Examination Guide for Physics: Principles & Problems

Defy the laws of physics.

It's been proven through years of classroom use...the "laws" of high school physics just don't hold with Merrill's *Physics: Principles & Problems*.

Law #1: Physics has to be complicated.

Physics doesn't have to be complicated. The success of *Physics: Principles & Problems* proves that simplicity is the key.

Law #2: Most students aren't motivated to take physics.

Students *are* motivated to take physics when they can see that it directly relates to the world around them.

Law #3: Average students can't handle the math.

Average students *can* handle the math in *Physics: Principles & Problems*...as they learn to solve traditional physics problems.

For the teacher only

Do your own evaluation of *Physics: Principles & Problems* by looking up the pages indicated. Or, for a quick overview, just turn the page.

Problem solving?
No problem.

Some physics programs offer an interesting solution to the difficulties students have with math problems: fewer math problems.

Physics: Principles & Problems offers a better solution: better support.

1. **Chapter openers** relate photos to real-life problems your students will learn to solve in each chapter.

2. **Clearly labeled example problems** (always in yellow) lead your students through every step of the math involved in solving problems.

3. **Practice exercises** immediately after the example problems check concept understanding and offer practice with problems that use math. An appendix of solutions to all practice exercises lets your students check their own progress.

4. **Problem solving hints** (always in blue) provide additional suggestions and strategies for applying physics concepts.

5. **Chapter reviews** cover all levels of difficulty.
   - **Questions** cover basic principles and concepts.
   - **Exercises** offer practice with formula substitution.
   - **Problems** involve both applying principles and using math. Most require the use of higher-level thinking skills or multiple steps.

Physics: Principles & Problems is a traditional, non-calculus-based physics program. An introductory chapter on fundamental algebra and trigonometry plus numerous in-text examples help your students build on first-year algebra concepts.

Magnetic Personalities

In a demonstration of the Meissner Effect, a magnet made of one of the lanthanoid metals is seen floating in the air above a superconductive disc. The superconductor has been cooled by immersing it in −196°C liquid nitrogen. Why is a lanthanoid magnet used instead of an ordinary ALNICO magnet? How is the magnet repelled from the superconductor material?

EXAMPLE

Voltage Drops in a Series Circuit

A 5.0-Ω resistor and a 10.0-Ω resistor are connected in series and placed across a 45.0-V potential difference. **a.** What is the effective resistance of the circuit? **b.** What is the current through the circuit? **c.** What is the voltage drop across each resistor? **d.** What is the total voltage drop across the circuit?

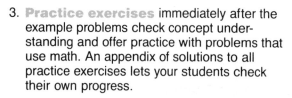

FIGURE 24–3. Use with the Example.

Given: $R_1 = 5.0\ \Omega$ Unknowns: R, I, V_1, V_2
$R_2 = 10.0\ \Omega$ Basic equation: $V = IR$
$V = 45.0\ V$

Solution:
a. $R = R_1 + R_2$
$= 5.0\ \Omega$

PROBLEM SOLVING

Drawing Schematic Diagrams

When drawing schematic diagrams, follow these steps.
1. Draw the symbol for the battery or other source of electric energy at the left side of the page. Put the positive terminal at the top.
2. Draw a wire following the conventional current out of the positive terminal. When you reach a resistor or other device, draw the symbol for it.
3. If you reach a point where there are two current paths, such as at a voltmeter, draw a † on the diagram and follow one path until the two paths join again. Then draw the second path.

Physics class should be more than just one problem after another.

Physics class can cause *you* problems, if your students don't truly understand the principles involved. Or they understand the principles but lack the math background. Or they can't follow the examples.

Open this Teacher Annotated Edition to any student page. You'll find a friendly, readable presentation of basic physics principles. You'll read about the many ways physics is used in our everyday world.

And you'll see, again and again, how *Physics: Principles & Problems* makes the connection from one principle to another . . . and from basic principles to problem solving.

Teaching support? Plan on it.

It's never been easier to plan ahead.

At the front of your Teacher Annotated Edition, you'll find page after page of chapter planning information—to help you prepare to teach each section, coordinate every component of the program, and plan interesting demonstrations and experiments. Detailed background information and lists of outside resources prepare you to answer any question. Complete solutions to all chapter review questions are also included here.

You can easily fit *Physics: Principles & Problems* to your needs.

The variety of problems and exercises means greater flexibility for you. You can choose to emphasize basic principles or problem solving and set the level of difficulty through the problems you assign. In addition, a wealth of components increases your options for labs, extra exercises and problems, and testing.

CHAPTER 1
A Mathematical Science

Overview

This chapter explains that physics concepts can be used to explain everyday phenomena. The second, meter, and kilogram are introduced as the fundamental units of time, distance, and mass in the SI system. Scientific notation is presented.

Students are shown that all measurements are subject to uncertainty. They learn that precision is limited by the smallest division on the measuring device and that accuracy is the degree to which the result agrees with an accepted value. When measurements are used in calculations, errors are compounded. Rules for determining the number of significant digits in a number and the number of significant digits in the result of a calculation conclude the chapter.

Planning Guide (5 Class Sessions)

Text Section		Demonstrations and Experiments		Other Program Components	
1:1 Physics: The Search for Understanding		Dem 1:1 Indirect Measurement	P	Skills	
1:2 Measurement and Scientific Methods	P	Exp 1 Measurement of Length	LM	Textbook Inventory	TRP
1:3 Metric System	P	Exp 2 Measurement of Mass and Density	LM	Mathematics Assessment	
1:4 Base and Derived Units	P	Dem 1:3 Estimating Measurements		Recording Measurements	
	P			Reading the Vernier Caliper	
				Propagation of Error	
1:5 Scientific Notation				Enrichment 1-1: What Is Time?	TRP
1:6 Prefixes Used with SI Units	P				
1:7 Addition and Subtraction in Scientific Notation	P			Teaching Master 1-1: Uncertainty in Measurement	TRP
1:8 Multiplication and Division in Scientific Notation	P			Teaching Master 1-2: Orders of Magnitude	TRP
	P			Minilab 1-1: Finding the Thickness of a Bean	TRP
1:9 Uncertainties of Measurements				Minilab 1-2: Models of the Solar System	TRP
1:10 Accuracy and Precision	S				
1:11 Significant Digits	S			Review Problems Masters	TRP
1:12 Operations Using Significant Digits	S			Enrichment 1-2: Estimating Orders of Magnitude	TRP
	S			Evaluation	TRP
					TRP

Performance Objectives

Upon completion of this chapter, your students will

1. define physics and list some applications. *1:1*
2. appreciate the difference in the approach to science by Galileo and the ancient Greeks. *1:2*
3. recognize the importance of the scientific methods. *1:2*
4. list the SI units for mass, length, and time. *1:3*
5. state the fundamental units and be able to distinguish between fundamental and derived units. *1:4*
6. demonstrate an ability to use scientific notation.
7. interpret common metric prefixes. *1:5*
8. be able to add and subtract large and small numbers using scientific notation. *1:6*
9. be able to multiply and divide small and large numbers using scientific notation. *1:7*
 1:8

10.

11.

12.

13. u
 m

Teaching the Chapter
Introduction

Using the Photo: Motion is indicated by the shape of the arms. The spiral arms curve and are not straight, indicating that the galaxy rotates. The spiral arms do not have uniform curvature, which indicates a difference in speed near the center compared with the outer edges. The tighter spiral indicates a higher speed near the center.

The chapter opener photograph can be used with Sections 1:1 and 1:2 to introduce the idea that the language of physics is mathematics and that physics utilizes measurements.

Demonstration: Pass out rulers to students and have them measure the thickness of a page in a book by measuring the thickness of 100 pages and dividing by 100. Record on the chalkboard the results of the measurement. Point out that each person should estimate to one hundredth of a centimeter since the smallest division on a meter stick is one tenth of a centimeter. Point out that dividing by 100 does not change the number of significant digits because 100 is an exact number.

1:1 Physics: The Search for Understanding

Chapters 1 and 2 deal with the mathematical skills needed for this course. Be careful not to intimidate students by doing too much math during the first few days. Plan to do some interesting and fun activities along with the math to motivate students. It is important throughout the course to relate physics to everyday situations.

Strive to know the ability of eac̲h̲
Use the Cl̲

each st
skills in

Giv
physics
on these
demonstr
phenome
number
dents will

1:2 Me
 Mer

Since o
sions will er
Galileo was
tions and me
he lived only
ceed throug
motion and l
cal developm

1:3 Metric

It is impo̲r
with the size
units. Use the

1 cm—widt
1 dm—widt
1 meter—di

1 g—mass of

Increase your options.

Teacher Resource Package

Ready-to-copy blackline masters are organized by chapter so it's easy for you to find what you need . . . when you need it. Our exclusive, time-saving booklet design means you handle only a few chapters at a time, while the storage case keeps the other booklets organized and ready on your bookshelf. Choose from safety pages, review and enrichment worksheets, minilabs, demonstrations, teaching masters, and tests for every chapter. In addition, extra lessons are provided on these three topics:

- Relativity
- Rotary motion
- Solid state physics

Laboratory Physics

A lab manual of 55 simple investigations using only basic equipment, for both qualitative and quantitative study of physics principles. Safety tips included with every investigation. A **Teacher Annotated Edition** is available.

Color Transparency Package

Twenty colorful overhead transparencies including some with overlays to make concepts clear.

Computer-Assisted Data-Checking Program

A quick, accurate way to verify the results of selected quantitative experiments in *Laboratory Physics.* For Apple II computers.

Teacher Annotated Edition

PHYSICS

Principles & Problems

AUTHORS

Paul W. Zitzewitz

Professor of Physics
Associate Dean of the College of Arts, Sciences, and Letters
University of Michigan-Dearborn
Dearborn, Michigan

James T. Murphy

Formerly Science Department Chairperson
Reading Memorial High School
Reading, Massachusetts

CONTENT CONSULTANTS

Craig Kramer

Physics Teacher
Bexley High School
Bexley, Ohio

Robert F. Neff

Physics Teacher
Suffern High School
Suffern, New York

Judith L. Doyle

Physics Teacher
Newark High School
Newark, Ohio

MERRILL PUBLISHING COMPANY

Columbus, Ohio

A Merrill Science Program

Physics: Principles & Problems
Physics: Principles & Problems, Teacher Annotated Edition
Physics: Principles & Problems, Teacher Resource Package
Physics: Principles & Problems, Transparency Package
Laboratory Physics
Laboratory Physics, Teacher Annotated Edition
Laboratory Physics, Computer-Assisted Data-Checking Software

Series Editor: Mary Beth Gallant; **Project Editor:** Madelaine Meek; **Editorial Assistant:** Diana Such
Project Designer: Karen P. Martino; **Project Artist:** Sheila Monroe-Hawkins;
  Illustrators: Dick Smith, Jim Shough, Don Robison
Photo Editors: Kenneth E. Stevenson, David T. Dennison
Production Editors: Annette Hoffman, Mary Ann Hopper

ISBN O-675-O2473-O

Published by
Merrill Publishing Company
Columbus, Ohio

3 4 5 6 7 8 9 10 11 12 13 14 15 VH 00 99 98 97 96 95 94 93 92 91
viT

Contents

Chapter-by-Chapter Teacher Guide

Includes: Teaching Techniques, Demonstrations, Detailed Solutions to Chapter Review, Performance Objectives, Planning Guide, Resources, and Background.

Philosophy

Physics: Principles & Problems employs a highly effective problem-solving method of teaching physics. The content is geared to produce a genuine understanding of the physical laws fundamental to all sciences. Physics concepts are introduced in the context of everyday applications relevant to the student. Each chapter covers basic ideas and illustrates how these basics interact in more complex concepts. The discussion of each topic is clarified and enhanced with abundant photographs and illustrations. Students are rarely asked to memorize details; rather, they are led to understand the basis for each major physics concept. This approach reduces student frustration and is a factor in promoting higher physics enrollments.

Physics: Principles & Problems, fifth edition, is arranged to present concepts in their most logical order. The importance of measurements in physics has been introduced first in order to emphasize the use of SI units and to reinforce the use of significant digits throughout the text. The second chapter demonstrates the use of algebra and graphing in physics while providing a review of these topics within the text. The discussion of trigonometry has been postponed until it is needed in Chapter 6 with the introduction of two-dimensional vectors. The concepts of momentum and energy are presented close together to emphasize the conservation laws. The quantum nature of light and electromagnetic radiation is developed only after a thorough introduction of electromagnetism.

The text uses problem solving as well as concept applications as one of the fundamental means of studying physics. *Example* problems have been revised to provide coherent models for solving physics and other quantitative problems. Variables are clearly identified both in words and symbols. Given and unknown quantities are isolated. Solutions are concisely presented. To allow students to become familiar with each new concept, a set of *Practice Exercises* follows most *Example* problems. Complete solutions for all *Practice Exercises* appear in a *Solutions Appendix* so that students will have immediate feedback about their understanding of the concept. Special attention is given to vector notation as well as proper significant digit operation.

The *Chapter Review* material has been revised and expanded with particular attention to increasing the number of questions and problems that require higher level, conceptual thinking.

Text Features

Organization and Sequence

Physics: Principles & Problems is designed for maximum flexibility in teaching. The text is divided into 31 chapters. Each chapter is then further divided into numbered sections that aid students in locating specific topics and assist you in arranging assignments.

The nature and role of measurements in physics is introduced in Chapter 1 to emphasize the quantitative nature of physics. Mathematical relationships are introduced in Chapter 2 to provide a brief review of algebra and graphing physical quantities. The mathematics review makes the text self-sustaining and eliminates the use of outside resources.

Mechanics is the first concept presented, and it provides the basis for discussing heat and states of matter. Wave phenomena are introduced and also used to describe sound and light. Electricity, magnetism, and electromagnetic waves follow. Atomic and nuclear physics complete the text with a discussion of quantum and elementary particle physics.

Readability

Readability aids in determining the success of a textbook in the classroom. A text that is easily comprehended by the majority of students in a class promotes student interest and involvement in the subject area. This feature, in turn, promotes teachability of the text and helps facilitate classroom management.

To control the reading level, careful attention has been given to vocabulary, sentence construction, paragraph structure, chapter organization, illustrations, and format.

The vocabulary in the text is consistent with the developmental level of the students for whom the text is designed. In addition, important science terms are printed in boldface or italic type when first presented. Some terms are followed by their phonetic spellings. Each term is then clearly defined and reinforced throughout the discussion.

An open format is achieved with wide margins and appropriate spacing between sections, problems, and illustrations. The typeface and size in which the text is set is another feature that enhances readability. Student notes are placed in the margin to serve as a reading aid and review guide. They provide a ready outline of the concepts discussed within the chapter and also make concise statements about those concepts.

The *Chapter Review* begins with a Summary that concisely reviews the major concepts and principles of the chapter. Each Summary statement is numbered and refers back to the appropriate section of the chapter.

Real World Applications

This edition of **Physics: Principles & Problems** has expanded the use of material to provide the students with visual links between physics concepts and real-world situations. Each chapter begins with a large color photograph and a problem that ties the photograph to the concepts presented in the chapter. This feature is designed to motivate student interest in the chapter and provide additional application of problem-solving skills. In addition over 300 color illustrations and graphs are included throughout the text. They serve to reinforce and clarify concepts presented in adjacent paragraphs.

Thirteen *Physics Focus* essays discuss current and relevant applications of concepts covered in the text. *For Your Information* margin features provide interesting highlights on research, technological applications, and quotes related to the text. Physics Careers are discussed in the *Appendix*.

Problem Solving

This text is designed for student success in problem solving. Your students' abilities to solve problems indicate how well they understand the basic principles in a chapter. Problem-solving skills are developed in a variety of ways throughout each chapter. As stated above, students are introduced to a problem-solving situation in the opening feature of each chapter.

Example problems are used extensively throughout the text to provide clear and logical models for solving physics problems. Each *Example* problem is clearly identified within a yellow tint block. Given or unknown variables are listed and basic equations relating the quantities are stated. The SI system of measurement is emphasized in the *Example* problems. Likewise, close adherence to the use of significant digits in each *Example* problem provides reinforcement for students in performing significant digit operations.

Practice Exercises follow most of the *Examples.* They are designed for students to check their understanding of the concepts presented in the *Examples* and preceding text. Answers to all *Practice Exercises* are provided in the *Solutions Appendix* to aid students in gaining confidence with the new material.

The *Chapter Review* provides several types of review material that focus on different levels of problem-solving skills. The Questions section contains recall questions to help students review the previous material and new vocabulary terms.

The Applying Concepts section provides a qualitative assessment of students' understanding of concepts presented in the chapter.

The Exercises are a quantitative review that covers either a single concept or requires relatively simple mathematical analysis. The Exercises provide an adequate review of the major concepts in each chapter.

The Problems can be used to individualize your course to the ability level of your students. The Problems are more challenging than the Exercises and can be used as enrichment. Therefore, you may wish to use them as supplementary material.

Role of Teacher Demonstration

Good teacher demonstrations are important in helping students visualize abstract concepts. Demonstrations allow for development of observational skills and proper techniques. Safety rules and procedures can be emphasized. Demonstrations can be preceded with a clearly identified problem; several demonstrations are designed for students to generate conclusions through observations. A good demonstration allows students to recognize and verbalize relationships as a result of their own experiences. Demonstrations allow you to present a maximum amount of text information while providing concrete and illustrative experiences. You will find demonstrations included with each chapter of the **Teacher Guide,** as well as references to demonstrations in the ***Teacher Resource Package.***

Supplementary Materials

Teacher Resource Package

The **Teacher Resource Package** is designed to enhance the *Physics: Principles & Problems* program by assisting the teacher in all areas of physics instruction. It is organized by chapter in six easy-to-use booklets. Use the **Teacher Resource Package** as a time-saving teaching aid in the planning, preparation, instruction, and evaluation of the high school physics course. The material provided includes a Program Planning Guide, Textbook Inventory, Mathematics Inventory, Lab Safety Guide, Physics Skills Masters, Supplemental Lessons, Teaching Masters, Mini-Lab/Demonstration Masters, Review Masters, Enrichment Masters, Evaluation Masters, and additional Tables.

Physics Skills Masters

The Physics Skills Masters are designed for use as paper and pencil exercises of fundamental reading and mathematical skills. The exercises stress the areas of measurement (SI units), problem solving, scientific reading, instrumentation, error analysis, and data analysis.

Teaching Masters

The Teaching Masters are designed to be used as transparencies and/or student reference sheets. They facilitate class discussion and aid in the reinforcement of basic physics concepts. Teaching Masters are provided for each chapter of the text.

Mini-Lab/Demonstration Masters

The Mini-Lab/Demonstration Masters are designed to aid both teacher and students through brief demonstrations of specific concepts.

Review Activity Masters

The Review Activity Masters contain pencil and paper exercises that are designed to aid student mastery of problem-solving skills. The exercises include both example problems and practice problems.

Enrichment Masters

The Enrichment Masters provide additional activities for the most motivated students. The exercises emphasize inference and other conceptual skills. Expansion of chapter concepts is often the goal of these exercises.

Evaluation Masters

The Evaluation Masters are designed to reinforce student learning, evaluate student progress, and discover areas of weakness in instruction. The program consists of a four-part test for each chapter. The sections include the following:
Discovering Concepts–a set of completion questions related directly to the fundamental definitions and ideas found in the chapter.
Understanding Concepts–a set of questions requiring students to select the correct answer from several choices.
Using Concepts–requires students to apply concepts and skills learned in solving mathematical problems.
Extending Concepts–requires students to apply learned concepts to an abstract situation.

The major focus of each chapter is to help students improve their knowledge of physics. These tests help you discover any weaknesses in instruction that may become apparent using the Evaluation Masters.

Additional Tables

The **Teacher Resource Package** contains supplementary tables of physical and mathematical data. These tables serve as a student aid in completing physics assignments by offering a readily available source of information.

Laboratory Program

The **Laboratory Physics** program is an integral part of the high school physics curriculum. It provides students with a variety of laboratory experiences that serve to reinforce physics principles. The quantitative aspects of laboratory procedures are emphasized. Each experiment involves the manipulation of apparatus, observation, data gathering and processing, and interpretation to form conclusions.

A suggested laboratory sequence can be found in the Planning Guide. By effectively correlating the laboratory experiments and textbook, students are able to understand physics concepts.

Data-Checking Software

This software package correlates with several of the quantitative experiments in **Laboratory Physics.** The software can be used by students as a check on their calculations or by teachers to aid in grading lab reports.

Transparency Package

Twenty four-color transparencies, many with overlays, are contained in this package. A Teacher Guide provides teaching suggestions and background material for each transparency.

Performance Objectives

What is a Good Performance Objective?

Statements of performance objectives can usually be divided into three distinct parts. First is a description of the conditions under which the desired behavior will be observed. Some examples include

"When presented with typical graph forms..."

"When asked to write the equation for..."

"After having read and discussed..."

A good performance objective includes a condition that tells causes or circumstances of behaviors that will be performed, and stimulates the student to accomplish the stated objective.

The second part of a well-stated performance objective is a clear description of exactly what behavior is to be observed. A good performance objective would avoid using such terms as "know about," "appreciate," or "sense the relationship between." Rather, a good performance objective will include terms that describe what you could observe students doing if they do "know about" or "appreciate." It is almost impossible to observe students "appreciating," but you can gather some evidence that they are appreciating science if they read science books for entertainment, request additional laboratory time before or after school, ask to perform a class demonstration, or express any other form of interest in physics.

In other words, a good performance objective uses verbs that express some type of observable action. Examples of such action verbs are: constructs, distinguishes between, expresses, identifies, lists, manipulates, matches, measures, recalls, states hypotheses, states orally, and observes.

The third part of a well-stated performance objective is a description of some level of performance or criteria that may help you know if the student or class has performed to the degree you have specified.

For example, if you were teaching students to use a balance, would you want all of your class to be able to accurately measure the mass of a solid or liquid? Would you feel satisfied if 90% of your class could perform this skill? 80%? 50%? Obviously, the level of performance would vary for each class, each student, each teacher, and each task.

By incorporating the three essential parts of a performance objective, you should come up with assertive statements, such as the following:

Conditions—tell you how to plan and organize your class, and what materials you will need.

Working individually, when given a laboratory balance, several solids, and a graduated cylinder...

Performance—tells you what student behaviors to look for.

Students will measure the masses of solids to the nearest 0.01 g and measure the volume of solids by liquid displacement. Students will be able to calculate the densities of the solids to the correct number of significant digits.

Criterion Measure—tells you how many students, or to what degree the objective should be achieved.

Of all the students, 95% will achieve 100% of the above objectives.

There may be several objectives in each section. Each objective is keyed to the appropriate section of the chapter. From these objectives, you should be able to determine and plan for the achievement of the objectives for each section of a chapter.

Remember, these performance objectives are not meant to be all-inclusive. You should supplement them with objectives from other sources and with those you write.

You will also find that the criterion or level of performance for each objective is not included. The intent was to create guidelines and not to state levels of expectancies for you. Only you can decide if 100% or only 50% of your students should be able to accomplish each task. You will need to develop and insert these criterion levels for your students based upon your materials and your situation.

How Do You Know You Have Achieved Your Objectives?

When you try to find out if students have learned anything, you probably give some form of written test—true-false, completion, matching, or essay type of examination. All of these forms of evaluation are important in determining whether or not students have achieved their objectives. Evaluation materials are available in the **Physics: Principles & Problems, Teacher Resource Package.**

Planning Guide

The Planning Guide for *Physics: Principles & Problems* is designed to help you arrange your physics course within the framework of a single academic year. This table suggests time allotments, levels of emphasis, and the use of laboratory experiments and films to plan a complete physics program. Using this guide you can gear the study pattern of each class to suit the needs and abilities of the students.

The suggested time allotments are those needed for class lecture time. Laboratory work and films will require extra time. You can best determine these needs because laboratory periods can vary from school to school.

Physics: Principles & Problems is designed to provide students with a strong background in physics by stressing the major concepts they will consistently apply throughout the course. In developing a unit plan the following breakdown may be helpful.

Mechanics	Chapters 1-11
Thermodynamics	Chapters 12-14
Wave Theory, Sound, and Optics	Chapters 15-20
Electricity and Magnetism	Chapters 21-27
Modern Physics	Chapters 28-31

It is a major goal of this text that students achieve a thorough understanding of each topic before proceeding to new material. To quote Sir Isaac Newton, "It is better to achieve a little with certainty than a great deal that one is not sure of."

Chapter	Sections	Lecture Time Days	Lecture Time Weeks	Emphasis	Suggested Experiments from *Laboratory Physics*
1	1:1-1:4	2		P	Measurement of Length
	1:5-1:8	2	1	P	Measurement of Mass and Density
	1:9-1:12	1		S	
2	2:1-2:4	3		P	Graphing Experimental Data
	2:5-2:6	2	1	P	
3	3:1	1		P	Measurement of Time
	3:2-3:4	3	1.5	P	
	3:5-3:7	2		P	
	3:8	1		P	
4	4:1-4:4	3		P	Graphical Analysis of Motion
	4:5-4:7	3	1.25	P	Graphical Analysis of Motion: Uniform Acceleration
5	5:1-5:5	2		P	Force and Acceleration
	5:6-5:7	2	1.25	P	Mass and Acceleration
	5:8-5:10	2		P	Friction
					Inertial Mass
6	6:1-6:6	3		P	Addition of Force Vectors
	6:7-6:8	1	1.25	S	
	6:9-6:11	2		S	
7	7:1-7:2	3		P	Analysis of the Path of a Projectile
	7:3-7:4	2	1	S	Centripetal Force
					The Pendulum
8	8:1-8:4	2		P	Kepler's Law of Equal Areas
	8:5-8:6	2	1.25	S	
	8:7	1		P	
	8:8	1		S	
9	9:1-9:3	3		P	Conservation of Momentum: Internal Force
	9:4	2	1.25	P	
	9:5	1		S	Conservation of Momentum: A Collision in Two Dimensions

Chapter	Sections	Lecture Time		Emphasis	Suggested Experiments from *Laboratory Physics*
		Days	Weeks		
10	10:1-10:2	2		P	Pulleys
	10:3	2	1	P	
	10:4-10:5	1		S	
11	11:1-11:3	3		P	Conservation of Energy:
	11:4-11:5	3	1.25	P	The Inclined Plane
12	12:1-12:5	2		S	The Conservation of Thermal Energy
	12:6-12:7	2	1.25	P	Specific Heat of a Metal
	12:8-12:10	2		P	Heat of Fusion of Ice
13	13:1-13:3	3		S	The Diameter of a Molecule
	13:4-13:6	3	1.25	S	Boyle's Law
14	14:1-14:2	1		S	Archimedes Principle
	14:3-14:5	2	1.25	S	
	14:6-14:8	2		S	
	14:9	1		S	
15	15:1-15:4	3		P	Wave Properties
	15:5-15:8	1	1.25	P	Pulses in a Ripple Tank
	15:9-15:10	2		P	Wavelength, Frequency, and Speed
					Refraction of Waves
					Diffraction and Interference of Waves
16	16:1-16:3	3		P	Speed of Sound in Air
	16:4-16:7	2	1	S	
17	17:1-17:4	2		P	Luminous Intensity and Efficiency
	17:5-17:6	2	1	P	of Light Bulbs
	17:7	1		P	
18	18:1	2		P	Law of Reflection of Light
	18:2-18:5	3	1.25	P	Snell's Law
	18:6-18:7	1		S	
19	19:1	1		P	Images Produced by Curved Mirrors
	19:2-19:7	2	1.5	P	Convex Lenses
	19:8-19:11	2		P	
	19:12-19:13	1		S	
20	20:1-20:2	2		P	Measuring the Wavelengths
	20:3	1	1	S	of Light Waves
	20:4	1		P	
	20:5	1		S	
21	21:1-21:3	2		P	Static Electricity
	21:4-21:5	2	1.25	P	Coulomb's Law
	21:6-21:7	1		P	
	21:8	1		S	
22	22:1-22:2	2		P	Charging and Discharging a
	22:3-22:4	1	1.25	P	Capacitor
	22:5	1		P	
	22:6-22:7	1		S	
	22:8	1		S	

Chapter	Sections	Lecture Time		Emphasis	Suggested Experiments from *Laboratory Physics*
		Days	Weeks		
23	23:1-23:4	2		P	Ohm's Law
	23:5	1		P	Electrical Equivalent of Heat
	23:6-23:7	2	1.25	P	
	23:8-23:9	1		S	
24	24:1-24:2	2		P	Series Circuits
	24:3-24:4	2	1.25	P	Parallel Circuits
	24:5-24:6	2		P	Series-Parallel Circuits
25	25:1-25:2	2		P	Magnetic Field Around Magnets
	25:3-25:4	2		P	Magnetic Fields Around a
	25:5	1	1.25	S	Current-Carrying Wire
	25:6-25:10	2		S	Current and Field Strength
26	26:1-26:5	4		P	Induced Current and Lenz's Law
	26:6-26:7	2	1.25	S	The DC Generator-The DC Motor
					Energy Transfer by an Electric Motor
27	27:1-27:2	3		P	Magnetic Field Strength (Magnetic
	27:3-27:6	2	1	S	Induction)
					Charge-to-Mass Ratio of the Electron
28	28:1-28:3	3		S	A Model for the Quantum Concept
	28:4-28:5	2	1	S	
29	29:1-29:2	2		P	The Spectra of Elements
	29:3-29:6	2	1.25	P	
	29:7	1		P	
	29:8	1		S	
30	30:1-30:2	2		P	Half-Life Simulation
	30:3-30:5	2	1.25	P	
	30:6-30:9	1		S	
	30:10-30:12	1		S	
31	31:1-31:2	2		P	Simulation of Nuclear Collisions
	31:3-31:5	2	1.25	P	
	31:6-31:7	2		P	

Equipment for Demonstrations

Suppliers

Audiovisual materials for purchase or rental may be obtained from the following distributors. All materials should be ordered months in advance, with alternate choices of dates for their use.

A list of university audiovisual distributors is included for your convenience. All audiovisual materials can be obtained from one of these suggested sources. The first reference is a good general source of information on physics audiovisual materials.

Audiovisual Resources

"A Potpourri of Physics Teaching Ideas," edited by Donna Berry, Published by the American Association of Physics Teachers.

AAPT
5112 Berwyn Road
College Park, MD 20740-4100

Bergwall Productions, Inc.
839 Stewart Ave
Garden City, NY 11530

Collier-Macmillan School
and Library Services
866 Third Ave.
New York, NY 10022

Ealing Film Loops
BFA Educational Media
2211 Michigan Ave.
Santa Monica, CA 90404

Ealing Film Loops
Cambridge, MA 02140

Education Development Center
39 Chapel St.
Newton, MA 02160

Educational Material and
Equipment Co.
46 Lafayette Ave.
New Rochelle, NY 10801

Encyclopaedia Britannica
Educational Corporation
425 North Michigan Ave.
Chicago, IL 60611

Handel Film Corp.
8730 Sunset Blvd.
West Hollywood, CA 90069

Learning Corporation of America
1350 Avenue of the Americas
New York, NY 10019

Metrologic Instruments, Inc.
P.O. Box 307
143 Harding Ave.
Bellmawr, NJ 08031

Pyramid Films
P.O. Box 1048
Santa Monica, CA 90406

Ross Books
P.O. Box 4340
Berkeley, CA 94794

Thomas Alva Edison Foundation
21000 West Ten Mile Road
Southfield, MI 48075

Time-Life Multimedia
100 Eisenhower Drive
Paramus, NJ 07652

WVIZ-TV
4300 Brookpark Road
Cleveland, OH 44134

University Rental Services

The University of Arizona
Film Library
Tucson, AZ 85719
(602) 621-3282

University of Illinois
Visual Aids Service
1325 South Oak
Champaign, IL 61820
(217) 333-1360

Indiana University
Audio Visual Center
Bloomington, IN 47405
(812) 335-2103

Kent State University
Audio-Visual Service
Kent, OH 44242
(216) 672-3456

Syracuse University
Film Rental Center
1455 E. Colvin
Syracuse, NY 13210
(315) 479-6631

Washington State Univ.
Audio-Visual Center
Pullman, WA 99164
(509) 335-4535

Equipment

Carolina Biological Supply Co.
2700 York Road
Burlington, NC 27215

Central Scientific Co.
11222 Melrose Avenue
Franklin Park, IL 60131

Fisher Scientific Co.
4901 W. LeMoyne
Chicago, IL 60615

Flinn Scientific Inc.
P.O. Box 219
Batavia, IL 60510

LaPine Scientific Company
6001 S. Knox Avenue
Chicago, IL 60629

McKilligan Supply Corporation
435 Main Street
Johnson City, NY 13790

Nasco
901 Janesville Avenue
Fort Atkinson, WI 53538

Sargent-Welch Scientific Co.
7300 N. Linder
Skokie, IL 60077

Sargent-Welch Scientific of Canada, Ltd.
285 Caryray Drive
Weston, Ontario, Canada M9L 1P3

Science Kit and Boreal Labs
777 E. Park Drive
Tonawanda, NY 14150

Ward's Natural Science
Establishment, Inc.
P.O. Box 1712
Rochester, NY 14603

A Mathematical Science

Overview

This chapter explains that physics concepts can be used to explain everyday phenomena. The second, meter, and kilogram are introduced as the fundamental units of time, distance, and mass in the SI system. Scientific notation is presented.

Students are shown that all measurements are subject to uncertainty. They learn that precision is limited by the smallest division on the measuring device and that accuracy is the degree to which the result agrees with an accepted value. When measurements are used in calculations, errors are compounded. Rules for determining the number of significant digits in a number and the number of significant digits in the result of a calculation conclude the chapter.

Planning Guide (5 Class Sessions)

Text Section		Demonstrations and Experiments		Other Program Components	
1:1 Physics: The Search for Understanding	P	Dem 1:1 Indirect Measurement		Skills	TRP
1:2 Measurement and Scientific Methods	P	Exp 1 Measurement of Length	LM	Textbook Inventory	
1:3 Metric System	P	Exp 2 Measurement of Mass and Density	LM	Mathematics Assessment	
1:4 Base and Derived Units	P	Dem 1:3 Estimating Measurements		Recording Measurements	
				Reading the Vernier Caliper	
				Propagation of Error	
				Enrichment 1-1: What Is Time?	TRP
1:5 Scientific Notation	P			Teaching Master 1-1: Uncertainty in Measurement	TRP
1:6 Prefixes Used with SI Units	P			Teaching Master 1-2: Orders of Magnitude	TRP
1:7 Addition and Subtraction in Scientific Notation	P			Minilab 1-1: Finding the Thickness of a Bean	TRP
1:8 Multiplication and Division in Scientific Notation				Minilab 1-2: Models of the Solar System	TRP
1:9 Uncertainties of Measurements	S			Review Problems Masters	TRP
1:10 Accuracy and Precision	S			Enrichment 1-2: Estimating Orders of Magnitude	TRP
1:11 Significant Digits	S			Evaluation	TRP
1:12 Operations Using Significant Digits	S				

Performance Objectives

Upon completion of this chapter, your students will

1. define physics and list some applications.   *1:1*

2. appreciate the difference in the approach to science by Galileo and the ancient Greeks.   *1:2*

3. recognize the importance of the scientific methods.   *1:2*

4. list the SI units for mass, length, and time. *1:3*

5. state the fundamental units and be able to distinguish between fundamental and derived units. *1:4*

6. demonstrate an ability to use scientific notation. *1:5*

7. interpret common metric prefixes. *1:6*

8. be able to add and subtract large and small numbers using scientific notation. *1:7*

9. be able to multiply and divide small and large numbers using scientific notation. *1:8*

10. show an awareness that all measured quantities have an uncertainty. *1:9*

11. be able to distinguish between accuracy and precision. *1:10*

12. demonstrate an understanding of the use of significant digits as a means of stating the precision of measured quantities. *1:11*

13. use significant digits correctly when recording measured data. *1:12*

Teaching the Chapter

Introduction

Using the Photo: Galaxies rotate as shown by studies of the Doppler shift of light from individual stars. Stars near the center of the galaxy move fastest, which causes the arms to curve. A tighter spiral indicates a higher speed near the center.

The chapter opener photograph can be used with Sections 1:1 and 1:2 to introduce the idea that the language of physics is mathematics and that physics utilizes measurements.

Demonstration: Pass out rulers to students and have them measure the thickness of a page in a book by measuring the thickness of 100 pages and dividing by 100. Record on the chalkboard the results of the measurement. Point out that each person should estimate to one hundredth of a centimeter since the smallest division on a meter stick is one tenth of a centimeter. Point out that dividing by 100 does not change the number of significant digits because 100 is an exact number.

1:1 Physics: The Search for Understanding

Chapters 1 and 2 deal with the mathematical skills needed for this course. Be careful not to intimidate students by doing too much math during the first few days. Plan to do some interesting and fun activities along with the math to motivate students. It is important throughout the course to relate physics to everyday situations.

Strive to know the ability of each of your students. Use the Checklist for Mathematics Assessment from the *Teacher Resource Package* and determine where each student needs practice. Teach or review the math

skills in Chapters 1 and 2.

Give an overview of the topics you will study in physics and do some of your favorite demonstrations on these topics. See the *Teacher Resource Package* for demonstration ideas. Emphasize that there are many phenomena that can be explained by a relatively small number of mathematical relationships and that students will see the pattern unfold during this course.

1:2 Measurement and Scientific Methods

Since our senses can fool us, showing optical illusions will emphasize the importance of measurement. Galileo was one of the first scientists to use observations and measurement as a source of knowledge, and he lived only a little over 300 years ago. As you proceed through the text and develop the equations of motion and laws of dynamics, emphasize the historical development of these concepts.

1:3 Metric System

It is important to help students become familiar with the size of everyday objects in terms of metric units. Use these approximations as examples.

    1 cm—width of a fingernail
    1 dm—width of a fist
    1 meter—distance from your nose to the end of
            your fingertips
    1 g—mass of a paper clip
    5 g—mass of a nickel
    1 kg—mass of a small box of sugar or a small brick
    2 mL—volume of a thimble
    2 L—large bottle of soda pop

Demonstration: Give students a list of objects in the room. Have students predict the size (length, width, height, or mass) of the object, and then allow them to measure each object using SI units.

1:5 Scientific Notation

1:6 Prefixes Used with SI Units

1:7 Addition and Subtraction in Scientific Notation

1:8 Multiplication and Division in Scientific Notation

Emphasize and practice using these common prefixes: *milli-, centi-, deci-, kilo-,* and *mega-.* Show the usefulness of scientific notation and powers of ten when dealing with very large numbers. Estimate periods of time in powers of ten. For example, there are about 70 heartbeats in a minute, or 7.0×10^1, and 700 heartbeats in ten minutes, or 7.0×10^2. Ask students how many heartbeats there would be in 1 000 minutes. ($7.0 \times 10^1 \times 10^3 = 7.0 \times 10^4$ heartbeats) In a million minutes (about 2 years) there would be $7.0 \times 10^1 \times 10^6$, or 7.0×10^7 heartbeats.

1:10 Accuracy and Precision

A good analogy to differentiate between precision and accuracy is the target analogy. Draw the targets as shown here.

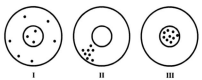

The dots represent bullet holes in the target. The first target shows good accuracy and poor precision; the second represents good precision and poor accuracy; the third represents good accuracy and good precision.

1:11 Significant Digits

When teaching significant digits, continually remind students of the exercise you did measuring the thickness of a page and the fact that everyone did not get the same answer because of uncertainty in measurement. When several measurements are used in a formula, the error is then compounded. Emphasize that significant digits represent the capabilities of the measuring instrument.

Resources

Literature

Berry, D., "Physics Boring? Says Who?" *The Science Teacher,* January, 1986, No. 1, pp. 38–40.

Hooper, W., "The Meter is Redefined," *The Physics Teacher,* January, 1987, p. 52.

McGahan, J.E., "A Game for Facilitating the Learning of Units in Physics," *The Physics Teacher,* April, 1977, pp. 233–234.

Swartz, C., *Prelude to Physics,* John Wiley and Sons, New York, 1983, pp. 1–4, 9–36.

Van Hise, Y., and Phillips, T., "What Do You Do the First Day of Physics Class?" *The Physics Teacher,* May, 1988, pp. 291, 292.

Software/Audiovisual

Powers of Ten, Pyramid Film, film
Datagraph II, Focus Media, Inc., Apple II software
Science Skills-Disk 1: Uncertainties, Mole Company, Apple II software

Chapter Review

QUESTIONS

1. Physics is the study of the basic physical laws that can be applied to all the sciences.
2. Fundamental units are units for mass, length, and time. Derived units are combinations of fundamental units.
3. seconds (time), meters (length), kilograms (mass)
4. Speed is m/s, km/h, or cm/s.
5. The International System of Units allows scientists all over the world to make measurements in the same system. Thus, scientists know exactly what is meant by measurements made by other scientists.
6. **a.** centimeter **b.** millimeter **c.** kilometer
7. **a.** derived **b.** kg/m^3
8. The final digit is estimated.
9. The precision of a measuring device is limited by the finest division on its scale.

10. a. Zeros are necessary to indicate the magnitude of the value, but there is no way of knowing whether or not the instrument used to measure the values actually measured the zeros. The zeros may serve only to locate the six.
  b. Write the number in scientific notation, including only the significant digits.

APPLYING CONCEPTS

1. Student answers will vary.

2. Student answers will vary.

3. a. less precise
  b. more accurate

4. Student answers will vary.

5. Student answers will vary.

6. Student answers will vary.

7. Only like terms can be added or subtracted. 5 m and 1 s cannot be added, but divided, 5 m/s becomes a velocity.

8. a. 365 days in a year
  b. The length of a meter stick is 1003.9 mm.

9. A meter stick's smallest division is a millimeter. Both answers should reflect a measurement to the nearest tenth of a centimeter, for example, 84.0 cm and 83.8 cm.

EXERCISES

1. a. 5×10^{24} m
  b. 1.66×10^{-19} m
  c. 2.033×10^{9} m
  d. 1.030×10^{-7} m

2. a. 3   **b.** 4   **c.** 1   **d.** 5

3. a. 3   **b.** 1   **c.** 3

4. a. 34.7 m
  b. 25.022 m
  c. 46.00 cm^2
  d. 3.1 kg

5. a. 6.12×10^9 s
  b. 2.94×10^{-6} m
  c. 1.25×10^{-4} kg
  d. 7.50×10^7 g

6. a. 2.9×10^9 m^2
  b. 2.0×10^5 m/s
  c. 1.3×10^{-6} km^2
  d. 1.9×10^2 kg/m^3

7. a. 7.4 mm
  b. 1 m
  c. 49.6 m^2
  d. 70.4 kg

8. a. 101.6 m
  b. 584 m^2

9. 2.4×10^2 m^3

10. 362.1 m

11. 48.2 kg

12. 69.2 m^2

PROBLEMS

1. 0.31 mg, 1021 μg, 0.000006 kg, 11.6 mg

2. The difference in area for the pans is
$$\pi\left(\frac{26 \text{ cm}}{2}\right)^2 - \pi\left(\frac{23 \text{ cm}}{2}\right)^2 = 120 \text{ cm}^2$$
$(120 \text{ cm}^2)(25¢/\text{cm}^2) = \$0.30$
Each pizza costs 30 cents more.

3. $D = m/V$, so $V = m/D$, $= (2.0 \times 10^{30} \text{ kg})/$
$(2.0 \times 10^{17} \text{ kg/m}^3) = 1.0 \times 10^{13} \text{ m}^3$
$V_{\text{sphere}} = (4/3)\,\pi r^3$, so $r^3 = 3V/4\pi$
$= 3(1.0 \times 10^{13} \text{ m}^3)/4\pi = 2.4 \times 10^{12} \text{ m}^3$;
$r = \sqrt[3]{2.4 \times 10^{12} \text{ m}^3} = 1.3 \times 10^4 \text{ m}$
$d = 2r = 2(1.3 \times 10^4 \text{ m})/(1.0 \times 10^3 \text{ m/km})$
$= 26$ km

4.

Side	Surface area	Volume	Surface Area
			Volume
(m)	(m^2)	(m^3)	
1.0	6.0	1.0	6
2.0	24	8.0	3
3.0	54	27	2
4.0	96	64	1.5
5.0	150	130	1.2
6.0	220	220	1

The table shows that surface area to volume ratio decreases with size. Silnce heat is lost through the walls of a building, tmhe large cube-shaped building would cost less to heat than the one-floor building with many wings.

5. a. An elephant's body has a small surface area to volume ratio. Wallowing in the water helps to cool it.
  b. The ears have a large surface area to volume ratio which allows rapid cooling.
  c. A large surface area to volume ratio allows rapid energy loss. Constant eating replenishes the lost energy.
  d. Like the hummingbird, the shrew has a large surface area to volume ratio and must eat large quantities of food to replace lost energy.

6. 9400 mL, 108 m, 51 mm

7. a. Rate = 2 drops/3 s, and there is 20 drops/cm^3 volume of water collected in one hour.
$(2 \text{ drops}/3 \text{ s})(3.6 \times 10^3 \text{ s/h})(1 \text{ cm}^3/20 \text{ drops})$
$(1 \times 10^{-3} \text{ dm}^3/\text{cm}^3) = 1 \times 10^{-1} \text{ dm}^3/\text{h}$
  b. $D = m/V$, so $m = DV = (1 \times 10^3 \text{ g/m}^3)$
$(1 \times 10^{-3} \text{ kg/g}) = (1 \times 10^{-1} \text{ dm}^3)$
$(1 \times 10^{-3} \text{ m}^3/\text{dm}^3) = 1 \times 10^{-4} \text{ kg}$

Mathematical Relationships

Overview

This chapter provides the mathematical background needed to understand and use the laws of physics. Practice is provided in manipulating algebraic equations that will be used later. The correct use of units in equations is emphasized.

When data is graphed, the relationship among the variables is often easier to determine. Identifying the dependent and independent variables and plotting them on the *y*- and *x*-axis, respectively, are tools for analyzing laboratory data. The graphed data can be used to decide if the relationship is linear, hyperbolic, or parabolic. If it is linear, the slope can be determined. The slope has physical units and, therefore, physical meaning.

As you continue to review math skills, take time to talk about physics and do some demonstrations to hold the interest of students for whom math is a challenge.

Planning Guide (5 Class Sessions)

Text Section		Demonstrations and Experiments		Other Program Components	
2:1 Graphing Data	P	Dem 2:1 Boyle's Law: an Inverse Relationship		Skills	TRP
2:2 Linear Relationships	P	Exp 3 Graphing Experimental		Graphing Techniques	
2:3 Parabolic Relationships	P	Data	LM	Interpreting Graphs	
2:4 Inverse Relationships	P			Factor-Label Method for	
				Converting Units	
				Dimensional Analysis	
				Teaching Master 2-1:	
				(a) Linear Relationship: Elongation	
				Versus Force	TRP
				Minilab 2-1: Gathering and	
				Analyzing Data	TRP
				Enrichment 2-1: Determining	
				Relationships from Graphs	TRP
2:5 Solving Equations Using Algebra	P			Teaching Master 2-1:	
2:6 Units in Equations	P			(b) Parabolic Relationship:	
				Position Versus Time	TRP
				Teaching Master 2-2:	
				(a) Inverse Relationship: Volume	
				Versus Pressure	
				(b) Graphical Relationships	TRP
				Review Masters	TRP
				Minilab 2-2: Measuring Height	
				Indirectly	TRP
				Evaluation	TRP

Performance Objectives

Upon completion of this chapter, your students will

1. demonstrate the ability to manipulate algebraic equations. *2:1*
2. use dimensional analysis to test the validity of an equation. *2:2*
3. distinguish between dependent and independent variables; interpret the meaning of linear, parabolic, and hyperbolic curves on graphs. *2:3*
4. recognize linear and direct relationships. *2:4*
5. recognize quadratic (parabolic) relationships. *2:5*
6. recognize inverse (hyperbolic) relationships. *2:6*
7. demonstrate a capacity to use the trigonometry of right triangles. *2:7*

Teaching the Chapter

Introduction

Using the Photo: While air and water resistance contribute to slowing the car after the accelerator is released, the road pushes on the car through the rotating tires. The role of the brakes is to slow the rotating wheels.

The chapter opener photograph can be used with Section 2:1 and the example of the braking distance of a car. It may also be used to develop the idea of types of variables.

Demonstration: Boyle's law can be used to demonstrate the inverse relationship between the volume of a gas and the pressure applied to it. Plug the end of a syringe and place pressure on the plunger. Read the volume of air in the syringe. Ask students to determine the independent variable (pressure) and the dependent variable (volume). Graph the data on the board or overhead. Have students choose divisions on the x- and y-axis. Discuss errors in the experiment and how these errors would affect the data.

Use this opportunity to discuss with students some important points to remember when communicating data. Some points you may want to discuss include titling graphs, labeling axes, and determining scale divisions.

2:1 Graphing Data

Emphasize that many of the relationships that will be studied throughout the year will be linear, parabolic, and hyperbolic (inverse). Help students learn the shapes of these curves and the equations that demonstrate the relationship of the two variables.

2:2 Linear Relationships

It is a good idea to discuss the choice of axis and how it affects the graph. Emphasize that the scales do not have to be identical on the x- and y-axes. Students may have learned otherwise in math class, and it may take some time to break the habit. The divisions should be chosen so the data extends about as far on the x-axis as it does on the y-axis. Make up some graphs with the line going up at a 45° angle. Make the x-axis the same scale on all the graphs, but make the y-axis a different scale. Ask students if all the graphs have the same slope. Hopefully they will realize that the slope is determined by reading values from the y- and x-axis and not just looking at the direction of the line. Now, on the same sets of axes, make a set of graphs as before but draw the slopes so that they are all the same. Practice making graphs and emphasize the importance of neatness. Use the Basic Skills Masters on graphing in the *Teacher Resource Package*. Make sure that your students are competent at graphing before using a computer graphing package.

2:3 Parabolic Relationships

Graphing equations is an important skill because it shows relationships in a dynamic rather than a static form. Illustrate this concept by distinguishing between a motion picture and a photograph. Give students practice in plotting data and drawing graphs. Try to find data of interest to the students, such as Henry (Hank) Aaron's home-run output. Use data from an astronomy book and plot the distance of Earth from the sun versus the time it takes the planet to go around the sun. Remind students to draw a smooth curve rather than "follow the dots" because measured quantities seldom fall exactly on the line. The smooth line, or curve, represents a best fit to experimental data.

2:5 Solving Equations Using Algebra

Help students become proficient at manipulating algebraic equations. Emphasize that it is always better to simplify and transpose equations when they are in symbolic form.

2:6 Units in Equations

Elaborate on the use of units in equations and stress unit cancellation methods. Explain how units can be used to check the correctness of an equation.

Resources

Literature

Ringel, Herbert, "Graphing Henry Aaron's Home-run Output," *The Physics Teacher,* January, 1974, p. 43.

Streuski, Ellen, "The Write Stuff," *The Science Teacher,* May, 1984, p. 88.

Swartz, Clifford, *Prelude to Physics,* John Wiley and Sons, New York, 1983, pp. 37–45.

Vargans, Marjorie F., "Writing Skills for Science Labs," *The Science Teacher,* November, 1986, pp. 29–33.

Software/Audiovisual

Graphical Analysis III, Vernier Software, Apple II

Mathematics for Science Series, Merlan Scientific, Ltd., Apple II

Datagraph II, Focus Media, Inc., Apple II

Visual Illusions, HRM, Apple II

Background

Several experiments require students to make graphs and then to manipulate data and regraph to obtain a straight line. Enrichment 2:1 in the *Teacher Resource Package* provides detailed information on this concept and gives several sets of data to graph, to manipulate, and to find the equation of the straight line including the slope. For advanced students, emphasize that the slope has physical meaning and must have units if the data gives units. This concept may be too mathematical for lower level students.

Chapter Review

QUESTIONS

1. temperature = independent variable; volume = dependent variable

2. **a.** temperature
   b. volume

3. ratio of vertical change to horizontal change, rise over run

4. Zero. The change in vertical distance is zero.

5. Negative because the change in vertical distance is negative for positive change in horizontal distance.

6. **a.** inverse
   b. direct
   c. direct with square of v

7. **a.** hyperbola
   b. straight line
   c. parabola

8. to check dimensional accuracy of answer as a check for correctness of problem setup

APPLYING CONCEPTS

1. **a.** longer because $d = vt$ and t is larger
   b. larger because the vertical distance increases more rapidly with speed

2. Answers will vary according to relationship chosen.

3. **a.** parabolic
   b. linear since y is being plotted versus the square of x, not x

4. Solve for k: $kv^2 = d$, $k = d/v^2$. From this it is seen that the units of k are $m/(m/s)^2 = s^2/m$.

5. **a.** air
   b. It would fall infinitely fast. Nothing can fall this fast.

EXERCISES

1. a.

b. straight line
c. $M = mV$, where m is the slope
d. mass/volume; density

2. a. $(4.23 \text{ cm})^3 = 75.7 \text{ cm}^3$
b. $M = (\text{density})(V) = (19.3 \text{ g/cm}^3)(75.7 \text{ cm}^3)$
1460 g

3. a.

b. the acceleration varies directly with the force
c. $F = ka$
d. $k = a/F$ so the units of k are $(\text{m/s}^2)/\text{N} = \text{m/s}^2 \cdot \text{N}$

4. a. $v = d/t = (2\pi)(1.50 \times 10^8 \text{ km})/(365 \text{ day}) \cdot (24 \text{ h/day}) = 1.08 \times 10^5 \text{ km/h}$
b. $v = (1.08 \times 10^5 \text{ km/h})(1000 \text{ m/km})/(3600 \text{ s/h}) = 3.00 \times 10^4 \text{ m/s}$

5. a. $v = d/t = (2\pi)(6.37 \times 10^3 \text{ km})/(24 \text{ h}) = 1.67 \times 10^3 \text{ km/h}$
b. $v = (1.67 \times 10^3 \text{ km/h})(1000 \text{ m/km})/(3600 \text{ s/h}) = 464 \text{ m/s}$

6. $\ell = gT^2/4\pi^2$, $g = 4\pi^2\ell/T^2$.

7. a. $1.5 \text{ min} = (1.5 \text{ min})/(60 \text{ min/h}) = 0.025 \text{ h}$, $d = vt = (20 \text{ km/h})(0.025 \text{ h}) = 0.5 \text{ km}$
b. $6000 \text{ m} = 6 \text{ km}$, $t = d/v = (6 \text{ km})/(30 \text{ km/h}) = 0.2 \text{ h}$

PROBLEMS

1. a. density of silver $= D = 10.5 \text{ g/cm}^3$. Since $D = M/V$, $M = DV = (10.5 \text{ g/cm}^3)(65.0 \text{ cm}^3) = 683 \text{ g}$
b. actual volume of silver $= V = M/D = (616 \text{ g})/(10.5 \text{ g/cm}^3) = 58.7 \text{ cm}^3$. Hollow volume $=$ given volume $-$ actual volume $= 65.0 \text{ cm}^3 - 58.7 \text{ cm}^3 = 6.3 \text{ cm}^3$

2. a.

b. hyperbola
c. Acceleration varies inversely with the mass.
d. $a = c/M$, $c = \text{constant} = 12$
e. $c = Ma$, so the units of c are $(\text{kg})(\text{m/s}^2) = \text{kg} \cdot \text{m/s}^2$

3. $v = d/t = (24 \text{ rev})(2\pi)(5.4 \text{ m/rev})/(10 \text{ min}) \cdot (60 \text{ s/min}) = 1.4 \text{ m/s}$

4. $(6.02 \times 10^{23})(1 \text{ cm}) = 6.02 \times 10^{23} \text{ cm}$ or $(6.02 \times 10^{23} \text{ cm})/(100 \text{ cm/m})(1000 \text{ m/km}) = 6.02 \times 10^{18} \text{ km}$

Motion in a Straight Line

Overview

The physics concepts and problem-solving techniques presented in this chapter are a foundation for later chapters. Procedures for problem solving are described in the Examples. The chapter emphasizes the importance of selecting the correct basic equation as essential to successful problem solving. Equations should be solved for the unknown before any numerical values are substituted for symbols.

Distance and speed are defined as scalar quantities and displacement and velocity as vector quantities. Vector addition using arrows is introduced.

The equations of motion are obtained from the definitions of velocity and acceleration. The acceleration due to gravity is introduced and the symmetry of motion for an object thrown into the air is discussed.

Planning Guide (7 Class Sessions)

Text Section		Demonstrations and Experiments		Other Program Components	
3:1 Position and Distance	P	Dem 3:1 Reaction Time Exp 4 Measurement of Time	LM	Minilab 3-1: Distance and Displacement	TRP
3:2 Average and Instantaneous Speed	P			Teaching Master 3-1: Vector Addition	TRP
3:3 Velocity and Speed	P				
3:4 Relativity of Velocity	S				
3:5 Acceleration	P	Dem 3:6 Galileo's Inclined Plane		Teaching Master 3-2: Constant Acceleration	TRP
3:6 Displacement During Uniform Acceleration	P				
3:7 Acceleration Due to Gravity	P				
3:8 Solving Motion Problems	P			Review Masters Enrichment 3-1: Problems Evaluation	TRP TRP TRP

Performance Objectives

Upon completion of this chapter, your students will

1. distinguish scalar from vector quantities, giving examples of each. *3:1*
2. describe, qualitatively, the relationship among distance moved, the time it takes, and the speed or velocity of the body. *3:1*
3. define and give an example of a frame of reference. *3:1*
4. define and give examples of instantaneous speed, distinguishing speed from velocity. *3:2, 3:3*
5. demonstrate the ability to calculate average speed

and velocity and to solve a velocity equation for the unknown.   3:2

6. distinguish distance from displacement, giving examples.   3:3

7. demonstrate the ability to calculate acceleration, both positive and negative.   3:5

8. write the equation for final velocity after acceleration, applying the equation in solution of problems.   3:5

9. write the two equations for the distance traveled during uniform acceleration and the equation for the final velocity of the object after acceleration over a given distance; apply the equations in solving problems; be able to recognize symmetry in motion problems.   3:6

10. be able to state the value for the acceleration due to gravity and demonstrate the ability to use this value in the equations of motion.   3:7

11. show the ability to use Table 3-1 to select the correct equation to use by analyzing the quantities present in the problem; demonstrate an orderly approach to problem solving.   3:8

Teaching the Chapter

Introduction

Using the Photo: The rate of change of speed, or acceleration, was zero. While each interval covered a larger distance, it took proportionally longer to travel, so the speed was constant. With no change of speed occurring, the acceleration is zero.

The photograph can be used to introduce or elaborate on topics in Section 3:1 on frame of reference, Sections 3:2 and 3:3 on velocity and average speed, and Section 3:5 on acceleration.

Demonstration: Have a student rest his or her elbow on a desktop. Hold an index card by the top and let the student put his or her thumb and forefinger on either side of the bottom of the card. Tell the student to catch the card when you drop it. The student should not be able to catch the card.

Have students determine their own reaction times. Divide the class into pairs and give each pair a metric ruler. One person in the pair holds the ruler at the top and the other person puts his or her thumb and forefinger on each side of the ruler at the bottom. The first person drops the ruler and the second one catches it. The position where it is caught is recorded. This procedure is done several times, and the average distance is used to calculate the reaction time using the equation $t = \sqrt{2d/g}$. Reaction times usually are approximately 0.2 s.

3:1 Position and Distance
3:2 Average and Instantaneous Speed
3:3 Velocity and Speed

The concept of scalars and vectors is confusing for students and it is necessary to emphasize that speed, like distance, is a scalar, and velocity, like displacement, is a vector.

3:5 Acceleration

Help students to differentiate between velocity and acceleration. Show students a graph that shows constant acceleration and another that shows constant velocity. This will help them to visualize that an acceleration of zero does not imply that an object is at rest.

3:6 Displacement During Uniform Acceleration

Demonstration: Try this version of Galileo's experiment on an inclined plane. Take a metal track or a board with a groove and mark off intervals in a ratio of 1:4:9:16 from the starting point. Let a ball roll down an incline. Make the slant small so the ball does not roll down too fast. Have students positioned at each mark and have them time how long it takes from the beginning to their mark. Find the ratio of these times. They should be in a ratio of 1:2:3:4. The students can then see that the distance traveled is related to the square of the time.

3:7 Acceleration Due to Gravity

Emphasize that neglecting air resistance allows for simple mathematical relationships. Point out that the motion of a stone falling from the ceiling in a classroom to the floor would be essentially the same in air or in a vacuum.

Differentiate between how far an object has gone and how fast it is going after one second. Students should be able to tell you that a body accelerates at -9.8 m/s². If you ask students what distance the body travels in 1 s, they will often say 9.8 m. Point out that the body started at rest and accelerated to 9.8 m/s in one second. Therefore, the body's average velocity during that second was 4.9 m/s, and the distance it traveled was 4.9 m.

Resources

Literature

Good, R. and Smith, M., "How Do We Make Students Better Problem Solvers?" *The Science Teacher,* April, 1987, pp. 31–36.

Martin, D., "Encouraging Critical Thought: Alternative Problem Forms," *The Physics Teacher,* May, 1988, pp. 288–289.

Peckman, G.D., *et al.* "If You Don't Have a Slicker, Does It Pay to Walk Quicker?" *The Science Teacher,* December, 1987, pp. 35–39.

Chapter Review

Questions

1. $a = \dfrac{v_f - v_i}{t}$ $\qquad$ $d = \dfrac{(v_f + v_i)t}{2}$

   $v_f = v_i + at$

2. Tables should indicate that, for a body accelerating uniformly from rest, distance traveled and speed attained are numerically the same at the end of two seconds.

Car	Speed (m/s)	Distance (m)
A	12	12
B	11	11
C	16	16
D	24	24

3. Both bodies have traveled the same distance. The body shot straight up rises to the same height from which the other body fell.

4. Earth pulls on the steel ball with more force than on the aluminum ball. However, the steel ball has more mass to be accelerated. Thus, both masses are accelerated equally.

5. Velocity is reduced at a constant rate as the ball travels up into the air. As the ball begins to drop,

Software/Audiovisual

Kinematics II, Vernier Software, Apple II software
A Tutorial on Motion, ComPress, Apple II software
Uniform Motion, Merlan Scientific Ltd, Apple II, Commodore Pet, Commodore 64 software

Background

When you discuss the position and velocity of an object, you are talking about its relativity to a fixed object, usually Earth. A train is moving at a constant velocity of 88 km/h with respect to Earth. A person on one of the train's cars throws a ball at 10 km/h to a person at the front end of the car. The ball will appear as if it is moving at 98 km/h, the sum of its velocity with respect to the train and the train's velocity with respect to Earth. When the ball is thrown to the back of the train, it appears to be going at 78 km/h with respect to Earth. However, it must be remembered that Earth is not stationary. Since everything in the universe is in relative motion, calculations with respect to Earth are only one part of an object's motion.

the velocity again begins to increase until it reaches the height from which it was initially released. At that point the ball will have the same velocity it had upon release. The acceleration is constant throughout its flight.

6. sheets of paper, parachutes, leaves, feathers

7. **a.** Yes. At the point where the acceleration acting on a body causes it to reverse the direction of its velocity, its velocity is zero. For instance, a body with an upward velocity is uniformly accelerated by gravity. When it reaches its maximum height, its velocity is zero, but gravitational acceleration is still acting on it. The body reverses direction and is accelerated downward.

   b. Yes. A body maintaining a constant speed in a circular path is constantly changing its direction of motion, and therefore, its velocity. For instance, a satellite in a circular orbit, a race car on a circular track, and a ball whirled around on a string, all maintain constant speed but their velocities are changing because the direction of their motions is constantly changing.

c. No. Any change in magnitude or in the directional component of the velocity of a body results in a change in velocity.

8. a. A body's velocity is positive or negative with respect to its direction of motion from some point of reference. One direction of motion is defined as positive, and velocities in that direction are considered positive. The opposite direction of motion is considered negative; and, likewise all velocities. An object undergoing positive acceleration is either uniformly increasing its velocity in the positive direction, or uniformly reducing its velocity in the negative direction.

   b. A car climbing a hill and running out of gas will eventually change the direction of its velocity while maintaining a constant acceleration. If we define the direction of motion uphill as positive, then after its motor stops, the car's velocity decreases, reaches zero, and then changes its direction of motion downhill. Throughout each change in the magnitude or direction of its velocity, the car is undergoing uniform negative acceleration.

Applying Concepts

1. A football is treated as a point when the conditions under study require a frame of reference beyond the football itself. For instance, it is treated as a point when you want to know how high or how far it travels; or, how long it is in the air (its hang time). However, when the conditions under study concern a frame of reference that only includes the football itself, it cannot be treated as a point. It must be treated as a football. For instance, questions about its spin or end-over-end motion include only the ball itself.

2. Yes. A ball thrown upward has a constant acceleration, g, throughout its entire flight. However, on the way up its velocity is positive, on the way down it is negative.

3. smaller speed from $v_f^2 = 2gd$, more time from $d = \frac{1}{2}gt$, or $t^2 = 2d/g$

4. a. In the equation $d = \frac{v_f^2 - v_i^2}{2g}$, the relationship between d and g is an inverse one. For instance, if g increases by three times, or $d = \frac{v_f^2 - v_i^2}{2(3g)}$, d becomes $\frac{1}{3}$. Therefore, a ball on Dweeb would rise to a height of only one-third that on Earth.

   b. With $v_f = 0$, the value d is directly proportional to the square of initial velocity, v_i. That is, $d = \frac{v_f^2 - (3v_i)^2}{2g}$. On Earth an initial velocity three times greater results in a ball rising nine times higher. On Dweeb, however, the height of nine times higher would be reduced to only three times higher because of d's inverse relationship to a g that is three times greater.

5. The thrown rock has greater speed and arrives first. Use $v_f^2 = v_i^2 + 2gd$ with only v_i changing and $v_f = v_i + gt$, or use $t = (v_f - v_i)/g$, noting that v_i is negative when an object is thrown downward. Both rocks accelerate the same.

6. The space shuttle travels a greater distance (scalar quantity) around Earth in getting to Edwards Air Force Base. Its displacement (vector quantity), however, is the position of its landing point, Edwards Air Force Base, from its starting (reference) point, Cape Canaveral, which is the same as it is for the NASA team.

Exercises

1. $d = vt = \frac{(55 \text{ km/h})(0.75 \text{ s})(1000 \text{ m/km})}{(3600 \text{ s/h})} = 11 \text{m}$

2. a. $v_f^2 = v_i^2 + 2ad$

$d = \frac{v_f^2 - v_i^2}{2a} = \frac{0 - (+55 \text{ m/s})^2}{(2)(-11 \text{ m/s}^2)} = 140 \text{ m}$

   b. $d = \frac{v_f^2 - v_i^2}{2a} = \frac{0 - (110 \text{ m/s})^2}{(2)(-11 \text{ m/s}^2)} = 550 \text{ m}$

3. $d = v_i t + \frac{1}{2}gt^2$

$t = \sqrt{\frac{2d}{g}} = \sqrt{\frac{(2)(-1.2 \text{ m})(6)}{(-9.8 \text{ m/s}^2)}} = 1.2 \text{ s}$

4. $v_f = v_i + at$

$a = \frac{v_f - v_i}{t} = \frac{96 \text{ m/s} - 32 \text{ m/s}}{8.0 \text{ s}}$

$= \frac{64 \text{ m/s}}{8.0 \text{ s}} = 8.0 \text{ m/s}^2$

5. a. $v_f = v_i + at$

$t = \frac{v_f - v_i}{a} = \frac{0 - (+155 \text{ m/s})}{-31.0 \text{ m/s}^2} = 5.00 \text{ s}$

   b. $d = v_i t + \frac{1}{2}at^2$

$$= (+155 \text{ m/s})(5.00 \text{ s}) + \frac{1}{2}(-31.0 \text{ m/s})(5.00 \text{ s})^2$$

$$= 388 \text{ m}$$

c. $v_f = v_i + at$

$$= (+155 \text{ m/s}) + (-31.0 \text{ m/s}^2)(8.00 \text{ s})$$

$$= -93 \text{ m/s} \quad \text{The rocket is moving in a}$$
direction opposite to its original
direction.

6. $v_f = v_i + at = 22 \text{ m/s} + (1.6 \text{ m/s}^2)(6.8 \text{ s})$

$$= 33 \text{ m/s}$$

7. $v_f = v_i + at$

$$= 2.35 \times 10^5 \text{ m/s} + (-1.10 \times 10^{12} \text{ m/s}^2) \times$$
$$(1.50 \times 10^{-7} \text{ s}) = 7.00 \times 10^4 \text{ m/s}$$

8. a. $v_f = v_i + at$

$$= 2.0 \times 10^1 \text{ m/s} + (23.1 \text{ m/s}^2)(20.0 \text{ s})$$

$$= 482 \text{ m/s}$$

b. $N = \dfrac{482 \text{ m/s}}{331 \text{ m/s}} = 1.46 \text{ times}$

9. $d = \dfrac{(v_f + v_i) t}{2} = \dfrac{(88 \text{ m/s} + 66 \text{ m/s})(12 \text{ s})}{2}$

$$= 920 \text{ m}$$

10. $d = \dfrac{(v_f + v_i) t}{2} = \dfrac{(75 \text{ m/s} + 145 \text{ m/s})(15 \text{ s})}{2}$

$$= 1650 \text{ m} = 1700 \text{ m}$$

11. $v_f^2 = v_i^2 + 2ad$

$$a = \dfrac{v_f^2 - v_i^2}{2d} = \dfrac{(600 \text{ m/s})^2 - 0}{(2)(0.9 \text{ m})}$$

$$= \dfrac{3.6 \times 10^5 \text{ m}^2/\text{s}^2}{1.8 \text{ m}} = 2 \times 10^5 \text{ m/s}^2$$

12. $v_i = v_f - at = 0 - (-9.0 \text{ m/s}^2)(8.0 \text{ s}) = 72 \text{ m/s}$

$$d = \dfrac{1}{2}(v_i + v_f) t = \dfrac{1}{2}(72 \text{ m/s} + 0 \text{ m/s})(8.0 \text{ s})$$

$$= 290 \text{ m/s}$$

13. $v_f = \sqrt{v_i^2 + 2ad}$

$$= \sqrt{0 + 2(5.0 \text{ m/s}^2)(5.0 \times 10^2 \text{ m})}$$

$$v_f = 72 \text{ m/s}$$

14. a. $v_f = v_i + gt = 0 + (-9.8 \text{ m/s}^2)(8.0 \text{ s})$

$$= -78 \text{ m/s (downward)}$$

b. $d = v_i t + \dfrac{1}{2}gt^2 = 0 + \dfrac{1}{2}(-9.8 \text{ m/s}^2)(8.0 \text{ s})^2$

$$= -310 \text{ m (downward)}$$

15. a. $v_f^2 = v_i^2 + 2gd$

$$d = \dfrac{v_f^2 - v_i^2}{2g} = \dfrac{(-73.5 \text{ m/s})^2 - 0}{(2)(-9.80 \text{ m/s}^2)}$$

$$= \dfrac{5402 \text{ m}^2/\text{s}^2}{-19.6 \text{ m/s}^2} = -276 \text{ m}$$

b. $v_f = v_i + gt$

$$t = \dfrac{v_f - v_i}{g} = \dfrac{-73.5 \text{ m/s} - 0}{-9.8 \text{ m/s}^2} = 7.5 \text{ s}$$

16. falling object $(v_i = 0)$

$$d = \dfrac{1}{2}gt^2 + v_i t$$

$$= \dfrac{1}{2}(-9.8 \text{ m/s}^2)(7.0 \text{ s})^2 = -240 \text{ m}$$

$d_{up} = d_{down}$
rising object $(v_i = 69 \text{ m/s})$

$$d = \dfrac{1}{2}gt^2 + v_i t$$

$$= \dfrac{1}{2}(-9.8 \text{ m/s}^2)(7.0 \text{ s})^2 + (69 \text{ m/s})(7.0 \text{ s})$$

$$= -240 \text{ m} + 480 \text{ m} = 240 \text{ m}$$

The distance is the same but the displacement is
the opposite.

17. $d = v_i t + \dfrac{1}{2}gt^2$

$$= 0 + \dfrac{1}{2}(-9.8 \text{ m/s}^2)(3.0 \text{ s})^2 = -44 \text{ m}$$

The ball rises 44 m, the same distance it falls.

18. $v_f^2 = v_i^2 + 2gd$

$v_f = \sqrt{v_i^2 + 2gd}$

$$= \sqrt{0 + (2)(-9.80 \text{ m/s}^2)(-12.0 \text{ m})}$$

$$= \sqrt{235.2 \text{ m}^2/\text{s}^2} = 15.3 \text{ m/s}$$

19. a. $d_{car} = v_i t + \dfrac{1}{2}at^2 = 0 + \dfrac{1}{2}(6.0 \text{ m/s}^2) t^2 =$

$$3.0 \ t^2 \ \text{m/s}^2$$

$$d_{truck} = v_i t + \dfrac{1}{2}at^2 = (21 \text{ m/s}) \ t$$

$d_{car} = d_{truck}$, when the truck overtakes the car
$3.0 \ t^2 \ \text{m/s}^2 = (21 \text{ m/s}) \ t$
$t = 7.0 \text{ s}$
$d_{car} = (3.0 \text{ m/s}^2)(7.0 \text{ s})^2 = 150 \text{ m}$

b. $v_f = v_i + at = 0 + (6.0 \text{ m/s}^2)(7.0 \text{ s}) = 42 \text{ m/s}$

Problems

1. a. $v_f = v_i + gt = (+6.0 \text{ m/s}) + (-9.8 \text{ m/s}^2)$
$$(2.0 \text{ s}) = -14 \text{ m/s}$$

b. The wrench was falling while the helicopter
was rising. The displacement of the wrench
below where it was released is given by

$$d_w = v_i t + \frac{1}{2}gt^2$$
$$= (+6.0 \text{ m/s})(2.0 \text{ s})$$
$$+ \frac{1}{2}(-9.8 \text{ m/s}^2)(2.0 \text{ s})^2$$
$$= -7.6 \text{ m}$$

Since the helicopter has risen (2.0 s)(6.0 m/s) or 12 m in this time, the wrench is 12 m + 7.6 or 20 m below the helicopter.

2. $d = \frac{1}{2}gt^2$, $t = \sqrt{\dfrac{2d}{g}}$

3. a. $v_i = \dfrac{(90.0 \text{ km/h})(1000 \text{ m/km})}{(3600 \text{ s/h})} = 25.0 \text{ m/s}$

$v_f = v_i + at$

$t = \dfrac{v_f - v_i}{a} = \dfrac{0 - (25.0 \text{ m/s})}{-10.0 \text{ m/s}^2} = 2.50 \text{ s}$

The car will travel
$d = vt = (25.0 \text{ m/s})(0.75 \text{ s}) = 18.75 \text{ m} = 19 \text{ m}$ before the driver applies the brakes. The total distance the car must travel to stop is

$d = 19 \text{ m} + v_i t + \frac{1}{2}at^2$

$= 19 \text{ m} + (25.0 \text{ m/s})(2.50 \text{ s})$

$+ \frac{1}{2}(-10.0 \text{ m/s}^2)(2.50 \text{ s})^2$

$= 50 \text{ m}$, yes it hits the barrier.

b. $d_{total} = d_{constant\ v} + d_{decelerating} = 40.0 \text{ m}$
$d_c = vt = (0.75 \text{ s}) v$
$d_d = -v^2/2a = -v^2/2(-10.0 \text{ m/s}^2) = v^2/20.0 \text{ m/s}^2$
$40 \text{ m} = (0.75 \text{ s}) v + v^2/20.0 \text{ m/s}^2$
$v^2 + 15v - 800 = 0$
Using the quadratic equation:
$v = 22 \text{ m/s}$ (The sense of the problem excludes the negative value.)

4. a. $t = \dfrac{d}{v}$ $t_{total} = t_1 + t_2$

$\dfrac{d}{90 \text{ km/h}} = \dfrac{0.5d}{50 \text{ km/h}} + \dfrac{0.5d}{v}$

$\dfrac{1}{v} = \dfrac{1}{45 \text{ km/h}} - \dfrac{1}{50 \text{ km/h}}$

$v = 450 \text{ km/h}$

b. no

5. Answers will vary. Use $v_i^2 = -2gd$.

6. Answers will vary. Use $v_i^2 = -2gd$.

7. a. Using $v_f^2 = v_i^2 + 2gd$, $v_f^2 = 2gd = 2(-9.80 \text{ m/s}^2)(1.20 \text{ m})$
$v_f = -4.85 \text{ m/s}$ (downward)

b. Using $v_f^2 = v_i^2 + 2gd$, $v_i^2 = -2gd = -2(-9.80 \text{ m/s}^2)(1.00 \text{ m})$, $v_i = 4.43 \text{ m/s}$

c. $a = (v_f - v_i)/t = (4.43 \text{ m/s} - (-4.85 \text{ m/s}))/0.010 \text{ s}$
$= +928 \text{ m/s}^2$, or some 95 times g

8. $v_f^2 = v_i^2 + 2ad$

$a = \dfrac{v_f^2 - v_i^2}{2d} = \dfrac{(44 \text{ m/s})^2 - 0}{2(3.5 \text{ m})}$

$= 2.8 \times 10^2 \text{ m/s}^2$, 28 times that of gravity

9. $v_i = \dfrac{(110 \text{ km/h})(1000 \text{ m/km})}{3600 \text{ s/h}} = 31 \text{ m/s}$

$v_f^2 = v_i^2 + 2ad$ with $v_f = 0$, $v_i^2 = -2 ad$, or

$d = \dfrac{-v_i^2}{2a} = \dfrac{-(31 \text{ m/s})^2}{2(-300 \text{ m/s}^2)} = 1.6 \text{ m thick}$

10. a. $v_f = v_i + at$

$a = \dfrac{v_f - v_i}{t} = \dfrac{(+444 \text{ m/s} - 0)}{1.80 \text{ s}}$

$= +247 \text{ m/s}^2$, or about $-25g$

b. $a = \dfrac{v_f - v_i}{t} = \dfrac{(0 - 444 \text{ m/s})}{2.15 \text{ s}}$

$= -207 \text{ m/s}^2$, or 21g

11. Use $d = \dfrac{(v_f + v_i) t}{2} = \dfrac{(444 \text{ m/s} + 0)(1.80 \text{ s})}{2}$

$= +400 \text{ m}$
while accelerating

$d = \dfrac{(0 + 444 \text{ m/s})(2.15 \text{ s})}{2} = +477 \text{ m}$
while braking

12. a. $v_f^2 = v_i^2 + 2ad$, or $v_f^2 = 2ad$

$a = \dfrac{v_f^2}{2d} = 3.1 \times 10^8 \text{ m/s}^2$

b. $d = \dfrac{(v_f + v_i) t}{2}$

$t = \dfrac{2d}{(v_f + v_i)} = \dfrac{2(2.0 \times 10^{-2} \text{ m})}{(3.5 \times 10^3 \text{ m/s} + 0)}$

$= 11 \times 10^{-6} \text{ s} = 11 \text{ microseconds}$

Graphical Analysis

Overview

Chapter 3 developed the equations of motion from the definitions of velocity and acceleration. Chapter 4 presents a graphical analysis of kinematics, which gives a dynamic picture of motion in contrast to the static picture given by numbers in equations. This chapter reinforces and builds upon the concepts of the previous chapter.

The shapes of the position-time, velocity-time, and acceleration-time motion graphs for constant velocity

and uniform acceleration are developed. The slopes and areas of these graphs are studied to gain additional information about the motions they describe. The slope of a position-time graph is the velocity of an object, and the slope of a velocity-time graph is the acceleration of the object. The area under the curve of the acceleration-time graph is the change in velocity of the object and the area under the curve of the velocity-time graph is the displacement of an object.

Planning Guide (6 Class Sessions)

Text Section			Demonstrations and Experiments		Other Program Components~	
4:1	Position-Time Graph for Constant Velocity	P	Intro Dem Tortoise and the Hare		Teaching Master 4-2: Position-Time Graph	TRP
4:2	Velocity from a Position-Time Graph	P	Exp 5 Graphical Analysis of Motion	LM		
4:3	Position-Time Graph for a Complete Trip	P	Exp 6 Graphical Analysis of Motion: Uniform Acceleration	LM		
4:4	Velocity-Time Graph for Constant Velocity	P				
4:5	Velocity-Time Graph for Uniform Acceleration	P			Minilab 4-1: Graphing Uniformly Accelerated Motion	TRP
4:6	Position-Time Graph for Uniform Acceleration	P			Teaching Master 4-1:	
4:7	Acceleration-Time Graph for Uniform Acceleration	P			(a) Constant Velocity	
					(b) Uniform Acceleration	TRP
					Review Masters	TRP
					Enrichment 4-1: Analyzing Motion Graphs	TRP
					Evaluation	TRP

Performance Objectives

Upon completion of this chapter, your students will

1. understand the meaning of a position-time graph of constant velocity.   *4:1*
2. be able to determine the slope of a curve on a position-time graph and calculate the velocity. *4:2*
3. interpret and plot position-time graphs for con-

stant and changing motion, negative positions, and varying slopes.   *4:3*

4. understand the meaning of the area under the curve on a velocity-time graph and be able to calculate the displacement from such a graph.   *4:4*

5. understand the relation of the position-time graph to the velocity-time graph; recognize the meaning of the parabolic shape; and interpret the slope at any point correctly.   *4:6*

6. understand that uniformly accelerated motion versus time must yield a straight line on an acceleration-time graph, and interpret and calculate the area under the curve.   *4:7*

Teaching the Chapter

Introduction

Using the Photo: A small mass will be at rest in the center of the saddle region between the two peaks (masses). In the center of the saddle, there is equal attraction for both masses. This is the only location in the picture where a small mass can be placed to produce a minimal attraction. Use this photograph with Section 4:6 to discuss the position-time graph for uniform acceleration. The three-dimensional graph has a shape similar to graphs found in this section.

Demonstration: This demonstration promotes skills in analyzing data, graphing data, and interpreting graphs. Set up two dot timers adjacent to each other. With the timers off, have one student take hold of the first timer's tape and walk 3 m forward. Have another student take hold of the second timer's tape and remain at the timer. Instruct both students that when the timers are started they are to walk at a constant velocity. The student having a head start should walk slower than the other student.

Start both timers simultaneously and stop both when the second student has caught up with the first. Have students mark off every fourth dot for 8 markings on each tape. Measure from the beginning of the tape to the first marking and then from the beginning to the second mark and so on through 8 marks.

Graph the total distance traveled versus time (four dots) for each tape on the same set of axes. Remember the first tape starts with 3 m at time zero. Fit straight lines to both sets of data and extrapolate the lines until they intersect. Read the graph to find the distance traveled by the walkers when they meet. Compare this value with the distance from the first dot to the last dot on the second tape. Compare the slopes of both lines.

4:1 Position-Time Graph for Constant Velocity

The following exercise may be helpful in teaching the difference between constant velocity and constant

acceleration. You will again use dot timers such as those in the introductory demonstration. You will start an activity and carry it through the chapter as each new concept is developed.

Discuss with students what the spacing looks like if the object pulling the tape through the timer is moving with a constant velocity. The spaces should all be equal. Have all students make a tape of constant velocity by pulling the tape through the timer as they walk away. They will have to move fairly quickly so the dots are easily distinguishable. Help students find a portion of the tape that shows constant velocity.

Have students mark off every fourth or fifth dot so there will be a couple of centimeters between each mark. Now have them measure from the beginning of the tape to the first mark, from the beginning of the tape to the second mark, and so on to about eight marks. Call each interval a tic of time, and make a graph of position versus time. The graph should be a straight line with a positive slope.

4:2 Velocity from a Position-Time Graph

The slope of a position-time graph is the velocity of an object. Have students find the slope of the position-time graph they made in Section 4:1. The units for the slope will be cm/tic. Emphasize that slope always carries units with it and these units should be used to identify what the slope represents.

4:4 Velocity-Time Graph for Constant Velocity

To make a velocity-time graph, have students cut the tape into pieces by cutting at each mark. Then make a bar graph by pasting the pieces on end next to each other. Even though there is some experimental error, this velocity-time graph should look like a horizontal line since all the pieces should be about the same length.

4:5 Velocity-Time Graph for Uniform Acceleration

Have students make a tape of constant acceleration by pulling the tape through the timer so that the spacing between the dots gets farther and farther apart. For the following exercise select a section of the tape that looks like constant acceleration. Allowing students to make the tapes in this way helps them to experience constant velocity and acceleration.

Have students again mark off every fourth or fifth dot so they have intervals of a few centimeters. Measure from the beginning of the tape to the first mark, from the beginning of the tape to the second mark, and so on to about eight marks. Have students record this data in a table and save it for the next section. Then have them cut the tape at each mark and make a bar graph as they did before. If the acceleration is constant, the graph should look like a straight line with a positive slope. Each bar represents the change in displacement in each successive time interval, or the area under the curve. It is easy to see that when something is accelerating, it travels farther in each successive time interval.

4:6 Position-Time Graph for Uniform Acceleration

To make a graph of position versus time, have students graph the data they recorded in the previous section before they cut the tape. This graph should look like a parabola. You can relate this to the equation for displacement from Chapter 3, $d = 1/2at^2$. The slope of this graph is velocity. The instantaneous velocity can be found by drawing a tangent line to the graph at a given point and determining its slope. Lead students to realize that the slope continually increases as does the velocity of an object that is accelerating.

4:7 Acceleration-Time Graph for Uniform Acceleration

Acceleration can be obtained from the slope of the velocity-time graph. Have students look at the bar graph they made and see that it has a constant positive slope with the units cm/tic^2. Students often have a hard time deciding whether to use slope or area to find a new quantity. Remind them that the unit of the slope

or area that they get from the units on the x- and y-axes indicates to them if they have the right quantity. For example, if they tried to take the area under the position-time graph, the units would be cm times seconds, which does not have physical meaning.

To summarize the concepts learned in this chapter, have students draw a position-time graph and a velocity-time graph for a person who walks to a friend's house at a constant pace, stops to talk for a while, and then runs home at a steady speed. Then have them draw the position-time graph for a person speeding up from a stoplight to the speed limit, traveling at the speed limit for a while, and then slowing down until reaching a stop sign. Finally, reverse the process, giving students some graphs and having them describe the sequence of events to go with the graphs.

If you have access to a sonic detector and the software that plots the motion of an object as it moves in front of the detector, the students can see the graph of their motion being produced as it is happening. This gives a visual picture immediately and can be very helpful. Some programs allow students to draw the velocity-time graphs for their position-time graphs. The correct graph is produced on the screen.

Resources

Literature

Miller, Jr., Franklin, *College Physics,* Harcourt Brace Jovanovich, San Diego, 1982, pp. 22–34.

Silberstein, E.P., "Graphically Speaking," *The Science Teacher,* May, 1986, pp. 41–45.

Swartz, Clifford, *Prelude to Physics,* John Wiley and Sons, Inc., New York, 1983, pp. 66–103.

Theriault, Robert, "Revved Up for Physics," *The Science Teacher,* December, 1986, pp. 39–40.

Van Heuvelen, Alan, *Physics: A General Introduction,* Little, Brown and Company, Boston, 1982, pp. 35–58.

Background

You may want to discuss motion which will give a negative displacementwith reference to a central point. For example, a certain person drives east at a constant velocity, and then stops for a while. Then, the person drives towards home at a constant velocity, passes home, drives west of home as far as he or she had gone east, stops for a while, and goes back home. The graph of position versus time will look like this:

Use the slope of the position-time graph to get the velocity-time graph.

The slope of the velocity-time graph will give acceleration-time.

This exercise may help students to have a more complete understanding of the graphical analysis of motion and to understand that negative quantities indicate direction.

Chapter Review

Questions

1. Slope of a position-time graph indicates velocity.
2. The area under a velocity-time curve represents displacement.
3. The slope of a velocity-time graph indicates acceleration.
4. When the velocity-time graph is a line parallel to the t-axis, the acceleration is zero.
5. Area beneath an acceleration-time graph represents change in velocity.
6. The velocity rises quickly at first, then the rate slows. At times the velocity remains constant for an instant, as gears are shifted. At succeeding gear shifts, the rate of increase in velocity decreases.
7. The average acceleration is largest in the interval AB and smallest in the interval DE. The instantaneous acceleration varies over each interval, start-

ing large and decreasing. It actually becomes zero at points B, C, and D where pauses due to shifting gears occur.

8. a. At the y-intercept, runner A is running ahead of runner B.
   b. Runner B is faster because the slope of the line representing runner B is larger than that of runner A.
   c. Runner B catches up with, and passes, runner A.

Applying Concepts

1. Both are straight lines through the origin. Slope of the runner's graph would be larger.
2. Both are straight lines through the origin. One has a positive slope, the other a negative slope. The absolute values of the two slopes are equal.

Chapter 4

3. Half a parabola, upside down, followed by a horizontal line at zero displacement after it hits the ground at 1 second.

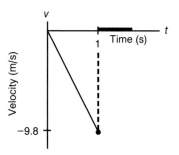

4. Straight line through origin with -9.8 m/s² slope until orange hits the ground at 1 s, then a horizontal line at zero velocity.

5. For the first 5 milliseconds, it has a uniform downward velocity. It then rapidly goes to zero velocity when it hits its target.

6. slope $= \Delta v/\Delta t = \dfrac{(13 \text{ m/s} - 0 \text{ m/s})}{(7 \text{ ms} - 5 \text{ ms})(1 \text{ s}/1000 \text{ ms})}$

$= \dfrac{13 \text{ m/s}}{0.002 \text{ s}} = 6.5 \times 10^3 \text{ m/s}^2$, or 6.5 km/s².

7. Velocity increases rapidly at first, then more slowly. Acceleration is greatest at the beginning, but is reduced as velocity increases. Eventually it is necessary for the driver to shift into second gear.

8. The acceleration is smaller just before the gear change because the slope is less at that point on the graph. Once the driver shifts and the gears engage, acceleration and the slope of the curve increase.

Exercises

1. a.

b. $d = \bar{v}t = (4 \text{ m/s})(2 \text{ s}) = 8$ m
c. $d = vt = (8 \text{ m/s})(4 \text{ s}) = 32$ m
d. $d = (10 \text{ m/s})(5 \text{ s}) + (20 \text{ m/s})(3 \text{ s})$
$= 50 \text{ m} + 60 \text{ m} = 110$ m
e. $a = \dfrac{\Delta v}{\Delta t} = \dfrac{16 \text{ m/s} - 0 \text{ m/s}}{4 \text{ s} - 0 \text{ s}} = 4 \text{ m/s}^2$
acceleration
f. $a = \dfrac{\Delta v}{\Delta t} = \dfrac{20 \text{ m/s} - 20 \text{ m/s}}{7 \text{ s} - 5 \text{ s}} = 0$ constant
velocity

2. a.

b. parabola
c. $d = 2t^2 = (2)(2.2 \text{ s})^2 = 9.7$ m
d. $d = \dfrac{(v_f + v_i)}{2}t$

$v_f = \dfrac{2d}{t} - v_i = \dfrac{(2)(18 \text{ m})}{3.0 \text{ s}} - 0 = \dfrac{36 \text{ m}}{3.0 \text{ s}} = 12$ m/s
The slope represents the speed at the end of 3.0 s.

3. a. $a = \dfrac{\Delta v}{\Delta t} = \dfrac{30 \text{ m/s} - 0 \text{ m/s}}{5 \text{ m/s}} = 6 \text{ m/s}^2$, N

b. $a = \dfrac{\Delta v}{\Delta t} = \dfrac{30 \text{ m/s} - 30 \text{ m/s}}{5 \text{ s}} = 0$

c. $a = \dfrac{\Delta v}{\Delta t} = \dfrac{20 \text{ m/s} - 30 \text{ m/s}}{5 \text{ s}} = -2 \text{ m/s}^2$

d. $a = \dfrac{\Delta v}{\Delta t} = \dfrac{0 - 20 \text{ m/s}}{5 \text{s}} = -4 \text{ m/s}^2$

4. a. $d = \dfrac{(v_f + v_i)}{2}t = \dfrac{(30 \text{ m/s} + 0)(5 \text{ s})}{2} = 75 \text{ m}$

b. $d = \bar{v}t = (30 \text{ m/s})(5 \text{ s}) = 150 \text{ m}$

c. $d = \dfrac{(v_f + v_i)}{2}t = \dfrac{(20 \text{ m/s} + 30 \text{ m/s})(5 \text{ s})}{2}$

$= 125 \text{ m}$

d. From $t = 15$ s to $t = 20$ s,
$d = \bar{v}t = (20 \text{ m/s})(5 \text{ s}) = 100 \text{ m}$
and from $t = 20$ s to $t = 25$ s
$d = \dfrac{(v_f + v_i)}{2}t = \dfrac{(0 \text{ m/s} + 20 \text{ m/s})(5 \text{ s})}{2}$

$= 50 \text{ m}$
Between $t = 0$ and $t = 25$ s
$d = 75 \text{ m} + 150 \text{ m} + 125 \text{ m} + 100 \text{ m} + 50 \text{ m} = 500 \text{ m}$

5. A − B = acceleration (in positive direction), B − C = constant velocity, C − D = deceleration (acceleration in negative direction), D − E = rest, E − F = acceleration in opposite (negative) direction, F − G = constant velocity, G − H = deceleration (acceleration in positive direction)

6. a.

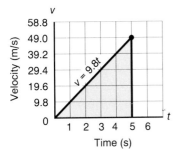

b. The area represents the distance through which the object fell (122.5 m).

7. a.

t(s)	d(m)
1	4.9
2	19.6
3	44.1
4	78.4
5	122.5

b.

c. They should be about 20 m/s and 39 m/s, but accurate values using data taken from the graph will be difficult to obtain.
$v_f = v_i + gt = 0 + (9.8 \text{ m/s}^2)(2 \text{ s}) = 20 \text{ m/s}$
$v_f = v_i + gt = 0 + (9.8 \text{ m/s}^2)(4 \text{ s}) = 39 \text{ m/s}$

8. a. A straight line through the origin.

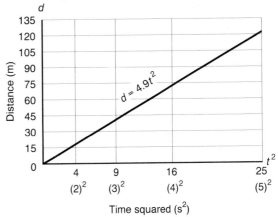

b. The slope will be 4.9 m/s² which is g/2, the proportionality constant between d and t^2.

c. Yes, since $d \propto t^2$.

9. a.

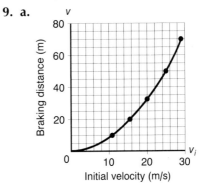

It appears to be half a parabola. This will be confirmed in part **d**.

b.

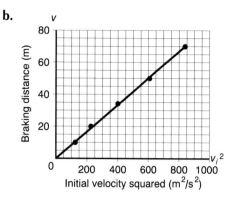

A straight line. Note that in both parts **a** and **b** all points will not fall on the curves because the given data is realistic data.

c. slope $= \dfrac{\Delta d}{\Delta v^2} = \dfrac{50\ \text{m} - 0\ \text{m}}{600\ \text{m}^2/\text{s}^2 - 0\ \text{m}^2/\text{s}^2}$

$= 0.0833\ \text{s}^2/\text{m}$

$1/\text{slope} = 12.0\ \text{m/s}^2$

d. Yes, since the equation can be written in the form $d = \left(-\dfrac{1}{2}a\right)v_i^2$, a straight line written

with slope $-\dfrac{1}{2}a$. Since $-2a = 12.0\ \text{m/s}^2$,

$a = -6.0\ \text{m/s}^2$.

10. a. It moves downward at about -13 m/s for about 5 ms. It then suddenly comes to a halt (accelerates).

b. about 6500 m/s².

c. 663 g's

d. area is almost rectangular:
$(-13\ \text{m/s})(0.006\ \text{s}) = -8$ cm. This is in agreement with the position-time graph where the hand moves from $+8$ cm to 0 cm, for a net displacement of -8 cm.

11. a. constant velocity
b. velocity

12. a. constant velocity
b. displacement

13. a. uniform acceleration
b. acceleration
c. displacement

14. velocity

15. a. parabola
b. instantaneous velocity
c. The slopes would be larger at higher points indicating larger velocities.

Problems

1. a.

(a.)

(b.)

(c.)

b.

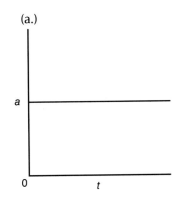

(a.)

(b.)

(c.)

2. a.

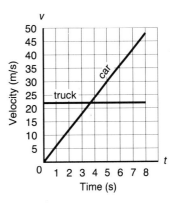

b. Yes. The position-time curves intersect at 7 seconds and position 150 m, as calculated. The velocity-time graph indicates a car velocity at 7 seconds of 42 m/s, as calculated.

3. a. $d_{Express} = v_i t + \frac{1}{2}at^2$

(36.0 m/s)(12.0 s) +

$\frac{1}{2}(-3.00 \text{ m/s}^2)(12.0 \text{ s})^2$

= 432 m − 216 m = 216 m

$d_{Local} = 100 \text{ m} + v_i t + \frac{1}{2}at^2$

= 100 m + (11.0 m/s)(12.0 s) + 0

= 100 m + 132 m = 232 m

On this basis no collision will occur.

b.

t	d(Local)	d(Express)
(s)	(m)	(m)
1	111	35
2	122	66
3	133	95
4	144	120
5	155	143
6	166	162
7	177	179
8	188	192
9	199	203
10	210	210
11	221	215
12	232	216

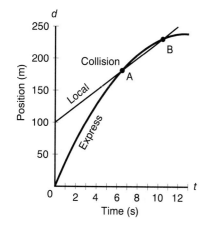

c. The collision occurs at point A (not B).

4. a.

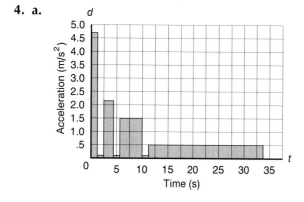

Acceleration is greatest between 0 and 3 seconds; least between 12 and 30 seconds.

b.

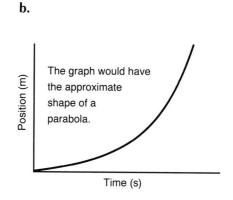

The graph would have the approximate shape of a parabola.

The position-time graph can be more accurately sketched by plotting the area under the given velocity-time graph versus time. For example, since the area of each square is (2.5 m/s) × (2.5 s) = 6.25 m, if the area under the graph up to 5 s is estimated to be 5.5 squares, then the distance traveled by the car in the first 5 s is (5.5 squares) × (6.25 m/square) = 34 m.

5. a. The table of positions for football (b), offensive receiver (r), and defensive safety (s) is generated from the following equations:
$$x_b = (11.4 \text{ m/s})t$$
$$x_r = 10 \text{ m} + (8.8 \text{ m/s})t$$
$$x_s = 8 \text{ m} + (9.5 \text{ m/s})t$$

t(s)	x_b(m)	x_r(m)	x_s(m)
0.0	0.0	10.0	8.0
1.0	11.4	18.8	17.5
2.0	22.8	27.6	27.0
3.0	34.2	36.4	36.5
3.6	41.0	41.7	42.2
3.8	43.3	43.4	44.1
4.0	45.6	45.2	46.0
4.2	47.9	47.0	47.9
4.4	50.2	48.7	49.8
4.6	52.4	50.5	51.7

b.

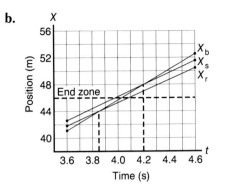

c. The positions of the football and the offensive receiver coincide at 3.85 s; those of the football and defensive safety at 4.2 s. The positions of the offensive receiver and defensive safety coincide at 2.86 s and this is not shown on the graph.

d. Since the football is caught in the end zone and the coincidence there is that of the football and the defensive safety, we conclude that the football is caught for an interception.

CHAPTER 5

Forces

Overview

Motion has been described in previous chapters by developing the basic motion equations and by doing a graphical analysis of motion. Chapter 5 deals with forces and how they affect motion. Newton's first law states that when all forces are balanced, an object will be at rest or will move with a constant velocity. The first law is often referred to as the law of inertia. Newton's second law states that an unbalanced force, referred to as the net force, causes acceleration. The unit of force is the newton, and one newton is the

force necessary to accelerate a 1-kg object at a rate of 1 m/s^2. Mass is a measure of the inertia of a body. Newton's third law states that every force is accompanied by an equal and opposite force.

Friction is a force that opposes the motion of two objects in contact. It is often the net force on an object. The force of friction is proportional to the coefficient of friction and the force normal to the two surfaces. Air friction is the force responsible for a body reaching a terminal velocity when it is in free fall.

Planning Guide (6 Class Sessions)

Text Section			Demonstrations and Experiments		Other Program Components	
5:1	Forces	P	Dem 5:1 Net Force		Teaching Master 5-1: Balanced	
5:2	Newton's First Law of		Exp 7 Force and Acceleration	LM	Forces	TRP
	Motion	P	Exp 8 Mass and Acceleration	LM	Demonstration 5-1: Newton's First	
5:3	Newton's Second Law of		Exp 9 Friction	LM	Law	TRP
	Motion	P			Demonstration 5-2: Inertia and	
5:4	The Unit of Force	P			Newton's First Law	TRP
5:5	Newton's Third Law of				Enrichment 5-2: Scientists Make	
	Motion	P			Headlines	TRP
					Enrichment 5-3: Time Lines	TRP
5:6	Mass and Weight	P				
5:7	Two Kinds of Mass	S				
5:8	Friction	P	Dem 5:8 Friction		Teaching Master 5-2: Sliding	
5:9	Acceleration When Two		Dem 5:10 Free Falling Cup		Friction	TRP
	Forces Act on an Object	P			Review Masters	TRP
5:10	The Fall of Bodies in the				Demonstration 5-3: Accceleration of	
	Air	P			Freely Falling Objects	TRP
					Demonstration 5-4. Frictional Effects	
					of Air	TRP
					Enrichment 5-1. Problems	TRP
					Evaluation	TRP

Performance Objectives

Upon completion of this chapter, your students will

1. name the four basic forces; know the relative strengths of the forces; and recognize that many seemingly different forces are actually electromagnetic in origin. 5:1
2. state the first law of motion; understand the concept of inertia; display an understanding of the universality of the first law. 5:2
3. state the second law of motion; understand that the first law is a special case of the second; display an understanding of the universality of the second law. 5:3
4. understand the definition of the newton; use the second law in solving problems. 5:4
5. state the third law of motion; understand that forces act in pairs on different bodies. 5:5
6. distinguish between weight and mass; understand the agent that gives rise to weight; use the second law to relate mass and weight. 5:6
7. differentiate between two concepts of mass. 5:7
8. demonstrate an understanding of the nature of frictional forces; be able to use the coefficient of friction in solving problems. 5:8
9. demonstrate an understanding of the meaning of net force and an ability to find the acceleration that results. 5:9
10. understand the definition of free fall and the origin of air resistance; recognize the reason terminal velocities exist. 5:10

Teaching the Chapter

Introduction

Using the Photo: Sky divers are accelerated at approximately 9.8 m/s^2 when they jump from a plane. Drag, a force due to friction from air resistance, depends on the speed of the falling object and its shape. Acceleration due to gravity remains constant. However, the net force is zero when the force due to the weight of the sky diver and the force of drag eventually become equal. With a net force of zero on the sky diver, the acceleration is zero also. So, the sky diver travels at a constant speed, which is his or her terminal velocity. A sky diver can reach his or her terminal velocity in about eleven seconds.

The photograph can be used to discuss Section 5:1 on forces, Section 5:3 on Newton's Second Law of Motion, Section 5:6 on weight, or Section 5:10 on terminal velocity.

Demonstration: Net forces cause masses to accelerate. This demonstration shows the relationship among net force, mass, and acceleration. Lay a pulley on a table. Attach one end of a string to a dynamics cart and put the string over the pulley. Hang weights on the other end of the string. Set different masses on the cart and accelerate the cart with the same weights hanging on the string over the pulley. Ask students to describe their observations and to explain how the two runs differed. Develop the idea that the same force produces less acceleration when the mass is greater, thus supporting $F = ma$.

Have a student use a spring scale to pull a 1-kg hooked mass on its side with a force of 1 N. Does the mass move? Reduce the friction on the surface or increase it by using sandpaper. What happens? Emphasize that the accelerating force is the net force. The net force is the force you apply minus the force of friction.

5:2 Newton's First Law of Motion

Ask students what they know about Newton's laws and inertia. Let students push or pull objects of different masses to get a physical feeling for forces. Do as many demonstrations as possible to reinforce the concepts of motion and force.

The simplicity of Newton's laws makes them difficult for students to appreciate. Emphasize that Newton's laws govern all motion. The result of a net force is the acceleration of a body, and if no net force exists, the body remains in equilibrium. Equilibrium means the body may be either at rest or moving with a constant velocity.

Ask students what they would think if their desk started to move. Ask students why a puck on an air table keeps moving when the force is removed.

5:6 Mass and Weight

Differentiate between mass and weight by emphasizing that mass is a measure of the amount of material present; weight is the gravitational force on the mass. Therefore, if you take an object to the moon, the amount of material in the object will not change, but the gravitational force on it will change. Prepare a chart of the weight of common objects in newtons to help students become familiar with the size of the newton. For example, a paper clip of mass 1 g, or 0.001 kg, weighs 0.0098 N. A nickel of mass 0.005 kg weighs 0.049 N. A person who has a mass of about 60 kg has a weight of 588 N.

5:8 Friction

The origin of frictional forces may be clarified using the analogy of two apparently smooth surfaces in contact with each other. A close-up view of the contact zone shows one rough surface meshing into another. Pieces of velcro are a good analogy.

Demonstration: Use a demonstration spring scale so the class can read the scale as you pull a brick across the table. Guide students to understand that it takes much more force to get the brick started than it does to keep it moving. Starting friction is called static friction. There are different coefficients of friction for static friction.

For friction studies, use a Teflon coated cookie sheet cut into 5 × 16-inch strips secured to a board with screws. Cover a 6 × 3 × 1-inch block of wood on the bottom and side with felt cloth. Show students that the force of friction is the same regardless of the size of the surfaces in contact.

5:9 Acceleration When Two Forces Act on an Object

Have students verbally describe net force. Have them write the equation $F = ma$ as $F_{net} = ma$ to remind them they must consider all the forces on the object. Have students draw diagrams for each problem, indicating forces on the object. A box can be used to represent the object. Put the mass of the object in the box and represent the forces on the box with arrows pointing in the direction of the force. Remind students that force is a vector, which has direction, whereas mass is a scalar, describable by a real number.

5:10 The Fall of Bodies in the Air

The concept of free fall might be discussed in terms of weightlessness in satellite orbit. As the force of gravity extends to satellite orbits, objects in orbit have weight. However, both the astronauts and the satellite in which they travel are in free fall, accelerating toward Earth at the same rate. Thus, the floor of the satellite does not exert a force on the astronauts, so they feel weightless. Similar effects occur in any object accelerating at a rate equal to gravity, such as elevators or airplanes.

Have volunteers ride up and down in an elevator and make a video of the scale readings as they accelerate and decelerate. Students can figure out the acceleration of the elevator from the scale readings.

When an object falls, it stops accelerating and reaches its terminal velocity when the force of the air resistance equals the weight of the object. Ask students to think of objects they see falling at a constant velocity. The terminal velocity depends on the weight of the object, the density of the air, and the size of the object.

Demonstration: Take a Styrofoam cup and punch a hole in its side near the bottom. Fill the cup with water and show how it leaks. Adjust the size of the hole so a steady stream of water comes out. Now refill the cup, this time placing your finger over the hole. Raise the cup over your head and release it to fall into a bucket. No water will leak through the hole on the trip down. Explain this, using the concepts of free fall and net force.

Resources

Literature

Brehmer, Steven, "Driving Home the Laws of Motion," *The Science Teacher,* December, 1981, p. 14.

Jensen, Larry, "Apparent Weight Losses in an Elevator," *The Physics Teacher,* October, 1976, pp. 436–439.

McGinley, P.H., "Cookie Sheet Friction," *The Physics Teacher,* September, 1973, p. 362.

Minstrell, Jim, "Getting the Facts Straight," *The Science Teacher,* January, 1983, p. 53.

Van Heuvelen, Alan, *Physics: A General Introduction,* Little, Brown and Co., Boston, 1982, p. 284–285.

Software/Audiovisual

General Physics Series Vol. III, Motion, Cross Educational Software, Apple II, IBM-PC software

Forces and Newton's Laws of Motion, Merlan Scientific Ltd., Apple II, Commodore 64, Commodore Pet software

Physics Demos: Mechanics, EduTech, Apple II software
The Mechanical Universe—High School Adaptation, Quad 1, Newton's Laws, Annenberg Project, 1985, video

Background

The formula for terminal velocity is

$$v_T = \sqrt{\frac{2W}{c_D \varrho A}}$$

where W is the weight of the object, c_D is the drag coefficient, ϱ is the density of air, and A is the cross sectional area of the object as seen along its line of motion. You can calculate the terminal velocity of a ping-pong ball weighing 2.9×10^{-2} N with a radius of 1.9×10^{-2} m and a drag coefficient of 0.6.

$$v_T = \sqrt{\frac{2W}{c_D \varrho A}} = \sqrt{\frac{2W}{c_D \varrho \pi r^2}}$$

$$= \sqrt{\frac{2\,(2.9 \times 10^{-2} \text{N})}{0.6\,(1.3 \text{ kg/m}^3)(\pi)(1.9 \times 10^{-2} \text{ m}^2)}}$$

$$v_T = 8.1 \text{ m/s}$$

A sky diver has a terminal velocity of about 54 m/s (120 mph) and a raindrop about 12 m/s.

Chapter Review

QUESTIONS

1. **a.** Newton's first law says that the state of motion of the ball will change if a net force acts on the ball. The net force on the ball is the friction force and the motion of the ball changes accordingly.
   b. The motion will not change if the acceleration of the ball is zero. Newton's second law, $F_{net} = ma$, indicates that the acceleration can be made zero by making the net force zero, either by eliminating friction, or by adding a force in the direction of motion to balance friction.

2. The mass would be the same. The weight would be ten times greater.

3. In both cases, the tendency of the package to remain at rest or in motion is the result of inertia. More specifically, if the friction force between the package and the seat is not large enough to accelerate the mass of the package at the same rate as the bus is accelerating then the bus will "outrun" the package. In the case of braking, insufficient friction force to decelerate the package at the same rate as the bus will result in the package "outrunning" the bus.

4. No. With no forces on it, it will continue at whatever velocity it had.

5. Friction between the hand cart and carton.

6. Terminal velocity is reached when air resistance equals the gravitational force. A batted ball is accelerated by the force of the bat, which can be much larger than the gravitational force.

7. The rock does pull on the Earth, but the Earth's enormous mass would undergo only a minute acceleration by such a small force. This would go undetected.

8. A large force is required to accelerate the mass of the bicycle and rider. Once the desired constant velocity is reached, a much smaller force is sufficient to overcome the everpresent frictional forces.

9. **a.** Yes. Its velocity changed direction, thus it was accelerated.
   b. The floor.

10. No. It only means forces on it were balanced. Example: an object hanging on a rope. The weight of the object is balanced by the tension in the rope.

APPLYING CONCEPTS

1. **a.** The car is suddenly accelerated forward. The seat accelerates the body, but the neck has to accelerate the head. This can hurt the muscles.
   b. The headrest pushes on the head, accelerating it in the same direction as the car.

2. The equal and opposite forces referred to in Newton's third law are acting on different objects.

The horse would pull on the cart and the cart would pull on him. The cart would have an unbalanced net force on it (neglecting friction) and would thus accelerate. Moral: never teach a horse only a little physics.

3. The shuttle is burning a large amount of its mass, the fuel, as it is launched. Since the force remains constant and the mass decreases, the acceleration increases.

4. Free fall, move to the moon, ride an elevator accelerating downward.

5. Each pulls on the other equally; Newton's third law. The Earth does accelerate toward the sky-diver, but the small force applied to the enormous mass of the Earth results in only a minute amount of acceleration.

6. Since friction depends on the nature of the surfaces (book/table) and the force pushing the surfaces together (book's weight), both would produce identical amounts of friction.

7. **a.** Velocity is increasing; distance traveled each second increases; acceleration is constant
   b. Velocity and acceleration all constant (acceleration is zero); distance continues to increase

8. The lighter, air-filled ping-pong ball reaches terminal velocity first. Because the force of gravity on the more massive concrete-filled ping-pong ball is larger, its terminal velocity is larger, and it strikes the ground first.

EXERCISES

1. $F = ma = (1750 \text{ kg})(+1.35 \text{ m/s}^2)$
   $= +2.36 \times 10^3 \text{ N}$.

2. $m = F/a = (+3.00 \times 10^3 \text{ N})/(+4.00 \text{ m/s}^2)$
   $= 750 \text{ kg}$

3. $F = ma$, where, since d and t are known, a can be found from $d = v_i t + (1/2)at^2$. Thus $a = 2d/t^2 = 2(+40 \text{ m})/(3.0 \text{ s})^2 = +8.9 \text{ m/s}^2$, so $F = (710 \text{ kg})(+8.9 \text{ m/s}^2) = +6.3 \times 10^3 \text{N}$.

4. **a.** Use $v_f^2 = v_i^2 + 2 gd = 2(9.80 \text{ m/s}^2)(10 \text{ m})$
   so $v_f = 14 \text{ m/s}$
   b. To find a, use $v_f^2 = v_i^2 + 2ad$ or
   $a = (v_f^2 - v_i^2)/2d$
   $= (0 - (14 \text{ m/s})^2)/2(2 \text{ m})$
   $= -49 \text{ m/s}^2$
   $F = ma = (65 \text{ kg})(-49 \text{ m/s}^2)$
   $= -3.2 \times 10^3 \text{ N}$

5. The rock would be 1/6 as hard to lift on the moon, since $W = mg$ and $g_{Earth} = 6g_{moon}$. There is no difference in the effort needed to throw the rock, neglecting air friction, since no gravitational force acts in the horizontal direction.

6. $g = w/m = (78.4 \text{ N})(7.50 \text{ kg}) = 10.5 \text{ m/s}^2$, downward

7. **a.** $W = mg = (5.0 \text{ kg})(-9.80 \text{ m/s}^2) = -49 \text{ N}$
   b. $ma = F_{net} = F_{appl} + W = 98 \text{ N} + (-49 \text{ N})$
   $= +49 \text{ N (up)}$
   $a = (+49 \text{ N})/(5.0 \text{ kg}) = +9.8 \text{ m/s}^2 \text{ (up)}$
   c. $v = at = (+9.80 \text{ m/s}^2)(10 \text{ s}) = +98 \text{ m/s}$ (up)
   d. Just the instrument weight, -49 N (down)
   e. The velocity becomes negative after it passes through zero. Thus, use $v_f = v_i + gt$, where $v_f = 0$, or $t = -v_i/g = -(+98 \text{ m/s})/(-9.80 \text{ m/s}^2) = 10 \text{ s}$.

8. The mass of the elevator is $m = W/g = (-30 \times 10^3 \text{ N})/(-9.8 \text{ m/s}^2) = 3.1 \times 10^3 \text{ kg}$. Now $ma = F_{net} = F_{appl} + W$ so that $F_{appl} = ma - W = (3.1 \times 10^3 \text{ kg})(1.0 \text{ m/s}^2) - (-30 \times 10^3 \text{ N}) = 3.3 \times 10^4 \text{ N}$.

9. Answers will vary. Example: 150 lb = 68 kg, $W = mg = (68 \text{ kg})(9.8 \text{ m/s}^2) = 670 \text{ N}$.

10. $T = ma = (70.0 \text{ kg})(1.50 \text{ m/s}^2) = 105 \text{ N}$

11. $ma = F_{net} = F_{appl} + W = F_{appl} + mg$, so $F_{appl} = ma - mg = (4500 \text{ kg})(2 \text{ m/s}^2) - (4500 \text{ kg})(-9.8 \text{ m/s}^2) = 5.3 \times 10^4 \text{ N}$.

12. $v_f^2 = v_i^2 + 2ad$ so $a = (v_f^2 - v_i^2)/2d = ((500 \text{ m/s})^2 - 0)/(2)(0.80 \text{ m}) = 1.6 \times 10^5 \text{ m/s}^2$ and $F = ma = (5.0 \times 10^{-3} \text{ kg})(1.6 \times 10^5 \text{ m/s}^2) = 800 \text{ N}$.

13. $v_f^2 = v_i^2 + 2ad$ so $a = (v_f^2 - v_i^2)/2d = ((36 \text{ m/s})^2 - 0)/(2)(2.5 \text{ m}) = 260 \text{ m/s}^2$
   $F = ma = (0.10 \text{ kg})(260 \text{ m/s}^2) = 26 \text{ N}$

14. $a = F/m = (-9000 \text{ N})/(1500 \text{ kg})$
   $= -6.0 \text{ m/s}^2$
   $d = (v_f^2 - v_i^2)/2a$
   $= ((0 - (20 \text{ m/s})^2)/(2)(-6.0 \text{ m/s}^2) = 33 \text{ m}$

15. $F_{appl} = ma - mg$
   $= (20 \text{ kg})(5 \text{ m/s}^2) - (20 \text{ kg})(-9.8 \text{ m/s}^2)$
   $= 296 \text{ N}$.
   No, this force is greater than 250 N, hence the sack rips.

16. Take the direction from the fish to the person as positive. The acceleration of the fish, and hence the line, will be obtained from $ma = F_{net} = F_{fish}$.

Thus $a = (F_{appl} + F_{fish})/m =$
$(38\ N - 40\ N)/(2.0\ kg) = -1.0\ m/s^2$.

17. a. $ma = F_{net} = F_{appl} - F_f = F_{appl} - ma =$
$40\ N - (5.0\ kg)(6.0\ m/s^2) = 10\ N$
b. $F_f = \mu F_N = \mu mg$ so $\mu F_f/mg =$
$(10\ N)(5.0\ kg)(9.8\ m/s^2) = 0.20$

18. $ma = F_{net} = F_{appl} - F_f$ where $F_f = \mu F_N = \mu mg$.
Therefore $a = (F_{appl} - \mu mg)/m = (700\ N -$
$(0.20)(200\ kg)(9.8\ m/s^2)/(200\ kg) = 1.5\ m/s^2$

19. a. $W = mg = (50\ kg)(9.8\ m/s^2) = 490\ N$
b. $F_f = \mu F_N = \mu W = (0.30)(490\ N) = 150\ N$,
static friction.
c. $F_f = \mu F_N = \mu W = (0.10)(490\ N) = 49\ N$,
sliding friction.
d. $ma = F_{net} = F_{appl} - F_f$ so $F_{appl} = ma + F_f =$
$(50\ kg)(30\ m/s^2) + 49\ N = 200\ N$

PROBLEMS

1. a. $F_f = ma = (925\ kg)(-12.2\ m/s^2)$
$= -1.13 \times 10^4\ N$, opposite direction of
motion
b. $\mu = F_f/mg$
$= (1.13 \times 10^4\ N)/(925\ kg)(9.8\ m/s^2) = 1.25$

2. $F = ma = (0.7\ kg)(-6500\ m/s^2)$
$= -4.6 \times 10^3\ N$ (upward)

3. The basic equation to be applied is $ma = F_{net} =$
$F_{appl} - W$, where the positive direction is taken
upward and F_{appl} is the force exerted by the scale.
The mass of the person is $m = W/g =$
$(490\ N)(9.8\ m/s^2) = 50\ kg$.
a. $a = 0$ so $F_{appl} = W = 490\ N$
b. $F_{appl} = ma + W$
$= (50\ kg)(2.2\ m/s^2) + 490\ N = 600\ N$
c. $a = 0$ so $F_{appl} = W = 490\ N$
d. $F_{appl} = ma + W$
$= (50\ kg)(-2.2\ m/s^2) + 490\ N = 380\ N$
e. $F_{appl} = ma + W$
$= (50\ kg)(-2.7\ m/s^2) + 490\ N = 355\ N$

f. $a = 0$ so $F_{appl} = W = 490\ N$
g. $a = -g$ so $F_{appl} = ma + W = m(-g) +$
$mg = 0$

4. The basic equation to be applied is $ma = F_{net} =$
$F_{appl} - W$, where the positive direction is taken
upward and F_{appl} is the force exerted by the scale.
The mass of the student is $m = W/g =$
$(836\ N)/(9.8\ m/s^2) = 85.3\ N$.
a. $a = (F_{appl} - W)/m =$
$(935\ N - 836\ N)/(85.3\ kg) = 1.16\ m/s^2$
b. $a = (F_{appl} - W)/m =$
$(782\ N - 836\ N)/(85.3\ kg) = -0.633\ m/s^2$
c. stopping, because the acceleration is less
and $t = \delta v/a$
d. $F_{appl} = W + ma = 836\ N + ma$. As the
elevator starts to descend a is negative and
the scale reads less than 836 N. When
constant downward velocity is reached, the
scale reads 836 N since the acceleration is
then zero. When the elevator is slowing at
the bottom, the acceleration is positive and
the scale reads more than 836 N.

5. $m = (20)(75\ kg) + 500\ kg = 2000\ kg$.
$W = mg = (2000\ kg)(9.8\ m/s^2) = 19\ 600\ N$
$ma = F_{net} = F_{appl} - W$, $a = (F_{appl} - W)/m =$
$(29\ 600\ N - 19\ 600\ N)/(2000\ kg) = 5.0\ m/s^2$

6. a. upward
b. $ma = F_{net}$ where m is the total mass being
accelerated. Take the direction of the physical
motion, smaller mass upward and larger mass
downward, to be the positive direction of
motion.
$m = m_1 + m_2 = 2.0\ kg + 3.0\ kg = 5.0\ kg$,
$F_{net} = -W_1 + W_2 = -m_1g + m_2g$
$= -(2.0\ kg)(9.8\ m/s^2) + (3.0\ kg)(9.8\ m/s^2)$
$= 9.8\ N$ (W_1 is negative since it acts in the
negative direction), $a = F_{net}/m$
$= (9.8\ N)/(5.0\ kg) = 2.0\ m/s^2$

Vectors

Overview

Vector and scalar quantities in one dimension were introduced in Chapter 3. This chapter deals with vectors in two dimensions. The graphical method of vector addition, utilizing the head-to-tail method, is introduced. The parallelogram method may produce the correct answer, but it does not teach the concepts of adding vector quantities. This chapter also shows how vector quantities act independently of one another.

When all forces on a point are balanced, the forces are in equilibrium. Two or more forces can be put in equilibrium by applying a force called the equilibrant, which is equal and opposite to the sum of the other forces.

A vector can be resolved into its horizontal and vertical components. On an inclined plane, the weight of an object is broken up into the force parallel to the plane and the force perpendicular to the plane.

Planning Guide (6 Class Sessions)

Text Section		Demonstrations and Experiments		Other Program Components	
6:1 Vector Addition; Graphical Method	S	Dem 6:1 Vector Addition		Teaching Master 6-1: Vector Addition	TRP
6:2 Vector Addition in Two Dimensions	P	Exp 10 Addition of Force Vectors	LM	Minilab 6-1: Components of Force Vectors	TRP
6:3 Independence of Vector Quantities	P	Dem 6:2 Independence of Vectors			
6:4 Vector Addition of Forces	P				
6:5 Vector Addition; Mathematical Method	P				
6:6 Addition of Several Vectors	S				
6:7 Equilibrium	S				
6:8 The Equilibrant	S				
6:9 Perpendicular Components of Vectors	P	Dem 6:9 Vector Components		Teaching Master 6-2:	
6:10 Gravitational Force and Inclined Planes	S	Dem 6:10 Coefficient of Friction		(a) Perpendicular Components of Vectors	
6:11 Non-perpendicular Components of Vectors	S	Dem 6:11 Non-perpendicular Components,		(b) Non-perpendicular Components of Vectors	TRP
				Review Masters	TRP
				Enrichment 6-1: Problems	TRP
				Enrichment 6-2: Coefficient of Friction	TRP
				Evaluation	TRP

Performance Objectives

Upon completion of this chapter, your students will

1. show an ability to add vectors by the graphical method, recognizing the commutative law of vector addition. *6:1*
2. recognize the independence of vector quantities. *6:3*
3. understand the addition of forces and be able to solve problems by graphical techniques. *6:4*
4. recognize the applications of elementary geometry and trigonometry to vector algebra and be able to solve problems using these methods. *6:5*
5. state the requirements for equilibrium. *6:7*
6. state the meaning of equilibrant; differentiating between resultant and equilibrant. *6:8*
7. specify the proper method of resolving vectors into perpendicular components; be able to choose axes and resolve vectors graphically. *6:9*
8. be able to specify axes, resolve vectors, and solve inclined plane problems. *6:10*
9. explain the resolution of nonperpendicular components. *6:11*

Teaching the Chapter

Introduction

Using the Photo: When sailing with the wind, the wind pushes a boat along in the same direction. The boat experiences frictional resistance from the water as it moves forward, thus causing it to move slower than the wind speed. Sailing at an angle to the wind creates a difference in pressure across the sail, creating a force which drives the boat forward. Water resistance opposes the forward force. As long as a net force acts on the sailboat, it will accelerate. In this manner, the terminal velocity can be in excess of the wind speed.

The photograph can be used with Sections 6:1–6:4 to illustrate vector addition of forces.

Demonstration: Going from a space diagram (an actual diagram of the situation) to a vector diagram requires a lot of practice. The following demonstration may help clarify this concept. Make a 20-N weight from two 1-kg masses and one 50-g mass tied in a square piece of cloth marked 20 N. Hang two spring scales calibrated in newtons above the chalkboard. Connect the scales with a piece of string and suspend the 20-N weight with a paper clip at the center of the string. Point out that the algebraic sum of the two forces shown on the scales is greater than 20 N. Ask students to relate the source of the extra force. Students sometimes add the forces like scalars and thus will not be able to account for the extra force.

Mark the directions of the three forces by running a piece of chalk along the strings. Record the magnitude of the three forces; removing the scales, strings, and weight, draw the appropriate vectors. Work through the vector addition to show that the sum of the two scale forces is 20 N straight up, which balances the weight down. Repeat with the 20-N weight suspended closer to one scale.

6:1 Vector Addition: Graphical Method

When vectors act at an angle to one another, they must be placed head-to-tail keeping the direction and magnitude the same. Before applying this to problems in the text, practice drawing the resultant of two vectors acting at several different angles.

6:2 Vector Addition in Two Dimensions

Demonstration: The idea that vectors act independently of one another is difficult for students to comprehend. Use this demonstration to illustrate this concept. Obtain a motorized car that goes at a relatively slow steady speed. Cut a long piece of shelf paper. Let the car go across the paper and time it with a stopwatch. Then let the car go across again as the paper is pulled perpendicular to the car's direction. Measure how long it takes the car to go across. Pull the paper so that it doesn't matter that the paper is moving, and notice that the time it takes the car to go across the paper is the same. Repeat the procedure, this time pulling the paper faster. This is similar to a boat crossing a river. If the boat heads straight across the river at a constant speed, it reaches the other side in the same time regardless of the speed of the river.

6:9 Perpendicular Components of Vectors

Demonstration: To demonstrate perpendicular components of forces, attach a large spring scale to a brick wrapped in paper and tied with a string. Start by holding the scale parallel with a bench and then raising the scale so that it acts on the brick at increasingly larger angles. Eventually the brick no longer will move horizontally, but it may be lifted off the bench. The horizontal component will decrease and the vertical component will increase as the angle increases.

Place a textbook on the bench. Have a student push on the book, first parallel to the bench, and then at increasingly larger angles. At some angle the book will not move no matter how hard it is pushed, because the horizontal component of the force is not enough to overcome friction.

6:10 Gravitational Force and Inclined Planes

Ask students what makes them slide down a slide. Most will answer that gravity is the force that makes them slide down. This is not incorrect, but point out that the gravitational force is straight down. Along the plane there must be a force that is due to gravity. Place a brick of known weight on an inclined plane. Hold the brick in place with a spring scale. Record the scale force as you raise the angle of the plane. Relate this scale reading to the force parallel to the plane in Figures 6–14 and 6–15.

Demonstration: To introduce the more advanced concept, coefficient of friction, use a block and give it a small push; sliding friction will slow it down. Raise the plane until the component of the block's weight along the plane balances the frictional force, and the block slides down at a constant velocity. Using the weight of the block, you can calculate the force parallel to the plane and the force perpendicular to the plane. The force that is parallel equals the frictional force, and the force that is perpendicular equals the normal force. You can find the coefficient of friction between the brick and the plane using $f = \mu F_N$.

Demonstration: Show students that as the angle between two forces increases, the tension in the strings increases. Hang two spring scales a distance apart above the chalkboard. Attach them with a string and hang a mass from the middle of the string. Read the scale as you make the angle larger. Notice that the force increases so much that it is off the scale. Point out that you cannot straighten the string because the tension approaches infinity. Using this demonstration, get a heavy rope and have two of the strongest stu-

dents in the class pull on each end as hard as they can to make it tight. Now ask if they think someone can pull on the rope and make them move sideways. Have a smaller person pull in the center of the rope perpendicular to the rope. A small force will pull the others over because the angle is so large that the small force causes a very large tension in the rope.

Resources

Literature

Edge, R.D., "Strength and Shape," *The Physics Teacher,* January, 1987, pp. 50–51.

Kagan, David T., "Statics and the Walkways Collapse," *The Science Teacher,* October, 1984, p. 59.

McDonald, Thomas, "Vector Racing," *The Science Teacher,* November, 1984, pp. 38–45.

Nelson, Jim, "Static Equilibrium," *The Science Teacher,* December, 1985, pp. 20–23.

Swartz, Clifford, *Prelude to Physics,* John Wiley and Sons, New York, pp. 111–122.

Software/Audiovisual

General Physics Series Vol. I-Vectors, Cross Educational Software, Apple II software

Vector Addition II, Vernier Software, Apple II software

Vectors and Linear Motion, Focus Media, Inc., Apple II software

Background

When an object hangs from the middle of a string, there is a simple formula for finding the tension in each string. The formula is

$$T = \frac{W}{2 \cos \theta/2}$$

This formula is derived as follows.

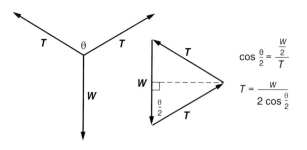

As θ approaches 180°, the tension goes to infinity. Another interesting derivation is to show that the coefficient of friction is equal to the tan θ where θ is the angle at which an object slides down a plane at constant speed. The derivation follows.

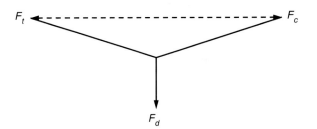

$F_N = F_W \cos \theta$

$F_\parallel = F_W \sin \theta$

If block slides at a constant speed, $F_\parallel = F_f$

$$\mu = \frac{F_f}{F_N} = \frac{F_W \sin \theta}{F_W \cos \theta}$$

$\mu = \tan \theta$

Chapter Review

QUESTIONS

1. When two or more forces act concurrently on an object and their vector sum is zero, the object is in equilibrium.

2. Vectors are added head to tail.

3. The resultant is drawn from the tail of the first vector to the head of the last vector. The head of the resultant vector coincides with the head of the last vector added.

4. Concurrent forces are two or more forces acting on the same point at the same time.

5. As the angle increases, the resultant decreases.

6. The vector sum of forces forming a closed triangle is zero. If these are the only forces acting on the object then the net force on the object is zero and the object is in equilibrium.

7. Find the resultant of the two forces. The equilibrant will be the negative of that.

8. The largest has magnitude 3 N + 4 N = 7 N

The smallest has magnitude 4 N − 3 N = 1 N

9. 10 mm

APPLYING CONCEPTS

1. **a.** same direction
   b. opposite directions
   c. no

2. 45°

3. Yes; make the angle between the handle and the horizontal smaller

4. the one that begins to slide at the larger angle

5. Method **b.** Vector consideration shows that if the rope is nearly straight then the car and tree forces are much greater than the driver force.

F_t ◄- ► F_c

F_d

6. Only the force perpendicular to the barbell contributes to lifting it. A grip in which the arms are extended straight forward from the body, so that all the force exerted is perpendicular to the bar, will exert less force on the weightlifter's arms. Spreading the arms so that the bar is gripped closer to the weights reduces the component of force perpendicular to the bar. The lifter must exert more total force for the perpendicular component to equal the force exerted when the arms are perpendicular to the bar.

7. When stretching a clothesline or strand of wire between two posts, there is no perpendicular component upward to balance the weight of the clothesline or wire. All the force exerted is horizontal to the weight. Stretching it to remove the last of the slack is an attempt to reduce the flexibility of the clothesline or wire and to increase the internal forces holding the line together; hence the need for superhuman strength.

EXERCISES

1.

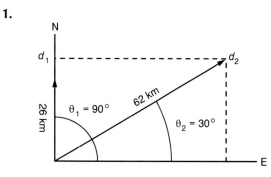

Add displacements by the component method:
$d_{1E} = d_1 \cos \theta_1 = (26 \text{ km}) \cos 90° = 0$
$d_{1N} = d_1 \sin \theta_1 = (26 \text{ km}) \sin 90° = 26 \text{ km}$
$d_{2E} = d_2 \cos \theta_2 = (62 \text{ km}) \cos 30° = 54 \text{ km}$
$d_{2N} = d_2 \sin \theta_2 = (62 \text{ km}) \sin 30° = 31 \text{ km}$
$d_E = d_{1E} + d_{2E} = 0 + 54 \text{ km} = 54 \text{ km}$
$d_N = d_{1N} + d_{2N} = 26 \text{ km} + 31 \text{ km} = 57 \text{ km}$
$d = \sqrt{(d_E)^2 + (d_N)^2}$
$\quad \sqrt{(54 \text{ km})^2 + (57 \text{ km})^2} = 79 \text{ km}$
$\tan \theta = 54 \text{ km}/57 \text{ km} = 0$
$\quad \theta = 43°$

2. Vector addition using the component method.

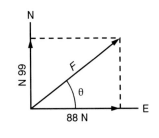

$F = \sqrt{(F_E)^2 + (F_N)^2}$
$\quad = \sqrt{(88 \text{ N})^2 + (66 \text{ N})^2}$
$\quad = 110 \text{ N}$

$\tan \theta = \dfrac{F_N}{F_E} = \dfrac{66 \text{ N}}{88 \text{ N}} = 0.75$
$\quad \theta = 37°$

3. Vector addition by component method.

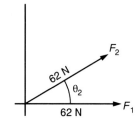

$F_{1h} = F_1 = 62 \text{ N}$
$F_{1v} = 0$
$F_{2h} = F_2 \cos \theta_2 = (62 \text{ N}) \cos \theta_2$
$F_{2v} = F_2 \sin \theta_2 = (62 \text{ N}) \sin \theta_2$
$F_h = F_{1h} + F_{2h} = 62 \text{ N} + (62 \text{ N}) \cos \theta_2$
$F_v = F_{1v} + F_{2v} = 0 + (62 \text{ N}) \sin \theta_2$
$F = \sqrt{(F_h)^2 + (F_v)^2}$
a. $F_h = 62 \text{ N} + (62 \text{ N}) \cos 0.0° = 124 \text{ N}$
$\quad F_v = 0 + (62 \text{ N}) \sin 0.0° = 0 \text{ N}$
$\quad F = \sqrt{(124 \text{ N})^2 + 0} = 124 \text{ N}$
b. $F_h = 62 \text{ N} + (62 \text{ N}) \cos 30.0° = 116 \text{ N}$
$\quad F_v = 0 + (62 \text{ N}) \sin 30.0° = 31.0 \text{ N}$
$\quad F = \sqrt{(116 \text{ N})^2 + (31.0 \text{ N})^2} = 120 \text{ N}$
c. $F_h = 62 \text{ N} + (62 \text{ N}) \cos 60.0° = 93.0 \text{ N}$
$\quad F_v = 0 + (62 \text{ N}) \sin 60.0° = 53.4 \text{ N}$
$\quad F = \sqrt{(93.0 \text{ N})^2 + (53.4 \text{ N})^2} = 107 \text{ N}$
d. $F_h = 62 \text{ N} + (62 \text{ N}) \cos 90° = 62 \text{ N}$
$\quad F_v = 0 + (62 \text{ N}) \sin 90° = 62 \text{ N}$
$\quad F = \sqrt{(162 \text{ N})^2 + (62 \text{ N})^2} = 88 \text{ N}$
e. $F_h = 62 \text{ N} + (62 \text{ N}) \cos 180°$
$\quad \quad = 62 \text{ N} + (62 \text{ N})(-1.00) = 0 \text{ N}$
$\quad F_v = 0 + (62 \text{ N}) \sin 180° = 0 \text{ N}$
$\quad F = 0 \text{ N}$

4. It decreases.

5. $a = \sqrt{(6.5 \text{ m/s}^2)^2 + (15 \text{ m/s}^2)^2} = 16 \text{ m/s}^2$
$\tan \theta = \dfrac{15}{6.5} = 2.31$
$\quad \theta = 67°$

6.

$F = 33$ N, due east

7. $v = \sqrt{(55 \text{ km/h})^2 + (225 \text{ km/h})^2} = 230$ km/h

$\tan \theta = \dfrac{225}{55} = 4.09$

$\theta = 76°$, north of east

8. Vector addition by component method.

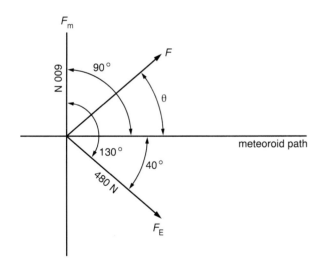

$F_{Eh} = (480 \text{ N}) \cos 40° = 370$ N
$F_{Ev} = -(480 \text{ N}) \sin 40° = -310$ N
$F_h = F_{mh} + F_{Eh} = 0 + 370 \text{ N} = 370$ N
$F_v = F_{mv} + F_{Ev} = 600 \text{ N} - 310 \text{ N} = 290$ N
$F = \sqrt{(F_h)^2 + (F_v)^2} = \sqrt{(370 \text{ N})^2 + (290 \text{ N})^2}$
   $= 470$ N

$\tan \theta = \dfrac{F_v}{F_h} = \dfrac{290 \text{ N}}{370 \text{ N}} = 0.784$

$\theta = 38°$ (from meteoroid path toward moon)

9. See solution to Exercise 3 for notation and method of solution using vector addition by components.
a. 30 N
b. 29 N
c. 21 N
d.

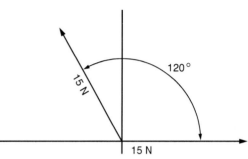

$F_h = 15 \text{ N} + (15 \text{ N}) \cos 120°$
   $= 15 \text{ N} - 7.5 \text{ N} = 7.5$ N
$F_v = (15 \text{ N}) \sin 120° = 13$ N
$F = \sqrt{(7.5 \text{ N})^2 + (13 \text{ N})^2} = 15$ N
e. 0 N

10. a.

$v = \sqrt{(3.8 \text{ m/s})^2 + (1.6 \text{ m/s})^2} = 4.1$ m/s

$\tan \theta = \dfrac{1.6}{3.8} = 0.421$

$\theta = 23°$ downstream
b. $t = \dfrac{d}{v} = \dfrac{240 \text{ m}}{3.8 \text{ m/s}} = 63$ s
c. $d = \bar{v}t = (1.6 \text{ m/s})(63 \text{ s}) = 1.0 \times 10^2$ m
11. See solution to Exercise 3 for notation and method of solution using vector addition by components.

a. 110 N

b.

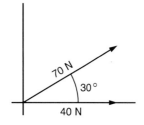

$F_h = 40 \text{ N} + (70 \text{ N}) \cos 30° = 100 \text{ N}$
$F_v = (70 \text{ N}) \sin 30° = 35 \text{ N}$
$F = \sqrt{(100 \text{ N})^2 + (35 \text{ N})^2} = 110 \text{ N}$
(result would differ from **a** if more than two significant figures were used)

c. 97 N

d. 81 N

e. 30 N

12. Vector addition by component method.

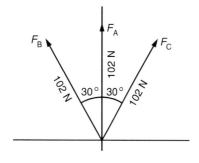

$F_{Ah} = 0 \text{ N}$
$F_{Av} = 102 \text{ N}$
$F_{Bh} = -(102 \text{ N}) \sin 30° = -51.0 \text{ N}$
$F_B = (102 \text{ N}) \cos 30° = 88.3 \text{ N}$
$F_{Ch} = (102 \text{ N}) \sin 30° = 51.0 \text{ N}$
$F_{Cv} = (102 \text{ N}) \cos 30° = 88.3 \text{ N}$
Since $F_h = F_{Ah} + F_{Bh} + F_{Ch} = 0 \text{ N} - 51.0 \text{ N} + 51.0 \text{ N} = 0.0 \text{ N}$,
$F = F_v = F_{Av} + F_{Bv} + F_{Cv} = 102 \text{ N} + 88.3 \text{ N} + 88.3 \text{ N} = 279 \text{ N}$

13. $d_N = d \sin \theta = (3.00 \times 10^2 \text{ km})(\sin 40°)$
$= 1.93 \times 10^2 \text{ km, north}$
$d_E = d \cos \theta = (3.00 \times 10^2 \text{ km})(\cos 40°)$
$= 2.30 \times 10^2 \text{ km, east}$

14.

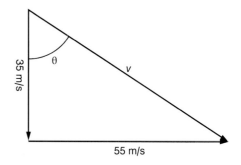

a. $v = \sqrt{(35 \text{ m/s})^2 + (55 \text{ m/s})^2} = 65 \text{ m/s}$

b. $\tan \theta = \dfrac{55 \text{ m/s}}{35 \text{ m/s}} = 1.57$, so $\theta = 58°$

15. a. $F_h = F \cos \theta = (95 \text{ N})(\cos 60°) = 48 \text{ N}$
$F_v = F \sin \theta = (95 \text{ N})(\sin 60°) = 82 \text{ N}$

b. $F_h = F \cos \theta = (95 \text{ N})(\cos 30°) = 82 \text{ N}$
$F_v = F \sin \theta = (95 \text{ N})(\sin 30°) = 48 \text{ N}$

16. $F_h = F \cos \theta = (92 \text{ N}) \cos 45° = 65 \text{ N}$
$F_v = F \sin \theta = (92 \text{ N}) \sin 45° = 65 \text{ N}$

17.

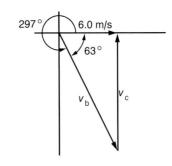

a. $v_c = (6.0 \text{ m/s}) \tan 63° = 12 \text{ m/s}, 90°$
b. $v_b = (6.0 \text{ m/s})/\cos 63° = 13 \text{ m/s}, 297°$
This is the velocity of the boat relative to the water. The velocity of the boat relative to Earth is 6 m/s, 0°.

18.

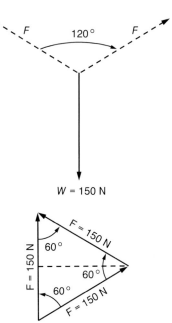

Forms an equilateral triangle—all sides are equal. Therefore, the two forces are 150 N each.

19.

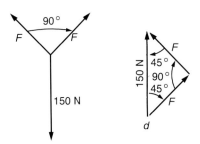

$F = (150 \text{ N}) \sin 45° = 106 \text{ N}$

20. a.

b.

c. Added head to tail, each arrangement of the vectors should give the same resultant. This is about 144 N at 16°.

PROBLEMS

1. $F_N = \pm(200 \text{ N}) \sin 30° [20 \text{ kg} + (1.5 \text{ kg} \times 30)](9.8 \text{ m/s}^2) = 637 \text{ N}$
$F_f = \mu F_N = (0.20)(637 \text{ N}) = 127 \text{ N}$
$F_h = 200 \text{ N} \cos 30° = 173 \text{ N}$
$a = F/m = (173 \text{ N} - 127 \text{ N})/65 \text{ kg} = 0.71 \text{ m/s}^2$

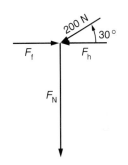

2. Solution by component method. Each of the first four forces is either horizontal or vertical as given. Only the fifth force requires resolution into components.
$F_{5h} = (50 \text{ N}) \cos 60° = 25 \text{ N}$
$F_{5v} = (50 \text{ N}) \sin 60° = 43 \text{ N}$
$F_h = F_2 + F_4 + F_{5h} = 40 \text{ N} + (-40 \text{ N}) + 25 \text{ N} = 25 \text{ N}$
$F_v = F_1 + F_3 + F_{5v} = 60 \text{ N} + (-80 \text{ N}) + 43 \text{ N} = 23 \text{ N}$
The resultant of the five forces is
$F = \sqrt{(25 \text{ N})^2 + (23 \text{ N})^2} = 34 \text{ N}$
$\tan \theta = \dfrac{23 \text{ N}}{25 \text{ N}} = 0.92, \theta = 43°$
Equilibrant: 34 N, 223°

3. $v = (5 \text{ km/h})(1000 \text{ m/km})/(3600 \text{ s/h}) = 1.39 \text{ m/s}$
$a = v/t = (1.39 \text{ m/s})/(1.5 \text{ s}) = 0.93 \text{ m/s}^2$
$ma = F_h = F \cos 45°$
$F = ma/\cos 45° = (10 \text{ kg})(0.93 \text{ m/s}^2)/\cos 45° = 13 \text{ N}$

4. a. $F_h = (100 \text{ N}) \cos 30° = 87 \text{ N}$
$a = F_h/m = (87 \text{ N})/(40 \text{ kg}) = 2.2 \text{ m/s}^2$

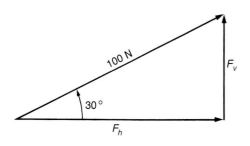

b. $F_v = (100 \text{ N}) \sin 30° = 50 \text{ N}$, upward.
$W = mg = (40 \text{ kg})(9.8 \text{ m/s}^2) = 390 \text{ N}$, downward
Floor force $= W - F_v = 390 \text{ N} - 50 \text{ N} = 340 \text{ N}$, upward

5. $d = \sqrt{(100 \text{ km})^2 + (500 \text{ km})^2} = 510 \text{ km}$
$\tan \theta = \dfrac{100}{500} = 0.2$
$\theta = 11°$, west of south

6. a. $F = W (\sin 30.0°) = 0.5 \ W$
$Ma = 0.5 \ Mg$
$a = 0.5 \ g = 4.9 \text{ m/s}^2$

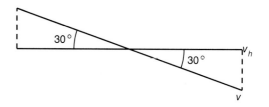

b. $v_f^2 = v_i^2 + 2ad$
$d = \dfrac{v_f^2 - v_i^2}{2a} = \dfrac{(24 \text{ m/s})^2 - 0}{(2)(4.9 \text{ m/s}^2)}$
$d = \dfrac{576 \text{ m}^2/\text{s}^2}{(2)4.9 \text{ m/s}^2} = 59 \text{ m}$

c. $v_h = v \cos 30° = (24 \text{ m/s})(0.866) = 21 \text{ m/s}$
$t = \dfrac{d}{v_h} = \dfrac{21 \text{ m}}{21 \text{ m/s}} = 1 \text{ s}$

7. a. $F_{||} = W \sin 20° = (325 \text{ N}) \sin 20°$
$= 111 \text{ N}$, down the plane.
b. zero
c. zero, Newton's First Law of Motion; an object will maintain a constant speed only if no net or unbalanced force acts on it.
d. $F_f = 211 \text{ N} - 111 \text{ N} = 100 \text{ N}$, down the plane.
e. $F_N = W \cos 20° = (325 \text{ N}) \cos 20° = 305 \text{ N}$
$F_f = \mu F_N$, so $\mu = F_f/F_N = (100 \text{ N})/(305 \text{ N}) = 0.33$

8. Solution by component method.
$F_{1h} = 0$ N
$F_{1v} = F_1 = 33$ N
$F_{2h} = (44$ N$) \cos 60° = 22$ N
$F_v = (44$ N$) \sin 60° = 38$ N
$F_h = 0$ N $+ 22$ N $= 22$ N

$F_v = 33$ N $+ 38$ N $= 71$ N
The resultant of the two given forces is
$F = \sqrt{(22 \text{ N})^2 + (71 \text{ N})^2} = 74$ N
$\tan \theta = \dfrac{71 \text{ N}}{22 \text{ N}} = 3.23, \theta = 73°$
Equilibrant: 74 N, 253°

Motion in Two Dimensions

Overview

This chapter extends the concepts of linear motion to curvilinear motion. The motion of projectiles is the result of an object having linear motion in two directions at the same time. The horizontal and vertical velocities of the moving object are completely independent of each other. The force that causes the curve of a projectile is gravity.

Circular motion is caused by a centripetal force, that always is directed toward the center of the circle. The velocity and centripetal acceleration of an object traveling in a circle always are at right angles to one another. The acceleration is directed toward the center of the circle and the velocity is directed along a tangent. The gravitational force provides the centripetal force for a satellite circling Earth. The velocity of a satellite is independent of its mass.

The pendulum and the spring are examples of simple harmonic motion, a motion that repeats itself. The period of a pendulum is dependent only on the acceleration due to gravity and the length of the pendulum. The period of the mass on a spring depends on its mass and the stiffness of the spring but not on the acceleration of gravity.

Planning Guide (5 Class Sessions)

Text Section	Demonstrations and Experiments	Other Program Components
7:1 Independence of Motion in Two Dimensions **P** **7:2** Projectile Motion **P**	Dem 7:1 Horizontally Launched Projectile, Galilean Relativity II Exp 11 Analysis of the Path of a Projectile **LM** Exp 12 Centripetal Force **LM** Exp 13 The Pendulum **LM** Dem 7:2 Parabolic Throw, Projectile Launched at an Angle	Teaching Master 7-1: (a) Frame of Reference (b) Projectile Motion **TRP** Demonstration 7-1: Independence of Horizontal and Vertical Motion **TRP** Demonstration 7-2: A Projectile Path Demonstrator **TRP** Demonstration 7-3: Centripetal Force **TRP**
7:3 Uniform Circular Motion **S** **7:4** Simple Harmonic Motion **S**	Dem 7:3 Centripetal Force, Disappearing Water Dem 7:4 Harmonic Motion	Teaching Master 7-2: Simple Harmonic Motion **TRP** Review Masters **TRP** Enrichment 7-1: Problems **TRP** Evaluation **TRP**

Performance Objectives

Upon completion of this chapter, your students will

1. display an understanding of the independence of the vertical and horizontal velocities of a projectile; begin to understand the notion of Galilean relativity and reference frames; and apply this knowledge in solving problems of projectiles launched horizontally. *7:1*

2. demonstrate an understanding of the motion of projectiles fired at an angle by solving problems illustrating such motion. *7:2*

3. demonstrate an understanding of centripetal

acceleration and Newton's second law applied to circular motion, and solve problems of circular motion. *7:3*

4. distinguish simple harmonic motion from other forms of vibratory motion; apply Newton's laws to the motion of a pendulum and mass on a spring. *7:4*

5. recognize resonance as a phenomenon often seen in daily life. *7:4*

Teaching the Chapter

Introduction

Using the Photo: Water sprayed from a fire hose, a garden hose, or a laboratory sink follows a characteristic parabolic path. Gravity is accelerating water droplets vertically downward while they continue traveling horizontally at a constant speed. The result is the parabolic path.

The photograph can be used with Sections 7:1 and 7:2 to discuss independence of motion in two dimensions and projectile motion.

Demonstration: This demonstration allows you to find the horizontal velocity of a dart shot from a toy dart gun by measuring the vertical height of the dart in the gun and the horizontal distance it travels. Shoot the dart gun several times horizontally from the same height above the floor. Measure the horizontal distance traveled each time and compute an average. Using the height of the dart, you can calculate the time it takes to reach the floor. Using this time of travel and the horizontal distance covered, you can compute the horizontal velocity. This demonstration will help to initiate a discussion about error in measurements. Be sure to use a soft rubber dart for safety reasons.

7:1 Independence of Motion in Two Dimensions

Demonstration: Use as many examples and demonstrations as possible to emphasize the idea of the independence of the horizontal and vertical motion of projectiles. Project the film loop *Galilean Relativity II—Object Dropped from an Aircraft* on the chalkboard. Mark the positions of the flare on the board. Draw horizontal and vertical lines at the positions of the flares to show that horizontal velocity is constant and vertical velocity increases. If this film loop is not available, enlarge Figure 7–1 several times and put pinholes in the middle of each ball. Project this onto the board using the overhead projector, and follow the procedure previously described. Emphasize the independence of the two motions.

7:2 Projectile Motion

Begin your discussion of projectiles by asking students what would happen if they threw a ball up in the air while riding in a car moving at a constant velocity. Many students will say that the ball will land behind them. Show them what will happen by showing the film loop *Galilean Relativity III—Projectile Fired Vertically* or by using a ballistics car. If you use the ballistics car, fire it while it is stationary and also while it is moving. Both the demonstration and the film loop show that an object shot straight up in the air from a vehicle moving horizontally will take the same path as a projectile fired at an angle. The horizontal motion has a constant velocity and the vertical motion is accelerated. You also can demonstrate this concept by holding a ball in your hand and walking with a constant velocity. If you throw the ball up in the air, it will come back down in your hand, providing that you have maintained a constant velocity.

You also can discuss the path of the projectile relative to the car and relative to the ground. Use this discussion to introduce the concept of frames of reference. If possible, show the PSSC film *Frames of Reference,* a classic on this topic.

Demonstration: Have a student throw a baseball from the top of the stadium. Measure the time it takes the ball to fall and the horizontal distance it travels. Use this data to find the vertical height and the vertical speed of the baseball.

Demonstration: Obtain a water-powered rocket and fire it at an angle. Measure the angle from which it is fired and the time it is in the air. From these measurements it is possible to calculate the initial velocity of the rocket and the height it reaches.

7:3 Uniform Circular Motion

It may be difficult to convince students that the acceleration of an object moving in a circle is toward the center of the circle. Develop the idea and demonstrate that the velocity at any instant is tangent to the circle. Tie a string to a cork and swing it in a circle. Let it go and observe that the cork flies off tangent to the circle.

Demonstration: When you swing an object in a circle, the speed may be constant, but since the direction is always changing, it is accelerating. Using a large jar and a plastic fishing bob, tie the bob to the lid of the jar so that the bob reaches about 2 cm from the bottom of the jar. Fill the jar with water and put the lid on the jar containing the bob. Turn the jar upside down. The bob will rise in the water. Do the following or have a student do so: Sit on a stool and hold the jar away from you while you spin on the stool. Encourage students to notice what will happen to the bob. The bob will point in toward you (toward the center of the circle) showing the direction of the acceleration.

Liquid accelerometers may also be used for this demonstration, but the liquid will flow in the opposite direction to the acceleration. If you hold the liquid accelerometer tangent to the circle as you spin, it will stay level showing there is no acceleration in that direction.

Demonstration: You can do a fun "trick" by making a pail out of a large juice can, using a wire hanger for the handle. Get a large sponge, wet it, squeeze it out, and put it in the bottom of the pail. Stand so the students cannot see into the pail. While you are talking about centripetal force, pour one-half cup of water into the pail. Swing it around and ask what will happen if you stop it at the top. After you stop the pail above your head, students should guess that there was a sponge in the can when no water came out.

Many students will ask about "centrifugal" force. Explain that this is a fictitious force that arises when the motion of an object moving in a circle is viewed. When you go around a sharp curve in a car, you feel like something is pushing you into the door. This pushing is incorrectly referred to as "centrifugal" force. You actually are trying to continue moving in a straight line, but the car door prevents you.

7:4 Simple Harmonic Motion

Ask students to describe the path of a ball dropped from a cliff. Then ask students what the path would look like if the ball were thrown faster and faster. Students should realize that if the ball were thrown fast enough, it would follow the curvature of Earth and circle the planet. The ball is constantly falling toward Earth. Point out that Newton figured this

out over three hundred years ago but scientists did not develop the technology to put the first satellite in orbit until recently.

Relate circular motion to simple harmonic motion. The projection of circular motion gives simple harmonic motion.

Demonstration: Obtain a Frisbee and fasten a cork to the edge so when you look along the edge of the frisbee, the cork sticks out. Put a needle through the middle of the frisbee so you can twirl it. Use a projector lamp to shine light on the edge of the frisbee as you twirl it. The projection of the cork will go back and forth in SHM.

Before doing the investigation "The Pendulum" in *Laboratory Physics* or giving students the formula for the period, ask them to devise an experiment to test the factors that affect the period of the pendulum. Then have students carry out the lab in detail.

Resources

Literature

Butcher, Frank, "Circular Motion Studies with a Toy Airplane," *The Physics Teacher,* December, 1987, pp. 572–573.

Gombka, W., and Steigauf, J., "The Falling Monkey Problem," *The Physics Teacher,* December, 1987, pp. 577–578.

Hartman, Charles, "Catapulting the Interest and Success of Physics Students," *The Physics Teacher,* December, 1986, pp. 556–557.

Lamb, William, "A Projectile Motion Bull's-Eye," *The Science Teacher,* February, 1985, pp. 30–33.

L'Hote, L.E., "Large Scale Use of a Liquid-Surface Accelerometer," *The Physics Teacher,* February, 1975, pp. 100–101.

McGehee, John, "Physics Student's Day at Six Flags/ Magic Mountain," *The Physics Teacher,* January, 1988, pp. 12–17.

Sumners, C., Contant, T., and Sethna, G., "Ride-on Physics," *The Science Teacher,* October, 1984, pp. 36–40.

VanHise, Y., "Physics With Fizz," *The Science Teacher,* September, 1987, pp. 54–57.

Software/Audiovisual

Concentrated Physics Concepts Part I: Mechanics Disk I, John Wiley and Sons, Apple II software

Experiments in Space: Projectile Motion, Ealing Film Loops, 8 mm film loop

Frames of Reference, PSSC, film

Free Fall and Projectile Motion, PSSC, film

Galilean Relativity II—Object Dropped from an Aircraft, Educational Material and Equipment Co., 8 mm film loop

Galilean Relativity III—Projectile Fired Vertically, Educational Material and Equipment Co., 8 mm film loop

University Physics, Disk I, Addison-Wesley, Apple II software

Background

It is possible to derive an equation to give the horizontal distance (range) of a projectile from the velocity given at an angle with the horizontal. The equation is

$$R = \frac{v_0^2 \sin 2\theta}{g}$$

Using this equation, you can show that the maximum range occurs when θ equals 45°. You can also show that the range will be the same for pairs of angles, 75° and 15°, 60° and 30°, 10° and 80°. A sketch of the paths would look like the diagram shown here. Encourage students to appreciate the symmetry of the motion.

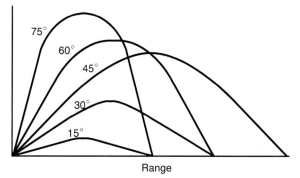

Range

Chapter Review

QUESTIONS

1. smallest at highest point, largest at lowest
2. Acceleration is constant; it doesn't change.
3. Circular motion results when the direction of the force is constantly perpendicular to the instantaneous velocity of the mass.
4. The period of a vibrating object is the time required for one vibration. The amplitude is the distance from rest position to the point of greatest displacement.
5. The force varies directly with the displacement. (It is directly proportional to the displacement.)
6. **a.** A, E = greatest vertical velocity
   b. All points. Horizontal velocity is constant and independent of vertical velocity.
   c. C = least vertical velocity
   d. The curve is a parabola.
7. **a.** low launch angle
   b. high launch angle
   c. low launch angle
8. Directly over it.
9. **a.** no
   b. yes, with constant speed
10. $T = 2\pi\sqrt{(\ell g)}$, so with g smaller, T would be longer.

APPLYING CONCEPTS

1. Yes. (In fact the monkey would be safe if it did not let go of the branch.) The vertical acceleration of the dart will be the same as that of the monkey. Therefore, the dart will be at the same vertical height when it reaches the monkey.
2. Both speed and angle of launch matter, so height does make a difference. Maximum range is achieved when the resultant velocity has equal vertical and horizontal components. In other words, a launch angle of 45°. For this reason, height as well as speed affects the range.
3. **a.** in your hand
   b. to the direction away from the center of the curve
4. According to Newton's laws, net force = zero means acceleration is zero. Passing through the equilibrium position, the acceleration has become zero and the velocity is a maximum.
5. Since $T = 2\pi\sqrt{(\ell g)}$, slide the bob down to lengthen the pendulum.
6. pulse rate, high tides, solar day, vernal equinox, full moon, dripping liquid, any form of natural pendulum

7. 20 m/s

8. $y = v_y t + \frac{1}{2}gt^2 = 0 + \frac{1}{2}(-9.80 \text{ m/s}^2)(1 \text{ s})^2 = -5$ m, no, the horizontal component of motion does not affect the vertical component

9. The outermost structure of the wheel will supply a centripetal force to resist the tendency of the moving colonists to fly off into space tangent to the radius at any point. To the colonists, this force could be interpreted as "gravity." "Down" will be in the direction of the outer rim of the wheel. If you have discussed centrifugal force and noninertial frames of reference, you might want to include these in your discussion.

EXERCISES

1. a. $x = v_x t$, so $t = x/v_x =$
$(+18.3 \text{ m})/(+44.8 \text{ m/s}) = 0.408$ s
   b. $y = (1/2)gt^2 = (1/2)(-9.80 \text{ m/s}^2)(0.408 \text{ s})^2 = -0.816$ m
   c. First half is 0.204 s in which it falls -0.204 m. It falls -0.612 m in the second half.
   d. The batter would think the ball is "sinking" because it seems to fall so much farther during the latter part of the flight.

2. Given v_x, y, and g, find x. $y = \frac{1}{2}gt^2$ and $t = x/v_x$ so, $y = \frac{1}{2}g(x/v_x)^2$. Thus $x^2 = v_x^2(2 y/g)$
$= (12.4 \text{ m/s})^2(2)(-0.32 \text{ m})/(-9.80 \text{ m/s}^2)$
$= 10.04 \text{ m}^2$; $x = 3.2$ m

3. $v_x^2 = (-xg/2)$ 480 m²/s²; $v_x = 22$ m/s.
Now $v_x = v \cos \theta$, so $v = v_x/\cos \theta = 31$ m/s

4. a. $v = 2\pi r/T$ where $r = 0.25$ m and
$T = (1/1800) \text{ min} = (1/30) \text{ s}$, so $v = 47$ m/s
   b. $a_c = v^2/r = (47 \text{ m/s})^2/(0.25 \text{ m})$
$= 8.9 \times 10^3 \text{ m/s}^2$
   c. $F_c = ma_c = (0.0050 \text{ kg})(8.9 \times 10^3 \text{ m/s}^2)$
$= 44$ N

5. $t = \sqrt{\dfrac{2d}{g}} = \sqrt{\dfrac{(2)(78.4 \text{ m})}{(9.8 \text{ m/s}^2)}} = 4.0$ s
$d = \bar{v}t = (8.0 \text{ m/s})(4.0 \text{ s}) = 32$ m

6. $y = v_y t + \frac{1}{2}gt^2$
Since initial vertical velocity is zero,
$t = \sqrt{\dfrac{2y}{g}} = \sqrt{\dfrac{(2)(176.4 \text{ m})}{(9.8 \text{ m/s}^2)}} = 6.0$ s
$x = v_x t = (22 \text{ m/s})(6.0 \text{ s}) = 130$ m

7. a. $y = v_y t + \frac{1}{2}gt^2$, since initial vertical velocity is zero,
$t = \sqrt{\dfrac{2y}{g}} = \sqrt{\dfrac{(2)(490 \text{ m})}{(9.8 \text{ m/s}^2)}} = 1.0 \times 10^1$ s
   b. $x = v_x t = (2.00 \times 10^2 \text{ m/s})(1.0 \times 10^1 \text{ s})$
$= 2.0 \times 10^3$ m

8. a. $y = v_y t + \frac{1}{2}gt^2$, since initial velocity is zero,
$t = \sqrt{\dfrac{2y}{g}} = \sqrt{\dfrac{(2)(1.225 \text{ m})}{(9.8 \text{ m/s}^2)}} = 0.50$ s
   b. $v_x = x/t = \dfrac{0.40 \text{ m}}{0.50 \text{ s}} = 0.80$ m/s

9. a. $y = v_y t + \frac{1}{2}gt^2$, since initial velocity is zero,
$t = \sqrt{\dfrac{2y}{g}} = \sqrt{\dfrac{(2)(61 \text{ m})}{(9.8 \text{ m/s}^2)}} = \sqrt{12.4 \text{ s}^2} = 3.5$ s
$v_x = x/t = \dfrac{23 \text{ m}}{3.5 \text{ s}} = 6.6$ m/s

10. a. $v_x = 59$ m/s, $v_y = 78$ m/s, $t = 2v_y/g = 16$ s
   b. $x = v_x t = 9.4 \times 10^2$ m
   c. Half of its flight time is 8.0 s. In that time it falls $y = (1/2)gt^2 = (1/2)(-9.80 \text{ m/s}^2)(8.0 \text{ s})^2$
$= 39$ m

11. First find the time the ball was in the air.
$v_y = v \sin 53.0° = (30.0 \text{ m/s})(0.799)$
$= 24.0$ m/s
$t_{up} = \dfrac{v_f - v_i}{g} = \dfrac{0 - (-24.0 \text{ m/s})}{-9.81 \text{ m/s}^2} = 2.54$ s
$t_{up} = t_{down}$
$t_{total} = t_{up} + t_{down} = 2.45 \text{ s} + 2.45 \text{ s} = 4.90$ s
$v_x = v(\cos 53.0°) = 30.0 \text{ m/s})(0.602)$
$= 18.1$ m/s
The distance the ball travels horizontally is
$x = v_x t = (18.1 \text{ m/s})(4.89 \text{ s}) = 88.5$ m
The distance the outfielder travels is
$x = v_x t = (4.00 \text{ m/s})(4.90 \text{ s}) = 19.6$ m
The distance between the batter and outfielder is
88.7 m + 19.6 m = 108.3 m

12. a. $a_c = \dfrac{4\pi^2 r}{T^2} = \dfrac{(4\pi^2)(1.3 \text{ m})}{(1.0 \text{ s})^2} = 51$ m/s²
   b. $F_c = ma_c = (7.00 \text{ kg})(51 \text{ m/s}^2) = 360$ N

13. a. toward center of record
   b. $a_c = v^2/r$ where $v = 2\pi r/T$, so $a_c = 4\pi^2 r/T^2$. Here $T = (1/33.33) \text{ min} = 1.80$ s. When $r = 5$ cm, $a_c = 0.61 \text{ m/s}^2$; at $r = 10$ cm, $a_c = 1.2 \text{ m/s}^2$, at $r = 15$ cm, $a_c = 1.8 \text{ m/s}^2$.
   c. frictional force between coin and record
   d. The largest radius because force to hold it is the greatest.

14. $F_c = ma_c$, where $a_c = v^2/r$. $v = 2\pi r/T$, so $a_c = 4\pi^2 r/T^2$. Solving for T, we find $T^2 = 4\pi^2 r/a_c = 4\pi^2 rm/F_c$ or $T = 2\pi \sqrt{(rm/F_c)} = 2.1$ s.

15. a. $T = 2\pi \sqrt{(\ell/g)} = 1.6$ s.

   b. Since period is proportional to the square root of the length, the pendulum would have to be four times as long, or 2.7 m.

   c. The period is proportional to the square root of the length, not the length, so the answer cannot be doubled.

16. a. $T = 2\pi r/v = 3.8 \times 10^{-6}$ s.

   b. $a_c = v^2/r$ and $F_c = ma_c$, so $a_c = 3.3 \times 10^{12}$ m/s^2 and $F_c = 5.5 \times 10^{-15}$ N

17. a. $F_c = m\dfrac{(4\pi^2 r)}{T^2} = \dfrac{(0.20 \text{ kg})(4\pi^2)(0.80 \text{ m})}{(1.0 \text{ s})^2}$
    $= 6.3$ N

   b. $F_c = ma_c$ and $a_c = v^2/r$ where $v = 2\pi r/T = 2\pi(0.80 \text{ m})/(0.5 \text{ s}) = 10$ m/s, so $a_c = 126$ m/s^2, $F_c = (0.20 \text{ kg})(64 \text{ m/s}^2) = 25$ N

   c. Ratio is 4:1 because velocity has doubled, acceleration doubled, squared, or multiplied by four.

18. a. $v = 2\pi r/T = 2\pi(50.0 \text{ m})/(14.3 \text{ s})$
    $= 22.0$ m/s $a_c = v^2/r$
    $= (22.0 \text{ m/s})^2/(50.0 \text{ m}) = 9.65$ m/s^2

   b. $F_c = ma_c = (615 \text{ kg})(9.65 \text{ m/s}^2)$
    $= 5.94 \times 10^3$ N

19. a. $v = 2\pi(6.4 \times 10^6 \text{ m})/(24 \text{ h} \times 3600 \text{ s/h})$
    $= 465$ m/s

   b. $a_c = v^2/r = (465 \text{ m/s})^2/(6.4 \times 10^6 \text{ m})$
    $= 0.034$ m/s^2

   c. $F_c = ma_c = (97 \text{ kg})(0.034 \text{ m/s}^2) = 3.3$ N

   d. $W = mg = (97 \text{ kg})(9.80 \text{ m/s}^2) = 950$ N

20. a. $v = 2\pi r/T = 2\pi(2.0 \text{ m})/(1/1.1 \text{ s}) = 14$ m/s.

   b. $a_c = v^2/r = (14 \text{ m/s})^2/r = 98$ m/s^2

   c. force of the drum

   d. Downward force of gravity $F = mg$. Frictional force $F_f = \mu F_N$. F_N is the force of the drum, ma_c. To balance $g = \mu a_c$, so we need $\mu = g/a_c = 0.10$

21.

$$T = 2\pi \sqrt{\frac{\ell}{g}} \text{ and } T' = 2\pi \sqrt{\frac{\ell}{2g}} \text{ so } \frac{T'}{T} =$$

$$\frac{2\pi \sqrt{\dfrac{\ell}{g}}}{2\pi \sqrt{\dfrac{\ell}{2g}}} = \sqrt{\frac{1}{2}}; T' = \sqrt{\frac{1}{2}} T = 0.7 T$$

PROBLEMS

1. $V = \sqrt{rg}$

$$r = m\frac{v^2}{g} = \frac{(120 \text{ m/s})^2}{9.8 \text{ m/s}^2} = \frac{14\ 600}{9.8} = 1500 \text{ m}$$

2. $\sin 60° = \dfrac{V_y}{10}$, $V_x = 8.7$ m/s; $\cos 60° = \dfrac{V_x}{10}$,
$V_x = 5.0$ m/s

   a. time for the ball to reach its peak is
$$t = \frac{v_f - v_o}{g} = \frac{0 - 8.7 \text{ m/s}}{-9.8 \text{ m/s}^2} = 0.9 \text{ s}$$
height of peak from floor is
$$d = t\left(\frac{v_f + v_o}{2}\right) = 0.9 \text{ s}\left(\frac{0 + 8.7 \text{ m/s}}{2}\right) = 3.9 \text{ m}$$
3.9 m $+ 1.8$ m $= 5.7$ m
time to fall from peak to height of basket is
$d = 5.7$ m $- 3.0$ m $= 2.7$ m
$y = v_y t + \frac{1}{2}gt^2$
2.7 m $= 0(t) + \frac{1}{2}(9.8 \text{ m/s}^2) t^2$
$t = 0.7$ s
total time in flight $= 0.9$ s $+ 0.7$ s $= 1.6$ s
time left in the game $= 2.0$ s $- 1.6$ s $= 0.4$ s

   b. $x = v_x t = (5.0 \text{ m/s})(1.6 \text{ s}) = 8.0$ m, since this is greater than the 6 m radius circle the player's team is awarded a 3 point goal and the player's team is ahead.

3. $t = \dfrac{x}{v_x} = 150 \text{ m}/500 \text{ m/s} = 0.3$ s
$y = v_y t + \frac{1}{2}gt^2 = 0(0.3 \text{ s}) + \frac{1}{2}(9.8 \text{ m/s}^2)(0.3 \text{ s})^2$
   $= 0.44$ m

4. $y = v_y t + \frac{1}{2}gt^2$
   $= 0(2.6 \text{ m/s}) + \frac{1}{2}(9.8 \text{ m/s}^2)(2.6 \text{ s})^2 = 33$ m
$x = v_x t = (2.8 \text{ m/s})(2.6 \text{ s}) = 7.3$ m

5.

$$T = 2\pi \sqrt{\frac{\ell_e}{g_e}} = 2\pi \sqrt{\frac{\ell_m}{g_m}}, \sqrt{\frac{\ell_e}{g_e}} = \sqrt{\frac{\ell_m}{g_m}} \text{ so}$$

$$\frac{\ell_e}{g_e} = \frac{\ell_m}{g_m}, \frac{1.0 \text{ m}}{9.8 \text{ m/s}^2} = \frac{\ell_m}{1.6 \text{ m/s}^2}, \ell_m = 0.16 \text{ m}$$

6. a. $y = v_y t + \frac{1}{2}gt^2$
    1001 m $= 0(t) + \frac{1}{2}(9.8 \text{ m/s}^2) t^2$, $t = 14.3$ s

   b. $(125 \text{ km/h})(1 \text{ h}/3600 \text{ s})(1000 \text{ m/km}) = 34.7$ m/s
$x = v_x t = (34.7 \text{ m/s})(14.3 \text{ s}) = 496$ m

Universal Gravitation

Overview

This chapter shows how Newton used the work of Kepler and Brahe in combination with his own work (the equation of centripetal acceleration) to identify the law governing the gravitational force and its universality. Newton realized that the force that makes an apple fall to the ground is the same force that holds the moon in orbit around Earth. This force is the centripetal force on the moon.

The method used by Cavendish to test the law of gravitation in the laboratory and experimentally determine G is described. The inverse-square-law relationship of weight to distance from the center of Earth is emphasized and shown graphically. Gravitational fields and Einstein's concept of gravity as an effect of space itself are introduced.

Planning Guide (6 Class Sessions)

Text Section	Demonstrations and Experiments	Other Program Components
8:1 Kepler's Laws of Planetary Motion **P** 8:2 Universal Gravitation **P** 8:3 Newton's Test of the Inverse Square Law **S** 8:4 Weighing Earth **S** 8:5 Satellites **S** 8:6 Weight and Weightlessness **P**	Dem 8:1 Cavendish Experiment, Ellipse Construction Exp 14 Kepler's Law of Equal Areas **LM**	Teaching Master 8-1: Planetary Motion **TRP** Teaching Master 8-2: (a) Gravitational Force **TRP** Minilab 8-1: Mass and Weight **TRP**
8:7 The Gravitational Field **P** 8:8 Einstein's Theory of Gravity **S**		Teaching Master 2-1: (b) Weight Versus Location **TRP** Review Masters **TRP** Enrichment 8-1: Problems **TRP** Evaluation **TRP**

Performance Objectives

Upon completion of this chapter, your students will

1. demonstrate an appreciation for the persistence required to gain scientific knowledge; list Kepler's laws of planetary motion. *8:1*

2. recognize how Kepler's laws are a result of universal gravitation; be able to calculate periods and radii of orbiting objects. *8:1, 8:3*

3. display an understanding of how Newton combined basic knowledge to arrive at a completely new law; (Students should not be requested to

learn the derivation.) understand the quantities on which the gravitational force depends. *8:2*

4. state the method used by Cavendish to determine G; understand the importance of knowing G. *8:4*

5. recognize that the motion of artificial satellites is circular motion about Earth; solve problems that relate the orbital velocity to distance from center of Earth. *8:5*

6. demonstrate an ability to define weightlessness and distinguish it from the condition of a mass

free of gravitational forces.   *8:6*

force.   *8:7*

7. describe gravitational fields; recognize that the field concept does not explain the origin of the

8. display an understanding of Einstein's concept of gravity.   *8:8*

Teaching the Chapter

Introduction

Using the Photo: Ann is correct. A satellite at Earth's surface would travel 8 km/s. Traveling faster would require the satellite to be in an orbit smaller than Earth's radius. Using $v = rg'$, $g' = G M_e/r^2$, and from Chapter 7, $v = 2\pi r/T$, the radius can be determined using the equation $r = \sqrt[3]{GM_eT^2/4\pi^2} = [(6.67 \times 10^{-11} \text{ N} \cdot \text{m}^2/\text{kg}^2)(6.00 \times 10^{24} \text{ kg})(4800 \text{ s})^2/(4)(3.14)^2]^{.333}$. The satellite's radius would be 6.06×10^6 m, which is less than Earth's radius of 6.37×10^6 m.

The photograph can be used with Sections 8:4–8:6 to discuss weighing Earth, satellites, and weightlessness.

Demonstration: A modified version of Cavendish's experiment can be used to demonstrate the gravitational attraction of masses. Tie a bottle filled with water to each end of a meter stick. Attach a mirror to the center of the meter stick and suspend this apparatus at its center from the ceiling with a long, thin wire. With the apparatus close to but not touching the floor, reflect the light from a laser off the mirror and onto a screen. (See diagram below.) Fill two large boxes with sand and place one near each of the two bottles. Note the movement of the light on the screen due to the twisting of the wire. Vary the distance between the boxes and the bottles and observe the light's movement. Now vary the amount of sand and/or water and again observe the change in twisting. Ask students how this demonstration shows the direct relationship between gravitational force and mass and the inverse square relationship between gravitational force and distance.

8:1 Kepler's Law of Planetary Motion

You may wish to explore with students the lives of Galileo, Kepler, Brahe, and Newton. It is important to emphasize that most famous discoveries use the work of people who came before the discoverer. Newton was well aware of this when he said, "If I have seen further than other men, it is because I stand on the shoulders of giants."

Demonstration: Use the following activity to review the construction of ellipses. Stick two suction-cup darts to the chalkboard. Make a loop of string to fit around the darts with plenty of string to spare. Put a piece of chalk in the loop and pull it tight. Draw an ellipse by rotating the chalk around the darts. Point out that the eccentricity of the ellipse, or its deviation from a circular path, is dependent on how far away the foci are from one another. Kepler discovered that the orbits of the planets are ellipses but they are not very eccentric, that is, they are very close to being circles.

8:2 Universal Gravitation

8:3 Newton's Test of the Inverse Square Law

The concept of an inverse square relationship between two variables is very important and will be used again in the study of electrostatics and light illumination. Ask students what happens to the force of attraction if you double the distance between two objects or what happens if you halve the distance. Emphasize the importance of Newton's "leap of the mind" in connecting the falling apple to the falling moon.

8:4 Weighing Earth

8:5 Satellites

8:6 Weight and Weightlessness

First have students calculate (a) the force of gravity between themselves and their nearest neighbor and (b)

Chapter 8

59T

the force of gravity between themselves and the moon, and then compare (a) and (b). (Have students assume a spherical person with a 20 cm radius.) Emphasize that everything in the universe attracts everything else and that the force they exert on Earth is the same as the force Earth exerts on them. However, Earth doesn't move because it is so massive compared to a person.

Ask students to describe their concept of weightlessness. Remind them that g decreases inversely with the square of the distance, so it gets very small but never equals zero. Weightlessness is being in free fall. The astronauts are weightless and many experience a "queasy feeling" in their stomachs when in orbit. You are weightless as you go over a hill on a roller coaster. Have students calculate an astronaut's weight in space, assuming the shuttle orbits at about 270 km and the diameter of Earth is 6400 km.

Ask students to describe what it would be like if the acceleration of gravity were 1/10 of what it is on Earth. How would it affect the way we walk, jump, or play baseball and football? Many students may have seen videos of astronauts on the moon, where g is 1.6 m/s^2. If possible, show the NASA film *Zero G.*

8:7 The Gravitational Field

A field describes some effect that an object will experience by being at a certain location. An object placed near Earth will accelerate toward Earth. Electric field is the force on a test charge, and magnetic field is the force on a moving charge. Gravitational field is the force on a mass.

8:8 Einstein's Theory of Gravity

Einstein introduced the concept of gravity as a peculiarity of space. Set up a sheet as shown in Figure 8–16 so students actually can see the change in the path of a small object as it approaches a large object.

Resources ━━━━━

Literature

Asimov, I., *Asimov's Biographical Encyclopedia of Science and Technology,* 2nd Edition, Doubleday and Co., Inc., Garden City, NY, 1982.

Evans, L., and Stevens, J.T., "Which Way Is Up?" *The Physics Teacher,* November, 1978, p. 561.

Leyden, Michael B., "The Elliptical Johannes Kepler," *The Science Teacher,* November, 1984, pp. 52–56.

Marion, J.B., and Hornyak, W.F., "Artificial Gravity," *General Physics with Bioscience Essays,* 2nd edition, John Wiley and Sons, Inc., New York, 1982, pp. 117–119.

Sayer, Gus A., "A Game of Gravity," *The Physics Teacher,* September, 1976, p. 359.

Whitman, John C., "Are Your Students Proportionality Literate?" *The Science Teacher,* November, 1987, pp. 37–39.

Wolfson, R., and Pasachoff, J.M., *Physics,* Little, Brown and Co., Boston, 1987, pp. 187–190.

Software/Audiovisual

Galileo, The Challenge of Reason, Learning Corporation of America, video

The Mechanical Universe-High School Adaptation, The Apple and the Moon, Annenberg Project, 1985, video

Newton: The Mind That Found the Future, Learning Corporation of America, video

Physics 1: Module E: Particle Dynamics and Gravity, Control Data Corp., IBM-PC software

Zero-G, HQa260A, NASA, film

Background ━━━━━

If you throw a ball up in the air, it comes down again. It is possible, however, to give an object a large enough speed that it will not come down. For an object to escape Earth's gravitational pull, the sum of the potential and kinetic energies must be zero. The sum approaches zero as the object moves farther from Earth. If v is the speed of a mass m_o at some distance r from Earth, m_e, then $KE = 1/2\ m_0 v^2$. Use calculus to show

$$PE = -\ \frac{Gm_e m_o}{r_e}$$

if $KE + PE = 0$

then $1/2\ m_0 v^2 - \dfrac{Gm_e m_o}{r_e} = 0$

and the escape speed is

$$v = \sqrt{\frac{2\ Gm_e}{r_e}}$$

This is the speed that must be given to an object at the distance r in order for it to escape to infinity. In this case r is the radius of Earth.

$$v = \sqrt{\dfrac{2(6.67 \times 10^{-11}\ \text{N} \cdot \text{m}^2/\text{kg}^2)(5.98 \times 10^{24}\ \text{kg})}{6.38 \times 10^6\ \text{m}}}$$

Since $1\ \text{N} \cdot \text{m/kg} = 1\ (\text{m/s})^2$, the units work out as follows:

$$v = 1.12 \times 10^4\ \text{m/s}$$

The object needs to be given a speed of 11.2 km/s to escape from Earth's gravitational pull. This can be calculated for any planet by substituting the mass of the planet for m_e and the planet's radius for r_e.

Chapter Review

Questions

1. Equal areas means if distance to planet is larger, speed is smaller. Hence, it moves faster when close.

2. No. The forces are third-law pairs, so they are equal and opposite.

3. $F = G\dfrac{m_1 m_2}{d^2}$, $m_1 = $ Earth's mass

   $m_2 = $ Object's mass

   $a = \dfrac{F}{m_2}$

   $a = G\dfrac{m_1}{d^2}$

   The acceleration is independent of the object's mass.

4. $F_g = G\dfrac{m_1 m_2}{d^2}$

   $= \dfrac{(6.67 \times 10^{-11}\ \text{N} \cdot \text{m}^2/\text{kg}^2)(1.00\ \text{kg})(1.00\ \text{kg})}{(1.00\ \text{m})^2}$

   $= 6.67 \times 10^{-11}\ \text{N}$

5. See text Section 8:4.

6. A force of 5-g means that the astronaut's weight is five times heavier than on Earth. The force exerted on the astronaut is five times the force of Earth's gravitational force.

7. Einstein's view is that gravity is an effect of the curvature of space due to the presence of mass, while Newton's view of gravity is a force acting directly between objects. Thus, according to Einstein, the attraction between Earth and the moon is the effect of the curvature of space caused by their combined masses.

8. a. 1830 N   b. 446 N   c. 198 N
   d. 792 N   e. 285 N
   Measure all distances from the center of Earth. Hence, 6400 km from Earth's surface is two Earth

radii and the weight reduces to $\frac{1}{4}$. At 12 800 km from Earth's surface, the weight would reduce to $\frac{1}{9}$, and so on.

Applying Concepts

1. See plot. Only bottom right is ok. Top two do not have sun at a focus; bottom left doesn't have planet in plane of ellipse.

2. No. Earth is more massive, so it would be at a location closer to the moon than halfway.

3. If $W = 4 \times 10^{-8}\ \text{N}$, then $m = W/g = (4 \times 10^{-8}\ \text{N})/(9.8\ \text{m/s}^2) = 4 \times 10^{-9}\ \text{kg}$

4. Its speed. It is falling all the time.

5. yes, weightless but not massless

6. The one further out has a longer period and moves more slowly. (v goes as $1/\sqrt{r}$, and T goes as r/v, or $\sqrt{r^3}$.

7. Period and orbital radius of at least one satellite.

8. From the radius and the orbital speed of a satellite, find the acceleration g' at a certain distance from the center. Then use $1/r^2$ dependence to find g at the tops of the clouds.

9. a. $v = R_e\sqrt{(g/r)}$, so small.
   b. decrease: The drag will slow it down causing the orbit to decay, so $v = R_e\sqrt{(g/r)}$ does not apply.

Exercises

1. $F = G\dfrac{m_1 m_2}{r^2}$

   $= \dfrac{(6.67 \times 10^{-11}\ \text{N} \cdot \text{m}^2/\text{kg}^2)(6.8\ \text{kg})(6.8\ \text{kg})}{(0.218\ \text{m})^2}$

   $= 6.5 \times 10^{-8}\ \text{N}$

2. $F = G\dfrac{m_1 m_2}{r^2}$, $m_2 = 2m_1$

$F = \dfrac{G(m_1)(2m_1)}{r^2}$, ${m_1}^2 = \dfrac{Fr^2}{2G}$

$m_1 = \sqrt{\dfrac{(2.75 \times 10^{-12}\ \text{N})(2.6\ \text{m})^2}{(2)(6.67 \times 10^{-11}\ \text{N} \cdot \text{m}^2/\text{kg}^2)}} = 0.37\ \text{kg}$

$m_2 = (2)(0.37\ \text{kg}) = 0.75\ \text{kg}$

3. $F = G\dfrac{m_1 m_2}{r^2}$

$= [(6.67 \times 10^{-11}\ \text{N} \cdot \text{m}^2/\text{kg}^2)(3.3 \times 10^5)$
$(6.0 \times 10^{24}\ \text{kg})(3.0 \times 10^2)(6.0 \times 10^{24}\ \text{kg})] \div$
$(7.8 \times 10^{11}\ \text{m})^2$

$= 3.9 \times 10^{23}\ \text{N}$

4. $(T_a/T_b)^2 = (r_a/r_b)^3$, so ${T_a}^2 = {T_b}^2\,(r_a/r_b)^3 =$
$(1.0\ \text{y})^2(5.2\ \text{AU}/1.0\ \text{AU})^3 = 141\ \text{y}^2$,
so $T_a = 12\ \text{y}$

5. a. $(r_a/r_b)^3 = (T_a/T_b)^2$, so ${r_a}^3 = {r_b}^3\,(T_a T_b)^2 =$
$(1.0\ \text{AU})^3(84\ \text{y}/1.0\ \text{y})^2 = 7.06 \times 10^3\ \text{AU}^3$,
so $r_a = 19\ \text{AU}$

b. $1\ \text{AU} = 1.50 \times 10^{11}\ \text{m}$,
so $19\ \text{AU} = 2.9 \times 10^{12}\ \text{m}$

6. $T^2 = r^2(4\pi^2/Gm)$, so $m = 4\pi^2 r^3/(GT^2)$

$= \dfrac{4\pi^2(1.50 \times 10^{11}\ \text{m})^3}{(6.67 \times 10^{-11}\ \text{N} \cdot \text{m}^2/\text{kg}^2)(3.16 \times 10^7\ \text{s})^2}$

$= 2.01 \times 10^{30}\ \text{kg}$

7. a. $r^3 = T^2 Gm/4\pi^2$

$= \dfrac{(7.465 \times 10^9 \text{s}^2)G(5.98 \times 10^{24}\ \text{kg})}{4\pi^2}$

$= 7.54 \times 10^{22}\ \text{m}^3 \qquad r = 4.23 \times 10^7\ \text{m}$

b. height $= 4.23 \times 10^7\ \text{m} - 6.37 \times 10^6\ \text{m}$
$= 3.59 \times 10^7\ \text{m}$

8. a. $(r_a/r_b)^3 = (T_a/T_b)^2$, so ${r_a}^3 = {r_b}^3(T_a/T_b)^2 =$
$(1.0\ \text{AU})^3(74\ \text{y}/1.0\ \text{y})^2 = 5.48 \times 10^3\ \text{AU}^3$,
so $r_a = 18\ \text{AU}$

b. Saturn and Uranus, just inside Uranus's orbit
(19 AU)

9. $T^2 = r^3(4\pi^2/Gm)$, so $m = 4\pi^2 r^2/(GT^2)$

$= \dfrac{4\pi^2(6.54 \times 10^{24}\ \text{m}^2)}{(6.67 \times 10^{-11})(6.9 \times 10^9\ \text{s}^2)}$

$= 5.6 \times 10^{26}\ \text{kg}$, or 94 Earth masses

10. $F = G\dfrac{m_1 m_2}{r^2}$

$= \dfrac{(6.67 \times 10^{-11}\ \text{N} \cdot \text{m}^2/\text{kg}^2)(8.0\ \text{kg})(6.0\ \text{kg})}{(2.0\ \text{m})^2}$

$= 8.0 \times 10^{-10}\ \text{N}$

11. a. $F = G\dfrac{m_1 m_2}{r^2}$

$= \dfrac{(6.67 \times 10^{-11}\ \text{N} \cdot \text{m}^2/\text{kg}^2)(8.0\ \text{kg})(8.0\ \text{kg})}{(5.0\ \text{m})^2}$

$= 1.7 \times 10^{-10}\ \text{N}$

b. $F = G\dfrac{m_1 m_2}{r^2}$

$= \dfrac{(6.67 \times 10^{-11}\ \text{N} \cdot \text{m}^2/\text{kg}^2)(8.0\ \text{kg})(8.0\ \text{kg})}{(5.0 \times 10^1\ \text{m})^2}$

$= 1.7 \times 10^{-12}\ \text{N}$

12. $m_1 = \dfrac{W}{g} = \dfrac{9.8 \times 10^2\ \text{N}}{9.8\ \text{m/s}^2} = 1.0 \times 10^2\ \text{kg}$

$m_2 = \dfrac{W}{g} = \dfrac{1.96 \times 10^2\ \text{N}}{9.8\ \text{m/s}^2} = 2.0 \times 10^1\ \text{kg}$

$F = G\dfrac{m_1 m_2}{r^2}$

$= [(6.67 \times 10^{-11}\ \text{N} \cdot \text{m}^2/\text{kg}^2)(1.0 \times 10^2\ \text{kg})$
$(2.0 \times 10^1\ \text{kg})] \div (4.0\ \text{m})^2$

$= 8.3 \times 10^{-9}\ \text{N}$

13. a. $F = G\dfrac{m_1 m_2}{r^2}$

$m = \sqrt{\dfrac{Fr^2}{G}} = \sqrt{\dfrac{(2.0 \times 10^{-7}\ \text{N})(30\ \text{m})^2}{(6.67 \times 10^{-11}\ \text{N} \cdot \text{m}^2/\text{kg}^2)}}$

$= \sqrt{2.698 \times 10^6\ \text{kg}^2} = 1.6 \times 10^3\ \text{kg}$

b. $F = ma$

$a = \dfrac{F}{m} = \dfrac{2.0 \times 10^{-7}\ \text{N}}{1.6 \times 10^3\ \text{kg}}$

$= 1.3 \times 10^{-10}\ \text{m/s}^2$

14. $F = G\dfrac{m_1 m_2}{r^2}$

$m_m = \dfrac{Fr^2}{Gm_e}$

$= \dfrac{(1.9 \times 10^{20}\ \text{N})(3.9 \times 10^8\ \text{m})^2}{(6.67 \times 10^{-11}\ \text{N} \cdot \text{m}^2/\text{kg}^2)(6.0 \times 10^{24}\ \text{kg})}$

$= 7.2 \times 10^{22}\ \text{kg}$

15. $F = ma$

$a = \dfrac{F}{m} = \dfrac{1.9 \times 10^{20}\ \text{N}}{7.2 \times 10^{22}\ \text{kg}}$

$= 2.6 \times 10^{-3}\ \text{m/s}^2$

16. $F = G\dfrac{m_1 m_2}{r^2}$

$= [(6.67 \times 10^{-11}\ \text{N} \cdot \text{m}^2/\text{kg}^2)(9.1 \times 10^{-31}\ \text{kg})$
$(1.7 \times 10^{-27}\ \text{kg})] \div (1.0 \times 10^{-10}\ \text{m})^2$

$= 1.0 \times 10^{-47}\ \text{N}$

17. $r_a{}^3 = r_b{}^3(T_a/T_b)^2 = (1.00 \text{ AU})^3$
$(225 \text{ days}/365 \text{ days})^2 = (1.00 \text{ AU})^3(0.380) = 0.380 \text{ AU}^3$, $r_a = 0.724 \text{ AU}$

18. No. Kepler's third law only relates periods and radii of two objects orbiting the same object.

Problems

1. $\dfrac{r^3}{T^2} = 3.35 \times 10^{18} \text{ m}^3/\text{s}^2$

$T = \sqrt{\dfrac{r^3}{3.35 \times 10^{18} \text{ m}^3/\text{s}^2}}$

$= \sqrt{\dfrac{(8)^3(1.5 \times 10^{11} \text{ m})^3}{(3.35 \times 10^{18} \text{ m}^3/\text{s}^2)}}$

$= 7.2 \times 10^8 \text{ s} = \dfrac{7.2 \times 10^8 \text{ s})}{(3.15 \times 10^7 \text{ s/yr})} = 23 \text{ yr}$

2. a. $F = G\dfrac{m_1 m_2}{r^2}$

$m_e = \dfrac{Fr^2}{Gm}$

$= \dfrac{(9.8 \text{ N})(6.4 \times 10^6 \text{ m})^2}{(6.67 \times 10^{-11} \text{ N} \cdot \text{m}^2/\text{kg}^2)(1.0 \text{ kg})}$

$= 6.0 \times 10^{24} \text{ kg}$

b. $V = \dfrac{4}{3}\pi r^3$

$= \dfrac{(4\pi)(6.4 \times 10^6 \text{ m})^3}{3} = 1.1 \times 10^{21} \text{ m}^3$

$D = \dfrac{M}{V} = \dfrac{6.0 \times 10^{24} \text{ kg}}{1.1 \times 10^{21} \text{ m}^3}$

$= 5.5 \times 10^3 \text{ kg/m}^3$

3. $F = Gm_1 m_2/d^2$

$= \dfrac{G(5.9 \text{ kg})(4.7 \times 10^{-2} \text{ kg})}{(5.5 \times 10^{-2} \text{ m})^2}$

$= 6.1 \times 10^{-9} \text{ N}$

4. $(T_a/T_b)^2 = (r_a/r_b)^3$, or $T_a{}^2 = T_b{}^2(r_a/r_b)^3 = (.5/1)^3 = 1/8$, or $T_a = 0.35$ lunar periods

5. $F = G\dfrac{m_1 m_2}{d^2}$

Earth on moon

$F_e = \dfrac{G(6.0 \times 10^{24} \text{ kg})(7.3 \times 10^{22} \text{ kg})}{(3.9 \times 10^8 \text{ m})^2}$

Sun on moon

$F_s = \dfrac{G(2.0 \times 10^{30} \text{ kg})(7.3 \times 10^{22} \text{ kg})}{(1.5 \times 10^{11} \text{ m})^2}$

$= 4.3 \times 10^{20} \text{ N}$

Ratio is $\dfrac{F_e}{F_s} = \dfrac{1.9}{4.3}$. The sun pulls more than twice as hard as the Earth on the moon.

6. Earth
$F_g = m_e a_e$

$a_e = \dfrac{F_g}{m_e} = \dfrac{1.9 \times 10^{20} \text{ N}}{6.0 \times 10^{24} \text{ kg}}$

$a_e = 3.2 \times 10^{-5} \text{ m/s}^2$

Moon
$F_g = m_m a_m$

$a_m = \dfrac{F_g}{m_m} = \dfrac{1.9 \times 10^{20} \text{ N}}{7.3 \times 10^{22} \text{ kg}}$

$a_m = 2.6 \times 10^{-3} \text{ m/s}^2$

No. Since the distance between them decreases as they accelerate toward each other, the gravitational force would increase and their acceleration would, in turn, increase.

CHAPTER 9

Momentum and Its Conservation

Overview

Momentum and conservation of momentum are concepts that are equivalent to Newton's second and third laws of motion. The rearrangement of $F = ma$ to $Ft = mv$ allows the second law to be applied to many everyday situations, especially sports and auto collisions.

The total momentum of a system will not change unless there is an external force exerted on the system.

When two skaters push against each other and go in opposite directions, there is no change in momentum. When two objects collide and stick together, there is also no change in momentum. When an object explodes momentum is also conserved. The law of conservation of momentum also includes objects colliding and going off at angles to one another.

Planning Guide (6 Class Sessions)

Text Section	Demonstrations and Experiments	Other Program Components
9:1 Momentum and Impulse **P** 9:2 Newton's Third Law and Momentum **P** 9:3 Law of Conservation of Momentum **P**	Dem 9:1 Egg Drop Exp 15 Conservation of Momentum: Internal Force **LM** Exp 16 Conservation of Momentum: A Collision in Two Dimensions **LM**	Teaching Master 9-1: Momentum **TRP** Teaching Master 9-2: Conservation of Momentum in Two Dimensions **TRP** Review Masters **TRP** Minilab 9-1: Velocity of a Softball **TRP** Demonstration 9-1: Newton's Third Law **TRP** Demonstration 9-2: Conservation of Momentum I **TRP** Demonstration 9-3: Conservation of Momentum II **TRP** Enrichment 9-1: Problems **TRP** Evaluation **TRP**
9:4 Internal and External Forces **P** 9:5 Conservation of Momentum in Two and Three Dimensions **S**		

Performance Objectives

Upon completion of this chapter, your students will

1. define momentum and impulse; recognize the connection between Newton's second law and the impulse-momentum equation; be able to calculate changes in momentum. *9:1*

2. recognize the connection between the third law of motion and conservation of momentum; define a closed, isolated system. *9:2*

3. State the law of conservation of momentum; recognize its implications, especially in collision problems. *9:3*

4. distinguish between external and internal forces and use this distinction in solving problems. *9:4*

5. explain the extension of the law of conservation of momentum to two or three dimensions; apply vectors to the solution of momentum conservation problems. *9:5*

Teaching the Chapter

Introduction

Using the Photo: Air bags allow the change in momentum, an impulse equal to force × time, to be transferred over a longer period of time. The longer time greatly reduces the force acting on a person's body (primarily the head). A rapid collision with the windshield or dashboard transfers momentum in a much shorter period of time, resulting in much larger forces.

Demonstration: The egg drop demonstration not only illustrates changing an object's momentum by applying an impulse, but also builds student enthusiasm because of the competition. Challenge students to design and construct a container that will protect a raw egg so it will remain unbroken when it is dropped. An upper story window or the back side of the school's football stadium serves as an excellent release site. It is important for students to see that the force must be minimized by maximizing the time of the impulse.

If time does not allow for the egg drop demonstration, a water balloon toss can be used as a substitute. Again point out that to minimize the force of catching the balloon, students should cradle it as it is caught, thus maximizing the time.

9:1 Momentum and Impulse

Take time to review Newton's second law because it leads directly into the concept of change in momentum. Be sure to make the distinction between momentum and change in momentum. Momentum is changed when an external force acts on a body. Have the students consider a sports car and a tractor-trailer truck. The truck's mass will always be larger than the sports car's mass. Ask students if the momentum of the truck will always be larger than the momentum of the car. If the velocity of the car is very large and the velocity of the truck is very small, the car's momentum can be larger than the truck's.

Sometimes it is convenient to manipulate the physical situation so the change in momentum will be maximized. For example, the longer a golf club is in contact with a ball, the more change in momentum will occur and the faster the ball will go. Another example is making the barrel of a cannon longer so the force applied to the cannonball will act over a longer period of time, making the cannonball go farther.

Ask students if they would land stiff-legged if they jumped from the lecture table to the floor. Most will probably say that they would bend their knees. Ask them why they do this. The change in momentum will be the same regardless of whether they bend their knees or not, but the size of F and t can be controlled. Since mv is constant, F can be made smaller if t is made longer. When the legs are bent, the time it takes to stop is increased and force is decreased. Football players are taught to roll when they fall down in order to minimize the force of the ground on their bodies as they come to a stop.

9:3 Law of Conservation of Momentum

Newton's third law is equivalent to the law of conservation of momentum. It is helpful to have equipment, such as an air track or an air hockey table, to demonstrate collisions. Collision balls hanging on a track or strings and steel balls are also useful.

Emphasize that there can be no change in momentum of a system unless there is an outside force on the system. If one body hits another in a closed system, the momentum gained by one body must equal the momentum lost by the other. There are basically two types of collisions in a straight line. The objects either collide and go off separately

$$m_A v_A + m_B v_B = m_A v_A' + m_B v_B'$$

or collide and stick together.

$$m_A v_A + m_B v_B = (m_A + m_B)v'.$$

Emphasize that whenever v_A and v_B have opposite directions, one must have a negative sign. Demonstrate some of these collisions. To make two objects stick together, use clay or Velcro.

9:4 Internal and External Forces

Relate the equation $m_A v_A' = -m_B v_B'$ to the recoil of a rifle and the way a rocket works. When a bullet is fired, the small bullet goes off at a high speed in one direction and the massive rifle moves at a small velocity in the opposite direction. This is analogous to a rocket that fires out exhaust gas in one direction and moves in the opposite direction. The rocket continues to accelerate until there is no more exhaust.

Ask students how they could get off the ice if they were stranded in the middle of a frozen lake with perfectly frictionless ice. Since the ice is frictionless, they could toss a shoe and move across the ice until they were able to get off the lake.

9:5 Conservation of Momentum in Two and Three Dimensions

In general, conservation of momentum takes into account collisions in two dimensions. As noted in the text, this fact can be applied to the game of billiards. If the balls make a glancing collision, they will move off at right angles to each other and conserve kinetic energy.

Have students experiment by colliding balls of the same size and mass and balls of the same size and different mass, such as golf balls and ping pong balls. Remind students to record their procedures and their observations as they do head on and glancing collisions by rolling the heavy ball into the light ball and the light ball into the heavy ball.

Resources

Literature

Brown, Jr., Robert J., "Another Newton's Sail-Boat," *The Physics Teacher*, December, 1972, p. 488.

Ficken Jr., George W., "Home Experiment Using a Garden Hose," *The Physics Teacher*, April, 1987, p. 218.

Marion, J.B., Hornyak, W.E., "Bone-Breaking Forces in Jumping," *General Physics With Bioscience Essays*, 2nd Edition, John Wiley and Sons, pp. 61–62.

Software/Audiovisual

Walker, Jearl, *Kinetic Karnival*, WVIZ-TV, video

The Mechanical Universe-High School Adaptation, Conservation of Momentum, Annenberg Project, 1985, video

University Physics, Disk I, Addison-Wesley, Apple II software

Vol. 4: Conservation Laws, Cross Ed. Software, IBM-PC software

Background

When an explosion takes place and pieces of objects fly off in several different directions, momentum is conserved. Since the momentum before the explosion was zero, the momentum after the explosion also must be zero. Therefore, the vectors representing momentum after the explosion must all be added head-to-tail to give a closed figure.

For example, assume an explosion occurs and a 1 kg piece goes north at 16 m/s and a 3 kg piece goes east at 4 m/s. The last piece has a mass of 2 kg. What is the magnitude and direction of the velocity of the piece? First draw the vector diagram putting in the known quantities. Remember that the vectors represent momentum.

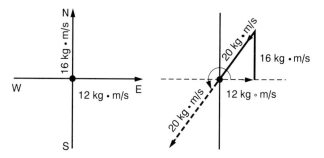

The unknown momentum is 20 kg m/s. Therefore, the unknown velocity for the 2 kg mass is 10 m/s. From the diagram, we can find that the angle is 233°.

Chapter Review

QUESTIONS

1. A conservation law states that a quantity is the same before and after an interaction.

2. You define an isolated system and examine it before and after the interaction.

3. **a.** There is a net external force, gravity, acting on it.
   b. the ball plus Earth

4. Yes. Must have a higher velocity such that mv(bullet) = mv(truck).

5. Momentum is conserved. The change in momentum of gases in one direction must be balanced by an equal change in momentum of the craft in the opposite direction.

6. By stopping the wheels and allowing the external frictional force of the road against the tires to stop the car. If there is no friction, for example, if the road is icy, then there is no external force and the car does not stop.

7. It must be moving with the velocity that the cue ball had just before the collision.

8. When the pistol is fired in the opposite direction, it provides the impulse needed to move the astronaut toward the capsule.

9. **a.** Impulses are the same, although opposite in direction.
   b. The catcher, because the time interval over which the force is exerted is smaller.

10. **a.** The change in momentum of your body is the same. Bending your knees increases the time, reducing the force.
   b. to increase the time of a collision, reducing the force

APPLYING CONCEPTS

1. Yes. If the smaller force acts for a long enough time, it can provide a larger impulse.

2. in the same direction, to increase the time of the collision, reducing the force

3. Momentum is conserved, so the momentum of block and bullet after the collision equals the momentum of the bullet before. The rubber bullet has a negative momentum after impact with respect to the block, so the block's momentum must be greater in this case. Bouncing beats sticking.

4. The example showed that, if they had equal masses, they would have moved off at half the speed. Thus, the moving truck must have had a more massive load.

5. It is transferred to Earth. Both Jim and Earth together must be considered as the system to use conservation of momentum.

6. It is transferred to Earth either directly or indirectly.

7. By shooting mass (exhaust gas) at high velocity in the same direction in which you are moving, its momentum would cause your ship's momentum to be decreased.

8. Consider the system to be the ball and wall (and Earth). The wall and Earth gain some momentum in the collision.

9. Rebounding presents the greater danger because it requires a greater change in momentum and therefore a greater impulse.

10. Held loosely the recoil momentum of the rifle works against only the mass of the rifle producing a larger velocity, striking your shoulder smartly. When held firmly against your shoulder, the recoil momentum must work against the mass of the rifle and yourself, resulting in a smaller velocity.

EXERCISES

1. $F\Delta t = (30.0 \text{ N})(0.16 \text{ s}) = 4.8 \text{ kg} \cdot \text{m/s}$

2. $\Delta p = F\Delta t = m\Delta v$
   $\Delta v = F\Delta t/m$
   $= (4.8 \text{ kg} \cdot \text{m/s})/(0.115 \text{ kg})$
   $= 42 \text{ m/s}.$

3. $\Delta p = m \Delta v = (76 \text{ kg})(9.4 \text{ m/s})$
   $= 7.1 \times 10^2 \text{ kg} \cdot \text{m/s}$
   $F = \Delta P/\Delta t = (7.1 \times 10^2 \text{ kg} \cdot \text{m/s})/(2.8 \text{ s})$
   $= 2.6 \times 10^2 \text{ N}$

4. $p_A + p_B = p'_A + p'_B = 0$, so
   $v_B = -v_A m_A/m_B$
   $= -(8.2 \text{ m/s})(95 \text{ kg})/(128 \text{ kg}) = -6.1 \text{ m/s}$

5. **a.** $d = (v_f + v_i)t/2$, so
   $t = 2d/v_i = 2(0.25 \text{ m})/(10 \text{ m/s})$
   $= 5.0 \times 10^{-2} \text{ s}$
   b. $F\Delta t = \Delta p$, so
   $F = \Delta p/\Delta t$
   $= (40 \text{ kg})(-10 \text{ m/s})/(5.0 \times 10^{-2} \text{ s})$
   $= -8 \times 10^3 \text{ N}$
   c. $F = ma$
   $m = F/a$
   $= (8 \times 10^3 \text{ N})/(10 \text{ m/s})$
   $= 800 \text{ kg, no}$
   d. Holding the infant on your lap would be dangerous both to yourself and to the infant.

6. **a.** $v_f = \sqrt{2gd}$
   $= \sqrt{2(9.8 \text{ m/s}^2)(2 \text{ m})}$
   $= 6.2 \text{ m/s}$
   $p = mv$
   $= (10 \text{ kg})(6.2 \text{ m/s})$
   $= 62 \text{ kg} \cdot \text{m/s}$
   The acceleration is downward, so
   $p = -62 \text{ kg} \cdot \text{m/s}.$
   b. Impulse equals Δp.
   $\Delta p = +62 \text{ kg} \cdot \text{m/s}$
   c. $d = (v_f + v_i)t/2$
   $t = 2d/v_f$
   $= 2(-1.0 \times 10^{-2} \text{ m})/(-6.2 \text{ m/s})$
   $= 3.2 \times 10^{-3} \text{ s}$
   $F = \Delta p/\Delta t$
   $= (62 \text{ kg} \cdot \text{m/s})/(3.2 \times 10^{-3} \text{ s})$
   $= 1.9 \times 10^4 \text{ N}$

d. $d = (v_f + v_i)t/2$

$t = 2d/v_f$

$= 2(-5.0 \times 10^{-2} \text{ m})/(-6.2 \text{ m/s})$

$= 1.6 \times 10^{-2} \text{ s}$

$F = \Delta p/\Delta t$

$= (62 \text{ kg} \cdot \text{m/s})/(1.6 \times 10^{-2} \text{ s})$

$= 3.8 \times 10^3 \text{ N}$

7. $p_A + p_B = p'_A + p'_B = 0$

$m_A v'_B = -m_B v'_B$

$v'_A/v'_B = -m_B/m_A$

$= -90/60$

$= -1.5$

The negative sign shows that the velocities are in opposite directions.

8. $p_A + p_B = p'_A + p'_B$

$m_A v_A = (m_A + m_B)v'$

$v_A = v'(m_A + m_B)/m_A$

$= (8.5 \text{ m/s})(2575 \text{ kg} + 825 \text{ kg})/$

(2575 kg)

$= 11 \text{ m/s}$

9. $p_A + p_B = p'_A + p'_B$

$m_A v_A = (m_A + m_B)v'$

$v' = m_A v_A/(m_A + m_B)$

$= \dfrac{(0.115 \text{ kg})(35 \text{ m/s})}{(0.115 \text{ kg} + 0.465 \text{ kg})}$

$= 6.9 \text{ m/s}$

10. a. $v_f^2 = 2gd$

$= 2(9.80 \text{ m/s}^2)(0.32 \text{ m})$

$v_f = 2.5 \text{ m/s}$

$p = mv$

$= (2.5 \text{ m/s})(60 \text{ kg})$

$= 1.5 \times 10^2 \text{ kg} \cdot \text{m/s}$

The acceleration is downward, so

$p = -1.5 \times 10^2 \text{ kg} \cdot \text{m/s}$.

b. Final momentum $= 0$,

so impulse $= +1.5 \times 10^2 \text{ kg} \cdot \text{m/s}$

c. $F = \dfrac{\Delta p}{\Delta t}$

$= (+1.5 \times 10^2 \text{ kg} \cdot \text{m/s})/(0.05 \text{ s})$

$= 3 \times 10^3 \text{ N}$

d. $W = mg$

$= (60 \text{ kg})(9.80 \text{ m/s}^2)$

$= 5.9 \times 10 \text{ N}$,

so this force is 5.1 times the dancer's weight.

11. a. $F\Delta t = \Delta p = m\Delta v$

$= (25 \text{ kg})(8 \text{ m/s} - 12 \text{ m/s})$

$= -100 \text{ kg} \cdot \text{m/s}$.

b. $F\Delta t = \Delta p = m\Delta v$

$= (25 \text{ kg})(-8 \text{ m/s} - 12 \text{ m/s})$

$= -500 \text{ kg} \cdot \text{m/s}$.

12. a. $p_i = 0$

$\Delta p = p_i$

$= (845 \text{ kg})(100 \text{ km/h})(1000 \text{ m/km})$

$(1\text{h}/3600 \text{ s})$

$= 2.3 \times 10^4 \text{ kg} \cdot \text{m/s}$.

b. $F = \dfrac{\Delta p}{\Delta t}$

$= \dfrac{2.3 \times 10^4 \text{ kg} \cdot \text{m/s}}{9.0 \times 10^{-1} \text{ s}}$

$= 2.6 \times 10^4 \text{ N}$

13. a. $m\Delta v = F\Delta t = (6.00 \text{ N})(10.0 \text{ s})$

$= 60.0 \text{ N} \cdot \text{s}$

b. $\Delta v = F\Delta t/m = (60.0 \text{ N} \cdot \text{s})/(3.00 \text{ kg})$

$= 20.0 \text{ m/s}$

14. $m\Delta v = F\Delta t$

$F = m\Delta v/\Delta t = (1.10 \times 10^3 \text{ kg})$

$(22.0 \text{ m/s} - 0 \text{ m/s})/(20.0 \text{ s})$

$= 1.21 \times 10^3 \text{ N}$

15. a. $\Delta p = m\Delta v$

$= (6.00 \times 10^2 \text{ kg})(44.0 \text{ m/s} - 10.0 \text{ m/s})$

$= 2.04 \times 10^4 \text{ N} \cdot \text{s}$

b. $F = m\Delta v/\Delta t$

$= (2.00 \times 10^4 \text{ N} \cdot \text{s})/(68.0 \text{ s})$

$= 3.00 \times 10^2 \text{ N}$

16. $p_A + p_B = p'_A + p'_B$

$m_A v_A + m_B v_B = m_A v'_A + m_B v'_B$

$v'_A = v'_B = v'$

$v' = \dfrac{m_A v_A}{(m_A + m_B)}$

$= \dfrac{(1245 \text{ kg})(28 \text{ m/s})}{(1245 \text{ kg} + 2175 \text{ kg})}$

$= 10 \text{ m/s}$

17. $p_A + p_B = p'_A + p'_B$,

$m_A v_A + m_B v_B = m_A v'_A + m_B v'_B$

$v'_A = (m_A v_A + m_B v_B - m_B v'_B)/m_A$

$= ((0.200 \text{ kg})(0.30 \text{ m/s}) + (0.100 \text{ kg})$

$(0.10 \text{ m/s}) - (0.100 \text{ kg})(0.26 \text{ m/s}))/$

(0.200 kg)

$= 0.22 \text{ m/s}$, in the original direction.

PROBLEMS

1. $\tan 30.0° = \dfrac{m\Delta v}{m_p \Delta v_p}$

$m\Delta v = m_p \Delta v_p \tan 30.0°$

$= (7600 \text{ kg})$

$(120 \text{ m/s})(0.577)$

$= 5.3 \times 10^5 \text{ kg} \cdot \text{m/s}$

$m_p \Delta v_p = m_g \Delta v_g = m\Delta v$

$m_g = \dfrac{m\Delta v}{\Delta v_g} = \dfrac{(5.3 \times 10^5 \text{ kg} \cdot \text{m/s})}{(3.2 \times 10^3 \text{ m/s})} = 170 \text{ kg}$

2. a. $\quad F_{\parallel} = F_w \sin \Theta = (24.5 \text{ N})(\sin 30.0°)$

$= 12.3 \text{ N}$

$F = ma, \; m = \dfrac{W}{g}$

$a = \dfrac{Fg}{W} = \dfrac{F_{\parallel}g}{F_W} = \dfrac{(12.3 \text{ N})(9.8 \text{ m/s}^2)}{24.5 \text{ N}}$

$= 4.9 \text{ m/s}^2$

$v_f^2 = 2ad = 2(4.9 \text{ m/s}^2)(1.00 \text{ m})$

$= 9.8 \text{ m}^2/\text{s}^2$

$v_f = 3.1 \text{ m/s}$

$p_A + p_B = p'_A + p'_B \; ; \; p_B = 0$

$m_A v_A = m_A v'_A + m_B v'_B$

$v'_A = v'_B = v'$

$m_A v_A = v'(m_A + m_B)$

$v' = \dfrac{m_A v_A}{(m_A + m_B)} =$

$\dfrac{(24.5 \text{ N}/9.8 \text{ m/s}^2)(3.1 \text{ m/s})}{((24.5 \text{ N} + 36.8 \text{ N})/9.8 \text{ m/s}^2)}$

$= 1.25 \text{ m/s}$

b. $F_f \Delta t = m\Delta v$

$\Delta t = \dfrac{m\Delta v}{F_f} =$

$\dfrac{(24.5 \text{ N} + 36.8 \text{ N})/(9.8 \text{ m/s}^2)(1.25 \text{ m/s})}{5.0 \text{ N}}$

$= 1.6 \text{ s}$

c. $d = v_i t = \dfrac{(1.2 \text{ m/s})(1.5 \text{ s})}{2}$

$= 1.0 \text{ m}$

3. a. $\Delta p_A = m_A v'_A - m_A v_A = m_A (v'_A - v_A)$

$= (5.0 \text{ g})(8.0 \text{ m/s} - 20.0 \text{ m/s})$

$= -6.0 \times 10^1 \text{ g} \cdot \text{m/s}$

b. $p_A + p_B = p'_A + p'_B$

$m_A v_A + m_B v_B = m_A v'_A + m_B v'_B$

$v'_B = \dfrac{(m_A v_A + m_B v_B - m_A v'_A)}{m_B} =$

$\dfrac{(5.0 \text{ g})(20.0 \text{ m/s}) + (10.0 \text{ g})(10.0 \text{ m/s}) - (5.0 \text{ g})(8.0 \text{ m/s})}{(10.0 \text{ g})}$

$= 16 \text{ m/s}$

$\Delta p_B = m_B v'_B - m_B v_B = m_B(v'_B - v_B)$

$= (10.0 \text{ g})(16 \text{ m/s} - 10.0 \text{ m/s})$

$= 6.0 \times 10^1 \text{ g} \cdot \text{m/s}$

4. $p_A + p_P + p_C = p'_A + p'_B + p'_C$

$m_A v_A + m_B v_B + m_C v_C = m_A v'_A + m_B v'_B + m_C v'_C$

$v'_A = v'_B = v'_C = v'$

$m_A v_A + m_B v_B + m_C v_C = v'(m_A + m_B + m_C)$

$v' = \dfrac{(m_A v_A + m_B v_B + m_C v_C)}{(m_A + m_B + m_C)} =$

$\dfrac{(92 \text{ kg})(5.0 \text{ m/s}) + (75 \text{ kg})(-2.0 \text{ m/s}) + (75 \text{ kg})(-4.0 \text{ m/s})}{(92 \text{ kg} + 75 \text{ kg} + 75 \text{ kg})}$

$= 0.04 \text{ m/s, over the goal line—touchdown!}$

5. Momentum before striking the ground

$p = mv$

$= (65 \text{ kg})(-10.4 \text{ m/s})$

$= -680 \text{ N} \cdot \text{s}$

Time from the instant the feet touch the ground until coming to rest

$d = \dfrac{(v_f + v_i)t}{2}$

$t = \dfrac{2d}{(v_f + v_i)} = \dfrac{(2)(0.50 \text{ m})}{(0 + (-10.4 \text{ m/s}))}$

$= 9.6 \times 10^{-2} \text{ s}$

$\Delta p = 680 \text{ N} \cdot \text{s}$ in coming to rest

$= F\Delta t$

$F = \dfrac{\Delta p}{\Delta t} = \dfrac{680 \text{ N} \cdot \text{s}}{9.6 \times 10^{-2} \text{ s}}$

$= 7.1 \times 10^3 \text{ N, upward}$

Work, Energy, and Simple Machines

Overview

This chapter familiarizes students with the calculation of work and power, thus paving the way for the consideration of energy in Chapter 11. The fundamentals of machines are also discussed. Mechanical advantage and ideal mechanical advantage are defined and used to calculate the efficiency of a machine.

Planning Guide (5 Class Sessions)

Text Section			Demonstrations and Experiments		Other Program Components	
10:1	Work	P	Exp 17	Pulleys	Teaching Master 10-1: Direction of	
10:2	Work and Direction of Force	P		**LM**	Force	**TRP**
10:3	Energy and Power	P				
10:4	Simple Machines	S			Teaching Master 10-2: Six Simple	
10:5	Mechanical Advantage	S			Machines	**TRP**
					Review Masters	**TRP**
					Minilab 10-1: Levers	**TRP**
					Enrichment 10-1: Bicycle	
					Mechanics	**TRP**
					Evaluation	**TRP**

Performance Objectives

Upon completion of this chapter, your students will

1. display an ability to calculate work done by a force. *10:1*
2. identify the force with the work it does. *10:2*
3. understand the relationship between work and energy. *10:3*
4. differentiate between work and power and correctly calculate power used. *10:3*
5. demonstrate knowledge of the types of simple machines and the relationship between machines and work. *10:4*
6. understand the concept of mechanical advantage and ideal *MA* and use them correctly in solving problems. *10:5*

Teaching the Chapter

Introduction

Using the Photo: The portion of the force doing the lifting is the component of force in a vertical direction. The farther the lifter's arms are apart, the greater the force needed to produce the same vertical component of force. The work required to lift a set of weights a given distance remains the same, although the applied force changes. Ricardo is correct.

This photograph can be used with Sections 10:1 and 10:2 on work and the direction of force.

Demonstration: A good way to teach the concepts of work and power is to measure "student power." The biggest student will not always be the most powerful. If possible, take students to a stairway or to the steps of the football stadium and measure the vertical height of the stairs. Measure the time it takes a student to run up the stairs. Have the student repeat this several times. Then calculate the average time. Convert the student's weight in pounds to newtons and calculate the work, $W = Fd$, and the power, $P = W/t$, where F is the weight, d is the vertical height of the stairs, and t is the time of travel.

If you are unable to go to a stairway, have a student lift some books from the floor to a tabletop. Measure the weight of the books, the height of the table, and the time it takes the student to lift the books. To lengthen the time, have the student lift the books up and down several times and measure the total distance. Work is the total distance lifted times the weight, while power is work divided by time.

10:1 Work

The concept of work is so familiar to everyone that the variety of understandings must be tailored for clarity and calculations in this chapter. Contrary to popular belief, no work is done unless distance is covered. Numerous examples drawn from everyday experiences can be discussed to create an interest in the study. Example: A person may push against a building until becoming tired. If the building does not move, no work is done.

10:2 Work and Direction of Force

Work, defined as the product of force and change in displacement, can be measured only when these factors are considered:
  (1) the displacement of the object
  (2) the magnitude of the force (always in the direction of the displacement).
Discuss with students some examples that they contribute. When you feel that the introduction is sufficient, continue with the following demonstrations.

Demonstration: Ask a student to push as hard as possible on a table. Begin the pushes straight down and continue to change the angle toward the horizontal until the table moves. Discuss what is happening with the class. This exercise can be extended with measurements and vector diagrams.

Demonstration: Do several examples finding the horizontal component of a force. Take a large demonstration spring scale and pull a brick across a table with the force at an angle. Have a student read the spring scale. Have another student measure the angle of the force. Find the horizontal component and calculate the work done in moving the brick one meter across the table. Contrast this with the work done when the same brick is lifted one meter.

10:3 Energy and Power

Demonstration: State that two students completing identical tasks accomplish the same amount of work regardless of the time it takes to do it. The one who completes the task in the shortest time demonstrates the most power.

10:4 Simple Machines
10:5 Mechanical Advantage

Emphasize that a machine decreases the force applied but not the work input. Ask students why machines are used. They may say to make a job easier or to help people do less work. To help students understand machines, do the following demonstration.

Demonstration: Set up a board at an angle. Pull a brick up the board and have a student read the scale. Record this as F_e. Measure the length of the incline and the height and record these as d_e and d_r respectively. Weigh the brick on the spring scale and record it as F_r. Now calculate the input work, output work, MA, IMA, and efficiency. It may be advantageous also to do this activity with a simple pulley to help differentiate among all the variables. Emphasize how much smaller the effort force is than the resistance force and that the purpose of a machine is to make the effort force as small as possible. Friction causes the work input to be larger than the work output.

Have several tools available for students to look at, such as a bottle opener, a car jack, a wrench, a nutcracker, and pliers. Discuss where the effort and resistance forces are when each machine is used.

Students can see that a screw is a modified inclined plane by cutting a piece of paper on the diagonal to make a triangle. Hold a pencil along the short side of the triangle and roll the paper around the pencil to get a spiral effect.

· The Minilab, "Levers," in the *Teacher Resource Package* can be done quite easily as it requires very little equipment. You may also wish to do the exercise on the mechanical advantage of the forearm as described in the literature resource "Body Levers." The forearm is a third-class lever and the force exerted by its muscle is many times the weight being lifted.

Resources

Literature

Chiapetta, Eugene L., "Body Levers," *The Science Teacher,* January, 1987, pp. 39–41.

Engel, C., and Girard, B., "Motorcycle Physics," *The Science Teacher,* January, 1983, p. 40.

Kolb, K.B., "Reciprocating Engine," *The Physics Teacher,* March, 1966, pp. 121–122.

Marion, J.B., and Hornyak, W.F., "Energetics of Running." In *General Physics with Bioscience Essays,* 2nd edition, John Wiley and Sons, Inc., New York, 1985, pp. 131–132.

Misiti, Jr., F.L., "Gear Up With Bike Mechanics," *The Science Teacher,* September, 1983, p. 35.

Wolfson, R., and Pasachoff, J.M., *Physics,* Little, Brown and Co., Boston, 1987, pp. 128–131.

Software/Audiovisual

Concentrated Physics Concepts Part I: Mechanics, Disk 2, John Wiley and Sons, Apple II software

University Physics, Disk I, Addison-Wesley, Apple II software

Work and Energy, J and S Software, Apple II software

Background

We have calculated work done for forces that are constant. Many important forces, including electrical and gravitational forces, vary with position. These forces vary inversely with the distance between the interacting objects. The force of a spring also varies as the spring stretches and is directly proportional to the distance it is stretched. Consider a force that varies with position as shown in the diagram.

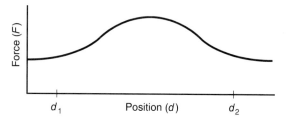

You cannot say that the work done is $F(d_2 - d_1)$ because the force varies and there is no single value of F. The region can be divided into small rectangles of width Δd and the areas of the rectangles determined and added together. If the width Δd is small enough, the force will be almost constant over that width. The area of one rectangle would be $F\Delta d$ and would represent the work done over that interval.

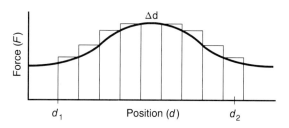

If you could make the width smaller and smaller, you would approach an infinite number of intervals. The sum of these infinitely small areas is called the definite integral. It would represent the total work done. Students taking calculus will be familiar with the integral; point out this application of integral calculus.

Chapter Review

Questions

1. Work is the product of force and the distance an object is moved in the direction of the force. Power is the time rate at which work is done.

2. .Both people are doing the same amount of work, as they are both climbing the same flight of stairs.

3. The person who climbs the stairs in 25 seconds expends the most power, as less time is needed to cover the distance.

4. Only the gravity and the upward normal force. They do no work because motion is perpendicular to them. There is no force in the direction of motion, so no work is done at all.

5. Pedals of a bike transfer work from the rider to the machine through a distance.

6. Your hand should be as far from the head as possible to make d_e as large as possible. The nail should be as close to the head as possible to make d_r as small as possible.

7. Increase the ratio of d_e/d_r to increase the ideal mechanical advantage of a machine.

8. No. The force of gravity is directed toward Earth and is perpendicular to the direction of motion of the satellite.

Applying Concepts

1. Each requires the same amount of work because Fd is the same.

2. Net work is zero. Carrying the carton upstairs requires positive work; carrying it back down is negative work. The work done in both cases is equal and opposite because the distances are equal and opposite. The student might arrange payments on the basis of the time it takes to carry paper, whether up or down, not on the basis of net work done.

3. You do positive work *on* the box because the force and motion are in the same direction. Gravity does negative work *on* the box because the force of gravity is opposite to the direction of motion. The net work done *on* the box is zero because the work done *by* you and *by* gravity are equal and opposite. However, the work done *by* you and *by* gravity are separate and do not cancel.

4. **a.** $W = Fd$ is independent of time, so the two do equal work.

   b. $P = \dfrac{W}{t}$, so Mo, who takes less time, expends more power.

5. Reduce friction as much as possible to reduce the resistance force.

Exercises

1. Find area under curve. It is a triangle, of area (base)(height)/2 = (0.25 m)(6.4 N)/2 = 0.80 J

2. $W = Fd \cos \theta$

   $\cos \theta = \dfrac{W}{Fd} = \dfrac{(1.20 \times 10^4 \text{ J})}{(125 \text{ N})(185 \text{ m})} = 0.519$

   $\theta = 58.7°$

3. **a.** 462 N is the horizontal component, so the tension is $\dfrac{462 \text{ N}}{\cos 56.0°} = 826$ N

b. $W = Fd = (462 \text{ N})(24.5 \text{ m}) = 1.13 \times 10^4$ J

c. force and displacement are in opposite directions, so $W = -(462 \text{ N})(24.5 \text{ m}) = -1.13 \times 10^4$ J

4. Only net vertical displacement counts.
   $W = Fd = (22 \text{ N})(0.35 \text{ m}) = 7.7$ J

5. **a.** $P = \dfrac{W}{t} = \dfrac{(145 \text{ N})(60.0 \text{ m})}{(25.0 \text{ s})} = 348$ W

   b. Either d is doubled or t is halved, so P is doubled to 6.96×10^2 W

6. $W = Fd = (150 \text{ kg})(9.8 \text{ m/s}^2)(8.0 \text{ m})$
   $= 1.2 \times 10^4$ J

7. **a.** $F_x = F \cos \theta$

   $F = \dfrac{F_x}{\cos \theta} = \dfrac{(805 \text{ N})}{\cos 32°} = 949$ N

   b. $W = F_x d = (805 \text{ N})(22 \text{ m}) = 1.8 \times 10^4$ J

   c. $P = \dfrac{W}{t} = \dfrac{1.8 \times 10^4 \text{ J}}{8.0 \text{ s}} = 2.3$ kW

8. $P = \dfrac{W}{t} = \dfrac{Fd}{t} = Fv = (6.0 \times 10^3 \text{ N})(15 \text{ m/s})$
   $= 90$ kW

9. $W = Fd$, where F is the weight of bucket plus soil. Soil mass is $(1.15 \text{ m}^3)(2.00 \times 10^3 \text{ kg/m}^3) = 2.30 \times 10^3$ kg. Its weight is 2.25×10^4 N, so total weight is 2.48×10^4 N. Thus, $W = Fd = (2.48 \times 10^4 \text{ N})(7.50 \text{ m}) = 1.86 \times 10^5$ J.

10. **a.** $W = Fd = mgd = (240 \text{ kg})(9.80 \text{ m/s}^2)(2.35 \text{ m}) = 5.53 \times 10^3$ J

    b. $d = 0$, so no work

    c. d is opposite of motion in part **a**, so W is also the opposite, -5.53×10^3 J

    d. No. He exerts no force, so he does no work, positive or negative.

    e. $P = \dfrac{W}{t} = (5.53 \times 10^3 \text{ J})/(2.5 \text{ s}) = 2.2$ kW

11. $P = \dfrac{W}{t} = \dfrac{mgd}{t}$

    $\dfrac{m}{t} = (35 \text{ L/min})(1.00 \text{ kg/L}) = 35$ kg/min

    Thus, $P = (35 \text{ kg/min})(1 \text{ min}/60 \text{ s})(9.80 \text{ m/s}^2)(110 \text{ m}) = 0.63$ kW

12. $P = \dfrac{W}{t} = \dfrac{Fd \cos \theta}{t}$

    $d = \dfrac{Pt}{F \cos \theta} = \dfrac{(64.6 \text{ W})(90.0 \text{ s})}{(115 \text{ N})(\cos 22.5°)} = 54.7$ m

13. F and d are parallel.

$$d = \frac{h}{\sin 30.0°} = \frac{(1.15 \text{ m})}{0.500} = 2.30 \text{ m}$$
$$W = Fd = (225 \text{ N})(2.30 \text{ m}) = 518 \text{ J}$$

14. $W_o = F_r d_r = (215 \text{ kg})(9.80 \text{ m/s}^2)(5.65 \text{ m})$
$$= 1.19 \times 10^4 \text{ J}$$

$$\frac{W_o}{W_i} \times 100\% = 72.5\%$$

$$W_i = \frac{W_o}{0.725} = \frac{(1.19 \times 10^4 \text{ J})}{(0.725)} = 1.64 \times 10^4 \text{ J}$$

15. **a.** $IMA = \dfrac{d_e}{d_r} = \dfrac{(3.90 \text{ m})}{(0.975 \text{ m})} = 4.00$

b. $MA = \dfrac{F_r}{F_e} = \dfrac{(1345 \text{ N})}{(375 \text{ N})} = 3.59$

c. $Efficiency = \dfrac{MA}{IMA} \times 100\%$
$$= \frac{3.59}{4.00} \times 100\% = 89.8\%$$

16. **a.** $W_i = Fd = (496 \text{ N})(2.10 \text{ m}) = 1.04 \times 10^3 \text{ J}$
b. $d = $ height raised $= 0.850 \text{ m}$
$$W_o = (115 \text{ kg})(9.80 \text{ m/s}^2)(0.850 \text{ m}) = 958 \text{ J}$$

c. $Efficiency = \dfrac{W_o}{W_i} \times 100\%$
$$= \frac{(958 \text{ J})}{(1.04 \times 10^3 \text{ J})} \times 100\%$$
$$= 92.1\%$$

Problems

1. **a.** $m = \dfrac{\Delta y}{\Delta x} = \dfrac{(5.0 \text{ N} - 0.0 \text{ N})}{(0.20 \text{ m} - 0.00 \text{ m})}$
$$= \frac{5.0 \text{ N}}{0.20 \text{ m}} = 25 \text{ N/m}$$
$$F = kd = (25 \text{ N/m})(0.20 \text{ m}) = 5.0 \text{ N}$$

b. $A = \dfrac{1}{2} lh = \left(\dfrac{1}{2}\right)(5.0 \text{ N})(0.20 \text{ m})$
$$= 0.50 \text{ J}$$

c. $W = \dfrac{1}{2} kd^2 = \left(\dfrac{1}{2}\right)(25 \text{ N/m})(0.20 \text{ m})^2$
$$= 0.50 \text{ J}$$

2. **a.** $W_{in} = W_{out} = W'_{in} = W'_{out}$
$$W_{in} = W_{out}$$
$$F_e d_e = F_r' d_r'$$
For the complex machine
$$IMA_c = \frac{d_e}{d_r'}$$

$$\frac{d_e}{d_r} = IMA; \frac{d'_e}{d'_r} = IMA'$$
$$d_r = d'_e$$
$$\frac{d_e}{IMA} = d_r = d'_e = (IMA')(d'_r)$$
$$d_e = (IMA)(IMA')(d_r')$$
$$\frac{d_e}{d_r'} = IMA_c = (IMA)(IMA')$$
$$= (3.0)(2.0) = 6.0$$

b. $\dfrac{F_r'}{F_e} = MA_c = \dfrac{(IMA) \times (eff)}{100\%}$
$$\frac{Fr'}{Fe} = \frac{(6.0)(60.0\%)}{(100\%)} = 3.6$$
$$F_e = \frac{F_r'}{3.6} = \frac{540 \text{ N}}{3.6} = 150 \text{ N}$$

c. $\dfrac{d_e}{d_r'} = IMA_c$
$$d_r' = \frac{d_e}{IMA_c} = \frac{12.0 \text{ cm}}{6.0} = 2.0 \text{ cm}$$

3. **a.** Mass lifted $= (550 \text{ dm}^3)(1000 \text{ cm}^3/\text{dm}^3)$
$$(0.82 \text{ g/cm}^3) = 4.5 \times 10^5 \text{ g}$$
$$= 450 \text{ kg}$$
$$W = F_w d = mg(h) = (450 \text{ kg})(9.8 \text{ m/s}^2)(25 \text{ m})$$
$$= 1.1 \times 10^5 \text{ J} = 110 \text{ kJ}$$

b. $P = \dfrac{W}{t} = \dfrac{(110 \text{ J})}{(35 \text{ s})} = 3.1 \text{ kW}$

4. **a.** $W = F_w h = (25 \text{ kg})(9.8 \text{ m/s}^2)(4.5 \text{ m})$
$$= 1.1 \times 10^3 \text{ J}$$
$$W = F_{ll} d$$
$$F_{ll} = \frac{W}{d} = \frac{(1.1 \times 10^3 \text{ J})}{18 \text{ m}} = 61 \text{ N}$$

b. $IMA = \dfrac{d_e}{d_r} = \dfrac{(18 \text{ m})}{(4.5 \text{ m})} = 4.0$

c. $MA = \dfrac{F_r}{F_e} = \dfrac{(25 \text{ kg})(9.8 \text{ m/s}^2)}{75 \text{ N}} = 3.3$
$$eff = \frac{MA}{IMA} \times 100\% = \frac{(3.3)}{(4.0)} \times 100\%$$
$$= 83\%$$

5. $v = 6.50 \text{ cm/s} = 0.0650 \text{ m/s}$
$$P = \frac{W}{t} = \frac{Fd}{t} = F\left(\frac{d}{t}\right) = Fv$$
$$P = F_w v$$
$$F_w = \frac{P}{v} = \frac{(188 \text{ W})}{(0.0650 \text{ m/s})} = 2.89 \times 10^3 \text{ N}$$

6. Total efficiency = 88% × 42% = 37%
Useful power = 5.5 kW × 37% = 2.0 kW =
2.0×10^3 W
$$P = \frac{W}{t} = \frac{Fd}{t} = F\left(\frac{d}{t}\right) = Fv$$

$P = F_w v$

$$v = \frac{P}{F_w} = \frac{(2.0 \times 10^3 \text{ W})}{(410 \text{ kg})(9.8 \text{ m/s}^2)} = 0.50 \text{ m/s}$$

Energy

Overview

The concept of work that was developed in Chapter 10 is now related to energy. Energy is defined as the capacity to do work. The forms of energy are related to the three basic forces. Each form can be either kinetic energy, the energy due to motion, or potential energy, the energy due to position. The joule is the unit for both work and energy.

The law of conservation of energy is one of the great generalizations of physics. This law states that energy may be transformed from one form to another, but it is never created or destroyed. The total amount of energy in the universe is constant.

The conservation of momentum in collisions was studied in Chapter 9. Momentum is conserved in any collision, but kinetic energy is conserved only in elastic collisions. In an inelastic collision, some of the kinetic energy is transformed into other forms of energy, such as heat or light.

Planning Guide (6 Class Sessions)

Text Section		Demonstrations and Experiments		Other Program Components	
11:1 Forms of Energy	P	Exp 18 Conservation of Energy:		Teaching Master 11-1:	
11:2 Work and Change in Kinetic		The Inclined Plane	LM	(a) Kinetic Energy and Work	
Energy	P			(b) Energy Conversion	TRP
11:3 Potential Energy	P				
11:4 Conservation of Energy	P			Teaching Master 11-2: Conservation of	
11:5 Conservation of Energy in				Energy	TRP
Collisions	P			Review Masters	TRP
				Minilab 11-1: Predicting the Landing	
				Spot of a Projectile	TRP
				Enrichment 11-1: Problems	TRP
				Evaluation	TRP

Performance Objectives

Upon completion of this chapter, your students will

1. define kinetic and potential energy. *11:1*
2. calculate kinetic energy and recognize that the change in kinetic energy is the work done on the object (work-energy theorem). *11:2*
3. recognize the arbitrary, but useful, nature of base or reference level of potential energy. *11:3*
4. demonstrate an ability to solve problems involving gravitational potential energy. *11:3*
5. state the law of conservation of energy; demonstrate understanding by solving problems involving energy changes. *11:4*
6. understand the difference between elastic and inelastic collisions. Recognize that mechanical energy is conserved only in elastic collisions, but momentum is conserved in both. *11:5*

Teaching the Chapter

Introduction

Using the Photo: Gravitational potential energy is increasing as the roller coaster is lifted. While the roller coaster is dropping, gravitational potential energy is transferred to kinetic energy. The kinetic energy and speed decrease as the roller coaster climbs the next hill. On a frictionless track, the roller coaster would have enough energy to carry it as high as it was initially. The total energy within the system remains constant.

This photograph can be used with Section 11:2 on potential energy and base levels, Section 11:3 on work and change in potential energy, and Section 11:5 on conservation of energy.

Demonstration: The study of energy can be introduced in this manner. Tie a very heavy mass, such as a kilogram mass, to the end of a rope. Tie the rope to the ceiling of the room. Stand with your head against a wall and pull the mass up to your face so the rope is taut. As you let the mass go, be careful to keep your head firmly against the wall. The pendulum will swing through an arc that brings the mass close to your face without touching it. Talk about the energy changing from potential energy at the ends of the arc to kinetic energy at the midpoint of the arc. Point out that between the ends and the midpoint of the arc, the mass has both potential and kinetic energy.

11:4 Conservation of Energy

Use a transformation of energy apparatus, such as one with a hand-cranked dynamo attached to a motor, bell, and lamp, to show students how you do work by turning the crank on the dynamo. Electrical energy is transformed into mechanical, light, and sound energy.

The concept of energy is a difficult one, so the more examples you can show of transforming work into various kinds of energy, the better. Even something as simple as discussing what happens when you rub your hands together will help students see that you are doing work, which produces thermal energy.

A spring-powered toy can be used to demonstrate that work (Fd) is done on a spring, stored in the form of potential energy, and then converted to kinetic energy.

Discuss and give examples of the consequences of the velocity squared term in the kinetic energy equation. A car gains kinetic energy as it goes from 0 to 55 km/h and as it goes from 55 km/h to 110 km/h. A person might think that the change in kinetic energy would be the same for both situations, but a simple calculation will show that doubling the speed increases the kinetic energy by a factor of four because velocity is squared. If the same force is used to stop the cars, the one with twice the speed will take four times the distance to stop.

11:5 Conservation of Energy in Collisions

A swinging-balls apparatus can be used for an effective discussion of conservation of energy in collisions. If you lift one ball and let it collide with the other four, it will stop and one ball will go out on the other end. Two balls hitting three will stop and two will go out on the other end. You might ask students why one ball does not go out with twice the speed when hit with two balls. You can show that momentum would be conserved by calculating kinetic energy before and after the collisions occur. Students will see that if one ball were to bounce out at twice the speed, the kinetic energy would increase, resulting in more energy than at the start.

You may wish to compare momentum with kinetic energy. Both momentum and kinetic energy deal with motion. When two bodies collide, momentum is transferred from one to the other. The resulting momentum could be zero, since momentum is a vector. When two objects collide, kinetic energy cannot be cancelled but it can be transformed to another form of energy. Energy is a scalar quantity, so the energy adds in a collision. Kinetic energy is proportional to v^2, and momentum is proportional to v. When you double the velocity, you increase kinetic energy by a factor of four and momentum by a factor of two. If you have two bullets, one with half the mass of the other but twice the velocity, they will both have the same momentum, but the smaller bullet will have twice the kinetic energy. The result is that the smaller, faster-moving bullet will penetrate what it hits more than the larger, slower-moving bullet.

Resources

Literature

Edge, R.D., "String and Sticky Tape Experiment," AAPT, Experiment 1.25.

Mammock, Frank M., "If Only Newton Had a Rocket," *The Science Teacher,* April, 1988, pp. 42–45.

Marion, J.B., and Hornyak, W.F., "Energetics of Jumping." In *General Science with Bioscience Essays,* 2nd edition, John Wiley and Sons, Inc., New York, 1985, pp. 137–141.

Rouché, B., and Rouché, C., "Tin Can Rally," *The Science Teacher,* September, 1988, pp. 78–79.

Zwart, J.W., "A Safe and Inexpensive Ballistic Pendulum," *The Physics Teacher,* October, 1987, pp. 447–448.

Software/Audiovisual

Concentrated Physics Concepts Part I: Mechanics, Disk 2, John Wiley and Sons, Apple II software

The Mechanical Universe-High School Adaptation, The Conservation of Energy, Annenberg Project, 1985, video

University Physics, Disk I, Addision-Wesley, Apple II software

Work and Energy, J and S Software, Apple II software

Background

One way to find the speed of a bullet is to use a ballistic pendulum. The calculation of the speed of a bullet requires the use of both conservation of momentum and energy. Assume that a 15-g bullet is shot into a 3.000-kg block of wood hanging at the end of a string. The block of wood with the bullet in it rises a height of 17 cm. To find the speed of the bullet, the problem should be worked in the opposite direction from which the events occur. First use conservation of energy to find the velocity of the block and bullet just after the bullet hits, and then use conservation of momentum to find the original velocity of the bullet.

Conservation of Energy

$$PE_{top} = KE_{bottom}$$

$$mgh = \frac{1}{2}mv'^2$$

$$v' = \sqrt{2gh} = \sqrt{2(9.8 \text{ m/s}^2)(.17 \text{ m})}$$

$$v' = 1.8 \text{ m/s for bullet and block}$$

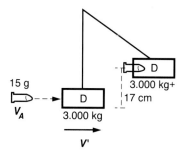

Conservation of Momentum

$$m_A v_A + m_B v_B = (m_A + m_B)v'$$

$$0.015 \text{ kg }(v_A) + 0 = (3.015 \text{ kg})(1.8 \text{ m/s})$$

$$v_A = 362 \text{ m/s for bullet}$$

Chapter Review

Questions

1. Forces transfer energy between points and between objects.

2. A wound-up watch spring has potential energy. Work was done to wind the spring. When running, a watch converts the potential energy of the spring into kinetic energy. When a watch runs down, its energy has been converted to heat and sound.

3. The Earth-sun system possesses both kinetic and potential energy. As a matter of fact, the two are constantly interchanging. This is why Earth moves faster along its orbit when closer to the sun, in accordance with Kepler's law.

4. a. The kinetic energy of the colliding bodies before the collision equals the kinetic energy of the bodies after the collision.
   b. conservation of momentum and energy
   c. conservation of momentum—some energy

changed to thermal energy

5. **a.** If the ball had bounced 8 m, the collision would have been perfectly elastic.
   b. If the ball had not bounced at all, the collision would have been perfectly inelastic.
   c. Some of the ball's kinetic energy is converted to heat and sound as it collides with Earth.

6. Even though the balls do not hit the ground at the same time, they have identical velocities and kinetic energies when they hit.

7. work by vaulter, kinetic energy of running, potential energy of bent pole, kinetic energy of rising vaulter, potential energy of vaulter at top of trajectory, kinetic energy of vaulter falling

8. The bowling ball on Earth will have the larger potential energy because potential energy is directly proportional to gravitational acceleration, g.

9. No, since the ball does not maintain a constant acceleration throughout its entire fall, some of its energy is transformed as it works against air resistance.

10. The semi-truck has more kinetic energy because kinetic energy is directly proportional to the mass of an object. The semi-truck also uses more fuel energy because fuel energy is likewise directly proportional to the mass of an object.

Applying Concepts

1. No. Gravity also does work on the box. Forces are balanced and there is no net work. Thus, there is no change in kinetic energy.

2. Yes. The net force acting on a car, the force exerted backwards by the road, does negative work on the car, reducing its kinetic energy.

3. Work is needed to change the potential energy of a car. By increasing the distance, d, the force, F, is reduced.

4. Kinetic energy is larger in winter, so potential energy must be smaller. Thus, potential energy is smaller when the distance to the sun is smaller.

5. Potential energy is greater, so E is greater. Thus, m is larger.

6. "Flubber" would violate the law of conservation of energy. Such a substance cannot exist as far as we know, at the present time.

7. The faster one rises four times as high because the kinetic energy at the bottom becomes potential energy at top, and kinetic energy is proportional to the square of the speed, while potential energy is proportional to the height.

8. Potential energy is doubled at the top, so kinetic energy is doubled at the bottom of the trajectory. Thus, the square of speed is doubled, so speed is larger by a ratio of $\sqrt{2}/1 = 1.414$.

Exercises

1. **a.** $W = Fd = (98 \text{ N})(50 \text{ m}) = 5000 \text{ J}$
   b. $\Delta PE = W = 5000 \text{ J}$
   c. $KE = \Delta PE = 5000 \text{ J}$

2. $KE = \frac{1}{2}mv^2 = \left(\frac{1}{2}\right)(1600 \text{ kg})(12.5 \text{ m/s})^2$
   $= 1.3 \times 10^5 \text{ J}$

3. $v = \dfrac{(108 \text{ km/h})(1000 \text{ m/km})}{(3600 \text{ s/h})} = 30.0 \text{ m/s}$
   $KE = \frac{1}{2}mv^2 = \left(\frac{1}{2}\right)(1500 \text{ kg})(30.0 \text{ m/s})$
   $= 6.8 \times 10^5 \text{ J}$

4. **a.** $W = KE$
   $Fd = \frac{1}{2}mv^2$
   $v^2 = \dfrac{2Fd}{m}$
   $v = \sqrt{\dfrac{2Fd}{m}} = \sqrt{\dfrac{(2)(201 \text{ N})(1.3 \text{ m})}{(0.30 \text{ kg})}}$
   $= 42 \text{ m/s}$
   b. $PE = \Delta KE$
   $mgd = \frac{1}{2}mv^2$
   $d = \dfrac{v^2}{2g} = \dfrac{(42 \text{ m/s})^2}{(2)(9.8 \text{ m/s}^2)}$
   $= 9.0 \times 10^1 \text{ m}$

5. **a.** $W = \Delta KE = \frac{1}{2}mv^2$
   $= \left(\frac{1}{2}\right)(1200 \text{ kg})(20 \text{ m/s})^2$
   $= 2.4 \times 10^5 \text{ J}$
   b. $d = \dfrac{(v_f + v_i)t}{2} = \dfrac{(20 \text{ m/s} + 0)(20.0 \text{ s})}{2}$
   $= 2.0 \times 10^2 \text{ m}$

c. $W = Fd$

$$F = \frac{W}{d} = \frac{(2.4 \times 10^5 \text{ J})}{(2.0 \times 10^2 \text{ m})}$$

$$= 1.2 \times 10^3 \text{ N}$$

d. $F_{net} = F_{forward} - F_{friction}$

$$F_{forward} = F_{net} + F_{friction}$$

$$= (1.2 \times 10^3 \text{ N}) + (450 \text{ N})$$

$$= 1.7 \times 10^3 \text{ N}.$$

6. $W = Fd = (410 \text{ N})(2.0 \text{ m}) = 820 \text{ J}$

$$W = \Delta KE$$

$$mgd = \Delta KE$$

$$d = \frac{\Delta KE}{mg} = \frac{820 \text{ J}}{32 \text{ N}} = 26 \text{ m}$$

7. a. $PE = mgh = (20 \text{ kg})(9.8 \text{ m/s}^2)(100 \text{ m})$

$$= 20\ 000 \text{ J}$$

b. $KE = \Delta PE = 20\ 000 \text{ J}$

c. $KE = \frac{1}{2}mv^2$

$$v = \sqrt{\frac{2KE}{m}} = \sqrt{\frac{(2)(20\ 000 \text{ J})}{(20 \text{ kg})}}$$

$$= 45 \text{ m/s}$$

8. a. $KE = \frac{1}{2}mv^2 = \left(\frac{1}{2}\right)(4.0 \text{ kg})(62 \text{ m/s})^2$

$$= 7.7 \times 10^3 \text{ J}$$

b. $W = Fd$

$$F = \frac{W}{d} = \frac{7.7 \times 10^3 \text{ J}}{22 \text{ m}} = 350 \text{ N}$$

9. a. $mv = (5.0 \times 10^5 \text{ kg})(8.0 \text{ m/s})$

$$= 4.0 \times 10^6 \text{ kg} \cdot \text{m/s}$$

b. Since momentum is conserved, it must be $4.0 \times 10^6 \text{ kg} \cdot \text{m/s}$.

c. Before the collision:

$$KE_1 = \frac{1}{2}mv^2$$

$$= \left(\frac{1}{2}\right)(5.0 \times 10^5 \text{ kg})(8.0 \text{ m/s})^2$$

$$= 1.6 \times 10^7 \text{ J}$$

$KE_2 = 0$, since it is at rest

After the collision:

$$KE = \frac{1}{2}mv^2$$

$$= \left(\frac{1}{2}\right)(5.0 \times 10^5 \text{ kg} + 5.0 \times 10^5 \text{ kg})(4.0 \text{ m/s})^2$$

$$= 8.0 \times 10^6 \text{ J}$$

d. While momentum was conserved during the collision, kinetic energy was not. The amount not conserved was turned into heat and sound.

10. a. $KE = \frac{1}{2}mv^2 = \left(\frac{1}{2}\right)(45 \text{ kg})(10.0 \text{ m/s})^2$

$$= 2.3 \times 10^3 \text{ J}$$

b. $KE = \frac{1}{2}mv^2 = \left(\frac{1}{2}\right)(45 \text{ kg})(5.0 \text{ m/s})^2$

$$= 5.6 \times 10^2 \text{ J}$$

c. $\dfrac{1/2\ (mv_1^2)}{1/2\ (mv_2^2)} = \dfrac{v_1^2}{v_2^2} = \dfrac{(10.0)^2}{(5.0)^2} = \dfrac{4}{1}$

11. $v = \dfrac{d}{t} = \dfrac{(1.8 \text{ km})(1000 \text{ m/km})}{(10.0 \text{ min})(60 \text{ s/min})} = 3.0 \text{ m/s}$

$$KE = \frac{1}{2}mv^2 = \left(\frac{1}{2}\right)(45 \text{ kg})(3.00 \text{ m/s})^2$$

$$= 2.0 \times 10^2 \text{ J}$$

12. $W = \Delta KE =$

$$\left(\frac{1}{2}\right)(15.0 \text{ kg})(7.50 \text{ m/s})^2 - \left(\frac{1}{2}\right)(15.0 \text{ kg})(3.20 \text{ m/s})^2$$

$$= 345 \text{ J}$$

$$d = \frac{W}{F} = \frac{345 \text{ J}}{10.0 \text{ N}} = 34.5 \text{ m}$$

13. a. $KE = \frac{1}{2}mv^2 = \left(\frac{1}{2}\right)(15.0 \text{ kg})(12.5 \text{ m/s})^2$

$$= 1170 \text{ J}$$

b. $\Delta PE = mgh = (15.0 \text{ kg})(9.80 \text{ m/s}^2)(20.4 \text{ m})$

$$= 3.00 \times 10^3 \text{ J}$$

c. $\Delta KE = \Delta PE = 3.00 \times 10^3 \text{ J}$

d. $KE = 1170 \text{ J} + 3.00 \times 10^3 \text{ J} = 4170 \text{ J}$

e. $v = \sqrt{\dfrac{2KE}{m}} = \dfrac{(2)(4170 \text{ J})}{15.0 \text{ kg}} = 23.6 \text{ m/s}$

14. a. $d_v = d \sin \theta = (16.0 \text{ m})(\sin 30.0°) = 8.00 \text{ m}$

$$\frac{1}{2}mv^2 = mgh$$

$$v = \sqrt{2gh} = \sqrt{(2)(9.80 \text{ m/s}^2)(8.00 \text{ m})}$$

$$= 12.5 \text{ m/s}$$

b. $KE = \frac{1}{2}mv^2 = \left(\frac{1}{2}\right)(10.0 \text{ kg})(12.5 \text{ m/s})^2$

$$= 781 \text{ J}$$

15. $PE = mgh$

$$h = \frac{PE}{mg} = \frac{1960 \text{ J}}{(10.0 \text{ kg})(9.80 \text{ m/s}^2)}$$
$$= 20.0 \text{ m}$$

Problems

1. a. $\Delta PE = Fd = (420 \text{ N})(1.00 \text{ m} - 0.40 \text{ m})$
$$= 250 \text{ J}$$

$$KE = \Delta PE = \frac{1}{2}mv^2$$

$$v = \sqrt{\frac{2KE}{m}} = \sqrt{\frac{(2)(250 \text{ J})}{(420 \text{ N}/9.8 \text{ m/s}^2)}}$$
$$= 3.4 \text{ m/s}$$

b. $W = PE - KE = 250 \text{ J} - \frac{1}{2}mv^2$

$$= 250 \text{ J} - \left(\frac{1}{2}\right)\left(\frac{420 \text{ N}}{9.8 \text{ m/s}^2}\right)(2.0 \text{ m/s})^2$$

$$= 250 \text{ J} - 86 \text{ J} = 164 \text{ J} = 160 \text{ J}$$

2. $KE_f = KE_i + PE_i$

$$\frac{1}{2}mv_f^2 = \frac{1}{2}mv_i^2 + mgh$$
$$v_i^2 = v_f^2 - 2gh$$
$$v_i = \sqrt{v_f^2 - 2gh}$$
$$= \sqrt{(7.5 \text{ m/s})^2 - (2)(9.8 \text{ m/s}^2)(2.0 \text{ m})}$$
$$= 4.1 \text{ m/s}$$

3. Momentum conservation:
$$m_b v = m_b v' + MV$$
Energy conservation:
$$\frac{1}{2}m_b v^2 = \frac{1}{2}m_b v'^2 + \frac{1}{2}MV^2$$
From momentum $v' = v - \dfrac{MV}{m_b}$

$$v^2 = \left(v - \frac{MV}{m_b}\right)^2 + \frac{MV^2}{m_b}$$

$$V = \frac{2v}{\left(1 + \dfrac{M}{m_b}\right)} = \frac{2(835 \text{ m/s})}{\left(1 + \left(\dfrac{104 \text{ kg}}{0.0042 \text{ kg}}\right)\right)}$$

$$= 6.7 \times 10^{-2} \text{ m/s}$$

4. Momentum conservation:
$$m_c v = m_c v' + m_b V$$
Energy conservation:
$$\frac{1}{2}m_c v^2 = \frac{1}{2}m_c v'^2 + \frac{1}{2}m_b V^2$$

From momentum $v' = v - \dfrac{m_b V}{m_c}$

$$v^2 = \left(v - \frac{m_b V}{m_c}\right)^2 + \frac{m_b V^2}{m_c}$$

$$V = \frac{2v}{\left(1 + \dfrac{m_b}{m_c}\right)} = \frac{(2)(44 \text{ m/s})}{\left(1 + \left(\dfrac{0.046 \text{ kg}}{0.220 \text{ kg}}\right)\right)}$$

$$= 73 \text{ m/s}$$

5. $v_f^2 = v_i^2 + 2ad$
$$2ad = v_f^2 - v_i^2$$
$$2\left(\frac{F}{m}\right)d = v_f^2 - v_i^2$$
$$Fd = \frac{1}{2}mv_f^2 - \frac{1}{2}mv_i^2$$
$$W = KE_f - KE_i$$

6. At top
$$PE = mgh = (28 \text{ kg})(9.8 \text{ m/s}^2)(4.8 \text{ m})$$
$$= 1.3 \times 10^3 \text{ J}$$
At bottom
$$KE = \frac{1}{2}mv^2 = \left(\frac{1}{2}\right)(28 \text{ kg})(3.2 \text{ m/s})^2$$
$$= 1.4 \times 10^2 \text{ J}$$
$$W_f = PE - KE = 1.2 \times 10^3 \text{ J}$$

Thermal Energy

Overview

This chapter introduces the concept of thermal physics using a microscopic point of view. It expands the concept of conservation of energy, and prepares students for the study of kinetic theory and gas laws presented in Chapters 13 and 14.

The first law of thermodynamics is treated as an extension of conservation of energy, with heat defined as the transfer of energy by means of a difference in temperatures. This definition of heat is carefully used throughout the chapter. Note this fact, because the common use of the noun "heat" is not consistent with this definition.

While the first law of thermodynamics does not prohibit heat flowing from a cold body to a hot body, the second law does. Entropy is described as the disorder of a system. Systems tend to move toward maximum entropy.

Planning Guide (6 Class Sessions)

Text Section		Demonstrations and Experiments		Other Program Components	
12:1 Theories, Hot and Cold	S	Dem 12:1 Hot or Cold?		Skill: Using a Physics Handbook	**TRP**
12:2 Thermal Energy and Temperature	S	Exp 19 The Conservation of Thermal Energy	**LM**	Demonstration 12-1: Galilean Thermometers	**TRP**
12:3 Equilibrium and Thermometry	S	Exp 20 The Specific Heat of a Metal	**LM**	Demonstration 12-3: Gravitational Energy to Thermal Energy	**TRP**
12:4 Temperature Scales	S	Exp 21 Heat of Fusion of Ice	**LM**		
12:5 The Kelvin or Absolute Scale	S	Dem 12:2 Heat Transfer			
12:6 The First Law of Thermodynamics	P			Teaching Master 12-1: Heat Engine **TRP**	
12:7 The Second Law of Thermodynamics	P				
12:8 Specific Heat	P	Dem 12:8 Contrasting Specific Heats, Water as a Coolant		Teaching Master 12-2: Heat Absorbed Versus Temperature	**TRP**
12:9 Conservation in Energy Transfer	P	Dem 12:9 Conservation of Heat Transfer		Review Masters	**TRP**
12:10 Change of State	P	Dem 12:10 Heat of Fusion		Demonstration 12-2: Specific Heat of a Metal and Water	**TRP**
				Enrichment 12-1: Problems	**TRP**
				Enrichment 12-2: The Invention of the Steam Engine	**TRP**
				Evaluation	**TRP**

Performance Objectives

Upon completion of this chapter, your students will

1. understand the nature of thermal energy as explained by the kinetic theory. *12:1*

2. define temperature and distinguish it from thermal energy. *12:2*

3. understand the process of reaching equilibrium

and its application to the measurement of temperature. *12:3*

4. describe the Celsius temperature scale. *12:4*

5. describe the Kelvin scale; demonstrate the ability to convert between Celsius and Kelvin. *12:5*

6. state the first law of thermodynamics; distinguish heat from work and both from thermal energy; define a heat engine, refrigerator, and heat pump. *12:6*

7. state the second law of thermodynamics; define entropy. *12:7*

8. define and display an understanding of specific heat; be able to calculate heat transfer. *12:8*

9. display an understanding of the application of conservation of energy to heat transfers; be able to calculate temperature changes due to heat transfer. *12:9*

10. define heats of fusion and vaporization; understand the microscopic basis of changes of state; calculate heat transfers needed to effect changes of state. *12:10*

Teaching the Chapter

Introduction

Using the Photo: When the bottle is opened, pressurized gas rapidly expands, doing work against the surrounding atmospheric pressure. Energy comes from the internal energy of the gas, which results in its temperature being reduced. The reduced temperature causes some of the water vapor to condense and form a fog as it cools. Use this photograph again when discussing Section 12:6 on the first law of thermodynamics and Section 12:10 on the change of state.

Demonstration: Place three beakers of water on your desk, one near 0°C, one near 20°C, and one near 50°C. Have a student put one hand in the coldest beaker of water and the other hand in the hottest beaker of water. After a minute or two, have the student put both hands in the beaker with the middle temperature. Ask the student to describe how the water in this beaker feels. The student will notice that it feels hot to one hand and cold to the other. This demonstration stresses the importance of using accurate measuring devices for measuring temperature.

12:3 Equilibrium and Thermometry

Thermal energy cannot be measured directly as we measure temperature with a thermometer. A thermometer makes use of some property that varies regularly with temperature, such as electrical resistance, color, magnetism, piezoelectric effect, or gas pressure. Thermometers depending on liquid expansion are used most often.

12:4 Temperature Scales

Thermometers are calibrated using two fixed points, such as the freezing point and boiling point of water. These points are marked with an arbitrary number. Explain to students that you could have a scale where water freezes at 50°S and boils at 200°S. Show them how to convert from one scale to another by using the ratio of the distances between the fixed points. The difference between boiling and freezing points of water is 200°S − 150°S on the S scale and 100°C − 0°C on the Celsius scale. This gives a ratio of 150°S to 100°C for the respective scales. For example, to convert 75°S to Celsius, a second ratio is established using the difference between this temperature and the freezing point of water on each scale; 75°S − 50°S = 25°S to X°C − 0°C = X°C. When set equal, these two ratios form a proportion for conversion based on distances from freezing: 150°S/100°C = 25°S/X°C, X = 17°C.

12:5 The Kelvin or Absolute Scale

The kelvin is one of the base units in the SI system. Note that the symbol K does not have a degree mark because the kelvin is a unit of measure. You can say that a body at 400 K is twice as hot as a body at 200 K. However, because 0°C is arbitrary, it does not make sense to say that a body at 30°C is twice as hot as a body at 15°C.

12:6 The First Law of Thermodynamics

Discuss the steps involved in cooling by a refrigerator. Ask students if a refrigerator can be used to cool a kitchen by opening the door. Explain that opening the door will cause the refrigerator to generate more heat in the kitchen as it runs longer and more Freon is

Chapter 12

warmed. Lead students to understand that to cool the kitchen, the refrigerator would have to be put in a doorway with the cooling coils outside. Then it would work like an air-conditioner and transfer the heat outdoors.

12:7 The Second Law of Thermodynamics

Do the demonstration shown in Figure 12–13. Put one drop of food coloring in water and let students watch it disappear. Ask students if they would expect the food coloring to go backwards and become a drop of color in the water again. Obviously they would not. Point out that we use the law of entropy to tell the sequence of events without realizing it. If we were given a series of pictures to put in chronological order, we would use the fact that things tend to go spontaneously to more disorder. For example, a log burns in a fire to produce ashes. If you had a series of pictures showing a pile of logs, a pile of ashes, and a pile of logs on fire, you would know there is only one way to put these in order of which event happened first, second, and third. Ashes will not become whole logs again. Irreversible processes can be explained by the law of entropy.

12:8 Specific Heat

Demonstration: Find the mass of a large glass marble. Cut a piece of lead sheet to the same mass. Heat the marble and the lead sheet in boiling water for a few minutes. While they are heating, measure out equal amounts of cold water into two polystyrene cups. Record the temperature. Ask the students to predict whether both materials will heat up the water the same amount since they are at the same temperature or if one of the materials will heat up the water more. Quickly transfer the marble to one cup and the lead to the other. Stir the water gently. When the temperatures level off, record them. The glass will cause a higher rise in temperature because glass has a higher specific heat than lead and gives off more heat as it cools each degree.

Demonstration: To demonstrate the differences in specific heat, warm a block of iron and an equal mass of water simultaneously over hot plates. After the water becomes only slightly warm, allow several drops of water to fall on the iron block. The sizzling noise will indicate that the iron is at a much higher temperature. Compare and discuss the specific heats of water and iron, and discuss why water makes such a good coolant.

12:9 Conservation in Energy Transfer

Demonstration: To show the predictability of final temperatures, pour equal amounts of cold and hot water of known temperatures into an empty polystyrene cup. Quickly stir the mixture and take its final temperature. Show that it is almost exactly midway between the two initial temperatures. Encourage students to discuss why the temperature might not be exactly at the midway point.

12:10 Change of State

Demonstration: Ask students which will cool water to a lower temperature, water at 0°C or ice at 0°C. Put equal masses of warm water into polystyrene cups. Record the temperatures and masses. Now add a small chunk of ice (enough so it will cool the water but also melt) to one cup. When the ice is all melted, record the temperature. Weigh the cup and water again, and subtract the original mass to find the mass of ice added. Add an equal amount of water at 0°C to the other cup. Record the final temperature after mixing. Some students will be surprised that the ice cools it to a lower temperature. This can start your discussion of heat of fusion.

Resources ▬▬▬▬▬▬▬▬

Literature

Dennis, Jr., Chandler M., "Newton's Law of Cooling or Is Ten Minutes Enough Time for a Coffee Break?" *The Physics Teacher,* October, 1980, pp. 532–533.

Epstein, L.C., and Hewitt, P.G., *Thinking Physics,* Insight Press, San Francisco, 1981, pp. 191–192.

Jones, Bruce, "A Stirring Experiment," *The Physics Teacher,* December, 1980, p. 671.

Stewart, Maurice B., "The Marquis of Worcester's Perpetual Motion Machine," *The Physics Teacher,* January, 1981, p. 37.

Switzer, Terry G., "Cheap Heat," *The Science Teacher,* April, 1986, pp. 32–34.

Software/Audiovisual

Kinetic Karnival, Cooking, WVIZ-TV, video

Chapter Review

QUESTIONS

1. The external energy of an object, such as a baseball in flight, is the sum of all energy outside of the object. The external energy of the baseball is the result of its motion and position above Earth. Thermal energy is the total kinetic and potential energy of all particles that compose the object.

2. Thermal energy is the sum of the kinetic and potential energies of the particles that make up an object. Temperature is the measure of the average kinetic energy of the particles of the object.

3. Heat is the measure of the internal kinetic energy transferred from objects of higher thermal energy to objects of lower thermal energy.

4. **a.** −2°C **b.** 271 K
5. **a.** 34°C **b.** 307 K
6. **a.** 20°C **b.** 293 K

7. Entropy is the measure of disorder in a system. If heat is added to an object, entropy is increased because the particles of the object exhibit a greater variety of speeds; hence, greater disorder and a higher degree of entropy.

8. The alcohol would cool faster since its specific heat would be less than that of water.

9. Freezing releases energy.

10. It takes less water than other liquids to transfer a given amount of heat to the air.

11. Yes. If it is at the melting or boiling point, energy added will go into potential energy.

12. The aluminum (specific heat 0.903 J/g · C°) can donate the most heat per gram to the ice in cooling through the same temperature change. The specific heat of lead is only 0.130 J/g · C°.

APPLYING CONCEPTS

1. Since the motion of the molecules of the brake are completely random, this will not happen. Statistically, the event is too unlikely to happen. The second law of thermodynamics prohibits such an event on this basis.

2. The metal knob and the wood are at the same temperature. However, the metal knob conducts the thermal energy of your fingers away from the point of contact much more rapidly than does the wood. Therefore, your fingers feel colder touching the metal than the wood.

3. Since we define temperature as the average kinetic energy of particles, by classical physics, temperature in a true vacuum is undefined.

4. No. Heat, not temperature, flows from the warmer to the colder object. The temperature changes are equal only if the product of the mass and specific heat of the two are the same.

5. $T_C = 1.5 \times 10^{7}°C$
   $T_K = 1.5 \times 10^{7}$ K
   $T_F = 2.7 \times 10^{7}°F$

   a. "Degrees" would not have been used if the Kelvin scale were used. It wouldn't matter anyway because 273 is insignificant compared to 1.5×10^{7}.

   b. It would matter between Celsius and Fahrenheit. Fahrenheit would be almost double.

6. Yes, oxidation of chemicals in the body releases thermal energy which is converted to mechanical energy by the body's muscles. The body's circulatory system acts as a cooling system and carries away waste heat.

7. **a.** One explanation is that the hot water evaporated faster, leaving less mass to freeze.

   b. If the pails are covered, evaporation is not a factor and the cold water freezes faster.

8. Vaporization. Changing liquid Freon to vapor requires energy. Heat is drawn from the air for this, so the air becomes cooler.

9. The freezing of the water releases thermal energy that slightly warms the air. Also, a layer of ice over the fruit slightly insulates the fruit from the cold.

10. Vaporization of water from the canvas requires energy that comes from the canteen, lowering its temperature.

11. No. The thermal energy output of a refrigerator equals the thermal energy in plus the electrical energy. Thus, more thermal energy is put into the room than taken out. The room warms up.

EXERCISES

1. $°C = K - 273 = 77 - 273 = -196°C$

2. $K = °C + 273.15 = -259.14 + 273.15$
$= 14.01$ K

3. $Q = mC\Delta T$
$= (50.0 \text{ g})(4.18 \text{ J/g} \cdot C°)(78.5°C)$
$= 1.6 \times 10^4$ J

4. $Q = mC\Delta T$
$= (50.0 \text{g})(0.903 \text{ J/g} \cdot C°)(100°C)$
$= 4.52 \times 10^3$ J

5. $\Delta E_A + \Delta E_B = 0$
$m_A C_A(T_f - T_{A,i}) + m_B C_B(T_f - T_{B,i}) = 0$
$T_f = \dfrac{m_A C_A T_{A,i} + m_B C_B T_{B,i}}{m_A C_A + m_B C_B}$
$= [(0.200 \text{ kg})(376 \text{ J/kg} \cdot C°)(100.0°C) +$
$(0.261 \text{ kg})(4180 \text{ J/kg} \cdot C°)(20.0°C)] /$
$[(0.200 \text{ kg})(376 \text{ J/kg} \cdot C°) + (0.261 \text{ kg})$
$(4180 \text{ J/kg} \cdot C°)]$
$= \dfrac{7520 \text{ J} + 21\ 819.6 \text{ J}}{75.2 \text{ J/C°} + 1090.98 \text{ J/C°}} = 24.6°C$

6. $Q_1 = mC\Delta T = (10.0 \text{ g})(2.06 \text{ J/g} \cdot C°)(20.0°C)$
$= 412$ J to warm the ice to 0°C
$Q_2 = mH_f = (10.0 \text{ g})(334 \text{ J/g})$
$= 3340$ J to melt the ice
$Q_3 = mC\Delta T = (10.0 \text{ g})(4.18 \text{ J/g} \cdot C°)(100.0°C)$
$= 4180$ J to warm the water to 100°C
$Q_4 = mH_v = (10.0 \text{ g})(2260 \text{ J/g})$
$= 22\ 600$ J to vaporize the water
$Q_5 = mC\Delta T = (10.0 \text{ g})(2.02 \text{ J/g} \cdot C°)(20.0°C)$
$= 404$ J to warm the steam to 120°C
$Q_{total} = Q_1 + Q_2 + Q_3 + Q_4 + Q_5$
$= 3.09 \times 10^4$ J

7. $\Delta T_{Zn} = \dfrac{C_W}{C_{Zn}} \Delta T_W$
$= \dfrac{4.18}{0.388}(1.00 \times 10^{2°}C) = 1080°C$

8. $Q = mC\Delta T = (165 \text{ g})(0.385 \text{ J/g} \cdot C°)(18°C)$
$= 1100$ J

9. $Q_{lost} = Q_{gained}$
$m_A C_A \Delta T = m_B C_B \Delta T$
$(1.00 \times 10^2 \text{ g})(C_T)(100.0°C - 21.6°C) =$
$(2.00 \times 10^2 \text{ g})(4.18 \text{ J/g} \cdot C°)(21.6°C - 20.0°C)$
$C_T = \dfrac{1340 \text{ J}}{7840 \text{ g} \cdot C°}$
$= 0.171 \text{ J/g} \cdot C$
$= 171 \text{ J/kg} \cdot K$

10. $Q = mH_v$
$H_v = \dfrac{Q}{m} = \dfrac{9870 \text{ J}}{40.0 \text{ g}} = 247 \text{ J/g}$

11. $\Delta E_A + \Delta E_B = 0$
$m_A C_A(T_f - T_{A,i}) + m_B C_B(T_f - T_{B,i}) = 0$
$T_f = \dfrac{m_A C_A T_{A,i} + m_B C_B T_{B,i}}{m_A C_A + m_B C_B}$
$= [(10.0 \text{ kg})(388 \text{ J/kg} \cdot C°)(71.0°C) +$
$(20.0 \text{ kg})(4180 \text{ J/kg} \cdot C°)(10.0°C)] \div$
$[(10.0 \text{ kg})(388 \text{ J/kg} \cdot C°) + (20.0 \text{ kg})$
$(4180 \text{ J/kg} \cdot C°)]$
$= 12.7°C$

12. $T_f = \dfrac{m_A T_{A,i} + m_B T_{B,i}}{m_A + m_B}$
$= [(6.0 \times 10^2 \text{ g})(90.0°C) +$
$(4.00 \times 10^2 \text{ g})(22°C)] /$
$[(6.0 \times 10^2 \text{ g}) + (4.00 \times 10^2 \text{ g})]$
$= 63°C$

13. $Q = mH_v = (60.0 \text{ g})(2260 \text{ J/g})$
$= 1.36 \times 10^5$ J to change steam to water
$Q = mC\Delta T = (60.0 \text{ g})(4.18 \text{ J/g} \cdot C°)(80.0°C) =$
2.01×10^4 J to cool water from 100.0°C
$\qquad\qquad$ to 20.0°C
$Q_{total} = 1.56 \times 10^5$ J

14. $Q_1 = mC\Delta T = (1.0 \times 10^3 \text{ g})$
$(0.14 \text{ J/g} \cdot C°)(347°C)$
$= 4.9 \times 10^4$ J to warm the mercury
from 10°C to 357°C
$Q_2 = mH_v = (1.0 \times 10^3 \text{ g})(306 \text{ J/g})$
$= 3.1 \times 10^5$ J to vaporize the mercury
$Q_{total} = Q_1 + Q_2 = 3.6 \times 10^5$ J

15. $Q = mH_f$
$= (2.00 \times 10^4 \text{ g})(334 \text{ J/g})$
$= 6.68 \times 10^6$ J

16. $Q = mC\Delta T$
$= (4.00 \times 10^2 \text{ g})(0.664 \text{ J/g} \cdot K)(80.0°C - 20.0°C)$
$= 1.59 \times 10^4$ J

17. $Q = mC\Delta T = (5.0 \text{ kg})(2060 \text{ J/kg} \cdot K)$
$(-4.0°C - (-17°C))$
$= 1.3 \times 10^5$ J

18. $Q = m_W C_W \Delta T + m_i C_i \Delta T$
$m_W = \dfrac{Q - m_i C_i \Delta T}{C_W \Delta T}$
$= [4.4 \times 10^6 \text{ J} - (2.50 \times 10^2 \text{ kg})$
$(450 \text{ J/kg} \cdot K)(25°C)] \div$
$[(4180 \text{ J/kg} \cdot K)(25°C)]$
$= 15$ kg

19. a. $Q = mC\Delta T$
$= (2.50 \times 10^2 \text{ g})(4.18 \text{ J/g} \cdot \text{K})(7.8°\text{C})$
$= 8200 \text{ J}$

b. $C_{lead} = \dfrac{Q}{m\Delta T} = \dfrac{8200 \text{ J}}{(8.00 \times 10^2 \text{ g})(80.0°\text{C})}$
$= 0.13 \text{ J/g} \cdot \text{K} = 130 \text{ J/kg} \cdot \text{K}$

20. $T_f = \dfrac{m_2 CT_{2,i} + m_1 CT_{1,i} - m_1 H_{f,1}}{m_1 C + m_2 C}$,
$T_{1,i} = 0.00°\text{C}$
$= [(400 \text{ g})(4.18 \text{ J/g} \cdot \text{C}°)(50.0°\text{C}) - (50.0 \text{ g})$
$(3.34 \times 10^2 \text{ J/g})] \div [((50.0 \text{ g}) +$
$(4.00 \times 10^2 \text{ g}))(4.18 \text{ J/g} \cdot \text{C}°)]$
$= 35.6°\text{C}$

21. $Q = mC\Delta T$
$C = \dfrac{Q}{m\Delta T} = \dfrac{5016 \text{ J}}{(5.00 \times 10^2 \text{ g})(10.0°\text{C})}$
$= 1.00 \text{ J/g} \cdot \text{C}°$

PROBLEMS

1. a. $-40°\text{C} = -40°\text{F}$
b. $574 \text{ K} = 574°\text{F}$
c. Celsius and Kelvin temperatures can never be the same.

2. $Q_{lost} = Q_{gained}$
$Q_{heater} = m_C C_C \Delta T_C + m_W C_W \Delta T_W$
$= (3.00 \times 10^2 \text{ g})(0.664 \text{ J/g} \cdot \text{C}°)$
$(85°\text{C}) + (250 \text{ g})(4.18 \text{ J/g} \cdot \text{C}°)(85°\text{C})$
$= 16 \text{ } 932 \text{ J} + 88 \text{ } 825 \text{ J} = 1.1 \times 10^5 \text{ J}$
$P = \dfrac{E}{t} = \dfrac{Q_{heater}}{t}$
$t = \dfrac{Q_{heater}}{P} = \dfrac{1.1 \times 10^5 \text{ J}}{3.00 \times 10^2 \text{ W}} = 370 \text{ s}$

3. a. $Q/t = \dfrac{1.0 \times 10^{11} \text{ kJ/day}}{(24 \text{ h/day})(3600 \text{ s/h})}$
$= 1.2 \times 10^6 \text{ kJ/s}$
$Q/t = (m/t)C\Delta T$
$\Delta T = \dfrac{Q/t}{(m/t)C}$
$= \dfrac{1.2 \times 10^6 \text{ kJ/s}}{(9.0 \times 10^4 \text{ kg/s})(4.18 \text{ kJ/kg} \cdot \text{C}°)}$
$= 3.2°\text{C}$

b. $4 \times 3.2°\text{C} = 13°\text{C}$, this temperature increase may cause serious damage to the ecology of the river.

4. $P = \dfrac{E}{t}$
$E = Pt = (30.0 \text{ W})(3600 \text{ s})$
$= 108 \text{ } 000 \text{ J}$
$m = \dfrac{Q}{H_v} = \dfrac{108 \text{ } 000 \text{ J}}{2260 \text{ J/g}}$
$= 47.8 \text{ g}$

5. $Q_{coal} = Q_{air}$
$(0.5)(m_c)\dfrac{Q}{m} = m_A C_A \Delta T_A$
$m_c = \dfrac{m_A C_A \Delta T_A}{(0.5)\dfrac{Q}{m}}$
$= [(1.70 \times 10^4 \text{ kg})$
$(1.1 \text{ kJ/kg} \cdot \text{C}°)(34°\text{C})] /$
$[(0.5)(3.35 \times 10^4 \text{ kJ/kg})]$
$= 38 \text{ kg}$

6. $m = Q/C\Delta T$
$= (2.9 \times 10^5 \text{ J})/(4180 \text{ J/kg} \cdot \text{K})(80 \text{ K})$
$= 0.87 \text{ kg} = 0.87 \text{ L}$

7. Change in thermal energy = heat added + work done $= -2.0 \text{ J} + (45 \text{ N})(0.24 \text{ m}) = 8.8 \text{ J}$

8. 375 mL would yeild 6.4 kJ. If climbing energy all goes into $PE = mgh$, then $h = 6.4 \text{ kJ/mg}$. Answer depends on weight. For a 65-kg (637 N) person, $h = 10 \text{ m}$, or about three flights.

9. $Q = KE = \dfrac{1}{2}mv^2 = \dfrac{1}{2}(750 \text{ kg})(23 \text{ m/s})^2$
$= 2.0 \times 10^5 \text{ J}$
$\Delta T = Q/mC$
$= (2.0 \times 10^5 \text{ J})/((15 \text{ kg})(450 \text{ J/kg} \cdot \text{K}))$
$= 30°\text{C}$

10. $Q = KE = \dfrac{1}{2}mv^2 = \dfrac{1}{2}(0.0042 \text{ kg})(275 \text{ m/s})^2$
$= 1.6 \times 10^2 \text{ J}$
$\Delta T = Q/mC$
$= (1.6 \times 10^2 \text{ J})/(0.0042 \text{ kg})(130 \text{ J/kg} \cdot \text{K})$
$= 290°\text{C}$

Gas Laws

Overview

The gas laws are a natural result of the kinetic-molecular theory and are an important verification of that theory. Boyle's law relates pressure and volume at constant temperature and Charles' law relates temperature and volume at constant pressure. These laws can be combined to relate pressure, volume, and temperature. The relationship between these same variables and the number of particles or moles of a sample of gas is shown by the ideal gas law. Many gases behave as ideal gases at moderate temperatures and pressures. Deviations become more significant at low temperature and high pressure where the gas behaves as a real gas with particles that do have volume and attraction for one another.

Planning Guide (6 Class Sessions)

Text Section		Demonstrations and Experiments		Other Program Components	
13:1 Assumptions of the Kinetic-Molecular Theory	S	Dem 13:1 Atmospheric Pressure: Karate Chop		Teaching Master 13-1: Volume Versus Pressure	**TRP**
13:2 Pressure	S	Exp 22 The Diameter of a Molecule	**LM**	Teaching Master 13-2: Volume Versus Temperature	**TRP**
13:3 Boyle's Law	S	Exp 23 Boyle's Law	**LM**	Review Masters	**TRP**
13:4 Charles' Law	S	Dem 13:2 Atmospheric Pressure: Bag in a Jar, Internal Pressure		Minilab 13-1: Charles' Law	**TRP**
13:5 The Ideal Gas Law	S	Dem 13:2 Atmospheric Pressure: Sticking Cups		Demonstration 13-1: Heating and Cooling a Gas	**TRP**
13:6 Real Gases	S	Dem 13:3 Boyle's Law		Demonstration 13-2: Compressibility of Air, A Cartesian Diver	**TRP**
		Dem 13:4 Charles' Law		Demonstration 13-3: Atmospheric Pressure	**TRP**
				Enrichment 13-1: Problems	**TRP**
				Enrichment 13-2: The Dunking Bird	**TRP**
				Enrichment 13-3: Scuba Diving	**TRP**
				Evaluation	**TRP**

Performance Objectives

Upon completion of this chapter, your students will

1. list the assumptions of the kinetic theory and the definition of an ideal gas. *13:1*

2. demonstrate an understanding of the concept of pressure and the definition of the pascal and other pressure units; understand the microscopic cause of gas pressure. *13:2*

3. state Boyle's law; demonstrate an ability to use the law in solving problems; understand the microscopic basis of it. *13:3*

4. state Charles' law; understand the relationship of this law to absolute zero; be able to solve problems using Charles' law. *13:4*

5. understand the formulation of the ideal gas law and be able to solve problems using it. *13:5*

6. understand the distinction between real and ideal gases and the limitations of the ideal gas law. *13:6*

Teaching the Chapter

Introduction

Using the Photo: The pressure at 30.0 m is 4.0 atmospheres. As the diver begins his ascent, the reduced pressure allows the air in the vest to expand. If no air were removed from the vest, its volume would increase four times by the time the diver reached the surface. Without a means to release excessive pressure, the vest would rupture.

This photograph can be used with Section 13.3 to discuss Boyle's law.

Demonstration: Lay a pine stick (0.5 cm × 3 cm × 60 cm) on a table with about 15 cm extending over the edge. Hit the stick on the end and let it go flying into the air. Put the stick back on the table and cover it with a newspaper so the paper is smooth and even with the edge of the table and about 15 cm of the stick extends over the table. Give the stick a sharp blow and it will break at the edge of the table. The pressure of the air on the paper held down the other end of the stick. **CAUTION:** *Be careful not to have anyone sitting close to you when you do this demonstration.*

13:2 Pressure

The introductory demonstration is valuable in illustrating the pressure of the atmosphere. Point out to students that the longest straw from which you can drink is 10.3 m long because that is the highest column of water the atmosphere can support. This is equivalent to 760 mm of mercury, the standard atmospheric pressure.

Demonstration: Take a plastic lunch bag and invert it over a wide-mouth jar. Push it down into the jar. Tape the edge of the bag to the outside of the jar. Now try to pull the bag out of the jar. You cannot do it because the atmospheric pressure is pushing down into the jar. When you pull up on the bag you increase the volume of air in the jar and lower its pressure. The atmospheric pressure is greater than the pressure in the jar. You encounter this situation sometimes when you try to unfold a plastic air mattress or inflatable plastic toy.

Demonstration: Blow a little air into a plastic sandwich bag and put it over the mouth of a wide-mouth jar. Tape the edge of the bag to the jar. Now try to push the bag down into the jar. It won't go down because the bag is filled with air, which is exerting a pressure.

Demonstration: Blow up a balloon about 1/3 of the way. Hold two small plastic cups against the sides of the balloon and blow it up further until about twice the size. The cups will now stick to the balloon by themselves. Ask students to explain. The curvature of the balloon increases and actually flattens out, increasing the volume of the air trapped in the cup and decreasing its pressure. The pressure outside the cups is now more and holds the cups on the balloon.

13:3 Boyle's Law

Demonstration: Insert the end of a large hypodermic syringe into a one-hole stopper. Plug the other end of the stopper with a piece of solid glass rod. Place weights on the plunger and see the volume decrease. If desired, data may be taken and a graph made. A scuba diver must be careful not to hold his or her breath when ascending because the pressure decreases on the lungs during ascension. Therefore, the volume of the lungs could increase too much or too rapidly and cause injury. **CAUTION:** *Be extremely careful while working with the hypodermic syringe. Always remove the needle before using it.*

13:4 Charles' Law

Demonstration: Using the syringe from the previous demonstration, place the syringe in water and heat the water. The volume of the syringe can be recorded at room temperature, boiling, and ice water temperatures. These points can be plotted on a graph of volume versus temperature. Extrapolation to zero volume gives an approximate value for absolute zero.

Resources

Literature

Carlson, W., "Boyle's Law Demonstration Using a Vacuum Gauge," *The Physics Teacher,* November, 1967, pp. 387–388.

Smith, Clyde J., "Archimedes' Principle Meets Charles' Law," *The Physics Teacher,* March, 1979, p. 187.

Taylor, Tim, "The Imploding Beer Can," *The Physics Teacher,* October, 1982, p. 458.

Background

It is interesting to compare the phase diagram for water to the phase diagram of CO_2. Note that the line between solid and liquid for water slants left and for carbon dioxide it slants right. When you apply pressure to water at a constant temperature, it changes from solid to liquid. When the same thing is done to carbon dioxide, it changes from liquid to solid, which is the more expected outcome. Water has the unusual property of being more dense as a liquid than as a solid. This fact explains why ice floats.

Other interesting points on the phase diagram are T and C. The point T on the graphs is called the triple point and is the point at which all three phases exist in equilibrium. Point C is the critical temperature and is the temperature above which a gas will not liquefy regardless of the pressure applied.

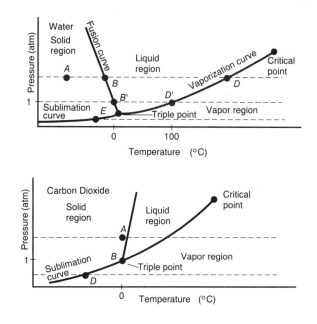

Chapter Review

QUESTIONS

1. See Section 13:1.
2. Collisions are perfectly elastic.
3. Force is a push or pull. Pressure is force per unit area.
4. weight of the air
5. $1 \text{ atm} = 1.013 \times 10^5 \text{ N/m}^2 = 1013 \text{ mb}$
   $= 760 \text{ Torr} = 101.3 \text{ kPa}$
6. $1 \text{ atm} = 760 \text{ mm} = 0.760 \text{ m}$,
   height $= 0.760 \text{ m} \times 3 = 2.28 \text{ m}$
7. The volume of a gas varies directly with the temperature.
8. The volume of a gas varies inversely with the pressure.
9. The temperature increases and, at constant volume, pressure varies directly with absolute temperature.
10. Decrease the pressure.
11. An ideal gas is an imaginary gas made up of particles with mass but no volume and with no attraction for each other. The differences between real gas and ideal gas are discussed in Section 13:6.

APPLYING CONCEPTS

1. a. Air pressure on the liquid in the glass pushes it up.
   b. 10.4 m, the height of a column of water supported by atmospheric pressure
2. Air pressure pushes on the open bottom holding water in place. When finger is released, air pressure pushes on both ends and gravity forces water out.
3. no atmospheric pressure to push the liquid up the straw
4. explode, pressure is greater inside the house pushing walls outward
5. Average velocity being zero does not mean average speed is zero.
6. At high pressure its volume would shrink more slowly than for an ideal gas, but at low temperatures it would behave like an ideal gas. It would never liquefy.
7. At constant pressure, all gases expand the same amount for a given temperature change. By graphing changes in volume versus kelvin temperature and extrapolating backwards, Charles arrived at a temperature for volume equal to zero. This value

indicated the possible location of absolute zero.

8. **a.** The division between the water and air moves toward the bottom of the glass.

   b. Volume decreases to one-half when pressure doubles. At the surface the air in glass experiences one atmosphere. To double the pressure to two atmospheres, the glass would have to be pushed to a depth of 10.4 m.

9. **a.** Air pressure on the water surface pushes the water up the glass.

   b. 10.4 m

EXERCISES

1. $28.5'' = 724$ Torr $= 965$ mb $= 96.5$ kPa;
   $31.0'' = 787$ Torr $= 1050$ mb $= 105$ kPa

2. **a.** $A = (0.20 \text{ m})(0.24 \text{ m}) = 0.048 \text{ m}^2$
   $F = (101 \text{ kN/m}^2)(0.048 \text{ m}^2) = 4.9 \times 10^3 \text{ N}$

   b. $m = \dfrac{W}{g} = \dfrac{(4.9 \times 10^3 \text{ N})}{(9.80 \text{ m/s}^2)} = 5.0 \times 10^2 \text{ kg}$

3. 32.0 psi = 2.18 atm
   Thus, absolute pressure is 3.18 atm, or 322 kPa.

4. $10.4 \text{ m}/0.9 = 12 \text{ m}$

5. $T_2 = \dfrac{V_2 T_1}{V_1} = \dfrac{(4.00 \text{ m}^3)(303 \text{ K})}{(2.00 \text{ m}^3)} = 606 \text{ K}, 333°C$

6. $\dfrac{(2.02 \times 10^5 \text{ N/m}^2)(30.0 \text{ m}^3)(-50°C + 273°C)}{(50.0 \text{ m}^3)(1.01 \times 10^5 \text{ N/m}^2)}$
   $= -5.40°C$

7. $\dfrac{(1.2 \text{ atm})(50.0 \text{ cm}^3)}{(0.30 \text{ atm})} = 2.0 \times 10^2 \text{ cm}^3$

8. $V_2 = \dfrac{V_1 T_2}{T_1} = \dfrac{(30.0 \text{ m}^3)(303 \text{ K})}{(278 \text{ K})} = 32.7 \text{ m}^3$

9. $T_1 = \dfrac{T_2 V_1}{V_2} = \dfrac{(91.0 \text{ K})(50.0 \text{ L})}{(30.0 \text{ L})} = 152 \text{ K}$

10. $p_2 = 1.0 \text{ atm} + \dfrac{(8.3 \text{ m})}{(10.4 \text{ m/atm})} = 1.8 \text{ atm}$
    $V_2 = \dfrac{p_1 V_1}{p_2} = \dfrac{(1.8 \text{ atm})(6.0 \text{ L})}{(1.0 \text{ atm})} = 11 \text{ L}$

11. For mercury, pressure increases 1.0 atm per 0.760 m of depth increase.

$p_1 = \dfrac{p_2 V_2}{V_1} = \dfrac{(1.00 \text{ atm})(0.500 \text{ cm}^3)}{(0.050 \text{ cm}^3)} = 10.0 \text{ atm}$

depth $= (10.0 \text{ atm} - 1.00 \text{ atm})(0.76 \text{ m/atm})$
$= 6.8 \text{ m}$

12. $T_2 = \dfrac{p_2 T_1}{p_1} = \dfrac{(2175 \text{ kPa})(40.0 \text{ K})}{(408 \text{ kPa})} = 213 \text{ K}$

13. $p_2 = \dfrac{p_1 T_2}{T_1} = \dfrac{(1.00 \text{ atm})(194 \text{ K})}{(573 \text{ K})} = 0.339 \text{ atm}$

14. $\dfrac{(228 \text{ K})(2.00 \text{ atm})(30.0 \text{ cm}^3)}{(1.00 \text{ atm})(50.0 \text{ cm}^3)} = 274 \text{ K} = 1°C$

15. $\dfrac{(2000 \text{ kPa})((10.0 \text{ m}^3)(40 \text{ K})}{(4.0 \times 10^2 \text{ kPa})(10.0 \text{ m}^3)} = 200 \text{ K}$

PROBLEMS

1. Her values extrapolate to zero at 30°S, which is her "absolute zero."

2. $n = \dfrac{(1.01 \times 10^5 \text{ Pa})(1.00 \times 10^{-6} \text{ m}^3)}{(8.31 \text{ Pa} \cdot \text{m}^3/\text{mol} \cdot \text{K})(293 \text{ K})}$
   $= 4.16 \times 10^{-5} \text{ mol} = 2.50 \times 10^{19} \text{ particles}$

3. **a.** $\dfrac{(1.0 \times 10^{-11} \text{ Torr})}{(760 \text{ Torr/atm})} = 1.3 \times 10^{-14} \text{ atm}$

   b. $(2.5 \times 10^{19} \text{ particles/atm})(1.3 \times 10^{-14} \text{ atm})$
   $= 3.3 \times 10^5 \text{ particles}$

4. $\dfrac{(200 \text{ g}/39.9 \text{ g/mol})(8.31 \text{ Pa} \cdot \text{m}^3/\text{mol} \cdot \text{K})(293 \text{ K})}{(510\,000 \text{ Pa})(1.0 \times 10^{-3} \text{ m}^3/\text{L})}$
   $= 24 \text{ L}$

5. $2.00 \text{ L} = 2.00 \times 10^{-3} \text{ m}^3$
   $\dfrac{(20.0 \text{ atm})(1.013 \times 10^5 \text{ Pa})(2.00 \times 10^{-3} \text{ m}^3)}{(8.31 \text{ Pa} \cdot \text{m}^3/\text{mole} \cdot \text{K})(323 \text{ K})}$
   $= 1.51 \text{ mol}$

   $m = (1.51 \text{ mole})(16.0 \text{ gram/mole}) = 24.2 \text{ grams}$

6. $\dfrac{(120.0 \text{ kPa})(20.0 \text{ L})}{(1.38 \times 10^{-23} \text{ L} \cdot \text{kPa/mol} \cdot \text{K})(296 \text{ K})}$
   $= 5.88 \times 10^{23} \text{ molecules}$

7. $0.760 \text{ m} \times 13.6 = 10.3 \text{ m}$

States of Matter

Overview

This chapter is a qualitative introduction to the properties of fluids and solids. Connections to the kinetic theory are stressed. Problems that deal with applications of fluids at rest (hydrostatics) and thermal expansion of solids provide interesting examples of the technological applications of physics. Bernoulli's principle is applied to fluids in motion and is used to explain the lift on an airplane wing as well as in automobile design. Pascal's principle is illustrated in the operation of hydraulic lifts that use fluids to multiply forces. The explanation of how ships built out of steel are able to float on water is dealt with using Archimedes' principle.

Various properties of the different states of matter are studied. Cohesive and adhesive forces of liquids are demonstrated by surface tension and capillary action, respectively. The transfer of kinetic energy is shown to cause a cooling effect during evaporation and a warming effect during condensation. Neon signs are an example of how electricity is conducted by a plasma and converted into visible light.

Planning Guide (6 Class Sessions)

Text Section	Demonstrations and Experiments	Other Program Components	
14:1 Fluids at Rest—Hydrostatics S **14:2** Fluids in Motion—Hydrodynamics S	Dem 14:1 Weight Versus Density, Cartesian Diver, Archimedes' Principle Exp 24 Archimedes' Principle **LM** Dem 14:2 Reducing Pressure, Bernoulli's Principle, Atmospheric Support	Teaching Master 14-1: (a) Hydraulic System (b) Archimedes' Principle Teaching Master 14-2: Bernoulli's Principle Demonstration 14-1: Bernoulli's Principle Demonstration 14-2: Atomizers Enrichment 14-1: Bernoulli's Equation	**TRP** **TRP** **TRP** **TRP** **TRP**
14:3 Liquids S **14:4** Surface Tension S **14:5** Evaporation and Condensation S	Dem 14:4 Surface Tension, Breaking Surface Tension	Minilab 14-1: Thermal Expansion of Liquids Demonstration 14-3: Surface Tension	**TRP** **TRP**
14:6 Solid State S **14:7** Elasticity S **14:8** Thermal Expansion of Matter S	Dem 14:8 Ball and Ring, A Bimetallic Strip	Demonstration 14-4: Thermal Expansion of a Solid Enrichment 14-2: Phase Diagrams	**TRP** **TRP**
14:9 Plasma S		Review Masters Evaluation	**TRP** **TRP**

Performance Objectives

Upon completion of this chapter, your students will

1. display an ability to define solids, liquids, gases, and plasmas in terms of their microscopic properties. *14:1*

2. understand the origin of Pascal's and Archimedes' principles and their respective applications to hydraulic machines and determination of buoyant force. *14:1*

3. explain Bernoulli's principle and its applications in producing lift; understand the difference between streamlined and turbulent flow. *14:2*

4. describe how cohesive and adhesive forces cause surface tension and capillary action, respectively. *14:4*

5. understand the origin of evaporation and condensation from the viewpoint of kinetic energy. *14:5*

6. display an understanding of the difference between solids and liquids on a microscopic level. *14:6*

7. display an understanding of the origin of thermal expansion; be able to solve problems in linear thermal expansion; state some examples of applications and difficulties caused by thermal expansion. *14:8*

8. define a plasma and give examples of plasmas in nature. *14:9*

Teaching the Chapter

Introduction

Using the Photo: The water level would drop. Jacqueline is more dense than the water. While on the air mattress, she displaces her weight of water. When she falls into the water, she displaces her volume of water, which is less than her weight. Less water is displaced while she is submerged than when she is on the air mattress; therefore, the pool water level drops.

The photograph can be used with Section 14:1 describing Archimedes' principle.

Demonstration: Obtain a small steel ball and a polystyrene ball that weigh the same. Have a student hold a ball in each hand and tell which is heavier. The student will probably say the steel ball. This can lead into your discussion of pressure and density. You may also discuss the importance of accurate measurements. Stress that we must be careful not to let our senses fool us when making observations.

14:1 Fluids at Rest—Hydrostatics

There are many interesting situations to discuss to help students differentiate between force and pressure. A person walking on snow will not sink if snowshoes are worn. The downward force is the same but the pressure is much less due to the increased area of the snowshoes. Ask students for other examples.

Demonstration: A Cartesian diver demonstrates properties of a fluid. A toy diver can be used or a diver can be constructed. Take a small test tube, fill it partially with water, cover the open end with part of a balloon, and fasten the balloon securely with a rubber band. Place the test tube in a clear-plastic pop bottle that is completely filled with water. Wait for the test tube to float in the water, glass end up. Cap the pop bottle securely, squeeze it, and the test tube should sink. You may have to experiment with the amount of water in the test tube needed to produce the dramatic effect. Explain how this demonstrates that fluids transmit pressure equally, and that liquids are much less compressible than gases.

Demonstration: To demonstrate Archimedes' principle, hang a 3-kg mass on a demonstration spring. Have another scale with a bucket on it that will be used to catch water. Place a second smaller bucket full of water inside the bucket on the scale. Let the 3-kg mass down into the water. Some of the water will overflow. Note the weight of the 3-kg mass. Remove the second bucket. Read the scale and calculate the weight of the displaced water. The weight of the water should equal the amount the weight that the 3-kg mass decreased. A simple project for students to do is to test which kind of cans of soda pop float. Ask students to find some explanation for their findings.

14:2 Fluids in Motion—Hydrodynamics

Demonstration: Tape a ping-pong ball to a string and hold it close to a rapid stream of water from the faucet. The pressure is reduced near the stream of water and the atmosphere pushes the ball toward the water.

Demonstration: Get a long-stemmed funnel and place a ping-pong ball in it. Blow through the stem as the funnel is turned upside down. The ping-pong ball will stay in the funnel as long as you keep blowing.

Demonstration: Insert a pin through an index card. Place the pin into the hole of a spool and blow into the hole from the other side. While blowing, turn the spool until the spool is upright and the card is on the bottom of the spool. The card will be supported by the atmosphere because the pressure is reduced between the spool and the card.

14:4 Surface Tension

Demonstration: Ask students if you can add anything to a full glass of water without its spilling. Then start adding pennies and see how many you can add before the water overflows. Surface tension keeps the water from spilling.

Demonstration: Float a needle on water by carefully placing it on the surface without touching the water with your fingers. Add a drop of detergent to break the surface tension and the needle sinks.

14:7 Elasticity

Demonstrate the difference in the elasticity between metals and nonmetallic solids. Also show the elastic limit, the point at which the bent metal no longer returns to its original shape.

14:8 Thermal Expansion of Matter

Demonstration: Obtain a ball and ring set to demonstrate thermal expansion. The ball slides through the ring. When the ball is heated, it won't fit through the ring. Ask students if the ball will fit through if both the ball and ring are heated. Most students will say no because they think the hole gets smaller as it is heated. Actually, the diameter of the hole gets larger and the hot ball fits through the hot ring. Point out to students that a metal lid on a jar can be loosened by running hot water on it.

Demonstration: Use a bimetallic strip to show how two metals expand by different amounts. When the strip is heated, it curls. This phenomenon is used in the construction of a thermostat. As the bimetallic

strip is heated, it curves, breaking an electrical circuit that turns the furnace off.

Expansion must be considered in many everyday situations. If one part of a glass is heated more than another, it may break. Pyrex is a special kind of glass that resists breaking with extreme changes. If you fill your gas tank on a hot day and then park your car in the sun, it may overflow because the cool gasoline heats up and expands. The dentist uses fillings that have the same expansion rate as teeth. Expansion joints are put in roadways and gaps are left in concrete sidewalks.

Water is very unusual because it contracts when heated from 0°C to 4°C and starts to expand above 4°C. Water has its maximum density at 4°C.

Resources ═══════════

Literature

Bauman, Robert P., "Archimedes Bath," *The Physics Teacher,* March, 1987, pp. 150, 151.

Edge, R.D., "Surface Tension," *The Physics Teacher,* December, 1988, pp. 586, 587.

Edge, R.D., "The Spin on Baseballs or Golfballs," *The Physics Teacher,* April, 1980, pp. 308, 309.

Haden, Hailey, "A Demonstration of Newtonian and Archimedian Forces," *The Physics Teacher,* April, 1964, pp. 176–177.

Jones, Robert N., "The Cartesian Diver," *The Physics Teacher,* September, 1973, p. 345.

Liem, Tik L., *Invitation to Science Inquiry,* Ginn Custom Publishing Co., Lexington, MA, 1981.

Miller, Jr., Franklin, *College Physics,* Harcourt Brace Jovanovich, San Diego, CA, 1982, p. 303.

Van Wyk, Steve, "Physics Problems for Physics Teachers," *The Physics Teacher,* March, 1987, pp. 177, 178.

Background ═══════════

The change from a solid directly to a gas is called sublimation. Solid CO_2 sublimes and is easy to use for a demonstration. Obtain some dry ice from an ice cream store and put a few small chips in a test tube with a balloon over the end. As the balloon expands, students observe that no liquid forms. This demonstration shows that gases exert pressure and occupy a lot more space than solids.

The thermal expansion of matter can be extended to volume. The formula for change in volume is very similar to the change in length, $\Delta V = V\beta\Delta T$. The symbol β stands for the coefficient of volume expansion and is 3 times α. α is the coefficient of linear expansion. If you have water in a glass cup and want to find the expansion of the water, you use the relative coefficient of volume expansion, which is the difference in the coefficients for glass and water.

Chapter Review

QUESTIONS

1. They are strongest in mercury and weakest in naptha.

2. Naptha for both, because weaker cohesive forces increase vaporization and decrease the boiling temperature.

3. Both fill any volume and consist of particles that are widely separated. The particles in plasmas are charged, while those in a gas are not.

4. Carbon tetrachloride, because the weight of the denser CCl_4 displaced by the steel would be greater than the same volume of water.

5. The adhesive forces of attraction between the candle wax, or paraffin, and the mold is greater than the cohesive forces of attraction among wax particles.

6. You break the attractive, cohesive forces between neighboring particles.

7. The soft glass of tube A expands three times as much as the Pyrex glass of tube B. The greater expansion of tube A gives it a wider opening or cross section than tube B. The equal volume of water fills the expanded cross section and thus will not rise as high in tube A. The lower coefficient of expansion of Pyrex glass prevents the glass from shattering with rapid increases and decreases in temperature.

8. It increases between 0 and 4°C, then falls as the temperature increases further.

9. Those in the plasma state are charged, those in the gaseous state are neutral.

10. It takes energy to vaporize the water in the canvas bag. The energy comes from the water, thus cooling it.

11. Cohesive forces are greater in water than in alcohol.

12. The body is cooled by vaporizing water (perspiration). Vaporization is reduced when there is already lots of water in the air.

APPLYING CONCEPTS

1. The razor blade should be placed carefully and flatly onto the surface of the water. This will reduce its weight per unit area of water surface on which it will rest. The surface tension of the water is then sufficient to support the reduced weight per unit area of the flat razor blade.

2. The hole increases. The cut-out circle expands as well.

3. The hot liquid causes the glass to expand. The hot inner surface expands first. It takes longer for the entire thick glass to reach a uniform temperature, and in that time, strains can occur that will cause the glass to break.

4. No. Aluminum has a higher coefficient of expansion than steel, and if the rod and ring are heated, the temperatures will be equal.

5. Colder steel is shorter, and a shorter pendulum oscillates faster, so clock will be fast.

6. Yes. Higher humidity means more vapor in the air, and less evaporation of water (perspiration) from the skin.

7. No. Archimedes' principle has no application under conditions of weightlessness.

EXERCISES

1. **a.** $\dfrac{F_1}{A_2} = \dfrac{F_2}{A_1}$

   $F_1 = \dfrac{F_2 A_2}{A_2}$

   $= \dfrac{(2.7 \times 10^3 \text{ N})(7.0 \times 10^{-2} \text{ m}^2)}{(2.1 \times 10^{-1} \text{ m}^2)}$

   $= 9.0 \times 10^2 \text{ N}$

   b. $V_1 = V_2$ and $A_1 h_1 = A_2 h_2$

   $h_1 = \dfrac{A_2 h_2}{A_1}$

   $= \dfrac{(2.1 \times 10^{-1} \text{ m}^2)(0.20 \text{ m})}{(7.0 \times 10^{-2} \text{ m}^2)}$

   $= 0.60 \text{ cm}$

2. a. 195 N + 8 N = 203 N

b. 195 N + 2 N = 297 N

In each case the buoyant force is equal to the weight of the water displaced. That is,

$W_{total} =$

$W_{aquarium} + ((W_{rock\ (fish)} - F_{buoyant}) + W_{water\ displaced})$.

3. $W_{net} = W - V\rho g$

$= 54\ N - (2.3 \times 10^{-3}\ m^3)$

$\qquad (1.00 \times 10^3\ kg/m^3)(9.8\ m/s^2)$

$= 54\ N - 23\ N = 31\ N$

4. The buoyant force will be twice as great as in Exercise 3.

$W_{net} = 54\ N - 2(23\ N) = 8\ N$

5. $W_{net} = W - V\rho g$

$= (2.8 \times 10^{-1}\ N) - (13\ cm^3)$

$(10^{-6}\ m^3/cm^3)(1.00 \times 10^3\ kg/m^3)(9.8\ m/s^2)$

$= (2.8 \times 10^{-1}\ N) - (1.3 \times 10^{-1}\ N)$

$= 1.5 \times 10^{-1}\ N$

$a = \dfrac{F}{m} = \dfrac{(1.5 \times 10^{-1}\ N)}{(2.8 \times 10^{-1}\ N/9.8\ m/s^2)} = 5.3\ m/s^2$

6. $W_{net} = W = F_{buoyant} = V\rho_{He}g - V\rho_{air}g$

$= (1.00\ m^3)(0.177\ kg/m^3)(9.80\ m/s^2) -$

$\qquad (1.00\ m^3)(1.20\ kg/m^3)(9.80\ m/s^2)$

$= -10.0\ N$

(Net buoyant force is 10.0 N upward.)

$W_{max} = 10.0\ N$

7. $\Delta L = L_i \alpha \Delta T$

$= (2.00\ m)(1.66 \times 10^{-5}{}^\circ C^{-1})(978^\circ C - 23^\circ C)$

$= 3.17 \times 10^{-2}\ m$

8. $F = W = mg$

$= (7.5\ kg)(9.8\ m/s^2)$

$= 74\ N$

$A = \pi r^2 = 3.14(5.0 \times 10^{-2}\ m)^2$

$= 7.9 \times 10^{-3}\ m^2$

$p = \dfrac{F}{A} = \dfrac{74\ N}{7.9 \times 10^{-3}\ m^2}$

$= 9.4 \times 10^3\ Pa = 9.4\ kPa$

9. a. $p = \rho h g$, $\rho_{H_2O} = 1.0\ g/cm^3 = 1000\ kg/m^3$

$p = (1000\ kg/m^3)(15\ m)(9.8\ m/s^2)$

$= 1.5 \times 10^5\ Pa$

$= 150\ kPa$

b. $p = (1000\ kg/m^3)(5.0\ m)(9.8\ m/s^2) = 54\ kPa$

10. $p = \rho h g$

$\rho_{oil} = 0.81\ g/cm^3 = 810\ kg/m^3$

$\rho_{H_2O} = 1000\ kg/m^3$

$h_{oil} = 2.5\ cm = 0.025\ m$

$h_{H_2O} = 6.5\ cm = 0.065\ m$

$p = p_{oil} + p_{H_2O} = ((810\ kg/m^3)(0.025\ m)$

$+ (1000\ kg/m^3)(0.065\ m))\ 9.8\ m/s^2$

$= 840\ Pa$

PROBLEMS

1. a. $F_2 = F_1\left(\dfrac{A_2}{A_1}\right)$, and the ratio of areas is the ratio

of squares of diameters, or

$F_2 = (3.0 \times 10^4\ N)\left(\dfrac{6.3\ mm}{22\ mm}\right)^2$

$= 2.5 \times 10^3\ N$

b. $MA = \dfrac{F_r}{F_e} = \dfrac{(2.5 \times 10^3\ N)}{(1.0 \times 10^2\ N)} = 25,$

and $IMA = \dfrac{l_e}{l_r}$, with $MA_, = IMA$

$l_e = (MA)l_r = 25\ (3.0\ cm) = 75\ cm$

2. $L_f = L_i + \alpha L_i (T_f - T_i)$

$T_f = T_i + \dfrac{(L_f - L_i)}{\alpha L_i}$

$= 20^\circ C + \dfrac{(1.2230\ cm - 1.2250\ cm)}{(12 \times 10^{-6}/^\circ C)(1.2250\ cm)}$

$= 20^\circ C - \dfrac{(2.0 \times 10^{-3}\ cm)}{(1.5 \times 10^{-5}\ cm/^\circ C)}$

$= 20^\circ C - 130^\circ C = -110^\circ C$

3. $\Delta V = \beta V_i \Delta T = (\beta_{alcohol} - \beta_{steel})V_i \Delta T$

$= (1100 \times 10^{-6}/^\circ C - 35 \times 10^{-6}/^\circ C)(\pi)$

$\qquad (1.000\ m)^2(5.000\ m)(30^\circ C)$

$= 5.0 \times 10^{-1}\ m^3 = 5.0 \times 10^2\ L$

4. $\Delta V = \beta V_i \Delta T$

$= (75 \times 10^{-6}/^\circ C)(1.78\ cm^3)(580^\circ C - 10^\circ C)$

$= 7.6 \times 10^{-2}\ cm^3$

5. $V_f = V_i + V_i \beta \Delta T = V_i(1 + \beta \Delta T)$

$V_i = \dfrac{V_f}{(1 + \beta \Delta T)}$

$= \dfrac{(2.56\ cm^3)}{(1 + (3)(1.66 \times 10^{-5}/^\circ C)(984^\circ C - 12^\circ C))}$

$V_i = 2.44\ cm^3$

6. a.

b.
$$F_{net} = F_W - F_{buoyant}$$
$$F_{buoyant} = F_W - F_{net}$$
$$= 920 \text{ N} - 750 \text{ N} = 170 \text{ N}$$
$$F_{buoyant} = V\rho_{water}\, g$$
$$V = \frac{F_{buoyant}}{\rho_{water}\, g}$$
$$= \frac{(170 \text{ N})}{(1.00 \times 10^3 \text{ kg/m}^3)(9.8 \text{ m/s}^2)}$$
$$= 1.7 \times 10^{-2} \text{ m}^3$$

c.
$$\rho_{object} = \frac{m}{V} = \frac{F_W}{V_g}$$
$$= \frac{(920 \text{ N})}{(1.7 \times 10^{-2} \text{ m}^3)(9.8 \text{ m/s}^2)}$$
$$= 5.5 \times 10^3 \text{ kg/m}^3$$

Waves and Energy Transfer

Overview

A knowledge of the nature of waves is basic to both sound and optics. All waves have the same general properties and follow the same laws. Thus although there are many kinds of waves, there is only one set of rules of wave behavior that need be learned. Waves in springs and water waves are used to demonstrate the laws of reflection, refraction, diffraction, and interference. Experiments show that sound and light waves which are not visible exhibit the same phenomena as these waves which are visible.

Planning Guide (6 Class Sessions)

Text Section		Demonstrations and Experiments		Other Program Components	
15:1 Types of Waves	P	Dem 15:1 A Wave Demonstrator		Teaching Master 15-1: Wavelength and	
15:2 Frequency, Wavelength, and		Exp 25 Wave Properties	**LM**	Frequency	**TRP**
Velocity	P	Exp 26 Pulses in a Ripple Tank	**LM**	Teaching Master 15-2: Interference	
15:3 Amplitude of a Wave	P	Exp 27 Wavelength, Frequency,		of Waves	**TRP**
15:4 Wave Speed in a Medium	P	Speed	**LM**	Demonstration 15-1: Slinky Wave	
15:5 Reflection and Transmission of		Exp 28 Refraction of Waves	**LM**	Demonstration	**TRP**
Waves at Boundaries	S	Exp 29 Diffraction and Interference			
15:6 Interference of Waves	P	of Waves	**LM**		
15:7 Standing Waves	S	Dem 15:3 Amplitude and Energy			
15:8 Reflection of Waves	P	Dem 15:4 Wave Velocity			
		Dem 15:6 Constructive and			
		Destructive Interference			
15:9 Refraction of Waves	P			Enrichment 15-1: Collapse of the	
15:10 Diffraction and Interference				Tacoma Narrows Bridge	**TRP**
of Waves	P			Enrichment 15-2: Ocean Waves	**TRP**
				Review Masters	**TRP**
				Evaluation	**TRP**

Performance Objectives

Upon completion of this chapter, your students will

1. recognize that waves transfer energy without the transfer of matter.   *15:1*

2. be aware that all waves exhibit the same behavior; distinguish between mechanical and electromagnetic waves, longitudinal and transverse waves; distinguish between a pulse and a wave.   *15:1*

3. define wavelength and frequency; state the equation defining the relationship among speed, wavelength, and frequency; solve problems using the equation.   *15:2, 15:5*

4. describe the relationship between the amplitude of a wave and the energy it transfers. *15:3*

5. understand that the speed of a wave depends on the medium. *15:4*

6. list the characteristics of the behavior of waves at the boundaries between media; solve problems involving that behavior. *15:5*

7. recognize that the wavelength, not the frequency changes at the boundary between media. *15:5*

8. state the principle of superposition; define constructive and destructive interference. *15:6*

9. describe the formation of standing waves; define node and antinode. *15:7*

10. state the law of reflection. *15:8*

11. describe the phenomenon of refraction in terms of the behavior of a transmitted wave. *15:9*

12. define diffraction of a wave around a barrier. *15:10*

Teaching the Chapter

Introduction

Using the Photo: The pedestrians set up a standing wave on the bridge. This phenomenon is called mechanical resonance. Energy was supplied from the people's footsteps. The amplitude of the vibrations increased as people walked in rhythm across the bridge.

This photograph can be used with Section 15:7 to discuss standing waves.

Demonstration: A wave demonstrator can be made by taking a piece of Mylar tape recorder tape about 2 m long and attaching one end to a support and the other end to a removable weight. Cut slits 3/8" long in the center of colored drinking straws. Put a small paper clip in the ends of the straws to increase the moment of inertia. Colored tape may be wrapped around one end of the straw to make the straw more visible. Thread the Mylar tape through the slit in the straws and put them at about 3-cm intervals. Wrap the tape around the end straws. Fix the top straw so it doesn't twist when it hangs. Hang a weight on the free end. This can now be used to demonstrate many wave phenomena.

15:1 Types of Waves

It is important to emphasize that the properties of the mechanical waves you are studying here apply to both sound waves which are mechanical waves and light waves which are electromagnetic waves. When you discuss the energy transferred by waves, remind the students that water waves transfer a great deal of energy as is shown by the destruction caused by giant waves in the ocean. Waves also destroy shorelines.

It is very important to have a Slinky, a more tightly wound spring, and ripple tank to use for demonstrations. If your budget permits, you can get enough of this equipment to have your students do many of the labs from the laboratory manual. If you can only afford one of each, then doing demonstrations will have to suffice. The ripple tank can be placed over an overhead projector and the patterns projected on a screen. The Slinky can be strung and hung as shown in the demonstration, "A Slinky Wave Demonstrator" in the *Teacher Resource Package.* Students can be involved in the demonstrations with the Slinky and can really see what is happening very easily. As you go through the chapter, do at least one demonstration with the Slinky or ripple tank for each new idea. All through the chapter are pictures of the demonstrations you can do.

Demonstration: Use the Slinky to demonstrate transverse and longitudinal waves.

15:2 Frequency, Wavelength, Velocity

Make sure your students really understand the meaning of frequency, wavelength, and velocity. Try to ask them questions so they will use the words. The concepts of period and frequency seem to be especially difficult. The two photographs in Figure 15–5 of a moving wave taken at one-second intervals should be helpful in visualizing the velocity of a wave.

15:3 Amplitude of a Wave

Demonstration: Have a student demonstrate a wave with a large amplitude and one with a small amplitude. Ask them which took more work. They will start to see that a wave with high amplitude also has high energy. Giant waves destroy ships because the energy level is high. If you wish, you can mention some of the topics you will be studying as you do the demonstrations. For example, a sound wave with a large dB reading would be a wave which would have a very large amplitude.

15:4 Wave Speed in Medium

Demonstration: The speed of a wave is dependent on the medium. This can be shown using the ripple tank by placing a piece of glass in the tank so the wave travels from deep water to shallow water. Using a hand strobe students can see that the frequency has not changed. They can also see that the wavelength has changed. Therefore the speed must have changed.

15:5 Reflection and Transmission of Waves at Boundaries

Do the demonstrations shown in Figures 15–9 and 15–10 for your students to show how waves are transmitted and reflected.

15:6 Interference of Waves

Demonstration: Have a student at each end of a Slinky send a pulse down the Slinky at the same time. First have them send the pulse on the same side so they can see it add up and then have them send it down the other side so they will cancel each other.

15:7 Standing Waves

It is worth investing in a string vibrator to show standing waves. It is very easy to identify the nodes and antinodes. You can vary the tension in the string and get different numbers of nodes and antinodes and therefore different numbers of wavelengths. It is a very good visual tool.

This is a good place to show the video of the Tacoma Narrows Bridge collapse. This is a must for your students.

15:8 Reflection of Waves

15:9 Refraction of Waves

15:10 Diffraction and Interference of Waves

In each of these sections there are excellent photographs of ripple tank demonstrations to do. These are described in detail in the lab manual. If you do not have ripple tanks for the whole class, then do these demonstrations with the ripple tank on the overhead projector.

Resources

Literature

Edge, R.D., "A Paper Wave to Explain the Doppler Shift," *The Physics Teacher,* September, 1987, pp. 400–401.

Fillmore, Keith, "Traveling Waves on a Rope," *The Physics Teacher,* May, 1983, p. 314.

Jensen, Harold C., "Hot Standing Waves," *The Physics Teacher,* May, 1968, p. 254.

Levenson, March D., "Wave Motion Demonstrator," *The Physics Teacher,* January, 1974, pp. 47, 48.

Scott, David M., *The Physics of Vibrations and Waves,* Merrill Publishing Co., Columbus, OH, 1986.

Walker, Jearl, *The Flying Circus of Physics, With Answers,* John Wiley and Sons, Inc., New York, 1977, pp. 99, 100, 261.

Warren, Williams, "Standing Waves on the Overhead Projector," *The Physics Teacher,* December, 1980, pp. 674, 675.

Audiovisual/Software

The Puzzle of the Tacoma Narrows Bridge Collapse, AAPT, video

Background

The following comments about the Tacoma Narrows Bridge Collapse are summarized from Jearl Walker's book, *The Flying Circus of Physics.* The bridge oscillated even when it was being built. It often made the workmen seasick. After the bridge opened, motorists would come from miles away to be on the bridge when it was in motion. One day the bridge went into a torsional oscillation which destroyed it in about an hour.

The question is why should a moderately strong steady wind cause such strong oscillations? It would appear that the large vertical plates on the bridge were probably responsible for the oscillations. Wind flowing around the plates caused pressure differences which ultimately made the bridge oscillate.

Chapter Review

QUESTIONS

1. Energy is transferred by particle transfer and by waves. There are many examples that can be given of each, a baseball and a bullet for particle transfer; sound waves and light waves.

2. The principal distinction is that electromagnetic waves seemingly require no medium, whereas mechanical waves do.

3. A transverse wave causes the particles of the medium to vibrate in a direction that is perpendicular to the direction in which the wave is moving. A longitudinal wave causes the particles of the medium to vibrate in a direction parallel with the direction of the wave. Surface waves have characteristics of both.

4. Once the pulse has passed, the point is exactly as it was prior to the advent of the pulse.

5. A pulse is a single disturbance in a medium, whereas a wave consists of several disturbances.

6. Wavelength is the linear distance from any given point on one wave to the corresponding point on the next wave. Frequency is the number of waves that pass a given point per unit time. The period is the time required for a wave to pass any given point or the time required to generate the wave.

7. Amplitude represents the energy content of a wave.

8. Speed of the waves cannot be changed; frequency can be changed by changing the frequency at which the waves are generated.

9. Amount of reflection is determined by the difference between the properties of the new medium and the properties of the old medium.

10. inverted

11. erect

APPLYING CONCEPTS

1. Frequency is the number of vibrations per second of a part of the medium. Velocity describes the motion of the wave, not the medium.

2. The speed of the wave is uniform, along the direction of the spring. The coil has a vibratory motion perpendicular to the spring.

3. first case longitudinal waves, second case transverse

4. The thin rope causes the vibrations in the thick one.

5. AM wavelengths are longer, and therefore the diffraction is more. The waves are bent more.

6. The period of the vibration must equal the time for the wave to go back and forth across the pan to create constructive interference.

7. No. The waves are not affected by interference, each continues to transfer energy.

8. Boundary A is more rigid.
   Boundary B is less rigid.
   Boundary C is less rigid.
   Boundary D is more rigid.

9. The bottom, because the difference in media is greater in this case.

10. A standing wave exists and the string can be touched at any of its five nodal points.

11. Bare areas are antinodal regions where there is maximum vibration. Sugar covered areas are nodal regions where there is no vibration.

EXERCISES

1. $v = f\lambda = \dfrac{1}{2.0 \text{ s}}(10.0 \text{ m}) = 5.0 \text{ m/s}$

2. a. $v = f\lambda = (4.8 \text{ Hz})(6.0 \text{ cm}) = 29 \text{ cm/s}$
   b. $T = 1/f = 1/(4.8 \text{ Hz}) = 0.21 \text{ s}$

3. a. $v = d/t = (4.4 \text{ m})/(1.8 \text{ s}) = 2.4 \text{ m/s}$
   b. $\lambda = v/f = vT = (2.4 \text{ m/s})(1.2 \text{ s}) = 2.9 \text{ m}$

4. $\lambda = c/f = (3.00 \times 10^8 \text{ m/s})/ (5 \times 10^{14} \text{ Hz})$
   $= 6 \times 10^{-7} \text{ m}$

5. a. $v = f\lambda = (1.00 \times 10^6 \text{ Hz})(1.50 \times 10^{-3} \text{ m})$
   $= 1.50 \times 10^3 \text{ m/s}$
   b. $T = \dfrac{1}{f} = \dfrac{1}{1.00 \times 10^6 \text{ Hz}} = 1.00 \times 10^{-6} \text{ s}$
   c. $T = 1.00 \times 10^{-6}$ s. The period and frequency remain unchanged.

6. a. $T = 4(0.18 \text{ s}) = 0.72 \text{ s}$
   b. $f = 1/T = 1/(0.72 \text{ s}) = 1.4 \text{ Hz}$

7. $d = 3.0 \text{ m}, t = 1/(0.30 \text{ Hz})$
   $v = d/t$
   $= (3.0 \text{ m})(0.30 \text{ Hz}) = 0.90 \text{ m/s}$

8. a. $f = (330 \text{ m/s})/(0.70 \text{ m})$
   $= 470 \text{ Hz}$
   b. $(470 \text{ Hz})(0.50 \text{ s}) = 240$ complete waves
   c. $d = vt$
   $= (330 \text{ m/s})(0.50 \text{ s})$
   $= 170 \text{ m}$

9. a. The amplitude is doubled.

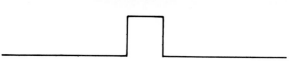

b. The amplitudes cancel each other.

c. If the amplitude of the first pulse is ½ of the second, the resultant pulse is ½ of the second.

PROBLEMS

1. $\lambda = 2(3.0 \text{ m}) = 6.0 \text{ m}$,
   $f = (14 \text{ waves})/(20 \text{ s})$
   $= 0.70 \text{ Hz}$
   $v = f\lambda = (0.70 \text{ Hz})(6.0 \text{ m})$
   $= 4.2 \text{ m/s}$

2. a. $v = f\lambda$
   $\lambda = \dfrac{v}{f} = \dfrac{3.0 \times 10^8 \text{ m/s}}{5.5 \times 10^5 \text{ Hz}}$
   $= 550 \text{ m}$

   $\lambda = \dfrac{v}{f} = \dfrac{3.0 \times 10^8 \text{ m/s}}{1.6 \times 10^6 \text{ Hz}}$
   $= 190 \text{ m}$

   b. $\lambda = \dfrac{v}{f} = \dfrac{3.0 \times 10^8 \text{ m/s}}{8.8 \times 10^7 \text{ Hz}}$
   $= 3.4 \text{ m}$

   $\lambda = \dfrac{v}{f} = \dfrac{3.0 \times 10^8 \text{ m/s}}{1.08 \times 10^8 \text{ Hz}}$
   $= 2.8 \text{ m}$

3. $t = \dfrac{1.80 \text{ s}}{2}$
   $= 0.900 \text{ s}$,
   the time for the wave to travel one way
   $d = vt = (1498 \text{ m/s})(0.900 \text{ s}) = 1350 \text{ m}$

4. $v = d/t$, so $d = vt$. We don't know t, only the difference in time Δt. Use $v_T t = v_L(t + \Delta t)$, solving for $t = v_L \Delta t/(v_T - v_L) = 98$ s. Then, $d = v_T t = (8.9 \text{ km/s})(98 \text{ s}) = 8.7 \times 10^2 \text{ km}$

5. the velocity of the needle

$f = 45 \text{ rpm} \cdot \dfrac{1 \text{ min}}{60 \text{ s}} = 0.75 \text{ rps,}$

$T = 1/f = 1/0.75 \text{ rps}$
$\quad\quad = 1.33 \text{ s}$

$c = 2\pi r = 2\pi(0.10\text{m}) = 0.63 \text{ m}$

$v = c/T = 0.63 \text{ m}/1.33 \text{ s} = 0.47 \text{ m/s}$

the frequency of sound

$f = v/\lambda = 0.47 \text{ m/s}/0.0025 \text{ m} = 190 \text{ Hz}$

6. $v = f\lambda = (0.600 \text{ m})(125 \text{ s}^{-1}) = 75.0 \text{ m/s}$

$\mu = \dfrac{m}{\ell} = \dfrac{1.50 \times 10^{3} \text{ kg}}{5.30 \text{ m}}$

$\quad\quad = 2.83 \times 10^{-4} \text{ kg/m}$

$T = v^2\mu$
$\quad = (75.0 \text{ m/s})^2(2.83 \times 10^{-4} \text{ kg/m}) = 1.59 \text{ N}$

CHAPTER 16

Sound

Overview

The characteristics and properties of waves studied in Chapter 15 are now applied to sound. Wave characteristics, such as velocity, frequency, and wavelength, are defined in terms of sound. Reflection and diffraction are illustrated as wave properties shared by sound. The production, transmission, and detection of sound are demonstrated using a variety of examples. Apparent changes in the frequency of a sound due to the relative movement of the source and/or the detector are explained by the Doppler shift.

In this chapter wave behavior is applied to sound, with an emphasis on music. Musical instruments are a rich source of examples of wave behavior. They can be used to illustrate pitch, intensity, beat notes, tone quality, and overtones. In the case of a wind instrument, the sound is produced by a vibrating reed or lips, which cause a column of air to resonate. The length of the column of air determines the pitch or frequency of the note. The loudness indicates the amplitude and is measured in decibels. Whether the sound produces consonance or dissonance depends on the ratio of the frequencies of the notes.

Planning Guide (5 Class Sessions)

Text Section			Demonstrations and Experiments		Other Program Components	
16:1	Sound Waves	P	Dem 16:1 The Doppler Toss,		Minilab 16-1: Pitch and Medium	**TRP**
16:2	The Doppler Shift	P	Sound Transmission, No Medium:		Demonstration 16-1: Sound Waves	
16:3	Pitch and Loudness	P	No Sound		Require a Medium	**TRP**
			Exp 30 Speed of Sound in Air	**LM**	Demonstration 16-2: The Doppler	
			Dem 16:3 Changing Pitch		Effect	**TRP**
16:4	Sources of Sound	S	Dem 16:4 Singing Pipes		Teaching Master 16-1: Resonance in	
16:5	Resonance	S	Dem 16:5 Resonating Glasses		Pipes	**TRP**
16:6	Detection of Sound	S	Dem 16:6 Detecting Sound		Teaching Master 16-2:	
16:7	The Quality of Sound	S	Dem 16:7 Stringed Harmonics,		(a) Beats	
			Swinging Overtones, Beats		(b) Consonances	**TRP**
					Review Masters	**TRP**
					Demonstration 16-3: Resonance	**TRP**
					Demonstration 16-4: Beats	**TRP**
					Enrichment 16-1: The Twelve Tone	
					Scale	**TRP**
					Enrichment 16-2: Ultrasound	**TRP**
					Enrichment 16-3: Thunder and	
					Lightning	**TRP**
					Enrichment 16-4: Shattered Glass	**TRP**
					Evaluation	**TRP**

Performance Objectives

Upon completion of this chapter, your students will

1. show knowledge of the nature of sound waves; list the wave behaviors of sound shared with other waves.   *16:1*
2. solve problems relating the frequency, wavelength, and velocity of sound waves.   *16:1*
3. define the Doppler shift.   *16:2*
4. list the properties of sound waves using the terms pitch and intensity or loudness; describe the meaning of the octave interval; use the decibel to define ratios of sound intensity.   *16:3*
5. describe the origin of sound in general and in various musical instruments in particular.   *16:4*
6. display an understanding of resonance, especially as applied to an air column; describe or sketch a standing wave; solve problems involving standing waves in resonating air columns.   *16:5*
7. list the parts of the ear and the function of each in detecting sound.   *16:6*
8. define timbre as sound quality; recognize the source of beat notes and solve problems involving beats; define overtones and their origins.   *16:7*

Teaching the Chapter

Introduction

Using the Photo: As a bat nears an object, the distance is shorter, so less time is required for an echo to return. The higher frequency sound has a smaller wavelength, approximately 3.4 mm (100 kHz), which provides greater detail about the object than waves having a longer wavelength.

The photograph can be used with Section 16:1 to discuss sound waves.

Demonstration: Install a buzzer in a foam ball. Start the buzzer and ask your students to predict what they will hear when the ball is thrown back and forth. Have two students throw the ball back and forth. Students should observe a sudden change in pitch when the ball changes direction. The pitch stays the same as the ball comes toward them and changes to a lower pitch when it goes away from them. This is an example of the Doppler shift.

16:1 Sound Waves

Sound waves need a medium in which to travel; the medium itself does not move from one place to another.

Demonstration: To show that a medium does not travel, have a student who plays the trumpet or trombone bring in his or her instrument. Dip the wide end of the instrument into a soap solution, being careful to check beforehand that soap will not damage the finish on the instrument. Let the student play a song and have the class notice that the soap solution stays in place. This shows that the air inside the trumpet is vibrating back and forth but not moving over some long distance.

Demonstration: Obtain a vacuum pump and a jar with a bell. Start the bell ringing and evacuate the jar. Students see the clapper hitting the bell but hear nothing. They should realize that this demonstration illustrates the fact that sound needs a medium.

16:2 The Doppler Shift

Demonstration: Tie a string to the foam ball with the buzzer used in the introductory demonstration and swing it in a circle to show the Doppler shift. Point out that when a siren passes you sounding at a constant frequency, its drop in pitch is a sharp drop and not a gradual change. Refer to the Background section for related equations.

The Doppler shift also applies to light waves. A star that is moving away from Earth will show a decrease in the frequency of the red line of its hydrogen spectrum as compared to the same line in the hydrogen spectrum on Earth.

16:3 Pitch and Loudness

The pitch of a vibrating object is related to the amount of material that vibrates. The more material that vibrates, the lower the pitch. Ask students which musical instruments have a lower pitch. Lead students to realize that the larger the instrument, the lower the pitch.

Demonstration: There are many ways you can demonstrate that pitch is related to the amount of vibrating matter. Hold a credit card or plastic ruler so it extends over the edge of the table. Pluck the card or ruler and observe its pitch. Then slide it slightly towards the center of a table, and pluck it again. Each time you change the overhanging length, see how the pitch varies.

16:4 Sources of Sound

Have several students bring in their musical instruments and explain to the class how they start the air vibrating to produce sound.

Demonstration: Obtain some stovepipe and a large Fisher burner. Cut two lengths of pipe 1 1/2 m long. Light the burner and hold one of the stovepipes over the burner. The stovepipe starts to make a foghorn noise. Put a piece of wire gauze about 25 cm up inside the other pipe. Hold this pipe over the burner until the gauze gets very hot and notice that the pipe makes no sound. The heated wire gauze causes the air compression to build up and the air column does not vibrate at the natural frequency of the pipe. When you remove the pipe from the burner, it vibrates in resonance with the air column and starts to make a loud foghorn noise. Tip it on its side and the noise stops because the rising warm air strikes the side of the pipe. Put the pipe upright again and the noise starts again. **CAUTION:** *Wear insulated gloves when holding the stovepipes over the burner to prevent burns.*

16:5 Resonance

Discuss everyday phenomena that are related to resonance. In order to go higher and higher on a swing, you must kick your feet in a certain rhythm. You are making the swing resonate. Your car may resonate at a certain speed and cause some part of it to have an annoying vibration. Troops need to break step when marching across a bridge so vibrations do not amplify.

Demonstration: Moisten your finger and rub it around the rim of a wine glass until the glass starts to hum. You are making the glass vibrate at its resonant frequency.

16:6 Detection of Sound

Sound is transmitted through bones and liquid in the ear until nerve fibers are stimulated and processed by the brain as sound.

Demonstration: Cut a metal coat hanger and shape it into a rectangular "U." Attach a piece of string about 1 m long to the ends of the metal. Drape the string over your head, making sure the hanger swings freely. Hold the string snugly in each ear and have someone tap the coat hanger. Then have someone tap the hanger when the string is not in your ears. Compare the intensity of the sound under both circumstances.

16:7 The Quality of Sound

Demonstration: Have someone who plays the violin or other stringed instrument demonstrate overtones, often referred to as harmonics. When the string is touched lightly in the middle, you hear the first overtone, which is one octave higher than the fundamental. When the string is touched lightly 1/3 of the way up, you hear the second overtone, which is an octave and a fifth above the fundamental. A student with a wind instrument can also demonstrate overtones by blowing with different amounts of force.

Demonstration: Use a piece of corrugated plastic tubing to demonstrate overtones. Swing it around at different speeds and you get a variety of notes. Talk about where the nodes and antinodes are and relate them to the fundamental and overtones. A different length tube will produce different pitches.

Demonstration: Obtain two slide whistles. Demonstrate beats by playing both whistles at the same time and adjust them so the pitch is just slightly different. You can also play combinations of notes that are consonant and dissonant.

Resonances

Literature

Burgard, James, "How to Hear a Mouse Roar," *The Physics Teacher*, November, 1971, p. 457.

Chandler, A.D., "A Sound-level Meter: A Sound Investment," *The Physics Teacher*, April, 1979, pp. 251–253.

Dwyer, Lester, "Demonstrations of Reflection and Diffraction of Sound," *The Physics Teacher*, May, 1968.

Edge, R.D., "Vibrations in Pipes," *The Physics Teacher*, May, 1980, pp. 383–384.

Falkenberg, Veralee, "A 'Sound' Investment," *The Physics Teacher*, January, 1972, pp. 44–45.

Hults, Morris G., "Sound Waves," *The Physics Teacher,* December, 1980, p. 671.

Miller, Jr., Franklin, *College Physics,* Harcourt Brace Jovanovich, San Diego, 1982, pp. 231–233.

Naegele, Carl J., "Resonance and Foghorns," *The Physics Teacher,* December, 1977, p. 559.

Rigden, John S., *Physics and the Sound of Music,* John Wiley and Sons, Inc., New York, 1977.

Zwicker, E., "Doing Physics, Pipe Music," *The Physics Teacher,* March, 1987, pp. 172–174.

Background

All types of wave motion exhibit the Doppler shift. Christian Johann Doppler (1803–1853) explained the phenomenon in 1842 and did experiments with trumpeters sounding a note as they sat on a flatcar pulled back and forth by a locomotive. Musicians with perfect pitch listened as the train approached and receded and showed that Doppler's equations were valid.

When the source of sound is in motion and the observer is stationary, the equation for the apparent frequency is

$$f' = \frac{f}{1 \pm \dfrac{v}{v_w}}$$

where v is the velocity of the source, v_w is the velocity of the sound and f is the stationary frequency of the sound. Use the " – " sign if the motion of the source of the sound is toward the observer and the " + " sign if the source is moving away from the observer.

If the observer is in motion, the equation is

$$f' = f \left(1 \pm \frac{v}{v_w}\right)$$

v is now the velocity of the observer. Use the " + " sign when the observer is moving toward the source of sound and the " – " sign when the observer is moving away from the source.

Chapter Review

QUESTIONS

1. The velocity of sound is greater in solids than in gases. Therefore, sound travels faster in steel rails than in air.

2. **a.** increases **c.** remains the same
   b. decreases **d.** remains the same

3. As a result of the Doppler shift,
   a. the pitch of the horn of a car moving toward you would increase.
   b. the pitch of the horn of a car moving away from you would decrease.

4. 100 times more intense

5. **a.** no change
   b. increases

6. $\lambda = 2l$ and $v = f\lambda$, so $v = 2fl$. If v increases and l remains unchanged, f increases.

7. sound quality or timbre

8. The slide of a trombone varies pitch by changing the length of the resonating column of vibrating air.

9. The frequency of the note is of natural resonance to the crystal causing its molecules to increase their amplitude of vibration as energy from the sound is accepted.

10. Molecules are closer together allowing a more rapid transfer of sound waves.

11. Sound is a mechanical wave and requires a medium (air) for transmission.

APPLYING CONCEPTS

1. Rewrite the script since sound waves cannot travel through a vacuum.

2. Sound waves in air consist of a series of compressions (maximum pressure) and rarefactions (minimum pressure) of air. As each compression of air reaches the ribbons, they move in the direction of wave motion, then back with each rarefaction.

3. Increased, the frequency is twice as high for an open pipe as for a closed pipe.

4. Ten firecrackers would have to explode together because 100 dB is ten times as loud as 90 dB.

5. by measuring the Doppler shift from sound reflected by the moving blood cells

6. **a.** They would differ in intensity. Larger insects would reflect more of the sound energy back to the bat.

b. An insect flying toward the bat would return an echo of higher frequency (Doppler shift). An insect flying away from the bat would return an echo of lower frequency.

7. While marching in-step a certain frequency is established which could resonate the bridge into destructive oscillation. No single frequency is maintained under "route step."

8. Light travels at 3.0×10^8 m/s while sound travels at 343 m/s. Officials would see the smoke before they would hear the pistol fire. The times would be less than actual, if sound were used.

EXERCISES

1. $d = vt = (343 \text{ m/s})(4.00/2 \text{ s}) = 686 \text{ m}$

2. The total distance the sound must travel is 6.00 m.
$t = d/v$
$\quad = (6.00 \text{ m})/(343 \text{ m/s}) = 0.0175 \text{ s}$

3. $v = f\lambda$
$\quad = (4.40 \times 10^2 \text{ Hz})(3.30 \text{ m}) = 1450 \text{ m/s}$

4. a. 100 dB is 10 times more intense than 90 dB.
b. 110 dB is 100 (10^2) times more intense than 90 dB.

5. a. $\lambda = v/f$
$\quad = (343 \text{ m/s})/(16.4 \text{ Hz}) = 20.9 \text{ m}$
$l = \lambda/2$
$\quad = (20.9 \text{ m})/(2) = 10.5 \text{ m}$
b. $f_c = f_o/2$
$f_c = (16.4 \text{ Hz})/2 = 8.20 \text{ Hz}$

6. 445 Hz $-$ 3 Hz $=$ 442 Hz and
445 Hz $+$ 3 Hz $=$ 448 Hz

7. $2f = (2)(370 \text{ Hz}) = 740 \text{ Hz}$
$3f = (3)(370 \text{ Hz}) = 1100 \text{ Hz}$
$4f = (4)(370 \text{ Hz}) = 1500 \text{ Hz}$

8. $3f = (3)(370 \text{ Hz}) = 1100 \text{ Hz}$
$5f = (5)(370 \text{ Hz}) = 1900 \text{ Hz}$
$7f = (7)(370 \text{ Hz}) = 2600 \text{ Hz}$

9. $f = v/\lambda$
$\quad = (343 \text{ m/s})/(0.0035 \text{ m}) = 9.8 \times 10^4 \text{ Hz}$

10. $\lambda = v/f$
$\quad = (1.50 \text{ km/s})(1000 \text{ m/km})/(4.25 \times 10^6 \text{ Hz})$
$\quad = (3.53 \times 10^{-4} \text{ m}$

11. a. 1 m $=$ 3.28 ft
1 mi $=$ 5280 ft
speed of sound $=$ 343 m/s
(5280 ft/mi)/(3.28 ft/m) $=$ 1610 m/mi

(343 m/s)/(1610 m/mi) $=$ (1/4.69) mi/s $\approx$ (1/5) mi/s; or, sound travels approximately one mile in 5 seconds.

b. 343 m/s $=$ 0.343 km/s $=$ (1/2.92) km/s $\approx$ 1/3 km/s; or, sound travels approximately one kilometer in 3 seconds. Therefore, divide the number of seconds by three.

12. $\lambda = 4L/3 = 4(27 \text{ cm})/3 = 36 \text{ cm}$
A note one octave higher is the first overtone of the fundamental. Resonances are spaced by 1/2 wavelength. Since the original whistle length of 27 cm $=$ 3/4 the wavelength of the first overtone (octave), then the shortest whistle length for the first overtone equals
$3\lambda/4 - \lambda/2 = \lambda/4 = 36 \text{ cm}/4 = 9 \text{ cm}$

13. $L = \lambda/2$, so $\lambda = 2L$; and, $v = f\lambda$, so $f = v/2L$
$\quad = (343 \text{ m/s})/(2)(0.836 \text{ m}) = 410 \text{ Hz}$
The ratio of a frequency one major third higher is 5:4, so (410 Hz)(5/4) $=$ 512 Hz
length of the second pipe
$L = v/2f = (343 \text{ m/s})/(2)(512 \text{ Hz}) = 335 \text{ mm}$

PROBLEMS

1. a. $\lambda = 4l = (4)(2.40 \text{ m}) = 9.60 \text{ m}$
$v = f\lambda$
$f = \dfrac{v}{\lambda} = \dfrac{343 \text{ m/s}}{9.60 \text{ m}} = 35.7 \text{ Hz}$
b. $f = 35.7 \text{ Hz} - 1.40 \text{ Hz} = 34.3 \text{ Hz}$
$v = f\lambda$
$\lambda = \dfrac{v}{f} = \dfrac{343 \text{ m/s}}{34.3 \text{ Hz}} = 10.0 \text{ m}$
$\lambda = 4l$
$l = \dfrac{\lambda}{4} = \dfrac{10.0 \text{ m}}{4} = 2.50 \text{ m}$
The difference in lengths is 2.50 m $-$ 2.40 m $=$ 0.10 m.

2. a. $f' = \dfrac{f(v - v_d)}{(v - v_s)} = \dfrac{(305 \text{ Hz})(343 \text{ m/s} - 0)}{(343 \text{ m/s} - 31 \text{ m/s})}$
$\quad = 340 \text{ Hz}$
b. $f' = \dfrac{f(v - v_d)}{(v - v_s)}$
$\quad = \dfrac{(305 \text{ Hz})(343 \text{ m/s} - (-21 \text{ m/s}))}{(343 \text{ m/s} - 31 \text{ m/s})}$
$\quad = 360 \text{ Hz}$

3. 440 Hz $+$ 3.0 Hz $=$ 443 Hz
$f' = f(v - v_d)/(v - v_s)$,
so $v_s = v - f(v - v_d)/f'$

$= (343 \text{ m/s}) - (440 \text{ Hz})(343 \text{ m/s} - 0)/(443 \text{ Hz})$

$= 2.3 \text{ m/s}$

4. major third ratio $= 5:4$

   $f' = f(v - v_d)/(v - v_s);$

   $v_s = v - f(v - v_d)/f'$

   $= (343 \text{ m/s}) - (343 \text{ m/s} - 0)/(5/4)$

   $= 69 \text{ m/s} = 250 \text{ km/h}$

   No, do not try the experiment.

5. $v = f\lambda,$

   so $\lambda = v/f = (343 \text{ m/s})/(550 \text{ Hz}) = 0.62 \text{ m}$

   For complete destructive interference to occur sound must travel $\frac{1}{2}$ wavelength farther from one speaker than the other, or 0.31 m. If the speakers are separated by 0.31 m or less, there is no destructive interference.

6. $49 \text{ cm} - 17 \text{ cm} = 32 \text{ cm}$, or 0.32 m

   Since the tube is closed at one end, $\frac{1}{2}\lambda$ exists between points of resonance.

   $\frac{1}{2}\lambda = 0.32 \text{ m}$, so $\lambda = 0.64 \text{ m}$

   $f = v/\lambda = (343 \text{ m/s})/0.64 \text{ m} = 540 \text{ Hz}$

Light

Overview

The ray model of light is introduced in preparation for its use in the following chapters on reflection and refraction of light. Michelson used the reflection of light from mirrors to obtain one of the first accurate measurements of the speed of light. The speed of light is now a defined quantity and celestial distances are measured in terms of the time it takes light to travel that distance as light years.

Electrical energy is converted into light energy in lamps. The illumination of a surface by a point source of light follows the inverse square law, $E = P/4d^2$.

The additive process of mixing colors of light is examined for white light passing through colored filters and combined together on a screen. The absorption of colors by pigments is used to explain color mixing by the subtractive process. Colors may also be formed when there is interference in thin films, such as soap or gasoline on water. Interference and polarization are explained using the wave nature of light. Polarized light is discussed as light oriented in only one plane that can be produced by passing light through a polarized filter or by the reflection of light.

Planning Guide (5 Class Sessions)

Text Section		Demonstrations and Experiments		Other Program Components	
17:1 The Facts of Light	P	Dem 17:1 Pinhole Camera,		Teaching Master 17-1:	
17:2 The Speed of Light	P	Correcting Vision		(a) The Electromagnetic Spectrum	
17:3 Sources of Light	P	Exp 31 Luminous Intensity and		(b) Measuring the Speed of Light	TRP
17:4 Transmission and Absorption		Efficiency of Light Bulbs	LM	Demonstration 17-1: Light Travels in	
of Light	S	Dem 17:3 Inverse Square Law		a Straight Line	TRP
				Demonstration 17-2: Inverse Square	
				Law	TRP
				Enrichment 17-1: Lights and	
				Shadows	TRP
17:5 Color	P	Dem 17:5 Color Addition, Color		Teaching Master 17-2: Polarization of	
17:6 Formation of Colors in Thin		Subtraction		Light	TRP
Films	S	Dem 17:6 Colorful Soap Films		Review Masters	TRP
17:7 Polarization of Light	P	Dem 17:7 Rotating Polarizing Filters		Minilab 17-1: Polarization of Light	TRP
				Enrichment 17-2: Polarization of	
				Light	TRP
				Enrichment 17-3: "The Light	
				Fantastic"	TRP
				Evaluation	TRP

Performance Objectives

Upon completion of this chapter, your students will

1. recognize that light is an electromagnetic wave and know its wavelength range. *17:1*

2. define a ray and give examples of evidence that light travels in straight lines. *17:1*

3. describe Michelson's method of measuring the speed of light; state the speed of light (to 1 or 3 significant digits); solve problems involving Michelson's method. *17:2*

4. define luminous intensity, luminous flux, and illuminance; solve illumination problems. *17:3*

5. define transparent, translucent, and opaque. *17:4*

6. display an understanding of the formation of color by the addition of light and by subtraction by pigments. *17:5*

7. explain the cause and give examples of interference in thin films. *17:6*

8. describe methods of producing polarized light. *17:7*

Teaching the Chapter

Introduction

Using the Photo: The small areas of the primary colors red, blue, and green are seen when the other two colors are blocked by the zebra. The yellow shadow is formed by the blue light being blocked and with red and green light falling on the screen. The cyan shadow is formed by red light being blocked and with blue and green light falling on the screen. The magenta shadow is formed by green light being blocked and with red and blue light falling on the screen.

This photograph also can be used with Section 17:5 to discuss color.

Demonstration: The fact that light travels in straight lines can be shown with a simple pinhole camera demonstration. Make several pinhole cameras for students' use. Use a thumbtack to punch a hole in the bottom of a polystyrene cup. Put a piece of waxed paper over the top of the cup and fasten it with a rubber band. Darken the room and light a candle a short distance from the pinhole. The students see an upside-down candle on the waxed paper formed by the rays coming through the pinhole. You can also let a little light in from the windows, and focus an object outside on the waxed paper. Draw a ray diagram to show how the image is formed.

17:1 The Facts of Light

Emphasize that we locate objects by assuming that light travels to our eyes in straight lines. This becomes very evident when you dive for an object on the bottom of a pool. The object is not where you think it is because the rays from the object are bent as they leave the water; you locate the object assuming the ray reflected from the object traveled in a straight line. This phenomenon of refraction will be studied in Chapter 18.

Demonstration: This demonstration is most effective with people who wear corrective lenses. Poke a hole in a 3″ × 5″ card. Have a student who wears glasses remove them and look at some printing. Now have the student look through the pinhole and the writing is much clearer. The eye is behaving like a pinhole camera. Two disadvantages to this kind of corrective measure are the small field of vision and reduction in the amount of light hitting the retina.

17:2 The Speed of Light

Compare the speed of light, 3×10^8 m/s, to the speed of sound, 3.4×10^2 m/s. Point out that the speed of light is six orders of magnitude larger than the speed of sound. Light seems to travel instantaneously, and we can assume this when estimating the distance of a thunderstorm. Sound travels at approximately 340 m/s. If you see a flash of lightning and count or time with the second hand of a watch how many seconds it is until you hear the thunder, you can multiply that by 340 m/s and have an idea how distant the storm is. Take time to discuss the different attempts of people such as Galileo, Roemer, and others, to find the speed of light. Students may find it interesting that Galileo's attempt to measure the speed of light failed because the distance involved made the time too short to be measureable. Roemer's measurement was only within 25 percent of the actual speed.

17:3 Sources of Light

Demonstration: A Mini-Mag Lite™ and a piece of circuit board are ideal for demonstrating the inverse square law. A Mini-Mag Lite may be ordered through a scientific equipment company or found in some hardware stores. The Mini-Mag flashlight has a bulb that acts as a good point source of light. The bulbs can be used without the flashlight if you make a holder for the bulb and a battery.

Darken the room. Shine the light through the piece of circuit board at a distance of 75 cm from the chalkboard. Have a student enclose a square of dots around the reflected light. Now move back to 1.5 m away and put a line around the same number of dots making a larger square. Compare the areas of the two squares and see that the second square is four times larger than the first even though the distance was only doubled. Emphasize the inverse square law and relate the concept of inverse square to Newton's Law of Gravitation.

17:5   Color

Demonstration: Set up three overhead projectors so they shine on the same screen. Cover each overhead's glass plate with cardboard with a hole cut in it. Place a different colored filter over each hole and arrange the projectors so the beams partially overlap on the screen. Experiment with several different colors of filters. Mix the three primary colors to get white light. You may get gray if the intensities are not exactly right.

Demonstration: The color that an object appears to be depends on the wavelengths of light the object reflects. Let white light reflect from a colored card or fabric and view it through a colored filter. You can also experiment by shining different colors of light on the card or fabric and note the color they appear. Discuss the application to clothing and interior design.

17:6   Formation of Colors in Thin Films

Soap film demonstrations are interesting as well as beautiful. A soap solution that will make lasting films can be made by combining 71 gm of Joy detergent, 184 gm of glycerine, and 227 gm of distilled water a few days in advance of intended use.

Demonstration: The following arrangement will project a soap film on a screen. A plexiglass tube about 15 cm long and 7 cm in diameter is ideal for holding the film. A soup can will suffice if the tube is not available. Set up a ring stand to hold the tube horizontally after you have dipped it in the soap solu-

tion and withdrawn it with a film on the end. Reflect light from the film and focus it on a screen with a long focal length lens. The film is wedge-shaped and multi-colored interference fringes are formed. There will be a dark spot on the bottom of the image of the film where it has gotten too thin or it has broken. Remind students that the image of the film is inverted, and that is why the dark spot is on the bottom. If you place a radio speaker at the far end of the tube from the soap film and play some music, you will get some very interesting wave patterns in the film on the screen.

Ask students what other objects produce colors similar to soap films. Some may say spilled gasoline. Ask if it always produces colors or it does only under certain conditions. Explain that the gasoline must be spilled on a wet pavement because the water allows for reflection from the bottom of the gasoline layer. This light interfering with light reflected from the top surface of the gasoline produces the colors. Gasoline spilled on dry pavement does not produce colors since dry pavement would not give a smooth enough surface for reflection from the back surface. Iridescence in butterfly wings, peacock feathers, and opals is caused by interference of light.

17:7   Polarization of Light

Use an oven shelf or refrigerator shelf and rope to demonstrate that the total transverse wave will only pass through an opening if its orientation is in the same plane as the opening. Only an electromagnetic wave in which the electric field is oriented in a plane different from the field of the polarizing filter is able to pass through. Distribute polarizing filters and have students look at light reflected from shiny surfaces. Have them test to see if any of the light will be blocked out as the filter is rotated. Ask them why one orientation of the filter will block out reflected light. If possible, have students take the filters outside and look at the sky and clouds and the light reflected from windows of buildings.

Demonstration: Put one piece of polarizing filter on the overhead and place a second filter on top. Rotate the top filter until the light has been blocked out. Ask students to explain what is happening. Have them observe how many degrees the filter has to be turned before it lets the maximum amount of light through again.

Resources

Literature

Anderson, Frank A., "Drawing Wave Diagrams for the Interference of Light," *The Physics Teacher*, March, 1973, p. 175.

Bartels, Richard A., "Using a Video Projector for Color-mixing Demonstrations," *The Physics Teacher*, April, 1982, pp. 247–248.

Connolly, Walter, "Color Mixing Using a Single Projector," *The Physics Teacher*, May, 1988, pp. 296–297.

Franklin, William R., "The Psychedelic Student-getter," *The Physics Teacher*, April, 1969, p. 227.

Gardner, Robert, "Colored Lights and Shadows," *The Physics Teacher*, October, 1978, p. 477.

Giancoli, Douglas C., *General Physics*, Prentice-Hall, Inc., Englewood Cliffs, NJ, 1984, pp. 732–737.

Patera, Russell, "Pinhole Glasses?" *The Physics Teacher*, September, 1978, p. 383.

Schroeder, M.C., and Smith, C.W., "Estimating the Speed of Light with a TV Set," *The Physics Teacher*, September, 1985, p. 360.

Background

Some substances are optically active and rotate the plane of polarized light. Optical activity is due to the asymmetry of the molecules. This can be shown when light is passed through a polarizer and then through a sugar solution. A second polarized filter, the analyzer, would cut out the light when its plane is rotated 90° to the polarizer if the sugar solution did not affect the polarized light. In order to block out the light coming through the sugar, the analyzer must be rotated at an angle other than 90°. The amount of rotation depends on the path length and the concentration of the solution.

This concept can be demonstrated by shining light through a sugar solution. Place a polarizing filter on top of an overhead projector. Put a plexiglas container, filled to a depth of 20 cm with corn syrup, on top of the polarizer. The light leaving this container is then passed through an analyzer. Note the changing of color as the analyzer is rotated through 360°. A microscope slide wrapped with overlapping transparent tape can be substituted for the container of corn syrup. Only certain types (the older brands that eventually turn yellow) of transparent tape are optically active.

Chapter Review

QUESTIONS

1. A transparent material is a material through which light can pass without distortion. A translucent material allows light to pass but distorts the light to the point where images are not discernable. An opaque material does not allow light to pass through.

2. A luminous body emits light. An illuminated body is one on which light falls and is reflected.

3. White light is a combination of all the colors, or at least the primary colors.

4. Black is not a color but is the absence of all color. An object appears to be black because little, if any, light is being reflected from it.

5. yellow, the sum of red and green light

6. Almost no light would get through. The red cellophane passes only red, but that is blocked by the green.

7. a. yellow
   b. yellow from the yellow light
   c. black, because blue contains neither red nor green light

8. Sound waves are longitudinal, not transverse waves. The particles of the medium move parallel to the motion of the wave rather than the perpendicular motion required for polarization.

9. Non-polarized light can be analyzed as half parallel to the filter, half perpendicular. Only the parallel half passes through.

10. The illumination on a surface is directly proportional to the intensity of the source and inversely proportional to the square of the distance of the surface from the source.

11. Black does not reflect any light.

APPLYING CONCEPTS

1. The 12-sided mirror would have to be rotated slower. It would now have to move 1/12 of a

rotation instead of 1/8 of a rotation in the same amount of time.

2. It is mainly illuminated. The filament is luminous, the frosted glass is illuminated. You can barely see the hot filament through the frosted glass.

3. It transmits all but blue; green and red.

4. **a.** It reflects only red and either absorbs or transmits blue and green.
   b. It transmits only red.
   c. They are absorbed.

5. Yellow-green, because less light has to be reflected to the eye for the object to be seen.

6. Blue will absorb the red and yellow light. Dark blue police cars would not be very visible. If a community wants its police cars to be visible, they should select a color other than dark blue.

7. No. Reflections off the top AND bottom surfaces are inverted. The film has to be $\lambda/2$ thick to reflect light.

8. Light scattered from the atmosphere is polarized, but that scattered from the clouds is not. By rotating the filter, the photographer can reduce the amount of polarized light reaching the film.

9. No. In the weightless environment, the soap film would not be thicker at the bottom.

EXERCISES

1. $v = \dfrac{d}{t}$

   $d = vt = (3.00 \times 10^8 \text{ m/s})(1.28 \text{ s})$
   $= 3.84 \times 10^8 \text{ m}$

2. $v = \dfrac{d}{t}$

   $t = \dfrac{d}{v} = \dfrac{(1.5 \times 10^8 \text{ km})(10^3 \text{ m/km})}{(3.00 \times 10^8 \text{ m/s})}$
   $= 5.0 \times 10^2 \text{ s}$

3. The mirror would move 1/8 rotation during the time light travels from one mountain to the other and back.

   $v = \dfrac{d}{t}$

   $t = \dfrac{d}{v} = \dfrac{(2)(40 \text{ km})(10^3 \text{ m/km})}{(3.00 \times 10^8 \text{ m/s})}$
   $= 2.7 \times 10^{-4} \text{ s}$

   $f = \dfrac{(1/8 \text{ rotation})}{(2.7 \times 10^{-4} \text{ s})} = 4.6 \times 10^2 \text{ Hz}$

4. $E = \dfrac{P}{4\pi d^2} = \dfrac{(405 \text{ } \ell\text{m})}{4\pi(4.0 \text{ m})^2} = 2.0 \text{ } \ell\text{x}$

5. Illumination $E \propto 1/d^2$; therefore, the illumination at screen B will be 1/4 of that at screen A since it is twice as far from the source.

6. No. Distance is doubled, so the illumination of the page is 1/4 as great.

7. $t = \dfrac{1}{f} = \dfrac{1}{5.00 \times 10^2 \text{ Hz}}$
   $= 2.00 \times 10^{-3} \text{ s for one rotation}$

   $t = \dfrac{1}{20}(2.00 \times 10^{-3} \text{ s}) = 1.00 \times 10^{-4} \text{ s}$

   $v = \dfrac{d}{t} = \dfrac{(3.00 \times 10^4 \text{ m})}{(1.00 \times 10^{-4} \text{ s})} = 3.00 \times 10^8 \text{ m/s}$

8. $E = \dfrac{I}{d^2}$

   $E_1 = E_2$

   $\dfrac{I_1}{d_1^2} = \dfrac{I_2}{d_2^2}$

   $I_2 = \dfrac{(I_1)(d_2^2)}{(d_1^2)}$

   $I_2 = \dfrac{(101 \text{ cd})(3.0 \text{ m})^2}{(5.0 \text{ m})^2}$
   $= 36 \text{ cd}$

9. $E = \dfrac{P}{4\pi d^2}$

   $P = 4\pi E d^2 = 4\pi(175 \text{ } \ell\text{x})(0.80 \text{ m})^2$
   $= 1.4 \times 10^3 \text{ } \ell\text{m}$
   Thus, the $100 - \text{W}$ ($1620 \text{ } \ell\text{m}$) setting is needed.

10. $E = \dfrac{P}{4\pi d^2}$

    $P = 4\pi E d^2 = 4\pi(160 \text{ } \ell\text{m/m}^2)(2.0 \text{ m})^2$
    $= 8.0 \times 10^3 \text{ } \ell\text{m}$

11. $E_1 = E_2$

    $\dfrac{P_1}{d_1^2} = \dfrac{P_2}{d_2^2}$

    $d_2 = d_1\sqrt{(P_2/P_1)} = (2.5 \text{ m})\sqrt{(2375/1445)}$
    $= 3.2 \text{ m}$

PROBLEMS

1. **a.** $v = \dfrac{d}{t}$

   $d = vt = (3.00 \times 10^8 \text{ m/s})(14 \text{ s})$
   $= 4.2 \times 10^9 \text{ m}$

b. $v = \dfrac{d}{t} = \dfrac{(4.2 \times 10^9 \text{ m})}{(42.5 \text{ h})}$

$= 28 \text{ km/s}$

c. $v = \dfrac{d}{t} = \dfrac{2\pi(1.5 \times 10^8 \text{ km})}{(365 \text{ d})}$

$= 30 \text{ km/s}$

2. $v = \dfrac{d}{t}$

$d = vt = (3.00 \times 10^8 \text{ m/s})(0.1 \text{ s})$

$= 3 \times 10^4 \text{ km}$

The mirror would be half this distance, or 15 000 km away. Earth is 40 000 km in circumference, so this is 3/8 of the way around Earth!

3. $E = \dfrac{P}{4\pi d^2}$

If P is reduced by a factor of 2, so must d^2. Thus, d is reduced by a factor of $\sqrt{2}$, becoming

$\dfrac{(3.3 \text{ m})}{\sqrt{2}} = 2.3 \text{ m}$

4. $E = \dfrac{P}{4\pi d^2}$

$E_1 = E_2$

$\dfrac{P_1}{d_1^2} = \dfrac{P_2}{d_2^2}$

$P_2 = \dfrac{(P_1)(d_2)^2}{(d_1)^2} = \dfrac{(1750 \text{ } \ell\text{m}(1.08 \text{ m})^2}{(1.25 \text{ m})^2}$

$= 1.31 \times 10^3 \text{ } \ell\text{m}$

Reflection and Refraction

Overview

The characteristics and behavior of waves were studied in Chapter 15. This chapter is concerned with the reflection and refraction of light, two properties that can be explained by treating light as a wave.

A ray optic treatment of the laws of reflection and refraction is presented. Elementary geometry and trigonometry are used to predict the behavior of light striking various boundaries. When light is reflected from a surface, the angle of incidence and the angle of reflection are equal. When light is refracted from one medium to another, Snell's law is used to compare the angle of incidence to the angle of refraction. The existence of critical angles is used to explain total internal reflection. Dispersion of light in a prism and in a water droplet are understood using the basic law of refraction.

Planning Guide (6 Class Sessions)

Text Section		Demonstrations and Experiments	Other Program Components	
18:1 The Law of Reflection	P	Dem 18:1 Reappearing Coin, Reflection Exp 32 Law of Reflection of Light **LM** Exp 33 Snell's Law **LM**		
18:2 Refraction of Light **18:3** Snell's Law **18:4** Index of Refraction and the Speed of Light **18:5** Total Internal Reflection	P P P P	Dem 18:2 Refraction by Water, Fat Finger, Refraction by Glass, Disappearing Objects Dem 18:5 A Fish's View, Trapped Light, Total Internal Reflection	Teaching Master 18-1: Refraction in Glass and Water Minilab 18-1: Index of Refraction Demonstration 18-1: The Red Sunset—Light Scattering Demonstration 18-2: Refraction—The Disappearing Act Demonstration 18-3: Total Internal Reflection	**TRP** **TRP** **TRP** **TRP** **TRP**
18:6 Effects of Refraction **18:7** Dispersion of Light	S S	Dem 18:7 Creating a Rainbow	Teaching Master 18-2: Refraction in Water Review Masters Enrichment 18-1: Problems Evaluation	**TRP** **TRP** **TRP** **TRP**

Performance Objectives

Upon completion of this chapter, your students will

1. state the law of reflection. *18:1*
2. distinguish between diffuse and regular reflection. *18:1*
3. define refraction; predict whether the ray will

bend toward or away from the normal when light moves from one medium into another. *18:2*
4. state Snell's law; apply the law to the solution of refraction problems. *18:3*
5. relate the index of refraction to the speed of light

in the medium; solve problems relating these two quantities. *18:4*

6. explain total internal reflection; define the critical angle. *18:5*

7. explain effects caused by the refraction of light in a medium with varying refractive index. *18:6*

8. explain the dispersion of light in terms of index of refraction. *18:7*

Teaching the Chapter

Introduction

Using the Photo: Rainbows are created when sunlight strikes raindrops at an angle of 40° to 42° with respect to the observer. The second rainbow is not a reflection of the first, but occurs at an angle of 50° to 54° from the observer. It is created as a result of a second internal reflection of the light within each raindrop. In the second reflection, the red and violet rays cross each other, causing a reversal of the color bands.

This photograph can be used with Section 18:5 on total internal reflection and Section 18:7 on dispersion of light.

Demonstration: Place a coin in the bottom of a polystyrene cup. Have students gather around the cup and move back until the coin just disappears from view. Have students remain while you pour water into the cup until it is full or the coin reappears. Ask students if they can explain what is happening. With only air in the cup, light traveled in a straight line. As the water is added, light is refracted from the water-air boundary and more of the cup's bottom is visible.

18:1 The Law of Reflection

Illustrate the law of reflection by bouncing a ball to a person across the room. Talk about the angle of incidence and the angle of reflection in terms of the ball reflecting off the floor and relate this to a light ray reflecting from a mirror, as in Figure 18–1.

Discuss the fact that a window will often act like a mirror. Ask students to explain this. If the side of a window near you is in a lit room and the other side of the window is in the dark of night, the window will behave like a mirror.

Demonstration: Many demonstrations can be done with a tank of water (an old fish tank could be used). With some added fluorescent dye or a little milk, you can see a laser beam when you shine it into the tank.

Place a mirror on the bottom of a tank. Shine a laser light on the mirror to see a ray of reflected light.

Move the beam to show different angles of incidence and reflection.

18:2 Refraction of Light

Refer to the introductory demonstration and explain how the light rays from the coin are bent as they come out of the water, allowing you to see the coin when the cup is full of water.

Demonstration: Shine a laser beam on a mirror on the bottom of the tank of water described in section 18:1. The beam will emerge and make a spot on the ceiling. Have students note that the spot is not directly in line with the beam being reflected from the mirror. The beam is bent away from the normal as it leaves the water because it is refracted.

Demonstration: Obtain a test tube large enough to put your finger in with room to spare. Fill the test tube with water and look at your "fat" finger due to refraction.

Demonstration: Put a glass square or triangle in the water tank. Shine a laser through the side of the tank and through the triangle or square so that the students can see the ray being bent. Pieces of glass or plastic in the shape of lenses will show how the beam is bent as it goes through lenses.

Demonstration: Several different ways of making objects disappear can be demonstrated. The dropper in a dropping bottle can be made to disappear if the air is forced out and the bulb released when the dropper is placed in microscope immersion oil. Pyrex will disappear in Anisole, and plexiglas cannot be seen when submerged in corn syrup.

18:3 Snell's Law

Have students do the lab "Snell's Law" in *Laboratory Physics*. Have students use the laser to check their diagrams. Shine the laser along the incident ray. The laser can be positioned so the beam just touches the paper. Students can see the beam go through and come out the other side along the rays drawn when they look through the glass square.

18:5 Total Internal Reflection

Demonstration: You can see how the world looks to a fish by placing a mirror face up on the bottom of a flat pan filled with water. Stick your finger in the water above the mirror and look straight down into the mirror. You see what the fish views when looking straight up. If you prop the mirror against the side of the pan, you see how the fish views things at an angle. At a particular angle, total internal reflection occurs. Place a coin in the bottom of the dish. Look in the mirror. If you see the coin in the mirror, the light from the coin has been reflected off the surface of the water. To find the correct angle to make this occur, lay the mirror flat and then slowly tilt it upwards along the side until the coin appears. This shows that the rays must have traveled up to the surface and been reflected back to the mirror.

Demonstration: Shine the laser through a right angle prism as in Figure 18–10. Put some chalk dust in the air so you can see the rays going in and coming out. Also shine the laser through a plexiglas rod curled at one end so students can see that the light is "trapped" inside the rod and comes out the end.

Demonstration: Place a mirror in the bottom of a tank of water as in Section 18:1. Shine a laser light on the mirror at an angle so that the ray reflected from the mirror will be totally reflected by the surface of the water. Put a piece of paper over the surface of the water to show that no light emerges from the water.

Point out that optical fibers are used in communication because the use of light and optical fibers allows many signals to be carried on a very small cable and over long distances.

18:7 Dispersion of Light

Everyone loves to see a rainbow or even a spectrum on the wall. When sunlight enters the room, hang a prism so the sun will shine through it and make a rainbow on your wall.

Demonstration: You can make a rainbow using a clear plastic box and an overhead projector. Orient the projector as if you were going to project an image on the front wall of the room. Tape a piece of paper over the upper mirror unit of the projector. Place a clear plastic box 3/4 full of water on the stage of the overhead. Turn off the lights, turn on the overhead projector, and see the rainbows on each side wall.

Resources

Literature

Derman, Samuel, "How the World Looks Underwater- A Demonstration for Nonswimmers," *The Physics Teacher,* October, 1982, pp. 474–475.

Derman, Samuel, "Solar Spectrum Projection," *The Physics Teacher,* January, 1978, p. 58.

Easton, D., "On Reflections in Ponds," *The Physics Teacher,* March, 1987, pp. 150–151.

Edgar, Dale, "Simulating Optical Fibers," *The Physics Teacher,* November, 1988, pp. 504–506.

Edge, R. D., "Optics of the Rear-View Mirror: A Laboratory Experiment," *The Physics Teacher,* April, 1986, pp. 221–223.

Greenlear, Robert, *Rainbows, Halos, and Glories,* Cambridge University Press, New York, 1980, pp. 1–21.

Ruiz, M. J., and Robinson, T. L., "Illusions with Plane Mirrors," *The Physics Teacher,* April, 1987, pp. 206–212.

Background

Figure 18–15 is a photograph of a rainbow and a diagram of the reflection and refraction by the droplet of water that causes the dispersion of the light. In the photograph you can see a faint second-order rainbow. Descartes was probably the first person to explain the formation of the primary and secondary rainbow in a treatise published in 1637. The second-order rainbow occurs because the light rays are reflected twice inside the drop before emerging. Descartes' explanation is still accepted today. According to Greenlear in his book, *Rainbows, Halos, and Glories,* the two rainbows are formed by rays from different drops coming to your eye even though every drop reflects and refracts in all possible ways.

Newton derived a formula for the angular size of the rainbow after multiple, N, reflections of the light inside the raindrops. For $N = 1$ the angle would be about 42° and for $N = 2$ about 51°. These are indeed the angles for the first two rainbows. Newton said that for $N = 3$ the light would be too faint to see the rainbow.

Edmund Halley worked on the problem and found for $N = 3$ and $N = 4$ the rainbows would appear around the sun. These would be difficult to see because of the brightness of the sun.

Chapter Review

QUESTIONS

1. When light is reflected from a smooth surface, the rays are reflected in the same order in which they are incident upon the surface. The result is an image of the origin of the rays. When light is reflected from a rough surface, it is reflected in many different directions. The rays are diffused or scattered. No image of the source results.

2. There are two possible answers to this question. The angle is 90°. However, the student might mention angles greater than the critical angle. Total internal reflection would mean no refracted rays.

3. Angle of incidence is larger than the angle of refraction.

4. Angle of incidence is smaller than angle of refraction.

5. Whenever a ray of light passes from one medium into another at some angle, the ray is refracted in such a way that the ratio of the sine of the angle of incidence to the sine of the angle of refraction is a constant for all angles of incidence.

6. $n = \dfrac{\sin i}{\sin r}$ $n = \dfrac{c}{v}$ $n_1 \sin \theta_1 = n_2 \sin \theta_2$

7. The term "critical angle" refers to the incident angle that causes the refracted ray to lie right along the boundary of the substance when a ray is passing from a dense to less dense medium. It may also be termed the incident angle, which, if exceeded, will cause total internal reflection.

8. Mirages are caused by a phenomenon of light refraction that is detailed in Section 18:6.

9. Red light; it is refracted the least by glass.

10. The spectrum of sunlight is called a continuous spectrum.

APPLYING CONCEPTS

1. Air and glass have the smaller critical angle. The critical angle for air and water is 48.6°. The critical angle for air and glass is 41°.

2.

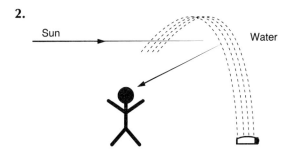

Sun — Water

3. (a) Blue travels slower in the prism.

4.

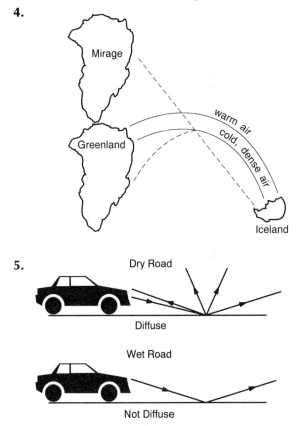

Mirage

Greenland

warm air

cold, dense air

Iceland

5.

Dry Road

Diffuse

Wet Road

Not Diffuse

6. You can only see a rainbow when the sun's rays come from behind you at an angle not greater than 42° with the horizon. When you are facing south in the northern hemisphere, the sun is never behind you at an angle of 42° or less.

7. The incident angles with which the three rays on the right strike the surface of the glass are greater

than the critical angle for glass, and total internal reflection occurs.

8. This illustrates light reflected at angles larger than the critical angle.

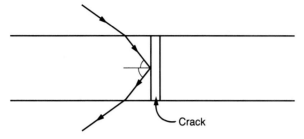

— Crack

9. **a.** 19.2°
   b. 30.0°
   c. It is refracted away from the normal.
   d. The ray leaving the glass is parallel to the ray entering the glass, but it is at a different location.

EXERCISES

1. **a.** 53°
   b. $2(53°) = 106°$
2. $2(90° - 36°) = 108°$
3. $\sin \theta_r = \dfrac{\sin \theta_i}{n} = \dfrac{\sin 60.0°}{1.5} = 0.58$
   $\theta_r = 35°$
4. $\sin \theta_r = \dfrac{\sin 36.0°}{1.33} = 0.442$
   $\theta_r = 26.2°$
5. **a.** $n = \dfrac{\sin \theta_i}{\sin \theta_r} = \dfrac{\sin 30.0°}{\sin 22.0°} = 1.34$
   b. water

6. $\sin \theta_r = \dfrac{\sin 60.0°}{2.42} = 0.358$
   $\theta_r = 21.0°$

7. $\sin \theta_r = \dfrac{(\sin \theta_i)(v)}{c} = \dfrac{(\sin 22°)(1.90 \times 10^8 \text{ m/s})}{(3.00 \times 10^8 \text{ m/s})}$
   $= 0.24$
   $\theta_r = 14°$

8. $n_1 \sin \theta_i = n_2 \sin \theta_r$
   $\sin \theta_r = \dfrac{(1.33)(\sin 23.2°)}{1.52} = 0.345$
   $\theta_r = 20.2°$

9. $\sin \theta_r = \dfrac{(1.61)(\sin 25.0°)}{1.36} = 0.500$
   $\theta_r = 30.0°$

10. $\sin \theta_r = \dfrac{(n_{water})(\sin \theta_i)}{n_{plastic}} = \dfrac{(1.33)(\sin 35.0°)}{(1.500)}$
    $= 0.509$
    The angle of refraction from the water into the plastic is equal to the angle of incidence from the plastic in the air.
    $\sin \theta_r = \dfrac{(1.500)(0.509)}{(1.00)} = 0.764$
    $\theta_r = 49.8°$

11. 8 mm

PROBLEMS

1. **a.** $\sin \theta_r = \dfrac{\sin 45°}{1.5} = 0.47$
   $\theta_r = 28°$
   b. $\theta_A = 90° - 28° = 62°$
   $\theta_B = 180° - (62° + 60°) = 58°$
   $\theta_C = 90° - 58° = 32°$

c. $\sin \theta_D = n \sin \theta_C = (1.5)(\sin 32°) = 0.80$

$\qquad \theta_D = 53°$

2. For red light

$$\sin \theta_r = \frac{(\sin 30.0°)}{2.410} = 0.207$$

$$\theta_r = 12.0°$$

For blue light

$$\sin \theta_r = \frac{(\sin 30.0°)}{2.450} = 0.204$$

$$\theta_r = 11.8°$$

3. a. For red light

$$\sin \theta_r = \frac{(\sin 30.0°)}{1.514} = 0.330$$

$$\theta_r = 19.3°$$

For blue light

$$\sin \theta_r = \frac{(\sin 30.0°)}{1.528} = 0.327$$

$$\theta_r = 19.1°$$

b.

	Diamond		Crown Glass	
	Red	Blue	Red	Blue
Angle of incidence	30.0°	30.0°	30.0°	30.0°
Angle of refraction	12.0°	11.8°	19.3°	19.1°
Difference	18.0°	18.2°	10.7°	10.9°

c. There is a much larger difference between the angles of incidence and refraction for diamond than for crown glass. This means that diamond has a much smaller critical angle. As a result, less light incident upon a diamond will pass completely through. Instead, more light will be reflected internally until it comes back out of the top of the diamond. Blue light has a smaller critical angle than red light. This means that more red light will emerge from a diamond than blue light. Hence, a diamond appears to have "fire."

4. $\sin \theta_i = \dfrac{(n_{water})(\sin 90°)}{(n_{crown\ glass})} = \dfrac{(1.33)(\sin 90°)}{1.52}$

$\qquad = 0.875$

$\qquad \theta_i = 61.0°$

5. $\sin \theta_r = \dfrac{\sin 45°}{1.52} = 0.465$

$\qquad \theta_r = 28°$

$\qquad \theta_i = 180° - (90° + 28°) = 62°$

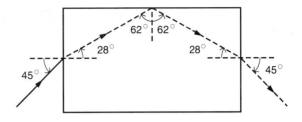

6. a. $\tan \theta_i = \dfrac{1.5\ m}{2.0\ m} = 0.75$

$\qquad \theta_i = 37°$

$\qquad \sin \theta_r = \dfrac{(1.33)(\sin 37°)}{1.00} = 0.80$

$\qquad \theta_r = 53°$

b. $\tan 53° = \dfrac{side\ opposite}{side\ adjacent}$

$\qquad side\ adjacent = \dfrac{side\ opposite}{\tan 53°} = \dfrac{1.5\ m}{\tan 53°}$

$\qquad = 1.1\ m$, shallower

7. a. $\sin \theta_G = \dfrac{(1.00)(\sin 40°)}{1.5} = 0.43$

$\qquad \theta_G = 25°$

b. $\sin \theta_W = \dfrac{(1.5)(\sin 25°)}{1.33} = 0.48$

$\qquad \theta_W = 29°$

c. $\sin \theta_W = \dfrac{(1.00)(\sin 40°)}{1.33} = 0.48$

$\qquad \theta_W = 29°$, the same

8. Time through vacuum

$$t = \frac{d}{v} = \frac{(1.5 \times 10^8\ km)(10^3\ m/km)}{(3.00 \times 10^8\ m/s)} = 500\ s$$

Time through water

$$v = \frac{c}{n} = \frac{(3.00 \times 10^8\ m/s)}{1.33} = 2.26 \times 10^8\ m/s$$

$$t = \frac{d}{v} = \frac{(1.5 \times 10^8\ km)(10^3\ m/km)}{(2.26 \times 10^8\ m/s)} = 660\ s$$

$$\Delta t = 660\ s - 500\ s = 160\ s$$

$$= (160\ s)(1\ min/60\ s) = 2.7\ min$$

Mirrors and Lenses

Overview

Ray optics techniques developed in the last chapter are used in Chapter 19 to analyze images formed by mirrors and lenses. Ray diagrams are used to find the location and size of images in plane mirrors. Images formed by curved mirrors and lenses are shown using ray diagrams, and equations are used to find the exact position and size of the images. The defects of spherical mirrors and lenses and the difference between real and virtual images are explained. The practical uses of curved mirrors and lenses in correcting eyesight and making telescopes and microscopes are summarized.

Planning Guide (7 Class Sessions)

Text Section	Demonstrations and Experiments	Other Program Components
19:1 Objects and Their Images in Plane Mirrors **P**	Dem 19:1 Multiple Reflections, Field of Reflection, Depth of Reflection Exp 34 Images Produced by Curved Mirrors **LM** Exp 35 Convex Lenses **LM**	Teaching Master 19-1: (a) Image Formed by a Plane Mirror **TRP** Minilab 19-1: Multiple Images Formed by Plane Mirrors **TRP** Demonstration 19-1: Cool Light **TRP** Demonstration 19-2: Burning the Candle at Both Ends **TRP**
19:2 Concave Mirrors **P** **19:3** Spherical Aberration and Parabolic Mirrors **S** **19:4** Real *vs.* Virtual Images **P** **19:5** Real Images Formed by Concave Mirrors **P** **19:6** Virtual Images Formed by Concave Mirrors **P** **19:7** Virtual Images Formed by Convex Mirrors **P**	Dem 19:2 Searchlight Dem 19:6 Images Formed by Concave Mirrors, Beam Splitter Dem 19:7 Images Formed by Convex Mirrors	Teaching Master 19-1: (a) Real Image Formed by a Concave Mirror **TRP** Teaching Master 19-2: (a) Virtual Image Formed by a Concave Mirror (b) Virtual Image Formed by a Convex Mirror Convex Mirror **TRP**
19:8 Lenses **P** **19:9** Real Images Formed by Convex Lenses **P** **19:10** Virtual Images Formed by Convex Lenses **P** **19:11** Virtual Images Formed by Concave Lenses **P**	Dem 19:9 Shrinking Lens Dem 19:11 The Growing Penny	Demonstration 19-3: Lens Combinations **TRP**
19:12 Chromatic Aberration **S** **19:13** Optical Instruments **S**		Review Masters **TRP** Enrichment 19-1: Problems **TRP** Enrichment 19-2: Telescopes **TRP** Evaluation **TRP**

Performance Objectives

Upon completion of this chapter, your students will

1. describe the image produced by a plane mirror. *19:1*
2. define focal point and explain the rules of ray tracing as applied to concave mirrors. *19:2*
3. define spherical aberration and describe the use of parabolic mirrors. *19:3*
4. distinguish between real and virtual images. *19:4*
5. explain the formation of real images by concave mirrors; use ray diagrams to locate the image; calculate the location using the mirror equation. *19:5*
6. explain and demonstrate using ray diagrams the formation of virtual, enlarged images by concave mirrors. *19:6*
7. explain and demonstrate using ray diagrams the formation of virtual images by convex mirrors, and calculate the location of these images. *19:7*

8. differentiate between concave and convex lenses. *19:8*
9. describe the formation of an image by a convex lens; use a ray diagram to locate the image; calculate the location using the lens equation. *19:9*
10. understand the derivation of the lens equation. *19:9*
11. describe the formation of a virtual image by a convex lens; diagram and calculate the location of these images. *19:10*
12. describe the formation of virtual images by concave lenses. *19:11*
13. define chromatic aberration and understand how it is eliminated. *19:12*
14. explain the operation of optical instruments such as the microscope and telescope. *19:13*

Teaching the Chapter

Introduction

Using the Photo: Jerrome is correct. It is a convex lens, which is able to project an inverted, real image on the screen.

The photograph can be used with Section 19:4 on real *vs.* virtual images, Section 19:8 on lenses, and Section 19:9 on real images formed by convex lenses.

Demonstration: Obtain two 20-cm square mirrors. Make a holder for the mirrors and tape the edges. Scrape a little hole in the paint on the back of one of the mirrors about 1/3 of the way down from the top of the mirror. Set the mirrors about 10 cm apart facing each other and place a soda pop can in between. Have students look through the hole at the large number of images formed and describe the characteristics of the successive images.

19:1 Objects and Their Images in Plane Mirrors

Obtain enough mirrors so each student can have one. If you have a glass and mirror repair store near you, they may cut up scraps of mirror for you and give them to you for free. Mirrors about 10 cm by 5 cm work well. Cut scraps of wood to fit the mirrors and

glue the mirrors onto the blocks so they stand. Have students stand the mirror on a line of notebook paper and try to write their names while looking at the pencil and paper in the mirror. If their names appear upright in the mirror, they have written the mirror image.

Demonstration: Ask students if they can see more of their face in a small mirror if they hold the mirror farther away. Have them test their predictions. They observe that they can still see the same amount of their face as they move the mirror away.

The optics of the rear view mirror in a car are very interesting. Discuss why an image is dimmed when the rear-view mirror is flipped up. The mirror is a back-silvered glass wedge. The mirror behaves like a regular mirror for day use. Since it is wedge-shaped, a fringe of color may appear at the top and bottom of the mirror, especially at night. When the mirror is turned up for night vision, the driver sees the image of the rear window reflected from the surface of the wedge, and the light reflected from the rear is deflected above the driver.

Demonstration: Place a plane sheet of glass in front of a beaker filled with water. Light a candle and place it in front of the glass sheet so its image appears to be in the water. This demonstration emphasizes that the image in a plane mirror is as far behind the mirror as the object is in front of the mirror.

19:2 Concave Mirrors

Concave mirrors are used as magnifying mirrors for shaving, applying makeup, and in reflecting telescopes. They are also used to make the beam of light in your car headlights. Often these mirrors are parabolic to avoid the spherical aberration.

Demonstration: Darken the room and hold a small light bulb (like the ones used on an optical bench) at the focal point of a large parabolic mirror and show how the light is reflected as a beam.

19:4 Real vs. Virtual Images

19:5 Real Images Formed by Concave Mirrors

19:6 Virtual Images Formed by Concave Mirrors

For each of the demonstrations in this chapter, use either a candle or a tubular, unfrosted, 25-W lamp with a straight filament to form a good, distinctive image. The relationships between object and image distances can be easily demonstrated even without an optical bench.

Demonstration: Hold a light source in one hand and a concave mirror in the other. First cast a large image on a wall and point out that the object is between C and F, but close to the focal point. Then hold the object far from the mirror and form a small image. Now hold the object between F and the mirror and demonstrate no real image is found. Only by looking into the mirror is the virtual image seen. Also show that you do not get an image anywhere when the object is at the focal point.

Demonstration: If you have a laser available, this simple set-up will let you split the laser beam into several rays. Take four or five microscope slides and stack them together. Place strips of cardboard between the slides at one end and form a wedge. Tape the slides together at the ends. Hold a laser vertically and shine it down on the wedge of slides held at an angle. Several beams will be reflected and can be sent through water with a little milk in it, making the rays more visible. Shine the rays through lenses in the water or reflect them from curved mirrors.

19:7 Virtual Images Formed by Convex Mirrors

Demonstration: Get a side-view mirror from a car and discuss the printing on the mirror that says, "Objects are closer than they appear." Pass around a convex mirror and have students hold it close to their faces and then move it away. Have them observe that the image is always right side up and smaller than their face. Compare this to the same exercise they did with the concave mirror (suggestion in margin notes).

19:8 Lenses

19:9 Real Images Formed by Convex Lenses

Demonstration: Use a convex lens and lamp to produce an image on a screen. Now ask what kind of image you will get if you have half a lens. Cover half the lens by taping paper over it or purchase half a lens for this purpose. Show that you still get the whole image even with half a lens. Now cover even more of the lens so only a sliver shows and you can still see the whole image.

Set up a fish tank and experiment with various objects to see what kinds of images they produce. Place a cup with printing on it in the tank. Now place an empty round-bottom flask in front of the cup and look at it. The double convex air lens behaves like a diverging lens. Look at the same printing when you fill the flask with water. Make a cylindrical air and water lens with a beaker and compare the writing on the cup. Have the students think of other experiments to try. Encourage them to predict what will happen and then test their predictions.

19:11 Virtual Images Formed by Concave Lenses

Demonstration: Place a penny heads up in the bottom of a test tube. Fill half of the test tube with water and look down into it. The penny looks small and far away because the meniscus behaves like a concave lens. Now fill the test tube to the top and add water until there is a convex surface. The penny appears much larger and closer.

Alert students to look for physics errors in books. For example, Golding's *Lord of the Flies* tells how a boy used his glasses to start a fire. Later in the book it says that the same boy suffered from myopia. Glasses that correct myopia are diverging and would not cause light to concentrate and start a fire.

19:13 Optical Instruments

Have students bring in old eyeglasses from near-sighted and farsighted people. Inspect the thickness of the edges and see what the image looks like when you look through them. Relate this to the diagrams in Figure 19–20.

Use some short and long focal length lenses to set up a simple microscope and telescope as described in this section of the text.

Resources

Literature

Clark, C. Bob, "His Specs–Use Them for Burning Glasses," *The Physics Teacher*, December, 1973, p. 522.

Conwell, C.R., and Paschal, J.S., "Kaleidoscope Physics," *The Science Teacher*, November, 1986, pp. 41–44.

Derman, Samuel, "An Optical Puzzle That Will Make Your Head Spin," *The Physics Teacher*, September, 1981, p. 200.

Edge, R.D., "Optics of the Rear-View Mirror: A Laboratory Experiment," *The Physics Teacher*, April, 1986, p. 197.

Ford, Kenneth W., "Why Is Your Image In a Plane Mirror Inverted Left-To-Right But Not Top-To-Bottom?" *The Physics Teacher*, April, 1975, pp. 228–229.

Insley, Peter, "Flying Halloween Witch," *The Physics Teacher*, October, 1988, p. 476.

Kruglak, H., "Swimming Pool Optics," *The Physics Teacher*, October, 1987, p. 440.

Linas, C.F., "Building a Telescope," *The Science Teacher*, December, 1988, pp. 33–34.

Miller, Jr., Franklin, *College Physics*, Harcourt Brace

Ouseph, P. J., "How Many Fish Are in the Tank?" *The Physics Teacher*, October, 1987, p. 440.

Background

It is interesting to consider the structure of other types of telescopes in addition to the astronomical telescope mentioned in the text. The largest telescopes use a concave mirror instead of an objective lens to form the real image. The concave mirror has the advantage of being much lighter than a lens and being free of chromatic aberration. Spherical aberration in the mirror is avoided by making the mirror parabolic rather than spherical. The larger telescopes have the advantage of having less fuzziness due to diffraction, and they can gather more light for a brighter image.

Radio telescopes use electromagnetic radiation of 10^{-3} m or more. The incoming radiation is focused on a receiving antenna at the focal point of a parabolic mirror.

Chapter Review

QUESTIONS

1. Image is erect, virtual, as far in back of the mirror as the object is in front of the mirror and the same size as the object. It is best to note that the image is not truly reversed in the full sense of the word but only appears to be reversed. Actually the correct optical term is that the image is perverted which refers to the same effect as is achieved when a rubber mask is turned inside-out.

2. The image will be between C and F, will be inverted, real, and smaller than the object.

3. The image will be at C, inverted, real, and the same size as the object.

4. The image will be beyond C, inverted, real, and larger than the object.

5. A virtual image cannot be cast upon a screen while a real image can. The rays that form a virtual image only appear to originate at the location of the image and actually originate elsewhere. The rays that form a real image do originate at the position of the image.

6. Object is between F and the mirror.

7. The image in a convex mirror is always virtual, erect, smaller than the object, and located closer to the mirror than the object.

8. All virtual images are erect and are the result of divergent rays.

9. The index of refraction of the material from which the lens is made determines focus.

10. The image will be between F and $2F$, inverted, real, and smaller than the object.

11. Light passing through a lens is slightly dispersed causing objects viewed through the lens to appear ringed with color. This effect is called chromatic aberration.

12. Rays parallel to the axis which strike the edges of a concave spherical mirror are not reflected through the focal point. This effect is called spherical aberration.

13. Convex mirrors are used as rearview mirrors on school buses. A convex mirror allows for a wide range of view allowing the driver to see a much larger area about the bus than is afforded by ordinary mirrors.

APPLYING CONCEPTS

1. concave with object beyond focal point

2. concave with object beyond center of curvature, convex with object anywhere

3. a. convex mirror
   b. It provides a wider field of view.

4. convex with object beyond focal point

5. No. Focal length depends only on law of reflection which is independent of index of refraction.

6. Yes. Refraction depends on difference in refractive indices at interface. Focal length will be increased.

7. a. infinity
   b. Yes; $\frac{1}{d_o} + \frac{1}{d_i} = \frac{1}{f} = 0$
   $d_i = -d_o$

8. No; the rays do not converge at a virtual image.

9. The film is run through the projector upside-down, so to speak.

EXERCISES

1. a.

b. $f = \dfrac{r}{2} = \dfrac{16.0 \text{ cm}}{2} = 8.0 \text{ cm}$

$\dfrac{1}{d_o} + \dfrac{1}{d_i} = \dfrac{1}{f}$

$d_i = \dfrac{f d_o}{(d_o - f)} = \dfrac{(8.0 \text{ cm})(16.0 \text{ cm})}{16.0 \text{ cm} - 8.0 \text{ cm}}$

$= 16.0 \text{ cm}$

c. $m = \dfrac{-d_i}{d_o} = \dfrac{-16.0 \text{ cm}}{16.0 \text{ cm}} = -1.0$

d. $m = \dfrac{h_i}{h_o}, \; h_i = m h_o = (-1.0)(15 \text{ mm})$

$= -15 \text{ mm}$

2. a.

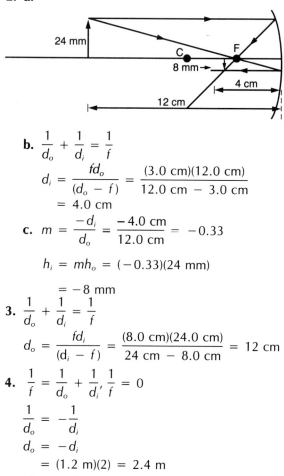

b. $\dfrac{1}{d_o} + \dfrac{1}{d_i} = \dfrac{1}{f}$

$d_i = \dfrac{f d_o}{(d_o - f)} = \dfrac{(3.0 \text{ cm})(12.0 \text{ cm})}{12.0 \text{ cm} - 3.0 \text{ cm}}$

$= 4.0 \text{ cm}$

c. $m = \dfrac{-d_i}{d_o} = \dfrac{-4.0 \text{ cm}}{12.0 \text{ cm}} = -0.33$

$h_i = m h_o = (-0.33)(24 \text{ mm})$

$= -8 \text{ mm}$

3. $\dfrac{1}{d_o} + \dfrac{1}{d_i} = \dfrac{1}{f}$

$d_o = \dfrac{f d_i}{(d_i - f)} = \dfrac{(8.0 \text{ cm})(24.0 \text{ cm})}{24 \text{ cm} - 8.0 \text{ cm}} = 12 \text{ cm}$

4. $\dfrac{1}{f} = \dfrac{1}{d_o} + \dfrac{1}{d_i}, \dfrac{1}{f} = 0$

$\dfrac{1}{d_o} = -\dfrac{1}{d_i}$

$d_o = -d_i$

$= (1.2 \text{ m})(2) = 2.4 \text{ m}$

5. The ray from top of head hits mirror halfway between eyes and top of head. Ray from feet hits mirror halfway between eyes and feet. Distance between the point the two rays hit the mirror is half the total height.

6. a.

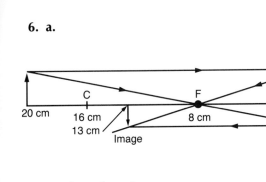

b. $\dfrac{1}{d_o} + \dfrac{1}{d_i} = \dfrac{1}{f}$

$d_i = \dfrac{d_o f}{d_o - f} = \dfrac{(20.0 \text{ cm})(8.0 \text{ cm})}{20.0 \text{ cm} - 8.0 \text{ cm}}$

$= 13 \text{ cm}$

7. a.

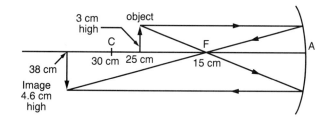

b. $\dfrac{1}{d_o} + \dfrac{1}{d_i} = \dfrac{1}{f}$

$d_i = \dfrac{d_o f}{(d_o - f)} = \dfrac{(25 \text{ cm})(15 \text{ cm})}{25 \text{ cm} - 15 \text{ cm}} = 38 \text{ cm}$

$\dfrac{h_i}{h_o} = \dfrac{-d_i}{d_o}$

$h_i = \dfrac{-d_i h_o}{d_o} = \dfrac{-(38 \text{ cm})(3.0 \text{ cm})}{25 \text{ cm}}$

$= -4.6 \text{ cm}$

8. a. $\dfrac{1}{d_o} + \dfrac{1}{d_i} = \dfrac{1}{f}$

$d_i = \dfrac{d_o f}{d_o - f} =$

$\dfrac{(30.0 \text{ cm})(15 \text{ cm})}{30.0 \text{ cm} - 15 \text{ cm}} = 3.0 \times 10^1 \text{ cm}$

b. $\dfrac{h_i}{h_o} = \dfrac{-d_i}{d_o}$

$h_i = \dfrac{-d_i h_o}{d_o} = \dfrac{-(3.0 \times 10^1 \text{ cm})(1.8 \text{ cm})}{30.0 \text{ cm}}$

$= -1.8 \text{ cm}$

9. a. $\dfrac{1}{d_o} + \dfrac{1}{d_i} = \dfrac{1}{f}$

$d_i = \dfrac{d_o f}{d_o - f} = \dfrac{(8.0 \text{ cm})(12 \text{ cm})}{8.0 \text{ cm} - 12.0 \text{ cm}}$

$= -24 \text{ cm}$

b. $\dfrac{h_i}{h_o} = \dfrac{-d_i}{d_o}$

$h_i = \dfrac{-d_i h_o}{d_o} = \dfrac{-(-24 \text{ cm})(3.0 \text{ cm})}{8.0 \text{ cm}}$

$= +9.0 \text{ cm}$

10. $\dfrac{1}{d_o} + \dfrac{1}{d_i} = \dfrac{1}{f}$

$d_i = \dfrac{d_o f}{d_o - f} = \dfrac{(3.0 \text{ m})(-0.16 \text{ m})}{3.0 \text{ m} - (-0.16 \text{ m})}$

$= -0.15 \text{ m} = -15 \text{ cm}$

11. $\dfrac{1}{d_o} + \dfrac{1}{d_i} = \dfrac{1}{f}$

$d_i = \dfrac{d_o f}{d_o - f}$

$= \dfrac{(8.0 \text{ cm})(30.0 \text{ cm})}{8.0 \text{ cm} - 30.0 \text{ cm}} = -11 \text{ cm}$

12. $\dfrac{1}{d_o} + \dfrac{1}{d_i} = \dfrac{1}{f}$

$d_i = \dfrac{d_o f}{d_o - f} = \dfrac{(10.0 \text{ m})(-0.060 \text{ m})}{10.0 \text{ m} - (-0.060 \text{ m})}$

$= -0.060 \text{ m} = -6.0 \text{ cm}$

13. a. $\dfrac{1}{d_o} + \dfrac{1}{d_i} = \dfrac{1}{f}$

$d_i = \dfrac{d_o f}{d_o - f} = \dfrac{(40.0 \text{ cm})(25.0 \text{ cm})}{40.0 \text{ cm} - 25.0 \text{ cm}}$

$= 66.7 \text{ cm}$

b. $\dfrac{h_i}{h_o} = \dfrac{d_i}{d_o}$

$h_i = \dfrac{d_i h_o}{d_o} = \dfrac{(66.7 \text{ cm})(h_o)}{40.0 \text{ cm}} = 1.67 \, h_o$

14. a. $r = 20 \text{ cm}, f = -10 \text{ cm}$

$\dfrac{1}{d_o} + \dfrac{1}{d_i} = \dfrac{1}{f}$

$d_i = \dfrac{f d_o}{(d_o - f)} = \dfrac{(-10.0 \text{ cm})(1.5 \text{ m})}{1.5 \text{ m} - (-10.0 \text{ cm})}$

$= -9.4 \text{ cm}$

b. $m = \dfrac{h_i}{h_o} = \dfrac{-d_i}{d_o} = \dfrac{-(-9.4 \text{ cm})}{(1.5 \text{ m})} = +0.063$

$h_i = m h_o = (0.063)(12 \text{ cm}) = 0.75 \text{ cm}$

15. $\dfrac{1}{d_o} + \dfrac{1}{d_i} = \dfrac{1}{f} = \dfrac{1}{25\text{ cm}} + \dfrac{1}{20\text{ cm}} = \dfrac{1}{11\text{ cm}}$

$f = 11\text{ cm}$

16. a. $\dfrac{1}{d_o} + \dfrac{1}{d_i} = \dfrac{1}{f}$

$d_i = \dfrac{fd_o}{(d_o - f)} = \dfrac{(13.5\text{ cm})(75.0\text{ cm})}{75.0\text{ cm} - 13.5\text{ cm}}$

$= 16.5\text{ cm}$

b. $h = \dfrac{d_i h_o}{d_o} = \dfrac{(16.5\text{ cm})(4.5\text{ cm})}{75.0\text{ cm}} = 9.9\text{ mm}$

17. From the lens equation, if d_o is decreased while f is constant, then d_i must increase.

18. Longer; $m = \dfrac{d_i}{d_o}$, so to increase m with d_o fixed, you increase d_i. From the lens equation, this means increasing f.

PROBLEMS

1. a. $\dfrac{1}{d_o} + \dfrac{1}{d_i} = \dfrac{1}{f}$

$d_i = \dfrac{d_o f}{(d_o - f)} = \dfrac{(12.0\text{ mm})(10.00\text{ mm})}{12.0\text{ mm} - 10.0\text{ mm}}$

$= 60.0\text{ mm}$

b. $m_o = \dfrac{-d_i}{d_o} = \dfrac{-60.0\text{ mm}}{12.0\text{ mm}} = -5.0$

c. $\dfrac{1}{d_o} + \dfrac{1}{d_i} = \dfrac{1}{f}$

$d_i = \dfrac{d_o f}{(d_o - f)} = \dfrac{(10.0\text{ mm})(20.0\text{ mm})}{10.0\text{ mm} - 20.0\text{ mm}}$

$= -20.0\text{ mm}$

d. $m_e = \dfrac{-d_i}{d_o} = \dfrac{-(-20.0\text{ mm})}{10.0\text{ mm}} = 2.00$

$m_{total} = (m_o)(m_e) = (-5.0)(2.00) = -10.0$

2. $\dfrac{1}{d_o} + \dfrac{1}{d_i} = \dfrac{1}{f}$

$d_i = \dfrac{d_o f}{(d_o - f)} = \dfrac{(16\text{ mm})(20\text{ mm})}{16\text{ mm} - 20\text{ mm}} = -80\text{ mm}$

$m = \dfrac{-d_i}{d_o} = \dfrac{-(-80\text{ mm})}{16\text{ mm}} = 5$

3. a. $\dfrac{1}{d_o} + \dfrac{1}{d_i} = \dfrac{1}{f}$

$d_i = \dfrac{d_o f}{d_o - f} = \dfrac{(3.0 \times 10^3\text{ mm})(50.0\text{ mm})}{3.0 \times 10^3\text{ mm} - 50.0\text{ mm}}$

$= 5.0 \times 10^1\text{ mm}$

$= 5.0\text{ cm}$

b. $\dfrac{1}{d_o} + \dfrac{1}{d_i} = \dfrac{1}{f}$

$d_i = \dfrac{d_o f}{d_o - f} = \dfrac{(125\text{ m})(1.00\text{ m})}{125\text{ m} - 1.00\text{ m}} = 1.00\text{ m}$

$= 1.00 \times 10^3\text{ mm}$

4. $\dfrac{h_i}{h_o} = \dfrac{-d_i}{d_o}$

$h_i = \dfrac{-d_i h_o}{d_o} = \dfrac{-(5.0\text{ cm})(0.50\text{ m})}{3.0\text{ m}} = -8.3\text{ mm}$

5. The image is the way another person sees you; left ear on right side.

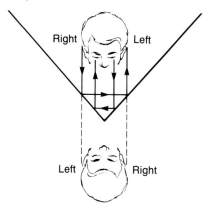

6. Total distance is $L_1 + L_2 + L_3$, which is twice the distance between the mirrors, less the thickness of your head.

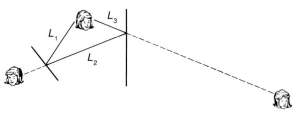

7. An enlarged, upright image only results from a concave mirror with object inside of the focal length.

$m = \dfrac{-d_i}{d_o}$

$d_i = -md_o = -(7.5)(14.0\text{ mm}) = -105\text{ mm}$

$\dfrac{1}{d_o} + \dfrac{1}{d_i} = \dfrac{1}{f}$

$f = \dfrac{d_o d_i}{(d_i + d_o)} = \dfrac{(14.0\text{ mm})(-105\text{ mm})}{14.0\text{ mm} - 105\text{ mm}}$

$= 16.2\text{ mm}$

radius of curvature $= (2)(16.2\text{ mm}) = 32.4\text{ mm}$

8. An enlarged, upright image requires a convex lens with the object inside the focal length.

$$m = \frac{-d_i}{d_o}$$

$$d_i = -md_o = -(7.5)(14.0 \text{ mm}) = -105 \text{ mm}$$

$$\frac{1}{d_o} + \frac{1}{d_i} = \frac{1}{f}$$

$$f = \frac{d_o d_i}{(d_i + d_o)} = \frac{(14.0 \text{ mm})(-105 \text{ mm})}{14.0 \text{ mm} - 105 \text{ mm}}$$

$$= 16.2 \text{ mm}$$

9.

$$\frac{h_i}{h_o} = \frac{DG}{AP} = \frac{GO}{OP} = \frac{d_i}{d_o} \text{ and } \frac{h_i}{h_o} = \frac{d_i}{d_o}$$

The shaded triangles FGD and FOB are similar. Since $BO = PA = h_o$,

$$\frac{GF}{OF} = \frac{DG}{BO} = \frac{h_i}{h_o} = \frac{d_i}{d_o} \text{ so, } \frac{GF}{OF} = \frac{d_i}{d_o}$$

But, $OF = f$ and $OG = d_i$, so the length of GF can be found from

$$GF = d_i - f$$

Substituting f for OF and $d_i - f$ for GF yields

$$\frac{GF}{OF} = \frac{d_i - f}{f} = \frac{d_i}{d_o} \text{ or } d_o d_i - f d_o = f d_i$$

Rearranging and dividing both sides by $f d_i d_o$ gives the lens equation

$$\frac{1}{d_o} + \frac{1}{d_i} = \frac{1}{f}$$

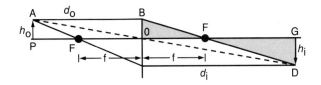

CHAPTER 20

Diffraction and Interference of Light

Overview

Diffraction and interference are the most important properties of waves. An understanding of how these effects occur is important not only to the study of light but also to the study of modern physics as presented in later chapters. This chapter presents a quantitative treatment of diffraction and interference that introduces students to the methods used in finding the wavelength of light or other forms of electromagnetic radiation. Interference from a single slit, double slit, and diffraction grating are all discussed. Changes in the diffraction pattern are shown as variables, such as the distance between adjacent slits, or the wavelength of light passed through a grating, are varied. The effect of diffraction on the resolving power of telescopes and microscopes is studied.

Planning Guide (5 Class Sessions)

Text Section	Demonstrations and Experiments	Other Program Components	
20:1 The Two-Slit Interference Pattern **P** 20:2 Measuring the Wavelength of a Light Wave **P**	Dem 20:1 Diffraction of Laser Light, Double-Slit Interference Exp 36 Measuring the Wavelengths of Light Waves **LM**	Teaching Master 20-1: (a) Formation of Interference Patterns **TRP** Teaching Master 20-2: (a) Double-Slit Interference (b) Single-Slit Interference **TRP** Demonstration 20-1: Interference of Paper Waves **TRP** Demonstration 20-3: Patterns on the Overhead Projector **TRP** Enrichment 20-1: Problems **TRP** Enrichment 20-2: Resolving Power of Telescopes and Microscopes **TRP** Enrichment 20-3: Diffraction and Interference **TRP**	
20:3 Single-Slit Diffraction **P** 20:4 Diffraction Gratings **P** 20:5 Resolving Power of Lenses **S**	Dem 20:3 Single-Slit Diffraction Dem 20:4 Diffraction Patterns, Diffraction Measurements	Teaching Master 20-1: (b) Spectrometer **TRP** Review Masters **TRP** Minilab 20-1: Diffraction Patterns— A Take-Home Lab **TRP** Demonstration 20-2: Diffraction Patterns with a Laser **TRP** Evaluation **TRP**	

Performance Objectives

Upon completion of this chapter, your students will

1. define diffraction of light using the wave model. *20:1*

2. display an understanding of how two slits produce a pattern of light and dark bands from the constructive and destructive interference of light waves. *20:1*

3. understand the geometry of interference from two slits; use the derived equation to calculate the wavelength of light waves. *20:2*

4. use geometry to explain how single-slit diffraction patterns occur; use the derived equation to relate the width of the pattern to slit width and light wavelength. *20:3*

5. explain the improvement in the diffraction pattern formed by a diffraction grating over two slits; understand the operation of a spectrometer. *20:4*

6. explain how diffraction effects cause a small lens to have limited resolution. *20:5*

Teaching the Chapter

Introduction

Using the Photo: Ridges in the butterfly's wing act as a diffraction grating. Multiple reflections from the ridges on the butterfly's wings create interference of the incident light. The effective optical thickness of the ridges and spaces between them is 225 nm or one-half of the observed 450 nm blue light. The intense blue color is seen as a result of constructive interference.

This photograph can be used with Section 20:1 to discuss the two-slit interference pattern.

Demonstration: Darken the room and shine a laser beam through a glass brick, a piece of shower door glass, or some other irregular piece of glass. Interesting patterns appear on the wall due to the diffraction and interference of the light rays.

20:1 The Two-Slit Interference Pattern

Demonstration: Place the ripple tank apparatus over an overhead projector and demonstrate the interference pattern that results from two slits or two point sources. Light waves behave in the same manner as these water waves.

Have students observe the interference patterns of light. Cut two slits as close together as possible in a 3" × 5" card or in exposed film. Pass around a double slit to each of your students. Darken the room and have students look at the filament of a showcase lamp. They can adjust the width of the slits by gently pulling on the edges of the card or film. Students observe several images of the filament as fringes along the edge of the bulb. The spacing of the fringes depends on the width of the slits.

Tape some red, clear, and blue plastic together so it can be placed in front of the filament and the light shines through all three pieces at the same time. Have students view the filament through the slits and observe the spacing between the fringes. Note how the spacing changes with the wavelength of light.

20:2 Measuring the Wavelength of a Light Wave

Have students do the lab "Measuring the Wavelengths of Light Waves" in *Laboratory Physics* to determine the identity of an unknown element. Obtain a spectrum chart and several different gas discharge tubes. Remove the labels from the tubes and replace them with numbers. Keep a key for yourself. Have students find the wavelength of as many lines in the spectrum as possible and match the pattern to one in the spectrum chart. The wavelengths may not agree exactly, but the students will be able to see a pattern and by process of elimination determine the identity of their unknown.

20:3 Single-Slit Diffraction

A simple variable width slit for studying single-slit diffraction can be made in the following way using two microscope slides, two single-edged razor blades, and some black electrical tape. Position the two razor blades with their edges together and sandwich them between the two microscope slides so the slit is parallel to the long side of the microscope slide. Wind electrical tape around each end of the pair of glass slides to keep them tight and to protect students against the sharp edge of the slide. The students can vary the slit width and observe the change in the width of the central maximum while viewing the filament of a showcase light bulb.

20:4 Diffraction Gratings

Inexpensive sheets of acetate film diffraction grating can be obtained from Edmund Scientific Co., 101

E. Gloucester Pike, Barrington, NJ, 08007-1380. Mount small pieces in slide holders and give them to your students so they can experiment on their own. Encourage them to look at different kinds of lights at night and share their findings. To make viewing a little easier, students can cut a 1 mm wide slot in the end of a toothpaste tube box and a 1 cm square hole in the other end. Put the diffraction grating over the square hole with the slits parallel to the slot in the box. View different light sources through the grating end of the box.

Demonstration: Diffraction patterns can be made from many everyday objects and a laser. Mount a finely marked ruler horizontally. Darken the room and aim the laser beam so it just grazes the ruler and illuminates about 3 cm of the ruler surface. Have a screen about 2 meters away and observe the diffraction pattern. Other objects that make interesting diffraction patterns are handkerchiefs, the eye of a needle, and wire gauze.

Demonstration: A laser can be used to find the spacing between the grooves on a 33-rpm record. Set a laser on a desk top and shine it on a record held vertically by a ring stand about 4 m from the laser. Put a piece of white paper on the wall as a screen for the light pattern. Measure the distance from the record to the screen (L) and the spacing between the maxima on the white paper (Δx). Calculate the spacing between the grooves (d) using the equation $d = \lambda L / \Delta x$. Use the wavelength of the light laser for λ. The calculation can be checked by using the frequency of revolution, 33 1/3 rpm, the width of the band used, and the playing time given for the band in the equation

$$d = \frac{\text{width of the band}}{(\text{frequency}) (\text{time for band})}$$

Resources

Literature

Anderson, Frank A., "Drawing Wave Diagrams for the Interference of Light," *The Physics Teacher*, March, 1973, p. 175.

Hirschman, Samuel, "Diffraction of Light Apparatus," *The Physics Teacher*, March, 1976, pp. 180-181.

Welty, Scott R., "Long-Playing Diffraction Grating," *The Physics Teacher*, March, 1981, p. 187.

Background

The resolving power of a microscope or telescope can be improved by either increasing the diameter of the lens or using shorter wavelength light. The lens serves as an opening for the light and actually behaves like a slit. The angular size of the central maximum of the pattern can be found using the equation $\theta_r = \lambda / .82\, D$, where λ is the wavelength of light shining on the lens and D is the lens diameter. The 0.82 D is the equivalent slit width for a lens of diameter D. This means that a parallel beam of light refracted by a lens does not produce a point image but gives a diffuse pattern whose angular radius is $\lambda / .82\, D$. To reduce the angular radius, the wavelength can be made smaller by using UV light. However, since glass does not transmit UV light, expensive quartz lenses would have to be used. X-ray microscopes have better resolving power, but conventional lenses are not usable, and complex mirror systems must be used. The small value of λ for electrons makes the electron microscope a very high resolution instrument, which can magnify 100 to 1000 times more than a visible light microscope.

Chapter Review

QUESTIONS

1. All wavelengths produce the line in the same place.

2. Decrease d or increase L.

3. A double-slit pattern consists of equally spaced lines of almost equal brightness. A single-slit pattern has a bright, broad central band and dimmer side bands.

4. The bands get wider and dimmer.

5. The interference pattern will be spread further apart for the 10^5 lines/cm grating.

6. the color with the smallest wavelength, violet

7. one-half the wavelength of the color

8. A full spectrum of color is seen. Because of the variety of wavelengths, dark fringes of one wavelength would be filled by bright fringes of another color.

9. by bending and spreading out waves allowing them to be received in more places

10. Diffraction gratings increase the intensity of the interference patterns, thereby producing stronger, sharper images of light that may otherwise be too faint to see.

11. Let the light fall on the double slit, and let the interference pattern fall on a sheet of paper. Measure the spacings between the bright bands, x, and use the equation

$$d = \lambda L / x$$

APPLYING CONCEPTS

1. Diffraction is most pronounced around obstacles approximately the same size as the wavelength of the wave. In our everyday experience, we do not encounter obstacles as small as would be required for the diffraction of light. We are more accustomed to obstacles of the size that diffract the much larger wavelengths of sound.

2. **a.** refraction **d.** refraction **f.** pigments
   b. refraction **e.** refraction **g.** diffraction
   c. pigments

3. Small apertures have large diffraction patterns that limit resolution.

4. The ridges act as a diffraction grating. Any blue light of wavelength approximately 4.40×10^{-7} m is reflected strongly from this grating.

5. Many diffraction gratings have a separation of about 2-4 times the wavelength they are being used with. A picket fence having a separation of about 10 cm could be used with wavelengths of about 30 cm or 0.3 m which is a longer wavelength microwave.

6. **a.** Loud, you are equidistant from the two speakers, so there is always reinforcement.
   b. The difference in distance from the two speakers is 1.0 m. The 1-m sound will be reinforced and will be loud; the 2-m wavelength sound will suffer destructive interference and be quiet.

EXERCISES

1. Students' diagrams should resemble Figure 20-1a on page 342.

2. $\lambda = xd / L$
   $= (1.90 \times 10^{-2}$ m$)(1.90 \times 10^{-5}$ m$)/0.800$ m
   $= 4.51 \times 10^{-7}$ m $= 451$ nm

3. $d = \lambda L / x$
   $= (5.42 \times 10^{-7}$ m$)(1.20$ m$)/4.00 \times 10^{-2}$ m
   $= 1.63 \times 10^{-5}$ m

4. $d = 1/(2.50 \times 10^3$ lines/cm$)$
   $= 4.00 \times 10^{-4}$ cm

5. $\lambda = xd / L$
   $= (1.65 \times 10^{-1}$ m$)(4.00 \times 10^{-6}$ m$)/1.00$ m
   $= 6.60 \times 10^{-7}$ m $= 660$ nm

PROBLEMS

1. $y = \dfrac{vL}{fw} = \dfrac{(330 \text{ m/s})(12 \text{ m})}{(550 \text{ Hz})(1.2 \text{ m})} = 6.0$ m
   The people are located 6.0 m to either side of the center of the wall opposite the window.

2. **a.** $\lambda = \dfrac{v}{f} = \dfrac{(3.0 \times 10^8 \text{ m/s})}{(600 \times 10^3 \text{ Hz})} = 500$ m
   b. The path difference is 19 500 m $-$ 17 500 m $= 2000$ m. The reception should be good since it is a multiple of the wavelength, so constructive interference will take place.

3. $y = (5.5 \times 10^{-7}$ m$)(0.050$ m$)/6.25 \times 10^{-3}$ m
   $= 4.4 \times 10^{-6}$ m

4. Band width is 4.4×10^{-3} mm. Coarse grains are $1/50$ mm $= 2.0 \times 10^{-2}$ mm, fine grains are $1/2000$ mm $= 5 \times 10^{-3}$ mm. Coarse is good enough.

5. $y = (5.45 \times 10^{-7}$ m$)(0.025$ m$)/3.0 \times 10^{-3}$ m
   $= 4.6 \times 10^{-6}$ m

6. $(4.6 \times 10^{-6}$ m$)/(1.5 \times 10^{-6}$ m/cell$) = 3$ cells. You need about 3 cells to tell light and dark edges. It would do no good to increase the resolution of the eye by using a larger iris because resolution is limited by cone separation in the retina.

7. $y = (5.00 \times 10^{-7}$ m$) (1 \times 10^5$ m$)/2.4$ m
   $= 2$ cm

8. **a.** $d = (4.0$ m$)(6.3 \times 10^{-7}$ m$)/0.021$ m
   $= 1.2 \times 10^{-4}$ m
   There are $1/1.2 \times 10^{-4}$ m $= 8.3 \times 10^3$ grooves/m, or 83 grooves/cm.
   b. Number of grooves is $(4.01$ min$)(33.333$ rev/min$) = 134$ grooves. $(134$ grooves$)/(1.6$ cm$)$
   $= 84$ grooves/cm.

9. $\lambda = y/f = (343$ m/s$)/325$ Hz $= 1.06$ m
   $x = \lambda L/d = (1.06$ m$)(4.5$ m$)/4.0$ m $= 1.2$ m

10. $\sin \theta = \lambda/d$;
    $d = 1/1.2 \times 10^4$ cm $= 8.33 \times 10^{-7}$ m
    red: $\sin \theta = 6.32 \times 10^{-7}$ m$/8.33 \times 10^{-7}$ m
    $= 0.76$; $\theta = 49°$
    blue: $\sin \theta = 4.21 \times 10^{-7}$ m$/8.33 \times 10^{-7}$ m
    $= 0.51$; $\theta = 30°$

CHAPTER 21

Electrostatics

Overview

Electrons around the positively charged nucleus can be transferred, causing a body to become positively or negatively charged. When charge is added to an insulator, it stays in one place; when it is added to a conductor, it spreads out all over. Like charges repel and unlike charges attract. A neutral object is attracted to either charge because the charged object induces separation of charge in the neutral object.

An electroscope can be used to determine the charge on an object. The electroscope is given a known charge. If a like charge is brought near the electroscope, its leaves spread farther apart, while an opposite charge brought near will cause the leaves to collapse. The force of attraction or repulsion is described by Coulomb's law.

Planning Guide (6 Class Sessions)

Text Section		Demonstrations and Experiments		Other Program Components	
21:1 The Electrical Atom	P	Dem 21:1 Electrostatic Air Cleaner		Teaching Master 21-1:	
21:2 Transferring Electrons	P	Exp 37 Static Electricity	LM	(a) Charging by Conduction and	
21:3 Conductors, Insulators, and		Exp 38 Coulomb's Law	LM	Induction	
Semiconductors	S	Dem 21:3 Insulator or Conductor			
21:4 Forces on Charged Bodies	P	Dem 21:4 ML-1, Repulsion of Like		Teaching Master 21-1:	
21:5 Charging by Induction	S	Charges, Homemade Electrostatic Devices		(b) Separation of Charge	TRP
				Minilab 21-1: Electrostatics	TRP
		Dem 21:5 Induction Versus Conduction		Demonstration 21-1: Using a	
				Van de Graaff Generator	TRP
				Demonstration 21-2:	
				Bending Water	TRP
21:6 Coulomb's Law	P	Dem 21:8 Charged Bodies Attract		Teaching Master 21-2:	
21:7 The Unit of Charge: The		Neutral Bodies		(a) Coulomb's Law	
Coulomb	P			(b) Electrostatic and Gravitational	
21:8 Forces on Neutral Bodies	S			Forces	TRP
				Review Masters	TRP
				Enrichment 21-1: Problems	TRP
				Enrichment 21-2: Lightning	TRP
				Evaluation	TRP

Performance Objectives

Upon completion of this chapter, your students will

1. outline the structure of the atom; know the charges on electron and proton; understand how charging occurs. *21:1*

2. know that charging is separation, not creation of charge. *21:2*

3. state the differences between conductors, insulators, and semiconductors. *21:3*

4. be able to summarize the observed forces between charged bodies; know how an electroscope detects the presence of charge and how an object is charged by conduction. *21:4*

5. explain separation of charge and charging by induction. *21:5*

6. state Coulomb's law and how the force depends on charges and their separation. *21:6*

7. state the SI unit of charge; understand the vector nature of the electric force; solve problems using Coulomb's law. *21:7*

8. understand the cause of the attractive force on neutral objects; list examples of this force. *21:8*

Teaching the Chapter

Introduction

Using the Photo: Charging by induction occurs. Negative charges on the bottoms of clouds induce a positive charge on the surface of Earth below the clouds. Most lightning that is seen is an electrical discharge between oppositely charged clouds and the ground.

This photograph can be used with Section 21:2 on transferring electrons, Section 21:5 on charging by induction, and Section 21:7 on the coulomb.

Demonstration: You can demonstrate the principle used in an electrostatic air cleaner using a Van de Graaff generator. Place a grounded point 15-20 cm from the dome of the generator and put a source of smoke between the bottom of the point and generator. The smoke will rise as it becomes charged by ions leaving the point. The particles are attracted to the dome.

Note: Electrostatic demonstrations do not work well in humid weather. For best results schedule this topic in dry weather. **CAUTION:** *Do not let students experiment with the generator unless supervised. Anyone with a medical heart problem should not work with the generator.*

21:2 Transferring Electrons

Emphasize that objects become charged by the transfer of electrons: adding excess electrons for a negative charge or the removal of electrons, creating a deficiency, for a positive charge. Protons are not transferred by ordinary means.

21:3 Conductors, Insulators, and Semiconductors

Demonstration: Charge an electroscope with a negatively charged rod, such as a rubber rod rubbed with fur. To show that some things are conductors and others are insulators, touch the electroscope with a glass rod. Nothing will happen because glass is an insulator. Touch the electroscope with a metal rod and it will discharge. Ask students to explain this result.

21:4 Forces on Charged Bodies

Emphasize the importance of making and recording accurate observations and differentiating between observations and explanations or interpretations. When students do the electrostatics lab, they observe objects moving toward or away from each other. They may hear a click or see something stick to a rod and then fall off. They do not see electrons flowing. Use the concept of electron flow in the interpretation.

Demonstration: To charge two objects similarly, hang two balloons from the ceiling and rub them each with fur. Students will observe that the balloons move away from one another and stay away. Point out that since you did the same thing to both balloons, you can assume the charge is similar and that like charges repel. Discuss students' observations and conclusions.

Demonstration: A simple electrophorous can be made by taping a polystyrene cup upside down on a metal disposable pie plate. Place a polystyrene plate upside down on a table and rub it with fur. Place the metal pie plate on top of the polystyrene plate using the cup for a handle. Touch the metal plate with your finger, remove your finger, and lift up the plate. It is now highly charged and can be used to charge an electroscope or pith balls. A paper clip with several pieces of fine string about 15 cm long can be attached to the pie plate and become charged.

Pith balls can be made by cutting a strip of aluminum foil the length of a plastic straw. Cut the foil wide enough to go around the straw one time and overlap a little. Rub the foil with a glue stick and glue the foil to the straw. Cut the straw into pieces one centimeter in length. Before the glue dries, roll back the foil and lay one end of a piece of thread in the foil and fasten it again. You now have a pith ball on a thread.

A simple electroscope can be made by taking an empty pop can and pulling the tab out so it is perpendicular to the top of the can. Turn a polystyrene cup upside down and lay the can on its side on top of the cup so the tab is horizontal. Cut a strip of aluminum foil about 0.5 cm wide and 5 cm long. Make a curve on one end and insert the end into the hole in the pop can tab so the foil can swing freely. Test it by bringing a charged rod near the can and see if the foil moves. Make the necessary adjustments until it moves.

21:5 Charging by Induction

Demonstration: Charge a rubber rod with fur and bring it near an electroscope. Have students tell what they observe. The leaves separate and then drop back again. Now touch the electroscope with the rod. You may want to rub the middle of the rod on the electroscope for the best charge transfer. Students will notice that the leaves diverge and stay that way when you take the rod away.

Emphasize that the results are very different when you bring a charged object *near* the electroscope as opposed to *touching* it. Touching the electroscope causes a transfer of electrons. As a result, the electroscope acquires a like charge. Bringing a charged rod near the electroscope causes a separation of charge that disappears as soon as the rod is removed. Charging by conduction means there is contact. Induction means there is no contact and therefore no transfer of charge.

21:6 Coulomb's Law

Electrostatic forces can be calculated using Coulomb's law. Point out the similarity between Coulomb's law and Newton's Universal Law of Gravitation; they are both inverse square laws. The electrostatic force is a much larger force than the gravitational force, by as many as 30 orders of magnitude (powers of ten).

Demonstration: Place polystyrene pieces in a polystyrene cup and in a metal cup. Ask students what will happen when the cups are placed on top of the generator. Then test to see what happens. The pieces remain in the metal cup and come bouncing out of the polystyrene cup. Ask what is the difference in the properties of the two cups. One cup is an insulator and the other a conductor. The charge is conducted to the outside of the metal cup but is on both the inside and the outside of the polystyrene cup. Therefore, the pieces in the polystyrene cup develop like charges and repel each other and the cup.

21:8 Forces on Neutral Bodies

Demonstration: There are many excellent demonstrations to do with the Van de Graaff generator. Take a pith ball and suspend it near the generator. It will be attracted and then repelled. Emphasize that neutral bodies are always attracted to charged bodies. Hold your hand a few inches from the generator. Discharge the pith ball and keep your hand near the generator so the pith ball bounces back and forth between your hand and the generator as it becomes charged and then discharged. It will move very quickly.

Resources ━━━━━━━━

Literature

Evans, L., and Stevens, J.T., "Kelvin Water Dropper Revisited," The Physics Teacher, December, 1977, pp. 548, 549.

Johnston, J.B., "Coulomb's Law on the Overhead Projector," The Physics Teacher, January, 1979, pp. 60, 61.

Miller, Jr., Franklin, College Physics, Harcourt Brace Jovanovich, San Diego, 1982, pp. 390-401.

Van Heuvelen, Alan, Physics, A General Introduction, Little, Brown, and Co., Boston, 1982, pp. 443-449.

Zwicker, Earl, "Doing Physics," The Physics Teacher, October, 1987, pp. 469, 470.

Background ━━━━━━━━

Suppose you have three charges arranged as in the diagram. Find the net force on the 2.0×10^{-6} C charge. The charge on the left end will repel it to the right and the charge on the right end will attract it to the right. Find each force individually and add them since they are both in the same direction.

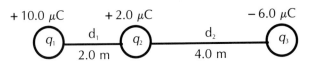

+ 10.0 μC   + 2.0 μC   − 6.0 μC

q_1 d_1 q_2 d_2 q_3

2.0 m   4.0 m

Force of repulsion between q_1 and q_2

$$F_1 = \frac{Kq_1q_2}{d_1^2}$$

$$= \frac{(9.0 \times 10^9 \; \frac{N \cdot m^2}{C^2})(10.0 \times 10^{-6} \; C)(2.0 \times 10^{-6} \; C)}{(2.0 \; m)^2}$$

$F_1 = 4.5 \times 10^{-2}$ N to the right

Force of attraction between q_2 and q_3

$$F_2 = \frac{Kq_2q_3}{d_2^2}$$

$$= \frac{(9.0 \times 10^9 \; \frac{N \cdot m^2}{C^2})(2.0 \times 10^{-6} \; C)(6.0 \times 10^{-6} \; C)}{(4.0 \; m)^2}$$

$F_2 = 6.8 \times 10^{-3}$ N to the right

Total force on q_2

$F_T = F_1 + F_2 = 5.2 \times 10^{-2}$ N to the right

Chapter Review

QUESTIONS

1. No. By conservation of charge, your hair must become negatively charged.

2. Use a known insulator to hold one end of the object against the electroscope. Touch the other end with the charged rod. If the electroscope indicates a charge, the object is a conductor.

3. Insulators: dry air, wood, plastic, glass, cloth, de-ionized water. Conductors: metals, tap water, your body. Semiconductors: silicon, germanium, gallium arsenide, selenium.

4. **a.** The leaves will move farther apart.
   b. The leaves will droop slightly.

5. He charged them while they were touching. They were the same size.

6. Similar: inverse-square dependence on distance, force proportional to product of two masses or charges. Different: only one sign of mass, so always attractive, while two signs of charge, so force is either attractive or repulsive.

7. The electrical force is much larger than the gravitational force.

8. It has been charged during drying.

9. Touching with an already-charged object, friction, or induction.

10. Metals contain free electrons while rubber has bound electrons.

APPLYING CONCEPTS

1. Rubbing it has charged it, and neutral particles are attracted to a charged object.

2. No; net charge is the difference between positive and negative charges. It can be zero.

3. **a.** No; neutral objects are attracted by either charge.
   b. It must be negative. Neutrals are never repelled.

4. Without touching the conductor, bring it close to, but not touching the rod. Then, momentarily touch the side of the conductor farthest from the rod. It will be charged by induction.

5. The charge in the cloud repels electrons on Earth, causing a charge separation. The side of Earth closest to the cloud is positive, resulting in an attractive force.

6. After charging sphere A and B equally, sphere B is touched to two other equally sized balls that are touching. The charge on B will be divided equally among all three balls leaving ⅓ the total charge on it.

7. To have the same force with one third the charge, the distance would have to be decreased such that $d^2 = 1/3$, or 0.58 times as far apart.

8. Ionized air molecules are absorbed by the charged insulator and discharge it.

9. The spheres all acquire the same charge and the same charge as the rod. Therefore, they are repelled from each other and the rod.

EXERCISES

1. $F = Kqq'/d^2 = (9.0 \times 10^9 \; N \cdot m^2/C^2)(1.8 \times 10^{-6} \; C)(-1.0 \times 10^{-6} \; C)/(0.014 \; m)^2 = -83$ N (attractive).

2. a. $2F$ **d.** $4F$

    b. $1/4F$ **e.** $3/4F$

    c. $1/9F$

3. $F = \dfrac{Kqq'}{d^2}$ $K = (9.0 \times 10^9 \text{ N} \cdot \text{m}^2/\text{C}^2)$

$= \dfrac{K(-1.6 \times 10^{-19} \text{ C})(-1.6 \times 10^{-19} \text{ C})}{(1.5 \times 10^{-10} \text{ m})^2}$

$= 1.0 \times 10^{-8} \text{ N}.$

4. $F_1 = \dfrac{Kqq'}{d_1^2} = \dfrac{K(4.5 \times 10^{-6} \text{ C})(4.5 \times 10^{-6} \text{ C})}{(0.04 \text{ m})^2}$

$= 110 \text{ N at } 90°$

The three spheres form a 3-4-5 right triangle, so $d_2 = 0.05 \text{ m}.$

$F_2 = \dfrac{Kqq'}{d_2^2} = \dfrac{K(4.5 \times 10^{-6} \text{ C})(4.5 \times 10^{-6} \text{ C})}{(0.05 \text{ m})^2}$

$= 73 \text{ N at } 37°$

Adding F_1 and F_2 as vectors, the net force is given by

$\sqrt{(110 \text{ N})^2 + (73 \text{ N})^2 - (2)(110 \text{ N})(73 \text{ N})(\cos 143°)}$

$= 170 \text{ N at } 143°.$

5. $F \propto \dfrac{1}{d^2}$ and $F \propto 1/(1/4)^2$, so $F = (16)(0.145 \text{ N})$

$= 2.32 \text{ N}.$

6. $F = Kqq'/d^2$, so $d = \sqrt{Kq^2/F} =$

$\sqrt{(9.0 \times 10^9 \text{ N} \cdot \text{m}^2/\text{C}^2)(1.6 \times 10^{-19} \text{ C})^2/(1.0 \text{ N})^2}$

$= 1.5 \times 10^{-14} \text{ m}$

7. $F = \dfrac{Kqq'}{d^2} = \dfrac{K(1.5 \times 10^{-5} \text{ C})(-1.5 \times 10^{-19} \text{ C})}{(1.5 \times 10^{-2} \text{ m})^2}$

$= -90 \text{ N}$

8. $F = Kq^2/d^2$, so $q = \sqrt{Fd^2/K}$

$= \sqrt{\dfrac{(6.4 \times 10^{-9} \text{ N})(3.8 \times 10^{-10} \text{ m})^2/}{(9.0 \times 10^9 \text{ N} \cdot \text{m}^2/\text{C}^2)}}$

$q = 3.2 \times 10^{-19} \text{ C}.$

9. $(-4.0 \times 10^{-17} \text{ C})/(-1.6 \times 10^{-19} \text{ C/electron})$

$= 250 \text{ electrons}.$

10. $d = \sqrt{Kqq'/F}$

$d = \sqrt{\dfrac{K(8.0 \times 10^{-4} \text{ C})(-3.0 \times 10^{-4} \text{ C})}{(-4.4 \times 10^3 \text{ N})}}$

$= 0.70 \text{ m}.$

11. $F = Kq^2/d^2 =$

$= \dfrac{(9.0 \times 10^9 \text{ N} \cdot \text{m}^2/\text{C})(-5.0 \times 10^{-5} \text{ C})}{(0.20 \text{ m})^2}$

$= 5.6 \times 10^2 \text{ N}.$

12. $F_1 = \dfrac{K(3.0 \times 10^{-6} \text{ C})(-2.0 \times 10^{-6} \text{ C})}{(0.050 \text{ m})^2}$

$= -2.2 \times 10^1 \text{ N, north}.$

$F_2 = \dfrac{K(3.0 \times 10^{-6} \text{ C})(-4.0 \times 10^{-6} \text{ C})}{(0.030 \text{ m})^2}$

$= -1.2 \times 10^2 \text{ N, south}.$

$F = F_2 - F_1$

$= (-1.2 \times 10^2 \text{ N}) - (-2.2 \times 10^1 \text{ N})$

$= -9.8 \times 10^1 \text{ N, south}.$

13. $F = \dfrac{Kq^2}{d^2}$, so $d = \sqrt{Kq^2/F}$

$d = \sqrt{\dfrac{(9.0 \times 10^9 \text{ N} \cdot \text{m}^2/\text{C})(-3.0 \times 10^{-6} \text{ C})}{(2.0 \text{ N})}}$

$= 0.20 \text{ m}.$

PROBLEMS

1. a. $mg = (1.0 \times 10^{-3} \text{ kg})(9.8 \text{ m/s}^2)$

$= 9.8 \times 10^{-3} \text{ N}.$

    b. $\tan 30.0° = \dfrac{F}{mg}$

$F = mg \tan 30.0°$

$= (1.0 \times 10^{-3} \text{ kg})(9.8 \text{ m/s}^2)(\tan 30.0°)$

$= 5.7 \times 10^{-3} \text{ N}.$

    c. $F = \dfrac{Kqq'}{d^2}$

$F = \dfrac{Kq^2}{d^2}$

$q = \sqrt{\dfrac{Fd^2}{K}}$

$= \sqrt{\dfrac{(5.7 \times 10^{-3} \text{ N})(3.0 \times 10^{-2} \text{ m})^2}{(9.0 \times 10^9 \text{ N} \cdot \text{m}^2/\text{C}^2)}}$

$= 2.4 \times 10^{-8} \text{ C}.$

2. The metal ball starts neutral. It is attracted toward the charged bell. When it hits, it becomes charged. The ball is now repelled. It is now attracted to the uncharged bell. It hits this bell discharging the ball. The entire process repeats.

3. a. yes
   b. positive by induction
   c. yes
   d. positive by conduction

4. number of molecules = $(1000 \text{ g})(6.02 \times 10^{23}$ molecules/mole$)/(18 \text{ g/mole})$
   $= 3.3 \times 10^{25}$ molecules
   $q = (1.6 \times 10^{-19} \text{ C/electron})(10 \text{ electrons/molecule})(3.3 \times 10^{25}$ molecules$)$
   $= 5.3 \times 10^{7}$ C.

5. a. $F_{net} = F_1 - F_2 = \dfrac{Kq_mq_l}{d^2} - \dfrac{Kq_mq_r}{d^2}$

$$= \dfrac{K(45 \times 10^{-6} \text{ C})(-67 \times 10^{-6} \text{ C})}{(0.72 \text{ m})^2} -$$
$$\dfrac{K(45 \times 10^{-6} \text{ C})(-83 \times 10^{-6} \text{ C})}{(0.72 \text{ m})^2}$$

   $= 13$ N, to the right.

b. $F_{net} = F_1 - F_2 = \dfrac{Kq_mq_l}{d^2} - \dfrac{Kq_mq_r}{d^2}$

$$= \dfrac{K(-83 \times 10^{-6} \text{ C})(-67 \times 10^{-6} \text{ C})}{(1.44 \text{ m})^2} -$$
$$\dfrac{K(-83 \times 10^{-6} \text{ C})(45 \times 10^{-6} \text{ C})}{(0.72 \text{ m})^2}$$

   $= -41$ N, to the left.

6. a. $(25 \text{ C})/(1.6 \times 10^{-19} \text{ C/electron}) = 1.6 \times 10^{20}$ electrons
   b. $\dfrac{(1.6 \times 10^{20} \text{ elec})(18 \text{ g /mole})}{(6.02 \times 10^{23} \text{ molecules/mole})}$
   $= 5.0 \times 10^{-3}$ g

7. a. A coin is $(5 \text{ g})/(58 \text{ g}) = 0.09$ of a mole. Thus it has $(0.09)(6.02 \times 10^{23}) = 5 \times 10^{22}$ atoms.
   b. $(5 \times 10^{22}$ atoms$)(28$ electrons/atom$) = 1 \times 10^{24}$ electrons
   c. $(1.6 \times 10^{-19}$ coulombs/electron$)(1 \times 10^{24}$ electrons$) = 2 \times 10^5$ coulombs

8. a. given: $q = +7.2 \times 10^{-6}$ C
   $q_1 = +3.6 \times 10^{-6}$ C
   $d_1 = 0.025$ m at 35°
   $q_2 = -6.6 \times 10^{-6}$ C
   $d_2 = 0.068$ m at 125°

   $F = \dfrac{Kq_1q_2}{d^2}$

   F_1 is repulsive, so force acts at $180° + 35° = 215°$
   F_2 is attractive, so force acts at 125°

   $F_1 = \dfrac{K(7.2 \times 10^{-6} \text{ C})(3.6 \times 10^{-6} \text{ C})}{(0.025 \text{ m})^2}$
   $= 3.73 \times 10^2$ N.

   $F_2 = \dfrac{K(7.2 \times 10^{-6} \text{ C})(-6.6 \times 10^{-6} \text{ C})}{(0.068 \text{ m})^2}$
   $= 9.3 \times 10^1$ N.

b. $F_R = 3.84 \times 10^2$ N at 201°.

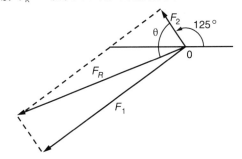

c. $F_R = \sqrt{F_1^2 + F_2^2} = 3.84 \times 10^2$ N
   $\tan \theta = \dfrac{3.73 \times 10^2 \text{ N}}{9.3 \times 10^1 \text{ N}} = 0.070,$
   $\theta = 76°$, angle $= 76° + 125° = 201°$

9. a. $F_C = \dfrac{Kq_1q_2}{d^2}$
   $= \dfrac{(9.0 \times 10^9 \text{ N} \cdot \text{m}^2/\text{C}^2)(1.6 \times 10^{-19} \text{ C})^2}{(5.3 \times 10^{-11} \text{ m})^2}$
   $= 8.2 \times 10^{-8}$ N.

b. $F_g = \dfrac{Gm_1m_2}{d^2}$ $G = 6.7 \times 10^{-11}$ N $\cdot$ m²/kg²

   $= \dfrac{G(9.11 \times 10^{-31} \text{ kg})(1.67 \times 10^{-27} \text{ kg})}{(5.3 \times 10^{-11} \text{ m})^2}$
   $= 3.6 \times 10^{-47}$ N.

c. Gravitational force is weaker by a huge factor of about 10^{39}!

The Electric Field

Overview

The abstract concept of the electric field is presented, using a gravitational field as an analogy. The use of N/C as the unit of electric field intensity reminds the students that the field is defined as force per unit charge.

Electrical potential is compared to gravitational potential. Electrical potential is defined as the change in potential energy of a unit charge in an electric field.

Potential differences are measured in volts.

The Millikan oil drop experiment is a good example of the use of uniform fields produced by parallel plates. Millikan showed that all electrons have the same charge.

Charge sharing is a useful application of energy minimization and describes the grounding process.

Planning Guide (6 Class Sessions)

Text Section		Demonstrations and Experiments	Other Program Components	
22:1 Electric Fields	P	Dem 22:1 Location of Charge		
22:2 Electric Field Intensity	P	Exp 39 Charging and Discharging a Capacitor **LM**		
		Dem 22:2 Electric Field Intensity		
22:3 Energy and the Electric Potential	P	Dem 22:5 Determining a Quantum Number	Teaching Master 22-1: Millikan's Oil Drop Experiment	**TRP**
22:4 The Electric Potential in a Uniform Field	P		Demonstration 22-1: Shielding the Electroscope	**TRP**
22:5 Millikan's Oil Drop Experiment	P		Demonstration 22-2: The Electric Pinwheel	**TRP**
22:6 Sharing of Charge	S	Dem 22:6 Grounding	Teaching Master 22-2: Charge Sharing	**TRP**
22:7 Electric Fields Near Conductors	S	Dem 22:8 Capacitor: Charge Storing	Review Masters	**TRP**
22:8 Storing Charges—The Capacitor	S		Demonstration 22-3: Properties of Capacitors	**TRP**
			Demonstration 22-4: Extent of an Electric Field	**TRP**
			Enrichment 22-1: Problems	**TRP**
			Evaluation	**TRP**

Performance Objectives

Upon completion of this chapter, your students will

1. define an electric field; give the direction of the field; distinguish between the field and field lines. *22:1*

2. relate electric field to the force on a test charge; solve force problems involving the field due to a point charge. *22:2*

3. define the electric potential difference in terms of work done in moving a unit charge; understand the units of potential difference; distinguish potential from potential difference. *22:3*

4. relate electric potential to gravitational potential; solve problems involving uniform electric fields. *22:4*

5. understand the use of electric fields by Millikan to determine the charge of the electron. *22:5*

6. demonstrate an understanding of the role of the

minimization of energy in the sharing of charge; define grounding; relate charge sharing to grounding. *22:6*

7. display an understanding of the location of charges on solid and hollow conductors; recognize the relation between conductor shape and electric field near the conductor. *22:7*

8. define capacitance; explain the principle of the capacitor; solve capacitor problems involving charge and potential difference. *22:8*

Teaching the Chapter

Introduction

Using the Photo: The ultra-high-voltage potential difference creates a strong electric field around the power line. Ions are accelerated toward the conductor, causing collisions with air molecules. This produces vast additional numbers of ions. During collisions in the ionized air, energy is released in the form of light, producing the glow seen as a corona. Power lines in our homes have weak electric fields, which do not ionize the air.

This photograph can be used with Section 22:7 on electric fields near conductors.

Demonstration: Place an empty coffee can on an insulating platform and charge it. Touch the inside of the can with a transfer disk (a metal sphere on an insulated handle) and then an electroscope. The leaves will remain limp. Repeat the procedure, this time touching the outside of the coffee can and then the electroscope. The leaves diverge, indicating all the charge is on the outside of the can.

22:2 Electric Field Intensity

Demonstration: To show that the field increases as you move toward the charge, hold a pith ball on a string on a stand about a meter away from the Van de Graaff generator. Slowly move the pith ball in so students can see that, as you get closer to the generator, the attraction to the Van de Graaff increases.

22:3 Energy and the Electric Potential

Electric potential is compared to gravitational potential. Use the analogy of hills and valleys for regions of high and low electric potential. A marble will roll down a hill to a valley where its gravitational potential is lowest. Likewise, a charge will move to a

region of lower electric potential. Work has to be done on a negative charge to separate it from a positive charge. Therefore, it will move spontaneously toward the positive charge to lower its potential. Remind students that a volt is one joule per coulomb. Potential difference is work per unit charge.

22:5 Millikan's Oil Drop Experiment

An oil drop apparatus or computer simulation can be used for the study of Millikan's oil drop experiment.

Demonstration: An experiment to show the reasoning Millikan used to find the charge on an electron can be done simply as a class demonstration. Fill film canisters with random numbers of pennies. Give one canister to each student. Weigh each film canister and record the results on the board. Students then arrange the masses in order from smallest to largest and find the differences. A pattern will emerge that will allow students to find the mass that will divide evenly into all the other mass differences. This is the mass of a penny. Students may check their results using a balance. Similar reasoning was used to determine the charge on an electron.

22:6 Sharing of Charge

Demonstration: Bring sharp and round grounded objects near an electrophorous or Van de Graaff to show the reduction of electric fields by grounding.

22:7 Electric Fields Near Conductors

The opening demonstration can be repeated here and discussed in more detail. Since the charges on a conductor are spread as far apart as they can be to make the potential as low as possible, the result is that all the charges move to the outer surface because it has larger area than the inner surface. This fact explains why it is safer to be inside your car in a lightning storm. If the car is struck by lightning, the charge will reside on the outside of the metal car.

22:8 Storing Charges—The Capacitor

Demonstration: Charge a Leyden jar by touching a charged electrophorous to the knob. This gives the inside of the jar a charge. If you charge the inside positively, the outside will become negatively charged as electrons move onto it from the ground. Repeated chargings build up a large charge difference. The charge on the inside and the charge on the outside are separated by a glass insulator. If the outside and inside are now connected, a spark will jump. Point out that this is the basic construction of a capacitor. Take apart a commercial capacitor to show its metal and plastic foils.

Capacitors are used to tune radio receivers, as condensers in ignition systems of cars, and in camera flash attachment circuits.

Resources

Literature

Epstein, Lewis C., and Hewitt, P., *Thinking Physics, Pt. II,* Insight Press, San Francisco, 1981, pp. 341–346.
Huff, G. Bradley, "Dissectible Leyden Jar," *The Physics Teacher,* May, 1986, p. 292.
Miller, Jr., Franklin, *College Physics,* Harcourt Brace Jovanovich, San Diego, 1982, pp. 410–427.
Swyer, L., and Thruman, B. N., "Is a Swimmer Safe in a Lightning Storm?" *The Physics Teacher,* May, 1980, pp. 388–389.

Chapter Review

QUESTIONS

1. See section 22:1 for detailed drawings.
2. The direction of an electric field is the direction of the force on a positive charge placed in the field. This would be away from a positive object and toward a negative object.
3. The volt is the change in potential energy, PE, resulting from moving a test charge q a distance d in a uniform field of intensity E; $V = \Delta PE/q = E \cdot d$.
4. $V = W/q = 12$ V
5. Charge is shared with Earth, which is an extremely large object.
6. The table is an insulator, or at least a very poor conductor.
7. A capacitor is a device that is made up of two conductors, or plates, isolated from each other by an insulator. As such, it stores charge. The larger the capacitance, the larger the charge that can be put on it for the same increase in the potential of the capacitor.
8. The 10-cm diameter sphere because the charges can be further apart, reducing potential rise as it is charged.
9. Joule; Volt
10. The concentration is greater at the corners.
11. Put a sufficiently large voltage across it.

APPLYING CONCEPTS

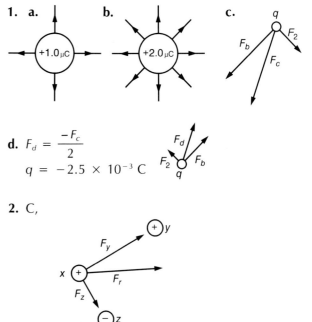

1. a.   b.   c.

d. $F_d = \dfrac{-F_c}{2}$

$q = -2.5 \times 10^{-3}$ C

2. C,

3. Slow; the larger the charge, the stronger the force, and thus the larger the (terminal) velocity.

4. **a.** No, their masses could be different.
   b. charge to mass ratio, q/m (or m/q)

EXERCISES

1. **a.** $E = \dfrac{F}{q} = \dfrac{8.0 \times 10^{-4} \text{ N}}{2.0 \times 10^{-4} \text{ C}} = 4.0 \text{ N/C}$
   b. It is toward the negative charge.

2. $q = \dfrac{1.4 \times 10^{-8} \text{ N}}{2.0 \times 10^{-4} \text{ N/C}} = 7.0 \times 10^{-5} \text{ C}$

3. $V = Ed = (1.5 \times 10^3 \text{ N/C})(0.080 \text{ m})$
   $= 1.2 \times 10^2 \text{ V} = 120 \text{ V}$

4. $E = \dfrac{50.0 \text{ V}}{0.020 \text{ m}} = 2500 \text{ V/m} = 2.5 \times 10^3 \text{ N/C}$

5. $W = qV = (0.15 \text{ C})(9.0 \text{ V}) = 1.4 \text{ J}$

6. $W = qV, q = \dfrac{W}{V} = \dfrac{1200 \text{ J}}{12 \text{ V}} = 1.0 \times 10^2 \text{ C}$

7. **a.** $q = \dfrac{F}{E} = \dfrac{8.5 \times 10^{-15} \text{ N}}{5.3 \times 10^3 \text{ N/C}} = 1.6 \times 10^{-18} \text{ C}$

   b. # electrons $= \dfrac{q}{q_e}$
   $$= \dfrac{1.6 \times 10^{-18} \text{ C}}{1.6 \times 10^{-19} \text{ C/electron}}$$
   $= 10$ electrons

8. $q = (6.8 \times 10^{-6} \text{ F})(15 \text{ V}) = 1.0 \times 10^{-4} \text{ C}$

9. **a.** $C = 75 \times 10^{-6} \text{ C}/15 \text{ V} = 5 \times 10^{-6} \text{ F}$
   b. It does not change.
   c. 30 V

10. $V = \dfrac{q}{C} = \dfrac{2.7 \times 10^{-3} \text{ C}}{5.4 \times 10^{-6} \text{ F}} = 5.0 \times 10^2 \text{ V}$

PROBLEMS

1. $W = \dfrac{1}{2}CV^2 = \dfrac{1}{2}(10.0 \times 10^{-6} \text{ F})(3.00 \times 10^2 \text{ V})^2$
   $= 0.450 \text{ J}$

2. **a.** $P = \dfrac{W}{t} = \dfrac{0.450 \text{ J}}{30 \text{ s}} = 2 \times 10^{-2} \text{ W}$

   b. $P = \dfrac{0.450 \text{ J}}{1.0 \times 10^{-4} \text{ s}} = 4.5 \times 10^3 \text{ W} = 4.5 \text{ kW}$

   c. Power is inversely proportional to the time. The shorter the time for a given amount of energy to be expended, the greater the power.

3. **a.** $W = (1/2)(61 \times 10^{-3} \text{ F})(10^4 \text{ V})^2 = 3.1 \times 10^6 \text{ J}$
   b. $P = W/t = (3.1 \times 10^6 \text{ J})/(1.0 \times 10^{-8} \text{ s})$
   $= 3.1 \times 10^{14} \text{ W}$
   c. $t = W/P = (3.1 \times 10^6 \text{ J})/(1.0 \times 10^3 \text{ W})$
   $= 3.1 \times 10^3 \text{ s}$

4. 1.63×10^{-19} C. Subtracting adjacent values, b-a, c-b, d-c, etc. yields 1.641×10^{-19} C, 3.30×10^{-19} C, 1.63×10^{-19} C, 3.35×10^{-19} C, 1.60×10^{-19} C, 1.63×10^{-19} C, 3.18×10^{-19} C, 3.24×10^{-19} C. There are two numbers, approximately 1.63×10^{-19} C and 3.2×10^{-19} C, which are common. Averaging each similar group produces one charge of 1.63×10^{-19} C and one charge of 3.27×10^{-19} C (which is two times 1.63×10^{-19} C). Dividing 1.63×10^{-19} C into each piece of data yields nearly whole number quotients indicating it is the value of an elementary charge.

5. $F = (8.0 \times 10^{-5} \text{ C})(50.0 \text{ N/C}) = 4.0 \times 10^{-3} \text{ N}$

6. **a.** $F = qE = (1.6 \times 10^{-19} \text{ C})(150 \text{ N/C})$
   $= 2.4 \times 10^{-17} \text{ N (upward)}$
   b. $F = mg = (1.7 \times 10^{-27} \text{ kg})(9.8 \text{ m/s}^2)$
   $= 1.7 \times 10^{-26} \text{ N (downward)}$, more than one billion times smaller.

7. **a.** $F = qE = (-1.6 \times 10^{-19} \text{ C})(10^5 \text{ N/C})$
   $= -1.6 \times 10^{-14} \text{ N}$ opposite the field.
   b. $a = (-1.6 \times 10^{-14} \text{ N})/(9.11 \times 10^{-31} \text{ kg})$

   $= 1.8 \times 10^{18} \text{ m/s}^2$

8. **a.** $Q = (82 \text{ protons})(1.6 \times 10^{-19} \text{ C/proton})$
   $= 1.3 \times 10^{-17} \text{ C}$

   $F = Eq$ and $F = \dfrac{KqQ}{d^2}$, so $E = \dfrac{KQ}{d^2}$
   $$= \dfrac{(9.0 \times 10^9 \text{ N} \cdot \text{m}^2/\text{C}^2)(1.3 \times 10^{-17} \text{ C})}{(10^{-10} \text{ m})^2}$$
   $= 1.2 \times 10^{13} \text{ N/C, outward}$

   b. $F = Eq = (1.2 \times 10^{13} \text{ N/C})(-1.6 \times 10^{-19} \text{ C})$
   $= -1.9 \times 10^{-6} \text{ N}$, toward the nucleus

Current Electricity

Overview

In the preceding chapters, static electricity, or charges at rest, were discussed. Chapter 23 deals with current electricity, which consists of a flow of electrons. The electrons keep moving because there is a source of potential difference, such as a battery or generator. A potential difference or voltage drop across a resistor is the result of the flow of current in that device. Thus, depending on the part of the circuit analyzed, current is either the result of or a cause of potential difference.

The study of current electricity involves the use of Ohm's law, $V = IR$, and wiring circuits with power supplies, resistors, ammeters, and voltmeters. Correct placement of the meters is very important. The voltmeter is placed in parallel and the ammeter is placed in series in a circuit.

When electrical energy is transmitted over wires, some energy is transformed into heat energy. This results in a decrease in efficiency.

Planning Guide (6 Class Sessions)

Text Section		Demonstrations and Experiments		Other Program Components	
23:1 Producing Electric Current	P	Dem 23:1 Generating Electricity		Skill: Using Voltmeters and	
23:2 Electric Circuits	P	Exp 40 Ohm's Law	LM	Ammeters	TRP
23:3 Rates of Energy Transfer	P	Exp 41 Electrical Equivalent of Heat	LM	Minilab 23-1: Electric Circuits	TRP
23:4 Resistance and Ohm's Law	P	Dem 23:2 Energy Transformations		Demonstration 23-1: Ohm's Law	TRP
		Dem 23:4 Ohm's Law		Enrichment 23-1: Problems	TRP
23:5 Diagramming Electric Circuits	P	Dem 23:5 Constructing Electric Circuits		Teaching Master 23-1: Symbols Used in Electric Circuit Diagrams	TRP
				Teaching Master 23-2: Simple Circuits	TRP
				Enrichment 23-2: Mystery Circuit Boards	TRP
23:6 Controlling Current in a Circuit	P	Dem 23:6 A Variable Resistor		Demonstration 23-2: Heating Effects of Electricity	TRP
23:7 Heating Effect of Electric Currents	P	Dem 23:7 Heating Effect of Electricity			
23:8 Transmission of Electric Energy	S			Review Masters	TRP
23:9 The Kilowatt Hour	S			Evaluation	TRP

Performance Objectives

Upon completion of this chapter, your students will

1. define an electric current; recognize the need for a potential difference if an electric current is to be maintained. *23:1*

2. recognize circuits as closed loops; understand the transfers of energy in circuits. *23:2*

3. define the ampere; explain the definition of

power in electric circuits; solve problems involving current and power. *23:3*

4. define resistance and use the definition to solve problems involving current flow and resistance. *23:4*

5. define Ohm's law; distinguish devices that obey Ohm's law from those that do not. *23:4*

6. diagram simple electric circuits; recognize the correct use of ammeters and voltmeters. *23:5*

7. explain the use of resistors in controlling current; solve problems using them. *23:6*

8. explain the relationship between electric and thermal energy. *23:7*

9. describe the reason for the use of high voltage lines in transmitting electric power. *23:8*

10. define kilowatt hour; solve problems involving the use and cost of electric energy. *23:9*

Teaching the Chapter

Introduction

Using the Photo: It is not a reasonable statement. Some electrical power is dissipated as heat during transmission. The amount of power lost is given by $P = I^2R$. Resistance of the power lines remains constant. When electrical energy is transmitted at a low voltage, such as 120 volts, and high current, a large amount of power is lost. A minimal amount of power is lost by transmitting energy at high voltage and low current. This photograph also can be used with Section 23:8 to discuss transmission of electric energy.

Demonstration: Make a simple voltaic cell from a lemon, a bare copper wire or strip, and a zinc-coated nail. Use a galvanometer to show the flow of electricity. If possible, show students a potato clock, which uses the same metals as above in a potato to run a clock. Also use a small hand cranked generator to light a light bulb, showing that work must be done to create electric energy.

23:2 Electric Circuits

You can use the popular water-flow analogy to help students understand that electrons flow when a difference in potential is maintained. If water is pumped to a reservoir, it will flow down to an empty reservoir through a pipe. When the water in both reservoirs reaches the same level, no more water flows. In an electric circuit, a battery or generator would be similar to the pump. The battery maintains a difference in electrical potential between the two points just as the pump maintains the difference in gravitational energy.

Demonstration: A commercially available transformation of energy apparatus has a hand cranked generator attached to a bell and a fan blade. Use the apparatus to show the work done to generate electric-

ity and then the electricity being transformed into other kinds of energy.

Cut apart some commercial cells to show their construction. **CAUTION:** *Do not touch the chemicals with your hands.*

23:3 Rates of Energy Transfer

Compare the current flowing through a 75-W light bulb connected to a 120-V source and an air conditioner rated at 2400 W connected to the same source by using the new equation $P = VI$. Discuss units in detail. Students have a tendency to use electrical units interchangeably. It is important to continually review the meaning of amp, ohm, volt, watt, and joule.

23:4 Resistance and Ohm's Law

Emphasize that resistance is constant at a certain temperature. A light bulb filament has very low resistance at first and then increases as it heats up. Point out that the resistance of a wire increases with the length and decreases as the cross sectional area increases. Resistance also depends on the type of material used.

Demonstration: Connect a few light bulbs in series with a battery and display the relationship among the current in the circuit, the voltage source, and the resistance of the lamp bulb.

23:5 Diagramming Electric Circuits

Demonstration: Set up a circuit for your students and identify the ammeter, voltmeter, resistor, switch, and power supply as you draw the diagram representing your circuit.

Discuss the meanings of series and parallel circuits. Point out that a voltmeter can be disconnected and the bulb still lights. This is a characteristic of something connected in parallel; it can be disconnected without breaking the circuit. However, if the ammeter is removed, it will break the circuit and the light goes out; this is a characteristic of something connected in series. Explain that when the meters are placed in the circuit, students must check that the + terminal of the meter is attached to the + side of the power source. This can be easily done by tracing the wires from the + side of the source to the + terminal of the meter. When students are setting up circuits, have them hook up the ammeter at the same time they connect the resistors. In this way, students can see that removing the ammeter results in a broken circuit. The voltmeter is put in last across the resistor like a bridge.

23:6 Controlling Current in a Circuit

Ask students if they have a dimmer switch in their dining room at home or one in their car to dim the dashboard lights. Ask them to describe how the dimmer works.

Demonstration: Collect different kinds of rheostats to show students. Hook one up in a circuit and show them how it is used to dim a light. Some students may have electric train sets with rheostats that control a train's speed. To make a rheostat, carve the wood off the middle section of a pencil. Using leads from a battery, clip one lead to the pencil point and rub the other lead along the graphite to change the length of graphite that is part of the circuit. Connect an ammeter to the circuit, and note the change in current as the length is varied.

23:7 Heating Effect of Electric Currents

Demonstration: Use an immersion heater to heat some water. Wrap the cup in foam packing to reduce heat loss. Put in a known mass of water and calculate the amount of energy needed to bring the water to boiling, using the formula $Q = mC\Delta t$. Find the power rating of the heater, and calculate the time needed to heat the water to boiling, using $Q = Pt$. Determine how close you come to the calculated time and discuss the errors involved.

23:8 Transmission of Electric Energy

Local power companies often have films available that can be helpful in teaching about transmission of electricity. Discuss safety in the home and the danger of using electrical appliances in the bathroom near a tub or basin filled with water. If you were to drop a hair dryer in the tub while taking a bath, the electricity would take the path of least resistance to ground, or through the water and you. A bird can sit on a high voltage wire without getting hurt because there is no potential difference between its legs. However, it would be very dangerous if one of its legs happened to touch the ground.

23:9 The Kilowatt Hour

Emphasize the idea that electric bills in kilowatt hours are billing for energy and not for power. Remind students that $W = Pt$ and W stands for work or energy. Have students bring in an electric bill from home. Have them record the wattage on every appliance and light bulb they use from the time they get up until they come to school. They should also record the amount of time each item is used. Have them find the total energy they used and then the cost, using the rate from the electric bill.

You may extend this activity by having students read the meter at the beginning and end of the week. During the week, keep a record of the wattage of all lights and appliances used and the approximate time they were used. Have students investigate ways they can save energy.

Resources ━━━━━━━━━━━

Literature

Lockhead, John, and Freddetta, Norman, "Student Conceptions of Simple Circuits," *The Physics Teacher*, March, 1980, pp. 194–198.

Miller, Jr., Franklin, *College Physics,* Harcourt Brace Jovanovich, San Diego, 1982, pp. 436–444.

Pynadata, V.D., "Do-It-At-Home Energy Exercise," *The Physics Teacher*, January, 1977, pp. 45–46.

Van Heuvelen, Alan, *Physics, A General Introduction,* Little, Brown and Co., Boston, 1982, pp. 478–491.

Background ━━━━━━━━━━━

The formula used to find the resistance of a piece of wire is $R = \varrho L/A$. The letter ϱ, rho, stands for resistivity; the value for ϱ is found on a table of resistivity. The following metals and alloys are listed in order of increasing resistivity: silver, copper, gold, aluminum, and nichrome. Nichrome is often used in heating elements. Copper is usually used for connecting wires since its resistivity is low. The letter L is the length in m and A is the cross sectional area in m².

Find the resistance of a piece of copper wire 2.0 m long and 2.0 mm in diameter. Its cross sectional area will be πr^2. The resistivity of copper is $1.68 \times 10^{-8} \ \Omega \cdot m$.

$$
\begin{aligned}
R &= \frac{\varrho L}{A} \\
&= \frac{\varrho L}{\pi r^2} \\
&= \frac{(1.68 \times 10^{-8} \Omega \cdot m)(2.0 \ m)}{\pi (.001 \ m)^2}
\end{aligned}
$$

$$R = 1.1 \times 10^{-2} \ \Omega$$

Chapter Review

QUESTIONS

1. **a.** electrical to heat and light
   b. electrical to heat and kinetic
   c. electrical to light and sound
2. The efficiency of a heater and the amount of power consumed are two important factors. Other factors include: rate of air flow, radiation pattern, and recommended area specifications.
3. increase voltage, decrease resistance
4. resistance and current
5. (1 kWh)(1000 W/kW)(3600 s/h)
   = 3.6×10^6 W · s
   = 3.6×10^6 J
6. $I = \dfrac{V}{R} = \dfrac{90 \ V}{45 \ \Omega} = 2 \ A$

7. $V = IR = (1.75 \ A)(16 \ \Omega) = 28 \ V$

8. **a.** in series
   b. in parallel

9. 1 C = 6.25×10^{18} electrons.
10. No potential difference exists across them.
11. A larger diameter wire has a smaller resistance.
12. It is halved.

APPLYING CONCEPTS

1. Smaller resistance. $P = IV$, where V is the same. $I = V/R$, so larger R has lower I, and thus lower P.
2. 50 W. $P = IV$, so higher P has higher I. $R = V/I$, so with same V, larger I means lower R.
3. Low resistance of cold filament allows high current initially and greater change in temperature, subjecting the filament to greater stress.
4. As the temperature increases, the average kinetic energy of the atoms in the wire increases making it more difficult to pass electrons.
5. By touching the fence and the ground, the cow encounters a difference in potential and conducts current, thus receiving a shock.
6. No. $R = V/I$ is $(1.5 \ V)/(45 \times 10^{-6} \ A) = 3.3 \times 10^4 \ \Omega$ at 1.5 V, but $R = (3.0 \ V)/(25 \times 10^{-3} \ A) = 120 \ \Omega$ at 3.0 V.
7. The potential difference is felt over the entire circuit and the electrons within the conducting wires move.
8. The 30A fuse allows more current to flow through the circuit, generating more heat which can be harmful to objects included in the circuit.
9. Electrons bumping into atoms give them an increase in their kinetic energy, thus raising the temperature of the wire.

EXERCISES

1. $P = VI = (120 \text{ V})(8.0 \text{ A}) = 960 \text{ W}$

2. $P = VI = (120 \text{ V})(1.2 \text{ A}) = 140 \text{ W}$

3. **a.** $P = VI = (3.0 \text{ V})(1.5 \text{ A}) = 4.5 \text{ W}$
   b. $E = Pt = (4.5 \text{ W})(10 \text{ min})(60 \text{ s/min})$
   $= 3.0 \times 10^3 \text{ J}$

4. $I = V/R = (75 \text{ V})/(15 \text{ }\Omega) = 5.0 \text{ A}$

5. $I = V/R$, so $V = IR = (0.5 \text{ A})(60 \text{ }\Omega) = 30 \text{ V}$.

6. I is proportional to V, so doubling V doubles I to 48 mA.

7. **a.** No. The voltage is increased by a factor of $(9.0)/(6.0) = 1.5$, but the current is increased by a factor of $(75)/(66) = 1.1$.
   b. $P = IV = (66 \times 10^{-3} \text{ A})(6.0 \text{ V}) = 0.40 \text{ W}$
   c. $P = IV = (75 \times 10^{-3} \text{ A})(9.0 \text{ V}) = 0.68 \text{ W}$

8. **a.** $V = IR$
   $$R = \frac{V}{I} = \frac{120 \text{ V}}{0.5 \text{ A}} = 240 \text{ }\Omega = 200 \text{ }\Omega$$
   b. $R_{cold} = \frac{1}{5}(200 \text{ }\Omega) - 40 \text{ }\Omega$
   c. $I = \frac{V}{R} = \frac{120 \text{ V}}{40 \text{ }\Omega} = 3 \text{ A}$

9. $Energy = Pt$
   $= (60.0 \text{ W})(30 \text{ min})(60 \text{ s/min})$
   $= 1.10 \times 10^5 \text{ J}$
   $Q = Pt$
   $= (60.0 \text{ W})(0.88)(30 \text{ min})(60 \text{ s/min})$
   $= 9.5 \times 10^4 \text{ J}$

10. **a.** $P = VI = (120 \text{ V})(0.50 \text{ A}) = 6.0 \times 10^1 \text{ W}$
    b. $E = Pt = (60 \text{ W})(5 \text{ min})(60 \text{ s/min})$
    $= 20000 \text{ J} = 2.0 \times 10^4 \text{ J}$

11. **a.** $P = IV = (210 \text{ A})(12 \text{ V}) = 2500 \text{ J/s}$
    b. $P = 2500 \text{ W}$

12. $I = \frac{V}{R} = \frac{30.0 \text{ V}}{20.0 \text{ }\Omega} = 1.50 \text{ A}$

13. $V = IR = (1.5 \text{ A})(4 \text{ }\Omega) = 6 \text{ V}$

14. $V = IR = (8.0 \text{ A})(15 \text{ }\Omega) = 120 \text{ V}$

15. **a.** $I = \frac{V}{R} = \frac{15 \text{ V}}{6 \text{ }\Omega} = 2.5 \text{ A} = 3 \text{ A}$
    b. $Q = I^2 Rt = (3 \text{ A})^2 (6 \text{ }\Omega)(10 \text{ min})(60 \text{ s/min})$
    $= 3.24 \times 10^4 \text{ J} = 3 \times 10^4 \text{ J}$

16. **a.** $I = \frac{P}{V} = \frac{30.0 \text{ W}}{120 \text{ V}} = 0.25 \text{ A}$
    b. $R = \frac{V^2}{P} = \frac{(120 \text{ V})^2}{30.0 \text{ W}} = 480 \text{ }\Omega$

PROBLEMS

1. **a.** $I = \frac{V}{R} = \frac{120 \text{ V}}{4.0 \text{ }\Omega} = 3.0 \times 10^1 \text{ A}$
   b. $Energy = Pt = \frac{V^2 t}{R}$
   $= \frac{(120 \text{ V})^2 (5.0 \text{ min})(60 \text{ s/min})}{4.0 \text{ }\Omega}$
   $= 1.1 \times 10^6 \text{ J}$
   c. $Q = mc\Delta T$
   $$\Delta T = \frac{Q}{mc} = \frac{(1.1 \times 10^6 \text{ J})}{(20.0 \text{ kg})(4180 \text{ J/kg} \cdot \text{C}°)}$$
   $= 13°C$
   d. $Cost = (1.1 \times 10^6 \text{ J/5 min})(30 \text{ min/day})$
   $(30 \text{ days})(1 \text{ kWh}/3.6 \times 10^6 \text{ J})(\$0.08/\text{kWh})$
   $= \$4.40$

2. **a.** $E = Pt$
   $= (5.00 \times 10^2 \text{ W})(30 \text{ min})(60 \text{ s/min})$
   $= 9 \times 10^5 \text{ J}$
   b. $Q = mc\Delta T$
   $$\Delta T = \frac{Q}{mc} = \frac{(0.5)(9 \times 10^5 \text{ J})}{(50.0 \text{ kg})(1100 \text{ J/kg} \cdot \text{C}°)} = 8°C$$
   c. $Cost = (500 \text{ J/s})(6 \text{ h/day})(3.6 \times 10^3 \text{ s/h})$
   $(30 \text{ days})(1 \text{ kWh}/3.6 \times 10^6 \text{ J})(\$0.08/\text{kWh})$
   $= \$7.20$

3. **a.** $I = \frac{V}{R} = \frac{110 \text{ V}}{22.0 \text{ }\Omega} = 5.0 \text{ A}$
   b. $E_w = mgd = (1 \times 10^4 \text{ kg})(9.8 \text{ m/s}^2)(8.0 \text{ m})$
   $= 7.8 \times 10^5 \text{ J} = 8 \times 10^5 \text{ J}$
   $E_m = IVt = (5.0 \text{ A})(110 \text{ V})(3600 \text{ s})$
   $= 2.0 \times 10^6 \text{ J}$
   $Eff = \frac{E_w}{E_m} \times 100\% = \frac{8 \times 10^5 \text{ J}}{2.0 \times 10^6 \text{ J}} \times 100\%$
   $= 40\%$

4. **a.** $P = IV = (0.050 \text{ A})(9.0 \text{ V}) = 0.45 \text{ W}$
   $= 4.5 \times 10^{-4} \text{ kW}$
   $Energy = Pt = (4.5 \times 10^{-4} \text{ kW})(300 \text{ h})$
   $= 0.14 \text{ kWh} = 0.1 \text{ kWh}$
   $\frac{Cost}{\text{kWh}} = \frac{\$0.90}{0.1 \text{ kWh}} = \$9/\text{kWh}$
   b. $Cost = \frac{\$0.08}{\text{kWh}}(0.1 \text{ kWh}) = 1 \text{ cent}$

5. **a.** $V = IR = (1 \times 10^{-3} \text{ A})(1 \times 10^5 \text{ }\Omega)$
   $= 1 \times 10^2 \text{ V} = 100 \text{ V}$
   b. $I = \frac{V}{R} = \frac{100 \text{ V}}{5 \times 10^3 \text{ }\Omega} = 2 \times 10^{-2} \text{ A}$
   $= 20 \text{ mA}$, loss of muscle control

c. $V = IR = (1 \times 10^{-3}\text{ A})(5 \times 10^3\ \Omega) = 5\text{ V}$

6. a. $I = 22\text{ mA}$
$R = V/I = (0.70\text{ V})/(2.2 \times 10^{-2}\text{ A}) = 32\ \Omega.$

 b. $I = 5.2\text{ mA}$
$R = V/I = (0.60\text{ V})/(5.2 \times 10^{-3}\text{ A})$
$= 120\ \Omega$

 c. No. Resistance depends on voltage.

7. a. $R = 143\ \Omega,\ 148\ \Omega,\ 150\ \Omega,\ 154\ \Omega,\ 154\ \Omega,$
$143\ \Omega,\ 143\ \Omega,\ 154\ \Omega,\ 157\ \Omega,\ 156\ \Omega.$

 b. Nichrome wire does not obey Ohm's law for all voltages. It obeys for voltages of $+8.00$ V to $+10.00$ V and in the -2.00 V to -4.00 V range. (See statement of Ohm's law, p 391.)

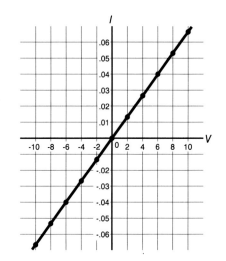

Series and Parallel Circuits

Overview

This chapter introduces series circuits, parallel circuits, and series-parallel circuits. Ohm's law is applied to find current and voltage throughout a circuit and the effective resistance of the whole circuit. A discussion of house wiring, fuses, circuit breakers, and ammeter and voltmeter use is also included. The danger of a short circuit producing high current and a large amount of heat is discussed.

An interesting application of circuitry is shown. Voltage dividers are used in circuits that contain light sensitive devices. As the amount of light striking a photoresistor decreases, its resistance increases. Circuits like these are used as a light meter or a switch that turns lights on and off depending on the amount of daylight present.

Planning Guide (7 Class Sessions)

Text Section		Demonstrations and Experiments		Other Program Components	
24:1 Series Circuits	P	Dem 24:1 Series Versus Parallel		Teaching Master 24-1:	
24:2 Voltage Drops in a Series	P	Exp 42 Series Circuits	**LM**	(a) Series Circuit	**TRP**
Circuit	P	Exp 43 Parallel Circuits	**LM**	Demonstration 24-1: Short Circuits	**TRP**
		Exp 44 Series-Parallel Circuits	**LM**		
24:3 Parallel Circuits	P	Dem 24:3 Parallel Circuits		Teaching Master 24-1:	
24:4 Applications of Parallel				(b) Parallel Circuit	**TRP**
Circuits	P			Demonstration 24-2:	
24:5 Series-Parallel Circuits	P			Parallel and Series Circuits	**TRP**
24:6 Ammeters and Voltmeters	P			Teaching Master 24-2:	
				Series and Parallel Circuits	**TRP**
				Review Masters	**TRP**
				Enrichment 24-1: Problems	**TRP**
				Evaluation	**TRP**

Performance Objectives

Upon completion of this chapter, your students will

1. describe a series circuit; define effective resistance; state how the effective series resistance is calculated; find the current in a series circuit. *24:1*

2. calculate voltage drops in series circuits; define a voltage divider; use in solving problems. *24:2*

3. describe a parallel circuit; state how the effective parallel resistance is calculated; find the current in branches of a parallel circuit. *24:3*

4. state the important characteristics of parallel circuits. *24:4*

5. describe a series-parallel circuit; state how effective resistance is found. *24:5*

6. distinguish between ammeters and voltmeters; state the important characteristics of each; describe how each is wired into a circuit. *24:6*

Teaching the Chapter

Introduction

Using the Photo: The 60-watt bulb will glow brighter. The resistance of the 60-watt light bulb is greater than the 100-watt light bulb. The power dissipated in the filament is $P = I^2R$. The same current flows in each light bulb, so the greater power is dissipated by the 60-watt light bulb. This photograph also can be used with Section 24:1 to discuss series circuits and Section 24:2 to discuss voltage drops in a series circuit.

Demonstration: Set up a power supply with three bulbs in series so students can easily see they are strung end-to-end and that there is only a single path through which current may flow. Light the bulbs, observe brightness, and unscrew one bulb so students can see that all the bulbs go out. Now set up the bulbs in parallel so the students can see that the pattern is like a series of stacked bridges. Observe the brightness and unscrew one bulb so students can observe that the rest of the bulbs stay lit.

24:2 Voltage Drops in a Series Circuit

To make the connection between circuit diagrams, actual circuits, and formulas comprehensible to your students, give them hands-on experience with the circuits and meters. Let students hook up resistors or light bulbs in series with a battery, ammeter, and switch and do the introductory demonstration themselves. Make sure conditions are safe. Remind students to check the polarity of the ammeter so that the ammeter is in the circuit in the correct orientation. Have students work from a circuit diagram and trace the diagram, placing the components in the circuit in the same order. The voltmeter should be put in last by hooking it in around the resistor like a bridge. Remind students that the voltmeter can be put in or taken out without breaking the circuit. Emphasize that when the ammeter is taken out of the circuit, the circuit is broken. As students change the position of the ammeter in the circuit, they will see that the current stays the same. When they move the voltmeter they will see that the voltages across the light bulbs all add up to the source voltage. If they add another light bulb, they will see that the light bulbs get dimmer and the current in the circuit decreases.

24:3 Parallel Circuits

Demonstration: Have students hook up two bulbs in parallel with a battery and a switch but without meters. Check the circuits. Now have them place the ammeter in the circuit so it will measure the total current. Have them add a third bulb and observe that the current increases. Students then may take the voltmeter and measure the voltage across the light bulbs so they can see the voltage drops are all the same. In order to measure the current through each branch, students must open the circuit between the resistor and the junction and insert the ammeter with the polarity correct. Students will observe that the current through each branch is less than the circuit's total current. When the current in all the branches is added together, it equals the total current. Have students reduce the circuit to one bulb and see that the voltage is still the same and the total current is lower than when there were several bulbs.

24:4 Applications of Parallel Circuits

Discuss why houses are wired in parallel. It would be very inconvenient if the lights all went out every time a bulb went out, or if they got dim when you turned on another lamp or used the toaster.

Perform the demonstration "Short Circuits" from the *Teacher Resource Package* showing how the short circuit causes the aluminum foil to melt. Collect a variety of different kinds of fuses and tell where they are used. Discuss the differences between fuse boxes and circuit breaker boxes and have students find out which they have in their houses. Point out that it is very dangerous to replace a fuse with a penny because the current could increase too much and cause a fire. The structure of the circuit breaker could be used as a lead-in to the next chapter on magnetism.

Discuss safety and the effect of current on the human body. The resistance of the human body when the skin is dry is about 10^5 ohms. It drops to about 1500 ohms for wet hands. Therefore, the current through the body from 120 V is about 1.2 mA for dry skin and 80 mA for wet skin. A person will feel a tingle at about 2 mA, at 10 to 20 mA there will be muscular effects, and by 20 mA a person will not be able to let go of a conducting wire. Respiratory paralysis occurs between 20 to 100 mA, and 100 mA to 3 A can be fatal. Stress the importance of handling electrical appliances, such as hair dryers, curling irons, and electric razors, with dry hands.

24:6 Ammeters and Voltmeters

Ammeters and voltmeters are constructed in such a manner that they will have a minimal effect on the circuit when they are being used to measure current and voltage. The construction of the two meters is very similar. They are both based on a moving coil galvanometer, a current-indicating device that depends on magnetic forces.

To make an ammeter, a low resistance shunt is placed in parallel with the galvanometer coil on the inside of the meter. This means that there is a very low resistance path for the current through this meter and thus it can be placed in series without affecting the circuit.

A voltmeter is made by placing a very high resistance resistor, called a multiplier, in series with the galvanometer coil. This gives the instrument a very high resistance and thus very little current will go through it when it is hooked in parallel in the circuit.

Discuss the importance of using a measuring device that does not change the properties of the circuit. Explain and emphasize the importance of a low resistance ammeter and high resistance voltmeter.

Resources

Literature

Keller, Clifton, "Mysterious Lights in Series and Parallel," *The Physics Teacher,* September, 1980, p. 460.

Marion, J.B., and Hornyak, W.F., *General Physics with Bioscience Essays,* John Wiley and Sons, Inc., New York, 1985, pp. 328–332.

Miller, Jr., Franklin, *College Physics,* Harcourt Brace Jovanovich, San Diego, 1982, pp. 454–472.

Van Heuvelen, Alan, *Physics, A General Introduction,* Little, Brown and Co., Boston, 1982, pp. 495–504.

Background

Faulty electrical devices can deliver lethal shocks. An electric heater could be a potential hazard if the high voltage becomes connected to the case by frayed insulation on the wires. If a person who is grounded touches the case, he or she will complete a path for the current to the ground. This kind of hazard can be avoided by the use of a three wire system. The third prong of a plug is connected by a wire to the case of the appliance. The third hole in the receptacle is connected to ground. Therefore, if there is faulty wiring in the appliance, the current is routed through the ground and not the person because the case and the ground have essentially no resistance between them.

Chapter Review

QUESTIONS

1. **a.** No current will flow in the resistor.
   b. The current in the resistor will remain the same.

2. In a series circuit, the current is opposed by each resistance in turn. Total resistance is the sum. In a parallel circuit, each resistance provides an additional path for current flow. The result is a decrease in total resistance.

3. No; the 30-Ω resistors can be used in parallel. Three 30-Ω resistors in parallel will give a 10-Ω resistance. Two 30-Ω resistors in parallel will give a 15-Ω resistance. This is a common but wasteful practice.

4. **a.** series   **d.** series   **g.** series
   b. series   **e.** parallel   **h.** parallel
   c. parallel   **f.** series   **i.** parallel

5. The purpose of a fuse is to prevent conductors from being overloaded with current and, through the resulting heating effect, causing fires. A fuse is simply a short length of wire which will melt from the same heating effect if the current is over a certain maximum.

6. A short circuit is an accidentally formed circuit which has extremely low resistance. A short circuit is dangerous because a low resistance across any potential difference will draw a large current. The heating effect can then cause a fire. A person standing in water who touches a conductor or light switch can also present the potential difference with a short circuit, which can produce disastrous results.

7. An ammeter must have low resistance because it is placed directly in the circuit. If its resistance were high, it would change the total resistance of the circuit and, thus, serve to reduce the current flowing in the circuit, thereby defeating its own purpose.

8. A voltmeter is placed in parallel with the portion of the circuit across which it is to measure the difference in potential. It must have very high resistance for the very same reason that an ammeter has low resistance. If the voltmeter had low resistance, it would lower the resistance of the portion of the circuit it is across and increase the current in the circuit. This would produce a higher voltage drop across the part of the circuit where the voltmeter is located and the meter would be defeating its own purpose.

9. It will be less than any of the resistors.

10. When one bulb burns out, the circuit is incomplete and they all go out.

APPLYING CONCEPTS

1. a. lower resistance: $P = IV$ $I = V/R$, so $P = V^2/R$ Smaller R means larger P.
   b. higher resistance: $P = IV$ $V = IR$, so $P = I^2R$ Larger R means larger P.

2. Connect four of them in series. The voltage drop across each will be 6 V/4 = 1.5 V.

3. The parallel circuit runs the battery dead first. Its total current would be four times that of the series circuit, thus using the energy twice as fast.

4. They are equal.

5. increased paths for electron flow

6. Appliances in parallel can be run independently of each other.

EXERCISES

1. a. $R = R_1 + R_2 = 20.0 \ \Omega + 5.0 \ \Omega = 25 \ \Omega$
   b. $I = \dfrac{V}{R} = \dfrac{50.0 \text{ V}}{25 \ \Omega} = 2 \text{ A}$
   c. $V_1 = IR_1 = (2 \text{ A})(20 \ \Omega) = 40 \text{ V}$
   $V_2 = IR_2 = (2 \text{ A})(5 \ \Omega) = 10 \text{ V}$
   d. $P_1 = IV_1 = (2 \text{ A})(40 \text{ V}) = 80 \text{ W}$
   $P_2 = IV_2 = (2 \text{ A})(10 \text{ V}) = 20 \text{ W}$

2. a. $\dfrac{1}{R} = \dfrac{1}{R_1} + \dfrac{1}{R_2} = \dfrac{1}{20.0 \ \Omega} + \dfrac{1}{5.0 \ \Omega}$
   $R = 4.0 \ \Omega$

b. $I = \dfrac{V}{R} = \dfrac{50.0 \text{ V}}{4.0 \ \Omega} = 12.5 \text{ A}$

c. $I_1 = \dfrac{V}{R_1} = \dfrac{50.0 \text{ V}}{20.0 \ \Omega} = 2.50 \text{ A}$

$I_2 = \dfrac{V}{R_2} = \dfrac{50.0 \text{ V}}{5.0 \ \Omega} = 1.0 \times 10^1 \text{ A}$

d. $V_1 = I_1 R_1 = (2.50 \text{ A})(20.0 \ \Omega)$
   $= 5.00 \times 10^1 \text{ V}$
   $V_2 = I_2 R_2 = (1.0 \times 10^1 \text{ A})(5.0 \ \Omega)$
   $= 5.0 \times 10^1 \text{ V}$

e. $P_1 = I_1 V_1 = (2.50 \text{ A})(5.0 \times 10^1 \text{ V})$
   $= 130 \text{ W}$
   $P_2 = I_2 V_2 = (1.0 \times 10^1 \text{ A})(5.00 \times 10^1 \text{ V})$
   $= 5.00 \times 10^2 \text{ W}$

f. With the same potential difference two resistors in parallel consume much more power than if they were wired in series.

3. a. $\dfrac{1}{R} = \dfrac{1}{R_1} + \dfrac{1}{R_2} = \dfrac{1}{16.0 \ \Omega} + \dfrac{1}{20.0 \ \Omega}$

$R = \dfrac{1}{0.1125 \ \Omega} = 8.89 \ \Omega$

b. $I = \dfrac{V}{R} = \dfrac{40.0 \text{ V}}{8.89 \ \Omega} = 4.50 \text{ A}$

c. $I_1 = \dfrac{V}{R_1} = \dfrac{40.0 \text{ V}}{16.0 \ \Omega} = 2.50 \text{ A}$

4. a. $\dfrac{1}{R} = \dfrac{1}{240 \ \Omega} + \dfrac{1}{240 \ \Omega} + \dfrac{1}{240 \ \Omega} + \dfrac{1}{240 \ \Omega}$

$= \dfrac{4}{240 \ \Omega}$

$R = \dfrac{240 \ \Omega}{4} = 6.0 \times 10^1 \ \Omega$

$I = \dfrac{V}{R} = \dfrac{120 \text{ V}}{6.0 \times 10^1 \ \Omega} = 2.0 \text{ A}$

b. $\dfrac{1}{R} = \dfrac{6}{240 \ \Omega}$

$R = \dfrac{240 \ \Omega}{6} = 4.0 \times 10^1 \ \Omega$

$I = \dfrac{V}{R} = \dfrac{120 \text{ V}}{4.0 \times 10^1 \ \Omega} = 3.0 \text{ A}$

c. $\dfrac{1}{R} = \dfrac{1}{4.0 \times 10^1} + \dfrac{1}{10.0 \ \Omega} = \dfrac{5}{40 \ \Omega}$

$R = \dfrac{40 \ \Omega}{5} = 8.0 \ \Omega$

$I = \dfrac{V}{R} = \dfrac{120 \text{ V}}{8.0 \ \Omega} = 15 \text{ A}$

5. a. $I = P/V = (75.0 \text{ W})/(120 \text{ V}) = 0.625 \text{ A}$
  b. $R = V/I = (120 \text{ V})/(0.625 \text{ A})$
    $= 190 \text{ }\Omega$
  c. $R = (120 \text{ V})/(0.30 \text{ A}) = 4.0 \times 10^2 \text{ }\Omega$
    an additional 210 Ω are needed.

6. a. $V_i = IR = (0.30 \text{ A})(190 \text{ }\Omega) = 57 \text{ V}$
    $V_R = (0.30 \text{ A})(210 \text{ }\Omega) = 63 \text{ V}$
  b. $P = IV = (0.30 \text{ A})(57 \text{ V}) = 17 \text{ W}$
  c. $P = IV = (0.30 \text{ A})(63 \text{ V}) = 19 \text{ W}$

7. $R_1 = VR_2/V_2 - R_2$
    $= (12 \text{ V})(100.0 \text{ }\Omega)/(4.0 \text{ V}) - 100.0 \text{ }\Omega$
    $= 200 \text{ }\Omega.$

8. Decreased

9. a. $R = V^2/P = (120 \text{ V})^2/(64 \text{ W})$
    $= 230 \text{ }\Omega$
  b. R is sum of resistances of 18 lamps, so each resistance is $(230 \text{ }\Omega)/18 = 13 \text{ }\Omega$
  c. $(64 \text{ W})/18 = 3.6 \text{ W}$

10. a. $R = (13 \text{ }\Omega)(17) = 220 \text{ }\Omega$
  b. $P = V^2/R = (120 \text{ V})^2/(220 \text{ }\Omega)$
    $= 65 \text{ W}$
  c. It increased!

11. $I = P/V$ and $R = V/I$, so $R = V^2/P$ Thus, R_{40}
    $= (120 \text{ V})^2/(40.0 \text{ W}) = 360 \text{ }\Omega$ $R_{60} = (120 \text{ V})^2/$
    $(60.0 \text{ W}) = 240 \text{ }\Omega$ $1/R = 1/(360 \text{ }\Omega) + 1/(240$
    $\Omega)$, so $R = 140 \text{ }\Omega$

12. a. $I_1 = \dfrac{V}{R_1} = \dfrac{150 \text{ V}}{75 \text{ }\Omega} = 2.0 \text{ A}$
  b. $I_2 = \dfrac{V}{R_2} = \dfrac{150 \text{ V}}{150 \text{ }\Omega} = 1.0 \text{ A}$
  c. $I = I_1 + I_2 = 2.0 \text{ A} + 1.0 \text{ A} = 3.0 \text{ A}$
  d. $\dfrac{1}{R} = \dfrac{1}{R_1} + \dfrac{1}{R_S} = \dfrac{1}{75 \text{ }\Omega} + \dfrac{1}{150 \text{ }\Omega} = \dfrac{3}{150 \text{ }\Omega}$
    $R = \dfrac{150}{3} \text{ }\Omega = 5.0 \times 10^1 \text{ }\Omega$
  e. $I = \dfrac{V}{R} = \dfrac{150 \text{ V}}{50 \text{ }\Omega} = 3.0 \text{ A}$, yes

13. a. $R = V^2/P = (120 \text{ V})^2/(275 \text{ W})$
    $= 52 \text{ }\Omega$
  b. $V_2 = VR_z/(R_1 + R_2)$
    $= (120 \text{ V})(52 \text{ }\Omega)/(2.5 \text{ }\Omega + 52 \text{ }\Omega)$
    $= 110 \text{ V}$
  c. $1/R = 1/(52 \text{ }\Omega) + 1/(12 \text{ }\Omega)$, $R = 9.8 \text{ }\Omega$
  d. $V_2 = VR_2/(R_1 + R_2)$
    $= (120 \text{ V})(9.8 \text{ }\Omega)/ 2.5 \text{ }\Omega + 9.8 \text{ }\Omega)$
    $= 96 \text{ V}$

14. a. $I = V/R = (15 \text{ V})/(10 \text{ }\Omega) = 1.5 \text{ A} = 2 \text{ A}$
  b. $R = V/I = (15 \text{ V})/(0.5 \text{ A}) = 30 \text{ }\Omega.$ thus, 30 $\Omega - 10 \text{ }\Omega = 20 \text{ }\Omega$

PROBLEMS

1. a. $R = V/I = (6.0 \text{ V})/(1.0 \text{ mA}) = 6.0 \text{ k}\Omega$
  b. Total $R = V/I = (6.0 \text{ V})/(0.5 \text{ mA}) = 12.0 \text{ k}\Omega.$
    Thus, external resistor $R' = 12.0 \text{ k}\Omega - 6.0 \text{ k}\Omega$
    $= 6.0 \text{ k}\Omega$
  c. Total $R = V/I = (6.0 \text{ V})/(0.25 \text{ mA}) = 24.0$
    $\text{k}\Omega.$ Thus, external resistor $R' = 24.0 \text{ k}\Omega -$
    $6.0 \text{ k}\Omega = 18.0 \text{ k}\Omega$
  d. Total $R = V/I = (6.0 \text{ V})/(0.75 \text{ mA}) = 8.0 \text{ k}\Omega.$
    Thus, external resistor $R' = 8.0 \text{ k}\Omega - 6.0 \text{ k}\Omega$
    $= 2.0 \text{ k}\Omega$
  e. Infinity at 0 deflection, 18 kΩ at 1/4, 6 kΩ at
    1/2, 2 kΩ at 3/4, 0 Ω at full-scale

2. $V_2 = VR_2/(R_1 + R_2)$. Since V_2 is more than half
    V, the voltage across R_2 is larger than that across
    R_1, so $R_2 > R_1$. $R_1 = VR_2/V_2 - R_2$
    $= (6.0 \text{ V})(330 \text{ }\Omega)/(5.0 \text{ V}) - 330 \text{ }\Omega = 66 \text{ }\Omega$

3. The equivalent resistance of the three $30.0^{-1} \text{ }\Omega$
    resistors in parallel is
    $$\dfrac{1}{R} = \dfrac{1}{30.0 \text{ }\Omega} + \dfrac{1}{30.0 \text{ }\Omega} + \dfrac{1}{30.0 \text{ }\Omega} = \dfrac{3}{30.0 \text{ }\Omega}$$
    $$R = \dfrac{30.0 \text{ }\Omega}{3} = 10.0 \text{ }\Omega$$
    $R_{Total} = 10.0 \text{ }\Omega + 10.0 \text{ }\Omega = 20.0 \text{ }\Omega$
    $$I_1 = \dfrac{V}{R_{Total}} = \dfrac{45.0 \text{ V}}{20.0 \text{ }\Omega} = 2.25 \text{ A}$$
    $V_1 = I_1R = (2.25 \text{ A})(10 \text{ }\Omega) = 22.5 \text{ V}$
    An ammeter has an internal resistance of zero, so
    $V_2 = V_3 = 45.0 \text{ V} - 22.5 \text{ V} = 22.5 \text{ V}$
    $$I_2 = \dfrac{V_2}{R_2} = \dfrac{22.5}{30.0 \text{ }\Omega} = 0.750 \text{ A}$$

4. In the 10-Ω resistor,
    $P_1 = I_1V_1 = (2.25 \text{ A})(22.5 \text{ V}) = 50.6 \text{ W}$
    In each of the 30-Ω resistors the power will be
    equal to
    $P = IV = (0.750 \text{ A})(22.5 \text{ V}) = 16.9 \text{ W}.$

5. The three 15-Ω resistors in parallel have an equiv-
    alent resistance of
    $$\dfrac{1}{R} = \dfrac{1}{15.0 \text{ }\Omega} + \dfrac{1}{15.0 \text{ }\Omega} + \dfrac{1}{15.0 \text{ }\Omega} = \dfrac{3}{15.0 \text{ }\Omega}$$
    $$R = \dfrac{15.0 \text{ }\Omega}{3} = 5.00 \text{ }\Omega$$

The equivalent resistance of the 40.0-Ω and 60.0-Ω in parallel is

$$\frac{1}{R} = \frac{1}{60.0\ \Omega} + \frac{1}{40.0\ \Omega} = \frac{2}{120\ \Omega} + \frac{3}{120\ \Omega}$$

$$= \frac{5}{120\ \Omega}$$

$$R = \frac{120\ \Omega}{5} = 24.0\ \Omega$$

The total resistance in the circuit is
$R_{Total} = 10.0\ \Omega + 5.00\ \Omega + 6.00\ \Omega + 24.0\ \Omega$
$= 45.0\ \Omega$

The total current passing through the circuit is I_3,

$$I_3 = \frac{V}{R_{Total}} = \frac{90.0\ V}{45.0\ \Omega} = 2.00\ A$$

$V_1 = I_3R = (2.00\ A)(10.0\ \Omega) = 20.0\ V$
$V_2 = I_3R = (2.00\ A)(6.00\ \Omega) = 12.0\ V$
I_3 divides itself equally in the three 15.0-Ω resistors,

so $I_1 = \frac{I_3}{3} = \frac{2.00\ A}{3} = 0.667\ A$

The voltage drop across the 15.0 Ω is
$V = IR = (2.00\ A)(5.00\ \Omega) = 10.0\ V$
The sum of the voltage drops across the resistors in the circuit is 90.0 V.
$90.0\ V = V_1 + 10.0\ V + V_2 + V_3$
$\qquad = 20.0\ V + 10.0\ V + 12.0\ V + V_3$
$\quad V_3 = 48.0\ V$

$$I_2 = \frac{V_3}{R} = \frac{48.0\ V}{60.0\ \Omega} = 0.800\ A$$

6. a. $R = 0.25\ \Omega + 0.25\ \Omega + 240\ \Omega = 240\ \Omega$

b. $I = \frac{V}{R} = \frac{120\ V}{240\ \Omega} = 0.50\ A$

$P = IV = (0.50\ A)(120\ V) = 60\ W$

c. $V = IR = (0.50\ A)(0.50\ \Omega) = 0.25\ V$

7. a. $\frac{1}{R} = \frac{1}{240\ \Omega} + \frac{1}{6.0\ \Omega}$

$\quad R = 5.9\ \Omega$

$\quad R_{eff} = 5.9\ \Omega + 0.25\ \Omega + 0.25\ \Omega = 6.4\ \Omega$

b. $I = \frac{V}{R} = \frac{120\ V}{6.4\ \Omega} = 19\ A$

c. $V = IR = (19\ A)(0.50\ \Omega) = 9.5\ V$

d. $V = 120\ V - 9.5\ V = 110\ V$
This will cause a momentary dimming.

8. a.

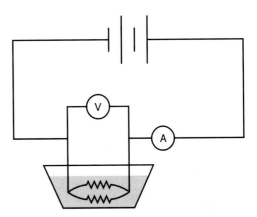

b. $\Delta Q = mc\Delta T = (100.0\ g)(4.2\ J/g \cdot C°)(75\ C°)$
$\qquad = 32\ 000\ J$
$\Delta Q = mL_v = (100.0\ g)(2300\ J/g)$
$\qquad = 230\ 000\ J$
$\Delta Q_{Total} = 32\ 000\ J + 230\ 000\ J = 260\ 000\ J$
Energy is provided at the rate of
$P = IV = (5.0\ A)(50.0\ V) = 250\ J/s$

The time required is $t = \dfrac{260\ 000\ J}{250\ J/s}$

$\qquad = 1.0 \times 10^3\ s$

9. a. $V = IR = (2\ A)(3\ \Omega) = 6\ V$
Resistors always reduce voltage, so the change is $-6\ V$.

b. The battery adds 6 V, so the voltage drop from A to C is zero.

c. $V = IR = (2\ A)(2\ \Omega) = 4\ V$ Again, it is negative. The battery drops the voltage by 12 V, so the total drop from A to D is 12 V + 4 V = 16 V.

Magnetic Fields

Overview

This chapter introduces the basic properties of magnets, the concept of the magnetic field, and the unit of magnetic induction. Both the SI unit of magnetic induction, tesla, and its equivalence, newton per ampere-meter, are used in this chapter. In Chapter 22, the electric field was defined. The electric field exerts forces on static charges. This is compared to the magnetic field, which exerts forces on moving charges.

This chapter contains less quantitative material than most, as right-hand rules are used to predict the direction of forces and fields. Electromagnetism is defined and the fields about variously shaped current-bearing wires are found by using right-hand rules. The force on a moving charge in a magnetic field is treated quantitatively.

Planning Guide (6 Class Sessions)

Text Section	Demonstrations and Experiments	Other Program Components
25:1 General Properties of Magnets **P** **25:2** Magnetic Fields Around Permanent Magnets **P**	Dem 25:1 Comparing Natural Forces, Which Is Magnetized? Exp 45 Magnetic Fields Around Magnets **LM** Exp 46 Magnetic Fields Around a Current-Bearing Wire **LM** Dem 25:2 Magnetic Field Lines Exp 47 Current and Field Strength **LM**	Minilab 25-1: A Simple Meter **TRP** Enrichment 25-1: The Doorbell **TRP** Enrichment 25-2: The Earth's Magnetic Field **TRP**
25:3 Electromagnetism **P** **25:4** Magnetic Field Near a Coil **P**	Dem 25:3 Oersted Apparatus Dem 25:4 Electromagnetics	Teaching Master 25-1: (a) Right-Hand Rule: Straight Wire (b) Right-Hand Rule: Electromagnet **TRP**
25:5 Magnetic Materials **S**	Dem 25:5 Magnetic Materials	
25:6 Forces on Currents in Magnetic Fields **P** **25:7** Measuring the Force on a Wire **S** **25:8** Galvanometers **S** **25:9** Electric Motors **P** **25:10** The Force on a Single Charged Particle	Dem 25:6 Jumping Wire, Aluminum Foil Wave	Teaching Master 25-2: Right-Hand Rule: Direction of Force **TRP** Review Masters **TRP** Demonstration 25-1: Magnetic Fields Around Current-Carrying Wires **TRP** Demonstration 25-2: Current-Carrying Wires in a Magnetic Field **TRP** Demonstration 25-3: Forces Between Parallel Current-Carrying Wires **TRP** Enrichment 25-3: Monopoles **TRP** Evaluation **TRP**

Performance Objectives

Upon completion of this chatper, your students will

1. list the properties of magnets.   25:1
2. describe the magnetic fields around permanent magnets and the field lines between like and unlike poles.   25:2
3. recognize that electric currents produce magnetic fields; describe the field around a current-carrying wire; explain the use of the right-hand rule in finding the direction of this field.   25:3
4. explain the magnetic field due to several loops of wire; apply the right-hand rule to determine the direction.   25:4
5. describe the origin of magnetism in materials. 25:5
6. define magnetic induction; explain the direction of the force on a current-carrying wire in a magnetic field.   25:6
7. list the factors that determine the force on a wire; solve problems involving a wire in a magnetic field.   25:7
8. explain the design and operation of the galvanometer.   25:8
9. explain the design and operation of the electric motor.   25:9
10. list the factors that determine the force on a moving charge in a magnetic field; solve problems involving this force.   25:10

Teaching the Chapter

Introduction

Using the Photo: Rare earth magnets have relatively strong magnetic fields and low masses. An ALNICO magnet would be too heavy, for its associated field, to be repelled from the superconductor. A superconductor has two properties—zero electrical resistance below some critical current and temperature and, in the presence of an external magnetic field, it will generate a surface current, which does not allow the magnetic field lines to penetrate the superconductor's surface. As a result, a magnetic repulsive force levitates the magnet above the superconductor. This photograph also can be used with the introduction to Chapter 25 to discuss magnetic materials, and with Section 25:6 to discuss forces on currents in magnetic fields.

Demonstration: Have some nails, paper clips, and thumbtacks lying on a table. Ask students what forces are being exerted on these objects. Bring a magnet near the objects and lift them off the table. The magnetic force is greater than the gravitational force. You may wish to review the fundamental forces in nature that were discussed in Chapter 5.

25:1 General Properties of Magnets

Do as many demonstrations and hands-on activities as possible in this chapter. Set up stations with the equipment needed to do labs, mini-labs, and demonstrations from the *Teacher Resource Package* and *Laboratory Physics.* Have students rotate to the different stations, observing and making notes of their observations. When all the activities are completed, discuss students' observations and summarize the meanings of their results.

Demonstration: Ask a student how he or she can tell, given two bars of iron, which is magnetized and which is not. If the student makes a T out of the bars of iron, the one that is not a magnet will not fasten to the middle of the other bar.

25:2 Magnetic Fields Around Permanent Magnets

Demonstration: Demonstrate field patterns with bar magnets and iron filings. You can do this for all to see using an overhead projector and a thin sheet of glass. Place magnets on the projector under the glass and sprinkle filings on the glass. Iron filings in a liquid encased in plastic may be used instead of loose filings.

25:3 Electromagnetism

Demonstration: A simple Oersted apparatus can be made by securing an inverted rectangular U-shaped metal bar to a piece of Lucite that fits on the overhead. Suspend a compass needle from the bar. When a large current is sent through the loop, the compass needle will line up perpendicular to the loop. Reversing the current reverses the direction the needle points. Pictures of this apparatus are in catalogs under Oersted's Law Apparatus.

25:4 Magnetic Field Near a Coil

Demonstration: Make several electromagnets, each with a different number of windings of wire. Show how the number of windings affects the strength of the electromagnet. Vary the current in one electromagnet to demonstrate the effect of current and remove the core to show its effect.

Mention some of the uses of electromagnets, such as circuit breakers and in lifting large bundles of scrap metal. Electromagnets may also be used to move cold iron ingots.

25:5 Magnetic Materials

Demonstration: Place sheets of various materials (wood, paper, cloth, aluminum foil, steel sheet) between a magnet and a paper clip. Use varying thicknesses to determine if thickness affects the ability of the magnet to pick up the paper clip. Magnetism penetrates most materials except those capable of being magnetized.

25:6 Forces on Currents in Magnetic Fields

Demonstration: Hang an insulated, flexible braided copper wire from two ring stands so it sags down to the table. Adjust the wire so it is hanging between the poles of a strong magnet. Place a 1.5 V battery and switch in the circuit. When you close the switch, the wire jumps. You can reverse the direction of the current or orientation of the magnet and observe the results.

Demonstration: Another demonstration to show the force on a current-carrying wire is to place a strip of very thin aluminum foil between the poles of horseshoe magnets. Stand up three strong horseshoe magnets about two inches apart so the poles alternate and they form a kind of tunnel. Run the aluminum foil between the magnets. Attach the ends of the foil with wire to a variable low-voltage DC power supply. Start out at low current and increase slowly. The aluminum strip arches in two places, showing there is a force on it. Reverse the current and observe. Very thin foil can be obtained by unrolling a 0.02 microfarad paper dielectric capacitor, which may be obtained in an electronic supply store.

25:9 Electric Motors

Help students understand that the armature of a motor turns because of the force on a current-carrying wire in a magnetic field. Obtain at least one St. Louis motor. Have students take turns doing "The DC Generator; the DC Motor" in *Laboratory Physics*.

25:10 The Force on a Single Charged Particle

Bringing a magnet near the face of an oscilloscope demonstrates the force of a magnetic field on a beam of electrons. Have students use the right-hand rule to predict the direction of the force.

Resources

Literature

Cipalla, A.J., "The Oersted Effect on the Overhead," *The Physics Teacher*, November, 1975, p. 475.

Edge, R.D., "Experiments with Nickels and Magnets," *The Physics Teacher*, February, 1981, pp. 124–126.

Ellis, Arthur B., "Superconductors—Better Levitation Through Chemistry," *Journal of Chemical Education*, October, 1987, pp. 836–841.

Fisher, Arthur, "Superconductivity," *Popular Science*, April, 1988, pp. 54–58.

Gottlieb, Herbert, "Force on Current Carrying Aluminum Foil," *The Physics Teacher*, November, 1967, p. 387.

Grace, G., and Barnhaed, R., "Current Technology—Superconductors," *The Science Teacher*, April, 1988, pp. 22–24.

Miller, Jr., Franklin, *College Physics*, Harcourt Brace Jovanovich, San Diego, 1982, pp. 482–487.

Nicklin, R.C., "Force Between Parallel Currents on the Overhead Projector," *The Physics Teacher*, September, 1978, p. 402.

Turner, Raymond, "A Physics Toy: Magnetic Seal and Ball," *The Physics Teacher*, December, 1987, pp. 568–569.

Wolsky, A.M., Giese, R.F., and Daniels, E.J., "The New Superconductors: Prospects for Applications," *Scientific American*, February, 1989, p. 60.

Software/Audiovisual

3-D Grapher; Waits, Scheick, Demana, New, and Edwards, Addison-Wesley.

Background

The formulas $F = BIL$ and $F = Bqv$ are good only when the current or charge is moving at right angles to the magnetic field. The formulas are really cross products, $F = qv \times B$ and $F = IL \times B$. A more general form of the equations is $F = qvB \sin \theta$ and $F = ILB \sin \theta$. θ is the angle between the wire and B or v and B. These equations allow you to calculate the force on a charged particle or current-bearing wire regardless of the angle. You can also see that the force is a maximum at 90° where $\sin \theta = 1$ and zero when v and B or the wire and B are parallel and $\sin \theta = 0$.

Chapter Review

QUESTIONS

1. Like poles repel one another; opposites attract.
2. iron, cobalt, and nickel
3. A temporary magnet is a magnet only while under the influence of another magnet. A permanent magnet needs no outside influence.
4. Move it to the other pole—if the same end is attracted, it is a temporary magnet. If the other end is attracted, it is a permanent magnet.
5. See text pg. 427
6. See text pg. 427
7. See text pg. 429
8. Grasp wire with the right hand keeping thumb pointing in the direction of the conventional current flow. Fingers will encircle wire and point in the direction of the field.
9. Grasp coil with the right hand keeping fingers encircling coil in the direction of the conventional current flow through the loops. Thumb of right hand will point at the north-seeking pole of the electromagnet.
10. Point fingers of the right hand in the direction of the magnetic field. Point thumb in direction of conventional current flow in wire. Palm of hand then faces in direction of force on wire.
11. Field is circular in the counter-clockwise direction.
12. **a.** between the two wires
    b. along a plane that is equal in distance from each wire
    c. along a plane that is equal in distance from each wire
13. parallel to the field
14. velocity forward, force upward, B is to the left.

APPLYING CONCEPTS

1. Use a compass. The N-pole of the compass needle is attracted toward the S-pole and vice-versa.
2. perpendicular to the plane of the coil. The right-hand rule would be used to find the direction of the field produced by the coil. The field in the room is in the same direction.
3. No; superconductors expel all magnetic fields from them. They are not attracted as are ferromagnetic elements.
4. The magnet causes the domains in the iron to point in the same direction. The charged rod separates the positive and negative charges in the insulator.
5. No; the force is always perpendicular to the velocity. No work is done. The energy is not changed.
6. equal by Newton's Third Law
7. The radii of the paths would be larger over the equator. The field is weaker there, so the force is smaller. The velocity is the same, so, given $a = v^2/r$, the radius must be larger.
8. No; new poles would form on the broken ends.

9. Wrap the wire around the compass. Briefly connect the wire to the battery. Use the right-hand rule to identify the direction of the field produced by the current. The end of the compass needle that points in the direction of the field is the N-pole.

10. The electrons are not all oriented and moving in the same direction.

11. No; if a field is parallel to the wire, no force would result.

EXERCISES

1. $B = \dfrac{F}{IL} = \dfrac{0.40 \text{ N}}{8.0 \text{ A} \times 0.50 \text{ m}}$
   $= 0.10 \text{ N/A} \cdot \text{m} = 0.10 \text{ T}$

2. $F = BIL = (0.30 \text{ N/A} \cdot \text{m})(6.0 \text{ A})(0.25 \text{ m})$
   $= 0.45 \text{ N}$

3. $B = \dfrac{F}{IL} = \dfrac{0.60 \text{ N}}{10.0 \text{ A} \times 1.50 \text{ m}} = 0.040 \text{ N/A} \cdot \text{m}$
   $= 4.0 \times 10^{-2} \text{ T}$

4. $F = BIL = (0.60 \text{ N/A} \cdot \text{m})(5.0 \text{ A})(0.80 \text{ m})$
   $= 2.4 \text{ N}$

5. $I = \dfrac{F}{BL} = \dfrac{0.12 \text{ N}}{(5 \times 10^{-5} \text{ N/A} \cdot \text{m})(0.80 \text{ m})}$
   $= 3 \times 10^3 \text{ A}$

6. $L = \dfrac{F}{BI} = \dfrac{3.6 \text{ N}}{(0.80 \text{ N/A} \cdot \text{m})(7.5 \text{ A})} = 0.60 \text{ m}$

7. $v = F/qB = \dfrac{4.1 \times 10^{-13} \text{ N}}{(0.61 \text{ N/A} \cdot \text{m})(1.6 \times 10^{-19} \text{ C})}$
   $= 4.2 \times 10^6 \text{ m/s}$

8. $F = Bqv \quad q = F/Bv$
   $\text{particles} = q\left(\dfrac{\text{charges}}{1.6 \times 10^{-19} \text{ C}}\right)$
   $= \dfrac{F}{Bv}\left(\dfrac{\text{charges}}{1.6 \times 10^{-19} \text{ C}}\right)$
   $= \dfrac{(5.78 \times 10^{-16} \text{ N})(\text{charges})}{(3.2 \times 10^{-2} \text{ T})(5.65 \times 10^4 \text{ m/s})}$
   $\qquad (1.6 \times 10^{-19} \text{ C})$
   $= 2 \text{ charges}$

9. $B = \dfrac{F}{qv} = \dfrac{(5.00 \times 10^{-12} \text{ N})}{(4.21 \times 10^7 \text{ m/s})(1.6 \times 10^{-19} \text{ C})}$
   $= 7.4 \times 10^{-1} \text{ T}$

10. $a = \dfrac{F}{m} = \dfrac{(5.00 \times 10^{-12} \text{ N})}{(1.88 \times 10^{-28} \text{ kg})}$
    $= 2.66 \times 10^{16} \text{ m/s}^2$

11. $F = (0.60 \text{ T})(1.6 \times 10^{-19} \text{ C})(2.5 \times 10^7 \text{ m/s})$
    $= 2.4 \times 10^{-12} \text{ N}$

12. $F = ma$
    $a = \dfrac{F}{m} = \dfrac{2.4 \times 10^{-12} \text{ N}}{9.11 \times 10^{-31} \text{ kg}} = 2.6 \times 10^{18} \text{ m/s}^2$

13. $F = (6.0 \times 10^{-2} \text{ T})(1.6 \times 10^{-19} \text{ C})(2.5 \times 10^6 \text{ m/s})$
    $= 2.4 \times 10^{-14} \text{ N}$

14. $I = F/BL = (1.8 \text{ N})/(0.40 \text{ T})(625 \text{ m})$
    $= 7.2 \text{ mA}$

15. **a.** $F/L = IB = (225 \text{ A})(5.0 \times 10^{-5} \text{ T})$
    $= 0.011 \text{ N/m}$
    b. north
    c. No; the force is much smaller than the weight of the wires.

16. $I = V/R = (15 \text{ V})/(8.0 \text{ }\Omega)$
    $= 1.88 \text{ A}$
    $L = 250\pi(0.025 \text{ m})$
    $= 19.6 \text{ m}$
    $F = BIL = (0.15 \text{ T})(1.88 \text{ A})(19.6 \text{ m}) = 5.5 \text{ N}$

PROBLEMS

1. **a.** $F = Bqv$
   $= (0.10 \text{ T})(1.6 \times 10^{-19} \text{ C})(3.0 \times 10^7 \text{ m/s})$
   $= 4.8 \times 10^{-13} \text{ N}$
   b. $r = \dfrac{mv^2}{F}$
   $= \dfrac{(1.67 \times 10^{-27} \text{ kg})(3.0 \times 10^7 \text{ m/s})^2}{4.8 \times 10^{-13} \text{ N}}$
   $= 3.1 \text{ m}$

2. **a.** P_2 to P_1
   b. $E = (20\ 000 \text{ J/C})(1.6 \times 10^{-19} \text{ C})$
   $= 3.2 \times 10^{-15} \text{ J}$
   $E = \dfrac{1}{2}mv^2$
   $v = \sqrt{\dfrac{2E}{m}} = \sqrt{\dfrac{(2)(3.2 \times 10^{-15} \text{ J})}{(9.0 \times 10^{-31} \text{ kg})}}$
   $= 8.4 \times 10^7 \text{ m/s}$
   c. clockwise

3. The spring will oscillate up and down. Current will cause the coils to attract each other, raising the coil from the mercury.

4. **a.** $R = V/I = (10 \text{ V})/(50 \times 10^{-6} \text{ A})$
   $= 2 \times 10^5 \text{ }\Omega = 200 \text{ k}\Omega$
   b. Total resistance $= 200 \text{ k}\Omega$, so series resistor is $200 \text{ k}\Omega - 1.0 \text{ k}\Omega = 199 \text{ k}\Omega$

5. **a.** $V = IR = (50 \times 10^{-6}$ A$)(1 \times 10^{3}$ $\Omega)$
$= 5 \times 10^{-2}$ V

b. $R = V/I = \quad \times 10^{-2}$ N$)/(1 \times 10^{-2}$ A$)$
$= 5.0$ Ω

c. $1/R_1 = 1/R - 1/R_2$
$= 1/5.0$ $\Omega - 1/(1.0 \times 10^{3}$ $\Omega)$
$R_1 = 5.0$ Ω

6. $F = Bqv = (16$ T$)(1.6 \times 10^{-19}$ C$)$
$(8.1 \times 10^{5}$ m/s$) = 2.1 \times 10^{-12}$ N,
upward (right-hand rule)

7. **a.** $F = BIL = (0.85$ T$)(15$ A$)(0.25$ m$) = 3.2$ N

b. $F = BIL \sin \theta$
$= (0.85$ T$)(15$ A$)(0.25$ m$)(\sin 45°) = 2.3$ N

c. 0.0 N

Electromagnetic Induction

Overview

The previous chapter discussed the magnetic fields around current-carrying wires and how these are used to convert electrical energy into mechanical energy in a motor. Chapter 26 introduces the generation of electric currents by the relative motion of a wire and a magnetic field. This is a conversion of mechanical energy into electrical energy. The current generated depends on the strength of the field, the length of the wire, and the velocity of the wire.

Generators can deliver AC or DC current. The effective voltage and current in an AC circuit can be calculated. Lenz's law explains back-*EMF* in a motor. As the current in a coil changes, an induced *EMF* appears and is called self-inductance. The opposition to alternating current flow by a coil is called inductive reactance.

Planning Guide (6 Class Sessions)

Text Section		Demonstrations and Experiments	Other Program Components	
26:1 Faraday's Discovery	P	Dem 26:1 Generating an EMF, Varying Induced Current	Teaching Master 26-1: Right-Hand Rule: Current Through a Conductor	TRP
26:2 Electromotive Force	P	Exp 48 Induced Current and Lenz's Law **LM**	Teaching Master 26-2: Direction of Current in a Loop in a Magnetic Field	TRP
26:3 Electric Generators	P	Exp 49 The DC Generator, the DC Motor **LM**	Demonstration 26-1: The Generator-Motor Effect	TRP
26:4 Alternating Current Generator	P	Exp 50 Energy Transfer by an Electric Motor **LM**	Enrichment 26-1: Michael Faraday	TRP
26:5 Lenz's Law	S	Dem 26:3 Motor or Generator?, Using Galvanometers as a Motor-Generator System	Enrichment 26-2: Trains and Hills	TRP
			Enrichment 26-3: Maglev Trains	TRP
26:6 Self-Inductance	S	Dem 26:7 Parameters of a DC Transformer, AC Transformer	Review Masters	TRP
26:7 Transformers	P		Minilab 26-1: Inducing Currents	TRP
			Evaluation	TRP

Performance Objectives

Upon completion of this chapter, your students will

1. explain the process by which a changing magnetic field produces an electric current. *26:1*

2. define *EMF*; state the meaning of the terms BLv that give the magnitude of the *EMF*; understand the limitations of this equation; apply to the solution of problems. *26:2*

3. explain the generation of current by a rotating armature in an electric generator; compare generators and motors. *26:3*

4. explain the difference between peak and effective current and voltage and use in solving problems. *26:4*

5. state Lenz's law; explain back-*EMF* and its relation

7. describe the transformer; explain the effect of the ratio of turns in the primary and secondary; solve transformer problems. *26:7*

6. explain the nature of self-inductance and its effects in AC and DC circuits. *26:6*

to energy transfer in motors and generators. *26:5*

Teaching the Chapter

Introduction

Using the Photo: The changing flux induces a current in the continuous aluminum ring. The current flowing in the ring creates a magnetic field that opposes the flux that induced the current (Lenz's law). Thus the ring is repelled. The split ring does not permit current to flow, so no opposing flux is created. This photograph also can be used with Section 26:1 to discuss Faraday's Discovery and Section 26:5 to discuss Lenz's Law.

Demonstration: Make a coil of heavy-gauge copper wire about 12 cm in diameter with about 60 loops of wire. Attach the ends of the wire to a flash bulb (AG1B flash bulbs work well). Now slowly put the bottom half of the coil through the poles of a **very** strong horseshoe magnet. Pull the coil out rapidly, and the flash bulb will light. This demonstration shows the generation of an *EMF* by movement of a wire in a magnetic field.

26:1 Faraday's Discovery

If possible, set up stations as in Chapter 25 to give students hands-on experience. If this is not possible, obtain large demonstration meters or overhead projection meters.

Demonstration: Connect a length of wire to a sensitive galvanometer and move the wire through the poles of a strong magnet. Show that the needle moves only when the wire moves and that the faster the motion, the greater the deflection. Show that the direction of the deflection depends on the direction of wire motion. Invert the magnet and see how it affects the direction of the current. Gather loops of wire and show how the length of wire affects the current. Make sure students realize that the wire could be stationary and the magnet in motion to give the same result. It is the relative motion that is important.

26:2 Electromotive Force

If an old microphone is available, take it apart to identify the magnet and coil of wire. Explain how the

sound waves vibrate the diaphragm and cause the coil of wire to move in the magnetic field, producing an *EMF* at the ends of the coil.

26:3 Electric Generators

Demonstration: Connect a simple motor (St. Louis type) to a battery and demonstrate the transformation of electrical energy to mechanical energy. Then disconnect the battery and connect a galvanometer to the wires. Flip the armature and show the transformation of mechanical to electrical energy. By varying the speed with which you flip the armature, you can easily demonstrate that the current generated is proportional to the speed with which the wire moves through the field.

Demonstration: You can also demonstrate the motor-generator with two galvanometers. Connect two identical galvanometers. Pick up one and wiggle it. You are providing mechanical energy and making the coil rotate in the magnetic field. An *EMF* is induced in the coil. The first galvanometer acts as a generator. The second galvanometer converts the electric energy from the first galvanometer into mechanical energy, and the needle moves. The second galvanometer acts as a motor.

26:5 Lenz's Law

Demonstration: Connect an ammeter in series with a motor. Have students observe current when the motor is turned on, running at high speed, and turning with a heavy load.

When the motor is first turned on, the current is fairly high. As the motor starts turning, its loop of wire cutting through the magnetic field acts as a generator. This produces a current that opposes the current supplied to the motor, and the ammeter reading drops.

26:7 Transformers

Obtain some induction coils for the study of the effects of the core and the number of windings on the

EMF induced in a transformer. If possible, have the students work with the coils.

Demonstration: Attach the terminals of a large coil to a dry cell and switch. Hook the terminals of a small coil to a galvanometer. Ask students what factors should be varied and then look at the galvanometer needle as you change them. Study the galvanometer readings as you vary the movement of the coil, the amount of coil you have overlapping, the amount of core inside the coil, and the opening and closing of the switch.

Demonstration: There are several demonstrations that can be done with a large AC induction coil. First make two coils with some heavy copper wire and close the circuit with a 1.5 V flashlight bulb. With the AC current in the induction coil, bring the coil with the bulb over the iron core. As you approach it, the bulb glows and gets brighter the closer you come. The bulb can burn out if you are not careful.

If students find the concepts of electricity very difficult, some kind of summary, perhaps in chart form, of Chapters 25 and 26 may help them better understand the concepts.

Chapter Review

QUESTIONS

1. They are similar in that electricity and magnetism are interrelated. They are different in that a steady electric current produces a magnetic field, but a change in magnetic field is needed to produce an electric current.

2. electromotive force
   It is not a force but a potential (energy per unit charge).

3. $EMF = BLv = (N/A \cdot m)(m)(m/s)$
$$= \frac{N}{A \cdot m} \left| \frac{m}{s} \right| \frac{m}{s} \left| \frac{1\ A}{1\ C/s} \right| \frac{1\ J}{1\ N \cdot m} = 1\ J/C = 1\ V$$

4. See page 450.

5. The armature of an electric generator consists of a number of wire loops wound around an iron core and placed in a strong magnetic field. As it rotates in the magnetic field, the loops cut through magnetic field lines and an electric current is induced.

Resources

Literature

Ferguson, J.L., "Turn-by-Turn Transformer Demonstration," *The Physics Teacher,* January, 1979, p. 59.

Harrich, Lloyd, "AC Made Visible," *The Physics Teacher,* October, 1984, p. 448.

Lantz, C., and Anderson, C.H., "Why Is the AC Power Line Grounded?" *The Physics Teacher,* April, 1980, p. 314.

Miller, Jr., Franklin, *College Physics,* Harcourt Brace Jovanovich, San Diego, 1982, pp. 501–504.

Miner, T.D., "Lenz's Law Demonstration," *The Physics Teacher,* November, 1968, p. 427.

Background

The formula $EMF = BLv$ is used only when B and v are at right angles to each other. In Chapter 25 this was discussed for the equations $F = BIL$ and $F = Bqv$. The general form of the equation for EMF is $EMF = Blv \sin \theta$ where θ is the angle between v and B. EMF is a maximum when θ is 90° and minimum when $\theta = 0°$ or the wire is moving parallel to the field. This can help students to understand the fluctuation in the magnitude of the current as the coil of wire is turned in the magnetic field.

6. Iron is used in an armature to increase the strength of the magnetic field.

7. In a generator, mechanical energy turns an armature in a magnetic field. The induced voltage causes current to flow. In a motor, a voltage is placed across an armature coil in a magnetic field. The voltage causes current to flow in the coil and the armature turns, producing mechanical energy.

8. In an alternating current generator, as the armature turns, the alternating current varies between some maximum value and zero. Since the current varies, the effective value of the current delivered by an alternating current generator is less than its maximum value.

9. An induced current always acts in such a direction that its magnetic properties oppose the change by which the current is induced.

10. current

11. a. Yes, voltage is greatest when the motion of the wire is horizontal, or perpendicular (90°) to the magnetic field lines. It decreases as the angle decreases between the motion of the wire and the magnetic field lines. Voltage is zero when the motion of the wire and the magnetic field lines are parallel.

b. The largest voltage is generated when the motion of the wire is horizontal and fully perpendicular to the magnetic field lines.

12. Move the magnet in or out through the coil.

13. The direction of the current reverses.

14. Change speed, length of wire (number of loops) in the magnetic field, and direction of motion.

15. It is larger a long time after the connection is made. The back-*EMF* opposes current flow just after the current starts to flow.

16. This is Lenz's law. Once the motor starts turning, it behaves as a generator and will generate current in opposition to the current being put into the motor.

17. An alternating current is always changing magnitude and direction. Therefore, self-induction is a constant factor. A direct current becomes steady quite rapidly and so there is no changing magnetic field after a short time.

18. The ratio of number of turns of wire in the primary to the number of turns of wire in the secondary determines the *EMF* ratio.

APPLYING CONCEPTS

1. No. Current and voltage change sign together. Energy transfer is proportional to the product I*V*, which is always the same sign.

2. The bulb will light because the current flows in the secondary circuit. This will happen whenever the primary current changes; it will glow both when the switch is closed and when it is opened.

3. Transformers allow distributing the energy at high potential, using it at low voltages, and reducing losses in transmission.

4. As Faraday discovered, only a *changing* magnetic field induces *EMF* and thus current flow.

5. The vacuum cleaner contains a motor, and thus a coil. The self-inductance produces a back-*EMF* that exists when the current to the motor is suddenly shut off.

6. a. Induced *EMF* is perpendicular to both the field and velocity, so field must be radial. Field lines go in toward S-pole, out from N-pole. By the right-hand rule, current is clockwise near S-pole, counter-clockwise near N-pole.

b. Near S-pole field inside the pipe is down, near N-pole it is up.

c. Induced field exerts an upward force on both poles.

7. There is potential energy in the stored water, kinetic energy in falling water and turning turbine, and electric energy in the generator.

8. No. It would violate the conservation of energy.

9. Yes. Energy is needed to light the lamp. It comes from your pedaling.

10. It would violate the law of conservation of energy. More energy would come out than went in. A generator would create energy, not just change it from one form to another.

11. The current flows from west to east.

EXERCISES

1. $EMF = BLv$
$$= (4.0 \times 10^{-2} \text{ T})(31 \text{ m})(15.0 \text{ m/s})$$
$$= 19 \text{ V}$$

2. a. $EMF = BLv$
$$= (0.30 \text{ T})(0.75 \text{ m})(16 \text{ m/s})$$
$$= 3.6 \text{ V}$$

b. $V = IR$
$$I = \frac{V}{R} = \frac{3.6 \text{ V}}{11 \ \Omega}$$
$$= 0.33 \text{ A}$$

3. $EMF = BLv = (0.50 \text{ T})(20.0 \text{ m})(4.0 \text{ m/s})$
$$= 4.0 \times 10^1 \text{ V}$$

4. a. $V_{eff} = 0.707 \ (V_{max})$
$$= 0.707 \ (150 \text{ V}) = 110 \text{ V}$$

b. $I_{eff} = 0.707 \ (I_{max})$
$$= 0.707 \ (30.0 \text{ A}) = 21.2 \text{ A}$$

c. $P_{eff} = I_{eff} \ V_{eff}$
$$= (21.2 \text{ A})(110 \text{ V}) = 2.3 \times 10^3 \text{ W}$$
$$= 2.3 \text{ kW}$$

5. a. $V_{max} = \dfrac{V_{eff}}{0.707} = \dfrac{220 \text{ V}}{0.707} = 310 \text{ V}$

b. $V = IR$
$$I = \frac{V}{R} = \frac{220 \text{ V}}{11 \ \Omega} = 2.0 \times 10^1 \text{ A}$$

6. The vertical component of magnetic field is
$B \sin 60° = (0.045 \text{ T})(\sin 60°) = 0.039 \text{ T}.$
$EMF = B_v Lv = (0.039 \text{ T})(2.5 \text{ m})(2.4 \text{ m/s})$
$\qquad = 0.23 \text{ V}$

7. $V_{eff} = 0.707 \, (V_{max}) = 0.707 \, (565 \text{ V}) = 399 \text{ V}$

8. a. $\dfrac{V_p}{V_s} = \dfrac{N_p}{N_s}$

$V_s = \dfrac{V_p N_s}{N_p} = \dfrac{(120 \text{ V})(1200)}{80} = 1800 \text{ V}$

b. $V_p I_p = V_s I_s$

$I_p = \dfrac{V_s I_s}{V_p} = \dfrac{(1800 \text{ V})(2.0 \text{ A})}{120 \text{ V}}$

$\qquad = 3.0 \times 10^1 \text{ A}$

c. $V_p I_p = (120 \text{ V})(3.0 \times 10^1 \text{ A}) = 3600 \text{ W}$
$V_s I_s = (1800 \text{ V})(2.0 \text{ A}) = 3600 \text{ W}$

9. a. $\dfrac{V_s}{V_p} = \dfrac{N_s}{N_p}$

$N_s = \dfrac{V_s N_p}{V_p} = \dfrac{(9.0 \text{ V})(475)}{(120 \text{ V})}$

$\qquad = 36 \text{ turns}$

b. $V_p I_p = V_s I_s$

$I_p = \dfrac{V_s I_s}{V_p} = \dfrac{(9.0 \text{ V})(125 \text{ mA})}{(120 \text{ V})}$

$\qquad = 9.4 \text{ mA}$

10. a. $\dfrac{N_p}{N_s} = \dfrac{V_p}{V_s} = \dfrac{1200 \text{ V}}{240\,000 \text{ V}} = \dfrac{1}{200}$

b. $V_p I_p = V_s I_s$

$I_s = \dfrac{V_p I_p}{V_s} = \dfrac{(1200 \text{ V})(40.0 \text{ A})}{240\,000 \text{ V}} = 0.20 \text{ A}$

11. $\dfrac{V_p}{V_s} = \dfrac{N_p}{N_s}$

$N_s = \dfrac{N_p V_s}{V_p}$

a. $N_s = \dfrac{(150)(6.0 \times 10^2 \text{ V})}{120 \text{ V}} = 750$

b. $N_s = \dfrac{(150)(3.0 \times 10^1 \text{ V})}{120 \text{ V}} = 37.5 = 38$

c. $N_s = \dfrac{(150)(6.0 \text{ V})}{120 \text{ V}} = 7.5$

12. The turns ratio is $\dfrac{8.0 \text{ V}}{24 \text{ V}} = \dfrac{1}{3}$.

Reversed it would be $\dfrac{3}{1}$.

Thus, the voltage would now be
$3(24 \text{ V}) = 72 \text{ V}.$

13. a. $\dfrac{V_p}{V_s} = \dfrac{N_p}{N_s} = \dfrac{(240 \text{ V})}{(120 \text{ V})} = \dfrac{2}{1}$

b. $V_p I_p = V_s I_s$

$I_p = \dfrac{V_s I_s}{V_p} = \dfrac{(120 \text{ V})(10.0 \text{ A})}{(240 \text{ V})}$

$\qquad = 5.0 \text{ A}$

14. $EMF = BLv$
$\qquad = (2.0 \times 10^{-2} \text{ T})(0.100 \text{ m})(1.0 \text{ m/s})$
$\qquad = 2.0 \times 10^{-3} \text{ V}$

$I = \dfrac{V}{R} = \dfrac{(2.0 \times 10^{-3} \text{ V})}{(875 \text{ }\Omega)}$

$\qquad = 2.3 \times 10^{-6} \text{ A}$

15. a. $\dfrac{V_p}{V_s} = \dfrac{N_p}{N_s}$

$V_s = \dfrac{V_p N_s}{N_p} = \dfrac{(1.20 \times 10^2 \text{ V})(1000)}{1}$

$\qquad = 1.20 \times 10^5 \text{ V}$

b. $V_p I_p = V_s I_s$

$I_s = \dfrac{V_p I_p}{V_s}$

$\qquad = \dfrac{(1.20 \times 10^2 \text{ V})(1.00 \times 10^2 \text{ A})}{(1.20 \times 10^5 \text{ V})}$

$\qquad = 0.100 \text{ A}$

PROBLEMS

1. a. The right-hand rule will show the current moving left.

b. The force will act in an upward direction.

2. a. $EMF = BLv$

$L = \dfrac{EMF}{Bv} =$

$\dfrac{12 \text{ V}}{(5.0 \times 10^{-5} \text{ T})(72.0 \times 10^3 \text{ m/h})(1/3600 \text{ s/h})}$

$\qquad = 1.2 \times 10^4 \text{ m}$

b. $V = IR$

$I = \dfrac{V}{R} = \dfrac{12 \text{ V}}{(2.6 \times 10^{-4} \text{ }\Omega/\text{m})(1.2 \times 10^4 \text{ m})}$

$\qquad = 3.8 \text{ A}$

3. a. 375 MW output means

$\dfrac{375 \text{ MW}}{(0.85)} = 441 \text{ MW input}$

b. $441 \text{ MW} = 441 \text{ MJ/s}$
$\qquad = 4.41 \times 10^8 \text{ J each second}$

c. $PE = mgh$

$m = \dfrac{PE}{gh} = \dfrac{(4.41 \times 10^8 \text{ J})}{(9.8 \text{ m/s}^2)(22 \text{ m})}$

$\qquad = 2.0 \times 10^6 \text{ kg each second}$

4. $EMF = BLv$

$\quad = \dfrac{(4.5 \times 10^{-5} \text{ T})(75 \text{ m})(950 \times 10^3 \text{ m/h})}{(3.6 \times 10^3 \text{ s/h})}$

$\quad = 8.9 \times 10^{-1} \text{ V}$

5. $EMF = BLv = (0.32 \text{ T})(0.40 \text{ m})(1.3 \text{ m/s})$

$\quad\quad\quad = 0.17 \text{ V}$

$\quad I = \dfrac{V}{R} = \dfrac{(0.17 \text{ V})}{(10 \text{ } \Omega)}$

$\quad\quad = 1.7 \times 10^{-2} \text{ A}$

6. a. $P = V_s I_s$

$\quad\quad V_s = \dfrac{P}{I_s} = \dfrac{(150 \text{ W})}{(5 \text{ A})}$

$\quad\quad\quad = 30 \text{ V}$

b. $\dfrac{30 \text{ V}}{9 \text{ V}} = \dfrac{10}{3}$

7. $V_p I_p = V_s I_s$

$\quad V_s = \dfrac{V_p I_p}{I_s} = \dfrac{(12 \text{ V})(3.0 \text{ A})}{(0.75 \text{ A})}$

$\quad\quad = 48 \text{ V}$

$\quad \dfrac{N_s}{N_p} = \dfrac{V_s}{V_p}$

$\quad N_p = \dfrac{N_s V_p}{V_s} = \dfrac{(1200)(12 \text{ V})}{(48 \text{ V})}$

$\quad\quad = 300 \text{ turns}$

Electric and Magnetic Fields

Overview

This chapter begins with the description of J. J. Thomson's experiment to find the electron mass. The masses of atoms and molecules are found using a mass spectrograph, which uses both magnetic and electric fields. The electric field accelerates the ions and the magnetic field deflects the ions according to mass.

Changing electric and magnetic fields couple to produce electromagnetic waves that move through space at the speed of light. The electromagnetic waves are produced by accelerated charges. The generation and reception of these electromagnetic waves is discussed.

Roentgen's discovery of high-frequency electromagnetic waves known as X rays is given. X rays are produced when high-speed electrons strike the anode of a cathode-ray tube. The kinetic energy of the electrons is converted into electromagnetic X rays.

Planning Guide (5 Class Sessions)

Text Section	Demonstrations and Experiments	Other Program Components
27:1 Mass of the Electron P **27:2** The Mass Spectrograph S	Dem 27:1 Interaction of Magnetic Fields Exp 51 Magnetic Field Strength (Magnetic Induction) **LM** Exp 52 Ratio of *g/m* for the Electron **LM** Dem 27:2 Path Deflecting	Teaching Master 27-1: Mass Spectrograph **TRP** Minilab 27-1: A Mass Spectrograph Model **TRP**
27:3 Electromagnetic Waves P **27:4** Production of Electromagnetic Waves S **27:5** Reception of Electromagnetic Waves S **27:6** X Rays S		Teaching Master 27-2: Electric and Magnetic Waves Through Space **TRP** Review Masters **TRP** Enrichment 27-1: Electromagnetic Waves **TRP** Enrichment 27-2: AM and FM Signals **TRP** Enrichment 27-3: Electromagnetic Fields and the Environment **TRP** Evaluation **TRP**

Performance Objectives

Upon completion of this chapter, your students will

1. describe Thomson's experiment measuring the mass-to-charge ratio of the electron; solve problems associated with this experiment. *27:1*

2. display an understanding of the mass spectrograph as an analytical tool; use data provided to solve problems. *27:2*

3. describe the coupling of electric and magnetic fields that produces electromagnetic waves. *27:3*

4. describe the generation of electromagnetic waves by accelerated charges; appreciate the use of resonance in many forms. *27:3, 27:4*

5. show knowledge of the frequency and wavelength of many common waves. *27:4*

6. explain the principles of the detection of electromagnetic waves. *27:5*

7. describe the nature and production of X rays. *27:6*

Teaching the Chapter

Introduction

Using the Photo: The parabolic reflector reflects very short-wavelength radio waves, just like a parabolic mirror reflects light. It produces a sharp reflected pattern as long as the dish is large compared to the wavelength of the radio frequency it is used to detect. This photograph can be used with Section 27:3 to discuss electromagnetic waves and Section 27:5 on reception of electromagnetic waves.

Demonstration: Use a cathode-ray tube to demonstrate that a magnetic field is associated with a moving stream of electrons. Approach the cathode-ray tube with the North pole of a magnet. Point out that the deflection of the beam is at right angles to the direction of the magnetic field. Remind students of the right-hand rule they learned in Chapter 25. **CAUTION:** *Do not let students operate the cathode-ray tube since it is a high-voltage piece of equipment.*

27:1 Mass of the Electron

The final chapters in the text deal with modern physics, which is rich in personalities and history. A brief sketch of the contributions of each of the famous scientists mentioned in these chapters will be helpful to the students. Most of the information provided in the notes for each section is from Asimov's book, *Biographical Encyclopedia of Science and Technology.* You may want to assign a scientist to each of your students to research and have them present reports on their scientist.

According to Asimov, J. J. Thomson was largely responsible for England's being at the forefront of subatomic particle physics for the first three decades of the twentieth century. Thomson's experiment on the charge-to-mass ratio for electrons opened up the field of subatomic particles.

Thomson was awarded the Nobel Prize in physics in 1906 for his work on the electron. At least six of Thomson's research assistants eventually won Nobel Prizes.

27:2 The Mass Spectrograph

Francis William Aston, the inventor of the mass spectrograph, worked under J. J. Thomson early in his career. Thomson had started experiments that showed all atoms of the same element did not have the same mass. Aston improved Thomson's instrument and designed it so all atoms of the same mass fell at the same line on a piece of photographic film. Neon was shown to have two lines, one for mass 20 and one for mass 22.

The instrument was called a mass spectrograph because it divided the elements into lines similar to a spectroscope. Aston was awarded the Nobel Prize in 1922 for his mass spectrograph.

Demonstration: Place a strong bar magnet on an overhead projector with a piece of plexiglas on top. Make the plexiglas large enough to extend about 20 cm over the edge of the overhead stage. Hold a piece of angle aluminum at an angle to the plexiglas and roll ball bearings down onto the plexiglas. Observe deflection by the magnet. Notice the effect of changing the speed or mass of the ball bearings.

27:3 Electromagnetic Waves

James Clark Maxwell was nicknamed Daffy by his peers because of his mathematical talents, which may have made him appear backward in other areas. He submitted original work to the Royal Society of Edinburgh at the age of fifteen. He met with William Nicol, the inventor of the Nicol prism, and became interested in light.

Maxwell became a professor at Aberdeen when he was twenty-six years old and made significant contributions to astronomy with his theory that Saturn's rings were not solid disks, but particles. Maxwell also worked on the kinetic theory of gases and is famous for working out the Maxwell-Boltzmann kinetic theory of gases. In 1871, Maxwell became the first physics professor at Cambridge. However, he lost most of his students because he talked over their heads. One student who remained and was inspired was J. J. Thomson.

Between the years of 1864 and 1873, Maxwell translated Faraday's description of magnetic lines of force into mathematical equations. He showed that electricity and magnetism cannot exist separately. He discovered that the speed of electromagnetic waves is the speed of light and further realized there is a whole spectrum of electromagnetic radiation of which light is only a part.

27:4 Production of Electromagnetic Waves

Piezoelectricity, from the Greek word meaning "to press," was discovered by Pierre Curie and his brother Jacques in 1880. They discovered that the potential across crystals of quartz and Rochelle salt varied directly with the pressure applied. Curie and his brother also realized that the reverse effect is possible. If a rapidly changing potential is applied, the crystal vibrates rapidly. These crystals are used in microphones and record players.

27:6 X Rays

The discovery of X rays is sometimes called the beginning of the Second Scientific Revolution. It is important to note that the discovery was somewhat accidental in nature. Wilhelm Konrad Roentgen was repeating some experiments on cathode rays previously done by William Crooke. While he was experimenting in a darkened room, he noticed a glow on a screen quite a distance away. He recognized that the cathode rays could not reach as far as the glowing material and that whatever was making this material glow was able to penetrate wood and other materials.

Roentgen recognized the importance of the discovery and kept it secret until he could do enough experiments to publish a paper. The medical use of X rays was immediately recognized. Unfortunately, the ability of X rays to cause cancer was not recognized until later. Roentgen was the first person to win the Nobel Prize in physics in 1901.

Resources

Literature

Asimov, Isaac, *Asimov's Biographical Encyclopedia of Science and Technology,* Doubleday and Company, Garden City, NY, 1982.

Gibney, Frank, editor, *How Things Work, Aerosols to Zippers,* Bantam/Britannica Books, New York, 1979, pp. 116–127.

Swartz, Clifford E., *Phenomenal Physics,* John Wiley and Sons, Inc., New York, 1981, pp. 655–683.

Young, Hugh D., "Radio and TV Reception," *The Physics Teacher,* March, 1984, p. 180.

Background

Why do AM signals fade when you drive under a bridge, but FM signals do not? The explanation has to do with the fact that FM wavelengths are small and AM wavelengths are long. The steel bridge behaves like a large mesh screen with holes a few meters in size. The shorter wavelength FM waves penetrate the girders quite well, but the longer wavelength AM waves are sometimes completely blocked.

Why does a TV picture flutter when a plane flies overhead? Television wavelengths are about one to six meters long. The airplane acts as a good reflector since it is much larger than the wavelength. The TV set receives two signals, one reflected directly from the transmitter and one reflected from the plane. The two wavelengths travel different distances to the TV receiver and may arrive in phase or out. As the plane moves, the path lengths change and the interference goes from constructive to destructive, causing fluttering in the picture.

Chapter Review

QUESTIONS

1. The top plate should be charged positively.
2. The magnetic field would be directed into the plane of the paper.
3. The magnetic field would be directed out the plane of the paper.
4. Electric fields are vertical and magnetic fields are horizontal.
5. Channel 2 requires a longer antenna because the length of an antenna is directly proportional to wavelength.
6. Channel 2 requires a larger capacitor because capacitance is inversely proportional to the EMF produced across the terminals of the antenna.
7. An induced magnetic field is always at right angles to the changing electric field.

8.
a. Radio waves have the longest wavelength.
b. X rays have the highest frequency.
c. All travel at the same velocity.

9. They vibrate.

10. Isotopes are atoms of the same element that have different masses.

APPLYING CONCEPTS

1. The antenna is 1 cm long.

2. Much larger, because the wavelength of microwave radiation is so much larger than that of visible light.

3. See Figure 27–6b.

4. Yes. The equation $v = \dfrac{E}{B}$ is independent of the mass or charge of the particle.

5. Change either both or neither, never only one.

6. By adjusting the capacitance of the antenna circuit the oscillation frequency of the circuit equals the frequency of the desired radio waves. Resonance occurs causing the electrons in the circuit to oscillate.

7. An AC generator supplies the changing electric field which in turn generates a changing magnetic field. A DC generator would only generate a changing electric field when turned on or off.

8. Microwaves are reflected by metal, thus keeping the energy from the soup. The ceramic mug transmits microwaves, whereas the water of the soup absorbs them.

EXERCISES

1. $r = \dfrac{mv}{Bq} = \dfrac{(1.7 \times 10^{-27} \text{ kg})(4.5 \times 10^4 \text{ m/s})}{(6.4 \times 10^{-2} \text{ T})(1.6 \times 10^{-19} \text{ C})}$
$= 7.5 \times 10^{-3}$ m
$C = 2\pi r = 2\pi(7.5 \times 10^{-3} \text{ m}) = 4.7 \times 10^{-2}$ m

2. $B = \dfrac{E}{v} = \dfrac{(5.8 \times 10^3 \text{ N/C})}{(3.6 \times 10^4 \text{ m/s})} = 1.6 \times 10^{-1}$ T

3. $v = \dfrac{Brq}{m} = \dfrac{(0.36 \text{ T})(0.2 \text{ m})(1.6 \times 10^{-19} \text{ C})}{(1.7 \times 10^{-27} \text{ kg})}$
$= 7 \times 10^6$ m/s

4.
a. $\dfrac{(4.0 \times 10^{-3} \text{ T})(2.0 \times 10^{-2} \text{ m})(1.6 \times 10^{-19} \text{ C})}{(9.11 \times 10^{-31} \text{ kg})}$
$= 1.4 \times 10^7$ m/s
b. $E = Bv = (4.0 \times 10^{-3} \text{ T})(1.4 \times 10^7 \text{ m/s})$
$= 5.6 \times 10^4$ N/C

5. $\dfrac{(2)(1.6 \times 10^{-19} \text{ C})(8.0 \times 10^{-2} \text{ T})^2(0.077 \text{ m})^2}{(2)(156 \text{ V})}$
$= 3.9 \times 10^{-26}$ kg

6. $\dfrac{3.9 \times 10^{-26} \text{ kg}}{1.67 \times 10^{-27} \text{ kg/u}} = 23$ u

7.
a. $\lambda = \dfrac{v}{f} = \dfrac{(3.0 \times 10^8 \text{ m/s})}{(85 \times 10^6 \text{ Hz})} = 3.5$ m
b. Length $= \dfrac{\lambda}{2} = \dfrac{3.5 \text{ m}}{2} = 1.8$ m

8. $E = qV = (1.6 \times 10^{-19} \text{ C})(4.0 \times 10^5 \text{ V})$
$= 6.4 \times 10^{-14}$ J

9. $\dfrac{(1.7 \times 10^{-27} \text{ kg})(5.4 \times 10^4 \text{ m/s})}{(6.0 \times 10^{-2} \text{ T})(1.6 \times 10^{-19} \text{ C})} = 9.6 \times 10^{-3}$ m

PROBLEMS

1.
a. $\dfrac{(2.0 \text{ T})(2)(1.6 \times 10^{-19} \text{ C})(0.15 \text{ m})}{6.6 \times 10^{-27} \text{ kg}}$
$= 1.5 \times 10^7$ m/s
b. $\dfrac{(6.6 \times 10^{-27} \text{ kg})(1.5 \times 10^7 \text{ m/s})^2}{2}$
$= 7.4 \times 10^{-13}$ J
c. $\dfrac{7.4 \times 10^{-13} \text{ J}}{2(1.6 \times 10^{-19} \text{ C})} = 2.3 \times 10^6$ V

2.
a. $E = qV = (1.6 \times 10^{-19} \text{ C})(1.0 \times 10^4 \text{ J/C})$
$= 1.6 \times 10^{-15}$ J
b. $f = \dfrac{E}{h} = \dfrac{(1.6 \times 10^{-15} \text{ J})}{(4)(6.6 \times 10^{-34} \text{ J/Hz})}$
$= 6.1 \times 10^{17}$ Hz

3. One proton mass out of 175×10^3 is 1/1750 of one percent, or about one two-thousandth of one percent differentiation ability.

4. $\dfrac{1}{(0.050 \text{ m})}\sqrt{\dfrac{(2)(4.5 \times 10^3 \text{ V})(9.11 \times 10^{-31} \text{ kg})}{(1.6 \times 10^{-19} \text{ C})}}$
$= 4.5 \times 10^{-3}$ T

5. $r = \dfrac{1}{B}\sqrt{\dfrac{2Vm}{q}} =$
$\dfrac{1}{(6.5 \times 10^{-2} \text{ T})}\sqrt{\dfrac{(2)(1.0 \times 10^3 \text{ V})(6.7 \times 10^{-27} \text{ kg})}{(2)(1.6 \times 10^{-19} \text{ C})}}$
$= 1.0 \times 10^{-1}$ m

6. $\dfrac{(28 \text{ u})(17.97 \text{ cm})}{16.23 \text{ cm}} = 31$ u

Chapter 27

Quantum Theory

Overview

The basic phenomena of quantum mechanics, beginning with radiation from incandescent bodies, are introduced in this chapter. Determination of Planck's constant is developed and the photoelectric effect is discussed quantitatively. As light of sufficient frequency shines on the cathode of a photocell, electrons are ejected. Variation of the potential difference across the cell is done until these electrons cease to flow to the anode. From the work done in stopping the electrons, determination of their maximum kinetic energy is made. The Compton effect is also presented as an aspect of the particle nature of electromagnetic radiation.

The remainder of the chapter presents the wave nature of particles. This presentation complements the particle nature of waves. Taken together, these complementary views give a better picture of the true nature of light.

Planning Guide (5 Class Sessions)

Text Section	Demonstrations and Experiments	Other Program Components

28:1 Radiation from Incandescent Bodies   **S**
28:2 Photoelectric Effect   **S**
28:3 The Compton Effect   **S**
	Dem 28:1 "Black Box"
	Exp 53 A Model for the Quantum Concept **LM**
		Teaching Master 28-1: Intensity of Blackbody Radiation Versus Temperature **TRP**
		Teaching Master 28-2:
		  (a) Photoelectric Effect
		  (b) KE_{max} of Photoelectrons Versus Temperature **TRP**
		Review Masters **TRP**
		Demonstration 28-1: Photoelectric Effect **TRP**
		Enrichment 28-1: The Electron Microscope **TRP**
		Enrichment 28-2: Einstein **TRP**

28:4 Matter Waves **S** **28:5** Particles and Waves **S**		Enrichment 28-3: For Stamp Collectors **TRP** Evaluation **TRP**

Performance Objectives

Upon completion of this chapter, your students will

1. display an understanding of the spectrum emitted by a hot body and the basics of the theory that explains this spectrum.   *28:1*

2. define the photoelectric effect; recognize that wave theory cannot explain this phenomenon but

the quantum theory can; solve problems involving the work function of materials, frequency of incident light, and kinetic energy of photoelectrons.   *28:2*

3. explain the Compton effect in terms of the photon colliding elastically with an electron.   *28:3*

4. describe experiments that demonstrate particle-like properties of the energy and momentum of electromagnetic radiation.   *28:2*

5. describe evidence of the wave nature of matter and solve problems relating wavelength to particle momentum.   *28:4*

6. recognize the dual nature of both electromagnetic radiation and matter and the impact of the Heisenberg uncertainty principle.   *28:5*

Teaching the Chapter

Introduction

Using the Photo: Jean was correct. The color of an incandescent body changes from a cherry red (cooler) color through yellow to white as it gets hotter. This photograph also can be used with Section 28:1 to discuss radiation from incandescent bodies.

Demonstration: Obtain a large carton (at least 0.5 m on one side) and paint the inside white or cover it with white paper. Make a hole about 3 cm in diameter in the center of one side. Have students look through the hole. Then ask them what color the box is on the inside. The box will appear to be black; the small amount of light that enters through the hole is reflected off the inside surfaces of the box many times. Some light is absorbed during each reflection, permitting only a minimal amount to come out.

28:1 Radiation from Incandescent Bodies

In 1900 Planck worked out a comparatively simple equation describing the distribution of radiation over the entire range of frequencies of electromagnetic radiation. He based his equation on the assumption that energy is not infinitely subdivisible. He said it existed in bundles, called quanta, that contained energy in direct proportion to the frequency. The constant, *h*, the ratio of the frequency of the radiation to the size of the quantum, is called Planck's constant. Planck found that the mathematics fit the experiments. However, he was uncomfortable with the quantum idea for many years, thinking that it had some meaning in nature. Einstein applied the quantum theory to the photoelectric effect, and Niels Bohr applied it to the structure of the atom. Planck won the Nobel Prize in 1918.

Planck's life was affected by World War II and the Hitler regime. One of his sons died in action and a second son was executed by the Hitler regime. Planck lived to see the end of the war and the destruction of Nazism. He died when he was ninety years old. Planck was named head of the Kaiser Wilhelm society, which was renamed the Max Planck Society in his honor.

28:2 Photoelectric Effect

Use the demonstration "Photoelectric Effect" in the *Teacher Resource Package*. The number of people involved in the development of the quantum theory and the sequence of events is interesting. Planck introduced the idea and Einstein extended the quantum theory to light. The year 1905 was an important one for Einstein. He published five papers in the German Yearbook of Physics and earned his Ph.D. In 1900 Planck had worked out an explanation of blackbody radiation using a quantum explanation for the radiation of energy. His work lay idle until Einstein applied it to explain why all wavelengths of light did not cause electrons to be emitted from certain metals. Classical physics could not explain this phenomenon. Einstein was awarded the Nobel Prize in 1921 for his work on the photoelectric effect, not for his theory of relativity as many people believe.

28:3 The Compton Effect

The fact that light travels in straight lines and casts sharp shadows led to the particle theory of light. The particle theory was revived when Compton's scattering of X rays showed that some of the scattered X rays lost energy. The only way he could explain this was to say that light behaved as a particle, or "photon," as he named it. This supported the view that light behaved as both a particle and a wave. His particle theory did not destroy the wave theory of light. Compton shared the Nobel Prize with Charles Wilson in 1927.

28:4 Matter Waves

De Broglie was educated at the Sorbonne in France and received his degree in history. He became involved in radio communication while in the French army in World War I. He was a radio engineer stationed at the Eiffel Tower. Radio communication sparked his interest in science, and in 1924, he obtained a doctorate degree in quantum theory.

De Broglie combined Einstein's and Planck's work to show that all particles have wave properties, such as wavelength and frequency, attributed to them. This wave-particle duality helped to make much more acceptable Einstein's idea that matter and energy are interconvertible. De Broglie was awarded the Nobel Prize in physics in 1929.

28:5 Particles and Waves

Heisenberg (1901 – 1976) had worked with Bohr and Arnold Sommerfeld on atomic structure. Heisenberg devised a mathematical relationship to explain the positions of spectral lines. He derived the equations in 1927 while on vacation in the North Sea to cure his hay fever. He also studied nuclear theory and predicted that hydrogen could exist in two forms dependent on the spin of the nucleus of the atom. This idea was used in devising a method for reducing the evaporation of liquid hydrogen, which proved useful when large quantities of liquid hydrogen were used a generation later as rocket fuel. Heisenberg stated that the position and momentum of a body cannot be determined simultaneously. The product of the error of the two measurements is approximately equal to Planck's constant. A bumper sticker, "Heisenberg May Have Slept Here," reminds us that he is famous for his uncertainty principle, which won him the 1932 Nobel Prize in physics.

Resources

Literature

Asimov, Isaac, *Asimov's Biographical Encyclopedia of Science and Technology,* Doubleday and Company, Garden City, NY, 1982.

Epstein, L. C., and Hewitt, P. G., *Thinking Physics,* Insight Press, San Francisco, 1981, pp. 208–211.

Sibers, Dennis, and Wilson, Alan, "Determining Planck's Constant Using a Light-Emitting Diode," *The Science Teacher,* February, 1989, pp. 44–46.

Swartz, Clifford E., *Phenomenal Physics,* John Wiley and Sons, Inc., New York, 1981, pp. 696–697.

Background

Photoelectric cells are used in exposure meters that convert light energy into electric energy. They are used in photography to determine the amount of light surrounding an object so the proper exposure settings may be found. The photoelectric cell is an iron plate coated with selenium and a thin layer of platinum. A honeycomb lens is placed on top of the cell. When light strikes the cell, selenium electrons start to move and a current is generated. The current increases as the amount of light increases. A current meter is calibrated in f-stop numbers and exposure times, allowing for perfect pictures.

Chapter Review

QUESTIONS

1. **a.** the rod glowing bright orange
   b. the rod glowing bright orange
2. Quantized means a quantity can have only certain values.
3. The energy levels of the oscillators in the wall of the hot body.
4. **a.** Blue has a lower frequency; tungsten has a higher threshold frequency.

b. Tungsten has a higher work function.

5. Each photon ejects a photoelectron. More intense light has more photons per second, thus it ejects more photoelectrons per second.

6. Each photon lacks the energy needed to eject an electron.

7. Elastic collisions transfer both momentum and energy. Only if photons have momentum can the equations be satisfied.

APPLYING CONCEPTS

1. Red photons do not have enough energy to cause the chemical reaction that exposes film.

2. No. Momentum would be zero.

3. The size of the baseball is about 0.10 m, whereas the de Broglie wavelength is 10^{-34} m, a factor of 10^{33} difference.

4. Diffraction and interference.

5. a. balanced force of gravity against force of electric field on charge

b. Balance force of electric field against that of magnetic field to find m/q, then use measured value of q.

c. Scatter off crystal, measuring angles of diffraction.

6. a. Measure kinetic energy of electron ejected from metal for at least two different wavelengths. Or, measure KE from known metal for only one wavelength.

b. Measure change in wavelength of X ray scattered from matter.

c. Measure angle diffracted by two slits or **grating**, or width of single-slit pattern, or angle bent through prism.

EXERCISES

1. $KE = qV$
$= (1.6 \times 10^{-19} \text{ C})(3.8 \text{ J/C}) = 6.1 \times 10^{-19} \text{ J}$

2. a. $\lambda = \dfrac{c}{f} = \dfrac{3.0 \times 10^8 \text{ m/s}}{1.2 \times 10^{15} \text{ Hz}} = 2.5 \times 10^{-7} \text{ m}$

b. $W = hf_o$
$= (6.6 \times 10^{-34} \text{ J/Hz})(1.2 \times 10^{15} \text{ Hz})$
$= (7.9 \times 10^{-19} \text{ J})(1 \text{ eV}/1.6 \times 10^{-19} \text{ J})$
$= 5.0 \text{ eV}$

c. $KE_{max} = \dfrac{hc}{\lambda} - hf_o$

$= \dfrac{(6.6 \times 10^{-34} \text{ J/Hz})(3.0 \times 10^8 \text{ m/s})}{(167 \times 10^{-9} \text{ m})(1.6 \times 10^{-19} \text{ J/eV})} - 5.0 \text{ eV}$

$= 7.4 \text{ eV} - 5.0 \text{ eV} = 2.4 \text{ eV}$

3. a. $\lambda = \dfrac{hc}{W}$

$= \dfrac{(6.6 \times 10^{-34} \text{ J/Hz})(3.0 \times 10^8 \text{ m/s})}{(4.7 \text{ eV})(1.6 \times 10^{-19} \text{ J/eV})}$

$= 2.6 \times 10^{-7} \text{ m}$

b. $KE = \dfrac{hc}{\lambda} - W$

$= \dfrac{(6.6 \times 10^{-34} \text{ J/Hz})(3.0 \times 10^8 \text{ m/s})}{(150 \times 10^{-9} \text{ m})(1.6 \times 10^{-19} \text{ J/eV})}$

$= 3.6 \text{ eV}$

4. $\lambda = \dfrac{6.6 \times 10^{-34} \text{ J/Hz}}{(3.3 \times 10^{-27} \text{ kg})(2.5 \times 10^4 \text{ m/s})}$

$= 8.0 \times 10^{-12} \text{ m}$

5. a. $v = \sqrt{\dfrac{2qV}{m}} = \sqrt{\dfrac{(2)(1.6 \times 10^{-19} \text{ C})(54 \text{ V})}{9.1 \times 10^{-31} \text{ kg}}}$

$= 4.4 \times 10^6 \text{ m/s}$

b. $\lambda = \dfrac{h}{mv} = \dfrac{6.6 \times 10^{-34} \text{ J/Hz}}{(9.1 \times 10^{-31} \text{ kg})(4.4 \times 10^6 \text{ m/s})}$

$= 1.6 \times 10^{-10} \text{ m}$

6. a.

$v = \sqrt{\dfrac{2KE}{m}} = \sqrt{\dfrac{(2)(0.025 \text{ eV})(1.6 \times 10^{-19} \text{ J/eV})}{1.67 \times 10^{-27} \text{ kg}}}$

$= 2.2 \times 10^3 \text{ m/s}$

b. $\lambda = \dfrac{h}{mv}$

$= \dfrac{6.6 \times 10^{-34} \text{ J/Hz}}{(1.67 \times 10^{-27} \text{ kg})(2.2 \times 10^3 \text{ m/s})}$

$= 1.8 \times 10^{-10} \text{ m}$

7. $\lambda = \dfrac{h}{mv} = \dfrac{6.6 \times 10^{-34} \text{ J/Hz}}{(1.67 \times 10^{-27} \text{ kg})(1.0 \times 10^6 \text{ m/s})}$

$= 4.0 \times 10^{-13}$ m

8. $W = \dfrac{1240}{\lambda_0}$ eV $\cdot$ nm

$= \dfrac{1240}{680 \text{ nm}}$ eV $\cdot$ nm

$= 18$ eV

PROBLEMS

1. a. $E = (3000 \text{ h})(3600 \text{ s/h})(1000 \text{ J/m}^2 \cdot \text{s})$

$= 1 \times 10^{10}$ J/m^2

b. Area $= \dfrac{4 \times 10^{11} \text{ J}}{(0.2)(1 \times 10^{10} \text{ J/m}^2)} = 2 \times 10^2$ m^2

2. a. $KE = \dfrac{1}{2}mv^2$

$v = \sqrt{\dfrac{2KE}{m}}$

$= \sqrt{\dfrac{(2)(13.65 \text{ eV})(1.60 \times 10^{-19} \text{ J/eV})}{9.11 \times 10^{-31} \text{ kg}}}$

$= 2.19 \times 10^6$ m/s

b. $\lambda = \dfrac{h}{mv}$

$= \dfrac{6.6 \times 10^{-34} \text{ J/Hz}}{(9.1 \times 10^{-31} \text{ kg})(2.19 \times 10^6 \text{ m/s})}$

$= 3.3 \times 10^{-10}$ m

c. 5.19 nm $= 51.9 \times 10^{-10}$ m

$\dfrac{3.3 \times 10^{-10}}{51.9 \times 10^{-10}} = \dfrac{1}{16}$ the radius of the atom

3. a. $\lambda = \dfrac{h}{mv}$

$v = \dfrac{h}{m\lambda}$

$= \dfrac{(6.6 \times 10^{-34} \text{ J/Hz})}{(9.1 \times 10^{-31} \text{ kg})(400 \times 10^{-9} \text{ m})}$

$= 2 \times 10^3$ m/s

b. $KE = \dfrac{(9.1 \times 10^{-31} \text{ kg})(2 \times 10^3 \text{ m/s})^2}{(2)(1.6 \times 10^{-19} \text{ J/eV})}$

$= 1 \times 10^{-5}$ eV

c. $\lambda = \dfrac{h}{mv}$

$v = \dfrac{h}{m\lambda} = \dfrac{6.6 \times 10^{-34} \text{ J/Hz}}{(9.1 \times 10^{-31} \text{ kg})(20 \times 10^{-9} \text{ m})}$

$= 3.6 \times 10^4$ m/s

$KE = \dfrac{1}{2}mv^2$

$= \dfrac{(9.1 \times 10^{-31} \text{ kg})(3.6 \times 10^4 \text{ m/s})^2}{2(1.6 \times 10^{-19} \text{ J/eV})}$

$= 4 \times 10^{-3}$ eV

4. $KE = hf - W$

$KE = 0$ for longest wavelength

$W = hf$

$W = 2.48 \text{ eV}(1.6 \times 10^{-19} \text{ J/eV})$

$= 4.0 \times 10^{-19}$ J

$f = \dfrac{W}{h} = \dfrac{4.0 \times 10^{-19} \text{ J}}{6.6 \times 10^{-34} \text{ J} \cdot \text{s}} = 6.0 \times 10^{14}$ Hz

$\lambda = \dfrac{c}{f} = \dfrac{3.0 \times 10^8 \text{ m/s}}{6.0 \times 10^{14} \text{ Hz}} = 5.0 \times 10^{-7}$ m

5. a. $f = \dfrac{v}{\lambda} = \dfrac{3.0 \times 10^8 \text{ m/s}}{3.5 \times 10^{-7} \text{ m}} = 8.6 \times 10^{14}$ Hz

$KE = hf - hf_0$

$= (6.6 \times 10^{-34} \text{ J} \cdot \text{s})(8.6 \times 10^{14} \text{ Hz}) -$
$(6.6 \times 10^{-34} \text{ J} \cdot \text{s})(6.7 \times 10^{14} \text{ Hz})$

$= 1.35 \times 10^{-19}$ J

$= 0.78$ eV

b. $f = \dfrac{v}{\lambda} = \dfrac{3.81 \times 10^8 \text{ m/s}}{5.5 \times 10^{-7} \text{ m}} = 5.5 \times 10^{14}$ Hz

This is less than f_0, so no electrons are ejected.

6. a. $v = \dfrac{h}{m\lambda}$

$= \dfrac{6.6 \times 10^{-34} \text{ J} \cdot \text{s}}{(9.1 \times 10^{-31} \text{ kg})(1.8 \times 10^{-10} \text{ m})}$

$= 4.0 \times 10^6$ m/s

$KE = \dfrac{1}{2}mv^2$

$= \dfrac{1}{2}(9.1 \times 10^{-31} \text{ kg})(4.0 \times 10^6)^2$

$= 7.4 \times 10^{-18}$ J

$$KE = qV$$

$$V = \frac{KE}{q} = \frac{7.4 \times 10^{-18} \text{ J}}{1.6 \times 10^{-19} \text{ C}} = 46 \text{ V}$$

b. $\quad v = \dfrac{h}{m\lambda} = \dfrac{6.6 \times 10^{-34} \text{ J} \cdot \text{s}}{(1.7 \times 10^{-27} \text{ kg})(1.8 \times 10^{-10} \text{ m})}$

$$= 2.2 \times 10^{3} \text{ m/s}$$

$$KE = \frac{1}{2}mv^{2}$$

$$= \frac{1}{2}(1.7 \times 10^{-27} \text{ kg})(2.2 \times 10^{3} \text{ m/s})^{2}$$

$$= 4.1 \times 10^{-21} \text{ J}$$

$$V = \frac{KE}{q} = \frac{4.1 \times 10^{-21} \text{ J}}{1.6 \times 10^{-19} \text{ C}} = 2.6 \times 10^{-2} \text{ V}$$

The Atom

Overview

This chapter presents the development of the modern theory of atomic structure. Ernest Rutherford directed alpha particles at gold foil and developed the nuclear model of the atom from his results. The mass and positive charge of an atom is contained in a small central core. Electrons orbit far from this nucleus, thus the atom's volume consists mainly of empty space. The movement of these electrons between energy levels of the atom is studied by means of absorption and emission spectra. The use of spectroscopy for identifi-cation of elements is shown. The Bohr model of the atom was able to predict the spectral lines of hydrogen but not of the next simplest atom, helium. These early models of the atom contributed to the wave model developed by Erwin Schroedinger.

The chapter concludes with an application of atomic theory, the laser. A discussion is given on how a laser works, the special properties of the laser's light, and the variety of applications of the laser.

Planning Guide (6 Class Sessions)

Text Section			Demonstrations and Experiments		Other Program Components	
29:1	The Nuclear Model	P	Dem 29:1 Rutherford's Model		Demontration 29-1: Models of the	
29:2	The Proton and the Neutron	P	Exp 54 The Spectra of Elements	**LM**	Atom—Rutherford's Experiment	**TRP**
29:3	Atomic Spectra	P	Dem 29:6 Quantum Circumferences		Teaching Master 29-1: Apparatus for	
29:4	The Bohr Model of the Atom	P			Absorption Spectra	**TRP**
29:5	Fluorescence and				Teaching Master 29-2: Energy	
	Phosphorescence	S			Levels	**TRP**
29:6	Predictions of the Bohr				Review Masters	**TRP**
	Model	P			Demonstration 29-2: A Statistical	
					Probability Demonstrator	**TRP**
					Enrichment 29-2: The Making of a	
					Model	**TRP**
29:7	Present Theory of the Atom	P	Dem 29:8 Laser Show		Enrichment 29-1: The Controversy	
29:8	Lasers	S			of the Laser Patent	**TRP**
					Evaluation	**TRP**

Performance Objectives

Upon completion of this chapter, your students will

1. explain the method used by Rutherford and co-workers to determine the structure of the atom; describe the Rutherford model.   *29:1*
2. describe the experimental results that suggested the existence of the neutron; contrast the proton with the neutron.   *29:2*
3. distinguish continuous from line spectra; contrast emission and absorption spectra; list some uses of spectroscopy.   *29:3*

4. list the assumptions used by Bohr to develop his atomic model; define energy levels and ground and excited states; display an understanding of the connection between photon energy and atomic energy changes. *29:4*

5. describe fluorescence and phosphorescence in terms of excited states of atoms. *29:5*

6. by reference to the text only, use the orbital radius

and energy level equations to solve problems using the Bohr model. *29:6*

7. display an appreciation of the contributions of the Bohr model and its shortcomings; describe the quantum mechanical model of the atom. *29:7*

8. describe a laser and the properties of laser light; display an understanding of the processes involved in the operation of the laser. *29:8*

Teaching the Chapter

Introduction

Using the Photo: Ultraviolet photons contain enough energy to excite atoms to higher energy levels. The light is absorbed at one energy level and part is re-emitted at a longer wavelength (lower energy), which is in the visible spectrum. The other energy is lost in collisions with other atoms. Daylight and infrared light have insufficient energy to excite the atoms. This photograph can be used with Section 29:5 to discuss fluorescence and phosphorescence.

Demonstration: Use the overhead projector to simulate Rutherford scattering. You will need a 19-cm × 30-cm glass dish, modeling clay, cardboard, and marbles. Cut a piece of cardboard 20 cm × 4.5 cm and place it across the dish slightly to one side of the center. Tape it in place. Make a clay piece shaped like a volcano that will fit under the cardboard. Place it under the cardboard near the center of the dish. Put a thin layer of clay at the end of the dish closest to the cardboard to catch the marbles. When placed on the overhead the students will see only the piece of card-board, which simulates the gold foil. Roll marbles at random from the end of the dish away from the clay. Sometimes the marbles bounce directly back. Other times they may deflect at an angle or continue moving. Use these results to discuss Rutherford's model of the atom.

29:1 The Nuclear Model

Ernest Rutherford was the second of twelve children and worked on his father's farm in New Zealand as he was growing up. He received a scholarship to New Zealand University and finished fourth in his class. He became interested in physics, and in 1895 received a scholarship to Cambridge University. He worked on radioactivity and was responsible for the names alpha and beta given to the particles emitted by

radioactive materials. Rutherford also discovered that some of the radiation was not affected by magnetic fields and called these gamma rays.

Rutherford is most famous for his experiment that shows the atom has a very concentrated dense nucleus. He bombarded gold foil, one fifty-thousandth of an inch thick, with alpha particles. Most of the alpha particles passed through the foil instead of being deflected, showing that the atom was mostly empty space. Rutherford won the Nobel Prize in 1908 for his theory of radioactive disintegration of elements, for determining the nature of the alpha particles, and for his theory of the nuclear atom. He was disappointed because he was awarded the Nobel Prize in chemistry and he considered himself a physicist. Rutherford was the first person to change one element into another by bombarding the nucleus with a particle.

29:2 The Proton and the Neutron

Chadwick was Rutherford's student at the University of Manchester. He then received the same scholarship to Cambridge that Rutherford had received. The experiments that led to the discovery of the neutron were originally done by Walther Bothe and the Joliot-Curies, but it was Chadwick who explained the results of these experiments. The neutron was difficult to find because uncharged particles do not ionize molecules in the air, which is the way most subatomic particles are detected. The neutron was shown to be a very useful particle for initiating nuclear reactions and Chadwick received the 1935 Nobel Prize in physics.

29:3 Atomic Spectra

Joseph Fraunhofer, the youngest of eleven children, was orphaned at the age of eleven. He was the only survivor when his home, a run-down tenement, collapsed a few years later. With some money he was given, he launched himself on a career as an optician. While testing some prisms, Fraunhofer discovered that the solar spectrum had dark lines in it and used this information to determine the gases in the sun's atmosphere. He was the first to use a grating of closely spaced thin wires to disperse light. Fraunhofer was considered a mere technician by the scientists of his day and was allowed to attend scientific meetings but not to address them.

29:4 The Bohr Model of the Atom

Bohr was a physics student and outstanding soccer player at the University of Copenhagen. He received his doctorate in 1911 and went to Cambridge to study with J. J. Thomson and Ernest Rutherford.

Bohr received the Nobel Prize in physics in 1922. He spent time in the United States in 1944 working on the atomic bomb project at Los Alamos. He also put his energies into the development of peaceful uses of atomic energy and organized the Peace Conference in Geneva in 1955.

29:5 Fluorescence and Phosphorescence

Materials that fluoresce glow only when light shines on them. Some detergents contain a fluorescent dye that makes white cloth look whiter, when actually the dye is fluorescing.

A mineral illuminated with ultraviolet light may glow, giving off different colors, due to the different elements in the mineral. Museums often have displays of such minerals. Some students may also have seen phosphorescent stickers in the shape of constellations that glow in the dark.

29:6 Predictions of the Bohr Model

Demonstration: Demonstrate the quantum number concept by taking a long strip of flexible corrugated plastic about 5 cm wide and bending it to form a circle. Show that it can fit together when you wrap it around in a circle only if the overlap is one wavelength long or multiples of a wavelength. Mark off a wavelength in the plastic to emphasize this point.

29:7 Present Theory of the Atom

Schroedinger was taught at home as a youngster and later received his degree from the University of Vienna. He was interested in both physics and philosophy. Like many other scientists of this era, Schroedinger was affected by World II. He had a professorship at the University of Berlin but returned to his native Austria because of Nazi activities. He was open about his dislike of the Nazis and nearly lost his life when he interfered with some storm troopers. In 1938 he left Austria for England and two years later went to Dublin, Ireland, to be a professor at the School for Advanced Studies. Schroedinger shared the Nobel Prize with Paul Dirac in 1933.

29:8 Lasers

The laser was preceded by the maser, which stood for "microwave amplification by stimulated emission of radiation." Both the laser and the maser were invented by Charles Townes, who won the Nobel Prize for physics in 1964, sharing it with Nikolai Basov. It is told he came up with the idea for the maser while sitting on a park bench in Washington, DC, early one morning. In the maser, ammonia molecules were excited by using heat or electricity to pump energy into them. They were stimulated to emit the energy by a beam of microwaves of natural frequency of the ammonia molecules.

In 1957, Townes began to devise a maser that would deliver infrared or visible light. He and Theodore Maiman made one using a ruby rod that emitted red light. The visible light masers were named lasers.

Demonstration: If you have a laser, do some demonstrations to show the color and intensity of the beam. Clap some erasers and shine the laser through the dust to show the intensity and color. If possible, view a hologram.

Physics Focus: For additional information on the STM, refer to the following articles: "Atomic bonds: Seeing the Links," *Science News*, September 16, 1986, p. 149; Kluger, Jeffrey, "A Dream Come True," *Discover*, January, 1989, p. 56.

Resources ━━━━━━━━━━━━━

Literature

Asimov, Isaac, *Asimov's Biographical Encyclopedia of Science and Technology*, Doubleday and Company, Garden City, NY, 1982.

Jeong, Tung H., *Laser Holography Experiments You Can Do...From Edison,* Thomas Alva Edison Foundation, Southfield, MI, 1987.

Metrologic Catalog and Laser Handbook, Metrologic Instruments, Inc., Bellmawr, NJ.

Raloff, Janet, "Seeking Coherent Answers," *Science News,* Volume 120, No. 12, pp. 184–187.

Schmidt, Ellen, "Laser Light Gets Everyone's Atten-

tion," *The Physics Teacher,* January, 1989, pp. 30–31.

Spradley, Joseph, "Hertz, and the Discovery of Radio Waves and the Photoelectric Effect," *The Physics Teacher,* November, 1988, pp. 492–497.

Unterseher, Fred, *Holography Handbook, Making Holograms the Easy Way,* Ross Books, Berkeley, CA, 1982.

Chapter Review

QUESTIONS

1. He directed a beam of charged alpha particles at a thin metal sheet and measured the number of particles deflected into various angles.

2. Neutrons and protons are approximately equal in mass. Protons are positively charged, whereas neutrons have no charge.

3. As the electrons undergo centripetal acceleration, they would lose energy and spiral into the nucleus. In addition, all atoms should radiate at all wavelengths, not discreet wavelengths.

4. a. Energy levels are quantized.
   b. Electrons do not radiate while they are in an allowed energy level.
   c. Photons are emitted or absorbed when an electron changes energy levels. Energy of a photon is equal to the difference in energy levels.

5. Photon wavelengths are determined by the difference in energies of allowed levels.

6. Six lines are possible. They are E_2-E_1, E_3-E_1, E_4-E_1, E_3-E_2, E_4-E_2, E_4-E_3. E_4-E_1 has the highest energy level.

7. The Bohr model has fixed orbital radii; the present model gives a probability of finding an electron at a location. The Bohr model allows for calculation of only hydrogen atoms; the present model can be used for all elements.

8. a. Lasers are directional and coherent.
   b. Blue light has a higher frequency and, therefore, higher energy.

9. Measure the time it takes for excited atoms to return to their ground states.

10. Microwave Amplification by Stimulated Emission of Radiation

APPLYING CONCEPTS

1. Money—it comes in only certain values, while water seems to come in any possible quantity.

2. Line spectrum—the light comes from a dilute gas.

3. The order of potassium and argon is reversed.

4. No, visible radiation is higher energy radiation than infrared.

5. Laser light is coherent and directional, thus it is more concentrated.

6. The maximum energy is 13.6 eV. This is also the ionization energy for hydrogen. The electron would have enough energy to leave the nucleus.

7. All down transitions from higher energy levels to the third energy level in hydrogen atoms yield photons with wavelengths greater than visible light; therefore, the protons emitted are infrared.

8. No, as the white light passed through Earth's atmosphere certain energies would be absorbed by the gases composing it. Its spectrum, therefore, would have black lines in it.

9. Since laser light is monochromatic only one line is seen.

EXERCISES

1. baseball diameter = 7.5 cm
distance to electron
$= 0.075 \text{ m} / (2.5 \times 10^{-15} \text{ m})(5 \times 10^{-9} \text{ m})$
$= 200 \text{ km}$

2. $r = n^2 k$, where $k = 5.3 \times 10^{-11}$ m
$r = (5)^2(5.3 \times 10^{-11} \text{ m}) = 1.3 \times 10^{-9}$ m
$r = (6)^2(5.3 \times 10^{-11} \text{ m}) = 1.9 \times 10^{-9}$ m

3. $E_2 = \dfrac{-13.6 \text{ eV}}{n^2} = \dfrac{-13.6 \text{ eV}}{(2)^2} = -3.4 \text{ eV}$

$E_3 = \dfrac{-13.6 \text{ eV}}{(3)^2} = -1.5 \text{ eV}$

$E_4 = \dfrac{-13.6 \text{ eV}}{(4)^2} = -0.85 \text{ eV}$

$E_5 = \dfrac{-13.6 \text{ eV}}{(5)^2} = -0.54 \text{ eV}$

$E_6 = \dfrac{-13.6 \text{ eV}}{(6)^2} = -0.38 \text{ eV}$

4. a. $(-0.38 \text{ eV}) - (-0.54 \text{ eV}) = 0.16 \text{ eV}$

b. $(-0.38 \text{ eV}) - (-1.50 \text{ eV}) = 1.12 \text{ eV}$

c. $(-0.85 \text{ eV}) - (-3.40 \text{ eV}) = 2.55 \text{ eV}$

d. $(-0.54 \text{ eV}) - (-3.40 \text{ eV}) = 2.86 \text{ eV}$

e. $(-0.54 \text{ eV}) - (-1.50 \text{ eV}) = 0.96 \text{ eV}$

5. a. $E = hf$
$hf = E_6 - E_5 = 0.16 \text{ eV}$
$f = \dfrac{(0.16 \text{ eV})(1.6 \times 10^{-19} \text{ J/eV})}{6.6 \times 10^{-34} \text{ J/Hz}}$
$= 3.9 \times 10^{13} \text{ Hz}$

b. $hf = E_6 - E_3 = 1.12 \text{ eV}$
$f = \dfrac{(1.12 \text{ eV})(1.6 \times 10^{-19} \text{ J/eV})}{6.6 \times 10^{-34} \text{ J/Hz}}$
$= 2.7 \times 10^{14} \text{ Hz}$

c. $hf = E_4 - E_2 = 2.55 \text{ eV}$
$f = \dfrac{(2.55 \text{ eV})(1.6 \times 10^{-19} \text{ J/eV})}{6.6 \times 10^{-34} \text{ J/Hz}}$
$= 6.1 \times 10^{14} \text{ Hz}$

d. $hf = E_5 - E_2 = 2.86 \text{ eV}$
$f = \dfrac{(2.86 \text{ eV})(1.6 \times 10^{-19} \text{ J/eV})}{6.6 \times 10^{-34} \text{ J/Hz}}$
$= 6.9 \times 10^{14} \text{ Hz}$

e. $hf = E_5 - E_3 = 0.96 \text{ eV}$
$f = \dfrac{(0.96 \text{ eV})(1.6 \times 10^{-19} \text{ J/eV})}{6.6 \times 10^{-34} \text{ J/Hz}}$
$= 2.3 \times 10^{14} \text{ Hz}$

6. a. $\lambda = \dfrac{c}{f} = \dfrac{3.0 \times 10^8 \text{ m/s}}{3.9 \times 10^{13} \text{ Hz}} = 7.7 \times 10^{-6} \text{ m}$

b. $\lambda = \dfrac{c}{f} = \dfrac{3.0 \times 10^8 \text{ m/s}}{2.7 \times 10^{14} \text{ Hz}} = 1.1 \times 10^{-6} \text{ m}$

c. $\lambda = \dfrac{c}{f} = \dfrac{3.0 \times 10^8 \text{ m/s}}{6.1 \times 10^{14} \text{ Hz}} = 4.9 \times 10^{-7} \text{ m}$

d. $\lambda = \dfrac{c}{f} = \dfrac{3.0 \times 10^8 \text{ m/s}}{6.9 \times 10^{14} \text{ Hz}} = 4.3 \times 10^{-7} \text{ m}$

e. $\lambda = \dfrac{c}{f} = \dfrac{3.0 \times 10^8 \text{ m/s}}{2.3 \times 10^{14} \text{ Hz}} = 1.3 \times 10^{-6} \text{ m}$

7. $E = 6.67 \text{ eV} + 2.15 \text{ eV} = 8.82 \text{ eV}$ which is E_9

8. $E = 8.81 \text{ eV} - 6.67 \text{ eV} = 2.14 \text{ eV}$

9. $f = (3.00 \times 10^8 \text{ m/s})/(10\,600 \times 10^{-9} \text{ m})$
$= 2.83 \times 10^{13} \text{ Hz}$
$hf = \dfrac{(2.83 \times 10^{13} \text{ Hz})(6.62 \times 10^{-34} \text{ J/Hz})}{(1.60 \times 10^{-19} \text{ J/eV})}$
$= 0.117 \text{ eV}$

10. a. $E = E_3 - E_2$
$= 1.9 \text{ eV}$
$E = hf$
$f = \dfrac{E}{h} = \dfrac{(1.9 \text{ eV})(1.6 \times 10^{-19} \text{ J/eV})}{6.6 \times 10^{-34} \text{ J/Hz}}$
$= 4.6 \times 10^{14} \text{ Hz}$
$\lambda = \dfrac{c}{f} = \dfrac{3.0 \times 10^8 \text{ m/s}}{4.6 \times 10^{14} \text{ Hz}} = 6.5 \times 10^{-7} \text{ m}$

b. $E = E_4 - E_3 = 0.65 \text{ eV}$
$E = hf$
$f = \dfrac{E}{h} = \dfrac{(0.65 \text{ eV})(1.6 \times 10^{-19} \text{ J/eV})}{6.6 \times 10^{-34} \text{ J/Hz}}$
$= 1.6 \times 10^{14} \text{ Hz}$
$\lambda = \dfrac{c}{f} = \dfrac{3.0 \times 10^8 \text{ m/s}}{1.6 \times 10^{14} \text{ Hz}}$
$= 1.9 \times 10^{-6} \text{ m}$

11. $E_4 - E_1 = (-0.85 \text{ eV}) - (-13.6 \text{ eV})$
$= 12.8 \text{ eV}$

12. $E = hf$
$f = \dfrac{E}{h} = \dfrac{(12.8 \text{ eV})(1.6 \times 10^{-19} \text{ J/eV})}{6.6 \times 10^{-34} \text{ J/Hz}}$
$= 3.1 \times 10^{15} \text{ Hz}$
$\lambda = \dfrac{c}{f} = \dfrac{3.0 \times 10^8 \text{ m/s}}{3.1 \times 10^{15} \text{ Hz}}$
$= 9.7 \times 10^{-8} \text{ m}$

PROBLEMS

1. a. $r = \dfrac{h^2}{4\pi^2 Kmq^2}n^2$
when $n = 1$, $r = 5.3 \times 10^{-11} \text{ m}$
when $n = 3$, $r = 4.8 \times 10^{-10} \text{ m}$

b. $F = \dfrac{Kq^2}{r^2}$
$= \dfrac{(8.99 \times 10^9 \text{ N} \cdot \text{m}^2/\text{C}^2)(1.6 \times 10^{-19} \text{ C})^2}{(4.8 \times 10^{-10} \text{ m})^2}$
$= 1.0 \times 10^{-9} \text{ N}$

c. $a = \dfrac{1.0 \times 10^{-9}\ \text{N}}{9.11 \times 10^{-31}\ \text{kg}} = 1.1 \times 10^{21}\ \text{m/s}^2$

d. $v = \sqrt{ar}$

$ = \sqrt{(1.1 \times 10^{21}\ \text{m/s}^2)(4.8 \times 10^{-10}\ \text{m})}$

$ = 7.3 \times 10^5\ \text{m/s or } 0.2\% \text{ of } c$

2. a. Yes, the atom is ionized.

$\dfrac{13.65\ \text{eV}}{n^2} = \dfrac{13.65}{4}\ \text{eV} = 3.4\ \text{eV}$

$E = hf = hc/\lambda = 6.0 \times 10^{-19}\ \text{J} = 3.7\ \text{eV}$

b. $3.7\ \text{eV} - 3.4\ \text{eV} = 0.3\ \text{eV} = 4.8 \times 10^{-20}\ \text{J}$

3. $f = c/\lambda = (3.00 \times 10^8\ \text{m/s})/(840 \times 10^{-9}\ \text{m})$

$ = 3.57 \times 10^{14}\ \text{Hz}$

$hf = \dfrac{(3.57 \times 10^{14}\ \text{Hz})(6.62 \times 10^{-34}\ \text{J/Hz})}{(1.60 \times 10^{-19}\ \text{J/eV})}$

$ = 1.48\ \text{eV}$

4. $E_1 = \dfrac{-2.17 \times 10^{-18}\ \text{J}}{1^2} = -2.17 \times 10^{-18}\ \text{J}$

$E_4 = \dfrac{-2.17 \times 10^{-18}\ \text{J}}{4^2} = -1.36 \times 10^{-19}\ \text{J}$

$E_4 - E_1 = 2.03 \times 10^{-18}\ \text{J}$

$M = \dfrac{2.03 \times 10^{-18}\ \text{J}}{(3.0 \times 10^8\ \text{m/s})^2} = 2.26 \times 10^{-35}\ \text{kg}$

5. $r = 5.3 \times 10^{-11}\ \text{m}$

$F_E = \dfrac{Kq_1 q_2}{r^2}$

$ = \dfrac{(9 \times 10^9\ \text{N} \cdot \text{m}^2/\text{C}^2)(1.6 \times 10^{-19}\ \text{C})^2}{(5.3 \times 10^{-11}\ \text{m})^2}$

$ = 8.2 \times 10^{-8}\ \text{N} \approx 10^{-7}\ \text{N}$

$F_G = \dfrac{Gm_1 m_2}{r^2}$

$ = \dfrac{G\,(1.67 \times 10^{-27}\ \text{kg})(9.1 \times 10^{-31}\ \text{kg})}{(5.3 \times 10^{-11}\ \text{m})^2}$

$ = 3.6 \times 10^{-47}\ \text{N} \approx 10^{-47}\ \text{N}$

$\dfrac{10^{-7}}{10^{-47}} = 10^{40},\ 40 \text{ orders of magnitude}$

6. $f = \dfrac{v}{\lambda} = \dfrac{3.0 \times 10^8\ \text{m/s}}{9.38 \times 10^{-8}\ \text{m}} = 3.2 \times 10^{15}\ \text{Hz}$

$E_N - E_1 = (6.6 \times 10^{-34}\ \text{J/Hz})(3.2 \times 10^{15}\ \text{Hz})$

$ = 2.11 \times 10^{-18}\ \text{J}$

$E_N = (-2.17 \times 10^{-18}\ \text{J}) + 2.11 \times 10^{-18}\ \text{J}$

$E_N = -6 \times 10^{-20}\ \text{J}$

$\dfrac{-2.17 \times 10^{-18}\ \text{J}}{N^2} = -6 \times 10^{-20}\ \text{J}$

$N^2 = 36$

$N = 6$

The Nucleus

Overview

The nucleus is a very small, dense body composed of protons and neutrons. The unstable nucleus undergoes radioactive decay, which produces alpha, beta, and gamma rays. The half-life of a radioactive isotope is the time required for half of the nuclei to decay. Nuclear reactions are produced by bombarding nuclei with protons, neutrons, alpha particles, electrons, or gamma rays. High energy protons for bombardment are produced by linear accelerators or synchrotrons. The Geiger counter, the Wilson cloud chamber, and the bubble chamber are ways of detecting particles emitted in radioactive decay.

Protons and neutrons, also called nucleons, are composed of still smaller particles called quarks. All matter appears to be made up of two families of particles, quarks and leptons.

Planning Guide (6 Class Sessions)

Text Section			Demonstrations and Experiments		Other Program Components	
30:1	Description of the Nucleus	P	Dem 30:1 Composition of an Isotope			
30:2	Isotopes	P	Mixture			
			Exp 55 Half-Life Simulation	**LM**		
30:3	Radioactive Decay	P	Dem 30:5 Half-Life		Teaching Master 30-1: Remaining	
30:4	Nuclear Reactions and				Nuclei Versus Half-Life	**TRP**
	Equations	P			Review Masters	**TRP**
30:5	Half-Life	P			Enrichment 30-1: Half-Life	**TRP**
30:6	Nuclear Bombardment	S			Teaching Master 30-2: Proton	
30:7	Linear Accelerators	S			Accelerator	**TRP**
30:8	The Synchrotron	S			Minilab 30-1: Distance Versus	
30:9	Particle Detectors	S			Intensity of Radiation	**TRP**
30:10	The Fundamental Particles	P	Dem 30:12 Discovering the Unknown		Evaluation	**TRP**
30:11	Particles and Antiparticles	S				
30:12	The Quark Model of Nucleons	S				

Performance Objectives

Upon completion of this chapter, your students will

1. define atomic number and mass number; find the charge and mass of the nucleus. *30:1*
2. define an isotope and a nuclide; calculate the number of neutrons, protons, and electrons in an isotope. *30:2*
3. describe the three modes of radioactive decay; explain the changes in atomic number and mass number accompanying each mode of decay. *30:3*
4. write equations for the three forms of decay. *30:4*
5. define half-life; calculate the amount of material and its activity remaining after a certain time. *30:5*

6. balance nuclear equations describing the result of nuclear reactions. *30:6*
7. describe the operation of a linear accelerator. *30:7*
8. describe the operation of a synchrotron. *30:8*
9. describe the operation of different radiation detectors. *30:9*
10. describe the two families of fundamental particles; explain the difference between fundamental particles and force carriers. *30:10*
11. describe antiparticles; calculate the energy of gamma rays emitted when particles annihilate with their antiparticles. *30:11*
12. follow the description of the quark model of the nucleon; understand the place of additional families of quarks and leptons in the quark model. *30:12*

Teaching the Chapter

Introduction

Using the Photo: Using the right-hand rule, a pair of particles of similar or identical mass but of opposite charge will spiral in opposite directions in an applied magnetic field. The pair of particles could be a positron-electron pair.

Demonstration: The recently published high school chemistry text entitled *ChemCom,* published by the American Chemical Society, has an excellent activity that demonstrates the composition of a mixture of isotopes. Pre-1982 and post-1982 pennies have different masses and can be used to represent two isotopes of the same element. Make up bags of ten pennies, each containing different mixtures of pre-1982 and post-1982 pennies. Give these bags and an additional penny of each type to students. Have students weigh and record separately the bag of ten pennies and each of the two single pennies. Then calculate the number of each isotope in the samples, using the following equation: total mass of pennies in mixture = (10 − P)(mass of pre-1982 penny) + (P)(mass of post-1982 penny), where P is the number of post-1982 pennies in the ten penny mixture.

30:3 Radioactive Decay

The discovery of radioactivity might be called a "lucky accident." Becquerel thought that fluorescent materials might give off X rays, so he wrapped some photographic plates in paper and put a piece of fluorescent material on top. He set this in the sunlight to fluoresce. When he checked the plates, they were fogged. He prepared some fresh plates but, because the weather had turned cloudy and he was unable to carry out his experiment, he set the plates and the fluorescent material in a drawer. After a while, he decided to take the plates out and develop them. Much to his surprise, the plates were fogged even though the material had not fluoresced. This phenomenon was caused by radioactivity.

30:5 Half-Life

Introduce half-life using the following example. Assume you have $4,000 and you spend half each year. Ask how much you would have left after seven years. Show how the solution of $31.25 is obtained by listing the amount left after each year through seven years.

Demonstration: Divide the class into groups and give each group a box containing 100 pennies. Have each group place all the pennies heads up. Then have students shake the box vigorously. Open the box and remove the pennies that are tails up. Count and record the remaining "undecayed pennies." Repeat this procedure five more times. Each shake represents a half-life. Plot a graph of the number of half-lives on the x-axis versus the number of undecayed pennies on the y-axis. Discuss the shape of the curve. Ask students if a radioactive substance is radioactive forever.

30:8 The Synchrotron

Atoms can be bombarded by particles from radioactive materials or by artificially accelerated particles. Irene Curie and Frederic Joliot used naturally occurring particles from radioactive materials. Sir John Cockcroft and Ernest Walton built an instrument to accelerate protons. They bombarded lithium with protons and produced alpha particles. This was the first reaction using artificially accelerated particles without the aid of natural radioactivity. Cockcroft and Walton won the 1951 Nobel Prize in physics.

The first cyclotron was built by Ernest Lawrence. The cyclotron deflects the paths of protons into circles and accelerates them to great speeds. The speeds become so great that the mass of the particles increases. This was predicted by Hendrik Lorentz and calculated by Einstein. In 1945, Edwin McMillan invented the synchrotron, which compensates for the increasing mass and reaches higher energy levels than the cyclotron.

30:9 Particle Detectors

One of the devices used to detect radioactive particles is the Wilson cloud chamber. Charles Wilson was interested in meteorology, specifically clouds. He hypothesized that clouds form by condensing vapor on ions in the air when there is no dust. He proved this using radioactive materials in a cloud chamber. Wilson won the Nobel Prize in 1927.

30:12 The Quark Model of Nucleons

The positron was discovered by Carl Anderson while he was studying tracks in a cloud chamber. A track that he found looked exactly like the tracks of an electron, but it curved the wrong way. He called the particle a positron.

Murray Gell-Mann, the son of an Austrian immigrant, was a brilliant young man. He received his Ph.D. from MIT at the age of 22. He became a full professor at the California Institute of Technology at the age of 26. His work was in the field of subatomic particles. He proposed the quark model of the atom in 1965 in an attempt to order the subatomic world.

Demonstration: Obtain several cigar boxes and put one metallic item and two nonmetallic items in each box. Seal the boxes and have students try to guess what is in them. Have students write down their observations and how their observations led them to make their guess.

Resources

Literature

Aubrecht, II, Gordon J., "Report on the Conference on the Teaching of Modern Physics," *The Physics Teacher*, December, 1986, pp. 540–546.

Boslough, John, "Worlds Within the Atom," *National Geographic*, May, 1985, pp. 634–663.

Fisher, Arthur, "Cosmic Order," *Popular Science*, May, 1983, pp. 72–76, 140.

"Fundamental Particles and Interactions, A Wall Chart of Modern Physics, By the Fundamental Particles and Interactions Chart Committee," *The Physics Teacher*, December, 1988, pp. 556–565.

Kowalski, Ludwik, "Simulating Radioactive Decay with Dice," *The Physics Teacher*, February, 1981, p. 113.

Stroink, G., "Radiation Safety in the Lab," *The Physics Teacher*, March, 1980, p. 207.

Background

There are many uses of radioactive substances. They are used in homes in ionizing smoke detectors and in offices in photocopying machines to reduce static. Manufacturing plants use them for product testing and paint curing. The authenticity of works of art is studied using radioactive substances. In agriculture, radioactive substances are used for measuring the utilization of fertilizers and the metabolism of pesticides.

Consumer groups have protested the use of radiation technology in the food industry. They say that there has not been enough research done on the products formed from radiation and used in such processes as inhibiting the sprouting of potatoes and onions, or delaying the ripening of fresh fruit and vegetables. Careful study must always occur to insure that technology which is beneficial to people in one way does not destroy it in another way.

Chapter Review

QUESTIONS

1. Transmutation is the change of one element into another by means of a nuclear reaction caused by radioactive decay or nuclear bombardment.
$$^{238}_{92}U \rightarrow {}^{234}_{90}TH + {}^4_2He$$

2. $A \rightarrow A - 4, Z \rightarrow Z - 2$

3. $A \rightarrow A, Z \rightarrow Z + 1$

4. $A \rightarrow A, Z \rightarrow Z - 1$

5. **a.** ${}^1_1p$ or ${}^1_1H$ **d.** ${}_{-1}^0e(e^-)$

   b. ${}^1_0n$ **e.** α or ${}^4_2He$

   c. ${}^0_1e(e^+)$

6. $\left(\dfrac{1}{2}\right)^3 = \dfrac{1}{8}$

7. a. electromagnetic, weak, gravity
  b. strong, electromagnetic, gravity
  c. weak

8. gamma since both are photons

9. a. F **b.** Am **c.** Ne **d.** Li

10. It accelerates using electrical force and the neutron has no charge.

APPLYING CONCEPTS

1. It would annihilate with an equivalent amount of matter, producing an extremely large amount of energy.

2. Each u quark has a charge of $+\dfrac{2}{3}$.

uuu $= 3\left(+\dfrac{2}{3}\right) = +2$ elementary charges

3. u $+ \bar{d} = +2/3 + (-(-1/3)) = +1$ elementary charge

4. a. u $+ \bar{u} = +2/3 + (-(+2/3)) = 0$ charge
  b. d $+ \bar{u} = -1/3 + (-(+2/3)) = -1$ charge
  c. d $+ \bar{d} = -1/3 + (-(-1/3)) = 0$ charge

5. No. Both Z and A are smaller than that of the α.

6. For the activity to fall to 1/8 its present amount you must wait three half lives, or 9 days.

7. Carbon is present in skeletons but not in metal armor.

8. Large; protons are farther apart and neutrons are able to decay.

EXERCISES

1. 12 neutrons

2. 8 neutrons

3. a. $112 - 48 = 64$ **e.** $1 - 1 = 0$
  b. $209 - 83 = 126$ **f.** $40 - 18 = 22$
  c. $208 - 83 = 125$ **g.** $132 - 54 = 78$
  d. $80 - 35 = 45$

4. $^{25}_{13}\text{Al} + ^{4}_{2}\text{He} \rightarrow ^{1}_{0}n + ^{28}_{15}\text{P}$

5. $^{2}_{1}\text{H} + ^{2}_{1}\text{H} \rightarrow ^{3}_{2}\text{He} + ^{1}_{0}n$

6. $4^{1}_{1}\text{H} \rightarrow ^{4}_{2}\text{He} + 2\,^{0}_{1}e$

7. $^{214}_{83}\text{Bi} \rightarrow ^{214}_{84}\text{Po} + ^{0}_{-1}e$

8. $^{210}_{84}\text{Po} \rightarrow ^{206}_{82}\text{Pb} + ^{4}_{2}\text{He}$

9. $^{56}_{24}\text{Cr} \rightarrow ^{56}_{25}\text{Mn} + ^{0}_{-1}e$

10. $^{227}_{92}\text{U} \rightarrow ^{223}_{90}\text{Th} + ^{4}_{2}\text{He}$

PROBLEMS

1. 280 years is 10 half-lives. $(\frac{1}{2})^{10}$ is equal to 9.8×10^{-4} or approximately $9.8 \times 10^{-2}\,\%$.

2. a. 48 h is two half-lives, therefore 24 h is one half-life.
  b. Determine the slope (at 24 hours) of the line of a graph of remaining nuclei versus time.

The slope is
9×10^{12} nuclei/second.

3. a. $v = \dfrac{d}{t}$

$t = \dfrac{d}{v} = \dfrac{\pi(2.0 \times 10^3\ \text{m})}{(3.0 \times 10^8\ \text{m/s})} = 2.1 \times 10^{-5}\ \text{s}$

  b. $\dfrac{(400 \times 10^9\ \text{eV}) - (8.0 \times 10^9\ \text{eV})}{2.5 \times 10^6\ \text{eV/revolution}}$
  $= 1.6 \times 10^5$ revolutions

  c. $t = (1.6 \times 10^5\ \text{rev})(2.1 \times 10^{-5}\ \text{s/rev})$
  $= 3.4\ \text{s}$

  d. $d = vt = (3.0 \times 10^8\ \text{m/s})(3.4\ \text{s})$
  $= 1.0 \times 10^9\ \text{m}$, or about 1 million km

4. 3200 counts to 100 counts represents 5 half-lives.
$\dfrac{30\ \text{h}}{5} = 6\ \text{h}$

5. $^{238}_{92}\text{U} \rightarrow ^{234}_{90}\text{Th} + ^{4}_{2}\text{He}$
$^{234}_{90}\text{Th} \rightarrow ^{234}_{91}\text{Pa} + ^{0}_{-1}e$
$^{234}_{91}\text{Pa} \rightarrow ^{234}_{92}\text{U} + ^{0}_{-1}e$
$A = 234$

6. $\dfrac{(6.02 \times 10^{23}\ \text{nuclei})}{14\ \text{g}} = \dfrac{N}{5\ \text{g}}$

$N = \dfrac{(6.02 \times 10^{23}\ \text{nuclei})(5\ \text{g})}{14\ \text{g}}$
$= 2 \times 10^{23}$ nuclei

After 2 half-lives only 1/4 of the nuclei are nondecayed.

$\left(\dfrac{1}{4}\right)(2 \times 10^{23}\ \text{nuclei}) = 5 \times 10^{22}$ nuclei

Nuclear Applications

Overview

In a nuclear reaction, the mass difference between the reactants and the products is converted into energy, according to $E = mc^2$. Bombardment of nuclei can produce radioactive isotopes not found in nature. These artificial radioactive nuclei are often used in medicine. Nuclear fission also occurs as a result of nuclear bombardment. The products of nuclear fission are similar in mass, and the reaction is accompanied by a large release of energy. Fusion is the combination of small nuclei into one, resulting in a large release of energy. Scientists hope that someday they will be able to use controlled fusion as a source of energy.

Planning Guide (6 Class Sessions)

Text Section		Demonstrations and Experiments	Other Program Components	
31:1 Forces Within the Nucleus	P	Dem 31:1 A Chain Reaction with Critical Mass	Teaching Master 31-1: Binding Energy Versus *A*	**TRP**
31:2 Binding Energy of the Nucleus	P		Review Masters	**TRP**
31:3 Artificial Radioactivity	P	Dem 31:4 A Domino Chain Reaction	Teaching Master 31-2: Nuclear Fission Chain Reaction	**TRP**
31:4 Nuclear Fission	P		Minilab 31-1: Penetrating Power of Radiation	**TRP**
31:5 Nuclear Reactors	P		Enrichment 31-1: Problems	**TRP**
			Enrichment 31-2: Nuclear Power	**TRP**
31:6 Nuclear Fusion	P		Enrichment 31-3: Nuclear Power—Pro and Con	**TRP**
31:7 Controlled Fusion	P		Evaluation	**TRP**

Performance Objectives

Upon completion of this chapter, your students will

1. recognize the role and nature of the strong force; define the nucleon and binding energy.   *31:1*
2. relate the energy released in a nuclear reaction to the difference in mass of the particles before and after the reaction.   *31:2*
3. define artificially produced radioactive isotopes; describe their medical uses; solve nuclear equations involving formation and decay of radioactive isotopes.   *31:3*
4. define nuclear fission and chain reaction; understand the source of energy in fission.   *31:4*
5. describe the operation of one or more types of nuclear reactors; understand the formation of plutonium in a reactor.   *31:5*
6. describe the fusion process and the formation of helium in the sun.   *31:6*
7. describe two approaches to controlled nuclear fusion.   *31:7*

Teaching the Chapter

Introduction

Using the Photo: High-speed charged particles (such as electrons) are given off from the fuel rods. The particles are traveling faster than the speed of light in water. As they pass through the water they produce the blue light, also known as Cherenkov radiation. The Cherenkov light is an electromagnetic shock wave, much like a sonic boom formed by an aircraft traveling faster than the speed of sound. This photograph also can be used with Section 31:2 to discuss binding energy of the nucleus and Section 31:5 to discuss nuclear reactors.

Demonstration: Give each student two corks. Turn your back to the class and toss a cork over your head toward the students. The student who gets hit should close his or her eyes and throw up in the air the two corks received earlier (not at another student). Other students who get hit should repeat the procedure. Then have students move closer together so they are taking up about half the space as before and repeat the procedure. Repeat the procedure a third time, having students move very close together. The closer together the students are, the faster the reaction. Almost everyone will get hit. Discuss the results. Students should observe that when people are spread out, it may take longer to get the chain reaction going. Compact groups start faster and react faster. This demonstrates chain reaction and critical mass.

31:2   Binding Energy of the Nucleus

The idea of binding energy came from William Harkins, who wondered about the difference in mass between the assembled nucleons and the same individual nucleons. He used Einstein's equation $E = mc^2$ to show that the mass would be changed into energy. The "mass numbers" of the individual isotopes were found using Francis Aston's mass spectrograph.

31:3   Artificial Radioactivity

When a substance is bombarded with neutrons, many of the nuclei in the substance become radioactive. The radiation is analyzed and used to identify the elements in the original sample. The procedure is known as neutron activation analysis. This method of analysis was used on a piece of Napoleon Bonaparte's hair and showed that the hair contained arsenic, meaning that Napoleon may have been poisoned. The discovery was made 150 years after Napoleon's death.

31:4   Nuclear Fission

Enrico Fermi discovered that neutrons were more effective in the bombarding of elements when they were slowed down. Fermi thought he had produced an element heavier than uranium when he bombarded uranium with neutrons. He was awarded the Nobel Prize for his work in 1938. In the midst of his work, Fermi had to leave Italy, where he was a professor at the University of Rome, because he was not a Fascist and his wife was Jewish. He came to the United States where he remained permanently. Fermi later discovered the chain reaction.

Lise Meitner (1878–1968), an Austrian-Swedish physicist, has a long list of accomplishments. She retired from physics at the age of 82 after devoting her whole life to it. One of her major accomplishments was the explanation of nuclear fission. Fermi had been incorrect in thinking his bombardment of uranium with neutrons produced elements heavier than uranium. It turned out that the products acted like barium. Meitner and her nephew Otto Frisch were the first to understand how barium was produced when uranium was bombarded with neutrons. Lise Meitner was the first woman to win the Fermi Award issued by the Atomic Energy Commission.

Demonstration: Stand one domino up and place two behind it in such a way that when the first domino falls, it will knock down the others. Then set 4 dominoes behind the 2, and 8 behind the 4, and so on. Space the dominoes so they will all fall in succession after you knock over the first one. This demonstrates a chain reaction.

31:5   Nuclear Reactors

Leo Szilard, a Hungarian-Austrian physicist, worked with Fermi on the first nuclear fusion reactor. Szilard was one of the people instrumental in building the atomic bomb. He was very much in favor of building the bomb, especially before the Germans could make one. However, when the bomb was completed for use, he had second thoughts about what they had created. He pleaded that the bomb not be used or that it be used only in uninhabited areas. He protested and tried to get people to ban nuclear warfare and testing and to use nuclear energy only for peaceful uses. He left the field of nuclear physics for biophysics and was awarded the Atoms for Peace Award in 1959.

Resources

Literature

Hewitt, Paul, "Why Is the Hot Spring Hot?" *The Physics Teacher*, May, 1987, p. 339.

Marzewski, Robert, "Chain Reaction Model," *The Physics Teacher*, November, 1988, p. 514.

Ostiek, V. J., and Bord, D. J., *Inquiry into Physics*, West Publishing Co., St. Paul, MN, 1987, p. 431.

Roeder, John, "Throwing Dice in the Classroom," *The Physics Teacher*, October, 1977, pp. 428–429.

Roeder, John, "Throwing Dice in the Classroom II," *The Physics Teacher*, April, 1980, pp. 302–304.

Watkins, Sallie, "Lise Meitner: The Making of a Physicist," *The Physics Teacher*, January, 1984, pp. 12–15.

Background

In order for a chain reaction to occur, a neutron must be absorbed by a uranium atom before it is lost to the surrounding environment. A neutron may bounce off many uranium atoms before it is absorbed by one. The size of the uranium core must be large enough so the chain will keep going. The critical mass is the smallest mass that allows the chain reaction to occur. The introductory demonstration shows how important the critical mass is.

The critical mass depends on the nature of the core and its shape. The greater the concentration of uranium-235 in the core, the less the critical mass. The use of slow neutrons rather than fast neutrons also reduces the critical mass.

Chapter Review

QUESTIONS

1. Sum of mass constituents less mass of the nucleus. It is related to binding energy through $E = mc^2$.

2. The incoming binding energy is less than the outgoing binding energy and, therefore, the reaction does go.

3. Not true. Iron is the most tightly bound element, and thus the most stable nucleus. It cannot decay by either fission or fusion.

4. A naturally radioactive material is one that is found to exist normally in ores and that displays radiations. Artificially radioactive material displays radiations only after being subjected to bombardment by particles.

5. Plasma confinement by magnetic fields and inertial confinement or laser implosion are being studied.

6. When a large atom, such as uranium, undergoes fission, the mass of the products is less than that of the original nucleus. An amount of energy equivalent to the difference in mass is released. However, when small nuclei fuse into a larger nucleus, the mass of the more tightly bound large nucleus is less, and the extra mass appears as energy.

7. tracer isotopes, PET scanner, destroy diseased cells

8. Neutrons must be released by a fissioned nucleus and absorbed by neighboring nuclei causing them to fission.

9. It slows neutrons, increasing their probability of being absorbed.

10. the rate of fission

APPLYING CONCEPTS

1. The water in the heat exchanger is radioactive; that used to generate steam is not.

2. No, plutonium is produced at the expense of uranium.

3. the fission fragments and neutrons

4. The nuclei that combine in the fusion process of stars require high kinetic energy to overcome the repulsive electrical forces among them.

5. Graphite is used as a moderator to slow neutrons in order to increase the probability of their being absorbed by $^{235}_{92}U$.

6. Fusion does not produce plutonium and results in fewer radioactive wastes than fission .

7. This refers to breeder reactors. Students should explain that fissionable plutonium in a reactor produces more plutonium than is used.

8. **a.** fission of 1 uranium nucleus = 200 MeV
   fusion of 4 hydrogen nuclei = 50 MeV

   b. Although the fission on one uranium nucleus produces more energy than the fusion of two hydrogen nuclei, there are over 100 times as many deuterium nuclei in a kilogram than there are uranium nuclei. Therefore the fusion of a kilogram of deuterium produces much more energy.

c. See answer to **b.**

EXERCISES

1. a. gold

    b. a. $^{200}_{80}Hg + ^{2}_{1}H \rightarrow ^{198}_{79}Au + ^{4}_{2}He$

2. a 7 protons = (7)(1.007825 u) = 7.054775 u

    7 neutrons = (7)(1.008665 u) = 7.060655 u

                            total = 14.11543 u

    mass of nitrogen nucleus = −14.00307 u

               mass defect = 0.11236 u

    b. (0.11236 u)(931 MeV/u) = 105 MeV

3. $Energy = \dfrac{105 \text{ MeV}}{14 \text{ nucleons}} = 7.5 \text{ MeV/nucleon}$

4. a. 6 protons = (6)(1.007825 u) = 6.046950 u

    7 neutrons = (7)(1.008665 u) = 7.060655 u

                     total = 13.107605 u

    mass of carbon nucleus = −13.00335 u

             mass defect = 0.10426 u

    b. (0.10426 u)(931 MeV/u) = 97.1 MeV

5. $F = K\dfrac{qq'}{d^2}$

    $= \dfrac{K(1.6 \times 10^{-19} \text{ C})(1.6 \times 10^{-19} \text{ C})}{(2.0 \times 10^{-15} \text{ m})^2} = 58 \text{ N}$

6. $^{7}_{3}Li + ^{1}_{1}H \rightarrow 2\,^{4}_{2}He$

7. a. $^{30}_{15}P \rightarrow ^{30}_{14}Si + ^{0}_{+1}e$

    b. $^{205}_{82}Pb \rightarrow ^{205}_{81}Tl + ^{0}_{+1}e$

8. a. $^{21}_{11}Na \rightarrow ^{21}_{10}Ne + ^{0}_{+1}e$

    b. $^{49}_{24}Cr \rightarrow ^{49}_{23}V + ^{0}_{-1}e$

9. a. $^{14}_{7}N + ^{4}_{2}He \rightarrow ^{18}_{9}F$

    b. $^{27}_{13}Al + ^{4}_{2}He \rightarrow ^{31}_{15}P$

10. a. $^{65}_{29}Cu + ^{1}_{0}n \rightarrow ^{65}_{28}Ni + ^{1}_{1}H$

    b. $^{14}_{7}N + ^{1}_{0}n \rightarrow ^{14}_{6}C + ^{1}_{1}H$

11. a. lithium

    b. a. $^{10}_{5}B + ^{1}_{0}n \rightarrow ^{7}_{3}Li + ^{4}_{2}He$

12. a. carbon

    b. $^{11}_{5}B + ^{1}_{1}p \rightarrow ^{11}_{6}C + ^{1}_{0}n$

    c. $^{11}_{6}C \rightarrow ^{11}_{5}B + ^{0}_{+1}e$

PROBLEMS

1. a. oxygen

    b. $^{18}_{9}F \rightarrow ^{18}_{8}O + ^{0}_{+1}e$

    c. Eight hours is about 4 half-lives, so 1/16 or 0.6 mg remains.

2. a. (2)(2.01410 u) − (4.00263 u) = 0.02557 u

    (0.02557 u)(931 MeV/u) = 23.8 MeV

    b. (23.8 MeV/molecule)(6.02 × 10²³ molecules/ mole)(1.6 × 10⁻¹⁹ J/eV)(10⁶ eV/MeV) = 2.29 × 10¹² J/mole

    c. $\dfrac{2.29 \times 10^{12} \text{ J}}{2.9 \times 10^{6} \text{ J/mole}} = 7.9 \times 10^{5} \text{ moles}$

3. a. $\dfrac{(6.02 \times 10^{23} \text{ atoms/mole})(1.00 \text{ kg})}{(0.235 \text{ kg/mole})}$

    $= 2.56 \times 10^{24} \text{ atoms}$

    b. (2.56 × 10²⁴ atoms/kg)(2.0 × 10² MeV/ atom)(1.6 × 10⁻¹⁹ J/eV)(10⁶ eV/MeV) = 8.2 × 10¹³ J/kg

    c. $\dfrac{3.0 \times 10^{9} \text{ J/s}}{8.2 \times 10^{13} \text{ J/kg}} = 3.7 \times 10^{-5} \text{ kg/s}$

    d. (3.7 × 10⁻⁵ kg/s)(3.15 × 10⁷ s/y) = 1.2 × 10³ kg/y

4. $Energy$ = (20 kilotons)(5.0 × 10¹² J/kiloton) = 1.0 × 10¹⁴ J

    $\dfrac{1.0 \times 10^{14} \text{ J}}{1.6 \times 10^{-19} \text{ J/eV}} = 6.3 \times 10^{32} \text{ eV}$

    $\dfrac{(6.3 \times 10^{32} \text{ eV})}{(2.0 \times 10^{2} \text{ MeV/atom})(10^{6} \text{ eV/MeV})} = 3.1 \times 10^{24} \text{ atoms}$

    $\dfrac{3.1 \times 10^{24} \text{ atoms}}{6.02 \times 10^{23} \text{ atoms/mole}} = 5.2 \text{ moles}$

    (5.2 moles)(0.235 kg/mole) = 1.2 kg

5. $^{238}_{92}U \rightarrow ^{234}_{90}Th + ^{4}_{2}He$

    $^{234}_{90}Th \rightarrow ^{234}_{91}Pa + ^{0}_{-1}e$

    $^{234}_{91}Pa \rightarrow ^{234}_{92}U + ^{0}_{-1}e$

    $^{234}_{92}U \rightarrow ^{230}_{90}Th + ^{4}_{2}He$

    $^{230}_{90}Th \rightarrow ^{226}_{88}Ra + ^{4}_{2}He$

    $^{226}_{88}Ra \rightarrow ^{222}_{86}Rn + ^{4}_{2}He$

6. mass defect

    = (232.0372 u) − (228.0287 u + 4.0026 u)

    = 0.0059 u

    total KE = (0.0059 u)(931 MeV/u)

    = 5.5 MeV

    KE for thorium nucleus = (5.5 MeV) − (5.3 MeV) = 0.2 MeV

7. $\dfrac{28.3 \text{ MeV}}{931 \text{ MeV/u}} = 0.0304 \text{ u}$

    2 neutrons + 2 protons

    = 2(1.008665 u) + 2(1.007825 u)

    = 4.0330 u

    (4.0330 u) − (0.0304 u) = 4.0026 u

We want your opinions!

We at Merrill Publishing feel that with this edition of *Physics: Principles & Problems,* we have produced a quality textbook program—but the final proof of that rests with you, the teachers who have had the opportunity to put our materials to use in your classrooms. That's why we would very much appreciate it if you would take the time to respond to any of the parts of this questionnaire that are appropriate for you. In doing so, you will be letting us know how good a job we've done and where we can work to improve. **In appreciation for your efforts, we will hold two drawings each year, awarding the win-** ners with their choice of a *graphing calculator, a freestanding globe, or a classroom cassette deck.* To be eligible, you would simply have to return this questionnaire on or before our April 30 drawing or on or before our November 30 drawing. Winners will be notified by mail.

Please note: 1) you need not have used all of the program components to respond to this questionnaire; 2) we encourage you to give us your honest and most candid opinions.

Excellent				Poor	**Student Text**
5	4	3	2	1	Format
5	4	3	2	1	Readability
5	4	3	2	1	Approach
5	4	3	2	1	Organization
5	4	3	2	1	Factual accuracy
5	4	3	2	1	Coverage of physics principles
5	4	3	2	1	Thoroughness of concept development
5	4	3	2	1	Visual impact
5	4	3	2	1	Treatment of new terms
5	4	3	2	1	Graphs
5	4	3	2	1	Problems
5	4	3	2	1	Illustrations
5	4	3	2	1	Glossary
5	4	3	2	1	Skills pages
					Teacher Annotated Edition
5	4	3	2	1	Teachability
5	4	3	2	1	Planning Guide
5	4	3	2	1	Demonstrations
5	4	3	2	1	Performance Objectives
5	4	3	2	1	Teaching aids
5	4	3	2	1	Chapter materials
5	4	3	2	1	Annotations
					Supplements
5	4	3	2	1	Teacher Resource Package
5	4	3	2	1	Laboratory Physics
5	4	3	2	1	Transparency Package
5	4	3	2	1	Laboratory, Physics, TE
5	4	3	2	1	Computer-Assisted Data-Checking Program

School Information

1. What is the grade level of the students you teach?   6   7   8   9   10   11   12
2. Total number of students in that grade?   1-50   51-100   101-200   200+
3. Average class size?   25 or less   26-30   31-35   41 or more
4. Total school enrollment?   1-200   201-500   501-1000   1000+
5. Ability level of your average class?   Basic   Average   Advanced
6. How appropriate in this text for your class?   Too easy   On level   Too difficult
7. How many years have you used this text?   1   2   3   4   5

Please feel free to include additional comments on a separate sheet.

- -

Fold

Name _____   Date _____

School _____

City _____   State _____   Zip _____

- -

Fold

BUSINESS REPLY MAIL
FIRST-CLASS MAIL   PERMIT NO. 284   COLUMBUS, OHIO

POSTAGE WILL BE PAID BY ADDRESSEE

MERRILL PUBLISHING COMPANY
A Bell & Howell Company

1300 Alum Creek Drive
P.O. Box 508
COLUMBUS, OH 43216-9889
ATTN: Elhi Research and Development

NO POSTAGE
NECESSARY
IF MAILED
IN THE
UNITED STATES

PHYSICS

Principles & Problems

AUTHORS

Paul W. Zitzewitz

Professor of Physics
Associate Dean of the College of Arts, Sciences, and Letters
University of Michigan-Dearborn
Dearborn, Michigan

James T. Murphy

Formerly Science Department Chairperson
Reading Memorial High School
Reading, Massachusetts

CONTENT CONSULTANT

Robert F. Neff

Physics Teacher
Suffern High School
Suffern, New York

MERRILL PUBLISHING COMPANY
Columbus, Ohio

A Merrill Science Program

Physics: Principles & Problems
Physics: Principles & Problems, Teacher Annotated Edition
Physics: Principles & Problems, Teacher Resource Package
Physics: Principles & Problems, Transparency Package
Laboratory Physics
Laboratory Physics, Teacher Annotated Edition
Laboratory Physics, Computer-Assisted Data-Checking Software

Authors

Paul W. Zitzewitz is a professor of physics and the Associate Dean of the College of Arts, Sciences, and Letters at the University of Michigan-Dearborn. He received his B.A. from Carleton College and M.A. and Ph.D. from Harvard University, all in physics. Dr. Zitzewitz has 17 years teaching experience and has published more than 50 research papers in the field of atomic physics.

James T. Murphy was formerly the chairperson of the Science Department at Reading Memorial High School in Reading, Massachusetts. He received his B.S. and M.Ed. from Massachusetts State University and his M.S. in physics from Clarkson College of Technology. Mr. Murphy taught biology, chemistry, physics, electronics, and general science at the junior and senior high school levels and authored numerous professional articles.

Content Consultant

Robert F. Neff has taught physics for 24 years at Suffern High School, Suffern, New York. He received his B.S. from Kenyon College and his M.S.T. from Cornell University. Mr. Neff has presented workshops on physics demonstrations to physics teachers across the country.

Reviewers

Delphia N. Bryant, Physics Teacher, Frederick Douglas High School, Atlanta, Georgia
Jack Grube, Science Coordinator, East Side Union High School District, San Jose, California
James C. Harpel, Physics Teacher, Horton Watkins (Ladue) High School, Ladue, Missouri
Mark Pilgrim, Physics Teacher, Chambersburg Area Senior High, Chambersburg, Pennsylvania
Ronald W. Revere, Physics Teacher, Wakefield Senior High School, Arlington, Virginia
Don Sparks, Science Dept. Chairperson, Physics Teacher, North Hollywood High School, North Hollywood, California
Kelly A. Wedding, Physics Teacher, Wichita Falls High School, Wichita Falls, Texas

Cover Photograph by Ralph Cowan

Series Editor: Mary Beth Gallant; **Project Editor:** Madelaine Meek;
Editorial Assistant: Colyene Garrabrant
Project Designer: Karen P. Martino; **Project Artist:** Sheila Monroe-Hawkins
  Illustrators: Dick Smith, Jim Shough, Don Robison
Photo Editors: Kenneth E. Stevenson, David T. Dennison
Production Editors: Annette Hoffman, Mary Ann Hopper; **Word Processor:** Peggy Doughty

ISBN-0-675-02472-2

Published by
Merrill Publishing Company
Columbus, Ohio

Preface

A study of physics and its applications is basic and vital to all students, whatever their educational goals. *Physics: Principles & Problems* appeals to students with a wide range of interests and can be used successfully for both classroom and individual study.

Physics: Principles & Problems provides a clear and straightforward presentation of the basic concepts of physics. These concepts are developed in a unified, logical sequence. Excessive detail has been omitted where it would obscure or confuse the main idea. However, care has been taken to identify frames of reference within which concepts are presented. These references are intended to enhance student awareness of the importance of defining an appropriate system when interpreting physical phenomena.

Mechanics, needed to interpret most phenomena, is the first concept presented. It is used to develop models for energy and matter. Wave phenomena are introduced as models for sound and light. Electromagnetic waves are developed from electricity and magnetism. Atomic and nuclear physics complete the text with an expanded discussion of quantum and elementary particle physics.

An understanding of the nature of measurements and mathematics is necessary in physics. To make the text self-sustaining, a brief review of algebra, trigonometry, and graphing using physical quantities is provided in Chapter 2. Thus, the need for outside resources is eliminated.

This text is written in a manner that bridges the gap between the understanding of a concept and the application of that concept to the solution of problems. Explanations are keyed to experiments and actual experiences, and lead students to an awareness of how physical laws operate in everyday phenomena. Conceptual and mathematical problem-solving skills are developed throughout the text. Photographs and artwork are used extensively throughout the text to illustrate concepts and their applications.

Physics: Principles & Problems reflects the consensus of recent recommendations made by curriculum committees, by teachers using this material, and by students. Following these guidelines, the authors have designed a physics program that is both manageable and realistic in terms of its expectations of students.

The authors wish to express their gratitude to the many physics students, teachers, and science educators who have made suggestions for changes based on their use of the previous editions of *Physics: Principles & Problems*.

To the Student

This physics textbook presents you with the basic physics concepts that will form a foundation for most of your studies of science and technology. These concepts are developed clearly and logically with applications from everyday experiences. Certain features of your textbook are designed to make the time you spend studying physics especially interesting and rewarding.

Each chapter is introduced with a photograph and a problem-solving feature. Chapter goals appear at the beginning of each chapter and give you an overall purpose for studying the chapter. Each chapter is divided into numbered sections that provide an outline of the chapter. Each chapter contains photographs and artwork that illustrate the concepts being presented. In some chapters, information is organized in tables and graphs.

Margin notes are carefully positioned throughout the text to highlight important terms and ideas. You can use these notes in organizing information for study and review. New terms are printed in boldface type and defined within the text when introduced. Additional information or interesting facts are noted in *For Your Information* entries.

Examples with step-by-step solutions are included throughout the text to provide you with a model for solving problems. Each *Example* emphasizes the thinking process involved in setting up a logical solution. These *Examples* are immediately followed by *Practice Exercises*. Complete solutions to the *Practice Exercises* are provided in a special *Solutions Appendix*. Thus, you can immediately check your understanding of the material just studied.

Some chapters contain a *Physics Focus*. This special feature provides information on a current topic in physics research as application of a physics concept.

A *Summary* at the end of each chapter provides you with a chapter overview. Comprehensive sets of *Questions* and *Concept Applications* are included at the end of each chapter for you to check your knowledge of concepts and to apply these concepts to everyday experiences.

Additional *Exercises* are also included at the end of each chapter along with more complex *Problems* which may combine several fundamental concepts. Together these *Exercises* and *Problems* provide you with numerous opportunities to practice and advance your physics problem-solving skills.

The *Readings* section at the end of each chapter includes readings from many recent popular scientific periodicals. These readings can help you expand your physics knowledge beyond the limitations of this textbook.

In addition to *Practice Exercise* solutions, the *Appendices* consists of a section on the laws of sines and cosines, reference tables, a listing of important physics equations according to sections, and a feature on physics-related careers. The reference tables include trigonometric tables, atomic masses of the elements, physical constants, and important equations. The career appendix includes descriptions and educational requirements for a variety of physics-related careers.

The *Glossary* is a ready reference for the definitions of new terms. The *Index* has been included to provide the page number where an item may be found.

Learn to use all the features of your textbook *Physics: Principles & Problems* to enhance your success in this course.

Table of Contents

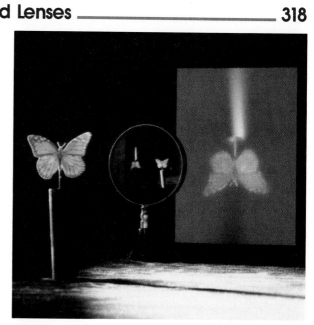

CHAPTER 1

Physics: A Mathematical Science

GOALS

1. You will gain an understanding of the nature of physics.
2. You will learn and use the SI system of measurement.
3. You will gain an understanding of the nature of measured quantities.

What is science? Science is usually defined as knowledge. Scientists are inquisitive people who look at the world around them with questioning eyes. Their observations lead them to search for the causes of what they see. What makes the sun shine? How do the planets move? Of what is matter made? More often than not, finding explanations to the original questions leads to more questions and experiments. What all scientists hope for are powerful explanations that describe more than one phenomenon and lead to a better understanding of the universe.

1:1 Physics: The Search for Understanding

Physics is the branch of knowledge that studies the physical world. Physicists investigate objects as small as atoms and as large as galaxies. They study the natures of matter and energy and how they are related. Sometimes the results of their work are only of interest to other physicists. Other times their work leads to devices such as lasers, calculators, or computers, which change everyone's life. As an example of how physics works, let us look at the history of one of the most important scientific advances of the last few years, superconductivity.

In September, 1986, two Swiss scientists working for IBM Corporation announced that they had discovered a new superconducting material that worked at temperatures as "high" as −243°C, 30 degrees above absolute zero. Until that time, materials were only superconducting at temperatures close to absolute zero, −273°C. This temperature is theoretically the lowest temperature possible. The new material was a ceramic, one that

Physics is the branch of knowledge that studies the physical world.

For Your Information

Basic research is what I am doing when I don't know what I am doing.
—Werner von Braun

2

Still Motion

Early telescopic observations revealed large numbers of faint, fuzzy patches of light. As a group these patches of light were called nebulae. Larger telescopes have revealed, however, that many nebulae are actually galaxies. Day after day an observer sees a spiral galaxy in the same way, with no apparent changes or movement. Yet it is universally accepted that spiral galaxies rotate about a center. As an observer, what indications are there to support galactic motion?

For Your Information

Other sciences use the results of physics.

SUGGESTION: List careers in which physics is required, such as architecture, physical therapy, medicine, and engineering. Refer students to the listing of physics-related careers in Appendix D.

does not normally conduct any electricity. This development was exciting because, although superconducting metals had been discovered in 1911, they worked only at very low temperatures. In 1973 an alloy had been found that worked at 23 degrees above absolute zero, but in the next 13 years no further progress had been made.

Within weeks after the discovery was announced, researchers in the United States, China, and Japan had repeated the experiments. That fall scientists tried different materials and increased the temperature to 52 degrees, then 77, then 90, then, in February, 1987, to 98 degrees above absolute zero ($-175°C$). In March, 1987, three thousand physicists jammed a hotel ballroom for eight hours to hear reports of experiments. In July, 1987, President Ronald Reagan held a press conference to watch a demonstration of a superconducting magnet and to announce a United States effort to apply the new developments. By the end of the same year, high school students had made superconductors that worked above $-196°C$.

Physicists and engineers have dreamed of many exciting applications for superconductors. They could carry electricity to cities from distant power plants without energy loss. They could be used in magnets that make nuclear fusion possible, that allow high-speed trains to "float" above the track, that could detect oil and minerals in Earth, or pinpoint diseased body tissue. Superconductors might make possible smaller, faster, more powerful computers. Until recently, the problem has been that superconductors worked at such low temperatures that they had to be cooled by liquid helium. Liquid helium is very expensive (more than $5 per liter) and difficult to store. The new superconductors can be cooled with liquid nitrogen, which costs about the same as soda pop. Now some of the dreams may be possible. But first the new materials, now as brittle as glass, must be modified so they can be made into flexible wires. An even more exciting possibility is the development of materials that are superconducting at room temperatures.

FIGURE 1-1. Many exciting applications of superconducting materials will be possible with the development of cheaper superconducting materials.

How did these discoveries occur? The original discovery, in 1911, was made by the Dutch physicist, Heike Kamerlingh Onnes. He had built new kinds of refrigerators that could reach previously unexplored low temperatures. He then studied the properties of gases, liquids, and solids under these new conditions. He noticed that mercury became a better electrical conductor when the temperature was lowered, but was totally surprised when all resistance disappeared at 4 degrees above absolute zero. Kamerlingh Onnes was an experimental physicist, one who worked in a research laboratory, often inventing and building the equipment he needed, and using insight, knowledge, and imagination to interpret the results. Many times the results had no immediate practical applications.

For over forty years after 1911 no one had developed a complete explanation of how materials could conduct electricity without loss. That is, there was no theory of superconductivity. In 1957 three American theoretical physicists, John Bardeen, Leon Cooper, and Robert Schrieffer, presented a theory that explained how superconductors work. Theoretical physicists use mathematics and, especially today, computers to construct a framework of explanations called a theory that explains experimental data and predicts new results. Theoreticians also need insight, imagination, and creativity. Their work is not done because no theory can yet explain how the new superconducting materials work.

We still have much to learn about the interactions of matter and energy. Sometimes experimental results come before the theoretical explanations. In other cases a theory predicts the result of an experiment that has not yet been done. Often physics has important applications to other sciences. Superconducting magnets are an important part of devices used by chemists to learn the structure of molecules, by biologists to trace molecules through cells, by physicians to find tumors in the brain.

Science and technology constantly interact. Often new equipment, such as the refrigerators Kamerlingh Onnes built, produce scientific results. Other times science results in new products. For example, engineers have built giant magnets and small, efficient motors and generators using superconductors. The applications of science affect the lives of all people more and more each year. For this reason, everyone needs an understanding of physics, as well as the other sciences, to make informed decisions about problems involving our rapidly changing society.

Perhaps the most surprising aspect of physics is that its results can be described by a small number of relationships, or laws. These laws often can be expressed using mathematics, which is often called the language of physics. For that reason, we begin the study of physics with a review of how measurements are made and how mathematics can be used to describe physical relationships.

1:2 Measurement and Scientific Methods

Starting in the fourth and fifth centuries B.C., Greek philosophers tried to determine what the world was made of. They believed in observing nature and then mentally fitting their observations into a logical framework or theory. Doing experiments to test their theories was not part of their method.

Physics involves both theory and experiment.

For Your Information

No number of experiments can prove me right; a single experiment can prove me wrong.
—Albert Einstein

FIGURE 1–2. Superconducting magnets are used in instruments that scan the brain of living subjects.

For Your Information

FIGURE 1–3. Much of your knowledge of physics will be gained in the laboratory through experimentation (a). The scientific method of studying events was developed by Galileo (b).

The writings of the early Greeks first came to Europe through Arabic translations in the twelfth century. Until the sixteenth century, Europeans accepted the Greek teachings as truth, with no need for verification. One of the first European scientists to claim publicly that knowledge must be based on observations and experiments rather than ancient books was Galileo Galilei (1564–1642). He questioned the belief that Earth is the center of the universe. He doubted Aristotle's views on physics, especially the idea that objects of large mass fall faster than objects of small mass. To prove Aristotle wrong, Galileo developed a systematic method of observation, experimentation, and analysis.

There is no single "scientific method." All scientists, however, study problems in an organized way. They combine systematic experimentation with careful measurement and analysis of results. From these analyses, conclusions are drawn. These conclusions are then subjected to additional tests to find out if they are valid. Since Galileo's time scientists all over the world have used these techniques and methods to gain a better understanding of the universe. Knowledge, skill, luck, imagination, trial and error, educated guesses, and great patience—all play a part. For example, the two Swiss scientists who discovered the new superconductors said they "felt free to try something crazy." The leader of the Houston, Texas, superconductor research group, Paul Chu said, "We feel we have an advantage over some other groups because we are not confined to conventional thinking. We think wildly."

a

b

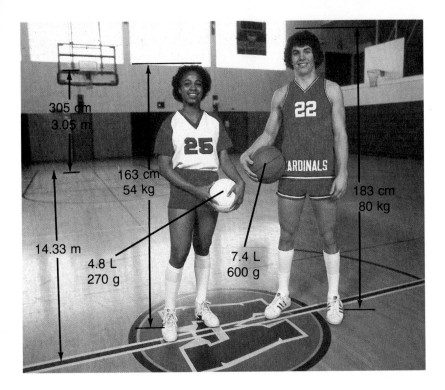

305 cm
3.05 m

163 cm
54 kg

183 cm
80 kg

14.33 m

4.8 L
270 g

7.4 L
600 g

For Your Information

When the metric system was proposed in 1792, a 10-hour clock was included in the plan. This part of the system was never accepted and was eventually abandoned.

For Your Information

Two cesium clocks would differ by only one second in 6 × 10^5 years. Two hydrogen maser clocks, perhaps the next standard, would differ by one second in one million years.

For Your Information

The National Institute of Standards and Technology was formerly known as the National Bureau of Standards.

The SI unit of time, the second, is based on a certain wavelength of light.

The unit of length is the meter.

The meter is defined as the distance traveled by light in a certain length of time.

Length is now defined by the distance light travels in a given amount of time.

The SI unit of mass is the kilogram.

1:3 Metric System

The metric system of measurement was created by French scientists in 1795. It is convenient to use because units of different sizes are related by powers of 10. An international committee determines the standards of the metric system. This committee has set up the International System of Units (SI). The SI is used throughout the world. SI units are emphasized throughout this text. The National Institutes of Standards and Technology (NIST) keeps the official standards for the units of length, mass, and time for the United States.

The standard unit of time is the **second** (s). The second was first defined as 1/86 400 of the mean solar day. A mean solar day is the average length of the day over a period of one year. In 1967, the second was redefined in terms of one type of radiation emitted by a cesium-133 atom.

The standard SI unit of length is the **meter** (m). The meter was first defined as one ten-millionth (10^{-7}) of the distance from the north pole to the equator, measured along a line passing through Lyons, France.

In the 20th century, physicists found that light could be used to make very precise measurements of distances. In 1960 the meter was redefined as a multiple of a wavelength of light emitted by krypton-86. By 1982, however, an even more precise length measurement defined the meter as the distance light travels in 1/299 792 458 second.

The third standard unit measures the mass of an object, the quantity of matter it contains. The **kilogram** is the only unit not defined in terms of the properties of atoms. It is the mass of a platinum-iridium metal cylinder kept near Paris. A copy is kept at the NIST.

Other standard SI units will be formally introduced later in this text.

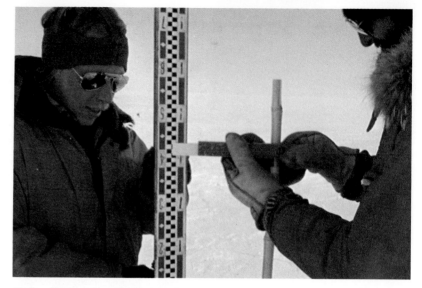

SUGGESTION: Emphasize the importance of writing every measurement with a unit. There are very few quantities that have no units. Index of refraction, *n*, and coefficient of friction, μ, are two.

The fundamental quantities of length, mass, and time are expressed in units of meters, kilograms, and seconds.

Derived quantities are combinations of fundamental units.

Volume is expressed in terms of length. The SI unit for volume is the cubic meter.

Scientific notation is used to write very small and very large quantities.

For Your Information

Note that spaces are used instead of commas to group long numbers such as 6 000 000 000 000. Many countries use commas as decimal points.

1:4 Base and Derived Units

The three fundamental quantities, length, mass, and time, are expressed in units of meters, kilograms, and seconds. Other quantities can then be described using these three units. For example, speed is found by dividing distance (length) by time. The speed of an object that travels 6 meters in 2 seconds is 3 m/s. Meter per second is a derived unit. Volume for rectangular solids is length times width (a length) times height (a length). The SI unit for volume is m³.

The quantity density is calculated by dividing mass by volume.

$$\text{density} = \frac{\text{mass}}{\text{volume}} = \frac{\text{mass}}{(\text{length})^3}$$

The SI unit for density is kilogram per cubic meter (kg/m³), which is a derived unit.

1:5 Scientific Notation

Scientists often work with very large and very small quantities. For example, the mass of Earth is about

6 000 000 000 000 000 000 000 000 kilograms

and the mass of an electron is

0.000 000 000 000 000 000 000 000 000 000 911 kilograms.

Written in this form, the quantities take up much space and are difficult to use in calculations. To work with such numbers more easily, we write them in a shortened form by expressing decimal places as powers of ten. This method of expressing numbers is called exponential notation. Scientific notation is based on exponential notation. In scientific notation, the numerical part of a measurement is expressed as a number between 1 and 10 multiplied by a whole-number power of 10.

$$M \times 10^n$$

In this expression, $1 \leq M < 10$ and n is an integer. For example, two kilometers can be expressed as 2×10^3 m. The mass of a softball is about 1.8×10^{-1} kg.

To write measurements using scientific notation, move the decimal point until only one digit remains on the left. Then count the number of places the decimal point was moved and use that number as the exponent of ten. Thus, the mass of Earth can also be expressed as 6×10^{24} kg. Note that the exponent becomes larger as the decimal point is moved to the left.

$$365 \text{ s} = 3.65 \times 10^2 \text{ s}$$
$$96\ 000 \text{ kg} = 9.6 \times 10^4 \text{ kg}$$
$$1\ 000\ 000 \text{ m} = 1 \times 10^6 \text{ m}$$

To write the mass of the electron in scientific notation, the decimal point is moved 31 places to the right. Thus, the mass of the electron can also be written as 9.11×10^{-31} kg. Note that the exponent becomes smaller as the decimal point is moved to the right.

$$0.007 \text{ kg} = 7 \times 10^{-3} \text{ kg}$$
$$0.000\ 63 \text{ m} = 6.3 \times 10^{-4} \text{ m}$$
$$0.000\ 000\ 950 \text{ s} = 9.50 \times 10^{-7} \text{ s}$$

Practice Exercises

Express the following measurements in scientific notation.

1. **a.** 5800 m
    b. 450 000 m
    c. 302 000 000 m
    d. 86 000 000 000 m
2. **a.** 0.000 508 kg
    b. 0.000 000 45 kg
    c. 0.003 600 kg
    d. 0.004 kg
3. **a.** 300 000 000 s
    b. 186 000 s
    c. 93 000 000 s

For Your Information

Since 1959, the yard has been legally defined by the NIST in terms of SI standards.
1 yard = 0.9144 meter (exactly)
1 inch = 2.54 centimeters (exactly)

FIGURE 1–6. Objects in the universe range from the very small to the unimaginably large.

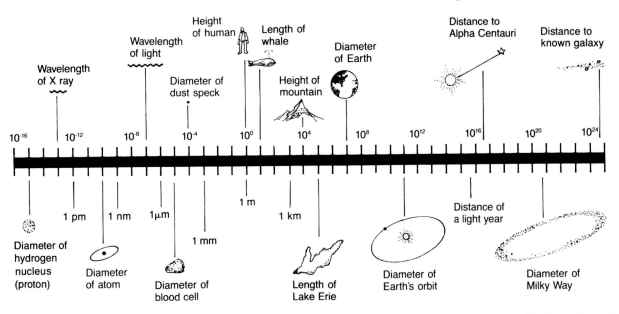

1:6 Prefixes Used with SI Units

One advantage of the metric system is that, like our numbering system, it is a decimal system. Prefixes are used to change SI units by powers of ten. Thus, one tenth of a meter is a decimeter, one hundredth of a meter is a centimeter, and one thousandth of a meter is a millimeter. Each of these divisions can be found on a meter stick. The prefixes that change SI units by a power of one thousand are most common. Thus, one thousand meters is a kilometer. The metric units for all quantities use the same prefixes. One thousandth of a gram is a milligram, and one thousand grams is a kilogram. To use SI units effectively, it is important to know the meanings of the prefixes in Table 1–1.

Metric units differ from one another by a factor of ten.

Prefixes are used to designate divisions and multiples of SI units.

SUGGESTION: Devise a mnemonic device for remembering the common prefixes deci, centi, milli, deka, hecto, and kilo.

TABLE 1–1

Prefixes Used with SI Units			
Prefix	**Symbol**	**Fractions**	**Example**
pico	p	1/1 000 000 000 000 or 10^{-12}	picometer (pm)
nano	n	1/1 000 000 000 or 10^{-9}	nanometer (nm)
micro	μ	1/1 000 000 or 10^{-6}	microgram (μg)
milli	m	1/1 000 or 10^{-3}	milligram (mg)
centi	c	1/100 or 10^{-2}	centimeter (cm)
deci	d	1/10 or 10^{-1}	decimeter (dm)
		Multiples	
tera	T	1 000 000 000 000 or 10^{12}	terameter (tm)
giga	G	1 000 000 000 or 10^{9}	gigameter (Gm)
mega	M	1 000 000 or 10^{6}	megagram (Mg)
kilo	k	1 000 or 10^{3}	kilometer (km)
hecto	h	100 or 10^{2}	hectometer (hm)
deka	da	10 or 10^{1}	dekagram (dag)

EXAMPLE

Conversion Between Units

What is the equivalent of 500 millimeters in meters?

Solution: From Table 1–1, we see the conversion factor is

1 millimeter = 1×10^{-3} meter

Therefore,

$$(500 \text{ mm}) \frac{(1 \times 10^{-3} \text{ m})}{1 \text{ mm}} = 500 \times 10^{-3} \text{ m} = 5 \times 10^{-1} \text{ m}$$

FIGURE 1–7. The meter stick contains decimeter, centimeter, and millimeter divisions.

Practice Exercises

4. Convert each of the following length measurements to its equivalent in meters.

   a. 1.1 cm   **b.** 76.2 pm   **c.** 2.1 km   **d.** 0.123 Mm

5. Convert each of these mass measurements to its equivalent in kilograms

   a. 147 g   **b.** 11 μg   **c.** 7.23 Mg   **d.** 478 mg

1:7 Addition and Subtraction in Scientific Notation

Suppose you need to add or subtract measurements expressed in scientific notation ($M \times 10^n$). If the numbers have the same exponent, you simply add or subtract the values of M and keep the same n.

Quantities to be added or subtracted must have the same exponents.

EXAMPLE

Adding and Subtracting with Like Exponents

a. 4×10^8 m $+ 3 \times 10^8$ m $= 7 \times 10^8$ m

b. 6.2×10^{-3} m $- 2.8 \times 10^{-3}$ m $= 3.4 \times 10^{-3}$ m

If the powers of ten are not the same, they must be made the same before the numbers are added or subtracted. Move the decimal points until the exponents are the same.

EXAMPLE

Adding and Subtracting with Unlike Exponents

SUGGESTION: After some practice changing exponents so numbers are to the same power of ten, teach students to use the exponent key on their calculators.

a. 4.0×10^6 m $+ 3 \times 10^5$ m

$= 4.0 \times 10^6$ m $+$

0.3×10^6 m

$= 4.3 \times 10^6$ m

b. 4.0×10^{-6} kg $- 3 \times 10^{-7}$ kg

$= 4.0 \times 10^{-6}$ kg $-$

0.3×10^{-6} kg

$= 3.7 \times 10^{-6}$ kg

Suppose you have to add a measurement made in meters to one made in kilometers. You first must convert the measurements to a common unit, then make the power of ten the same. Finally you add or subtract.

EXAMPLE

Adding and Subtracting with Unlike Units

a. 4.1 m $+$ 1.5468 km $=$ 4.1 m $+$ 1546.8 m

$=$ 1550.9 m $=$ 1.5509 km

b. 2.31×10^{-2} g $+$ 6.1 mg $=$ 23.1 mg $+$ 6.1 mg $=$ 29.2 mg

c. 2.03×10^2 m $+$ 1.057 km $=$ 2.03×10^2 m $+ 10.57 \times 10^2$ m

$=$ 12.60×10^2 m $=$ 1.260 km

a
b

FIGURE 1–8. Professor Stephen Hawking, an astrophysicist, is currently studying black holes (a). Astronaut Sally Ride was chosen as the first woman to take part in a space shuttle mission (b).

Practice Exercises

Solve the following problems. Express your answers in scientific notation.

6. a. 5×10^{-7} kg $+ 3 \times 10^{-7}$ kg
    b. 4×10^{-3} kg $+ 3 \times 10^{-3}$ kg
    c. 1.66×10^{-19} kg $+ 2.30 \times 10^{-19}$ kg
    d. 7.2×10^{-12} kg $- 2.6 \times 10^{-12}$ kg
7. a. 6×10^{-8} m^2 $- 4 \times 10^{-8}$ m^2
    b. 3.8×10^{-12} m^2 $- 1.90 \times 10^{-11}$ m^2
    c. 5.8×10^{-9} m^2 $- 2.8 \times 10^{-9}$ m^2
    d. 2.26×10^{-18} m^2 $- 1.80 \times 10^{-18}$ m^2
8. a. 5.0×10^{-7} mg $+ 4 \times 10^{-8}$ mg
    b. 6.0×10^{-3} mg $+ 2 \times 10^{-4}$ mg
    c. 3.0×10^{-14} mg $+ 2 \times 10^{-15}$ mg
    d. 4.00×10^{-12} mg $+ 6.0 \times 10^{-13}$ mg
9. a. 5.0×10^{-1} μm $- 4 \times 10^{1}$ nm
    b. 6.0 mm $- 2 \times 10^{-4}$ m
    c. 3.0×10^{-2} pg $- 2 \times 10^{-5}$ ng
    d. 8.2 km $- 3 \times 10^{2}$ m

1:8 Multiplication and Division in Scientific Notation

Quantities expressed in scientific notation do not need to have the same exponents before they are multiplied or divided. Multiply the values of *M*, then add the exponents. The units are multiplied.

The product of two numbers expressed in scientific notation is the product of the values of *M* times 10 raised to the sum of their exponents.

EXAMPLE

Multiplication Using Scientific Notation

a. $(3 \times 10^{6}$ m$)(2 \times 10^{3}$ m$) = 6 \times 10^{6+3}$ m$^2 = 6 \times 10^{9}$ m^2
b. $(2 \times 10^{-5}$ m$)(4 \times 10^{9}$ m$) = 8 \times 10^{9-5}$ m$^2 = 8 \times 10^{4}$ m^2
c. $(4 \times 10^{3}$ kg$)(5 \times 10^{11}$ m$) = 20 \times 10^{3+11}$ kg $\cdot$ m
$$= 2 \times 10^{15} \text{ kg} \cdot \text{m}$$

Quantities expressed in scientific notation with different exponents also can be divided. Divide the values of M, then subtract the exponent of the divisor from the exponent of the dividend.

The quotient of two numbers expressed in scientific notation is the quotient of the values of M times 10 raised to the difference of their exponents.

EXAMPLE

Division Using Scientific Notation

a. $\dfrac{8 \times 10^6 \text{ m}}{2 \times 10^3 \text{ s}} = 4 \times 10^{6-3} \text{ m/s} = 4 \times 10^3 \text{ m/s}$

b. $\dfrac{8 \times 10^6 \text{ kg}}{2 \times 10^{-2} \text{ m}^3} = 4 \times 10^{6-(-2)} \text{ kg/m}^3 = 4 \times 10^8 \text{ kg/m}^3$

Practice Exercises

Find the value of each of the following quantities.

10. a. $(2 \times 10^4 \text{ m})(4 \times 10^8 \text{ m})$

  b. $(3 \times 10^4 \text{ m})(2 \times 10^6 \text{ m})$

  c. $(6 \times 10^{-4} \text{ m})(5 \times 10^{-8} \text{ m})$

  d. $(2.50 \times 10^{-7} \text{ m})(2.50 \times 10^{16} \text{ m})$

11. a. $\dfrac{6 \times 10^8 \text{ kg}}{2 \times 10^4 \text{ m}^3}$ c. $\dfrac{6 \times 10^{-8} \text{ m}}{2 \times 10^4 \text{ s}}$

  b. $\dfrac{6 \times 10^8 \text{ kg}}{2 \times 10^{-4} \text{ m}^3}$ d. $\dfrac{6 \times 10^{-8} \text{ m}}{2 \times 10^{-4} \text{ s}}$

12. a. $\dfrac{(3 \times 10^4 \text{ kg})(4 \times 10^4 \text{ m})}{6 \times 10^4 \text{ s}}$ b. $\dfrac{(2.5 \times 10^6 \text{ kg})(6 \times 10^4 \text{ m})}{5 \times 10^{-2} \text{ s}^2}$

1:9 Uncertainties of Measurements

Often several scientists measure the same quantities and compare the data they obtain. Each scientist must know how trustworthy the data are. For this reason, the knowledge of how well a measurement was made is very important.

Every measurement, whether made by a student or a professional scientist, is subject to uncertainty. The length of a ruler can change with changes of temperature. An electric measuring device is affected by magnetic fields near it. In one way or another, all instruments are subject to external influences. Uncertainties in measurement cannot be avoided.

In addition to uncertainties due to external causes, the accuracy of a measurement is affected by the person making the reading. One common source of error comes from the angle at which an instrument is read. In a car, the passenger's reading of the gas gauge and the driver's reading of the same gauge can be quite different. From the passenger's viewpoint, the gauge may read empty. From the driver's seat, the gauge may read one-quarter full. The driver's reading is the more correct one. The difference in the readings is a parallax error. **Parallax** (PAR uh laks) is the apparent shift in the position of an object when it is viewed from various angles. Although it is really the reference point behind the object that changes, it is the object that appears to have moved. When in the passenger seat, your eyes line up the gauge needle with the empty mark on the scale. If

For Your Information

Any error that can creep in, will. It will be in the direction that will do most damage to the calculation.
—Murphy's law

All measurements are subject to uncertainties.

Parallax is a common cause of uncertainty in measurements.

FIGURE 1–9. A parallax example is shown when a car's gasoline gauge is viewed from the passenger's seat (a) and the driver's seat (b). Note the apparent difference in readings.

a   b

you move to the driver's seat, the needle almost lines up with the one-quarter mark. Laboratory instruments must be read at eye level and straight on to avoid parallax errors. See Figure 1–9.

1:10 Accuracy and Precision

Precision is the degree of exactness to which the measurement of a quantity can be reproduced. For example, a student was conducting an experiment to determine the speed of light. Several trials were made that yielded values ranging from 3.000×10^8 m/s to 3.002×10^8 m/s, with an average of 3.001×10^8 m/s. This led the student to report that the speed of light is $(3.001 \pm 0.001) \times 10^8$ m/s. The speed of light might range from 3.000×10^8 m/s to 3.002×10^8 m/s. The precision of the measurement was 0.001×10^8 m/s.

The precision of a measuring device is limited by the finest division on its scale. The smallest division on a meter stick is a millimeter. Thus, a measurement of any smaller length with a meter stick can be only an estimate. There is a limit to the precision of even the best instruments.

Accuracy is the extent to which a measured value agrees with the standard value of a quantity. In the measurement of the speed of light, the accuracy is the difference between the student's measurement and the defined value of the speed of light, quoted to the same precision: 2.998×10^8 m/s. Thus, the accuracy is 3.001×10^8 m/s $- 2.998 \times 10^8$ m/s $= 0.003 \times 10^8$ m/s. You can see that a precise measurement might not be accurate.

The accuracy of an instrument depends on how well it agrees with a currently accepted standard. The accuracy of measuring devices should be checked regularly. They can be calibrated by using them to measure quantities whose values are accurately known. Uncertainties in measurement affect the accuracy of a measurement. However, the precision is not affected since readings are still stated in terms of the smallest division on the instrument.

1:11 Significant Digits

Because the precision of all measuring devices is limited, the number of digits that are valid for any measurement is also limited. Suppose you measure the length of a strip of metal with a meter stick. The smallest division on the meter stick is a millimeter. You should read the scale to the

Precision is the degree of exactness to which a measurement can be reproduced.

The precision of an instrument is limited by the smallest division on the measuring scale.

The accuracy of a measurement describes how well the result agrees with an accepted value.

SUGGESTION: Discuss examples of measurements that are precise without being accurate and vice versa. How could accuracy be described if there were no standard value?

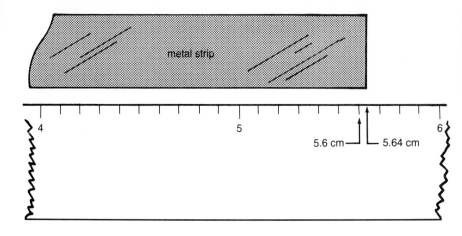

nearest millimeter and then estimate any remaining length as a fraction of a millimeter. The metal strip in Figure 1–10 is somewhat longer than 5.6 centimeters, or 56 millimeters. Looking closely at the scale, you can see that the end of the metal strip is about four-tenths of the way between 56 and 57 millimeters. Therefore, the length of the strip is best stated as 56.4 millimeters. The last digit is an estimate. It might not be 4 but is likely not larger than 5 or smaller than 3. Thus your measurement contains three significant digits. They are the two digits you are sure of, 5 and 6, and the one, 4, that is an estimated digit.

Suppose that the end of the metal strip is right on the 56 millimeter mark. In this case, you should record the measurement as 56.0 millimeters. The zero indicates that the strip is not 0.1 millimeter more or less than 56 millimeters. The zero is a significant digit because it transmits information. It is the uncertain digit because you are estimating it. The last digit given for any measurement is the uncertain digit. *All nonzero digits in a measurement are significant.*

Zeros are often a problem. The zero mentioned in 56.0 millimeters is significant. However, a zero that only serves to locate the decimal point is not significant. Thus the value of 0.0026 kilogram contains two significant digits. The measurement of 0.002060 kilogram contains four significant digits. The final zero indicates a reasonable estimate.

There is no way to tell how many of the zeros in the measurement 186 000 m are significant. The 6 may have been the estimated digit and the three zeros may be needed only to place the decimal point. Or, all three zeros may be significant because they were measured. To avoid confusion, such measurements are written in scientific notation. In the number that appears before the power of ten, all the digits are significant. Thus, 1.860×10^5 m has four significant digits. To summarize, the following rules are used to determine the number of significant digits.

1. Nonzero digits are always significant.
2. All final zeros after the decimal point are significant.
3. Zeros between two other significant digits are always significant.
4. Zeros used solely for spacing the decimal point are not significant.

a

b

FIGURE 1–11. The micrometer (a) and analytical balance (b) are used to obtain very precise measurements of length and mass, respectively.

Practice Exercises

13. State the number of significant digits in each measurement.

a. 2804 m	**d.** 0.003 068 m
b. 2.84 m	**e.** 4.6×10^5 m
c. 0.0029 m	**f.** 4.06×10^5 m

14. State the number of significant digits for each measurement.

a. 75 m	**d.** 1.87×10^6 ml
b. 75.00 mm	**e.** 1.008×10^8 m
c. 0.007 060 kg	**f.** 1.20×10^{-4} m

1:12 Operations Using Significant Digits

The result of any mathematical operation with measurements can never be more precise than the least precise measurement. Suppose you measure the lengths 6.48 meters and 18.2 meters. You are asked to find the sum of the two lengths. The length 18.2 meters is precise only to a tenth of a meter. The result of any mathematical operation with measurements cannot be more precise than the least precise measurement. Therefore, the sum of the two lengths can be precise only to a tenth of a meter. First add 6.48 meters to 18.2 meters to get 24.68 meters. Then round off the sum to the nearest tenth of a meter. The correct value is 24.7 meters. Subtraction is handled the same way. To add or subtract measurements, first perform the operation, and then round off the result to correspond to the least precise value involved.

The sum or difference of two values is as precise as the least precise value.

EXAMPLE

Significant Digits—Addition and Subtraction

Add 24.686 m + 2.343 m + 3.21 m.

Solution:

$$\begin{array}{r} 24.686 \text{ m} \\ 2.343 \text{ m} \\ \underline{3.21 \text{ m}} \\ 30.239 \text{ m} = 30.24 \text{ m} \end{array}$$

Note that 3.21 m is the least precise measurement. Round off the result to the nearest hundredth of a meter. Follow the same rules for subtraction.

A different method is used to find the correct number of significant digits when multiplying or dividing measurements. After performing the calculation, note the factor with the least number of significant digits. Round the product or quotient to this number of digits.

The number of significant digits in a product or quotient is the number in the factor with the lesser number of significant digits.

EXAMPLE

Significant Digits—Multiplication

Multiply 3.22 cm by 2.1 cm.

Solution:

$$
\begin{array}{r}
3.\,2\,\textcircled{2}\ \text{cm} \\
2.\,\textcircled{1}\ \text{cm} \\
\hline
\textcircled{3}\,\textcircled{2}\,\textcircled{2} \\
6\ \ 4\ \textcircled{4} \\
\hline
6.\,\textcircled{7}\,\textcircled{6}\,\textcircled{2}\ \text{cm}^2
\end{array}
$$

This is correctly stated as 6.8 cm².

SUGGESTION: Emphasize that all measurements have some error. When you use measurements in a formula, the significant digit rules help obtain a meaningful answer.

The least precise factor, 2.1 cm, contains two significant digits. Therefore the product has only two. Note that each circled digit is doubtful, either because it is an estimated measurement or is multiplied by an estimated measurement. Since the 7 in the product is doubtful, the 6 and 2 are certainly not significant. The answer is best stated as 6.8 cm².

EXAMPLE

Significant Digits—Division

Divide 36.5 m by 3.414 s.

Solution: $\dfrac{36.5\ \text{m}}{3.414\ \text{s}} = 10.69$ m/s. This is correctly stated as 10.7 m/s.

Be sure to record all measurements made during an experiment with the correct number of significant digits. The number of significant digits shows the precision of the instrument. When using a calculator, be particularly careful to record your answer with the proper number of significant digits, even though the calculator shows additional, meaningless digits.

Avoid reporting all the digits given by a calculator. Report only significant digits.

FIGURE 1–12. When using a calculator in answering problems, it is important to note that your answers cannot be more precise than the least precise quantity involved.

It is important to understand that significant digits are only considered when calculating with measurements. Because of the uncertainty in all measurements, it is important to let anyone who is using your data know exactly how precise your values are.

Practice Exercises

15. Add 6.201 cm, 7.4 cm, 0.68 cm, and 12.0 cm.

16. Subtract
  a. 8.264 g from 10.8 g.
  b. 0.4168 m from 475 m.

17. Perform the following multiplications.
  a. 131 cm × 2.3 cm
  b. 3.2145 km × 4.23 km

18. Perform the following divisions.
  a. 20.2 cm ÷ 7.41 s
  b. 3.1416 cm ÷ 12.4 s
  c. 3.21 m × 1.2 m ÷ 0.009 m
  d. (20.2 cm − 11.41 cm) ÷ 1.34 cm

CHAPTER 1 REVIEW

SUMMARY

1. Physics is the study of matter and energy and their relationships. **1:1**

2. Physics is basic to all other sciences. **1:1**

3. A knowledge of physics makes us, as citizens, better able to make decisions about questions related to science and technology. **1:1**

4. Scientists study problems in an organized way, using many techniques. **1:2**

5. The meter, kilogram, and second are the fundamental units of length, time, and mass in the SI system. **1:3**

6. SI units of different sizes are related by powers of ten. **1:3**

7. Derived units are a combination of fundamental units. **1:4**

8. Large and small measurements, often used in physics, are most clearly written using scientific notation. **1:5**

9. Prefixes are used to change SI units by powers of 10. **1:6**

10. To be added or subtracted, numbers must be raised to the same power of 10. **1:7**

11. Quantities written in scientific notation need not have the same power of 10 to be multiplied or divided. **1:8**

12. All measurements are subject to some uncertainty. **1:9**

13. Precision is the degree of exactness with which a quantity is measured. **1:10**

14. Accuracy is the extent to which the measured and accepted values of a quantity agree. **1:10**

15. For a given measurement, the number of significant digits is limited by the precision of the measuring device. **1:11**

16. The last digit in a measurement is always an estimate. Only one estimated digit is significant. **1:11**

17. The result of any mathematical operation made with measurements can never be more precise than the least precise measurement. **1:12**

QUESTIONS

1. Define physics.
2. What differences are there between fundamental units and derived units?
3. What are the fundamental units in the SI system?
4. Express speed in terms of fundamental units.
5. What is the importance of the International System of Units?
6. Give the proper name for each multiple of the meter listed.
   a. 1/100 m   b. 1/1000 m   c. 1000 m
7. The density of an object is defined as its mass per unit of volume.
   a. Does density have a fundamental or derived unit?
   b. What is the SI unit for density?
8. How does the last digit differ from the other digits in a measurement?
9. What determines the precision of a measurement?
10. a. Why is it difficult to tell how many significant digits are in a measured value such as 76 000?
    b. How can the number of significant digits in such a number be made clear?

APPLYING CONCEPTS

1. Give some examples of applications of the results of work by physicists.
2. Locate the size of the following objects in Figure 1–6.
   a. The width of your thumb.
   b. The thickness of a page in this book.
   c. The height of your classroom.
   d. The distance from your house to school.
3. Suppose a student measures the speed of light to be 2.999×10^8 m/s with an uncertainty of 0.006×10^8 m/s.
   a. Is this measurement more or less precise than the example on p. 14?
   b. Is it more or less accurate?
4. Make a chart of sizes of objects similar to Figure 1–6. Include only objects you have measured. Some should be less than one millimeter, others several kilometers.
5. Make a chart of time intervals similar to Figure 1–6. Include intervals like the time between heartbeats, the time between presidential elections, the average lifetime of a human, the age of the United States, and so forth. Find as many very short and very long examples as you can.
6. Some of the branches of physics you will investigate study motion, the properties of materials, sound, light, electricity and magnetism, properties of atoms, and nuclear physics. Identify at least one example of an application of each branch.
7. Why can quantities with different units never be added or subtracted but can be multiplied or divided? Give examples to support your answer.
8. Give an example of a measurement that is
   a. accurate but not precise.
   b. precise but not accurate.
9. Two students use a meter stick to measure the width of a lab table. One records an answer of 84 cm and the other 83.78 cm. Explain why neither answer is recorded correctly.

EXERCISES

1. Express the following numbers in scientific notation.
   a. 5 000 000 000 000 000 000 000 000 m
   b. 0.000 000 000 000 000 000 166 m
   c. 2 033 000 000 m
   d. 0.000 000 103 0 m
2. State the number of significant digits in each measurement.
   a. 248 m   c. 64.01 m
   b. 0.000 03 m   d. 80.001 m
3. State the number of significant digits in the following measurements.
   a. 2.40×10^6 kg
   b. 6×10^8 kg
   c. 4.07×10^{16} m
4. Add or subtract as indicated.
   a. 16.2 m + 5.008 m + 13.48 m
   b. 5.006 m + 12.0077 m + 8.0084 m
   c. 78.05 cm² − 32.046 cm²

d. 15.07 kg − 12.0 kg

5. Add or subtract as indicated.

   a. 5.80×10^9 s $+ 3.20 \times 10^8$ s

   b. 4.87×10^{-6} m $- 1.93 \times 10^{-6}$ m

   c. 3.14×10^{-5} kg $+ 9.36 \times 10^{-5}$ kg

   d. 8.12×10^7 g $- 6.20 \times 10^6$ g

6. Multiply or divide as indicated.

   a. $(6.2 \times 10^{18}$ m$)(4.7 \times 10^{-10}$ m$)$

   b. $(5.6 \times 10^{-7}$ m$) \div (2.8 \times 10^{-12}$ s$)$

   c. $(8.1 \times 10^{-4}$ km$)(1.6 \times 10^{-3}$ km$)$

   d. $(6.5 \times 10^5$ kg$) \div (3.4 \times 10^3$ m$^3)$

7. Students did the following problems on their calculators, reporting the results shown. Give the answer to each using the correct number of significant digits.

   a. 5.32 mm + 2.1 mm = 7.4200000 mm

   b. $\dfrac{8.29 \text{ m}}{7} = 1.184285714$ m

   c. 13.597 m × 3.65 m = 49.6290500 m^2

   d. 83.2 kg − 12.804 kg = 70.3960000 kg

8. A yard is 33.21 m long and 17.6 m wide.

   a. What length of fence must be purchased to enclose the entire yard?

   b. What area must be covered if the yard is to be fertilized?

9. The length of a room is 16.40 m, its width is 4.5 m, and its height is 3.26 m. What volume of air does the room contain?

10. The sides of a quadrangular plot of land are measured. The lengths are 132.68 m, 48.3 m, 132.736 m, and 48.37 m. What is the perimeter of the plot as can best be determined from these measurements?

11. A water tank has a mass of 3.64 kg when empty and a mass of 51.8 kg when filled to a certain level. What is the mass of the water in the tank?

12. A rectangular floor has a length of 15.72 m and a width of 4.40 m. Calculate the area of the floor to the best possible value using these measurements.

PROBLEMS

1. Rank the following mass measurements from smallest to largest: 11.6 mg, 1021 μg, 0.000 006 kg, 0.31 mg.

2. Tony's Pizza Shop ordered new 23-cm pizza pans (9-inch pans). By mistake, 26-cm (10-inch) pans were delivered. Tony says that the difference is too small to worry about. As Tony's accountant, what would you say knowing materials cost about 0.25 cents per square centimeter?

3. Studies show that nuclear matter is unbelievably dense. Neutrons have a density of about 2.0×10^{17} kilograms per cubic meter (more than 200 000 000 tons per cubic centimeter). Pulsars are thought to be the compact remnants of old stars that have collapsed due to gravity. These stars form rapidly spinning, spherical bodies consisting entirely of neutrons. Let us assume that the sun is sufficiently large to form a pulsar. Calculate the diameter in kilometers of the pulsar formed from the sun if it were to collapse completely so that its density equaled that of neutrons. The mass of the sun is about 2.0×10^{30} kg.

4. Make a table listing the surface areas and volumes of cubes having sides that measure 1 m, 2 m, 3 m, 4 m, 5 m, and 6 m respectively. Add a third column listing the ratio of the surface area to volume for each cube. (For example, the first ratio is six to one.) Suppose you are on a building committee to design a new high school building for a town that has cold winters. Part of the committee favors a one-story building with many wings. A second group wants a cube-shaped building with several stories. You know that heating is a major cost in the operation of a school and that heat loss takes place through the walls, ceilings, and floors of buildings. How would you vote in this matter? Explain.

5. On the basis of what you have found in regard to the ratios of surface areas to volumes in Problem 4, explain the following facts.

   a. Elephants like to wallow in cool streams.

   b. Elephants have large ears containing many veins.

   c. A hummingbird (one of the smallest birds) eats almost constantly from sunrise to sunset.

   d. A shrew (one of the smallest mammals) will attack and kill animals much larger than itself to satisfy its tremendous appetite.

6. Many labels give metric equivalents of English quantities. Examples are: 12 fluid ounces (9354.66 mL), 353 ft (107.59 m), 2.0 inches

(50.80 mm). Report each metric equivalent using the correct number of significant digits.

7. Water drips from a faucet into a flask at the rate of two drops every 3 seconds. A cubic centimeter (cm^3) contains 20 drops.
    a. What volume of water, in cubic decimeters (dm^3), will be collected in 1 hour?
    b. If 1 cubic decimeter (dm^3) has a mass of 1000 g, what is the mass, in kilograms, of the water collected?

READINGS

Cole, K. C., "Beyond Measurement." *Discover*, October, 1983.

Hildebrandt, Stefon, *Mathematics and Optimal Form.* Scientific American Books, New York, NY, 1984.

Hooper, William, "The Meter Is Redefined." *The Physics Teacher*, January, 1987.

Shamos, Morris H. (editor), *Great Experiments in Physics.* Dover Publications, Inc., New York, NY, 1987.

Wolsky, A. M., R. F. Giese, and E. J. Daniels, "The New Superconductors: Prospects for Applications." *Scientific American*, February, 1989.

CHAPTER 2

Mathematical Relationships

For Your Information

Equations and graphs are both means of expressing relationships among variables.

GOALS

1. You will review basic graphing techniques.
2. You will learn how analysis of a graph can lead to an algebraic equation.
3. You will review solving equations.

Physics often uses mathematics as its language. The general results of many observations and experiments, called laws, can usually be written in the form of algebraic equations. Probably the most famous physics equation is Einstein's $E = mc^2$. This equation describes the law of the equivalence of mass and energy.

How do you find an equation to describe experimental results? Frequently a graph of the results is used. In this chapter you will see how data describing the distance a car travels while braking to a stop can be expressed by an equation. You will learn that one of the most powerful ways of analyzing data is to display them as a graph.

2:1   Graphing Data

One of the most important skills to learn in driving a car is how to stop it safely. No car can "stop on a dime." The faster the car is going, the farther it travels before it stops. When you studied for your driver's license, you probably found a table showing how far a car moves beyond the point at which the driver makes a decision to stop.

One state manual shows that a car travels a certain distance between the time the driver decides to stop the car and the time he puts on the brakes. This is called the "thinking distance." When the brakes are applied, the car slows down and travels the "braking distance." Table 2–1 shows these distances, together with the total stopping distance for various speeds. The table shows both SI quantities as well as, in parentheses, English units used in the driver's manual.

SUGGESTION: Have students bring in graphs from newspapers or magazines. Evaluate the graphs in terms of construction and usefulness.

Forced Stop

As a car brakes or skids to a stop, the braking usually occurs in a non-linear manner. Weather conditions, road surface, and tire conditions are variables that affect stopping. As the car brakes to a halt, what actually exerts the force on the car to stop it?

Stopping distance

FIGURE 2–1. The total stopping distance is the sum of the thinking and braking distances. Graphs (a) and (b) display the same information in two different ways.

SUGGESTION: Point out that grid-squares may have different scales on the x- and y-axes as in Figure 2–1.

FIGURE 2–2. Knowing when and how to apply brakes safely is an important part of a driver's test.

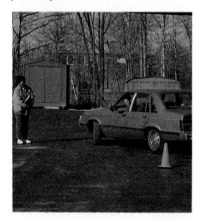

TABLE 2–1

Thinking and Braking Distances vs Speed								
Original speed		Thinking distance		Braking distance		Total distance	
m/s	(mph)	m	(ft)	m	(ft)	m	(ft)
11	(25)	8	(27)	10	(34)	18	(61)
16	(35)	12	(38)	20	(67)	32	(105)
20	(45)	15	(49)	34	(110)	49	(159)
25	(55)	18	(60)	50	(165)	68	(225)
29	(65)	22	(71)	70	(231)	92	(302)

The first step in analyzing data is to look at them carefully. Which variable did the experimenter (the driver) change? In our example, it was the speed of the car. Thus speed is the **independent,** or manipulated, variable. The other two variables, thinking and braking distance, changed as a result of the change in the speed. These quantities are called **dependent,** or responding, variables.

How do the distances change for a given change in the speed? Notice that the thinking distance increases by about the same amount for each increase in speed. However, the braking distance increases much more as the speed increases. The relationship between the distances and speed can be seen more easily if the data are plotted on a graph. To avoid confusion, you should plot two graphs, one of thinking distance and the other of braking distance.

PROBLEM SOLVING

Plotting Graphs

These steps will help you plot graphs from data tables.

1. Identify the independent and dependent variables. The independent variable is plotted on the horizontal, or x-axis. The dependent variable is plotted on the vertical, or y-axis. In our example, speed is plotted on the x-axis, and distance is plotted on the y-axis.

2. Decide on the range of the independent variable to be plotted. In the example, data is given for speeds between 11 and 29 m/s. A convenient range for the x-axis might be 0–35 m/s.
3. Decide if the origin (0, 0) is a valid data point. When the speed is zero, thinking and stopping distances are obviously both zero. In this case then, your graph should include the origin. Extend it beyond 35 m/s. Spread out the data as much as possible. Let each space on the graph paper stand for a convenient unit. Choose 2, 5, or 10 spaces to represent 10 m/s.
4. Number and label the horizontal axis.
5. Repeat Steps 2–4 for the dependent variable.
6. Plot your data points on the graph.
7. Draw the best straight line or smooth curve that passes through as many data points as possible. *Do not use a series of straight line segments that "connect the dots."*
8. Give the graph a title that clearly tells what the graph represents.

2:2 Linear Relationships

The graph of thinking distance versus speed is a straight line. The dependent variable varies linearly with the independent variable.

The relationship of the two variables shown in this graph can be written as an equation

$$y = mx + b$$

where m and b are constants called the slope and y-intercept, respectively. Each constant can be found from the graph. The slope, m, is the ratio of the vertical change to the horizontal change. To find the slope, select two points, A and B, as far apart as possible on the line. They should not be data points. The vertical change, or rise, Δy, is the difference in the vertical values of A and B. The horizontal change, or run, Δx, is the difference in the horizontal values of A and B. The slope of the graph is then calculated as

$$m = \frac{\text{rise}}{\text{run}} = \frac{\Delta y}{\Delta x} = \frac{(20 - 0) \text{ m}}{(27 - 0) \text{ m/s}} = \frac{20 \text{ m}}{27 \text{ m/s}} = 0.74 \text{ s}$$

Notice that units have been kept with the variables.

For Your Information

It takes a fully loaded super-tanker, traveling at a normal speed of 16 knots, at least 20 minutes to stop. If an immobile object appeared suddenly as much as 3 miles away, a collision would occur.

The independent variable is controlled by the experimenter.

The dependent variable changes as a result of the change in the independent variable.

The independent variable is plotted on the x-axis.

The dependent variable is plotted on the y-axis.

The slope (m) of a graph is $\Delta y/\Delta x$.

SUGGESTION: Stress the value of units to check equations.

Thinking Distance Versus Speed

A smooth curve is drawn through as many plotted points as possible.

FIGURE 2–3. The graph indicates a linear relationship between thinking distance and car speed.

2:2 Linear Relationships 25

The y-intercept, b, is the point at which the line crosses the y-axis, and is the y value when the value of x is zero. In this case, when x is zero, the value of y is 0 meters. For special cases like this, when the y-intercept equals zero, the equation becomes $y = mx$. The quantity y varies directly with x.

The value of y does not always increase with increasing x. If y gets smaller as x gets larger, then $\Delta y/\Delta x$ is less than zero, and the slope is negative.

After drawing the graph and obtaining the equation, check to see if the results make sense. The slope indicates the increased thinking distance for an increase in speed. It has units of meters/(meters/second), or seconds. Thus it is a time. It is the amount of time your body takes from the instant the message to stop the car registers in your brain until your foot hits the brake pedal.

2:3 Parabolic Relationships

Figure 2–4 is the graph of the braking distance versus speed, completed as suggested in the Problem Solving. Note that the relationship is not linear.

The smooth line drawn through all the data points curves upward. You cannot draw a straight line through all the points. Such graphs are frequently parabolas, indicating that the two variables are related by the equation

$$y = kx^2$$

where k is a constant. This equation shows that y varies directly with the square of x. The constant k shows how fast y changes with x^2. In Chapters 4 and 5 we will discuss variables that are related by this equation, and learn why braking distance depends on speed in this way.

2:4 Inverse Relationships

Some variables are related by the type of graph shown in Figure 2–5. In this case, a plot has been made of the volume of a fixed amount of gas in a

FIGURE 2–4. The graph indicates a parabolic relationship; braking distance varies as the square of the original speed.

26 Mathematical Relationships

Boyles Law

Volume (cubic centimeters) vs. Pressure (kPa)

FIGURE 2–5. The graph shows the inverse relationship between gas volume and gas pressure.

A hyperbola results when one variable depends on the inverse of the other.

bicycle pump with a plugged hose. The pressure on the gas has been increased by pressing on the pump handle. When the pressure is doubled, the volume is reduced to one-half its original volume. This relationship is an inverse variation. The graph is a hyperbola, not a straight line. The general equation for an inverse relationship is $xy = k$ or $x = k \times (1/y)$. In Chapter 13 you will learn the reason why a gas behaves in this manner.

In inverse variation, the product of the two variables is a constant.

2:5 Solving Equations Using Algebra

From your graph of the thinking distance versus speed, you obtained an equation relating the two variables. If we represent the thinking distance by d, the speed of the car by v, and the slope, which we discovered had units of time, t, the equation is

$$d = vt, \text{ or } d = tv$$

Note that this last equation is the same as $y = mx$. The distance, d, is the dependent variable. The speed, v, is the independent variable. The slope (m) is the time, t. You can use this equation to find d if you know v and t. What if, however, you know d and t and want to find v? You can solve the equation above for v. First, place the term containing v on the left side.

$$vt = d$$

To get v alone on the left side, but not change the value of the relationship, divide both sides of the equation by t. Thus

$$v = \frac{d}{t}$$

That is, the speed of the car is equal to the thinking distance divided by the thinking time. If an equation contains several factors, the same process is followed until the unknown is isolated on the left side of the equation. The steps can be performed in any sequence; just be sure you perform the same operations on both sides of the equation.

SUGGESTION: Drill students extensively on solving algebraic expressions similar to those you will use later in the course so students will be able to concentrate on the physical concepts.

The quantity in an equation that is required is the unknown.

EXAMPLE

Solving Equations

Solve the following equation for x.

$$\frac{ay}{x} = \frac{cb}{s}$$

Solution: Multiply both sides by x.

$$ay = \frac{cbx}{s}$$

Rearrange to bring x to the left side.

$$\frac{cbx}{s} = ay$$

Divide both sides by cb.

$$\frac{x}{s} = \frac{ay}{cb}$$

Multiply both sides by s.

$$x = \frac{asy}{cb}$$

Algebraic equations are manipulated by performing the same operations on each side of the equation.

EXAMPLE

Solving Equations

Solve the following equation for x: $y = mx + b$.

Solution:

Rearrange to bring x to the left side. $mx + b = y$

Subtract b from both sides. $mx = y - b$

Divide both sides by m. $x = (y - b)/m$

Solve equations for the unknown, placing it on the left-hand side of the equal sign.

Practice Exercises

1. Solve the following equation for b. $y = mx + b$

2. Solve the following equations for v.

    a. $d = vt$ **c.** $a = \dfrac{v^2}{2d}$

    b. $t = \dfrac{d}{v}$ **d.** $\dfrac{v}{a} = \dfrac{b}{c}$

3. Solve each of these equations for E.

    a. $f = \dfrac{E}{s}$ **b.** $m = \dfrac{2E}{v^2}$ **c.** $\dfrac{E}{c^2} = m$

4. Solve the equation $v^2 = v_0^2 + 2ad$ for d.

5. Solve each of these equations for a.

    a. $v = v_0 + at$

    b. $y = v_0 t + \frac{1}{2}at^2$

    c. $v^2 = v_0^2 + 2ay$

    d. $v = \sqrt{2as}$

6. Solve each of these equations for x.

    a. $w = fx$

    b. $g = \dfrac{f}{x}$

    c. $n = \dfrac{x}{y} - m$

    d. $d = ax^2 - d_0$

2:6 Units in Equations

Suppose you want to find the area of a wood plank. The plank is 15.0 cm wide and 2.50 m long. If you simply multiply length times width, you get 37.5 cm · m. This is not very useful because area is measured in m^2 or cm^2. Thus, you should first make sure all terms in an equation have the same units. In this case, change the width to 0.150 m. When you multiply length by width, you obtain an area of 0.375 m^2.

All terms in an equation must have the same units.

Most physical quantities have units as well as numerical values. When you substitute a value into an equation, you must write both the value and the unit. If your answer has the wrong units, you have probably made an error in your solution. When a term has several units, you can operate on the units like any other mathematical quantity.

Always include units with values in equations.

EXAMPLE

Operating on Units

If $v = 11.0$ m/s and $t = 6.00$ s, find d using $d = vt$. Find the units for d.

Solution: $d = vt = (11.0 \text{ m/s})(6.0 \text{ s}) = 66.0 \text{ m/s} \cdot \text{s} = 66.0 \text{ m}$

Note that the units on the right, meters, are the units for distance. By inspecting the units, you will often be able to tell when you have set up the equation incorrectly.

Units provide a useful way of checking the correctness of an equation.

Practice Exercises

7. Identify the answers to these exercises using consistent units.

    a. Find the area of a rectangle 2 mm by 30 cm.

    b. Find the perimeter of a rectangle 25 cm by 2.00 m.

8. Find which of the following equations are incorrect.

    a. area = (length)(width)(height)

    b. time = distance/speed

    c. distance = (speed)(time)^2

$$A^2 + B^2 = C^2$$

One of the most well-known aspects of triangle geometry is the Pythagorean Theorem: the square of the hypotenuse of a right triangle is equal to the sum of the squares of the other two sides. The theorem is named for Pythagoras, a Greek who proved the relationship in C. 540 B.C.

In his early years, Pythagoras traveled extensively to learn various techniques of counting and manipulation of numbers. Pythagoras was not financially successful until he started a school for wealthy aristocrats in Crotona, Italy. This school developed into the Pythagorean Brotherhood, which mixed mathematics, philosophy, and religion.

Members of the Brotherhood worshiped numbers, believed in reincarnation, and agreed to credit the Brotherhood with any mathematical discovery. Many discoveries demonstrated scientific insight that was not widely accepted until centuries later. The brothers believed that Earth was a sphere and that the sun and planets had independent movement. At the time few, if any, outsiders considered these theories to have merit, but 2000 years later Copernicus, Galileo, and Kepler proved that the ideas of the Brotherhood were correct.

Through experimentation with bells, flutes, and strings, Pythagoras established the relationship between mathematics and the musical scale and developed concepts of octaves and harmonics. The whole-number relationship between musical notes lead Pythagoras to classify integers as perfect, friendly, or tolerable. He considered even numbers as feminine and odd numbers as masculine. The number "1" was neuter and held sacred as the number from which all others were formed. Numbers were used to describe colors and personality traits.

Through a combination of mysticism and science, Pythagoras made major contributions to physics and mathematics, but the famous theorem was not his original idea. Although credited with proving the theorem, Pythagoras actually stated something known by the Babylonians hundreds of years earlier.

CHAPTER 2 REVIEW

SUMMARY

1. Data are plotted in graphical form to show the relationship between two variables. **2:1**

2. The independent variable is the one the experimenter changes. It is plotted on the x- or horizontal axis. The dependent variable, which changes as a result of the changes made by the experimenter, is plotted on the y- or vertical axis. **2:1**

3. A graph in which data lie in a straight line is a graph of a linear relationship. **2:2**

4. A linear relationship can be represented by the equation $y = mx + b$. **2:2**

5. The slope, m, of a straight-line graph is the vertical change (rise) divided by the horizontal change (run). **2:2**

6. The graph of a parabolic relationship is a rising curve. It represents an equation $y = kx^2$. **2:3**

7. A hyperbolic graph represents an equation $xy =$ constant, an inverse relationship. **2:4**

8. When solving an equation for a quantity, you must add, subtract, multiply, or divide in order to put that quantity alone on the left side of the equation. **2:5**

9. Units should always be included when solving problems. The units must be the same on both sides of the equation. If this is not true, the equation is wrong. **2:6**

QUESTIONS

1. During a laboratory experiment, the temperature of the gas in a balloon is varied and the volume of the balloon is measured. Which quantity is the independent variable? Which quantity is the dependent variable?

2. When plotting a graph of the experiment in Question 1,

   a. what quantity is plotted horizontally?

   b. what quantity is plotted vertically?

3. Define the slope of a straight-line or linear graph.

4. Data are plotted on a graph and the value on the y-axis is the same for each value of the independent variable. What is the slope? Why?

5. Suppose you receive $5.00 at the beginning of a week and spend $1.00 each day for lunch. You prepare a graph of the amount you have left versus the day. Would the slope of this graph be positive, zero, or negative? Why?

6. According to the formula $F = mv^2/r$, what relationship exists between

   a. F and r?

   b. F and m?

   c. F and v?

7. For the above question, what type of graph would be drawn for

   a. F versus r?

   b. F versus m?

   c. F versus v?

8. How may units be used to check if an equation is written correctly?

APPLYING CONCEPTS

1. A person who has consumed alcohol usually has longer reaction times than a person who has not.

Thus, the time between seeing a stoplight and hitting the brakes would be longer for the drinker than for the nondrinker.

   a. For a fixed speed, would the "thinking distance" for such a driver be longer or shorter than for a nondrinking driver?

   b. Would the slope of the graph of thinking distance versus speed have a larger or smaller slope?

2. Think of a relationship between two variables. In baseball you might consider the relationship between the distance the ball is hit and the speed of the pitch. Determine which is the independent variable and which is the dependent variable. In this example, the speed of the pitch is the independent variable. Choose your own relationship. If you can, think of other possible independent variables for the same dependent variable.

3. A relationship between the independent variable x and the dependent variable y can be written using the equation $y = ax^2$, where a is a constant.

   a. What is the shape of the graph of y versus x?

   b. If $z = x^2$, what would be the shape of the graph $y = az$?

4. The graph of braking distance versus car speed is a parabola. Thus we write the equation $d = kv^2$. The distance, d, has units, meters, and velocity, v, has units meters/second. How could you find the units of k? What would they be?

5. Aristotle said that the quickness of a falling object varies inversely with the density of the medium in which it is falling.

   a. According to Aristotle, would a rock fall faster in water (density 1000 kg/m³), or in air (density 1 kg/m³)?

   b. How fast would a rock fall in vacuum? Based on this, why did Aristotle say that there could be no such thing as a vacuum?

EXERCISES

1. During an experiment, a student measured the mass of 10.0 cm³ of alcohol. The student then measured the mass of 20.0 cm³ of alcohol. In this way the data in Table 2–2 were collected.

TABLE 2–2

Volume (cm³)	Mass (g)
10.0	7.9
20.0	15.8
30.0	23.7
40.0	31.6
50.0	39.6

  a. Plot the values given in the table and draw the curve that best fits all points.

  b. Describe the resulting curve.

  c. Use the graph to write an equation relating the volume to the mass of the alcohol.

  d. Find the units of the slope of the graph. What is the name given to this quantity?

2. Density is the ratio of the mass of an object to its volume. Gold has a density of 19.3 g/cm³. A cube of gold measures 4.23 cm on each edge.

  a. What is the volume of the cube?

  b. What is its mass?

3. During a class demonstration, an instructor placed a 1-kg mass on a horizontal table that was nearly frictionless. The instructor then applied various horizontal forces to the mass and measured the rate at which the mass gained speed (was accelerated) for each force applied. The results of the experiment are shown in Table 2–3.

TABLE 2–3

Force (N)	Acceleration (m/s²)
5.0	4.9
10.0	9.8
15.0	15.2
20.0	20.1
25.0	25.0
30.0	29.9

  a. Plot the values given in the table and draw the curve that best fits all points.

  b. Describe, in words, the relationship between force and acceleration according to the graph.

  c. Write the equation relating the force and the acceleration that results from the graph.

  d. Find the units of the slope of the graph.

4. The average distance between Earth and the sun is 1.50×10^8 km.

  a. Calculate the average speed, in km/h, of Earth assuming a circular path about the sun.

  b. Convert your answer from km/h to m/s. Show all units.

5. The radius of Earth is 6.37×10^3 km.

  a. Find the speed, in km/h, resulting from the rotation of Earth, of a person standing on the equator.

  b. Convert your answer to m/s.

6. Solve the equation

$$T = 2\pi\sqrt{\frac{\ell}{g}}$$

for ℓ; for g.

7. Find the answers to these problems using consistent units.

  a. Find the distance a bike travels in 1.5 minutes, if it is traveling at a constant velocity of 20 km/hr.

  b. How long would it take a car to travel 6000 m if its velocity is a constant 30 km/hr?

PROBLEMS

1. The density of silver is 10.5 g/cm³.

  a. What is the mass of 65.0 cm³ of silver?

  b. When placed on a beam balance, the 65.0-cm³ piece of silver has a mass of only 616 g. What volume of the piece is hollow?

2. The teacher who performed the experiment in Exercise 3 then changed the procedure. The mass was varied while the force was kept constant. The acceleration of each mass was then recorded. The results are shown in Table 2–4.

TABLE 2–4

Mass (g)	Acceleration (m/s²)
1.0	12.0
2.0	5.9
3.0	4.1
4.0	3.0
5.0	2.5
6.0	2.0

a. Plot the values given in the table and draw the curve that best fits all points.

b. Describe the resulting curve.

c. According to the graph, what is the relationship between mass and the acceleration produced by a constant force?

d. Write the equation relating acceleration to mass given by the data in the graph.

e. Find the units of the constant in the equation.

3. A child rides a merry-go-round horse that is 5.4 m from the center. The ride lasts 10 minutes. During this time the ride makes 24 revolutions. Find the speed of the child in meters/second.

4. Assume that a small sugar cube has sides 1 cm long. If you had a box containing 1 mole of sugar cubes and lined them up side by side, how long would the line be? 1 mole $= 6.02 \times 10^{23}$ units.

READINGS

Begley, Sharon, "Finding Order in Disorder: The Science of Chaos Reveals Nature's Secrets." *Newsweek,* December 21, 1987.

Friberg, Joran, "Numbers and Measures in the Earliest Written Records." *Scientific American,* February, 1984.

Gardner, Martin, "Slicing Pi Into Million." *Discover,* January, 1985.

Goehl, John F., Jr., "Is the Extrapolation Linear?" *The Physics Teacher,* February, 1988.

CHAPTER 3

Motion in a Straight Line

GOALS

1. You will gain an understanding of the fundamental quantities of motion: position, velocity, and acceleration.
2. You will learn to use the equations that relate the acceleration, velocity, and displacement of an object undergoing constant acceleration in one direction.
3. You will learn and practice an organized, systematic approach to solving physics problems.

Emphasize the simplicity and universality of the material in this chapter.

Take a moment to think of things that move. Now, can you think of anything that does not move? People walk, run, and ride bicycles. Cars and planes carry people rapidly from place to place. Earth rotates once each day and revolves about the sun once each year. The sun also rotates with the Milky Way, which itself is moving within its group of galaxies. Because motion is common to everything in the universe, we begin our study of physics with a study of motion.

All motion can be described in terms of the position, velocity, and acceleration of an object. To simplify matters, we will set up a few ground rules.

First, we will only describe motion, not try to explain its causes. Second, we will begin by studying objects that move only in straight lines. Third, we will study objects as if they were point objects, not three-dimensional bodies. For example, if we describe the motion of a bicycle, we will mentally step back until the bike and its rider look like tiny points.

3:1 Position and Distance

To describe the motion of an object you have to know where it is. The location of an object is its position. Figure 3–1 is a drawing of two cars on a road. What is the position of car A? Its position must be described in

How Fast Faster?

While bicycling, Jose noticed it took 1.3 seconds to pedal from the beginning of one center line segment to the beginning of the next. During the next interval, he timed 2.7 seconds to travel two segments. During the third interval, it took 4.0 seconds to travel three segments. The center line segments were 2 meters long and spaced 10 meters apart. Determine Jose's acceleration over the three intervals.

terms of its relationship to some reference point. You might choose the "O" mark on the scale. You would then place the zero point of a ruler on the O and measure the separation between it and car A as 8.0 cm. That is, A is 8.0 cm to the right of O. What is the position of car B? Measure its separation from O and you will find that it is 1.0 cm to the left of O.

In making O the reference point, you have chosen a "frame of reference." You could have chosen the left edge of the figure, the edge of the page, some point on your desk, the front of the room, or any other location. The separation between car A and the reference point would be different in each case. The **position** of an object is the separation between that object and a reference point. Distance, on the other hand, needs no reference frame. You measure the distance between two objects by measuring their separation. The separation between car A and car B is 9.0 cm no matter where you put the end of your ruler.

Distance differs from position in a second way. Both a distance and a direction are needed to describe position. Point A is a certain distance to the right of O. Although the direction can be described in terms of left and right, it is more conveniently described by using plus (+) and minus (−) signs. Positive (+) directions are to the right of the reference point; negative (−) directions are to the left. Thus the position of A is +8.0 cm and the position of B is −1.0 cm. Distance, on the other hand, involves only a length measurement, never direction. A quantity that has only a magnitude, or size, is called a **scalar** (scā-ler). A quantity that has both size and direction is called a **vector.** Thus, distance is a scalar, while position is a vector. We will soon find other quantities that are scalars and vectors.

3:2 Average and Instantaneous Speed

Suppose the cars in Figure 3–1 move from one position to another. The faster an object moves, the more its position changes in a fixed amount of time, and the greater is its speed. We define the **speed** of an object to be the distance it travels divided by the time it takes. Speed is a rate, a ratio between two different quantities. For example, if a car travels a distance of 100 m in 10 seconds, its speed is 100 m divided by 10 s, or 10 m/s.

If a car travels a distance of 200 kilometers in 2.00 hours, its average speed is (200 km)/(2.00 h) = 100 km/h. During some of that time, however, it may have been going much faster than 100 km/h; at other times it may have been going slower. Possibly it stopped. Its average speed is still the total distance divided by the total time interval. The **average speed** of an object that moves a distance d during a time interval t is $\bar{v}$ (v-bar) and can be calculated using the equation

$$\bar{v} = \frac{d}{t}$$

The instantaneous speed of a car is shown on its speedometer. It is the speed measured at a particular instant in time. Rather than measuring the distance moved over one hour, you must measure it over one second, or over an even smaller unit of time. The time interval must be small enough so that the speed is constant over that interval. Only if the speedometer indicated the same speed for the entire trip would the average and instantaneous speed be the same.

Any distance unit and any time unit can be used to calculate speed. In this textbook we will mostly use meters per second and kilometers per hour.

FIGURE 3-2. One of the first high-speed photographs was taken in 1878. The vertical lines are 68 cm apart. The time between exposures is 1/25 second. What is the average speed of the horse in m/s?   17 m/s

Instantaneous speed is the speed of an object at a particular moment in time.

FIGURE 3-3. The speedometers in most cars register the instantaneous speed of the car (a). Some new speedometers contain microcomputers that calculate the average speed for the trip as well (b).

a

b

PROBLEM SOLVING

An easy way to change from one unit to another is by using conversion factors. To convert a speed given in km/h to m/s, you must first change kilometers to meters, then hours to seconds. The value of a quantity does not change when it is multiplied by 1. Any quantity divided by its equivalent equals one. Since 1000 m = 1 km and 3600 s = 1 h, we can make the following conversion factors.

$$\frac{1000 \text{ m}}{1 \text{ km}} = 1$$

$$\frac{1 \text{ h}}{3600 \text{ s}} = 1$$

Therefore, to change a speed in km/h to m/s, first multiply it by an appropriate distance conversion factor and then by a time conversion factor. For example, 100 km/h becomes

$$\frac{100 \text{ km}}{1 \text{ h}} \times \frac{1000 \text{ m}}{1 \text{ km}} \times \frac{1 \text{ h}}{3600 \text{ s}} = 27.8 \text{ m/s}$$

This method of converting one unit to another unit is called the factor-label method of unit conversion. Unit labels are treated as mathematical factors and can be divided out. If the final units do not make sense, check your factors. You may find that a factor has been either inverted or stated incorrectly.

FIGURE 3–4. This high-speed French train travels commercially at speeds close to 305 km/h. The train moves as a single unit, giving it an exceptionally smooth ride. Japanese and German railroads are working on magnetically-suspended trains that can reach speeds of 480 km/h.

SUGGESTION: To help students get used to everyday speeds in metric, use this table.

km/h	mi/h	m/s
40 km/h =	25 mi/h =	11 m/s
80	50	24
100	62	28
120	75	33

Always include units with quantities when solving problems.

Units can be converted by multiplying by a factor of unit magnitude.

EXAMPLE

Calculating Average Speed

A bicycle rider travels 22 kilometers in 3.25 hours. What is the average speed of the rider in m/s?

Given: distance
$d = 22$ km
time interval
$t = 3.25$ h

Unknown: average speed ($\bar{v}$)

Basic equation: $\bar{v} = \dfrac{d}{t}$

Solution: $\bar{v} = \dfrac{d}{t} = \dfrac{22 \text{ km}}{3.25 \text{ h}}$

$= 6.8$ km/h

$= 6.8 \text{ km/h}\left(\dfrac{1000 \text{ m/km}}{3600 \text{ s/h}}\right) = 1.9$ m/s

For Your Information

Vector quantities not only have magnitude and direction, but also follow a special set of rules of combination. The product of a scalar and a vector is a scalar. The product of two vectors may be either a scalar or a vector. Often we are only interested in the magnitudes of vectors.

If any two of the three quantities are known, the third quantity can be found. For example, if the average speed and time interval are known, then the distance traveled can be found by rearranging the equation.

$$v = \frac{d}{t} \text{ or } d = vt$$

The correctness of this equation can be checked by examining the units. The quantity d has units meters. The quantity vt has units (m/s)s = m. This is an indication that the equation is correct.

EXAMPLE

Distance Traveled at an Average Speed

The high-speed train in Figure 3–4 travels from Paris to Lyons at an average speed of 227 km/h. The trip takes 2.00 hours. How far is Lyons from Paris?

Given: average speed $\bar{v}$ = 227 km/h   **Unknown:** distance d
time interval t = 2.00 h

Basic equation: $\bar{v} = \dfrac{d}{t}$

Solution: $\bar{v} = \dfrac{d}{t}$ so $d = \bar{v}t$

d = (227 km/h)(2.00 h) = 454 km

Practice Exercises

1. A person walks 13 km in 2.0 h. What is the person's speed in km/h and m/s?
2. A high school athlete runs 1.00×10^2 m in 12.20 s. What is the speed in m/s and km/h?
3. Light from the sun reaches Earth in 8.3 min. The speed of light is 3.00×10^8 m/s. How far (in kilometers) is Earth from the sun?
4. Suppose a car travels at a constant speed of 10 m/s. How far would it move in 1 hour? In 1 minute? In 1 second? In 1 millisecond? In 1 microsecond? In 1 nanosecond?

3:3 Velocity and Speed

A car can move either direction on a road. A car with a speed of 10 m/s starting at a position +50 m from a reference point could reach either +60 m or +40 m in one second. Recall that +50 m means 50 m to the right of the reference point. The speed would be the same, but the direction would be different. The **velocity** of an object describes both its speed and its direction. An object moving toward more positive positions has a positive velocity. Thus the car moving from +50 m to +60 m would have a velocity of +10 m/s; the car moving from +50 m to +40 m, −10 m/s. As in Figure 3–5, an arrow can be used to indicate the velocity of an object. By convention, arrows that point to the right show positive velocities; arrows pointing to the left indicate negative velocities.

Notice that an object can have a negative position but still have a positive velocity. If the car moved from −47 m to −27 m in 2.0 s, it would have a velocity of +10 m/s.

Both position and displacement are vectors; they can be either positive or negative. In books, vectors are written in boldface type. Thus displacement, written **d**, is a vector, but distance, written d, is a scalar.

Speed is a scalar quantity. It can be described completely by a magnitude. Velocity is a vector. It must have both a magnitude and a direction.

Speed and velocity describe the change in position through time.

SUGGESTION: Make up several simple examples of distance versus displacement and have the students make up some.

Distance is a scalar quantity; displacement is a vector quantity.

FIGURE 3–5. Arrows show the direction of velocity.

20m   30m   40m   50m   60m

The net change in position of an object is called its displacement. That is, the **displacement** of an object is the distance between its final position, d_f, and its initial position, d_i.

$$d_f - d_i = \Delta d$$

Suppose the position of the object changed between the initial time, t_i, and the final time, t_f. Then the motion occurred during the time $\Delta t = t_f - t_i$. The average velocity of the object is the ratio of the displacement to the time interval:

$$\bar{v} = \frac{d_f - d_i}{t_f - t_i} = \frac{\Delta d \text{ (m)}}{\Delta t \text{ (s)}}$$

Often the initial time is set equal to zero. In this case $\Delta t = t_f$, or more simply, t.

EXAMPLE

Distance, Displacement, Speed, and Velocity

A car is driven 8.0×10^1 km west in 1.0 h and then 7.0×10^1 km east in 2.0 h. East is the positive direction. What is the average velocity and average speed of the car in km/h?

For Your Information

Given:
    first displacement d_1 = 80 km west
                   = −80 km
    first time interval t_1 = 1.0 h
second displacement d_2 = 70 km east
                    = +70 km
    second time interval t_2 = 2.0 h

Unknowns:
    average velocity $\bar{v}$
    average speed $\bar{v}$

Basic equation: $\bar{v} = \dfrac{\Delta d}{\Delta t}$

Solution:
    total displacement = Δd = −80 km + 70 km
                      = −10 km
    total time interval = Δt = 1.0 h + 2.0 h
                    = 3.0 h
             $\bar{v}$ = −10 km/3.0 h
               = −3.3 km/h

but

    total distance = Δd = 80 km + 70 km
                = 150 km
      $\bar{v}$ = 150 km/3.0 h = 50 km/h

Notice that distance and displacement can be very different quantities. If the object moves from position A to position B, and back to A, the displacement is zero, but the distance is twice the distance between A and B. The magnitude of the displacement equals the distance only if the motion is all in one direction.

40   **Motion in a Straight Line**

Practice Exercises

5. A cross country runner runs 5.0 km east along the course, then turns around and runs 5.0 km west along the same path. She returns to the starting point in 40 min. What is her average speed? Her average velocity?

6. A bullet is shot from a rifle with a speed of 720.0 m/s.
   a. What time is required for the bullet to strike a target at a position +324 m?
   b. What is the velocity of the bullet in km/h?

3:4 Relativity of Velocity

Have you ever noticed when flying that once an airplane is in smooth, level flight, you have no sense of how fast the plane is moving? You could measure the speed of passengers walking up and down the aisle, just as you could when the plane was stopped on the ground. You might find that they are moving at +2 m/s or −2 m/s, depending on their direction. If a person on the ground could see into the plane, however, that person would see the situation differently. If the plane were moving at a typical velocity of +200 m/s, then the ground observer would see the passengers moving at +202 m/s or +198 m/s. Just as you must define a reference frame for measuring position, you have to define a reference frame for measuring velocity. Normally a reference frame that moves with Earth is chosen.

You probably noticed that to find the velocity of the walking passengers as seen from the ground, you simply added the velocity of the plane to the velocity of the passenger. In 1905 Albert Einstein pointed out that this rule does not work when the velocities are near the speed of light, 299 792 458 m/s. In fact, if the passengers and people on the ground measured the speed of light emitted by a lamp on the plane, both groups would measure exactly the same velocity! This fact was central to Einstein's theory of special relativity.

The velocity of an object depends on the frame of reference in which it is measured.

For Your Information

Two physicists, Albert Abraham Michelson and Edward Williams Morley, tried to measure the speed of light when it traveled both with and against the motion of Earth. Their efforts failed when they could find no change. This failure was later explained by Einstein's theory of relativity, which showed that the speed of light in a vacuum never varies.

Practice Exercises

7. You are a passenger on a bus moving at a velocity of +20 m/s. You run quickly to the front of the bus at +3 m/s, then back to the rear at −2 m/s. What would be your velocity as seen from the reference frame of the street
   a. when running toward the front?
   b. when running toward the rear?

8. A car is traveling at a constant speed of 90 km/h. It is passed by a truck moving at 105 km/h. From the point of view of the car, what is the truck's speed?

3:5 Acceleration

An airplane is at rest at the start of the runway; it has zero velocity. When cleared for takeoff by the tower, the pilot opens the throttle. After 10 seconds the airspeed indicator shows +30 m/s. After 20 seconds it shows +60 m/s. When 30 seconds have elapsed the airspeed is +90 m/s and the plane lifts off. In each 10 second interval the airplane's velocity increases by 30 m/s. Thus the velocity increases +3 m/s each second. The airplane has accelerated down the runway.

The **average acceleration** is the change in velocity divided by the interval of time. The change in velocity is the difference between the final velocity and the initial velocity. The equation used to calculate the average acceleration is

$$\bar{a} = \frac{v_f - v_i}{t_f - t_i} = \frac{\Delta v \ (\text{m/s})}{\Delta t \ (\text{s})}$$

As in the case of velocity, often we set $t_i = 0$, so $\Delta t = t_f$, and

$$\boxed{\bar{a} = \frac{v_f - v_i}{t}}$$

FIGURE 3–6. Once cleared for take-off, a pilot must maintain acceleration down the runway in order to reach takeoff velocity before running out of runway.

Speed is measured in meters per second, m/s, so the magnitude of acceleration is measured in (m/s)/s, or m/s/s. This unit is read "meters per second per second." There are two "pers" because acceleration is a rate of a rate. More often the unit for acceleration is written as m/s² and read "meters per second squared."

Just as position and velocity are vectors—numbers with both magnitude and direction—so is acceleration. In straight-line motion, acceleration can be either positive or negative. When the speed increases, the change in velocity is a positive number and the acceleration is positive; when velocity decreases, the acceleration is negative.

If the change in velocity is the same in each time interval, the acceleration is constant, or uniform. Under the special condition of constant, or uniform, acceleration, the average and instantaneous acceleration are the same. Unless specifically stated otherwise, all problems in this textbook will assume constant acceleration.

EXAMPLE

Calculating Acceleration

The velocity of a car increases from +2.0 m/s to +16 m/s over a 3.5-s interval. What is the car's acceleration?

Given: initial velocity   Unknown: acceleration $\bar{a}$
$v_i = +2.0$ m/s
final velocity   Basic equation: $\bar{a} = \dfrac{v_f - v_i}{t}$
$v_f = +16$ m/s
time interval
$t = 3.5$ s

Solution: $\bar{a} = \dfrac{v_f - v_i}{t} = \dfrac{+16 \text{ m/s} - 2.0 \text{ m/s}}{3.5 \text{ s}}$

$= +4.0$ m/s^2

When velocity is constant, the acceleration is zero. Suppose the airplane lands. As it approaches the runway to land, it slows down. Its speed decreases over a period of time. The final speed is smaller than the initial speed, so the change in velocity is a negative number. Thus the acceleration also is negative.

Does an object with negative acceleration always slow down? Think about backing a car down a long driveway. Remember that velocity is a vector. If we have defined the forward direction to be positive, then the backward direction is negative and the velocity of the car is negative. If the car starts moving backwards very slowly, but then speeds up, its final velocity will be more negative than its initial velocity. As a result, both the change in velocity and the acceleration will be negative, even though the car is going faster. When the car reaches the end of the driveway, the driver puts on the brakes and comes to a stop. Then the final velocity will be less negative than the initial velocity. The acceleration will be positive, even though the car is moving slower.

Position, velocity, and acceleration are vectors. Both magnitude and direction must be given.

A vector quantity requires that the direction be indicated, even though the direction is not used in the calculation.

EXAMPLE

Negative Acceleration

A car backs up. Its speed changes from −2.0 m/s to −9.0 m/s in 2.0 s. Find its acceleration.

Given: initial velocity   Unknown: acceleration (a)
$v_i = -2.0$ m/s
final velocity   Basic equation: $a = \dfrac{v_f - v_i}{t}$
$v_f = -9.0$ m/s
time interval
$t = 2.0$ s

Solution: $a = \dfrac{v_f - v_i}{t} = \dfrac{-9.0 \text{ m/s} - (-2 \text{ m/s})}{2.0 \text{ s}}$

$= -3.5$ m/s^2

An object can be accelerating even if its instantaneous velocity is zero.

Acceleration is the same whether the velocity is positive, negative, or zero.

Final velocity can be found from the initial velocity, acceleration, and time interval.

Can an object have a nonzero acceleration if its instantaneous velocity is zero? Think of a car climbing a hill and running out of gas. We will define velocity uphill to be positive. After its engine stops, the car's positive velocity gets smaller, so its acceleration is negative. Soon the velocity reaches zero. Only an instant later the car starts moving backward, down the hill. Its velocity is now negative. Even if you measure the change in velocity over a very small interval of time, you will find the final velocity more negative than the initial velocity. The acceleration will be negative whether the velocity is positive, zero, or negative.

Practice Exercises

9. An Indy-500 race car's velocity increases from +4.0 m/s to +36 m/s over a 4.0-s period. What is its acceleration?

10. The same race car slows from +36 m/s to +15 m/s over 3.0 s. What is its acceleration?

11. A car is coasting backwards down a hill at −3.0 m/s when the driver gets the engine started. After 2.5 s the car is moving uphill at a velocity of +4.5 m/s. What is the acceleration over the 2.5-s time interval?

12. A bus is moving at 25 m/s. The driver steps on the brakes, and the bus stops in 3.0 s. What is the acceleration of the bus?

13. Suppose the bus took twice as long to stop. How would the acceleration be related to the acceleration you found above?

How can you find the velocity of an object when you know the acceleration and the time over which the acceleration occurred? To answer this question, rearrange the equation for acceleration and solve it for the final velocity.

$$a = \frac{v_f - v_i}{t}$$

$$v_f - v_i = at$$

$$\boxed{v_f = v_i + at}$$

EXAMPLE

Final Velocity After Uniform Acceleration

If a car with a velocity of $+2.0$ m/s accelerates at a rate of $+4.0$ m/s^2 for 2.5 s, what is its final velocity?

Given: initial velocity

$v_i = +2.0$ m/s

acceleration

$a = +4.0$ m/s^2

time interval

$t = 2.5$ s

Unknown: final velocity (v_f)

Basic equation: $v_f = v_i + at$

Solution: $v_f = v_i + at$

$= +2.0$ m/s $+ (+4.0$ m/s$^2)(2.5$ s$)$

$= +12$ m/s

Practice Exercises

14. A race car accelerates from rest at $+7.5$ m/s^2 for 4.5 s. How fast will it be going at the end of that time?

15. A golf ball rolls up a hill on a Putt-Putt hole.

    a. If it starts with a velocity of $+2.0$ m/s and accelerates at a rate of -0.5 m/s^2, what is its velocity after 2.0 s?

    b. If the acceleration occurs for 6.0 s, what is its final velocity?

    c. Describe, in words, the motion of the golf ball.

16. A bus traveling at $+30$ km/h accelerates at $+3.5$ m/s^2 for 6.8 s. What is its final velocity in km/h?

3:6 Displacement During Uniform Acceleration

When an object is moving with constant velocity, its displacement can be found by multiplying its velocity by the time interval. The same equation can be used to find distance if the object is uniformly accelerating, as long as the average velocity is used.

Consider a car accelerating uniformly from $+15$ m/s to $+25$ m/s for 3.0 seconds. The car will move smoothly through the whole set of velocities between $+15$ m/s and $+25$ m/s. The middle or average velocity is $+20$ m/s. The average velocity of a uniformly accelerating object is always the middle velocity.

The average velocity of a uniformly accelerating object is the middle velocity.

Velocity (m/s, N)

Average velocity

FIGURE 3–8. The average velocity of a uniformly accelerated object is the middle velocity.

The middle velocity of the car can be found by adding the final velocity and the initial velocity and dividing the sum by two. That is,

$$\bar{v} = \frac{v_f + v_i}{2}$$

Thus the average velocity of the car in the example is

$$\bar{v} = \frac{+25 \text{ m/s} + 15 \text{ m/s}}{2} = +20 \text{ m/s}$$

To find the displacement of a uniformly accelerating object during a time interval, multiply the average velocity calculated above by the time interval to obtain

$$d = \frac{(v_f + v_i)t}{2} = \frac{1}{2}(v_f + v_i)t$$

In 3.0 seconds the car discussed above will undergo a displacement of +60 m.

EXAMPLE

Displacement During Uniform Acceleration

What is the displacement of a train as it is accelerated uniformly from +11 m/s to +33 m/s in a 20.0 s interval?

Given: initial velocity
$v_i = +11$ m/s
final velocity
$v_f = +33$ m/s
time interval $t = 20.0$ s

Unknown: displacement (*d*)

Basic equation: $d = \dfrac{(v_f + v_i)t}{2}$

Solution: $d = \dfrac{(v_f + v_i)t}{2} = \dfrac{(+33 \text{ m/s} + 11 \text{ m/s})(20.0 \text{ s})}{2}$

$= +4.4 \times 10^2$ m

Practice Exercises

17. A race car starts from rest and is accelerated uniformly to +41 m/s in 8.0 s. What is the car's displacement?

18. A race car traveling at +44 m/s is uniformly accelerated to a velocity of +22 m/s over an 11-s interval. What is its displacement during this time?

19. A rocket traveling at +88 m/s is accelerated uniformly to +132 m/s over a 15-s interval. What is the rocket's displacement during this time?

20. An engineer must design a runway to accommodate airplanes that must reach a ground speed of +61 m/s before they can take off. These planes are capable of being accelerated uniformly at the rate of +2.5 m/s/s.

    a. How long will it take the planes to reach takeoff speed?

    b. What must be the minimum length of the runway?

If the initial velocity, acceleration, and time interval are known, the displacement of the object can be found by combining equations already used. The final velocity of a uniformly accelerated object is $v_f = v_i + at$. Displacement of an object with uniform acceleration is $d = \frac{1}{2}(v_f + v_i)t$. Substitute the final velocity from the first equation for v_f in the second equation.

$$d = \tfrac{1}{2}(v_f + v_i)t = \tfrac{1}{2}((v_i + at) + v_i)t = \tfrac{1}{2}(2v_i + at)t$$

$$\boxed{d = v_i t + \tfrac{1}{2}at^2}$$

There are two terms in this equation. The first term, $v_i t$, is the displacement of an object moving with constant velocity v_i. The second term, $\frac{1}{2}at^2$, gives the displacement of the object starting from rest and moving with uniform acceleration. The sum of these two terms gives the displacement of an object that starts with an initial velocity and accelerates uniformly.

SUGGESTION: If a problem asks for t and t comes out negative, an error has been made.

SUGGESTION: Give examples that show how the two displacements add. Include both negative initial velocities and negative acceleration.

The displacement can also be found from the initial velocity, acceleration, and time interval.

EXAMPLE

Calculating Displacement from Acceleration and Time Interval

A car starting from rest accelerates at $+6.1$ m/s^2 for 7.0 s. How far does the car move?

Given: initial velocity
   $v_i = +0$ m/s
   acceleration
   $a = +6.1$ m/s^2
   time interval $t = 7.0$ s

Unknown: displacement (d)
Basic equation: $d = v_i t + \frac{1}{2}at^2$

Solution: $d = v_i t + \frac{1}{2}at^2$
   $= (+0$ m/s$)(7.0$ s$) + (\frac{1}{2})(+6.1$ m/s$^2)(7.0$ s$)^2$
   $= 0 + 150$ m $= +150$ m

Practice Exercises

21. An airplane starts from rest and accelerates at a constant rate of $+3.00$ m/s^2 for 30.0 s before leaving the ground. What is its displacement during this time interval?

22. Starting from rest, a race car moves 110 m in the first 5.0 s of uniform acceleration. What is the car's acceleration?

23. A jet plane traveling at $+88$ m/s lands on a runway and comes to rest in 11 s.
   a. Calculate its uniform acceleration.
   b. Calculate the distance it travels.

24. A driver brings a car traveling at $+22$ m/s to a full stop in 2.0 s.
   a. What is the car's acceleration?
   b. How far does it travel before stopping?

25. A bicyclist approaches the crest of a hill at $+4.5$ m/s. She accelerates down the hill at a rate of $+0.40$ m/s^2 for 12 s. How far does she move down the hill during this time interval?

26. A car moves at +12 m/s and coasts up a hill with an acceleration of −1.6 m/s².

    a. What is the car's displacement after 6.0 s?

    b. What is it after 9.0 s?

    c. Explain your answers.

The displacement is the same if initial and final velocities are exchanged and the sign of the acceleration is reversed.

    The equations for final velocity and displacement can be combined to form an equation relating initial and final speed, acceleration, and distance, but not time. We first rewrite the two equations,

$$d = \frac{(v_f + v_i)t}{2} \text{ and } v_f = v_i + at$$

The second equation is now solved for t and substituted in the first, resulting in

$$d = \frac{v_f + v_i}{2} \times \frac{v_f - v_i}{a} = \frac{v_f^2 - v_i^2}{2a}$$

Final velocity can also be found from the initial velocity, acceleration, and distance traveled.

Solving for v_f^2 yields

$$\boxed{v_f^2 = v_i^2 + 2ad}$$

This equation relates acceleration, distance, and initial speed to final speed. The equation can be solved without knowing the time interval over which the acceleration takes place.

EXAMPLE

Calculating Acceleration from Distance and Speed

    An airplane must reach a speed of 71 m/s for takeoff. If the runway is 1.0 km long, what must the acceleration be?

Given: initial speed   **Unknown:** acceleration a
      $v_i = 0$ m/s   **Basic equation:** $v_f^2 = v_i^2 + 2ad$
      final speed
      $v_f = 71$ m/s
      distance
      $d = 1$ km $= 1.0 \times 10^3$ m

SUGGESTION: You might discuss how this example would change if the plane took off backwards, i.e., at −71 m/s. To have the results make sense, both d and a would have to be negative.

Solution: $v_f^2 = v_i^2 + 2ad$ so

$$a = (v_f^2 - v_i^2)/2d$$
$$= ((71 \text{ m/s})^2 - 0)/2(1.0 \times 10^3 \text{ m})$$
$$= 2.5 \text{ m/s}^2$$

    Consider the reverse of this problem. The plane lands going 71 m/s. It slows to a halt at an acceleration of −2.5 m/s². How far does it travel? We use the same basic equation, solved for the distance.

$$d = \frac{v_f^2 - v_i^2}{2a}$$

$$d = \frac{(0 \text{ m/s})^2 - (71 \text{ m/s})^2}{2(-2.5 \text{ m/s}^2)} = +1.0 \times 10^3 \text{ m}$$

Notice that the distance traveled is the same. The motion in these two cases is said to be symmetrical. The conditions at the beginning and end of the motion are reversed, and the solutions are equivalent. Symmetry often plays an important role in physics problems.

Practice Exercises

27. An airplane accelerates from a speed of 2.0×10^1 m/s at the constant rate of 3.0 m/s^2 over a distance of 530 m. What is its speed after moving this distance?

28. The pilot stops the same plane in 484 m using an acceleration of -8.0 m/s^2. How fast was the plane moving before braking began?

29. Police find skid marks 60 m long on a highway showing where a car made an emergency stop. Assuming that the acceleration was -10 m/s^2 (about the maximum for dry pavement), how fast was the car going? Was the car exceeding the 80 km/h speed limit?

3:7 Acceleration Due to Gravity

Galileo was the first to show that all bodies fall to Earth with a constant acceleration. It does not matter what the mass of the body is, from how high it is dropped, or whether it is dropped or thrown. As long as air resistance can be ignored, the acceleration is the same.

All freely falling bodies accelerate at the same rate.

Acceleration due to gravity is given a special symbol, **g.** Since it is a vector, it must have both a direction and a magnitude. We will choose "up" as our positive direction, so a falling body has a negative velocity, and its acceleration is also negative. On Earth, a freely falling body has an acceleration, **g,** of -9.80 m/s^2. Actually, **g** varies slightly, from -9.790 m/s^2 in southern Florida to -9.810 m/s^2 in northern Maine. It is smaller at high altitudes, for example, -9.789 m/s^2 on the top of Pike's Peak. We will use a typical value of -9.80 m/s^2. Thus, if a ball is dropped from the top of a building, it starts with zero velocity and in each second of fall gains a downward velocity of -9.80 m/s.

SUGGESTION: Students should learn the value -9.80 m/s^2.

The acceleration of a freely falling body is -9.80 m/s^2 (toward Earth).

If a ball is thrown up from the ground, it starts with a positive velocity, say $+20$ m/s. The acceleration of the ball is -9.80 m/s^2, so its velocity gets smaller. After about 2 seconds it will have zero velocity and be at its highest point. The velocity, however, is still changing at the rate of -9.80 m/s^2. On the way down, the ball's velocity is negative and becomes more negative at the rate of -9.80 m/s^2. After it has fallen for about 2 seconds, the ball will be once again on the ground. It has spent 4 seconds in the air. It rises the same distance during the first two seconds as it falls during the final two seconds. The equation for uniformly accelerated motion is symmetrical.

All problems involving motion of falling bodies can be solved by using the equations developed in this chapter with the acceleration, **a,** replaced by **g.** Thus you would use

SUGGESTION: Stress the modeling process used here. Solutions of this simplified model provide a guide to solving problems where g varies and air resistance is important.

$$v_f = v_i + gt$$
$$v_f^2 = v_i^2 + 2gd$$
$$d = v_i t + \tfrac{1}{2}gt^2$$

FIGURE 3–9. Before opening his parachute, a sky diver's downward speed increases by about 10 m/s each second.

Negative values of g, v_f, and d indicate a downward direction.

EXAMPLE

Freely Falling Bodies

A brick falls freely from a high scaffold at a construction site. **a.** What is its velocity after 4.0 s? **b.** How far does it fall during this time?

Given: acceleration of gravity
$g = -9.80$ m/s^2
initial velocity
$v_i = 0$ m/s
time interval $t = 4.0$ s

Unknowns: a. v_f **b.** d

Basic equations: a. $v_f = v_i + gt$
b. $d = v_it + \frac{1}{2}gt^2$

Solution: a. $v_f = v_i + gt = 0$ m/s $+ (-9.80$ m/s$^2)(4.0$ s$)$
$v_f = -39$ m/s
b. $d = v_it + \frac{1}{2}gt^2 = 0$ m/s $+(\frac{1}{2})(-9.80$ m/s$^2)(4.0$ s$)^2$
$= (\frac{1}{2})(-9.80$ m/s$^2)(16$ s$^2) = -78$ m

The negative displacement means that the final position is lower than the initial position.

3:8 Solving Motion Problems

Several equations for solving motion problems have been introduced in this chapter. How do you know which one(s) to use in solving a problem? The equations are listed in Table 3–1, together with a list of the quantities related by each equation.

TABLE 3–1

Equations of Motion for Uniform Acceleration				
Equation	**Quantities Related**			
$v_f = v_i + at$	v_i	v_f	a	t
$d = \frac{1}{2}(v_f + v_i)t$	v_i	d	v_f	t
$d = v_it + \frac{1}{2}at^2$	v_i	d	a	t
$v_f^2 = v_i^2 + 2ad$	v_i	d	v_f	a

SUGGESTION: Have students copy Table 3–1 on a 3 × 5 card to have in front of them as they do homework or problems in class. This will help them to learn these questions.

FIGURE 3–10. A lobbed ball experiences constant acceleration. As the ball rises its speed decreases, which can be seen as smaller intervals of distance traveled, and as it falls its speed increases.

50   **Motion in a Straight Line**

PROBLEM SOLVING ━━━━━━━━━━

In order to solve problems in which you must choose the equation to be solved, follow this procedure.

Note that each equation has at least one of the four variables d, v, a, or t missing. All include the initial velocity as well as the initial time (0) and initial position (also zero).

When solving motion problems, or, indeed, any physics problem, use an orderly procedure like the one listed below.

1. Read the problem carefully.
2. Identify the quantities that are given in the problem.
3. Identify the quantity that is unknown, the one you have to find.
4. Select the equation that contains the given and unknown quantities.
5. Solve the equation for the unknown quantity using algebra.
6. Substitute the values given in the problem, along with their proper units, into the equation and solve it.
7. Check to see if the answer is in the correct units.
8. Check to see if the numerical value of your answer is reasonable.

SUGGESTION: Show students other methods for solving this problem. For example, from symmetry, the initial and final velocities of the whole trip are equal in magnitude but opposite in direction. Use $v_f = v_i + gt$ to find t for the whole trip.

Each of the equations developed in this chapter has one quantity missing.

EXAMPLE

Acceleration Due to Gravity

A tennis ball is thrown straight up with an initial speed of $+22.5$ m/s. It is caught at the same distance above ground from which it was thrown. **a.** How high does the ball rise? **b.** How long does the ball remain in the air?

SUGGESTION: Emphasize the symmetry in the motion of an object thrown up in the air and coming back down.

Given: $v_i = +22.5$ m/s (upward)
$g = -9.80$ m/s²

Unknowns: a. d **b.** t

Basic equations: $v_f = v_i + gt$
$d = v_i t + \frac{1}{2}gt^2$
$v_f^2 = v_i^2 + 2gd$
$d = \frac{1}{2}(v_f + v_i)t$

SUGGESTION: Stress the value of the symmetry. Compare to a movie run in reverse.

Solution:

a. At the top of the ball's flight, the instantaneous velocity of the ball is zero. Thus the final velocity for the upward part of the ball's flight will be zero. Therefore we know v_i and g, but need d. Use the equation $v_f^2 = v_i^2 + 2gd$, solving it for d. With $v_f = 0$, $0 = v_i^2 + 2gd$ or $2gd = -v_i^2$.

Thus $d = \dfrac{-v_i^2}{2g} = \dfrac{-(22.5 \text{ m/s})^2}{2(-9.80 \text{ m/s}^2)} = 25.8$ m

The direction is up (positive) so $d = +25.8$ m.

b. From symmetry, we know that the times required for the rising and falling parts of the flight will be the same. Thus the time to rise is half the total time. Thus we know v_f and g, but need t. Use $v_f = v_i + gt$. With $v_f = 0$, we solve for t, obtaining

$t = \dfrac{-v_i}{g} = \dfrac{-(22.5 \text{ m/s})}{(-9.80 \text{ m/s}^2)} = 2.30$ s

Thus the total trip time is 4.60 s.

EXAMPLE

Finding Displacement When Velocities and Times Are Known

A spaceship accelerates uniformly from $+65.0$ m/s to $+162.0$ m/s in 10.0 seconds. How far does it move?

Given: $v_i = +65.0$ m/s   Unknown: displacement d

$v_f = +162.0$ m/s

$t = 10.0$ s   Basic equation: $d = \dfrac{(v_f + v_i)t}{2}$

Solution: $d = \dfrac{(v_f + v_i)t}{2}$

$= \dfrac{(+162.0 \text{ m/s} + 65.0 \text{ m/s})(10.0 \text{ s})}{2}$

$= +1.14 \times 10^3$ m $(+1.14$ km$)$

Practice Exercise

30. A spacecraft traveling at a velocity of $+1210$ m/s is uniformly accelerated at -150 m/s^2. If the acceleration lasts for 8.68 seconds, what is the final velocity of the craft? Explain your results in words.

CHAPTER 3 REVIEW

SUMMARY

1. All motion can be described in terms of the position, velocity, and acceleration of the object. **Introduction**

2. A scalar quantity is described completely by its magnitude, while a vector quantity requires both magnitude and direction. **3:1**

3. The position of an object is its separation from a reference point. **3:1**

4. Average speed is the total distance traveled divided by the elapsed time. **3:2**

5. Instantaneous speed is the speed of an object at any given instant. **3:2**

6. Displacement is a vector quantity giving the magnitude and direction of an object's change of position. **3:1**

7. Average velocity is the displacement (net distance from starting point) divided by the elapsed time. **3:3**

8. It is necessary to define a frame of reference when measuring velocity. **3:4**

9. Acceleration is the ratio of the change in velocity to the time interval over which it occurs. **3:5**

10. Constant acceleration is called uniform acceleration. **3:5**

11. The acceleration of gravity is -9.80 m/s^2 near Earth. **3:7**

12. Motion problems can be solved using one or more of the formulas in Table 3–1. **3:8**

QUESTIONS

1. Write a summary of the equations for displacement, velocity, and time of a body experiencing uniformly accelerated motion.

2. Four cars start from rest. Car A accelerates at 6.0 m/s². Car B accelerates at 5.4 m/s². Car C accelerates at 8.0 m/s², and Car D speeds up at 12 m/s². In the first column of a table, show the speed of each car at the end of 2.0 s. In the second column, show the distance each car travels during the same two seconds. What conclusion do you reach about the speed attained and the distance traveled by a body starting from rest at the end of the first two seconds of acceleration?

3. An object shot straight up rises for 7.0 s before gravity brings it to a halt. A second object falling from rest takes 7.0 s to reach the ground. Compare the distances traveled by the objects during the 7.0 s period.

4. Explain why an aluminum ball and a steel ball of similar size, dropped from the same height, reach the ground at the same time.

5. Describe the changes in the velocity of a ball thrown straight up into the air. Then describe the changes in its acceleration.

6. Give some examples of falling objects for which air resistance cannot be ignored.

7. **a.** Can a body have a zero velocity and be accelerating?
   b. Can a body have constant speed and a changing velocity?
   c. Can a body have constant velocity and a changing speed?
   Explain your answers.

8. **a.** Can a body have a negative velocity and a positive acceleration?
   b. Can a car change the direction of its velocity when traveling with a constant acceleration?

APPLYING CONCEPTS

1. List some conditions under which a football may be treated as a point. When can it not be so treated?

2. Can the velocity of an object change when its acceleration is constant? If you answer yes, give an example. If you answer no, explain why.

3. On the moon, **g** is one sixth of its value on Earth. Will an object dropped by an astronaut hit the ground with a smaller or larger speed than on Earth? Will it take less time or more time to fall?

4. A ball is thrown vertically upward with the same initial velocity on Earth and on planet Dweeb, which has three times the gravitational acceleration as Earth.
   a. How does the maximum height reached by the ball on Dweeb compare with the maximum height on Earth?
   b. If the ball on Dweeb were thrown with three times greater initial velocity, how would that change your answer to **a?**

5. One rock is dropped from a cliff, a second rock is thrown downward. When they reach the bottom, which rock has a greater speed? Which has a greater acceleration? Which arrives first?

6. A NASA team oversees a space shuttle launch at Cape Canaveral and then travels to Edwards Air Force Base in California to supervise the landing. Which group of people, the astronauts or the NASA team, has the greater displacement?

EXERCISES

1. You are driving down a street in a car at 55 km/h. Suddenly a child runs into the street. If it takes you 0.75 s to react and apply the brakes, how many meters will you have moved before you begin to slow down?

2. A race car can be slowed with acceleration of −11 m/s².
   a. If the car is going +55 m/s, how many meters will it take to stop?
   b. Repeat for a car going 110 m/s.

3. An astronaut drops a feather from 1.2 m above the surface of the moon. If the acceleration of gravity on the moon is one sixth the acceleration on Earth, how long does it take the feather to hit the surface?

4. Find the uniform acceleration that causes an object's speed to change from 32 m/s to 96 m/s in an 8.0-s period.

5. A rocket traveling at +155 m/s is accelerated at a rate of −31.0 m/s².
   a. How long will it take before the instantaneous speed is 0 m/s?

b. How far will it travel during this time?

c. What will be its velocity after 8.00 s?

6. A car with a velocity of +22 m/s is accelerated uniformly at the rate of +1.6 m/s^2 for 6.8 s. What is its final velocity?

7. Determine the final velocity of a proton that has an initial velocity of +2.35 × 10^5 m/s and then is accelerated uniformly in an electric field at the rate of −1.10 × 10^{12} m/s^2 for 1.50 × 10^{-7} s.

8. A supersonic jet that is flying at 2.0 × 10^2 m/s is accelerated uniformly at the rate of 23.1 m/s^2 for 20.0 s.

a. What is its final speed?

b. The speed of sound is 331 m/s in air. How many times the speed of sound is the plane's final speed?

9. Determine the displacement of a plane that is uniformly accelerated from +66 m/s to +88 m/s in 12 s.

10. How far does a plane fly in 15 s while its velocity is changing from +145 m/s to +75 m/s at a uniform rate?

11. If a bullet leaves the muzzle of a rifle with a speed of 600 m/s, and the barrel of the rifle is 0.9 m long, at what rate is the bullet accelerated while in the barrel?

12. A car comes to rest after a uniform acceleration of −9.0 m/s^2 for 8.0 s. What distance does it travel during this time?

13. A plane travels a distance of +5.0 × 10^2 m while being accelerated uniformly from rest at the rate of +5.0 m/s^2. What final speed does it attain?

14. A stone falls freely from rest for 8.0 s.

a. Calculate its final velocity.

b. What distance does the stone fall during this time?

15. A weather balloon is floating at a constant height above Earth when it releases a pack of instruments.

a. If the pack hits the ground with a velocity of −73.5 m/s, how far does the pack fall?

b. How long does the pack fall?

16. Consider the objects in Question 3. The first object has an initial velocity of +69 m/s. Calculate the displacement of each object. Do your results support your answer to Question 3?

17. During a baseball game, a batter hits a long fly ball. If the ball remains in the air for 6.0 s, how high does it rise? Hint: Calculate the height using the second half of the trajectory.

18. A student drops a rock from a bridge to the water 12.0 m below. With what speed does the rock strike the water?

19. When a traffic light turns green, a waiting car starts off with a constant acceleration of +6.0 m/s^2. At the instant the car begins to accelerate, a truck with a constant velocity of +21 m/s passes in the next lane.

a. How far will the car travel before it overtakes the truck?

b. How fast will the car be traveling when it overtakes the truck?

PROBLEMS

1. A wrench falls from a helicopter that is rising steadily at +6.0 m/s. After 2.0 s,

a. what is the velocity of the wrench?

b. how far below the helicopter is the wrench?

2. Now that you know about acceleration, test your reaction time. Ask a friend to hold a ruler just even with the tip of your fingers. Then have your friend drop the ruler. Measure the number of centimeters that the ruler falls before you can catch it and calculate your reaction time. Use an average of several trials to give more accurate results. The reaction time for most people is more than 0.15 second.

3. a. A driver of a car going 90.0 km/h suddenly sees the lights of a barrier 40.0 m ahead. It takes the driver 0.75 s to apply the brakes, and the maximum acceleration during braking is −10.0 m/s^2. Determine if the car hits the barrier.

b. What is the maximum speed at which the car could be moving and not hit the barrier 40.0 m ahead? Hint: The distance traveled at constant speed plus the distance decelerating equals the total distance traveled.

4. You plan a trip on which you want to average 9.0 × 10^1 km/h. You cover the first half of the trip at an average speed of only 5.0 × 10^1 km/h.

a. What must your average speed be in the second half of the trip to meet your goal? Note that the velocities are based on half the distance, not half the time.

    b. Is this a reasonable speed?

5. Have someone measure how high you jump vertically. Then calculate the speed with which you leave the ground.

6. Throw a ball vertically along the side of a building so you can estimate its height. Calculate the velocity with which it leaves your hand.

7. A tennis ball is dropped from 1.20 m above the ground. It rebounds to a height of 1.00 m.

    a. With what speed does it hit the ground?

    b. With what speed does it leave the ground?

    c. If the tennis ball were in contact with the ground for 0.010 s, find its acceleration while touching the ground. Compare to its acceleration g.

8. A baseball pitcher throws a fastball at a speed of 44 m/s. The acceleration occurs as the pitcher holds the ball in his hand and moves it through an almost straight-line distance of 3.5 m. Calculate the acceleration, assuming it is uniform. Compare the acceleration to that of gravity.

9. Highway safety engineers build soft barriers so that cars hitting them will slow down at a safe rate. A person wearing a safety belt can stand an acceleration of -300 m/s². How thick should barriers be to safely stop a car that hits a barrier at 110 km/h?

10. Rocket-powered sleds are used to test the responses of humans to acceleration. Starting from rest, one sled can reach a speed of 444 m/s in 1.80 s and be brought to a stop again in 2.15 s.

    a. Calculate the acceleration of the sled when starting and compare it to g.

    b. Find the acceleration of the sled when braking and compare it to g.

11. How far does the rocket sled in Problem 10 travel while accelerating and while braking?

12. Engineers are developing new types of guns that might someday be used to launch satellites as if they were bullets. One such gun can give a small object a velocity of 3.5 km/s moving it through only 2.0 cm.

    a. What acceleration does the gun give this object?

    b. Over what time interval does the acceleration take place?

READINGS

Easton, D., "The Stoplight Dilemma Revisited." *The Physics Teacher,* January, 1987.

Goldman, Terry, Richard J. Hughes, and Michael Martin Nieto, "Gravity and Antimatter [new ideas challenge independence of gravitational acceleration for mass and substance]." *Scientific American,* March, 1988.

Hammer, Signe, "The Riddle of Turbulence." *Science Digest,* May, 1984.

Nalence, Eugene E., "Using Automobile Road Test Data." *The Physics Teacher,* May, 1988.

CHAPTER 4

Graphical Analysis of Motion

GOALS

1. You will be able to produce and read graphs to analyze the motion of objects in terms of displacement, velocity, and acceleration.
2. You will be able to use graphs to identify relationships among the quantities describing an object in motion based on the shape of a curve, the slope of a curve or its tangent lines, and the area under a curve.

SUGGESTION: Practice graphing using the Skills section of the TRB.

For Your Information

"Mathematics is the door and the key to the sciences."
—Roger Bacon

SUGGESTION: Emphasize the difference between distance, displacement, and position.

SUGGESTION: Enlarge the graphs in the text and make overhead transparencies for teaching this chapter.

When velocity is constant, displacement varies directly with time.

Graphs are one of our most useful tools. We use them to determine relationships among quantities. For instance, a straight line indicates that one quantity varies directly with another. A parabola always means that one quantity varies as the square of another. The straight line and parabola are curves that you will see as you study motion graphs. By interpreting the curves of motion graphs, you will be able to determine the relationships among an object's displacement, velocity, acceleration, and time.

4:1 Position-Time Graph for Constant Velocity

A jet airplane travels at a constant velocity of $+260$ m/s. The equation describing motion at constant velocity is $d = vt$. To create a graph of the plane's motion, first make a table listing times and corresponding displacements of the plane. Figure 4–1 includes a table of positions for the first 5 seconds of travel, assuming the plane was located at the position $+100$ m at $t = 0$ seconds. The data are then plotted on a graph with time as the independent variable and position as the dependent variable. A straight line best represents the data. This graph shows that there is a linear relationship between displacement and time. The y-intercept of the graph shows the position of the object at $t = 0$.

Field Trip

This three-dimensional graph illustrates the gravitational field of two different and equal masses. The strength of attraction as a function of the distance from each mass is shown. The steeper the height of the graph, the greater the force of attraction for another mass placed nearby. In reference to the graph, where could a small mass be placed to remain at rest?

Position versus Time

Time (s)	Position (m)
0	100
1	360
2	620
3	880
4	1140
5	1400

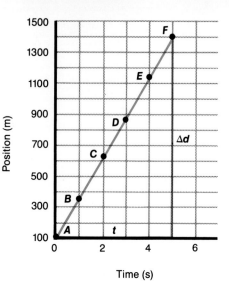

SUGGESTION: When finding the slope, use the curve rather than data points and form the largest possible triangles to increase precision.

4:2 Velocity from a Position-Time Graph

The slope of the curve of a graph is the rise divided by the run. On a position-time graph the rise is the change in position, or displacement of the object. The run is the time interval during which the change in position occurred. That is

$$\text{slope} = \frac{\text{rise}}{\text{run}} = \frac{d}{t}$$

The slope of a graph is $\Delta y/\Delta x$.

For more accurate results, always use the largest possible rise and run when finding the slope. In Figure 4–1 the slope of the line between points A and F is given by

$$\text{slope} = \frac{\text{rise}}{\text{run}} = \frac{\Delta d}{t} = \frac{+1400 \text{ m} - 100 \text{ m}}{5 \text{ s} - 0 \text{ s}} = \frac{+1300 \text{ m}}{5 \text{ s}} = +260 \text{ m/s}$$

From the equation you can see that the unit of slope is meters per second, the unit of velocity. The slope of a position-time graph is the velocity of the object.

The slope of a curve on a position-time graph is the velocity.

4:3 Position-Time Graph for a Complete Trip

Figure 4–2 is a position-time graph for a short car trip. The velocity of the car for each part of the trip can be found by determining the slope of the line for that part. From A to B

$$\text{slope} = \frac{d}{t} = \frac{+200 \text{ m}}{10 \text{ s}} = +20 \text{ m/s}$$

Between points B and C the line is horizontal, and

$$\text{slope} = \frac{d}{t} = \frac{0 \text{ m}}{10 \text{ s}} = 0 \text{ m/s}$$

A steep slope on a position-time graph indicates high velocity. When the slope is zero, the object is at rest.

The car is at rest.

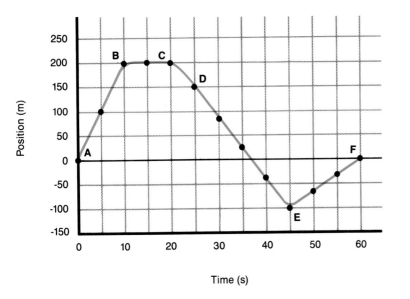

FIGURE 4–2. A position-time graph for a short car trip.

Between points C and D, the position of the car decreases; it moves back toward its original position. The displacement is negative.

A negative value on a position-time graph indicates a negative displacement.

$$\text{slope} = \frac{d}{t} = \frac{-50 \text{ m}}{5 \text{ s}} = -10 \text{ m/s}$$

The slope is negative.

Thus the velocity is also negative, showing that the car is moving in a direction opposite to its original direction. Between points D and E the velocity is given by

A negative slope on a position-time graph shows that the object is moving in the direction opposite to its original direction.

$$\text{slope} = \frac{d}{t} = \frac{-250 \text{ m}}{20 \text{ s}} = -12.5 \text{ m/s}$$

The slope and velocity are both more negative. The velocity has the same negative value for the entire segment, even though the position at point E is negative. That is, the car passed the starting point. Between points E and F

$$\text{slope} = \frac{d}{t} = \frac{+100 \text{ m}}{15 \text{ s}} = +6.7 \text{ m/s}$$

The velocity again is positive. The car is once more moving in the original direction.

The average velocity of the total trip is the change in position between points A and F divided by the total time. The average velocity is zero because positions A and F are the same. For a round trip, the average velocity is zero. What is the average speed?

4:4   Velocity-Time Graph for Constant Velocity

A velocity-time graph of motion is the most useful of all motion graphs. The data in Figure 4–1 were used to plot a position-time graph of an airplane flying at constant velocity. A plot of the velocity versus time is

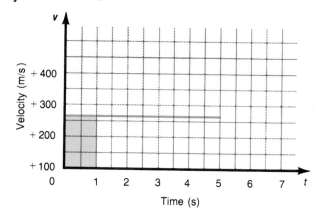
Velocity versus Time

shown in Figure 4–3. Every point on the line has the same vertical value because the velocity is constant. The line is parallel to the t-axis.

The slope of the line is the rise divided by the run. The rise is the change in velocity and the run is the time interval. Therefore,

$$\text{slope} = \frac{\text{rise}}{\text{run}} = \frac{v_f - v_i \ (\text{m/s})}{t \ (\text{s})} = a \ (\text{m/s}^2)$$

The slope of the line on the velocity-time graph is the acceleration of the object. For the airplane of Figure 4–3, the acceleration is zero.

A velocity-time graph can also be used to find the displacement of an object. Note the shaded area under the line in Figure 4–3. The vertical side of this area is the velocity, $v = +260$ m/s. The horizontal side is the time interval, $t = 1.0$ s. The area of this rectangle is $vt = (+260 \text{ m/s})(1.0 \text{ s}) = +260$ m. This quantity is the displacement of the plane in 1.0 second. Thus the area under the line is equal to the displacement of the object from its original position at time t.

At the end of 3.0 seconds, the area under the line would be $vt = (+260 \text{ m/s})(3.0 \text{ s}) = +780$ m. This is the distance the plane would travel from its original position in three seconds.

Displacement increases linearly with time. Note that the curve of a position-time graph for constant velocity is a straight line.

The velocity-time graph of constant velocity is a line parallel to the t-axis.

Practice Exercises

1. A plane flies in a straight line at a constant speed of $+5.0 \times 10^1$ m/s.
   a. Construct a table showing the position or displacement of the plane at the end of each second for a 10-s period.
   b. Use the data from the table to plot a position-time graph.
   c. Show that the slope of the line is the velocity of the plane. Use at least two different sets of points along the line.
   d. Plot a velocity-time graph of the plane's motion for the first 6 s of the 10-s interval.
   e. Find the displacement of the plane between the seventh and tenth seconds.

Position versus Time

FIGURE 4–4. Use with Practice Exercises 2, 3, and 4.

Time (s)

2. Use the position-time graph in Figure 4–4 to find
   a. how far the object travels between $t = 0$ s and $t = 40$ s.
   b. how far it travels between $t = 40$ s and $t = 70$ s.
   c. how far it travels between $t = 90$ s and $t = 100$ s.

3. Use Figure 4–4 to find
   a. the velocity of the object during the first 40 s.
   b. the velocity of the object between $t = 40$ s and $t = 70$ s.
   c. the velocity of the object between $t = 70$ s and $t = 90$ s.
   d. the velocity of the object between $t = 90$ s and $t = 100$ s.

4. Use the position-time graph, Figure 4–4, to construct a table showing the average velocity of the object during each 10-s interval over the entire 100 s.

5. Plot a velocity-time graph using the table from Exercise 4.

6. A car moves along a straight road at a constant velocity of $+4.0 \times 10^1$ m/s.
   a. Plot a position-time graph for the car.
   b. Find the slope of the curve using two different points along the line.
   c. Plot a velocity-time graph for the car. What does the area under the curve of the graph represent?
   d. Calculate the area under the curve of the graph between the fifth and sixth seconds. What does this area represent?

7. A cyclist maintains a velocity of $+5.0$ m/s N. The location is $+250$ m south of point A.
   a. Plot a position-time graph of the cyclist's location from point A at 10.0-s intervals for 60.0 s.
   b. What is the position in terms of location A after 60.0 s?
   c. What is the displacement from the original position after 60.0 s?

8. A person drives a car at a constant $+20$ m/s for 60 seconds. The car runs out of gas, so the driver, carrying an empty gasoline can, walks

4:4 Velocity-Time Graph for Constant Velocity 61

at +1.5 m/s for 120 seconds to the nearest gas station. After the 180 seconds it takes to fill the can, the driver walks back to the car at a slower 1.2 m/s. The car is then driven back home at −20 m/s.

a. Draw a velocity-time graph for this problem. You will have to calculate the distance the driver walked to the station in order to find the time it took to walk back to the car.

b. Draw a position-time graph for the problem from the areas under the curves of the velocity-time graph.

FIGURE 4–5. A velocity-time graph for uniformly accelerated motion.

Velocity versus Time

Time (s)	Velocity (m/s)
0	0
1	+20
2	+40
3	+60
4	+80
5	+100

4:5   Velocity-Time Graph for Uniform Acceleration

A jet plane starts from rest on a runway. It is accelerated uniformly at the rate of +20 m/s^2. The table in Figure 4–5 lists velocities for the first five seconds of the plane's motion. The velocity-time plot of these data is a straight line passing through the origin. The equation that describes the velocity of a uniformly accelerated object starting from rest is $v_f = at$.

As you have seen, the acceleration of an object is the slope of the curve of a velocity-time graph. For uniform acceleration, the slope of the line is constant over its entire length.

As you have also seen, for an object moving with constant velocity, the area under the curve of a velocity-time graph is the displacement of the object. It is true that for any velocity-time graph, including uniformly accelerated motion, the area under the curve is the displacement of the object.

Look at the shaded area under the curve between points A and B on Figure 4–5. The shaded area is a triangle with altitude 40 m/s. The base of the triangle is the time, t. The area of a triangle is found by multiplying the product of the base and altitude by one half. The altitude, here 40 m/s, is the velocity attained by the plane when it accelerates at 20 m/s^2 for two seconds. That is, $v = at$. The base is simply t. The area of the triangle is

$$\text{area} = \frac{1}{2} \text{ base} \times \text{height}$$

$$\text{area} = \frac{1}{2}(at)(t) = \frac{1}{2}at^2 = d$$

The velocity-time graph of constant acceleration is a straight line that passes through the origin.

The slope of the curve of a velocity-time graph is the acceleration.

The area under a velocity-time graph is displacement.

SUGGESTION: You may have some students who are enrolled in calculus. This is a good place to mention that taking the slope is equivalent to taking a derivative, and finding the area under a curve is equivalent to integrating.

62   Graphical Analysis of Motion

This is the equation for the displacement of an object undergoing uniform acceleration from rest. Therefore, the area under the curve of a velocity-time graph represents the displacement of the object.

4:6 Position-Time Graph for Uniform Acceleration

Figure 4–7 includes a table of the positions of the jet plane for the first five seconds of its acceleration. The positions could have been determined either by measuring the area under the curve of the velocity-time graph or by using the equation

$$d = \frac{1}{2}at^2$$

The data were then plotted on the position-time graph shown. The curve

SUGGESTION: Make one overhead transparency of a parabola, a second of position-time axes. Moving the parabola left and right, up and down shows motion with various initial positions and velocities, but constant acceleration. The curvature of the parabola represents acceleration.

Position versus Time

Time (s)	Position (m)
0	+ 0
1	+ 10
2	+ 40
3	+ 90
4	+ 160
5	+ 250

FIGURE 4–7. A position-time graph for uniformly accelerated motion.

of the position-time graph is half a parabola. A curve with a parabolic
shape shows that one quantity varies directly with the square of the other.

The slope of a position-time graph is the velocity of the object. As you
have seen, when an object's velocity is constant, its position changes the
same amount each second. Therefore the position-time graph is a straight
line with a constant slope. However, if the object is accelerated, during
each second it travels a greater distance than it did the second before. The
position-time graph for accelerated motion is a parabola, and the slope
does change. Figure 4–8 is an enlargement of the position-time graph for
the jet plane. Suppose you want to find the slope of the curve at point P.

Draw a line tangent to the curve at point P. The slope of the tangent line is
the instantaneous velocity at point P. Point P is at the time 3 seconds. A
tangent line is drawn, and

$$\text{slope} = \frac{\text{rise}}{\text{run}} = \frac{+270 \text{ m} - 0 \text{ m}}{6.0 \text{ s} - 1.5 \text{ s}} = \frac{+270 \text{ m}}{4.5 \text{ s}} = +60 \text{ m/s}$$

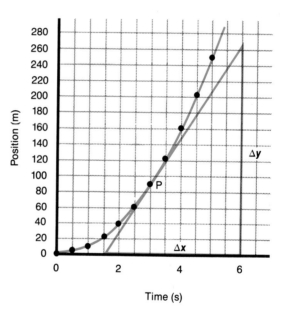

The velocity at the end of 3 seconds for an object that accelerates at
+20 m/s² is +60 m/s, which agrees with the velocity-time graph for the jet
plane.

4:7 Acceleration-Time Graph for Uniform Acceleration

Acceleration that does not change in time is uniform or constant acceleration. If acceleration is constant, an acceleration-time graph is a line
parallel to the t-axis. The acceleration of the jet plane is plotted against
time in Figure 4–9. As expected, the acceleration-time curve is a straight
line parallel to the t-axis.

Note that the area under the curve of the acceleration-time graph is the
change in velocity of the plane from its value at $t = 0$. At any point along

Acceleration versus Time

the *t*-axis, the area under the line is a rectangle with sides *a* and *t*. Therefore the area of the rectangle is *at*. This area is equal to the change in velocity, $v_f - v_i$, which is equal to *at*. In this case the plane started from rest, $v_i = 0$ m/s, so the area represents the final velocity, v_f. For example, at the end of 3 seconds, the area is $(+20 \text{ m/s}^2)(+3 \text{ s}) = 60$ m/s.

PHYSICS FOCUS

Three-Dimensional Computer Graphing

From the time René Descartes developed graphing techniques in the mid-17th century, researchers have used graphs in every physical science. In many experiments scientists can gain more insight by studying the graph of an event than by studying the event itself. The development of more precise measuring tools has led to complex experiments that can yield hundreds of pages of numbers. As numerical data become more abundant, the importance of graphs increases. Physical correlations may be hidden in volumes of numbers but can become obvious when the values are plotted. In such cases the graphs are as important as the original data.

Computer-generated three-dimensional graphing is a technique currently used in all areas of physics. Variables plotted on the X, Y, and Z axes can be manipulated, tabulated, substituted, and analyzed instantaneously. It is now possible to do exploratory data analysis to find physical relationships not identified in the past. Many universities offer courses such as Descriptive Statistical Graphing and Three-Dimensional Graphing Analysis to students of the physical sciences. Computer software companies produce dozens of programs with 2-D and 3-D plotting capabilities. As graphs become even more complex, it becomes increasingly important for all students of the physical sciences to have a knowledge of graphing fundamentals.

SUMMARY

1. Graphs are useful in finding mathematical relationships among quantities. **Introduction**
2. The slope of a position-time graph is the velocity of an object in motion. **4:2**
3. If the position-time graph is parallel to the *t*-axis, the slope is zero. The velocity of the object is zero. **4:3**
4. If the position-time graph is a straight line, the object is moving with constant velocity. **4:3**
5. The velocity-time graph of an object with constant velocity is a line parallel to the *t*-axis. **4:4**
6. The slope of the line on a velocity-time graph is the acceleration of the object. **4:4**
7. The area under the curve of a velocity-time graph is the displacement of the object. **4:4**
8. A velocity-time graph for a uniformly accelerated object is a straight line. **4:5**
9. The slope of a velocity-time graph is the acceleration of the object. **4:5**
10. The area under the curve of a velocity-time graph is the displacement of the object. **4:5**
11. If the position-time graph is half a parabola, the object is undergoing uniform acceleration. Position varies with the square of the time. **4:6**
12. An acceleration-time graph of an object with uniform acceleration is a line parallel to the *t*-axis. The area under the curve is the change in velocity of the object. **4:7**

QUESTIONS

1. What does the slope of a position-time graph indicate?
2. What quantity is represented by the area under a velocity-time curve?

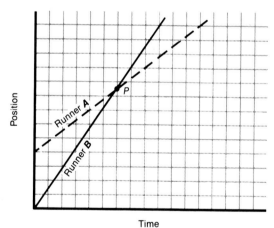

FIGURE 4–11. Use with Question 8.

3. What does the slope of a velocity-time graph indicate?
4. If a velocity-time curve is a straight line parallel to the *t*-axis, what can be deduced about the acceleration?
5. What quantity is represented by the area under an acceleration-time curve?
6. Figure 4–10 shows a velocity-time graph for an

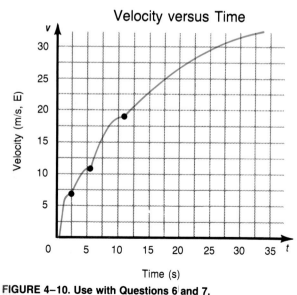

FIGURE 4–10. Use with Questions 6 and 7.

automobile on a test track. Describe the changes in velocity with time.

7. Study Figure 4–10. During what interval is the acceleration largest? During what interval is it smallest?

8. Figure 4–11 is a position-time graph of two people running.
   a. Describe the position of runner A relative to runner B at the y-intercepts.
   b. Which runner is faster?
   c. What occurs at point P and beyond?

APPLYING CONCEPTS

1. A walker and a runner leave your front door at the same time. They move in the same direction at constant velocities. Describe the position-time graphs of each.

2. Two people leave a lamppost at the same time. One walks east, the other west, both at the same speed. Describe the position-time graphs of the two people.

3. An orange falls out of a window 4.9 m above the ground. When it hits the ground, it splatters and stays at rest. Describe and sketch the position-time graph for the orange.

4. Describe and sketch the velocity-time graph for the orange.

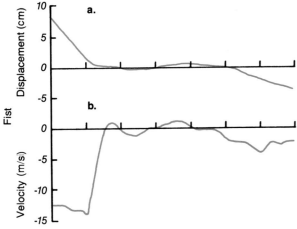

FIGURE 4–12. Use with Applying Concepts 5 and 6 and Exercise 10.

5. Figure 4–12 shows the velocity of a fist versus time during a karate blow. Describe in words the motion of the fist.

6. Estimate the acceleration of the fist when it hits the target by finding the slope of the velocity-time graph in Figure 4–12b.

7. The graph in Figure 4–10 on page 66 shows the velocity-time graph for an accelerating automobile on a test track. The three "notches" in the curve occur where the driver shifts gears. Describe the changes in velocity and acceleration of the car while it is in first gear.

8. Is the acceleration just before a gear change larger or smaller than the acceleration just after the gear change? Explain your answer.

EXERCISES

1. The velocity of an automobile changes over an 8-s time period as shown in Table 4–1.
   a. Plot the velocity-time graph of the motion.
   b. Determine the distance the car travels during the first 2.0 s.
   c. What distance does the car travel during the first 4.0 s?
   d. What distance does the car travel during the entire 8.0 s?
   e. Find the slope of the line between $t = 0$ s and $t = 4.0$ s. What does this slope represent?
   f. Find the slope of the line between $t = 5.0$ s and $t = 7.0$ s. What does this slope indicate?

TABLE 4–1

Time (s)	Velocity (m/s)	Time (s)	Velocity (m/s)
0.0	0.0	5.0	20.0
1.0	4.0	6.0	20.0
2.0	8.0	7.0	20.0
3.0	12.0	8.0	20.0
4.0	16.0		

2. The total distance a steel ball rolls down an incline at the end of each second of travel is given in Table 4–2.
   a. Draw a position-time graph of the motion of the ball. When setting up the axes use five divisions for each 10 m of travel on the d-axis. Use five divisions for each second of time on the t-axis.
   b. What type of curve is the line of the graph?

c. What distance has the ball rolled at the end of 2.2 s?

d. Find the slope of the line at $t = 3.0$ s. What does this slope show?

TABLE 4–2

Time (s)	Distance (m)
0.0	0.0
1.0	2.0
2.0	8.0
3.0	18.0
4.0	32.9
5.0	50.0

3. Use Figure 4–13 to find the acceleration of the moving object

   a. during the first 5 s of travel.

   b. during the second 5 s of travel.

   c. between the tenth and the fifteenth second of travel.

   d. between the twentieth and twenty-fifth second of travel.

4. Refer to Figure 4–13 to find the distance the moving object travels

   a. between $t = 0$ s and $t = 5$ s.

   b. between $t = 5$ s and $t = 10$ s.

   c. between $t = 10$ s and $t = 15$ s.

   d. between $t = 0$ s and $t = 25$ s.

Velocity versus Time

FIGURE 4–13. Use with Exercises 3 and 4.

5. Use the intervals marked on the graph in Figure 4–14 to describe the motion of the object.

FIGURE 4–14. Use with Exercise 5.

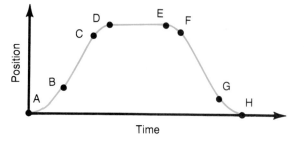

6. Make a table of the velocities of an object at the end of each second for the first 5 s of free-fall from rest.

   a. Use the data in your table to plot a velocity-time graph.

   b. What does the total area under the curve represent?

7. a. Compute the total distance that the object in Exercise 6 has fallen at the end of each second.

   b. Use the distances calculated in part **a** to plot a position-time graph.

   c. Find the slope of the curve at the end of 2 and 4 s. What are the approximate slopes? Do these values agree with the table of speeds in Exercise 6?

8. Use the data prepared in Exercise 7 to plot a position versus time-squared graph.

   a. What type of curve is obtained?

   b. Find the slope of the line at any point. Explain the significance of the value you obtain.

   c. Does this curve agree with the equation $d = 1/2gt^2$?

9. Data in Table 4–3, taken from a drivers' handbook (see Chapter 2), show the distance a car travels when it brakes to a halt from a specific initial velocity.

TABLE 4–3

Initial velocity (m/s)	Braking distance (m)
11	10
15	20
20	34
25	50
29	70

a. Plot the braking distance versus the initial speed. Describe the shape of the curve you obtain.

b. Plot the braking distance versus the square of the initial velocity. Describe the shape of the curve you obtain.

c. Calculate the slope of your graph from part **b.** Find the value and units of the quantity 1/slope of the curve.

d. Does this curve agree with the equation $v_i^2 = -2\ ad$? What is the value of a?

10. Figure 4–12 shows the position-time and velocity-time graphs of a karate expert using a fist to break wooden boards.

a. Use the velocity-time graph to describe the motion of the expert's fist during the first 10 ms.

b. Estimate the slope of the velocity-time graph to determine the acceleration of the fist when it suddenly stops.

c. Express the acceleration as a multiple of the gravitational acceleration, **g.**

d. Determine the area under the velocity-time curve to find the distance the fist moves in the first 6 ms. Compare with the position-time graph.

11. Look at Figure 4–15.

a. What kind of motion does this graph represent?

b. What does the slope of the line represent?

FIGURE 4–15.

12. Look at Figure 4–16.

a. What kind of motion does this graph represent?

b. What does the area under the curve of the graph represent?

FIGURE 4–16.

13. Look at Figure 4–17.

a. What kind of motion does this graph represent?

b. What does the slope of the line represent?

c. What does the area under the curve represent?

FIGURE 4–17.

14. Look at Figure 4–18. What does the area under the curve of this graph represent?

FIGURE 4–18.

FIGURE 4–19.

Time

15. Look at Figure 4–19, which is a position-time graph of uniform acceleration.
    a. What type of curve does this graph represent?
    b. What does the slope of the line taken at any point represent?
    c. How would slopes taken at higher points on the line differ from those taken at lower points?

PROBLEMS

1. To accompany each of the graphs in Figure 4–20, draw
    a. a velocity-time graph.
    b. an acceleration-time graph.
2. a. Draw velocity-time and position-time graphs for the car and truck in Review Exercise 19, page 54, Chapter 3.
    b. Do the graphs confirm the answer you calculated for the exercise?
3. An express train, traveling at 36.0 m/s, is accidentally sidetracked onto a local train track. The express engineer spots a local train exactly 1.00×10^2 m ahead on the same track and traveling in the same direction. The engineer jams on the brakes and slows the express at a rate of 3.00 m/s^2. The local engineer is unaware of the situation. If the speed of the local is 11.0 m/s, will the express be able to stop in time or will there be a collision? To solve this problem, take the position of the express when it first sights the local as a point of origin. Next, keeping in mind that the local has exactly a 1.00×10^2 m lead, calculate how far each train is from this point at the end of the 12.0 s it would take the express to stop.
    a. On the basis of your calculations, would you conclude that there is or is not a collision?
    b. The calculations you made in part **a** do not allow for the possibility that a collision might take place before the end of the twelve seconds required for the express to come to a

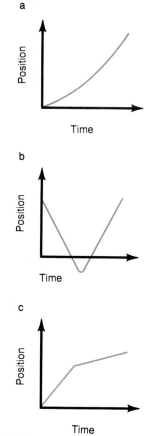

FIGURE 4–20.

halt. To check on this, take the position of the express when it first sights the local as the point of origin and calculate the position of each train at the end of each second after sighting. The local will always be $100 + 11t$ meters from the origin while the express will be

$$v_i t + \tfrac{1}{2}at^2 \text{ meters from the origin}$$

Make a table showing the distance of each train from the origin at the end of each second. Plot these positions on the same graph and draw two lines.

    c. Use your graph to answer part **a**.
4. The velocity-time graph of Figure 4–10 can be used to find both the acceleration and the displacement of the car.
    a. Carefully read the graph and calculate the acceleration of the car at several different

times. Choose three times in the first 10 seconds, and three more in the next 20 seconds. Note the small level places on the graph where the driver shifted gears. Now make an acceleration-time graph. At what times is the acceleration largest and smallest? Do your answers agree with those of Question 7, page 67?

b. Sketch the position-time graph of Figure 4–10.

5. During a football game, the quarterback rolls out to his right with two huge linebackers in close pursuit. An instant before the linebackers bury him at the 50-yard (46-m) line, he releases a towering pass down the sideline. The ball sails toward the end zone with a horizontal velocity of +11.4 m/s. At the instant the pass is released by the quarterback, the offensive receiver is crossing the 40-yard (36-m) line, along the sideline at a velocity of +8.8 m/s. The defensive safety is 2.0 m behind the offensive receiver and moving down the sideline at a velocity of +9.5 m/s. The pass reaches a maximum height of 21.6 m and is caught in the endzone. Determine if the football is caught for a touchdown or an interception, as follows. (Assume no air resistance.)

   a. Generate a table showing the positions, from the point of release of the football, of the foot-

ball, the offensive receiver, and the defensive safety from the time the football was released, $t = 0$, until it was caught, in 0.2-s intervals.

   b. Plot the positions on the same position-time graph and draw three lines.

   c. Identify and describe what is happening at the three points of intersection among the three lines.

   d. Determine if the football is caught for a touchdown or an interception.

READINGS

Bartusiak, Marcia, "Mapping the Sea Floor from Space." *Popular Science*, February, 1984.

Gardner, Martin, "The Computer As Scientist." *Discover*, June, 1983.

"Newton Vindicated—Einstein Too! [experiment upholds Newton's second law of motion]." *Sky and Telescope*, May, 1987.

"3-D Graphing." *Byte*, January, 1989.

Silk, Joseph, "The Large-Scale Structure of the Universe." *Scientific American*, October, 1983.

CHAPTER 5

Forces

GOALS

1. You will gain an understanding of the relationship between forces and changes in motion.
2. You will be able to use Newton's laws of motion to determine the behavior of bodies that have forces acting on them.
3. You will understand the difference between weight and mass.

For Your Information

Newton's laws of motion, his concepts of the motion of fluids, and his theory that gravity is proportional to mass are contained in his *Principia*, published in 1687. This work became the basis of the scientific method and the foundation of physics for the next 200 years.

SUGGESTION: Discuss the meaning of the word *force* in physics. Compare this with everyday uses of the word. Emphasize that the term as used in physics has a very specific meaning.

Imagine that you are at a baseball game where you can see the pitcher but not the batter. You see the pitched ball first moving toward home plate until it disappears from view, and then reappears moving in the opposite direction. Obviously the ball has interacted with something. You know intuitively that the velocity of an object does not change unless it interacts with something that exerts a force on it.

The exact connection between force and change in velocity was first stated by Isaac Newton (1642–1727). He started work on his laws of motion in 1665, but did not publish them until 1687. Even though we now know that Newton's laws of motion must be modified at velocities near the speed of light and for objects the size of atoms, his three laws still summarize the relationship between forces and the motion of a body.

5:1 Forces

What is a force? You might define **force** as a push or a pull. For example, the pull of gravity accelerates an apple falling from a tree toward Earth. Then, when the apple hits the ground, it rapidly comes to a halt. Forces sometimes cause accelerations; at other times they stretch, bend, or squeeze an object. The study of forces and the motion that results is called **dynamics.** Although you might list hundreds of different forces, physicists have been able to group them all into just four kinds.

The first force that Newton described, the **gravitational force,** is an attractive force that exists between all objects. The gravitational force between Earth and the sun holds Earth in its orbit. The gravitational force of the moon on Earth causes tides. Despite its effects on our daily lives, the gravitational force is the weakest of the four forces.

Going Down

As Galileo demonstrated, at a given location, all objects are uniformly accelerated by gravity. These skydivers will achieve a terminal velocity of 250 km/hr. What is their final acceleration? Why do skydivers reach a terminal velocity as they fall toward Earth?

Forces that give materials their strength, their ability to bend, squeeze, stretch, or shatter, are examples of the **electromagnetic force.** Charged particles at rest exert electric forces on each other. Charged particles in motion produce magnetic forces. Electric and magnetic forces are related to each other and are both aspects of a single force, the electromagnetic force. It is very large compared to gravitational forces. We will discuss this force in detail later in this book.

The two remaining forces are less familiar because they act mainly within the nucleus of an atom. The strongest is the **strong nuclear force** that holds the particles in the nucleus together. It is hundreds of times stronger than electromagnetic forces, but it only acts over distances the size of the nucleus. The fourth force is called the **weak force.** It is actually a form of electromagnetic force, and is involved in the radioactive decay of some nuclei.

Many physicists believe that the unification of electricity and magnetism into a single force, as well as the recent unification of the electromagnetic force with the weak force, suggests that there is really only one force. They have constructed theories called Grand Unified Theories (GUTs) and Supersymmetric theories that seek to demonstrate this unification. At this time, however, the theories are incomplete and do not fully agree with experiments.

5:2 Newton's First Law of Motion

Suppose you place a wooden block on a carpeted floor and give it a push. The block will stop almost as soon as you remove your hand. If the floor has a smooth surface instead of carpet, the block may slide farther. If you have an extremely smooth block and an oiled floor, the block might slide at almost constant speed for a long distance without any additional pushes. A steel ball rolling on a hard floor might roll at constant speed until it strikes a wall.

FIGURE 5–1. Galileo studied acceleration due to gravity by rolling metal balls down smooth ramps and timing them with a water clock.

Galileo was the first to see that no more force was needed to keep a body in motion at constant velocity than to let it remain at rest. Newton's first law of motion really restates some of Galileo's ideas.

According to Galileo and Newton, only an unbalanced or net force acting on an object will change its motion. Consider an object that has no net force on it. If it is at rest, it will remain at rest. If it is moving at constant speed in a straight line, it will continue to do so. The tendency of an object to remain in the same state of motion is called **inertia.** For this reason, **Newton's first law** is often called the law of inertia. It states that *a net or unbalanced force is needed to change the state of motion of an object.*

Figure 5–3 pictures a simple experiment that demonstrates Newton's first law. Lay an index card over a drinking glass. Place a penny on the card, centered over the glass. With the flick of a finger, give the card a quick horizontal push. The card moves away, but the penny drops into the glass. Why does the penny not accelerate with the card? The smooth card does not exert much horizontal force on the penny. With little horizontal force on it, the penny does not move sideways very fast. With the card no longer under it, however, there is a net downward force, so the penny accelerates downward, falling into the glass.

According to Newton's first law, there is no real difference between an object at rest and one moving with constant velocity. Consider the two sailboats in Figure 5–4. One sailboat is at rest; the other is moving in a straight line at a constant speed of +10 km/h. The boat at rest has two forces acting on it. The weight of the boat pulls it downward. The force of the water pushes it upward. The two forces have equal magnitudes but opposite directions. Thus they are balanced—their sum is zero, and the boat remains at rest.

FIGURE 5–2. On a perfectly smooth floor, a ball will regain the height from which it was rolled. With no incline, it will continue in motion in a straight line at a constant speed.

Newton's first law is sometimes called the law of inertia.

For Your Information

Newton's first law defines the type of frame of reference, sometimes called an inertial frame of reference, in which his laws of motion operate.

FIGURE 5–3. A quick snap of a finger can knock the card from under a coin, allowing the coin to drop into the glass.

a

b

c

FIGURE 5–4. When forces are balanced, there is no acceleration.

Water — Velocity = 0 km/h — Weight

Water — Water — Wind — Velocity = 10 km/h, E — Weight

The sailboat moving with constant velocity has four forces acting on it. The two opposite vertical forces are equal in size. In the horizontal direction, the force of the wind on the sails pushes the boat forward, while the water exerts a force on the boat's hull that opposes the force of the wind. These two forces also are equal in size but opposite in direction, and so their sum is also zero. Thus there is no net force on the boat and it continues to move with constant velocity.

Suppose the wind should suddenly stop. The only remaining horizontal force would be that of the water on the hull, pushing it backward. With an unbalanced force acting on the boat, the velocity would change, causing the boat to slow down.

5:3 Newton's Second Law of Motion

We know that a net force causes acceleration, but how are force and acceleration related? Consider pushing a bowling ball. The harder you push, the faster the ball will reach a given speed. Thus the larger the force, the larger the acceleration. Acceleration is directly proportional to force.

Acceleration also depends on mass. The same force on a basketball would accelerate it much more than the bowling ball. Newton found that acceleration was inversely proportional to mass. These relationships are true in general and are stated in **Newton's second law:** *the acceleration of a body is directly proportional to the net force on it and inversely proportional to its mass.* As the net force acting on an object increases, so does its acceleration. However, if the object's mass increases, the acceleration decreases. Newton's second law may be summarized in an equation

$$a = \frac{F}{m}$$

or more commonly,

$$\boxed{F = ma}$$

Force and acceleration both have direction as well as size. The acceleration is in the same direction as the force causing it.

5:4 The Unit of Force

Newton's second law defines the unit of force. A force of magnitude one newton (N) causes a mass of one kilogram to accelerate at a rate of one meter per second squared. That is

$$F = ma = (1.00 \text{ kg})(1.00 \text{ m/s}^2) = 1.00 \text{ N}$$

SUGGESTION: Emphasize that the force in *F* = *ma* is the unbalanced force or net force. It might be good to write the word "net" before the *F* when using the equation as a reminder.

Newton's second law says that an unbalanced force causes a change in motion.

The most familiar form of Newton's second law is *F* = *ma*.

A force of one newton will accelerate a one-kilogram mass at a rate of one meter per second per second.

EXAMPLE

Using Newton's Second Law to Find Force

What unbalanced force is required to accelerate a 1500 kg race car at $+3.00$ m/s^2?

Given: mass   Unknown: force, F
     $m = 1500$ kg   Basic equation: $F = ma$
     acceleration
     $a = +3.00$ m/s^2

Solution: $F = ma$
$$= (1500 \text{ kg})(+3.00 \text{ m/s}^2)$$
$$= +4500 \text{ N (in the direction of acceleration)}$$

SUGGESTION: Emphasize that the student will need to substitute kg·m/s^2 in equations where they want to check units.

FIGURE 5–5. By reducing the mass of a race car, designers are able to increase the acceleration possible without increasing force.

EXAMPLE

Finding Force When Acceleration Must Be Calculated

An artillery shell has a mass of 55 kg. The shell is fired from the muzzle of a gun with a velocity of $+770$ m/s. The gun barrel is 1.5 m long. What is the average force on the shell while it is in the gun barrel?

Given: mass   Unknown: average force (F)
     $m = 55$ kg   Basic equation: $F = ma$
     final velocity
     $v_f = +770$ m/s
     distance accelerated
     $d = +1.5$ m

Solution: You cannot use $F = ma$ directly because you do not know a. However, given the final velocity and distance, and knowing the initial velocity is zero, first find a using $v_f^2 = v_i^2 + 2ad$.

$$v_f^2 = v_i^2 + 2ad \text{ or } a = \frac{v_f^2 - v_i^2}{2d} = +2.0 \times 10^5 \text{ m/s}^2$$

$F = ma = (55 \text{ kg})(+2.0 \times 10^5 \text{ m/s}^2) = +1.1 \times 10^7 \text{ N}$. Does the large size of the force surprise you?

The direction is in the direction of the larger velocity, the positive direction.

Practice Exercises

1. Together a motorbike and rider have a mass of 275 kg. The rider slows the motorbike at -4.50 m/s^2. What is the net force on the motorbike? What does the negative sign signify?

2. When a shot-putter exerts a net force of $+140$ N on a shot, the shot has an acceleration of $+19$ m/s^2. What is the mass of the shot?

3. A 7.3-kg bowling ball sliding down a smooth ramp has a net force of $+19$ N exerted on it. What is its acceleration?

4. Imagine a spider with mass 7.0×10^{-5} kg moving downward on its thread. The net force on the spider is $+1.2 \times 10^{-4}$ N. What is the acceleration of the spider? Explain the sign.

5:5 Newton's Third Law of Motion

If you try to accelerate a bowling ball by kicking it, you will feel the force of the ball on your foot. If you exert a force on a baseball to stop it, the ball also exerts a force on you. These are examples of the forces described in **Newton's third law:** *for every force on an object there will always be an equal and opposite force exerted by that object.*

Forces always come in pairs. When one object exerts a force on a second object, the second object exerts an equal and opposite force on the first. According to Newton's third law, there is no situation in which one force acts on a single object. Every interaction involves at least two objects and two equal but opposite forces.

These equal and opposite forces are often called **action-reaction forces** or pairs. However, this does *not* imply that the action force was created first and caused the reaction force. In all cases, the two forces came into being at exactly the same time. Either force could be considered the action force and the other the reaction force.

Let us analyze the forces involved when you pick up a bowling ball, as in Figure 5–6. When your hand exerts a force on the ball, the ball exerts an equal but opposite force on your hand. These two forces make up one pair of action-reaction forces. A second pair is made up of the gravitational force Earth exerts on the ball, and the equal but opposite force the ball exerts on Earth. As you examine the diagram, note that in each pair there are two equal but opposite forces acting on *two different* objects, your hand and the ball.

SUGGESTION: Have students identify force pairs acting in situations like pushing, walking, driving a car, and so forth.

Forces always come in pairs, between pairs of objects.

Newton's third law states that an action force has an equal but opposite reaction force.

The action and reaction forces act on different bodies.

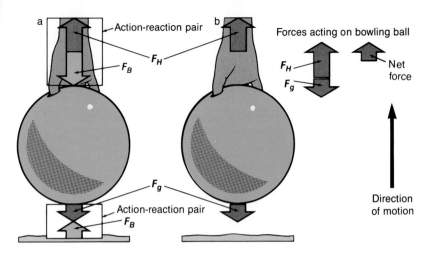

a

Action-reaction pair

F_H

F_B

b

Forces acting on bowling ball

F_H

F_g

Net force

F_g

Action-reaction pair

F_B

Direction of motion

FIGURE 5–6. Each pair of action-reaction forces is equal (a). However, there is a net upward force on the bowling ball, causing it to accelerate upward (b).

In our bowling ball example, it appears there are no unbalanced forces, so why does the ball accelerate upward? To understand why, we need to isolate the bowling ball and examine only the forces acting on it. There are only the force of your hand directed upward and the force of gravity pulling downward. When you lift the ball, the force exerted by your hand is greater than the force of gravity, so the ball accelerates upward.

Note that action-reaction force pairs are always equal in magnitude and act on different objects. Forces that cause acceleration described by Newton's second law always act on the same object and are not necessarily equal.

SUGGESTION: Emphasize that the action and reaction forces act on different bodies, but that accelerating or net forces act on the same body.

5:6 Mass and Weight

Walking home from school, you come to a box on the ground and give it a good kick. If the box goes sailing, you know it has a small inertia; it has a small mass. If the box hardly accelerates at all, it must have a large inertia and a large mass. This is an example of the definition of mass as the measure of the inertia of an object. One way to measure the inertial mass of an object is by exerting a known force on it and measuring its acceleration.

Suppose you pick up the box and then let it drop. It will accelerate downward. Thus Earth must be exerting a downward force on the box. The gravitational force exerted by a large body, usually Earth, is called **weight.** Weight is measured in newtons like all other forces. A medium sized apple weighs about one newton.

You can weigh an object with a spring scale. When a force is exerted on a spring, it stretches. The amount of stretch is proportional to the force. When an object is attached to a spring scale, the scale exerts an upward force on the object while Earth exerts a downward force. When the two forces are balanced, the scale measures the force needed to balance the weight of the object.

The weight of an object can be found using Newton's second law of motion. On the surface of Earth, all objects falling freely accelerate at an acceleration, **g**, of 9.80 m/s² down. The force accelerating them is $F = mg$. Therefore the force exerted on a 1.00 kg mass is 9.80 N down.

SUGGESTION: Hang kilogram masses on a spring scale calibrated in newtons.

Mass is sometimes defined as the quantity of matter in an object.

Weight is the gravitational force of an object.

FIGURE 5–7. The weight of a medium apple is about one newton.

SUGGESTION: Note that we are using only magnitudes when discussing the force of gravity and the acceleration due to it.

SUGGESTION: Be very careful to use the terms *mass* and *weight* accurately. Continue to remind students of the difference. You might even want to give students a bonus point if they catch someone, including you, misusing either term.

To determine the weight of an object, Newton's second law may be written in the form

$$W = mg$$

The weight of any object is proportional to its mass. It is a vector quantity pointed toward the center of Earth. Rather than indicate direction by using a negative sign, we will use the word "down" when direction is needed.

EXAMPLE

Calculating Weight

Find the weight of a 5.00-kilogram mass.

$$W = mg = (5.00 \text{ kg})(9.80 \text{ m/s}^2)$$
$$= 49.0 \text{ kg} \cdot \text{m/s}^2$$
$$= 49.0 \text{ N}$$

It is very important that you understand the fundamental difference between mass and weight. Weight depends on the acceleration due to gravity, and thus may vary from location to location. A person weighs less on the top of a high mountain, even though he or she has the same mass. A bowling ball with a mass of 7.3 kg weighs 71 N on Earth, but only 12 N on the moon, where the acceleration due to gravity is 1.6 m/s². However, if you tried to kick a bowling ball across the surface of the moon, it would be just as hard to accelerate as on Earth because its mass would be the same.

Practice Exercises

All measurements for exercises 5 and 6 are at sea level; $g = 9.80$ m/s².

5. What is the weight of each of the following objects?
   a. 2.00 kg bag of sugar
   b. 108 kg football player
   c. 870 kg automobile
6. Find the mass of each of these weights.
   a. 98 N
   b. 80 N
   c. 0.98 N
7. How much force must a scale exert to balance a 20 N stone? In what direction?
8. An astronaut with mass 75 kg travels first to Mars, then into interplanetary space. What is his weight
   a. on Earth?
   b. on Mars where $g = 3.8$ m/s²?
   c. in interplanetary space?

5:7 Two Kinds of Mass

We discussed one way of determining mass by using the property of inertia. The **inertial mass** of an object is the ratio of the unbalanced force exerted on it and its acceleration,

$$m = \frac{F}{a}$$

A second method compares the gravitational force exerted on an unknown mass to the gravitational force exerted on a known mass. The unknown mass is placed on a pan at the end of a beam balance, or lever. Known masses are placed on a pan at the other end of the beam. When the pans balance, the force of gravity is the same on each pan. Then the masses on either side of the balance must be the same. The mass measured this way is called the **gravitational mass,** m_g.

In Section 5:6 you calculated the gravitational force, W, exerted on a mass using $W = m_g g$, where m_g is the gravitational mass. If this force, W, is the only force on the object, then $W = F$, and the object will accelerate according to Newton's second law, $F = m_i a$, where m_i is the inertial mass. Since $W = F$, $m_g g = m_i a$. All objects fall with acceleration g as long as gravitational and inertial masses are equal.

In 1916 Albert Einstein (1879–1955) used the equivalence of inertial and gravitational masses as one foundation for his general theory of relativity. Recently, however, several experiments have seemed to find small differences between the gravitational and inertial masses. Their results suggest that materials with high density, such as lead, fall more slowly than materials with low density, like aluminum. The investigators suggest that there is a "fifth force" exerted by Earth that slightly repels objects with high density. Experiments done by other physicists have produced different results, and at this time, no one knows for sure whether the fifth force actually exists.

For Your Information

When Ernest Rutherford, a Nobel Prize recipient for his research on radioactivity, was asked what he thought of Einstein's theory of relativity, he replied, "Oh, that stuff. We never bother with that in our work."

–Stephen Leacock
Common Sense and the Universe

SUGGESTION: Inertial mass can also be measured by finding the period of oscillation of a mass hanging on a spring, Figure 5–8.

SUGGESTION: Point out that a spring scale measures weight.

SUGGESTION: Mention to students that Baron Eotvos of Hungary was the first to show experimentally that the two masses are equal to high precision.

FIGURE 5–8. A beam balance (a) allows you to compare an unknown mass to a known mass. Using an inertial balance (b), you can calculate the mass from the back and forth motion of the mass.

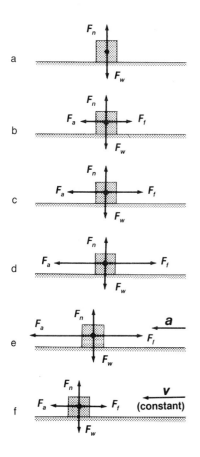

5:8 Friction

Slide your hand across a tabletop. The force you feel opposing the motion of your hand is called friction. It acts when brakes slow a bike or car, when a sailboat moves through water, and when a sky diver falls through the air. If there were no friction, whenever you tried to walk, you would slide as if you were on ice. Without friction, tires would spin and cars would not move. An eraser could not grip your homework paper and remove a mistake.

Friction is the force that opposes the motion of two surfaces that are in contact. The direction of the force is parallel to the surface and in a direction that opposes motion. To understand the cause of friction, you must recognize that on a microscopic scale, all surfaces are rough. When two surfaces rub, the high points of one surface temporarily bond to the high points of the other. The electromagnetic force causes this bonding force.

If you try to push a heavy box along the floor, you will find it very hard to start it moving, Figure 5–9. The force that opposes the start of motion between two surfaces that are not already in relative motion is **static friction.** However, once the box starts moving, the force of friction decreases. Because the surfaces are already in relative motion, this smaller force is called **sliding friction.** The force of sliding friction is less than that of static friction. Thus a car will stop faster when the wheels do not skid.

How large is the force of sliding friction? Slide your book across the desk. It slows down. To keep it moving at constant velocity, you must apply a constant force that is the same size as the frictional force, but in the opposite direction. See Figure 5–10. By measuring the applied force, F_A, you can determine the force of friction, F_f. Experimentally it has been found that the force of friction depends only on the nature of the surfaces in contact and the force pushing the surfaces together. This result can be expressed by an equation for the magnitude

$$F_f = \mu F_N$$

In this equation μ (mu), called the **coefficient of friction,** is a value describing the nature of the surfaces in contact. F_N, called the normal force, is the force exerted by the table on the book. It is the force pushing the surfaces together. The normal force (F_N) always acts perpendicular to the surfaces in contact. When the book is resting on a horizontal surface, the normal force is numerically equal to the weight of the book (W), the force of the book on the table. If you use your hands to push down on the

FIGURE 5–9. A greater and greater horizontal force, F_a is applied to a box (a–d). An equal force of static friction acts in the opposite direction to keep the box from moving. When F_a exceeds the force of static friction, the box accelerates (e). The box will move at a constant velocity if F_a is then reduced until it equals the force of sliding friction (f).

Friction acts in a direction parallel to the surfaces in contact and opposes the motion.

The coefficient of friction is the ratio of the force of friction, F_f, and the force of pressing the surfaces together, F_N.

FIGURE 5–10. Four forces are shown acting on a box moving to the right with a constant horizontal velocity.

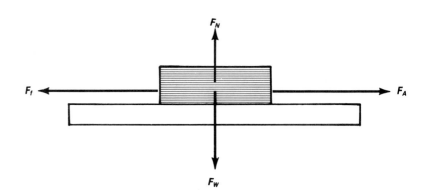

book, the force of the book on the table increases, and the normal force of the table upward on the book also increases.

In most cases, the coefficient of sliding friction for two surfaces in contact is independent of the amount of surface area in contact and the velocity of motion.

Friction does not depend on the areas of the surfaces in contact.

PROBLEM SOLVING

When solving problems involving more than one force on an object, always start by sketching a neat drawing of the object. Then draw arrows representing all the forces acting on the object. Label each force with the cause of the force. Be specific. Examples are "weight," "force of string," "normal force exerted by table," "force of friction." Remember that *ma* is not a force, but the mass times the acceleration.

Static friction is always larger than sliding friction.

EXAMPLE

Sliding Friction

A smooth wooden block is placed on a smooth wooden tabletop, as shown in Figure 5–11. A force of 14.0 N is necessary to keep the 40.0 N block moving at a constant velocity. **a.** What is the coefficient of sliding friction for the block and table? **b.** If a 20.0 N weight is placed on the block, what force will be required to keep the block and weight moving at constant velocity?

SUGGESTION: We will not be calculating static friction.

Given: $F_A = 14.0$ N
　　　　$W = 40.0$ N
　　　　$W' = 20.0$ N

Unknowns: **a.** coefficient of sliding friction (μ)
　　　　　b. force of friction (F_f)

Basic equations: $F_A = F_f$
　　　　　　　　$F_f = \mu F_N$
　　　　　　　　$F_N = W$
　　　　　　　　$F_N = W + W'$

SUGGESTION: The normal force is the sum of all the forces acting perpendicular to the two surfaces. It is equal to the weight when the object is moving horizontally and there are no other forces acting on it that have a component perpendicular to the two surfaces.

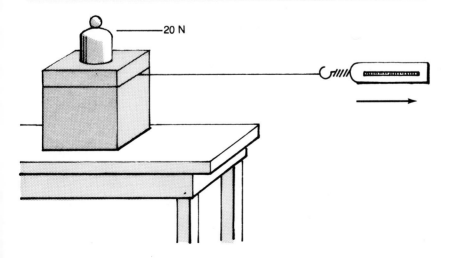
20 N

FIGURE 5–11. Use with the Example.

Solution:

a. $\mu = \dfrac{F_f}{F_N} = \dfrac{F_A}{W}$

$\dfrac{F_A}{W} = \dfrac{14.0\ \text{N}}{40.0\ \text{N}}$

$= 0.350$

b. $F_f = \mu F_N$

$= \mu(W + W')$

$= (0.350)(40.0\ \text{N} + 20.0\ \text{N})$

$= 21.0\ \text{N}$

Note that μ depends only on the surfaces in contact, and so is the same for the two parts of the Example.

Practice Exercises

9. A 52-N sled is pulled across a cement sidewalk at constant speed. A horizontal force of 36 N is exerted. What is the coefficient of sliding friction between the sidewalk and the metal runners of the sled?

10. Suppose the sled in Exercise 9 is on packed snow. The coefficient of friction is now only 0.12. If a person weighing 650 N sits on the sled, what force is needed to slide the sled across the snow at constant speed?

11. The coefficient of sliding friction between rubber tires and wet pavement is 0.50. The brakes are applied to a 750-kg car traveling 30 m/s, and the car skids to a stop.
    a. What is the size and direction of the force of friction that the road exerts on the car?
    b. What would be the size and direction of the acceleration of the car?
    c. How far would the car travel before stopping?

12. If the car's tires did not skid, the coefficient of friction would have been 0.70. Would the force of friction have been larger, smaller, or the same? Would the car have come to a stop in a shorter, the same, or a longer distance?

FIGURE 5–12. By reducing frictional forces, the hydrofoil boat can maintain higher speeds than an ordinary boat.

5:9 Acceleration When Two Forces Act on an Object

In Newton's second law of motion, $F = ma$, the force, F, that causes the mass to accelerate is the net force acting on the mass. In Figure 5–13a, a 10 kg mass rests on a frictionless, horizontal surface. A +100 N force is exerted horizontally on the mass. The resulting acceleration is

$$a = \frac{F}{m} = \frac{+100 \text{ N}}{10 \text{ kg}} = +10 \text{ m/s}^2$$

SUGGESTION: Relate net force to net income to help students understand the meaning of *net*.

An unbalanced force causes a mass to accelerate.

a

a = 10 m/s²

100 N

μ = 0.0

b

a = 8.0 m/s²

μ = 0.20

F_f

FIGURE 5–13. When acted upon by a 100-N force, the acceleration of a 10-kg mass on a frictionless surface (a) is greater than the acceleration of a 10-kg mass on a rough surface (b).

If the same mass rests on a rough surface, friction will oppose the motion. In Figure 5–13b, the frictional force is −20 N. The negative sign indicates that the force acts in a direction opposite the applied force, which is positive. Any mass's acceleration will be the result of the net force acting on it. The net force is the vector sum of the applied force and frictional force. In one dimension you take the vector sum by adding the forces, paying attention to the signs. That is,

$$\begin{aligned} F_{net} &= F_{applied} + F_f \\ &= +100 \text{ N} + (-20 \text{ N}) \\ &= +80 \text{ N} \end{aligned}$$

and the resulting acceleration is given by

$$a = \frac{F_{net}}{m} = \frac{+80 \text{ N}}{10 \text{ kg}} = +8.0 \text{ m/s}^2$$

The direction of the acceleration is positive, in the direction of the applied force.

Other forces besides friction act on objects. Consider a 10.0-kg stone lying on the ground. The stone is at rest; the net force on it is zero. The weight of the stone, W, is 98.0 N in a downward direction. The ground exerts an equal and opposite force, 98.0 N, upward. The net force is

$$\begin{aligned} F_{net} &= F_{ground} + W \\ &= 98.0 \text{ N} + (-98.0 \text{ N}) \\ &= 0 \text{ N} \end{aligned}$$

The force of friction is in the direction opposite to the motion of the body.

The net force is the vector sum of all forces acting on a body.

The weight of an object is one of the forces acting on an object.

$F = 148$ N

10 kg

$W = 98$ N

FIGURE 5–14. A mass is accelerated upward if the total force exerted upward is greater than the weight.

How can the stone be given an upward acceleration? Suppose a person exerts a 148 N upward force on the stone. The net force is

$$F_{net} = F_{person} + W$$
$$= +148.0 \text{ N} + (-98.0 \text{ N})$$
$$= +50.0 \text{ N}$$

The net force acting on the stone is 50 N upward. The acceleration of the stone can be found from Newton's second law:

$$a = F/m = (+50 \text{ N})/(10 \text{ kg}) = +5 \text{ m/s}^2$$

The stone will be accelerated upward at +5 m/s².

EXAMPLE

Forces on an Accelerating Object

A spring scale hangs from the ceiling of an elevator. It supports a package that weighs 25 N. **a.** What upward force does the scale exert when the elevator is not moving? **b.** What force does the scale exert when the elevator accelerates upward at +1.5 m/s²? Use Figure 5–15.

Given: weight of package
$W = 25$ N
acceleration
a. $a = 0$ m/s²
b. $a = +1.5$ m/s²

Unknown: upward force, F_{scale}

Basic equations: $F_{net} = ma$
$F_{net} = F_{scale} + W$
$W = mg$

Solution: **a.** Because $a = 0$, $F_{net} = 0$, so
$$F_{scale} = -W$$
$$= -(-25 \text{ N}) = 25 \text{ N (up)}$$
Weight is 25 N down, so the scale supplied 25 N up.
b. Now $a = +1.5$ m/s². Therefore $F_{net} = m(+1.5 \text{ m/s}^2)$
$W = mg$, so $m = W/g = (25 \text{ N})/(9.80 \text{ m/s}^2) = 2.6$ kg
Thus $F_{net} = (2.6 \text{ kg})(+1.5 \text{ m/s}^2) = +3.9 \text{ N (up)}$
$F_{net} = F_{scale} + W$ so
$$F_{scale} = F_{net} - W$$
$$= +3.9 \text{ N} - (-25 \text{ N}) = +29 \text{ N (up)}$$
That is, the scale indicates a larger weight when the elevator accelerates upward.

FIGURE 5–15. Use with the Example.

a Elevator   b Elevator

25 N

$a = 0$ m/s² $a = +1.5$ m/s²

Practice Exercises

13. A rubber ball weighs 49 N.
    a. What is the mass of the ball?
    b. What is the acceleration of the ball if an upward force of 69 N is applied?
14. A small weather rocket weighs 14.7 N.
    a. What is its mass?

b. The rocket is carried up by a balloon. The rocket is released from the balloon and fired, but its engine exerts an upward force of 10.2 N. What is the acceleration of the rocket?

15. The space shuttle has a mass of 2×10^6 kg. At lift-off the engines generate an upward force of 30×10^6 N.

    a. What is the weight of the shuttle?

    b. What is the acceleration of the shuttle when launched?

    c. The average acceleration of the shuttle during its 10 minute launch is 13 m/s². What velocity does it attain?

    d. As the space shuttle engines burn, the mass of the fuel becomes less and less. Assuming the force exerted by the engines remains the same, would you expect the acceleration to increase, decrease, or remain the same? Why?

16. A certain sports car accelerates from 0 to 60 mph in 9.0 s (average acceleration = 3.0 m/s²). The mass of the car is 1354 kg. The average frictional force during acceleration is 280 N. Find the force required to give the car this acceleration.

5:10 The Fall of Bodies in the Air

Astronauts on the surface of the moon dropped a hammer and a feather together. These objects hit the surface at the same time. Without any air, all objects fall with the same acceleration. On Earth the acceleration is 9.80 m/s².

In air, however, an additional force acts on moving bodies. Air resistance, sometimes called the drag force, is a frictionlike force. As an object moves through the air, it collides with air molecules that exert a force on it. The force depends on the size and shape of the object, the density of the air, and the speed of motion. Suppose you drop a ping-pong ball. Just

An object in freefall (in a vacuum) has only the force of gravity acting on it. Its acceleration is equal to **g**.

The force of air molecules striking a moving object is called air resistance.

SUGGESTION: The film loop showing an astronaut dropping a hammer and feather on the moon and on Earth could be shown here.

FIGURE 5–16. In a vacuum, a coin and feather fall with the same acceleration.

after you drop it, it has very little velocity, and thus very small drag force. The downward force of gravity is larger than the upward drag force and the ball accelerates downward. As its velocity increases, so does the drag force. At some later time the drag force equals the force of gravity. The net force is zero, and the velocity of the ball becomes constant. This constant velocity is called the **terminal velocity.**

The terminal velocity of a ping-pong ball in air is only 9 m/s. A basketball has a terminal velocity of 20 m/s, while a baseball can fall as fast as 42 m/s. Skiers increase their terminal velocities by decreasing drag force. They hold their bodies in an "egg" shape and wear very smooth clothing and streamlined helmets. A sky diver can control terminal velocity by changing body shape. A spread-eagle position gives the slowest speed, about 60 m/s. After the parachute opens, the terminal velocity is about 5 m/s.

CHAPTER 5 REVIEW

SUMMARY

1. Dynamics is the study of forces and the changes in motion they cause. **5:1**

2. The four basic forces are the gravitational, electromagnetic, and strong and weak nuclear forces. **5:1**

3. Newton's first law states that an object with no net (unbalanced) force acting on it will either continue at rest or in a state of constant speed in a straight line. **5:2**

4. The tendency of an object to remain in the same state of motion is called inertia. **5:2**

5. Newton's second law states that when a net (unbalanced) force acts on an object, the resulting acceleration varies directly with the force and inversely with the mass of the object. **5:3**

6. One newton (N) is the force necessary to accelerate a 1-kg mass at a rate of 1 m/s². **5:4**

7. Newton's third law states that forces always exist in pairs. When one object exerts a force on a

second object, the second exerts an equal and opposite force on the first. **5:5**

8. Mass is a measure of the inertia of a body. Weight is a measure of the gravitational force on a body. **5:6**

9. Gravitational mass and inertial mass are two essentially different concepts. The gravitational and inertial masses of a body, however, are numerically equal. **5:7**

10. Friction is the force that opposes the relative motion of two objects in contact. **5:8**

11. The magnitude of the sliding friction force is equal to the product of the coefficient of friction and the normal force. **5:8**

12. Net force is the vector sum of forces acting on the body. **5:9**

13. A body falling in air reaches terminal velocity when the upward force of air resistance equals the downward force of gravity. **5:10**

QUESTIONS

1. A ball is rolled across the top of a table and slowly comes to a stop.

   a. Using Newton's first law of motion, explain why the ball stops.

   b. Using Newton's second law, explain under what conditions the ball would have remained in motion.

2. An object on Earth has a mass of 3.0 kg. What would be the mass of the object if it were taken to

Jupiter where the acceleration of gravity is 10 times that of Earth?

3. Why does a package on the seat of a bus slide backward when the bus accelerates quickly from rest? Why does it slide forward when the driver applies the brakes?

4. A spacecraft is accelerated away from Earth by its rockets. Once the craft reaches a high velocity and is far from Earth, must it continue to fire its rockets to keep moving? Explain.

5. A carton of books is placed on a hand cart. When the cart is accelerated, the carton also accelerates. What supplies the force that accelerates the carton?

6. The terminal velocity of a baseball is 43 m/s, but a batted ball can go well over 50 m/s. Why?

7. A rock is dropped from a bridge to a valley below. Earth pulls on the rock and it accelerates downward. According to Newton's third law, the rock must also be pulling on Earth, yet we do not notice the Earth accelerating upward. Explain.

8. Why do you push harder on the pedals of a bicycle when it first starts moving than when it is moving with a constant velocity?

9. A basketball falls to the floor and bounces up.
   a. Is a force required to make it bounce? Why?
   b. If a force is needed, what supplies the force?

10. Suppose the acceleration of an object is zero. Does this mean no forces are acting on it? Give an example supporting your answer.

APPLYING CONCEPTS

1. If a car in an accident is struck from behind, passengers often incur a neck injury that is called whiplash.
   a. Using Newton's laws of motion, explain what happens.
   b. How does a headrest reduce whiplash?

2. According to legend, a horse learned Newton's laws. When it was told to pull a cart, it refused, saying that if it pulled the cart forward, according to Newton's third law there would be an equal and opposite reaction force. Thus there would be balanced forces on the cart and, according to Newton's second law, the cart would not accelerate. How would you reason with the horse?

3. When the space shuttle is launched from Earth, a constant force is applied and the shuttle accelerates upward. As the flight progresses, its rate of acceleration increases. Explain.

4. When people go on a diet, most say they want to lose weight. Describe some methods that would allow them to decrease their weight without decreasing their mass.

5. A skydiver jumps from an airplane and accelerates toward Earth. Which has the greater pull on the other, the Earth or the skydiver? Does Earth accelerate toward the skydiver?

6. Which creates a greater force of friction: sliding your physics book across a table on its back cover or along one of its edges?

7. a. As an object free falls in a vacuum, which of the parameters (distance, velocity, acceleration) vary and which remain constant during succeeding seconds of time?
   b. If the above object experienced air resistance and reached terminal velocity, what would your answer be now?

8. Two ping-pong balls, one filled with air and the other with concrete, are dropped at the same time from a helicopter. Both experience air resistance as they fall. Which ball reaches terminal velocity first? Do both hit the ground at the same time? Why?

EXERCISES

1. A towrope is used to pull a 1750-kg car, giving it an acceleration of $+1.35$ m/s^2. What force does the rope exert?

2. A race car undergoes a uniform acceleration of $+4.00$ m/s^2. If the net force causing the acceleration is $+3.00 \times 10^3$ N, what is the car's mass?

3. A race car has a mass of 710 kg. It starts from rest and travels $+40$ m in 3.0 s. The car is uniformly accelerated during the entire time. What net force is applied to it?

4. A 65-kg swimmer jumps off a 10 m high tower.
   a. Find the swimmer's velocity when hitting the water.
   b. The swimmer comes to a stop 2 m below the surface. Find the net force exerted by the water.

5. Compare the effort needed to lift a 10-kg rock on Earth and on the moon. Now compare the effort needed to throw the same rock horizontally.

6. A 7.50-kg object is placed on a spring scale. If the scale reads 78.4 N, what is the acceleration of gravity at that location?

7. The instruments attached to a weather balloon have a mass of 5.0 kg.
   a. What do the instruments weigh?
   b. The balloon is released and exerts an upward force of 98 N on the instruments. What is the acceleration of the balloon and instruments?
   c. After the balloon has accelerated for 10 seconds, the instruments are released. What is the velocity of the instruments at the moment of their release?
   d. What net force acts on the instruments after their release?
   e. When does the direction of their velocity first become downward?

8. An elevator that weighs 3.0×10^3 N is accelerated upward at 1.0 m/s². What force does the cable exert to give it this acceleration?

9. If 2.2 lb = 1 kg, what is your mass in kg? What is your weight in newtons?

10. How much tension must a rope withstand if it is used to accelerate a 70.0 kg skier behind a boat at 1.50 m/s²?

11. A 4500-kg helicopter accelerates upward at 2 m/s². What lift force is exerted by the air on the propellers?

12. How much force is needed to accelerate a 5.0 g bullet from rest to a speed of 500 m/s over a distance of 0.80 m?

13. To throw a 0.10 kg baseball, a pitcher accelerates the ball from rest to 36 m/s through a distance of 2.5 m. Calculate the average force exerted by the pitcher in throwing the ball.

14. A force of −9000 N is used to stop a 1500 kg car traveling at 20 m/s. What braking distance is needed to bring the car to a halt?

15. The maximum force a grocery sack can withstand and not rip is 250 N. If 20 kg of groceries are lifted from the floor to the table with the acceleration of 5 m/s², will the sack hold?

16. A person fishing hooks a 2.0 kg fish on a line that can only sustain a maximum of 38 N of force before breaking. If the fish can exert a force of 40 N during part of the fight, what is the minimum acceleration with which the line must be played out during this time in order not to break the line?

17. A force of 40 N accelerates a 5.0 kg ball at 6.0 m/s² along a horizontal surface.
   a. How large is the frictional force?
   b. What is the coefficient of friction?

18. A 200 kg crate is pushed horizontally with a force of 700 N. If the coefficient of friction is 0.20, calculate the acceleration of the crate.

19. A sled of mass 50 kg is pulled along snow-covered, flat ground. The static friction coefficient is 0.30, and the sliding friction coefficient is 0.10.
   a. What does the sled weigh?
   b. What force will be needed to start the sled moving?
   c. What force is needed to keep the sled moving at a constant velocity?
   d. Once moving, what total force must be applied to the sled to accelerate it 3.0 m/s²?

PROBLEMS

1. In Chapter 4 you calculated the braking acceleration for a car based on data in a drivers' handbook. The acceleration was −12.2 m/s².
   a. If the car has a mass of 925 kg, find the frictional force and state the direction.
   b. Find the coefficient of friction for this car's tires on the road.

2. In Chapter 4 you found that when a karate strike hits wooden blocks, the hand undergoes an acceleration of −6500 m/s². Medical data indicates the mass of the forearm and hand to be about 0.7 kg. What is the force exerted on the hand by the blocks?

3. A person weighing 490 N stands on a scale in an elevator.
   a. What does the scale read when the elevator is at rest?
   b. The elevator starts to go up and accelerates the person at +2.2 m/s². What does the scale read now?
   c. What is the reading on the scale when the elevator rises at a constant velocity?

d. The elevator slows down at -2.2 m/s^2 as it reaches the proper floor. What does the scale read?

e. The elevator descends, accelerating at -2.7 m/s^2. What does the scale read?

f. What does the scale read when the elevator descends at a constant velocity?

g. Suppose the cable snapped and the elevator fell freely. What would the scale read?

4. A student takes a bathroom scale into an elevator on the 64th floor of a building. The scale reads 836 N.

a. As the elevator moves up, the scale reading increases to 935 N, then decreases back to 836 N. Find the acceleration of the elevator.

b. As the elevator approaches the 64th floor, the scale reading drops as low as 782 N. What is the acceleration of the elevator?

c. Using your results from parts a and b, explain which change in velocity, starting or stopping, would take the longer time.

d. Explain the changes in the scale you would expect on the ride back down.

5. Safety engineers estimate that an elevator can hold 20 persons of 75-kg average mass. The elevator itself has a mass of 500 kg. Tensile strength tests show that the cable supporting the elevator can tolerate a maximum force of 29 600 N. What is the greatest acceleration that the elevator's motor can produce without breaking the cable?

6. A 2.0-kg mass and a 3.0-kg mass are attached to a lightweight cord that passes over a frictionless pulley. The hanging masses are left free to move.

a. In what direction does the smaller mass move?

b. What is its acceleration?

READINGS

Brancazio, Peter, "Sir Isaac and the Rising Fast Ball." *Discover,* July, 1984.

Easton, D., "Weightlessness and Free Bodies." *The Physics Teacher,* November, 1983.

Frenkel, Karen A., "The Leading Edge." *Forbes,* December, 1984.

Kyke, C., "How Weight Affects Bicycle Speed." *Bicycling,* April, 1988.

Shopf, Bruce, "Pivoting Windmills." *Popular Science,* January, 1984.

Vectors

GOALS

1. You will gain an understanding of vector quantities.
2. You will be able to produce vector diagrams and geometric solutions for problems involving vector quantities.
3. You will be able to solve algebraically problems involving vector quantities and objects in equilibrium.

SUGGESTION: Review what was learned about vectors in Chapter 3. Chapter 6 introduces vectors in two dimensions.

For Your Information

The word *vector* comes from the Latin word meaning to carry.

A vector quantity can be shown as an arrow-tipped line segment (length indicates magnitude; arrow indicates direction).

SUGGESTION: Vectors are not easy for students to visualize. Demonstrations, such as those suggested in the Teacher Guide at the front of this book, may help them gain understanding.

Have you ever had to move a heavy crate up several steps? Even if it were too heavy to lift, you might be able to push the crate up a ramp easily. By using the ramp, you decrease the force you need to exert to raise the crate from the street to the top of the steps. By using the ramp, you take advantage of the vector nature of forces. Forces, like displacement and velocity, are vector quantities. In this chapter, mathematical operations involving vectors will be studied. We will investigate the result of several forces acting in more than one dimension on an object.

6:1 Vector Addition; Graphical Method

A vector quantity can be represented by an arrow-tipped line segment. The length of the line, drawn to scale, represents the magnitude of the quantity. The direction of the arrow indicates the direction of the quantity. This arrow-tipped line segment represents a vector.

The sum of any two vectors can be found graphically. Consider a person who walks 200 m east, pauses, and then continues 400 m east. To find the total change in position of the person, the vector quantities must be added. In Figure 6–1a, A and B are vectors representing the two segments of the person's walk. The vectors are added by placing the tail of one vector at the head of the other vector. Neither the direction nor the length of either vector is changed during the process. A third vector is then drawn connecting the tail of the first vector to the head of the second vector. This third vector represents the sum of the first two vectors. It is called the **resultant** of A and B. The resultant is always drawn from the tail of the first vector to the head of the last vector.

Run with the Wind

The world speed sailing record is held by sailboards. In recent years, many board sailors have surpassed the earlier speed records held by catamarans. A recent top speed of 20.8 m/s was set in an 18 m/s wind. How is it possible to sail faster than the wind speed?

a

Scale: 1 division = 100 m
A= 200 m, E   B = 400 m, E

R= 600 m, E

b

Scale: 1 division = 100 m
B = 400 m, E   A = 200 m, E

R = 600 m, E

FIGURE 6–1. Vectors are added by placing the tail of one vector at the head of the other vector. The resultant, R, represents the sum of A and B (a). The order of addition does not matter (b).

SUGGESTION: Ask students if they have ever walked or ridden a bike in a strong wind, or if they have been in a rowboat or canoe on a stream with a strong current. What happened?

In adding two vectors graphically, a third vector is drawn from the tail of the first to the head of the second. This vector, the resultant, is the sum of two vectors.

FIGURE 6–2. The vector sum of B + A is the same as the vector sum of A + B.

FIGURE 6–3. A boat traveling 9.4 m/s at 32° north of east can also be described as traveling both east at 8.0 m/s and north at 5.0 m/s at the same time.

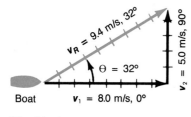

Scale: 1 division = 1 m/s

V_R = 9.4 m/s, 32°
v_2 = 5.0 m/s, 90°
θ = 32°
Boat v_1 = 8.0 m/s, 0°

When vectors are added, the order of addition does not matter. The tail of A could have been placed at the head of B. Figure 6–1b shows that the same vector sum would result.

To find the magnitude of the resultant, measure its length using the same scale used to draw A and B. In this situation, the total change in position is 200 m east + 400 m east = 600 m east. If the person had turned after moving 200 m east and walked 400 m west, the change of position would have been 200 m east + 400 m west or 200 m west. Note that in both cases, the vectors are added head to tail, and the directions are not changed.

6:2 Vector Addition in Two Dimensions

Now let us consider motion in two dimensions. In Figure 6–2, A and B represent the two displacements of a student who walked 95 m east and 55 m north. The vectors are added by placing the tail of one vector at the head of the other vector. The resultant of A and B is drawn by connecting the tail of the first vector with the head of the second vector. To find the magnitude of the resultant, R, measure its length and evaluate it using the same scale used to draw A and B. Its direction is found with a protractor. The direction is expressed as an angle measured counterclockwise from the horizontal (0°). In Figure 6–2, the resultant displacement is 110 km at 30° above the horizontal.

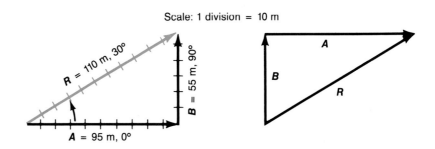

Scale: 1 division = 10 m

R = 110 m, 30°
B = 55 m, 90°
A = 95 m, 0°
A
B
R

6:3 Independence of Vector Quantities

Perpendicular vector quantities act independently. Consider a motorboat that heads east at 8.0 m/s across a river flowing north at 5.0 m/s. The boat starts on the west side and travels 8.0 meters east in one second. It also travels 5.0 meters north in the same second. The velocity north does not change the velocity east. Neither does the velocity east change the velocity north. These two perpendicular velocities are independent of each other. *All perpendicular vector quantities behave in this manner.*

In Figure 6–3, the two velocities of the boat are represented by vectors. When these vectors are added, the resultant velocity, v_R, is 9.4 m/s at 32° from the horizontal. In one second, this resultant velocity will carry the motorboat 8.0 meters due east and 5.0 meters due north. You can think of the boat as traveling east at 8.0 m/s and north at 5.0 m/s at the same time. You can also think of it as traveling 9.4 m/s in the direction 32° north of east. Both statements have the same meaning.

94 Vectors

Suppose that the river is 80 meters wide. Because the boat's velocity is 8 m/s east at all times, it will take the boat 10 seconds to cross the river. However, the boat will also be carried 50 meters downstream during this 10 seconds. In no way does the downstream velocity change the velocity of the boat with respect to the water.

Vectors act independently; one vector cannot change the other.

6:4 Vector Addition of Forces

Force vectors are added in the same way as velocity vectors. Forces that act on the same point at the same time are called **concurrent forces.**

Concurrent forces act on the same point at the same time.

In Figure 6–4, a force of 45 N and a force of 65 N act concurrently on point *P*. The smaller force acts in the direction of 60°, the larger force acts at 0°. The resultant, **R,** is the sum of the two forces. Forces **A** and **B** are drawn to scale. **R** is found by moving **A** along **B** without changing its direction until the tail of **A** is located at the head of **B**. The resultant is drawn from the tail of the first vector to the head of the second vector. The magnitude of **R** is determined using the same scale used for **A** and **B**. The angle is found with a protractor. In this case, **R** is 96 N acting in a direction of 24°. A force of 96 N acting in a direction of 24° will have exactly the same effect as a force of 45 N at 60° and a force of 65 N at 0° acting concurrently.

Moving a vector changes neither its magnitude nor its direction.

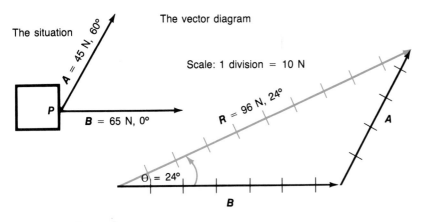

FIGURE 6–4. The resultant force of two forces acting on a point can be determined graphically.

Practice Exercises

Draw vector diagrams to solve each problem.

1. After walking 11 km due north from camp, a hiker then walks 11 km due east.
   a. What is the total distance walked by the hiker?
   b. Determine the total displacement from the starting point.
2. A plane flying at 90° at 1.00×10^2 m/s is blown toward 180° at 5.0×10^1 m/s by a strong wind. Find the plane's resultant velocity and direction.
3. A motorboat heads due east at 16 m/s across a river that flows due north at 9.0 m/s.
   a. What is the resultant velocity (speed and direction) of the boat?
   b. If the river is 136 m wide, how long does it take the motorboat to reach the other side?

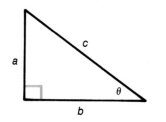

FIGURE 6–5. Some vector sums can be determined using right triangles.

SUGGESTION: Use the mnemonic device, SOHCAHTOA, to remember that sin = opp/hyp, cos = adj/hyp, and tan = opp/adj.

For Your Information

Physics Term Made Easy
Hypotenuse: Animal-like rhinoceros but with no horn or nose.

The Pythagorean theorem can be used to find the length of the third side of a right triangle.

FIGURE 6–6. A vector diagram can be used to approximate the mathematical solution.

SUGGESTION: If students have calculators with trig functions, encourage them to solve the problems using the calculator rather than tables.

SUGGESTION: Have students practice several of these problems. First have them predict what the resultant will be, then construct the vector diagram.

c. How far downstream is the boat when it reaches the other side of the river?

4. While flying due east at 120 km/h, an airplane is carried due north at 45 km/h by the wind. What is the plane's resultant velocity?

6:5 Vector Addition; Mathematical Method

The sum of any two vectors can be determined using algebra and trigonometry. Trigonometry is the area of mathematics that deals with the relationships among angles and sides of triangles. If two vectors are perpendicular, a right angle is formed when the tail of the second vector is placed at the head of the first. The resultant vector, drawn from the tail of the first to the head of the second, is the hypotenuse of the resulting right triangle. The resultant can be calculated using the Pythagorean theorem.

$$c^2 = a^2 + b^2$$

In Figure 6–5, c is the **hypotenuse** (side opposite the right angle) and sides a and b are the legs of a right triangle.

The interior angle, θ, may be found by using the trigonometric function of tangent. The tangent (tan) of an angle is the ratio of the length of the side opposite the right angle to the length of the side adjacent to the angle.

In Figure 6–5, $\tan \theta = \dfrac{a}{b}$.

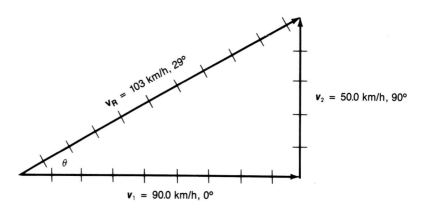

$v_R = 103$ km/h, 29°

$v_2 = 50.0$ km/h, 90°

$v_1 = 90.0$ km/h, 0°

EXAMPLE

Finding the Resultant Algebraically

An airplane flying toward 0° at 90.0 km/h is being blown toward 90° at 50.0 km/h. What is the resultant velocity of the plane?

Given: plane velocity (v_1)
= 90.0 km/h, 0°
wind velocity (v_2)
= 50.0 km/h, 90°

Unknown: resultant velocity (v_R)

Basic equation: $c^2 = a^2 + b^2$
or $v_R{}^2 = v_1{}^2 + v_2{}^2$

Solution: The vector v_R is the hypotenuse of a right triangle. Its magnitude is given by
$$v_R = \sqrt{v_1{}^2 + v_2{}^2}$$

$$v_R = \sqrt{(90.0 \text{ km/h})^2 + (50.0 \text{ km/h})^2}$$
$$= \sqrt{1.06 \times 10^4} \text{ km/h}$$
$$v_R = 1.03 \times 10^2 \text{ km/h}$$

The angle, θ, is found by

$$\tan \theta = \frac{\text{opposite side}}{\text{adjacent side}}$$
$$= \frac{50.0 \text{ km/h}}{90.0 \text{ km/h}}$$
$$\tan \theta = 0.556$$

A calculator or Table C–6 in the Appendix shows that 0.556 is the tangent of 29°. Therefore, θ is 29°. The resultant velocity, v_R, is 103 km/h at 29°.

If two vectors are acting at angles other than 90°, one way to determine the resultant mathematically is by using the law of cosines and the law of sines. These are discussed in Appendix D.

For Your Information

The product of two vector quantities may be different from the product of their magnitudes. There are two ways of multiplying two vectors—one gives a scalar product, the other, a vector product. **a** and **b** are two concurrent vectors differing in direction by the angle θ. The product of **a** · **b**, called the dot product, is a scalar, $ab \cos \theta$. The product of **a** × **b** or **b** × **a**, called the cross product, is another vector, **c**, whose magnitude is $ab \sin \theta$ or $-ab \sin \theta$, respectively.

PROBLEM SOLVING

> Whenever solving vector addition algebraically, draw a careful sketch of the vectors and check that your answer agrees with the sketch.

Either the law of sines and cosines or resolution of vectors into components can be used for these problems.

Practice Exercises

Solve each exercise graphically or mathematically, depending on your instructor's directions.

Remember that the Pythagorean theorem can be used for right triangles only.

5. A 110-N force and a 55-N force act on point P. The 110-N force acts at 90°. The 55-N force acts at 0°. What is the magnitude and direction of the resultant force?

6. A motorboat travels at 8.5 m/s. It heads straight across a river 110 m wide.
   a. If the water flows at a rate of 3.8 m/s, what is the boat's resultant velocity?
   b. How much time does it take the boat to reach the opposite shore?

7. A boat heads directly across a river 41 m wide at 3.8 m/s. The current is flowing at 2.2 m/s.
   a. What is the resultant velocity of the boat?
   b. How much time does it take the boat to cross the river?
   c. How far downstream is the boat when it reaches the other side?

Remember that directions are measured counterclockwise from the horizontal.

8. A 42-km/h wind blows toward 215°. What is the resultant velocity of a plane that flies toward 125° at 152 km/h?

6:6 Addition of Several Vectors

Often more than two forces act concurrently on the same point. To determine the resultant of three or more vectors, follow the same proce-

a

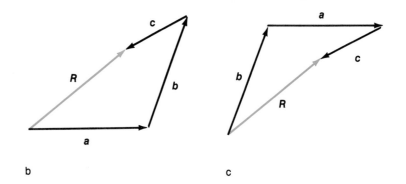

b

c

FIGURE 6–7. In (a) the three forces act concurrently on point *P*. In (b) and (c) the vectors are added graphically. The resultant is the same in both diagrams.

dure you use to add two vectors. Place the vectors head-to-tail. The order of addition is not important. In Figure 6–7a, the three forces, *a, b,* and *c,* act concurrently on point *P*. In Figures 6–7b and 6–7c, the vectors are added graphically. Note that the resultant is the same in both sketches although two different orders of addition are used. When placing vectors head-to-tail, the direction of each must not be changed.

SUGGESTION: Discuss examples of situations where there is no equilibrant and predict what it will be. Then draw the diagram and compute it.

6:7 Equilibrium

When two or more forces act concurrently on an object, and their vector sum is zero, the object is in **equilibrium.** An object in equilibrium has no acceleration because the forces on it are balanced. An example of equilibrium is the case in which two equal forces act in opposite directions on an object, as shown in Figure 6–8. The resultant force is zero.

Equilibrium occurs when the sum of forces acting at a point is zero.

FIGURE 6–8. When the dogs Darby and Spanky pull with equal force in opposite directions, the forces on the toy are in equilibrium, and the toy does not move. The resultant force is zero (a). Two equal forces exerted in opposite directions on the toy produce equilibrium (b).

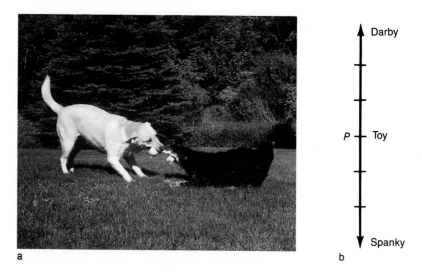

a

b

Figure 6–9 shows a point *P* with three concurrent forces acting on it. The 3-N force and the 4-N force are at right angles to each other. When the three vectors are added head-to-tail, they form a closed triangle, as in Figure 6–9. The vector sum is zero because the length of the resultant is zero. Therefore, the three forces produce no net force on point *P*. Point *P* is in equilibrium.

FIGURE 6–9. Vectors in equilibrium give a resultant of zero.

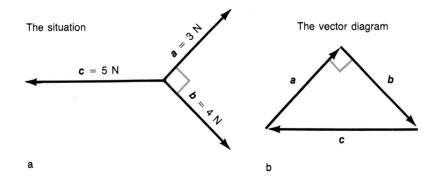

The situation

The vector diagram

a

b

SUGGESTION: Point out that physical conditions dictate the directions of the components. Component forces are the result of real agents: ropes, planes, gravity, friction, etc.

6:8 The Equilibrant

When two or more forces act on a point and their vector sum is not zero, a force can be found that will produce equilibrium. This force is called the **equilibrant** (ee KWIL uh bruhnt) **force**. The equilibrant force is the single additional force that, if applied at the same point as the other forces, will produce equilibrium. In Figure 6–10, the equilibrant force is a 10-N force whose direction is opposite to the direction of the resultant.

To find the equilibrant force of two or more concurrent forces, first find the resultant force. The equilibrant force is equal in magnitude to the resultant, but opposite in direction.

An equilibrant force balances the forces acting on a point to produce equilibrium.

The equilibrant is equal in magnitude to the resultant, but opposite in direction.

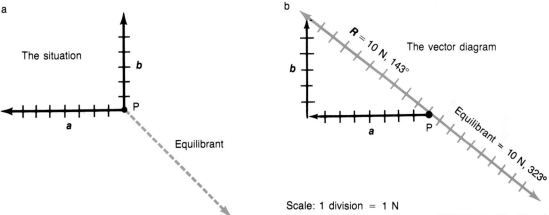

Scale: 1 division = 1 N

FIGURE 6–10. To determine the equilibrant of two forces acting at an angle of 90° with each other, first find the resultant of the two forces.

Practice Exercises

9. A force of 55 N acts due west on an object. What added single force on the object produces equilibrium?

10. Two forces act concurrently on point P. One force is 6.0×10^1 N horizontally. The second force is 8.0×10^1 N vertically.

    a. Find the magnitude and direction of the resultant.

    b. What is the magnitude and direction of the equilibrant?

11. A 62-N force acting at 30.0° and a second 62-N force acting at 60° are concurrent forces.

    a. Determine the resultant force.

    b. What is the magnitude and direction of their equilibrant?

12. A 36-N force acts at 225°. A 48-N force acts at 315°. The two forces act on the same point. What is the magnitude and direction of their equilibrant?

6:9 Perpendicular Components of Vectors

We have seen that two or more vectors acting in different directions from the same point may be replaced by a single vector, the resultant. The resultant has the same effect as the original vectors.

It is also possible to begin with a single vector and think of it as the resultant of two or more vectors, each acting in a direction different from the original vector. These vectors are called the **components** of the given vector. Most of the time, we are concerned with finding the vertical and horizontal components of a given vector.

The process of finding the effective value of a component in a given direction is called **vector resolution.** Consider the sled being pulled in Figure 6–11. A 58-N force is exerted on a rope held at an angle of 30° with the horizontal. This force pulls both forward and upward on the sled. The force that pulls the sled forward is the horizontal component (F_h). The force that pulls the sled upward is the vertical component (F_v).

a

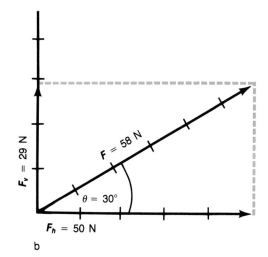

b

FIGURE 6–11. The force used to pull a sled can be resolved into its vertical and horizontal components.

The value of the horizontal and vertical components of **F** can be found by first drawing a set of perpendicular axes, Figure 6–11. One axis is in the horizontal direction. The other axis is in the vertical direction. The vector that represents the force in the rope, **F,** is then drawn to scale at the proper angle with the horizontal axis. To resolve that force into the components F_v and F_h, draw perpendicular lines from each axis to the tip of the force vector. The magnitudes of the two components can then be measured using the scale used for **F.** Note that the resultant of F_v and F_h is the original force.

As can be seen from Figure 6–12, F_v and F_h can be found using trigonometry. In this case,

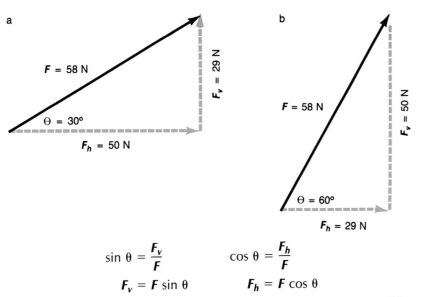

a

$F = 58$ N

$\theta = 30°$

$F_h = 50$ N

$F_v = 29$ N

b

$F = 58$ N

$\theta = 60°$

$F_h = 29$ N

$F_v = 50$ N

$$\sin \theta = \frac{F_v}{F} \qquad \cos \theta = \frac{F_h}{F}$$

$$F_v = F \sin \theta \qquad F_h = F \cos \theta$$

The directions of F_v and F_h can be found from the vector diagram. If the value for either F_v or F_h is positive, it is up or to the right. If F_v is negative, it is down.

When the person pulling the sled lowers the rope, decreasing θ, the horizontal component is increased. On the other hand, if the angle between the rope and the horizontal is increased to 60°, the horizontal component decreases to 29 N. Thus, the magnitude of the components change as the direction of the force changes.

In adding nonperpendicular vectors, first find the components of those vectors. Then add the vertical and horizontal components separately. Finally, combine the sums vectorally to form the resultant vectors.

PROBLEM SOLVING

In resolving velocity and displacement vectors, let one axis represent a right-left (0°, 180°) direction. Let the second axis represent an up-down (90°, 270°) direction.

Vector resolution can be used to add two or more vectors that are not perpendicular to each other. First, each vector is resolved into its vertical and horizontal components. Then the vertical components of all the vectors are added together to produce a single vector that acts in the vertical direction. Likewise, all of the horizontal components of the vectors are added together to produce a single horizontal vector. The resulting vertical and horizontal vectors can be added together to obtain a resultant, using the methods described in Sections 6:2 and 6:5.

EXAMPLE

Resolving a Velocity Vector Into Its Components

A wind with a velocity of 40.0 km/h blows at 30.0°, Figure 6–13.
a. What is the component of the wind's velocity toward 90°? **b.** What is the component of the wind's velocity toward 0°?

Given: $v = 40.0$ km/h, 30.0°   Unknowns: v_N, v_E

Solution: To find the northerly component, v_N, use the relation

$$\sin 30.0° = \frac{v_N}{v}$$

Then $v_N = v(\sin 30.0°)$

$$= (40.0 \text{ km/h})(0.500)$$

$$v_N = 20.0 \text{ km/h}, 90.0°$$

To find the horizontal component, v_E, use the relation

$$\cos 30.0° = \frac{v_E}{v}$$

Then $v_E = v(\cos 30.0°)$

$$= (40.0 \text{ km/h})(0.866)$$

$$v_E = 34.6 \text{ km/h}, 0.0°$$

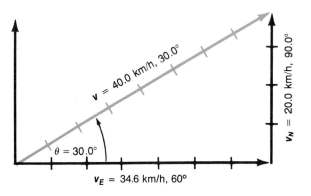

FIGURE 6–13. A velocity vector V can be resolved into north and east components.

Practice Exercises

13. A heavy box is pulled across a wooden floor with a rope. The rope forms an angle of 60° with the floor. A tension of 8.0×10^1 N is maintained on the rope. What force is actually pulling the box across the floor?

14. An airplane flies toward 149° at 5.0×10^2 km/h. At what rate is the plane moving?

    a. toward 90°   **b.** toward 180°

15. By applying a force of 72 N along the handle of a lawn mower, a student can push it across the lawn. Find the horizontal component of this force when the handle is held at an angle with the lawn of

    a. 60.0°   **b.** 40.0°   **c.** 30.0°

16. A water skier is towed by a speedboat. The skier moves to one side of the boat in such a way that the tow rope forms an angle of 55° with the direction of the boat. The tension on the rope is 350 N. What would be the tension on the rope if the skier were directly behind the boat?

6:10 Gravitational Force and Inclined Planes

The gravitational force acting on an object is directed toward the center of Earth. This means that the object's weight, **W**, acts perpendicular to the surface of Earth. It can be represented by a vertical vector directed down.

Figure 6–14 shows a trunk resting on an inclined plane. The weight of the trunk, **W**, can be resolved into two components perpendicular to each other. One component, $F_\perp$, is called the perpendicular force and acts perpendicular to the incline. The second component, $F_\parallel$, is called the parallel force and acts parallel to the incline.

The right triangle formed by the surface of the incline and the right triangle formed by **W**, $F_\perp$, and $F_\parallel$ are similar triangles because corresponding sides are mutually perpendicular. If θ and **W** are both known, a vector diagram similar to Figure 6–14 can be drawn, and the force **W** resolved into the components $F_\parallel$ and $F_\perp$ by the graphical method. An easier method is to calculate the values of $F_\parallel$ and $F_\perp$ using the trigonometric functions of right triangles.

SUGGESTION: Note that in Chapter 5, F_N was equal to the weight, but here on the incline it is only related to weight by $F_N = W \cos \theta$.

The correct choice of axes to use in inclined plane problems is the set perpendicular to the plane.

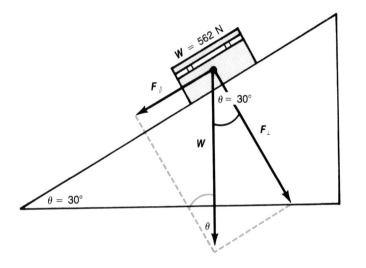

FIGURE 6–14. The weight vector **W** is resolved into two components. One component acts parallel to the plane. The other acts perpendicular to the plane.

EXAMPLE

Finding $F_\perp$ and $F_\parallel$

A trunk weighing 562 N is resting on a plane inclined at 30° from the horizontal, Figure 6–14. Find the magnitudes of the parallel and perpendicular components of the weight.

Given: W = 562 N   **Unknowns:** perpendicular force ($F_\perp$),
            θ = 30.0°   parallel force ($F_\parallel$)

Solution: $\sin \theta = \dfrac{F_\parallel}{W}$ so $F_\parallel = W \sin \theta$ $\cos \theta = \dfrac{F_\perp}{W}$ so $F_\perp = W \cos \theta$

$F_\parallel$ = (562 N)(sin 30.0°) $F_\perp$ = (562 N)(cos 30.0°)
     = (562 N)(0.500)   = (562 N)(0.866)
     = 281 N   = 487 N

W = 562 N

F∥ = 431 N

θ = 50°

W

θ = 50°

F⊥ = 361 N

FIGURE 6–15. As the angle of the incline increases, the component of the weight acting parallel to the plane increases. The component that acts perpendicular to the plane decreases.

Note that as the incline in Figure 6–15 becomes steeper, $F_\parallel$ becomes greater and $F_\perp$ becomes less.

Are there any other forces besides the force of gravity on the trunk? The inclined plane exerts a force perpendicular to its surface, called the normal force. The trunk has no acceleration in the direction perpendicular to the plane, and so the forces in that direction must be balanced. Therefore, the normal force of the plane on the trunk, F_N, is equal and opposite to the perpendicular component of the weight on the plane, $F_\perp = W \cos \theta$.

If there is no friction between the trunk and the plane, then the only force in the direction along the plane is the parallel component of weight, $F_\parallel = W \sin \theta$. According to Newton's second law, the acceleration of the trunk is then $a = \dfrac{F_\perp}{m} = \dfrac{W}{m} \sin \theta$. But, $\dfrac{W}{m} = g$, so the acceleration of the trunk is $a = g \sin \theta$. As the plane becomes more horizontal, the acceleration approaches zero. When the plane is tilted more vertically, the acceleration approaches closer to $g = -9.80$ m/s².

EXAMPLE

Finding Acceleration Down a Plane

The 562 N trunk is on an ice-covered plane inclined at 30.0° from the horizontal. Find the acceleration of the trunk down the plane.

Given: $W = 562$ N   **Unknown:** acceleration down the plane (**a**)

$\theta = 30.0°$ **Basic equations:** $F = ma$

$W = mg$

$F_\parallel = W \sin \theta$

Solution: $F_\parallel = W \sin \theta$

$= mg \sin \theta$

$a = \dfrac{F}{m} = \left(\dfrac{mg}{m}\right) \sin \theta = g \sin \theta$

$= (-9.80 \text{ m/s}^2)(0.500) = -4.90 \text{ m/s}^2$

The negative sign indicates the acceleration is down the plane.

The resolution of weight on an inclined plane can be used to measure the coefficient of friction. Put a coin on one of your textbooks. Now slowly lift the cover. The coin will remain at rest until the cover reaches a large enough angle for the coin to begin to accelerate down the book. The downward force along the cover is the parallel component of the weight. As long as the angle of the cover is not too large, the component is balanced by the static friction force. When the force down the cover exceeds the frictional force, the coin starts to move. Now static friction is replaced by sliding friction, which is a smaller force. With a net force on the coin, it accelerates down the book. If you measure the angle when the coin first begins to move, you can determine the coefficient of static friction. Try different objects and books. Which combination has the greatest friction? The least?

EXAMPLE

Finding the Coefficient of Static Friction

A coin placed on the cover of a book just begins to move when the cover makes an angle of 38° with the horizontal, Figure 6–16. What is the coefficient of static friction between the cover and coin?

Given: angle of inclined plane
$\theta = 38°$

Unknown: μ

Basic equations: $F_f = \mu F_N$
$F_\perp = W \cos \theta$
$F_\parallel = W \sin \theta$

FIGURE 6–16. Use with the Example.

Solution: When motion is just ready to start, friction is at its maximum and the forces, both parallel and perpendicular to the book cover, are balanced.
perpendicular forces $= F_N = F_\perp = \cos \theta$
parallel forces $= F_f = F_\parallel = W \sin \theta$
But $F_f = \mu F_N$
$W \sin \theta = \mu(W \cos \theta)$
This means that $\mu = \dfrac{\sin \theta}{\cos \theta}$
$= \tan \theta = \tan 38° = 0.78$

Practice Exercises

17. The 562-N trunk is placed on an inclined plane that forms a 66° angle with the horizontal.
    a. Calculate the values of $F_\perp$ and $F_\parallel$.
    b. Compare your results with those given above for the same trunk on a 30° incline.
18. A car weighing 1.2×10^4 N is parked on a 36° slope.
    a. Find the force tending to cause the car to roll down the hill.
    b. What is the force the car exerts perpendicular to the hill?

6:11 Nonperpendicular Components of Vectors

In Section 6:9, a single vector was resolved into two components at right angles to each other. A vector, however, can be resolved into components that lie in any direction as long as their vector sum is equal to the original vector. In some cases, it may be necessary to resolve a vector into components that are not at right angles to each other.

A sign that weighs 40 N is supported by ropes A and B, Figure 6–17a. Three forces act on the sign. They are the force of rope A, the force of rope B, and the force due to gravity, the weight of the sign. The weight of the sign, 40 N, acts straight down. Because the sign is in equilibrium, the forces of the two ropes must produce a resultant force, R, 40 N straight up to balance the weight of the sign: $A + B = R$. Thus, the magnitude and direction of the resultant of the forces in the two ropes is known, although the force in each rope is not known.

Figure 6–17b shows how **R** can be resolved into two components to find the force in each rope. Draw the known, **R,** and two lines that represent the directions of ropes *A* and *B*.

The vector **R** is then resolved into two components—one in the direction of rope *A* and one in the direction of rope *B*. You can resolve **R** by constructing a parallelogram. The broken lines in Figure 6–17b represent the parallel sides that are drawn to complete the parallelogram. These broken lines intersect the lines representing the forces of ropes *A* and *B*. In so doing, they define the magnitude of the components of **R**. The two components, **a** and **b,** are then measured using the scale of the diagram to find the force in each rope.

The force turns out to be 52 N in each rope. Note that when **a, b,** and **W** are added, as in Figure 6–17c, they form a closed triangle. This triangle indicates a vector sum of zero. Thus, the sign hangs in equilibrium. Is it surprising that the force in each rope is larger than the weight of the sign? Try different angles. As the angle between the ropes becomes smaller, the component forces also become smaller. When the angle is zero the weight is shared equally, and each rope exerts only 20 N.

FIGURE 6–17. Resolving the force R into the nonperpendicular components a and b.

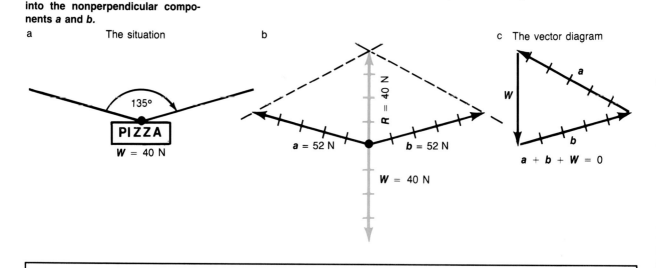

a   The situation   b   c   The vector diagram

135°

PIZZA

W = 40 N

R = 40 N

a = 52 N   **b** = 52 N

W = 40 N

W

a

b

a + **b** + **W** = 0

CHAPTER 6 REVIEW

SUMMARY

1. The resultant is the sum of two or more vectors. **6:1**

2. Addition of two vectors is performed by placing the tail of the second vector at the head of the first vector. The resultant vector is drawn by connecting the tail of the first vector to the head of the second vector. **6:1, 6:2**

3. Vector quantities act independently of each other. **6:3**

4. Force vectors can be added in the same way as velocity vectors. **6:4**

5. Vectors may be added graphically or mathematically. **6:5**

6. The resultant of several concurrent vectors can be found by the same procedures used for adding two vectors. **6:6**

7. When no net force acts on a point object, it is in equilibrium. **6:7**

8. The equilibrant is the single force that is equal in magnitude and opposite in direction to the resultant of several forces acting on a point. **6:8**

9. A vector can be resolved into two perpendicular components. **6:9**

10. The weight of an object on an inclined plane can be resolved into two perpendicular components. One component, $F_{\parallel}$, acts parallel to the plane; the other component, $F_{\perp}$, acts perpendicular to the plane. **6:9**

QUESTIONS

1. What is meant by equilibrium?
2. How are vectors added graphically?
3. When two or more vectors are added graphically, how is the resultant found?
4. What is meant by the term concurrent forces?
5. How does the resultant of two vectors change as the angle between the two vectors increases?
6. What is the sum of three vectors that form a triangle? Assuming that the vectors are forces, what does this imply about the object on which the forces act?
7. How can the equilibrant of two or more concurrent forces be found?
8. What is the largest possible resultant of two concurrent forces with magnitudes of 3 N and 4 N? What is the smallest possible resultant? Make a sketch to demonstrate your answers.
9. A vector drawn 15 mm long represents a velocity of 30 m/s. How long should you draw a vector to represent a velocity of 20 m/s?

APPLYING CONCEPTS

1. Two dogs pull on a toy. One pulls with a force of 10 N, the other with a force of 15 N.
   a. In what relative directions can they act to give the toy the largest possible acceleration?
   b. In what relative directions can the dogs act to give the toy the smallest acceleration?
   c. Can they ever result in zero acceleration?
2. At what angle of an inclined plane are the parallel and perpendicular components of an object's weight equal?
3. A lawn mower is pushed across a lawn. Can the horizontal component of the force be increased without changing the force applied to the handle of the mower? Explain.

4. A student puts two objects on a physics book and carefully tilts the cover. At a small angle, one object starts to slide. At a larger angle, the other begins to slide. Which has the greater coefficient of friction?
5. A driver is trying to get a car unstuck from some mud using a long line of strong rope. Which method would allow the greater force to be exerted on the car? Why?
   a. The driver ties one end of the rope to the car and pulls on the other end.
   b. The driver ties one end on the car and the other to a tree, then pushes on the rope perpendicular to it, about halfway between the two ends.
6. Weight lifting or "pumping iron" has become very popular in the last few years. When lifting a barbell, which grip will exert less force on the lifter's arms, one in which the arms are extended straight forward from the body so they are at right angles to the bar or one in which the arms are spread so that the bar is gripped closer to the weights? Explain.
7. When stretching a clothesline or a strand of wire between two posts, it is relatively easy to pull one end of the line hard enough to remove most of the slack. However, it is almost always necessary to resort to some mechanical device that can exert a greater-than-human force to take out the last of the slack to make the line completely horizontal. Why is this true? Disregard any stretching of the line.

EXERCISES

1. A salesperson leaves the office, drives 26 km due north, then turns onto a second highway and continues in a direction of 30.0° north of east for 62 km. What is the total displacement of the salesperson from the office?

2. Two players kick a soccer ball at exactly the same time. One player's foot exerts a force of 66 N north. The other player's foot exerts a force of 88 N east. What is the magnitude and direction of the resultant force on the ball?

3. Two forces of 62 N each act concurrently on a point P. Determine the magnitude of the resultant force acting on point P when the angle between the forces is as follows.

    a. 0.0° **b.** 30.0° **c.** 60.0° **d.** 90.0° **e.** 180°

4. In Exercise 3, what happens to the resultant of two forces when the angle between them increases?

5. A weather station releases a weather balloon. The balloon's buoyancy accelerates it straight up at 15 m/s². A wind accelerates it horizontally at 6.5 m/s². What is the magnitude and direction (with reference to the horizontal) of the resultant acceleration?

6. What is the vector sum of a 65-N force acting due east and a 32-N force acting due west?

7. A plane flies due north at 225 km/h. A wind carries it due east at 55 km/h. What is the magnitude and direction of the plane's resultant velocity?

8. A meteoroid passes between the moon and Earth. A gravitational force of 6.0×10^2 N pulls the meteoroid toward the moon. At the same time, a gravitational force of 4.8×10^2 N pulls it toward Earth. The angle between the two forces is 130°. The moon's force acts in a direction perpendicular to the meteoroid's original path. What is the resultant magnitude and direction of the force acting on the meteoroid? State the direction in reference to the meteoroid's original path. (Figure 6–18 is not a vector diagram. It is intended to show direction only.)

FIGURE 6–18. Use with Exercise 8.

9. Two 15-N forces act concurrently on point P. Find the magnitude of their resultant when the angle between them is

    a. 0.0° **b.** 30.0° **c.** 90.0° **d.** 120.0° **e.** 180.0°

10. A boat travels at 3.8 m/s and heads straight across a river 240 m wide. The river flows at 1.6 m/s.

    a. What is the boat's resultant velocity?

    b. How long does it take the boat to cross the river?

    c. How far downstream is the boat when it reaches the other side?

11. Determine the magnitude of the resultant of a 4.0×10^1-N force and a 7.0×10^1-N force acting concurrently when the angle between them is

    a. 0.0° **b.** 30.0° **c.** 60.0° **d.** 90.0° **e.** 180.0°

12. Three people attempt to haul a heavy sign to the roof of a building by using three ropes attached to the sign. Person A stands directly above the sign and pulls straight up on a rope. Person B and Person C stand on either side of Person A. Their ropes form 30.0° angles with Person A's rope. A force of 102 N is applied on each rope. What is the net upward force acting on the sign?

13. A plane travels on a heading of 40.0° north of east for a distance of 3.00×10^2 km. How far north and how far east does the plane travel?

14. A descent vehicle landing on the moon has a vertical velocity toward the surface of the moon of 35 m/s. At the same time it has a horizontal velocity of 55 m/s.

    a. At what speed does the vehicle move along its descent path?

    b. At what angle with the vertical is this path?

15. A lawn mower is pushed across a lawn by applying a force of 95 N along the handle of the mower. The handle makes an angle of 60.0° with the horizontal.

    a. What are the horizontal and vertical components of the force?

    b. The handle is lowered so it makes an angle of 30.0° with the horizontal. What are the horizontal and vertical components of the force?

16. A force of 92 N is exerted on a heavy box using a rope. The rope is held at an angle of 45° with the horizontal. What are the vertical and horizontal components of the 92-N force?

17. A river flows toward 90°. A riverboat pilot heads the boat 297° and is able to go straight across the river at 6.0 m/s.

    a. What is the velocity of the current?

    b. What is the velocity of the boat?

18. A street lamp weighs 150 N. It is supported equally by two wires that form an angle of 120° with each other. What is the tension of each of these wires?

19. If the angle between the wires in Problem 18 is changed to 90.0°, what is the tension of each of the wires?

20. Three forces act concurrently on point P. Force *a* has a magnitude of 80.0 N and is directed at 60.0°. Force *b* has a magnitude of 70.0 N and is directed at 0.0°. Force *c* has a magnitude of 40.0 N and is directed at 315°.

   a. Graphically add these three forces in the order *a* + *b* + *c*.

   b. Graphically add these three forces in the order *c* + *b* + *a*.

   c. What is noted about the solutions in each case?

PROBLEMS

1. A brick layer applies a force of 100 N to each of two handles of a wheelbarrow. Its mass is 20 kg and it is loaded with 30 bricks, each of mass 1.5 kg. The handles of the wheelbarrow are 30° from the horizontal and the coefficient of friction is 0.20. What initial acceleration is given the wheelbarrow?

2. Five forces act simultaneously on Point *A*: the first 60 N at 90°; the second 40 N at 0°; the third 80 N at 270°; the fourth 40 N at 180°; and the fifth 50 N at 60°. What is the magnitude and direction of a sixth force that produces equilibrium at Point *A*?

3. A gardener pushes on the handle of a 10 kg lawn spreader. The handle makes a 45° angle with the horizontal. The gardener wishes to accelerate the spreader from rest to 5 km/h in 1.5 s. What force must be applied to the handle? Neglect friction.

4. A 40 kg crate is pulled across a floor with a rope. A force of 100 N is applied at an angle of 30° with the horizontal. Calculate:

   a. The acceleration of the crate.

   b. The upward force the floor exerts upon it as it is pulled. Neglect friction.

5. A ship sets out to sail 500 km due south but a severe storm blows it due east 100 km from its starting point. How far and in what direction must the ship sail to reach its desired destination?

6. A mass, *M*, starts from rest and slides down the frictionless incline as shown. As it leaves the incline, its speed is 24 m/s (Figure 6–19).

   a. What is the acceleration of the mass while on the incline?

   b. What is the length of the incline?

   c. How long does it take the mass to reach the floor after it leaves the top of the incline?

FIGURE 6–19. Use with Problem 6.

7. In order to slide a 325-N trunk up a 20.0°-inclined plane at a constant speed, a force of 211 N is exerted parallel to the plane.

   a. What is the component of the weight parallel to the plane?

   b. The sum of the component of the weight, the applied force, and friction must total to what?

   c. What is the net force parallel to the plane? Why?

   d. What is the friction force?

   e. What is the coefficient of friction?

8. A 33-N force acting at 90° and a 44-N force acting at 60° act concurrently on point P. What is the magnitude and direction of a third force that produces equilibrium at point P?

READINGS

Aquirre, J. M., "Student Preconceptions About Vector Kinematics." *The Physics Teacher*, April, 1988.

Browne, Malcolm W., "Slippery Skins for Speedier Subs." *Discover*, April, 1984.

Crane, Richard, "Frisbees, Can Lids, and Gyroscopic Effects." *The Physics Teacher*, May, 1983.

Gilmore, C. P., "Spin Sail Harnesses Mysterious Magnus Effect." *Popular Science*, January, 1984.

MacKeown, P. K., "Gravity is Geometry." *The Physics Teacher*, December, 1984.

Motion in Two Dimensions

For Your Information

SUGGESTION: Ask what force makes the projectile move horizontally and what force makes it move vertically. Emphasize that there is only a vertical force on a projectile in the absence of air resistance.

Projectile motion is the curved motion of an object that is projected into the air.

GOALS

1. You will gain an understanding of the fundamentals of two-dimensional motion.
2. You will recognize the concepts on which projectile motion, uniform circular motion, and simple harmonic motion are based.
3. You will be able to solve problems based on these three types of two-dimensional motion.

The pitcher winds up and throws. The ball lands in the center of the catcher's mitt. But in what direction did the pitcher throw the ball to get it there? As soon as the ball leaves the pitcher's hand, the gravitational force acts on it, accelerating it toward Earth. The ball is a projectile; the path it follows is its trajectory. In this chapter we will study the motion of projectiles and other objects that move in two dimensions according to Newton's laws.

7:1 Independence of Motion in Two Dimensions

The photograph of two falling golf balls, Figure 7–1, was made with a strobe light that flashed 30 times each second. One ball was thrown horizontally at 2.0 m/s, the other ball was simply dropped. Notice that the thrown ball moves the same distance to the right between each time interval. That is, its horizontal velocity is constant. The dropped ball also has a constant horizontal velocity—zero. In each case there is no net horizontal force on the ball, so there is no horizontal acceleration.

The golf ball photograph shows a remarkable property of motion. Look carefully at the vertical displacement of the balls. At each flash, the vertical position of the dropped ball is the same as that of the thrown ball. This means that in terms of its vertical motion, the thrown ball acts just as if it had been dropped. In addition, the change in vertical position between each flash is the same for the two balls. This indicates that their vertical velocities also must be equal. The spaces between images grow larger because the balls are accelerated downward by the force of gravity.

$v_x + v_y$

John and Sally observed these water droplets sprayed into a sink. Recalling Newton's first law of motion, John states that he does not understand why the droplets are not traveling in a straight line. Sally indicates that the phenomenon is easily explained. What explanation does she give?

SUGGESTION: Point out to students that if an observer moved to the right at the correct speed, the ball projected horizontally would appear to fall straight down.

FIGURE 7–1. A flash photograph of two golf balls released simultaneously. Both balls were allowed to fall freely, but one was projected horizontally with an initial velocity of 2.00 m/s. The light flashes are 1/30 s apart.

The trajectory is the path of a projectile.

The horizontal and vertical velocities of a projectile are independent.

A frame of reference is the viewpoint of an observer of the motion. The shape of a trajectory depends on the frame of reference of the observer.

The photograph shows that the horizontal motion of the thrown ball does not affect its vertical motion at all.

Suppose that a bus passes as you stand by the side of a road. A passenger in the bus accidentally drops an apple out the window. Imagine that you can watch the apple only. What path will you see it take? The apple has the same horizontal velocity as the bus. The path will be curved like that of the thrown golf ball. Now think about what the path would look like to the passenger. Both the passenger and the apple move with the same horizontal velocity. Thus the passenger will see a straight path like that of the dropped golf ball. The trajectory as seen by the two observers will be different, but both observers will agree that it takes the same time for the apple to hit the ground. Thus the shape of the trajectory and the horizontal motion depend on the viewpoint, or frame of reference, of the observer. The time of fall does not.

The independence of vertical and horizontal motion can be used to determine the location and the time of fall of thrown objects. Consider

FIGURE 7–2. To observer A, the apple falls straight down. To observer B, the path of the apple is a parabola.

112 Motion in Two Dimensions

first a motion with constant horizontal velocity. If we call the horizontal displacement x and the horizontal velocity v_x, then the horizontal displacement at time t is

$$x = v_x t$$

In the same way, we will use y and v_y to describe the vertical displacement and velocity of the object. The equation describing the vertical motion is that of a body falling with constant acceleration. In fall time, t

$$y = v_y t + \tfrac{1}{2} g t^2$$

Horizontal velocity is constant; vertical velocity is constantly changing because of gravity.

Remember that displacement is the change in position, the final position less the initial position. Up is the positive direction, so the displacement of an object that moves downward is negative.

EXAMPLE

Projectile Launched Horizontally

A stone is thrown horizontally at $+15$ m/s from the top of a cliff 44 m high. **a.** How long does the stone take to reach the bottom of the cliff? **b.** How far from the base of the cliff does the stone strike ground? **c.** Sketch the trajectory of the stone.

Given: horizontal velocity
$v_x = +15$ m/s
initial vertical velocity
$v_y = 0$ m/s
vertical acceleration
$g = -9.80$ m/s^2
initial height 44 m

Unknowns: a. time interval t
b. horizontal
displacement x
Basic equations: $x = v_x t$
$y = v_y t + \tfrac{1}{2} g t^2$

Solution: If the initial height is 44 m, then the vertical displacement is $y = -44$ m.

a. $y = v_y t + \tfrac{1}{2} g t^2$, or with $v_y = 0$, $y = \tfrac{1}{2} g t^2$. Thus

$$t^2 = \frac{2y}{g}$$

$$= \frac{2(-44\text{ m})}{-9.80\text{ m/s}^2} = 9.0\text{ s}^2$$

$$t = \sqrt{9.0\text{ s}^2} = 3.0\text{ s}$$

b. $x = v_x t$
$= (+15\text{ m/s})(3.0\text{ s}) = +45\text{ m}$

c. See Figure 7–3.

Trajectory of stone

FIGURE 7–3. The path of a projectile thrown horizontally.

SUGGESTION: Have the students describe the path, with respect to Earth and the truck, of a ball shot straight up from a truck moving with a constant velocity.

Practice Exercises

1. A stone is thrown horizontally at a speed of $+5.0$ m/s from the top of a cliff 78.4 m high.
   a. How long does it take the stone to reach the bottom of the cliff?
   b. How far from the base of the cliff does the stone strike the ground?
   c. What are the horizontal and vertical components of the velocity of the stone as it hits the ground?
2. How would the three answers to Exercise 1 change if

FIGURE 7–4. The path of this diver can be analyzed by treating the diver as a projectile fired at an angle with the horizontal.

The trajectory of a projectile is a parabola.

FIGURE 7–5. The flight of a golf ball can be described in terms of horizontal and vertical components.

a. the stone were thrown with twice the horizontal speed?

b. the stone were thrown with the same speed but the cliff were twice as high?

3. A steel ball rolls with constant velocity on a tabletop 0.950 m high. It rolls off and hits the ground +0.352 m from the edge of the table. How fast was the ball rolling?

4. A beach ball, moving with a speed of +1.27 m/s, rolls off a pier and hits the water 0.75 m from the end of the pier. How high is the pier above the water?

PROBLEM SOLVING

When solving a projectile motion problem, the first task is to determine the horizontal and vertical components of the initial, or launching, velocity. Then the parts of the problem involving either component of the motion can be solved separately. For the sake of clarity, we will ignore air resistance in all problems involving projectile motion.

7:2 Projectile Motion

Figure 7–5a shows what happens when a golf ball, launched horizontally, bounces off a hard surface. After each bounce the ball begins a new trajectory. Figure 7–5b shows the vertical and horizontal velocity components during one of the bounces. The horizontal component, v_x, is constant because there is no force being exerted in the horizontal direction. The vertical component is large and positive at the beginning and decreases to zero at the top of the bounce. It then increases in the negative

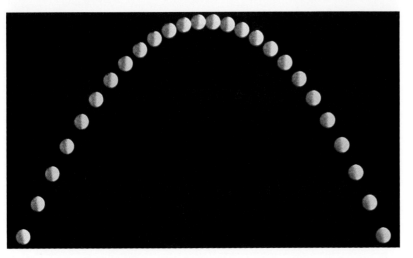

FIGURE 7–6. The time interval between each position of the ball is
1/30 of a second.

SUGGESTION: Relate projectiles to
various sports to get student interest.

direction as the projectile falls. When the object returns to its launch
height, the vertical speed is the same as it was at launch, but its direction
is reversed. The range is the horizontal distance traveled, R, in this figure.

The velocity of a projectile is resolved
into horizontal and vertical
components.

EXAMPLE

Projectiles Not Launched Horizontally

In the first complete bounce of the golf ball in Figure 7–5, the initial
velocity of the ball was 4.36 m/s at an angle of 81° above the horizontal. Find **a.** how long it took the ball to land, **b.** how high the ball
bounced, **c.** what its range was.

Given: initial velocity
v_i = 4.36 m/s at 81°

Unknowns: a. time in flight t
b. maximum vertical
displacement (height) y
c. range R

Basic equations: $x = v_x t$
$$y = v_y t + \tfrac{1}{2}gt^2$$

Find components of a vector by using
$v_x = v \cos \theta$, $v_y = v \sin \theta$. Note that
$v_x = v_y$ when $\theta = 45°$.

Solution: components of initial velocity
$$v_x = v_i \cos \theta = (4.36 \text{ m/s})(\cos 81°) = (4.36 \text{ m/s})(0.156)$$
$$= 0.680 \text{ m/s}$$
$$v_y = v_i \sin \theta = (4.36 \text{ m/s})(\sin 81°) = (4.36 \text{ m/s})(0.988)$$
$$= 4.31 \text{ m/s}$$

a. When it lands, the height $(y) = 0$.
$y = v_y t + \tfrac{1}{2}gt^2 = 0$. Therefore,
$$t = \frac{-2v_y}{g}$$
$$t = \frac{-2(4.31 \text{ m/s})}{(-9.80 \text{ m/s}^2)}$$
$$= 0.88 \text{ s}$$

When solving vector problems, the
horizontal and vertical motions are
treated separately.

b. The maximum height occurred at half the flight time, or 0.44 s after launch.

$$y = v_y t + \tfrac{1}{2} g t^2$$
$$= (4.31 \text{ m/s})(0.44 \text{ s}) + \tfrac{1}{2}(-9.8 \text{ m/s}^2)(0.44 \text{ s})^2$$
$$y = 1.9 \text{ m} - 0.95 \text{ m} = +0.95 \text{ m (up)}$$

c. The range is given by

$$R = v_x t$$
$$= (0.680 \text{ m/s})(0.88 \text{ s})$$
$$= 0.60 \text{ m}$$

SUGGESTION: Emphasize again that horizontal motion is constant in the absence of friction. The gravitational force makes the projectile slow down on the way up and speed up on the way down.

PROBLEM SOLVING

Always check a problem to see if your answers are reasonable. In this case, you can use the photo and the knowledge that there were 30 flashes per second. The flight time was calculated to be 0.88 s. At 30 flashes/second this would be 26.4 flashes. You can count 26 flash intervals during this bounce, so the answer is reasonable. The calculated maximum height is 0.95 m and the range is 0.60 m. The ratio of these two is 1.58/1. On the photo the ratio is 44 mm/28 mm = 1.57/1, also in reasonable agreement.

Practice Exercises

5. A golf ball is hit with a velocity of 24.5 m/s at 35.0° above the horizontal. Find
   a. the range of the ball.
   b. the maximum height of the ball.
6. A player kicks a football from ground level at 27.0 m/s at an angle of 30.0° above the horizontal. Find
   a. its "hang time," that is, the time the ball is in the air.
   b. the distance the ball travels before it hits the ground.
   c. its maximum height.
7. The kicker now kicks the ball with the same speed, but at 30.0° from the vertical, or 60.0° from the horizontal. Find
   a. its "hang time," that is, the time the ball is in the air.
   b. the distance the ball travels before it hits the ground.
   c. its maximum height.
8. Using the results for Exercises 6 and 7, compare qualitatively the flight times, ranges, and maximum heights for projectiles launched with high and low trajectories, when the high angle is the complement of the low angle. (The complement of angle θ is (90° − θ).)

7:3 Uniform Circular Motion

Your body cannot sense constant speed, but it is a sensitive accelerometer. Your stomach can sense the acceleration of an elevator or of an

If motion is circular, the centripetal acceleration is always at right angles to the instantaneous velocity of the object.

airplane in rough weather. Have you ever ridden in an amusement park ride similar to the one in Figure 7-7? If you have, you are aware of how your body feels when it is being accelerated. When the ride is not starting or stopping, the speed is constant, but the velocity is changing because its direction is changing. In this ride, the riders move with uniform circular motion.

You can find the acceleration of a body moving in a circle at constant speed by drawing a vector diagram like Figure 7-8a. Points A and B are two successive positions of an object that is moving with uniform circular motion. The radius of the circle is r. The radius and speed are constant, so the velocity is always perpendicular to the radius. That is, it is tangent to the circle. The vector v_1 represents the instantaneous velocity of the object at A. The vector v_2 represents the instantaneous velocity of the object at B. Note that the two vectors have the same length, but their directions are different.

Acceleration is the change in velocity, Δv, divided by the time interval, Δt. Δv is the difference between the two vectors, v_1 and v_2. To find Δv, place v_1 and v_2 tail to tail. In Chapter 6 you found a vector sum by placing two vectors head to tail. Consider Figure 7-8b. You can see that vector v_2 is the sum of v_1 and Δv. That is,

$$v_2 = v_1 + \Delta v, \text{ or}$$
$$\Delta v = v_2 - v_1$$

The size of Δv can be found by using a ratio of the sides of similar triangles ABC and DEF. The distance traveled by the object between point A and point B is the arc AB. If we choose A and B so they are close together, then arc AB is approximately equal to chord AB. Thus

$$\frac{\Delta v}{v} = \frac{chord \ AB}{r}$$

FIGURE 7-8. Vector diagrams can be used to analyze uniform circular motion.

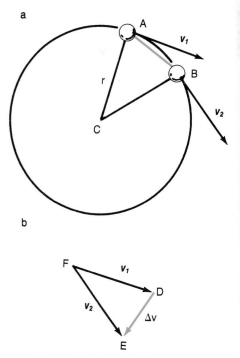

Vectors are subtracted by placing them tail to tail.

But the distance traveled in the time interval Δt is just $v\Delta t$. Thus we obtain

$$\frac{\Delta v}{v} = \frac{v\Delta t}{r}$$

Since acceleration is $\boldsymbol{a} = \dfrac{\Delta v}{\Delta t}$ we find

$$a = \frac{\Delta v}{\Delta t} = \frac{v^2}{r}$$

The direction of Δv can be seen in Figure 7–8b. By letting positions A and B become very close together, Δv is almost perpendicular to the two velocity vectors. That is, it is in the direction of the radius, pointing toward the center of the circle. Newton originated the word centripetal (sen TRIP uht uhl) for a quantity that always points toward the center of the circle. Centripetal means "center seeking." For this reason we call the acceleration just defined centripetal acceleration and write

$$a_c = \frac{\Delta v}{\Delta t} = \frac{v^2}{r}$$

Centripetal acceleration always points toward the center of the circle. It is directly proportional to the square of the speed and inversely proportional to the radius of the circle.

It is often difficult to measure the speed of an object, but easier to measure the time needed to make a complete revolution, T. The distance traveled is the circumference of the circle, $2\pi r$. The constant speed can be expressed as $v = 2\pi r/T$. This expression for v can be substituted into the equation for centripetal acceleration to yield

$$a_c = \frac{4\pi^2 r}{T^2}$$

b

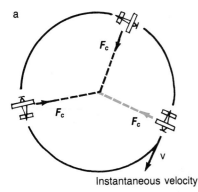

FIGURE 7–9. The force on a model plane in flight is directed toward the center of the circle (a). The plane would move in a straight path if the strings were cut (b).

a

Instantaneous velocity

A body is not accelerated unless a net force acts on it. The acceleration is in the same direction as the force. What supplies the force that gives a body centripetal acceleration? In the case of the amusement park ride, the drum exerts a force against the backs of the riders. The force that causes the centripetal acceleration of a model plane flying in a circle is the force of the string, often called the tension in the string. The moon orbits Earth with nearly uniform circular motion. Earth's gravity is the force that causes this acceleration. Because the force, as well as the acceleration, is toward the center of the circle, these forces are often called centripetal forces. To understand centripetal acceleration, it is very important to identify the source of the force. Then Newton's second law can be written in the form

Centripetal acceleration, like centripetal force, is always directed toward the center of the circle.

$$F_c = ma_c = \frac{mv^2}{r} = m\left(\frac{4\pi^2 r}{T^2}\right)$$

In what direction does an object fly if the force giving it centripetal acceleration suddenly stops? Consider an Olympic hammer thrower. The "hammer" is a heavy ball on a chain that the thrower whirls in a circle. As he whirls it at greater and greater speeds, his arms and the chain supply the force that gives it centripetal acceleration. At the correct time, he lets go of the chain. The hammer flies off in a straight line tangent to the circle. After its release, only the gravitational force is acting on it.

EXAMPLE

Uniform Circular Motion

SUGGESTION: Swing a stopper around in a circle and discuss its speed and velocity and what makes it keep moving in a circle.

A 0.013-kg rubber stopper is attached to a 0.93-m length of string. The stopper is swung in a horizontal circle, making one revolution in 1.18 s. **a.** Find the speed of the mass. **b.** Find its centripetal acceleration. **c.** Find the force the string exerts on it.

Given: mass $m = 0.013$ kg   Unknowns: **a.** speed v
      radius of circle $r = 0.93$ m   **b.** acceleration a_c
      period $T = 1.18$ s   **c.** force F_c

Basic equations: **a.** $v = \dfrac{2\pi r}{T}$ **c.** $F_c = ma_c$

        b. $a_c = \dfrac{v^2}{r}$

Solution: **a.** velocity $= \dfrac{\text{distance}}{\text{time}} = \dfrac{2\pi r}{T} = \dfrac{2(3.14)(0.93 \text{ m})}{1.18 \text{ s}}$

          $= \dfrac{5.8 \text{ m}}{1.18 \text{ s}} = 5.0$ m/s

     b. acceleration $a_c = \dfrac{v^2}{r} = \dfrac{(5.0 \text{ m/s})^2}{0.93 \text{ m}}$

          $= 27$ m/s^2 (radially inward)

   c. force $F_c = ma_c = (0.013 \text{ kg})(27 \text{ m/s}^2)$

          $= 0.35$ N (radially inward)

FIGURE 7–10. Vibrating objects undergo simple harmonic motion.

In simple harmonic motion, the force varies directly with the displacement from equilibrium.

For Your Information

The frequency of an object in SHM is equal to the inverse of the period, $f = 1/T$.

FIGURE 7–11. Simple harmonic motion can be shown by the vibrating of a mass on a spring.

Practice Exercises

9. Suppose the mass of the rubber stopper in the Example problem on page 119 is doubled, but all other quantities remain the same. How would the velocity, acceleration, and force change?

10. If the radius in the Example were twice as large, but all other quantities remained the same, how would velocity, acceleration, and force change?

11. Finally, if the stopper were swung in the same circle so it had a period half as large as in the Example, how would the answers change?

12. A runner moving at a speed of 8.8 m/s rounds a bend with a radius of 25 m.

  a. Find the centripetal acceleration of the runner.

  b. What supplies the force needed to give this acceleration to the runner?

7:4 Simple Harmonic Motion

A playground swing moves back and forth over the same path. A vibrating guitar string, a pendulum, and a mass on a rubber band or spring are other examples of back and forth or vibrational motion.

In each case, the object has an equilibrium or resting position. After the object is pulled away from the resting position, a force in the system pulls it back toward equilibrium. The force might be gravity, as in the case of the swing or pendulum. It could also be the stretch of the rubber band, guitar string, or spring. *If the force varies directly with the displacement, the motion is called* **simple harmonic motion** (SHM).

Objects in SHM can be described by two quantities, period and amplitude. The period, T, is the time needed to repeat one complete cycle of motion. The amplitude of the motion is the maximum distance the object moves from equilibrium position.

The force that a spring exerts increases linearly with the amount it is stretched or compressed. This relationship is called Hooke's law. The force is a restoring force. That is, it acts to oppose the force that stretched or compressed the spring. Because the force is also linear, the movement

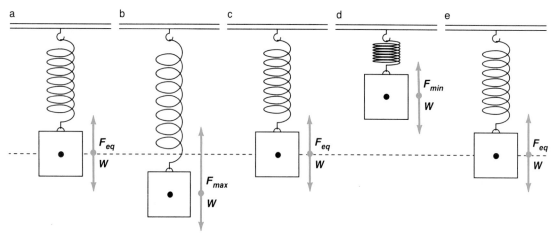

a   b   c   d   e

of a mass suspended on a spring is another example of simple harmonic motion.

Let us follow a mass on a spring through one complete cycle. At the equilibrium point, as shown in Figure 7–11a, the weight of the mass is balanced by the force of the spring, F_1. Suppose you exert enough force to pull the mass down a few centimeters, as shown in Figure 7–11b. When you let go, the restoring force of the spring is more than the weight. There is a net upward force, so the mass is accelerated upward. As the mass rises, the spring is stretched less and less. The force it exerts gradually decreases. As a result, the net force, and thus the acceleration, is less.

When the mass returns to its equilibrium position, the net force is again zero. Does the mass stop? According to Newton's laws, a force is needed to change motion. With no net force, the mass continues with its upward motion. When the mass is above the equilibrium position, the weight is larger than the force exerted by the spring. There is a net downward force and downward acceleration. The speed of the mass decreases. When the speed is zero, the mass is as high as it will go. Even though the speed is zero, there is a net downward force, and the mass accelerates down. When it again reaches the equilibrium position there is no force, but the downward motion continues. When the mass returns to its lowest location, the cycle of motion starts over. One period, T, has elapsed. The period depends on the mass and stiffness of the spring. It does not depend on the amplitude of the motion.

For Your Information

Galileo is said to have discovered the periodic nature of the motion of a pendulum while watching the swinging of a chandelier in the cathedral in Pisa. Galileo discovered the principle of the pendulum when he was a teenager.

The period is the time required to finish one complete revolution.

The period of a spring can be calculated using the equation $T = 2\pi\sqrt{m/k}$, where k is the constant describing the stiffness of the spring.

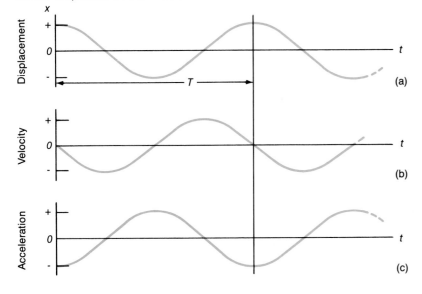

Figure 7–12 shows graphs of the position, velocity, and acceleration of the mass through two periods. Notice that the speed is largest when the acceleration is zero, that is, when the distance from the equilibrium position is also zero. At the high and low points of the motion the acceleration is greatest, but the speed is zero; the mass is at rest for an instant.

The swing of a pendulum also demonstrates SHM. A simple pendulum consists of a mass (the bob) suspended by a string of length ℓ. The bob swings back and forth. The force on the bob when it is pulled away from

FIGURE 7–12. The graph in (a) shows the displacement, *d*, with respect to time, *t*. The velocity, *v*, and acceleration, *a*, with respect to time are shown in (b) and (c), respectively. Note how the amplitudes and the relative phases of the three curves are related.

A pendulum making small swings undergoes simple harmonic motion.

a

A   E   B

b

FIGURE 7–13. The motion of a simple pendulum (a). The motion of the pendulum of a clock is an example of simple harmonic motion (b).

The period of a pendulum depends on its length and the acceleration due to gravity, but not on its mass.

FIGURE 7–14. The gravitational acceleration of a pendulum can be resolved into two components.

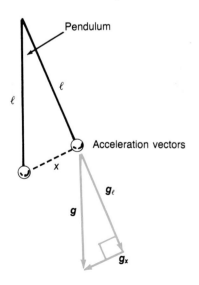

Pendulum

ℓ

ℓ

x

Acceleration vectors

g_ℓ

g

g_x

the vertical is shown in Figure 7–14. The gravitational force, the weight, W, is resolved into two components. F_y is parallel to the string. It is balanced by the force exerted by the string. The component F_x is at right angles to the direction of the string. This component is unbalanced and is the net force that causes the acceleration of the bob. When the bob is pulled to the right, F_x is to the left, and vice versa. That is, the component of the weight, F_x, is a restoring force. Further, for small angles (θ less than 15°) the magnitude of F_x is proportional to the displacement of the bob. Thus pendulum motion is an example of SHM.

The period of the simple pendulum of length ℓ is given by the equation

$$T = 2\pi\sqrt{\frac{\ell}{g}}$$

Notice that the period depends only on the length of the pendulum, not its mass or amplitude. A measurement of the length and period of a pendulum can be used to measure the local value of the gravitational acceleration, g.

The amplitude of any vibrating object can be greatly increased by applying small external forces at regular intervals of time. This effect is called **mechanical resonance.** You were probably first introduced to resonance when you learned to "pump" a playground swing. You found that you could increase the amplitude of the swing if you applied forces to it at just the right times. The time interval between the applied forces had to equal the period of the swing. Other familiar examples of mechanical resonance include rocking a car to free it from a snow bank and jumping up and down on a trampoline or diving board. Resonances can also cause damage. Soldiers do not march across bridges in cadence. The rhythm of their steps could create large oscillations caused by their steps resonating

FIGURE 7–15. A swing is an example of a simple pendulum.

SUGGESTION: Relate simple harmonic motion to the projection of circular motion.

with the natural period of the bridge. The Tacoma Narrows bridge swung so violently in a windstorm that it broke apart because the wind forces resonated with the bridge's natural frequency of motion.

Practice Exercises

13. What is the length of a simple pendulum whose period is 1.00 s? Assume normal g.

14. If $f = 1/T$ for an object in SHM, write the equation for f of a pendulum in terms of ℓ and g.

15. Using the formula from Exercise 14, find the frequency of a pendulum 0.40 m long.

16. What is the period of the pendulum in Exercise 15?

For Your Information

The bridge that replaced the Tacoma Narrows bridge was built with air passages through the road surface to give the road a variable frequency.

For Your Information

Physics you can do: Use a yo-yo or any other mass on the end of a string to get some experience with resonance. First gently swing the mass back and forth to get a feel for its natural motion. Then, very slightly vibrate the hand holding the string back and forth. First try longer periods of motion, then speed them up until they match the natural period. Finally, go to much faster vibrations. Note that the movement of the mass is much greater when the period of your hand's motion equals the natural period.

FIGURE 7–16. Jumping up and down on a trampoline is an example of mechanical resonance.

SUMMARY

1. The horizontal and vertical motions of a projectile are independent of one another. **7:1**

2. If air resistance is ignored, a projectile moves with constant velocity horizontally and constant acceleration vertically. **7:2**

3. The trajectory of a projectile launched at an angle depends on the horizontal and vertical components of its initial velocity. **7:2**

4. A body moving in uniform circular motion has a constant speed and is accelerated toward the center of the circle. **7:3**

5. An object moving with simple harmonic motion (SHM) moves back and forth with a constant period. **7:4**

6. Mechanical resonance can greatly increase the amplitude of SHM when a small periodic net force acts on an oscillating object at its natural period. **7:4**

QUESTIONS

1. Where in its trajectory is the speed of a projectile smallest? largest?

2. Describe the variations in the acceleration of a projectile over its trajectory.

3. What relationship must exist between an applied force and a moving mass if uniform circular motion is to result?

4. Distinguish between the period and the amplitude of a pendulum.

5. Describe the relationship between the force and the displacement in simple harmonic motion.

6. Consider the trajectory of the ball in Figure 7–17.

   a. At which point is the vertical velocity the greatest?

   b. At which point is the horizontal velocity the greatest?

   c. Where is the vertical velocity least?

   d. Name the curve traveled by the ball.

FIGURE 7–17. Use with Question 6.

7. Trajectories for two batted baseballs are shown in Figure 7–18. Choose the trajectory for which

   a. the flight time is smallest.

   b. the flight time is largest.

   c. the horizontal velocity is largest.

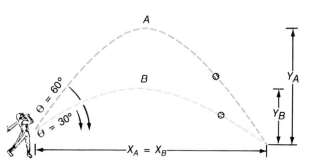

FIGURE 7–18. Use with Question 7.

8. An airplane pilot flying at constant velocity and altitude drops a flare. Ignoring air resistance, where will the plane be relative to the flare when the flare hits the ground?

9. Discuss whether you can go around a curve

   a. with zero acceleration.

   b. with constant acceleration.

10. Suppose an astronaut carries a pendulum to the moon. Would the period of the pendulum be shorter, longer, or the same on the moon as on Earth?

APPLYING CONCEPTS

1. A zoologist standing on a high platform aims a tranquilizer gun at a monkey hanging from a distant tree branch by one hand. The barrel of the gun is parallel to the horizontal. Just as the zoologist pulls the trigger, the monkey lets go of the branch and begins to fall. Will the dart hit the monkey?

2. A friend who is competing in the long jump asks you to explain the physics of this event. Does the height of the jump make any difference? What does influence the length of the jump?

3. Imagine you are sitting in a car tossing a ball straight up into the air.
   a. If the car moves with constant velocity, will the ball land in front of, behind, or in your hand?
   b. If the car rounds a curve at constant speed, where will the ball land?

4. When a mass vibrating on a spring passes through the equilibrium position, there is no net force on it. Why is the velocity not zero at this point? What quantity is zero?

5. If you find a pendulum clock running slightly fast, how can you adjust it to keep better time? Explain.

6. Name several naturally occurring repetitive phenomena that might be used as fairly reliable time standards.

7. A batter hits a pop-up straight up over home plate at an initial velocity of 20 m/s. The ball is caught by the catcher at the same height that it was hit. At what velocity will the ball land in the catcher's mitt?

8. A student is practicing with a remote-controlled race car on the balcony of a 6th-floor condominium. An accidental turn sends the car through the railing and off the edge of the balcony. How far does the car fall in 1 s? Does the distance the car falls depend on the velocity with which it speeds off the edge?

9. To provide "gravity" for future space colonists, engineers have proposed a giant wheel rotating around a central axis. Why would this design simulate gravity? Which way is down?

EXERCISES

1. A pitched baseball is thrown horizontally a distance of +18.3 m at +44.8 m/s.
   a. How long does the ball take to reach home plate?
   b. How far does the ball drop during its flight?
   c. Find the distance the ball drops during the first and second halves of its flight.

d. How does a batter react to such a pitch?

2. A dart player throws a dart horizontally at a speed of +12.4 m/s. The dart hits the board 0.32 m below the height from which it was thrown. How far away is the player from the board?

3. A pitched ball is hit by a batter at a 45° angle. It just clears the outfield fence, 98 m away. The fence is the same height as the pitch, so make the height of the fence zero. Find the velocity of the ball when it left the bat.

4. A high-speed fan rotates at 1800 revolutions per minute. A piece of gum with a mass of 0.0050 kg is stuck to a blade 25 cm from the center.
   a. Find the velocity of the gum.
   b. What is the acceleration of the gum?
   c. What force is needed to hold the gum to the blade?

5. A stone is thrown horizontally at 8.0 m/s from a cliff 78.4 m high. How far from the base of the cliff does the stone strike the ground?

6. A bridge is 176.4 m above a river. If a lead-weighted fishing line is thrown from the bridge with a horizontal speed of 22 m/s, what horizontal displacement does it have before striking the water?

7. a. If an object falls from a resting height of 490 m, how long does it remain in the air?
   b. If the object has a horizontal velocity of 2.00 × 10^2 m/s when it begins to fall, what horizontal displacement will it have?

8. A toy car runs off the edge of a table that is 1.225 m high. If the car lands 0.40 m from the base of the table,
   a. how long does it take for the car to fall to the floor?
   b. What is the horizontal velocity of the car?

9. Divers at Acapulco dive from a cliff that is 61 m high. If the rocks below the cliff extend outward for 23 m, what is the minimum horizontal velocity a diver must have to clear the rocks safely?

10. A mortar shell is fired at an angle of 53° with a speed of 98 m/s.
    a. How long is the shell in the air?
    b. How far does it travel before hitting the ground?
    c. How high does it reach?

11. A baseball is hit at 30.0 m/s at an angle of 53.0° with the horizontal. An outfielder runs 4.00 m/s toward the infield and catches the ball. What was the original distance between the batter and the outfielder?

12. During the hammer throw, an athlete whirls a 7.00-kg hammer tied to the end of a 1.3-m chain in a horizontal circle. The hammer moves at the rate of 1.0 rev/s.
    a. What is the centripetal acceleration of the hammer?
    b. What is the tension in the chain?

13. A coin is placed on a phonograph record revolving at 33⅓ revolutions per minute.
    a. In what direction is the acceleration of the coin, if any?
    b. Find the acceleration of the coin when it is placed 5, 10, and 15 cm from the center of the record.
    c. What force accelerates the coin?
    d. At which of the three radii listed in **b** would the coin be most likely to fly off? Why?

14. A string can exert a force of 4 N without breaking. The string is used to whirl a 0.5-kg mass in a horizontal circle. A 0.87-m length is used. Find the minimum period at which the mass can be swung without the string breaking.

15. A pendulum has a length of 0.67 m.
    a. Find its period.
    b. How long would the pendulum have to be to double the period?
    c. Why is your answer to part **b** not just double the length?

16. In a cyclotron, protons with mass 1.657×10^{-27} kg move in a circular path of radius 1.20 m in a large electromagnet. If the velocity of the protons is 2.0×10^6 m/s, find
    a. the time it takes the protons to complete one revolution.
    b. the force the magnet exerts on the protons.

17. A child whirls a yo-yo in a horizontal circle. The yo-yo has a mass of 0.20 kg and is attached to a string 0.80 m long.
    a. If the yo-yo makes one complete revolution each second, what force does the string exert on it?

    b. If the child increases the speed of the yo-yo to 2 revolutions per second, what force does the string now exert?
    c. What is the ratio of answer (b) to (a)? Why?

18. It takes a 615-kg racing car 14.3 s to travel at a uniform speed around a circular racetrack of 50.0 m radius.
    a. What is the acceleration of the car?
    b. What average force must the track exert on the car's tires to produce this acceleration?

19. An early major objection to the idea that Earth is spinning on its axis was that Earth would turn so fast at the equator that people would be thrown off into space. Show the error in this logic by calculating
    a. the speed of a person at the equator. The radius of Earth is about 6400 km.
    b. the centripetal acceleration of the person.
    c. the force needed to hold a 97-kg person in place at the equator.
    d. the force of gravity (weight) of such a person.

20. Look at the carnival ride in Figure 7–7. It has a 2.0-m radius and rotates 1.1 times per second.
    a. Find the speed of a rider.
    b. Find the centripetal acceleration of a rider.
    c. What produces this acceleration?
    d. When the floor drops down, riders are held up by friction. What coefficient of friction is needed to keep the riders from slipping?

21. A yo-yo is oscillating like a pendulum on the end of its string of length ℓ. Just as the yo-yo passes the midpoint of its swing, the operator loops the string so it is exactly half its original length. In terms of the original period, T, what is the new period?

PROBLEMS

1. A 75-kg pilot flies a plane in a loop. At the top of the loop, where the plane is completely upside-down for an instant, the pilot hangs freely in the seat and does not push against the seat belt. The airspeed indicator reads 120 m/s. What is the radius of the plane's loop?

2. Trailing by two points, and with only 2.0 s remaining in the game, a player shoots the basketball at an angle of 60° with the horizontal at a velocity of 10 m/s. The ball is released 1.8 m

above the floor and swishes the net of the basket, which is 3.0 m above the floor.

  a. How much time is left in the game when the basket is made?

  b. Shots made outside a semicircle of 6-m radius from a spot directly beneath the basket are awarded 3 points, while those inside score 2 points. Did the player tie the game or put the team ahead?

3. A gun is sighted directly at a target 150 m away. If the bullet has a velocity of 500 m/s as it leaves the barrel of the gun, how far below the target does the bullet strike?

4. A watermelon is rolled off a high diving platform with a velocity of 2.8 m/s and lands in the water 2.6 s later. How high is the platform, and how far from the base of the platform does the watermelon land?

5. Find the length of a pendulum oscillating on the moon that would have the same period as a 1.0 m pendulum oscillating on Earth. The moon's gravity is one-sixth of Earth's.

6. An airplane traveling 1001 m above the ocean at 125 km/h is to drop a box of supplies to shipwrecked victims below.

  a. How many seconds before being directly overhead should the box be dropped?

  b. How far horizontally is the plane from the victims when it is dropped?

READINGS

Brancazio, Peter, "Getting a Kick Out of Physics." *Discover*, November, 1984.

Buethe, Chris, and Dick Simon, "Physics at the Indy 500." *The Physics Teacher*, May, 1988.

Eskow, Dennis, "A Mach 20 Airliner." *Popular Mechanics*, November, 1984.

Flynn, George J., "The Physics of Aircraft Flight." *The Physics Teacher*, September, 1987.

Greenslade, Thomas, "More Bicycle Physics." *The Physics Teacher*, September, 1983.

Lamb, William, "Bulldozing Your Way Through Projectile Motion." *Science Teacher*, November, 1983.

Strange, Curtis, "Curtis in Control: You Can't Play Golf Until You Have Control Over Your Swing and Over Yourself." *Golf Magazine*, November, 1988.

CHAPTER 8

Universal Gravitation

SUGGESTION: Use this chapter to emphasize how a theory develops and how many people contribute to new theories.

GOALS

1. You will gain a knowledge and understanding of the law of universal gravitation.
2. You will be able to use Newton's and Kepler's laws to describe the motion of Earth and other planets, as well as objects near Earth.
3. You will understand the concepts of weightlessness and freefall and relate these to Einstein's theory of relativity.

For Your Information

Edmund Halley was a clerk for the Royal Society. He edited sections of Newton's *Principia* and even paid for its printing.

For Your Information

". . . from the time of Kepler to that of Newton, and from Newton to Hartley, not only all things in external nature, but the subtlest mysteries of life and organization and even of the intellect and moral being, were conjured within the magic circle of mathematical formulae."
–Samuel Taylor Coleridge

Comets were once considered bearers of evil omens. These mysterious bodies appeared without warning, spouting bright tails that sometimes covered one quarter of the sky. Edmund Halley studied one comet carefully in 1682. He recognized that it was the same comet seen in 1607 and 1531. Based on Newton's law of universal gravitation, Halley and others were able to show that comets were merely one of a large number of objects that circled the sun. The origin and composition of comets is still a mystery, however. One of the artificial satellites that approached Comet Halley in 1987 captured photographs of the peanut-shaped core of the comet.

8:1 Kepler's Laws of Planetary Motion

As a boy of fourteen in Denmark, Tycho Brahe (1546–1601) observed an eclipse of the sun on August 21, 1560. Amazed that astronomers had predicted the event, he vowed to become an astronomer. In 1563 he observed two planets in conjunction, that is, located at the same point in the sky. The time that all the current books predicted for this event was wrong by two days, so Brahe decided to dedicate his life to making accurate predictions of astronomical events.

Brahe traveled throughout Europe for five years studying astronomy and collecting instruments. In 1576 he persuaded King Frederick II of Den-

Round and Round

An astronaut, the space shuttle, and a satellite are seen floating nearby, all apparently weightless. Kim and Ann are debating whether or not it is possible for a satellite to have an Earth orbit with a period of 80 minutes and a corresponding velocity of 8.05×10^3 m/s. Kim states that a satellite permitted to fall toward Earth would increase its velocity to the desired speed and go into a lower orbit. Ann believes that it is impossible for a satellite to travel that fast in Earth orbit. Who is correct?

FIGURE 8–1. An early engraving of Tycho Brahe at work in his laboratory.

SUGGESTION: Tell your students why Kepler was driven to find the true paths of planets after finding Tycho's measurements were wrong by only eight minutes of arc (one-fourth the width of the moon).

Tycho Brahe made very accurate measurements of the positions of planets and stars before the telescope was invented.

For Your Information

Galileo was summoned to appear before the Inquisition in 1633 and forced to reject the Copernican theory that Earth moves about the sun.

SUGGESTION: Explain that Kepler's laws are now known to be the result of conservation of energy and angular momentum.

FIGURE 8–2. An imaginary line from Earth to the sun sweeps out equal areas each second whether Earth is close to or far from the sun.

mark to give him the island of Hven, where Brahe then built the finest observatory of its time. For over 20 years Brahe carefully recorded the positions of the planets and stars. Telescopes had not been invented, so he used huge instruments like those in Figure 8–1.

In 1597, out of favor with the new Danish King, Brahe moved to Prague where, in 1600, the German Johannes Kepler (1571–1630) became one of his assistants. Kepler wanted to use a sun-centered system to explain Brahe's exact data. He was convinced that geometry and mathematics could be used to explain the number, distance, and motion of the planets. By doing a careful mathematical analysis of Brahe's data, Kepler discovered three laws that still describe the behavior of every planet and satellite. However, the theories he developed to explain his laws are no longer considered correct. The three laws can be stated as follows.

1. The paths of the planets are ellipses with the sun at one focus.
2. An imaginary line from the sun to a planet sweeps out equal areas in equal time intervals whether the planet is close to or far from the sun (Figure 8–2).

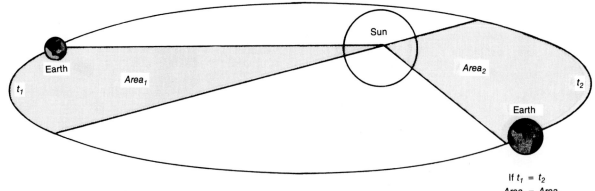

3. The ratio of the squares of the periods of any two planets revolving about the sun is equal to the ratio of the cubes of their average distances from the sun. Thus if T_a and T_b are their periods and r_a and r_b their average distances,

$$\left(\frac{T_a}{T_b}\right)^2 = \left(\frac{r_a}{r_b}\right)^3$$

Notice that the first two laws apply to each planet, moon, or satellite individually. The third law relates the motion of several satellites about a single body. For example, it can be used to compare the distances and periods of the planets about the sun or the distances and periods of the moon and artificial satellites around Earth.

SUGGESTION: Actually these laws are applicable to motion in any conic section (ellipse, parabola, hyperbola, as well as circle).

For Your Information

Johannes Kepler's eyesight was so poor that he could not use a telescope himself. That did not stop him, however, from discovering the scientific principles involved in the manner in which a telescope handled light.

EXAMPLE

Using Kepler's Third Law to Find an Orbital Period

Galileo discovered four moons of Jupiter. Io, which he measured to be 4.2 units from the center of Jupiter, has a period of 1.8 days. He measured the radius of Ganymede's orbit as 10.7 units. Use Kepler's third law to find the period of Ganymede.

Given: for Io
period T_b = 1.8 days
radius r_b = 4.2 units
for Ganymede
radius r_a = 10.7 units

Unknown: Ganymede's period T_a

Basic equation: $\left(\dfrac{T_a}{T_b}\right)^2 = \left(\dfrac{r_a}{r_b}\right)^3$

Solution: $T_a{}^2 = T_b{}^2\left(\dfrac{r_a}{r_b}\right)^3$

$$= (1.8 \text{ days})^2 \left(\frac{10.7 \text{ units}}{4.2 \text{ units}}\right)^3$$

$$= (3.2 \text{ days}^2)(16.5)$$

$$= 52.8 \text{ days}^2$$

$$T_a = 7.3 \text{ days}$$

For Your Information

Kepler calculated that the first voyages to the moon would take four hours. He felt that the passengers should take narcotics to endure the trip.

FIGURE 8–3. The planet Jupiter and its moons (a). Io, one of Jupiter's moons, appears yellow because of sulfur deposits (b). Callisto, the fourth moon of Jupiter, is covered with ice (c).

a

b

c

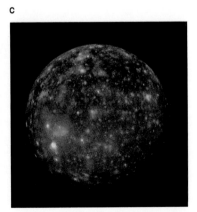

Notice that when working ratio problems, you do not need to convert all units to meters and seconds. You must, however, use the same units throughout the problem.

EXAMPLE

Using Kepler's Third Law to Find an Orbital Radius

The fourth moon of Jupiter, Callisto, has a period of 16.7 days. Find its distance from Jupiter using the same units Galileo used.

Given: for Io
period T_b = 1.8 days
radius r_b = 4.2 units
for Callisto
period T_a = 16.7 days

Unknown: Callisto's radius r_a

Basic equation: $\left(\dfrac{T_a}{T_b}\right)^2 = \left(\dfrac{r_a}{r_b}\right)^3$

Solution: $r_a{}^3 = r_b{}^3\left(\dfrac{T_a}{T_b}\right)^2$

$$= (4.2 \text{ units})^3\left(\dfrac{16.7 \text{ days}}{1.8 \text{ days}}\right)^2$$

$$= (74.1 \text{ units}^3)(86.1)$$

$$= 6.38 \times 10^3 \text{ units}^3$$

$$r_a = 18.5 \text{ units}$$

PROBLEM SOLVING

When working with equations that involve squares and square roots, or cubes and cube roots, your solution is more precise if you keep at least one extra digit in your calculations until you reach the end. When you use Kepler's third law to find the radius of the orbit of a planet or satellite, first solve the cube of the radius, then take the cube root. This is easier to do if your calculator has a cube-root key ($\sqrt[3]{}$). If your calculator has a key y^x (or x^y), you can also find the cube root. Check the instructions of your calculator, but you usually enter the cube of the radius, press the y^x key, then enter .3333333 and press equals.

Practice Exercises

1. Earth moves more slowly in its orbit in summer than in winter. Is it closer to the sun in summer or in winter?

2. An asteroid revolves around the sun with an orbital radius twice that of Earth. Find the period of the asteroid in earth years.

3. Mars is, on the average, 1.52 times as far from the sun as is Earth. Find the time required for Mars to circle the sun in earth days.

4. The moon has a period of 27.3 days and is 3.90×10^5 km from the center of Earth. Find the period of an artificial satellite that is 6.70×10^3 km from the center of Earth.

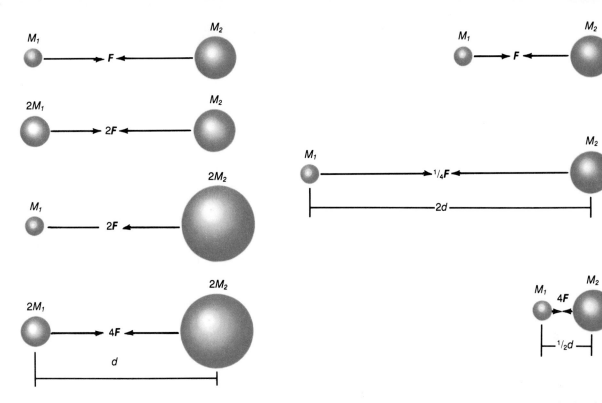

8:2 Universal Gravitation

Kepler was, perhaps, the first modern physicist. He was the first scientist to base laws on precise observations, to express them in terms of equations, and to suggest a physical reason for the laws. Some 45 years later, in 1666, Isaac Newton was living at home in rural England because the plague had closed all schools. Newton had used mathematical arguments to show that if the path of a planet were an ellipse, in agreement with Kepler's first law, then the net force on the planet must vary inversely with the square of the distance between the planet and the sun. That is, he could write an equation

$$F \propto \frac{1}{d^2}$$

where the symbol $\propto$ means "is proportional to," and d is the average distance between the centers of the bodies. He further showed that the force was in the direction of a line connecting the centers of the bodies. But Newton could go no further because he could not measure the magnitude of the force, F.

Newton later wrote that the sight of a falling apple made him think of the problem of the motion of the planets. Newton recognized that the apple fell straight down because Earth attracted it. Might not this force extend beyond the trees, to the clouds, to the moon, and even beyond? Gravity could even be the force that attracts the planets to the sun. Further, Newton's own third law of motion said that the apple would also attract Earth. Newton.decided that the force of attraction must be proportional to the mass of the apple and the mass of Earth. Finally, he was so

FIGURE 8-4. The gravitational force between any two bodies varies directly as the product of their masses and inversely as the square of the distance between them.

Newton proposed that the motion of the moon around Earth was the result of the gravitational forces between Earth and the moon.

The gravitational force varies inversely with the square of the distance between the bodies.

SUGGESTION: Have the class practice the inverse square relationship orally using many different examples.

Newton proposed that the force that causes objects to fall to Earth exists between all other bodies, even the sun and planets.

For Your Information

There is one part of the legend of Newton and the apple that is not true. When the apple fell, it did not hit Newton on the head.

FIGURE 8–5. Gravitational forces hold the stars in their relative positions in this spiral galaxy.

The law of universal gravitation is valid for any two bodies.

confident that the laws that governed motion on Earth could work anywhere that he assumed that the force of attraction acted between any two masses, m_1 and m_2. Thus he wrote

$$F = G\,\frac{m_1 m_2}{d^2}$$

The gravitational force is proportional to the mass of each of the two bodies.

where G is a universal constant. This equation means that if the mass of a planet were doubled, the force of attraction would be doubled. Similarly, if the planet were attracted toward a star with twice the mass of the sun, the force would be twice as great. And, if the planet were twice the distance from the sun, the force would be only one-quarter as strong.

SUGGESTION: Note that d is the distance between the centers of mass of the objects. It took Newton 20 years to prove that this law is valid for large bodies as well as point particles.

8:3   Newton's Test of the Inverse Square Law

If Newton's idea that Earth's attraction of an apple extended to the moon were correct, he would not need to measure the force directly. The force of Earth's gravity on the moon is

Newton tested the law of universal gravitation as applied to the motion of the moon about Earth.

$$F_{grav} = G\,\frac{M_e M_m}{r_{em}{}^2}$$

where M_e is the mass of Earth, M_m the mass of the moon, and r_{em} the radius of the moon's orbit about the center of Earth. Newton did not know G, M_e, or M_m, but he found a way of calculating the product GM_e. On the surface of Earth the gravitational force on a mass m is its weight, mg. Calling R_e the radius of Earth, he wrote

$$mg = G\,\frac{M_e m}{R_e{}^2} \quad \text{or} \quad GM_e = gR_e{}^2$$

SUGGESTION: Point out that Newton couldn't determine the proportionality constant because the mass of Earth was unknown.

Thus

$$F_{grav} = M_m g\!\left(\frac{R_e}{r_{em}}\right)^2$$

134   Universal Gravitation

Now he applied his second law. The acceleration of the moon is its centripetal acceleration. The acceleration is written in terms of the period of the moon, T. That is, T is the time required for the moon to make one revolution about Earth.

$$M_m g \left(\frac{R_e}{r_{em}}\right)^2 = M_m \frac{4\pi^2 r_{em}}{T^2}$$

Newton solved this equation for the period of the moon, obtaining

$$T = \frac{2\pi}{R_e} \sqrt{\frac{r_{em}^3}{g}}$$

Newton knew g, the radius of Earth, R_e, and that the radius of the moon's orbit is 60 Earth radii. He calculated $T = 27$ days. The correct period of the moon is $27\frac{1}{3}$ days. Newton knew that the numbers he had put into the formula were approximations, and wrote that his calculation "answered pretty nearly."

Newton's gravitational law applied to the motion of the moon. Would it also explain the motion of the planets about the sun? Newton used the symbol M_p for the mass of the planet, M_s for the mass of the sun, and r_{ps} for their distance apart. He then used the second law, $F = ma$, with F the gravitational force and a the centripetal acceleration. That is

Newton's second law, $F = ma$, states that if the force varies as $1/d^2$, so does the resulting acceleration.

$$G \frac{M_s M_p}{r_{ps}^2} = M_p \frac{4\pi^2 r_{ps}}{T_p^2}$$

where T_p is the time required for the planet to make one complete revolution about the sun. He rearranged the equation in the form

$$\frac{T_p^2}{r_{ps}^3} = \frac{4\pi^2}{M_s G}$$

This equation is Kepler's third law: the square of the period is proportional to the cube of the distance. The proportionality constant depends only on the mass of the sun and Newton's universal gravitational constant, G. It

Thin wire

Large mass

Small mass

FIGURE 8–7. Cavendish verified the existence of gravitational forces between masses by using an apparatus similar to that shown.

Cavendish tested the law of universal gravitation between small masses on Earth.

SUGGESTION: Because the law of gravitation is universal, G is the same for any two bodies. Knowing G, Cavendish could determine the mass of Earth.

does not depend on any property of the planet. Thus Newton's law of gravitation not only leads to Kepler's third law but it also predicts the value of the constant. In our derivation of this equation we have assumed the orbits of the planets are circles. Newton found the same result for elliptical orbits.

8:4 Weighing Earth

As you know, the force of attraction between two objects on Earth is very small. You cannot feel the slightest attraction even between two massive bowling balls. In fact, it took 100 years after Newton's work before an apparatus was sensitive enough to measure the force. In 1798 the Englishman Henry Cavendish (1731–1810) used equipment like that sketched in Figure 8–7. A rod about 20 cm long had two small lead balls attached. The rod was suspended by a thin wire so it could rotate. Cavendish measured the force needed to rotate the rod through given angles. Then he placed two large lead balls close to the small ones. The force of attraction between the balls caused the rod to rotate. By measuring the angle through which it turned, Cavendish was able to find the force between the masses. He found that the force agreed with Newton's law of gravitation.

Cavendish measured the masses of the balls and the distances between their centers. Substituting these values for force, mass, and distance into Newton's law, he found the value of G.

Newton's law of universal gravitation says

$$F_g = G\,\frac{m_1 m_2}{d^2}$$

When m_1 and m_2 are measured in kilograms, d in meters, and F_g in newtons, then $G = 6.67 \times 10^{-11}$ Nm²/kg². For example, the attractive gravitational force between two bowling balls, each of mass 7.26 kg, with

FIGURE 8–8. This map shows variations in the force of gravity throughout the United States and Canada. Milligals are units of gravitational acceleration.

their centers separated by 0.30 m is

$$F_g = \frac{(6.67 \times 10^{-11} \text{ Nm}^2/\text{kg}^2)(7.26 \text{ kg})(7.26 \text{ kg})}{(0.30 \text{ m})^2} = 3.91 \times 10^{-8} \text{ N}$$

Cavendish's experiment is often called "weighing the earth." You know that on Earth's surface the gravitational attraction of Earth is the weight of an object: $F_g = W = mg$. According to Newton, however, $F_g = GM_em/R_e^2$. The two results must be equal, so $g = GM_e/R_e^2$. Because Cavendish measured the constant G, we can rearrange this equation as $M_e = gR_e^2/G$. Using modern values of the constants we find

$$M_e = \frac{(9.80 \text{ m/s}^2)(6.37 \times 10^6 \text{ m})^2}{6.67 \times 10^{-11} \text{ Nm}^2/\text{kg}^2} = 5.96 \times 10^{24} \text{ kg}$$

Comparing the mass of Earth to that of a bowling ball, you can see why the gravitational attraction of everyday objects cannot be easily sensed.

Newton's law can also be used to find the weight of an object at any given distance from Earth. Since $W = F_g$,

$$W = \frac{GM_em}{d^2}$$

Thus the weight of an object of mass m varies inversely with the square of its distance, d, from the center of Earth. The weight of a body is slightly less on high mountains than at sea level.

Because the mass of an object does not depend on gravitational force, we can rewrite the equation for weight in terms of the acceleration due to gravity, at any distance from Earth, g'.

$$g' = \frac{W}{m} = G\frac{M_e}{d^2}, \text{ or } g' = g\left(\frac{R_e}{d}\right)^2$$

By examining the second equation you can see that for an object on the surface of Earth $d = R_e$, and $g' = g$. When the object is 6400 km above Earth's surface $d = 2R_e$ and $g' = g/4$. Figure 8–11 shows how weight depends on the distance from the center of Earth.

8:5 Satellites

Newton used the Figure 8–10 to illustrate a "thought experiment." Consider a cannon on a high mountain that shoots a cannonball horizontally. During the first second the ball is in flight it falls 4.9 m. The ball follows a parabolic trajectory (D). If the speed of the ball increases, the ball will travel farther around Earth, but it will still fall 4.9 m in the first second of flight. Meanwhile, the surface of Earth is curved. If the ball goes just fast enough, after one second it will reach a point where Earth has

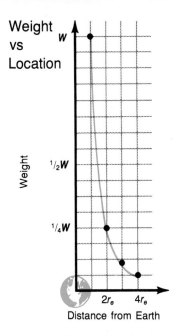

Weight vs Location

FIGURE 8–9. The change in gravitational force with distance follows the inverse square law.

Cavendish was able to measure, experimentally, the constant G in Newton's law of universal gravitation.

SUGGESTION: Comment on the fact that Kepler's constant is just for objects revolving around the sun and will be different for objects revolving around other bodies, whereas Newton's constant G is the same throughout the universe.

FIGURE 8–10. If the cannonball travels 8 km horizontally in 1 s, it will fall the same distance toward Earth as Earth falls from the cannonball.

curved 4.9 m away from the horizontal. That is, the curvature of Earth will just match the curvature of the trajectory, and the ball will orbit Earth.

Figure 8–10 shows that Earth curves away from a line tangent to its surface at a rate of 4.9 meters for every 8 km. That is, the altitude of the line tangent to Earth at *A* will be 4.9 m above Earth at *B*. If the cannonball in Figure 8–10 were given a horizontal velocity so that it could travel from *A* to *B* in one second, it would fall 4.9 m and arrive at *C*. The altitude of the ball would not have changed. The cannonball would fall toward Earth at the same rate that Earth's surface curves away. An object with a horizontal speed of 8 km/s will keep the same altitude and circle Earth as an artificial satellite.

Newton's thought experiment ignored air resistance. The mountain would have to be more than 150 km above Earth's surface to be above almost all the atmosphere. A satellite at this altitude encounters no air resistance and can orbit Earth for a long time.

The force of gravity on a satellite, its weight, provides the centripetal force to maintain its circular motion.

A satellite in an orbit that is always the same height above Earth moves with uniform circular motion. Its centripetal acceleration is $a_c = v^2/r$. Now, the acceleration of the satellite at radius r from the center of Earth is $g' = g(R_e/r)^2$, so we can write $g' = v^2/r$. We finally solve this equation for the velocity a satellite must have to orbit Earth to find

$$v^2 = g'r \text{ or } v = R_e\sqrt{\frac{g}{r}}$$

The same equation could be used for satellites of any other planet if the surface acceleration, g, and planetary radius, R, were used in place of g and R_e.

The velocity of a satellite is independent of its mass.

Note that the orbital velocity and period are independent of the mass of the satellite. Satellites are accelerated to the speeds needed to achieve orbit by large rockets, such as the shuttle booster rocket. The acceleration

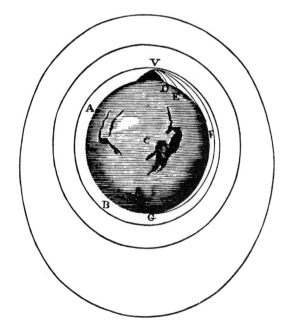

FIGURE 8–11. The drawing is from Newton's "Systems of the World." It shows the trajectories of a body projected with different speeds from a high mountain. Newton knew that a projectile would orbit Earth if its speed were great enough. The trajectories from point *V* to points *D, E, F*, and *G* are the paths of objects with greater and greater horizontal velocities.

of any mass must follow Newton's law, $\textbf{F} = m\textbf{a}$, so a more massive satellite requires more force to put it into orbit. Thus the mass of a satellite is limited by the capability of the rocket used to launch it.

A satellite must be given a large velocity to place it into orbit.

Practice Exercises

5. Calculate the velocity that a satellite must have in order to orbit Earth. Use $g = 9.80$ m/s^2.

6. During the lunar landings, the command module orbited close to the moon's surface while waiting for the lunar module to return from the surface. The diameter of the moon is 3570 km and the acceleration of gravity on the moon is 1.60 m/s^2.
   a. At what velocity did the command module orbit the moon?
   b. In how many minutes did the module complete one orbit?

7. Mercury has an acceleration of gravity on the surface of 3.78 m/s^2 and a radius of 2440 km.
   a. What is the speed of a satellite in orbit 265 km above the surface?
   b. What is the period of the satellite?

8. We can consider the sun to be a satellite of our galaxy, the Milky Way. The sun, mass 2.0×10^{30} kg, revolves around the center of the galaxy with a radius of 2.2×10^{20} m. The period of one rotation is 2.5×10^8 years.
   a. Find the approximate mass of the galaxy.
   b. Assuming the average star in the galaxy has the mass of the sun, find the number of stars.
   c. Find the speed with which the sun moves around the center of the galaxy.

8:6 Weight and Weightlessness

You have probably seen astronauts on the space shuttle working and relaxing in "zero-g" or "weightlessness." The shuttle orbits Earth about 400 km above its surface. At that distance $g' = 8.7$ m/s^2. Earth's gravity certainly is not zero in the shuttle. In fact, gravity causes the shuttle to circle Earth. Just as with Newton's cannonball, the shuttle and everything in it are falling freely toward Earth.

How do you measure weight? You either stand on a spring scale or hang an object from a scale. Weight is found by measuring the force the scale exerts in opposing the force of gravity. As we saw in Chapter 3, if you stand on a scale in an elevator that is accelerating downward, your weight is reduced. If the elevator is in freefall, that is, accelerating downward at 9.80 m/s^2, then the scale exerts no force on you. Your weight is zero. So it is in an orbiting satellite. The satellite, the scale, you, and everything else in it are accelerating toward Earth with acceleration g'.

Weight is the gravitational force of Earth on an object.

The acceleration due to gravity is independent of the mass of the object.

8:7 The Gravitational Field

Many common forces are contact forces. Friction is exerted where two objects are in contact. You touch the rope that you pull; you touch the box that you push. Gravity is different; it acts on an apple falling from a tree and on the moon in orbit. It acts on you in midair. That is, gravity acts

FIGURE 8–12. Astronauts in training experience a moment of weightlessness in a diving aircraft.

SUGGESTION: Have students calculate their weights at the height of a satellite and on the moon. Discuss the question of weightlessness in satellites. Point out that objects are weightless in satellites because everything, including the weighing device, is freefall.

Gravitational force diminishes as you go very far away from Earth but it is never zero.

For Your Information

Little Miss Muffet
Sits on her tuffet
In a nonchalant sort of a way.
With her force field around her
The spider, the bounder,
Is not in the picture today.
— Frederick Winsor
The Space Child's
Mother Goose

The gravitational field describes the acceleration a body would experience if placed at a certain location.

The field strength varies inversely with the square of the distance from Earth.

over a distance. Newton himself was uneasy with such an idea. How can the sun exert a force on Earth 150 million kilometers away?

In the nineteenth century Michael Faraday invented the concept of the field to explain how a magnet attracts objects. Later this concept was applied to gravity. Every body with mass is surrounded by a gravitational field. The field acts on a second body resulting in a force of attraction. The field acts on that body at the location of the body. Explaining gravity in terms of a gravitational field makes the idea of a force acting at a distance unnecessary.

To find the strength of the gravitational field, place a small body of mass m in the field and measure the force. The field strength, g, is the force divided by the mass, F/m. The direction of g is in the direction of the force. Thus

$$g = \frac{F}{m}$$

Note that the field is just the acceleration of gravity at the location of the mass. The unit of the field strength is N/kg. It is independent of the size of the test mass. The field can be represented by a vector of length g and pointing toward the object producing the field. We can picture the gravitational field of Earth as a collection of vectors surrounding Earth and pointing toward it. The strength of the field varies inversely with the square of the distance from the center of Earth.

140   Universal Gravitation

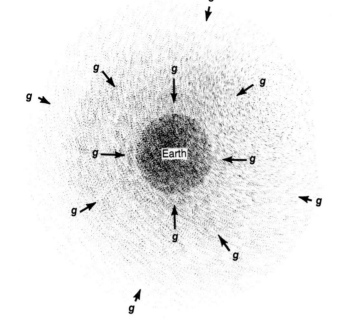

FIGURE 8–13. Vectors can be used to show Earth's gravitational field.

8:8 Einstein's Theory of Gravity

Newton's law of universal gravitation allows us to calculate the force that exists between two bodies because of their masses. The concept of a gravitational field allows us to picture the way gravity acts on bodies far away. Neither explains the origin of gravity.

Albert Einstein (1879–1955) proposed that gravity is not a force, but an effect of space itself. According to Einstein, a mass changes space about it. Mass causes space to be curved, and other bodies are accelerated because they move in this curved space.

One way to picture how space is affected by mass is to compare it to a large two-dimensional rubber sheet, Figure 8–14. The yellow ball on the sheet represents a massive object. It forms an indentation. A marble rolling across the sheet simulates the motion of an object in space. If the marble moves near the sagging region of the sheet, its path will be curved. In the same way, Earth orbits the sun because space is distorted by the two bodies.

Einstein's theory, called the general theory of relativity, makes predictions that differ from the predictions of Newton's law. One of the basic postulates of the theory is the *principle of equivalence*. In very general terms, this principle says that if a person were enclosed in an airtight box, there is no experiment that could be done within the box to tell whether the box was in freefall on Earth or drifting in outer space. It also predicts that in a vacuum, all bodies, regardless of mass, fall with the same acceleration. In every test, Einstein's theory has been shown to give the correct results.

Perhaps the most interesting prediction is the deflection of light by massive objects. In 1919, during an eclipse of the sun, astronomers found that light from distant stars that passed near the sun was deflected in agree-

The gravitational field does not explain *why* a body is accelerated.

Einstein said that a body, for example, Earth, changes the space around it, and the acceleration of another body is a result of the change in space.

Einstein's concept of gravity fits with every experimental test.

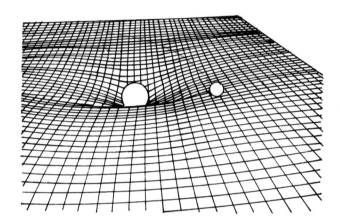

FIGURE 8–14. Matter causes space to curve just as a mass on a rubber sheet curves the sheet around it. Moving bodies, near the mass, follow the curvature of space.

For Your Information

ment with Einstein's predictions. Astronomers have seen light from a distant, bright galaxy bent as it passes by a closer, dark galaxy. The result is two or more images of the bright galaxy. If the object is massive enough, light leaving it will be totally bent back to the object. No light ever escapes. Such an object, called a black hole, has been identified as a result of its effect on nearby stars.

Einstein's theory is not yet complete. It does not explain how masses curve space. Physicists are still working to understand the true nature of gravity.

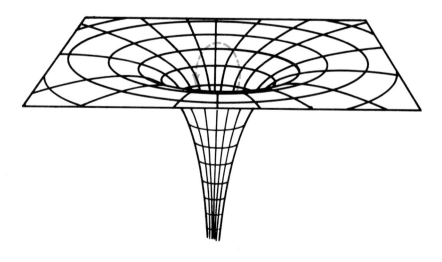

FIGURE 8–15. A black hole is so massive and of such unimaginable density, that light leaving it will be bent back to the black hole.

CHAPTER 8 REVIEW

SUMMARY

1. Kepler's laws of planetary motion state that planets move in elliptical orbits, that they sweep out equal areas in equal times, and that the ratio of the square of the periods of any two planets is equal to the ratio of the cube of their distances to the sun. **8:1**

2. Newton's law of universal gravitation states that the force between two bodies depends on the product of their masses divided by the square of the distance between their centers. It is along a line connecting their centers. **8:2**

3. Kepler's laws are a result of Newton's law of gravitation. **8:3**

4. The mass of the sun can be found from the period and radius of a planet's orbit. The mass of the planet can be found only if it has a satellite orbiting it. **8:3**

5. Cavendish was the first to measure the attraction between two bodies on Earth. **8:4**

6. A satellite in a circular orbit accelerates toward Earth at a rate equal to the acceleration of gravity, g', at its orbital radius. **8:5**

7. An object is weightless if it is in freefall. **8:6**

8. All bodies have gravitational fields surrounding them that can be represented by a collection of vectors representing the acceleration of gravity at all locations. **8:7**

9. Einstein's theory of gravity, general relativity, describes gravitational attraction as a property of space itself. **8:8**

QUESTIONS

1. According to Kepler's second law, does a planet move faster along its orbital path when it is close to or far away from the sun?

2. The moon and Earth are attracted to each other by gravitational force. Does the more massive Earth attract the moon with a greater force than the moon attracts Earth? Explain.

3. The force of gravity acting on an object near Earth's surface is proportional to the mass of the object. Why does a heavy object not fall faster than a light object?

4. Two 1.00-kg masses are 1.00 m apart. What is the force of attraction between them?

5. How did Cavendish demonstrate that a gravitational force of attraction exists between two small bodies?

6. During space flight, astronauts often refer to forces as multiples of the force of gravity on the Earth's surface. What does a force of 5-g mean to an astronaut?

7. Newton assumed that gravitational force acts directly between Earth and the moon. How would Einstein's view of the attraction between the two bodies differ from Newton's view?

8. The radius of Earth is about 6.40×10^3 km. A 7.20×10^3-N spacecraft travels away from Earth. What is the weight of the spacecraft these distances from Earth's surface?

   a. 6.40×10^3 km   **d.** 1.28×10^4 km

   b. 1.92×10^4 km   **e.** 2.56×10^4 km

   c. 3.20×10^4 km

APPLYING CONCEPTS

1. For each of the orbits shown in Figure 8–16, tell whether or not it is a possible orbit for a planet.

FIGURE 8–16. Use with Applying Concepts 1.

Possible orbits for satellites

2. A spacecraft traveling from Earth to the moon reaches a point where the gravitational attraction of the moon equals that of Earth. Would this location be when the craft is halfway to the moon? Explain.

3. We found that the force of attraction between two bowling balls 30 cm apart was about 4×10^{-8} N. What would be the mass of an object with this weight?

4. How do you answer the question, "What keeps a satellite up?"

5. Chairs in an orbiting spacecraft are weightless. If you were on board and barefoot, would you stub your toe if you kicked one? Explain.

6. Compare two artificial satellites, one 400 km above the surface, the other 600 km. Which has the longer period? Which moves at the greater speed?

7. What information do you need to find the mass of Jupiter?

8. A reference book lists the surface acceleration of gravity on Jupiter as 22.9 m/s² and its equatorial diameter as 143 000 km. Assuming that Jupiter's diameter was measured from photographs showing only the tops of clouds, how could the surface gravity be determined?

9. Examine the equation relating the speed of an orbiting satellite and the distance from the center of Earth.

   a. Does a satellite with a large or small radius have the greater velocity?

   b. When a satellite is too close to Earth, it can get into the atmosphere where there is air drag. As a result its orbit gets smaller. Does its speed increase or decrease?

EXERCISES

1. Two bowling balls each have a mass of 6.8 kg. They are located next to one another with their centers 21.8 cm apart. What gravitational force do they exert on each other?

2. Two spherical balls are placed so their centers are 2.6 meters apart. The force between the two balls is 2.75×10^{-12} N. What is the mass of each ball if one ball is twice the mass of the other ball?

3. Use the following data to compute the gravita-

tional force the sun exerts on Jupiter.
   mass of Earth = 6.0×10^{24} kg
   mass of the sun = 3.3×10^5 times the mass of Earth
   mass of Jupiter = 3.0×10^2 times the mass of Earth
   distance between Jupiter and the sun = 7.8×10^{11} m

4. Jupiter lies at an average distance from the sun of 5.2 AU (5.2 times as distant as Earth). Find Jupiter's orbital period in earth years.

5. Uranus requires 84 years to circle the sun. Find the distance from the sun to Uranus

   a. in AU.

   b. in m.

6. Find the mass of the sun (in kg) using Earth's average distance of 1.50×10^{11} m and its orbital period.

7. Consider a satellite with a period of exactly 24 hours. This type of satellite is called "geosynchronous."

   a. Find its orbital radius in m.

   b. How far from the surface of Earth would the orbit be?

8. Comet Halley returns every 74 years.

   a. Find the average distance the comet is from the sun.

   b. Look up planetary orbits and decide between which two planets this comet is located.

9. Mimas, a moon of Saturn, has an orbital radius of 1.87×10^8 m and an orbital period of about 23 hours. Find the mass of Saturn.

10. Assume the distance, d, between the centers of the two masses. Two balls have their centers 2.0 m apart. One has a mass of 8.0 kg. The other has a mass of 6.0 kg. What is the gravitational force between them?

11. a. What is the gravitational force between two 8.00-kg spherical masses that are 5.0 m apart?

    b. What is the gravitational force between them when they are 5.0×10^1 m apart?

12. Two large spheres are suspended close to each other. Their centers are 4.0 m apart. One sphere weighs 9.8×10^2 N. The other sphere has a weight of 1.96×10^2 N. What is the gravitational force between them?

13. Two satellites of equal mass are put into orbit 30 m apart. The gravitational force between them is 2.0×10^{-7} N.
    a. What is the mass of each satellite?
    b. What is the initial acceleration given to each satellite by the gravitational force?
14. The mass of Earth is 6.0×10^{24} kg. If the centers of Earth and the moon are 3.9×10^8 m apart, the gravitational force between them is about 1.9×10^{20} N. What is the approximate mass of the moon?
15. Use Newton's second law of motion to find the acceleration given the moon by the force in Exercise 14.
16. The mass of an electron is 9.1×10^{-31} kg. The mass of a proton is 1.7×10^{-27} kg. They are about 1.0×10^{-10} m apart in a hydrogen atom. What gravitational force exists between the proton and the electron of a hydrogen atom?
17. Venus has a period of revolution of 225 earth days. Find the distance between the sun and Venus using the distance between the sun and Earth as one distance unit. (This unit is called the astronomical unit, or AU.)
18. Mars has a moon, Phobos, with a period of 7 hours 39 minutes. Can you find its orbital radius using Kepler's third law and any data given in this section? Explain.

PROBLEMS

1. If a small planet is located eight times as far from the sun as Earth (1.5×10^{11} m), how many years would it take the planet to orbit the sun?
2. Using the fact that a 1.0-kg mass weighs 9.8 N on the surface of Earth and the radius of Earth is roughly 6.4×10^6 m,

    a. calculate the mass of Earth.
    b. calculate the average density of Earth.
3. An apparatus like the one Cavendish used to find G has a large lead ball 5.9 kg in mass and a small one 0.047 kg. Their centers are separated by 0.055 m. Find the force of attraction between them.
4. A satellite is placed in orbit with an orbital radius half the radius of the moon's orbit. Find its period in units of the period of the moon.
5. The moon is 3.9×10^5 km from the Earth's center and 1.5×10^8 km from the sun's center. If the masses of the moon, Earth, and sun are 7.3×10^{22} kg, 6.0×10^{24} kg, and 2.0×10^{30} kg, respectively, find the ratio of the gravitational forces exerted by Earth and the sun on the moon.
6. Suppose the moon ceased to revolve around Earth. Using information from Problem 5, with what acceleration would Earth begin to move toward the moon? With what acceleration would the moon begin to move toward Earth? Would the accelerations remain constant as the moon and Earth approached each other? Why?

READINGS

Adney, Kenneth J., "Applying Kepler's Third Law." *The Physics Teacher*, November, 1987.

Fisher, Arthur, "Testing Einstein Again with a Relativity Satellite." *Popular Science*, August, 1983.

Oppenheimer, Steve, "The Search for Gravity Waves." *Science Digest*, March, 1984.

"Overcoming the Human Factor [cosmonauts deal with problems living in space]." *U.S. News and World Report*, May 16, 1988.

Spetz, Gary, "Detection of Gravity Waves." *The Physics Teacher*, May, 1984.

CHAPTER 9

Momentum and Its Conservation

GOALS

1. You will gain an understanding of the quantity of motion, called momentum.
2. You will learn how to use the law of conservation of momentum to analyze the motion of colliding objects.
3. You will learn that Newton's third law is equivalent to the law of conservation of momentum.

For Your Information

Nature and Nature's laws lay hid in night: God said, "Let Newton be," and all was light.
Epitaph on Newton from *The Works of Alexander Pope*

Physics, as you know, is the study of matter and motion. In our course so far we have concentrated on the details of how changes in motion occur. In this chapter and in Chapter 10, we will take a slightly different point of view. Rather than studying forces and the acceleration that results from an interaction, we will look at a system before and after an interaction takes place. We will look for properties of the system that remain constant. Such properties are said to be conserved.

As an example, suppose you place several sugar cubes in a box and close it. We can call the box and the sugar in it a **system,** a defined collection of objects. Shake the box hard for several minutes. When you open it, you find that the shapes of the cubes have changed. In addition, there are sugar grains in the box that were not there before. It would be almost impossible to apply Newton's laws to each of the forces that were acting while the box was shaken. Instead, we can look for a property of the system that remains constant. A balance would show that the mass of the sugar and the box remains the same. The mass is conserved. Over the past century, physicists have found that studying conserved properties has produced great success in solving problems and understanding the principles of the physical world.

9:1 Momentum and Impulse

Suppose a heavy bowling ball and a light *bocce* ball roll across the floor at the same velocity. It takes more force to stop the more massive ball in the same time interval. Now consider two bowling balls of equal mass

Air Force

Traveling at a high rate of speed, a car and its passengers possess a great deal of momentum. A sudden stop or a head-on collision exerts tremendous force on the passengers in an extremely short period of time. How does an airbag help to reduce the danger to the passengers during such an occurrence?

FIGURE 9–1. A light bowling ball (a) generally has less momentum when it reaches the pins than a heavier ball (b). Notice the difference in pin action between the two photographs.

rolling horizontally. If one ball is moving faster than the other, a larger force is needed to stop it in the same time interval than to stop the slower one. Obviously both the velocity and the mass of a moving object help determine what is needed to change its motion. Newton called the product of the mass and velocity of a body the "quantity of motion." Today we call this quantity **momentum.** Momentum is a vector quantity that has the same direction as the velocity of the body.

According to Newton's first law, if no net force acts on a body, its velocity is constant. If we consider only a single isolated object, then its mass cannot change. If its velocity is also constant, then so is its momentum, the product of its mass and velocity. That is, if a single body has no net force acting on it, its momentum is constant. Its momentum is conserved.

Newton's second law describes how the velocity of a body is changed. Let us rewrite Newton's second law using the definition of acceleration as the change in velocity divided by the time interval.

$$\boldsymbol{F} = m\boldsymbol{a} = \frac{m\Delta\boldsymbol{v}}{\Delta t}$$

Multiplying both sides of the equation by Δt, we have the equation

$$\boldsymbol{F}\Delta t = m\Delta\boldsymbol{v}$$

The left side of this equation, the product of the net force and the time interval over which it is exerted, is called the **impulse.** Impulse is a vector in the direction of the force. The unit for impulse is the newton · second (N · s).

Momentum is the product of an object's mass and velocity and is represented by $\boldsymbol{p}$. The equation for momentum is

$$\boxed{\boldsymbol{p} = m\boldsymbol{v}}$$

The unit for momentum is kilogram · meter/second (kg · m/s). If the mass of an object is constant, then a change in its velocity results in a change in its momentum. Under these conditions

$$\Delta\boldsymbol{p} = m\Delta\boldsymbol{v}$$

Thus we see that the impulse given to an object is equal to the change in its momentum.

$$F\Delta t = \Delta p$$

This equation is often called the **impulse-momentum** theorem. The equality of impulse and change in momentum is another way of writing Newton's second law. Often the force is not constant during the time it is exerted. In that case, the average force is used in the impulse-momentum theorem.

Impulse is the product of the average force and the time interval over which the force is exerted. A large change in momentum occurs only when there is a large impulse. A large impulse, however, can result from either a large force acting over a short time, or a smaller force acting over a longer time. What happens to the driver when a crash suddenly stops a car? An impulse is needed to bring the driver's momentum to zero. The steering wheel can exert a force over a short length of time. An air bag reduces the force exerted on the driver by greatly increasing the length of time the force is exerted.

FIGURE 9–2. Seat belts provide the impulse necessary to bring a driver's momentum to zero.

SUGGESTION: Involve students in a discussion of the importance of follow-through in sports, or "cushioning" a fall.

EXAMPLE

Calculating Momentum

A baseball of mass 0.14 kg is moving at +35 m/s. **a.** Find the momentum of the baseball. **b.** Find the velocity at which a bowling ball, mass 7.26 kg, would have the same momentum as the baseball.

a. Given: mass $m = 0.14$ kg   **Unknown:** momentum p
          velocity $v = +35$ m/s   **Basic equation:** $p = mv$

Solution: $p = mv = (0.14 \text{ kg})(+35 \text{ m/s}) = +4.9 \text{ kg} \cdot \text{m/s}$

b. Given: momentum   **Unknown:** velocity v
          $p = +4.9 \text{ kg} \cdot \text{m/s}$ **Basic equation:** $p = mv$
          mass $m = 7.26$ kg

Solution: $p = mv$ so $v = \dfrac{p}{m} = \dfrac{+4.9 \text{ kg} \cdot \text{m/s}}{7.26 \text{ kg}} = +0.67$ m/s

EXAMPLE

Impulse and Momentum Change

A 0.144-kg baseball is pitched horizontally at +38 m/s. After it is hit by a bat, it moves at −38 m/s.

a. What impulse did the bat deliver to the ball?

b. If the bat and ball were in contact 0.80 ms, what was the average force the bat exerted on the ball?

c. Find the average acceleration of the ball during its contact with the bat.

Indicate the direction of the impulse, force, and acceleration.

FIGURE 9–3. A pitcher provides impulse *Ft* to the baseball (a). The ball moves in the direction of the impulse with momentum *mv*. Likewise, a batter provides impulse *Ft* to the bat, which moves with momentum *mv* (b). The bat provides impulse *Ft* to the ball, which is equal and opposite to the impulse provided to the bat by the ball (c). The ball moves off with a change in momentum equal to the impulse from the bat, and the bat moves with momentum changed by an amount equal to the impulse it received from the ball (d).

a. **Given:** mass $m = 0.144$ kg
initial velocity
$v_i = +38$ m/s
final velocity
$v_f = -38$ m/s

Unknown: impulse $F\Delta t$
Basic equation: $F\Delta t = \Delta p$

Solution: $F\Delta t = \Delta p = mv_f - mv_i = m(v_f - v_i)$
$= (0.144 \text{ kg})(-38 \text{ m/s} - (+38 \text{ m/s}))$
$= (0.144 \text{ kg})(-76 \text{ m/s})$
$= -11 \text{ kg} \cdot \text{m/s}$ (in the direction of the batted ball)

b. **Given:** momentum change
$\Delta p = -11$ kg · m/s
time interval
$\Delta t = 0.80$ ms $= 8.0 \times 10^{-4}$ s

Unknown: average force F
Basic equation: $F\Delta t = \Delta p$

Solution: $F\Delta t = \Delta p$ so $F = \dfrac{\Delta p}{\Delta t} = \dfrac{-11 \text{ kg} \cdot \text{m/s}}{0.80 \text{ ms}} = \dfrac{-11 \text{ kg} \cdot \text{m/s}}{8.0 \times 10^{-4} \text{ s}}$
$= -1.4 \times 10^4$ N (in the direction of the batted ball)

c. **Given:** average force
$F = -1.4 \times 10^4$ N
mass
$m = 0.144$ kg

Unknown: average acceleration a
Basic equation: $F = ma$

Solution: $F = ma$ so $a = \dfrac{F}{m}$

$= \dfrac{-1.4 \times 10^4 \text{ N}}{0.144 \text{ kg}}$

$= -9.7 \times 10^4$ m/s², about 10 000 g!

Practice Exercises

1. A compact car, mass 725 kg, is moving at +100 km/h.
   a. Find its momentum.
   b. At what velocity is the momentum of a larger car, mass 2175 kg, equal to that of the smaller car?
2. A 0.145-kg baseball is pitched at 42 m/s. The batter hits it horizontally to the pitcher at 58 m/s.
   a. Find the change in momentum of the ball.
   b. If the ball and bat were in contact 4.6×10^{-4} s, what would be the average force while they touched?
3. A snowmobile has a mass of 2.50×10^2 kg. A constant force acts upon it for 60.0 s. The snowmobile's initial velocity is 6.00 m/s and its final velocity 28.0 m/s.
   a. What is its change in momentum?
   b. What is the magnitude of the force that acts upon it?
4. A car weighing 15 680 N and moving at 20.0 m/s is acted upon by a 6.40×10^2 N force until it is brought to a halt.
   a. What is the car's mass?
   b. What is its initial momentum?
   c. What is the change in the car's momentum?
   d. How long does the braking force act on the car to bring it to a halt?

9:2 Newton's Third Law and Momentum

The Example in Section 9:1 involved a type of collision. The baseball collided with the bat. In the collision, the momentum of the baseball changed as a result of the impulse given it by the bat. The bat exerted a force on the ball. By Newton's third law, the ball must have exerted an

For Your Information

Because his mother wanted him to be a farmer, Newton dropped out of school when he was a teenager.

FIGURE 9–4. Momentum is transferred when billiard balls collide. However, some momentum is lost due to friction between the balls and the table. If we consider the billiard balls and table together as a system, momentum is conserved.

SUGGESTION: Newton's third law is another way of stating the conservation of momentum.

SUGGESTION: Point out that when a truck and car collide, the force of the car on the truck is equal to the force of the truck on the car. You will need to emphasize this many times.

A single force cannot exist. Every force on a body is accompanied by an equal and opposite force on another body.

A system is isolated if no net external force acts on it.

The momentum gained by one body in an interaction is equal to the momentum lost by the other body.

equal and opposite force on the bat. Thus the bat also received an impulse. The force on the bat is in the direction opposite the force on the ball, so the impulse given to the bat must be in the opposite direction as well. By the impulse-momentum theorem, the momentum of the bat must have changed. Its forward momentum was reduced as a result of its impact with the ball.

The momentum change of the bat may not be obvious because the bat is held by a batter who stands on soil, usually wearing spiked shoes for greater friction. In almost all natural processes, many forces are exerted, so to study the impulses and changes in momentum further, we have to choose a simpler system.

In order to study momentum changes in collisions, we must use a closed, isolated system. Remember, a system is a collection of objects. Objects neither enter nor leave a closed system. A system is isolated if no unbalanced external forces are exerted on it. Two balls on a billiard table are an isolated system as long as friction is small enough to be ignored and as long as neither ball hits the bumper at the edge of the table.

Suppose ball A is moving with momentum p_A and ball B with momentum p_B. They collide, and ball B exerts force F on ball A. The balls are in contact for a time Δt, so the impulse given ball A is $+F\Delta t$. The momentum of ball A is changed by an amount equal to the impulse; $\Delta p = F\Delta t$. The new momentum of ball A is represented by $p'_A = p_A + \Delta p$.

During the collision, ball A also exerts a force on ball B. According to Newton's third law, the force ball A exerts on ball B is equal in magnitude but opposite in direction to the force B exerts on A. The time interval is the same, so the impulse given ball B is $-F\Delta t$. The momentum of B is changed by an amount $-\Delta p$ that is equal in size but opposite in direction to the momentum change of ball A; $-\Delta p = -F\Delta t$. Thus the new momentum of ball B is $p'_B = p_B + (-\Delta p)$.

The momentum of ball B decreased while the momentum of ball A increased. The momentum lost by B equals the momentum gained by A. For the whole system consisting of the two balls, the net change in momentum is zero. That is, the final momentum of the system equals the initial momentum of the system; $p_A + p_B = p'_A + p'_B$. The total momentum before the collision is the same as the total momentum after the collision. That is, the momentum of the system is not changed; it is conserved. In summary,

FIGURE 9–5. Ball A is moving with momentum p_A, while ball B is moving with momentum p_B (a). When they collide, the impulses provided to the balls are equal in magnitude, but opposite in direction (b). After the collision, ball A moves with new momentum p'_A, while ball B moves with new momentum p'_B (c).

Object	Ball A	Ball B	System
Initial momentum	p_A	p_B	$p_A + p_B$
Impulse	$+F\Delta t$	$-F\Delta t$	0
Momentum change	$+\Delta p$	$-\Delta p$	0
Final momentum	p'_A	p'_B	$p'_A + p'_B$

a

b

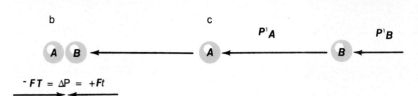

c

9:3 Law of Conservation of Momentum

The total momentum of an isolated system always remains constant.

The **law of conservation of momentum** states: *The momentum of any closed, isolated system does not change.* It does not matter how many objects are in the system. It is only necessary that no objects enter or leave the system and that there are no net external forces on the system. Because all interactions are collisions in one form or another, the law of conservation of momentum is a very powerful tool.

As an example, consider two freight cars A and B, each with a mass of 3.0×10^5 kg, as seen in Figure 9–6. Car B is moving at $+2.2$ m/s while car A is at rest. The system is composed of the cars A and B. Assume that the cars roll without friction so there are no net external forces. Thus the two cars are a closed, isolated system and momentum is conserved. The two cars collide and are coupled together. We will use conservation of momentum to find the velocity of the coupled cars.

SUGGESTION: Emphasize the importance of identifying objects A and B and keeping all quantities carefully labeled.

Because the masses of the cars are equal, we can write $m_A = m_B = m$. The initial velocity of A is zero, so $v_A = 0$ and $p_A = 0$. Thus the initial momentum of the system is

$$p_A + p_B = p_B = mv_B$$

After the collision, the two coupled cars move with the same velocity, $v'_A = v'_B = v'$. Because the masses are also equal, $p'_A = p'_B = mv'$. Therefore the final momentum of the system is

$$p'_A + p'_B = 2mv'$$

By the law of conservation of momentum,

$$p_A + p_B = p'_A + p'_B$$
$$mv_B = 2mv'$$
$$v_B = 2v'$$
$$\text{or } v' = \tfrac{1}{2}v_B$$

FIGURE 9–6. The total momentum of the freight car system after collision is the same as the total momentum of the system before collision.

After the collision, the two cars move together with half the velocity of the moving car B before the collision, or $+1.1$ m/s. The momentum of the two cars before the collision is given by

$$
\begin{aligned}
p_A + p_B &= m_A v_A + m_B v_B \\
&= (3.0 \times 10^5 \text{ kg})(0 \text{ m/s}) + (3.0 \times 10^5 \text{ kg})(+2.2 \text{ m/s}) \\
&= +6.6 \times 10^5 \text{ kg} \cdot \text{m/s}
\end{aligned}
$$

The final momentum of the system is given by

$$
\begin{aligned}
p'_A + p'_B &= m_A v'_A + m_B v'_B \\
&= (3.0 \times 10^5 \text{ kg})(+1.1 \text{ m/s}) + (3.0 \times 10^5 \text{ kg})(+1.1 \text{ m/s}) \\
&= +6.6 \times 10^5 \text{ kg} \cdot \text{m/s in the direction of car } B\text{'s original} \\
&\quad \text{motion}
\end{aligned}
$$

We can also examine the changes in momentum of the parts of the system. The change in momentum of car A is

$$
\begin{aligned}
\Delta p_A &= p'_A - p_A \\
&= m_A v'_A - m_A v_A \\
&= (3.0 \times 10^5 \text{ kg})(1.1 \text{ m/s}) - (3.0 \times 10^5 \text{ kg})(0 \text{ m/s}) \\
&= +3.3 \times 10^5 \text{ kg} \cdot \text{m/s}
\end{aligned}
$$

The change in momentum of car B is

$$
\begin{aligned}
\Delta p_B &= p'_B - p_B \\
&= m_B v'_B - m_B v_B \\
&= (3.0 \times 10^5 \text{ kg})(1.1 \text{ m/s}) - (3.0 \times 10^5 \text{ kg})(+2.2 \text{ m/s}) \\
&= -3.3 \times 10^5 \text{ kg} \cdot \text{m/s}
\end{aligned}
$$

The momentum lost by one object in a collision is gained by the other.

The momentum lost by car B (-3.3×10^5 kg $\cdot$ m/s) is equal to the momentum gained by car A ($+3.3 \times 10^5$ kg $\cdot$ m/s).

This example shows there are two important aspects of any collision. First, for the closed, isolated system as a whole, the total momentum is the same before and after the collision.

$$
p_A + p_B = p'_A + p'_B
$$

Momentum is only transferred in a collision. Total momentum is constant.

Second, momentum is transferred from one part of the system to another part.

$$
\Delta p_A = -\Delta p_B
$$

EXAMPLE

Conservation of Momentum—1

A glider of mass 0.355 kg moves along a friction-free air track with a velocity of 0.095 m/s. It collides with a second glider of mass 0.710 kg moving in the same direction at a speed of 0.045 m/s. After the collision, the first glider continues in the same direction with a velocity of 0.035 m/s. What is the velocity of the second glider after the collision?

Given: $m_A = 0.355$ kg   Unknown: v'_B
$\quad\quad v_A = +0.095$ m/s   Basic equation: $p_A + p_B = p'_A + p'_B$
$\quad\quad m_B = 0.710$ kg
$\quad\quad v_B = +0.045$ m/s
$\quad\quad v'_A = +0.035$ m/s

Solution: $p_A + p_B = p'_A + p'_B$, so $p'_B = p_B + p_A - p'_A$
$$m_B v'_B = m_B v_B + m_A v_A - m_A v'_A$$
or
$$v'_B = \frac{m_B v_B + m_A v_A - m_A v'_A}{m_B}$$
$$= \frac{(0.710\ kg)(+0.045\ m/s) + (0.355\ kg)(+0.095\ m/s)}{0.710\ kg}$$
$$- \frac{(0.355\ kg)(+0.035\ m/s)}{0.710\ kg}$$
$$= \frac{(+0.053\ kg \cdot m/s)}{(0.710\ kg)} = +0.075\ m/s$$

Practice Exercises

5. A 0.105-kg hockey puck moving at 48 m/s is caught by a 75-kg goalie at rest. With what speed does the goalie slide on the ice?

6. A 35.0-g bullet strikes a 5.0-kg wooden block and embeds itself in the block. The block and bullet fly off together at 8.6 m/s. What was the original velocity of the bullet?

7. A 35.0-g bullet moving at 475 m/s strikes a 2.5-kg wooden block. The bullet passes through the block, leaving at 275 m/s. The block was at rest when it was hit. How fast is it moving when the bullet leaves?

8. A 0.50-kg ball traveling at 6.0 m/s collides head-on with a 1.00-kg ball moving in the opposite direction at a velocity of −12.0 m/s. The 0.50-kg ball moves away at −14 m/s after the collision. Find the velocity of the second ball.

9:4 Internal and External Forces

In the Example in Section 9:3, two railroad cars collided and coupled. They exerted forces on each other. The forces among objects within a system are called internal forces. The total momentum of the system is conserved because it is closed and isolated.

An internal force cannot change the total momentum of a system.

What if we define our system as car A only? When car A collides with car B, an external force is acting. The system is no longer isolated, and the momentum of the system is not conserved. You see, it is very important to define the system carefully.

Consider the two skaters shown in Figure 9–7 as an isolated, closed system. Skater A has a mass of 60.0 kg; skater B has a mass of 45.0 kg. The skaters are standing still on smooth ice. The force of friction can be neglected. The initial momentum of the system is zero. Skater A pushes skater B away. Only an internal force has been exerted, so the momentum of the system is conserved. We can find the relative velocities of the two skaters using conservation of momentum.

Define the system carefully! A force can be either internal or external, depending on the definition of the system.

SUGGESTION: Other kinds of internal forces are explosions and releasing compressed springs.

$$p_A + p_B = p'_A + p'_B$$
$$0 = p'_A + p'_B$$

or

$$p'_A = -p'_B$$
$$m_A v'_A = -m_B v'_B$$
$$v'_A = -\left(\frac{m_B}{m_A}\right) v'_B$$
$$v'_A = -\left(\frac{45.0 \text{ kg}}{60.0 \text{ kg}}\right) v'_B$$
$$= -0.75 v'_B$$

FIGURE 9–8. The total momentum of an isolated system is constant.

Since the initial momentum of the system is zero, the vector sum of the momenta after the collision must also be zero. Therefore, the momenta of the two skaters are equal and opposite. Their velocities, however, are not equal. The larger skater moves more slowly than the smaller one.

The system we defined included the two skaters. Therefore, when one skater pushed on the other, the force was an internal force. The momentum of the system remained the same. On the other hand, if we had defined the system as including only skater B, there would have been an external force, and the momentum of the system would have changed.

A system can contain more than two objects. For example, a small container filled with gas is a system consisting of many particles. The gas particles are constantly colliding with each other and the container. Their momenta are changing with every collision. Each particle, however, can gain only the momentum lost by another particle during a collision. For this reason, the total momentum of the system does not change. The total momentum of an isolated system is constant.

How does a rocket accelerate in space? This is another example of conservation of momentum. A rocket combines fuel and oxidizer and expels the hot gases from the exhaust at high speed. At first the rocket with its unburned fuel moves forward at some constant speed. It has a momentum mv. After the firing, the mass of the burned fuel is moving backward with high relative velocity. In order to conserve momentum, the rocket, with its mass reduced by the burned fuel, must move with increased speed in the forward direction.

FIGURE 9–9. A rocket accelerating in space represents an isolated system in which momentum is conserved.

EXAMPLE

Conservation of Momentum—2

A cannon at rest with mass 1.20×10^3 kg fires a 53-kg mass in a horizontal direction at 67 m/s. The cannon can roll without friction on Earth. What is the velocity of the cannon after firing the shot?

Given: $m_A = 1.2 \times 10^3$ kg   Unknown: v'_A

  $v_A = 0$ m/s   Basic equation: $p_A + p_B = p'_A + p'_B$

  $m_B = 53$ kg

  $v_B = 0$ m/s

  $v'_B = +67$ m/s

Solution: $p_A + p_B = p'_A + p'_B$

  But $v_A = v_B = 0$, so $p_A = p_B = 0$, and

  $p'_A = -p'_B$

  $m_A v'_A = -m_B v'_B$

  $v'_A = -\dfrac{m_B v'_B}{m_A}$

  $v'_A = -\left(\dfrac{(53 \text{ kg})(+67 \text{ m/s})}{1.2 \times 10^3 \text{ kg}}\right)$

  $= -3.0$ m/s

The cannon recoils in a direction opposite that of the moving projectile.

Practice Exercises

9. A 4.00-kg model rocket is launched, shooting 50.0 g of burned fuel from its exhaust at an average velocity of 625 m/s. What is the velocity of the rocket after the fuel has burned? (Ignore effects of gravity and air resistance.)

FIGURE 9–10. Use with Practice Exercise 11.

10. Two campers dock a canoe. One camper steps onto the dock. This camper has a mass of 80.0 kg and moves forward at 4.0 m/s. With what speed and direction do the canoe and the other camper move if their combined mass is 110 kg?

11. A thread holds two carts together on a frictionless surface as in Figure 9–10. A compressed spring acts upon the carts. After the thread is burned, the 1.5-kg cart moves with a velocity of 27 cm/s to the left. What is the velocity of the 4.5-kg cart?

12. A 50.0-g projectile is launched with a horizontal velocity of 647 m/s from a 4.65-kg launcher moving at 2.00 m/s. What is the velocity of the launcher after the projectile is launched?

9:5 Conservation of Momentum in Two and Three Dimensions

To this point we have considered momentum in one dimension only. The law of conservation of momentum, however, holds for all isolated, closed systems. It is true regardless of the directions of the particles before and after they collide.

Figure 9–11a shows a billiard ball striking another ball at rest. The momentum of the moving ball is represented by the vector p_A. The momentum of the ball at rest is zero. Therefore, the total momentum of the system is the vector p_A going toward the right. After the collision, the momenta of the two balls are represented by the vectors p'_A and p'_B. Figure 9–11b shows that the vector sum of p'_A and p'_B equals the original

SUGGESTION: Emphasize that the same principles are used here as in Section 9:4, but since angles are involved, triangles must be used. Therefore arithmetic addition will not work here and trigonometry must be used.

Momentum is conserved even if motion occurs in two or three dimensions.

The total momentum is the vector sum of the momenta of all the parts of a system.

FIGURE 9–11. The law of conservation of momentum holds for all isolated, closed systems, regardless of the directions of objects before and after they collide (a). The vector sum of the momenta is constant (b).

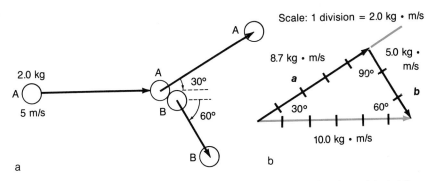

a

momentum, **p**$_A$. The components of the vectors can also be added. The initial momentum has no vertical or y component, so the vector sum of the vertical components of the two balls, **p**$_{yA}$ and **p**$_{yB}$, must be zero. They are equal in magnitude but opposite in direction. The sum of the horizontal components, **p**$_{xA}$ and **p**$_{xB}$, is equal to the original momentum.

EXAMPLE

Conservation of Momentum in Two Dimensions

A 2.00-kg ball, A, is moving at a velocity of 5.00 m/s. It collides with a stationary ball, B, also of mass 2.00 kg (Figure 9–12). After the collision, ball A moves off in a direction 30.0° to the left of its original direction. Ball B moves off in a direction 90.0° to the right of ball A's final direction. **a.** Draw a vector diagram to find the momentum of ball A and of ball B after the collision. **b.** Find the velocities of the balls after the collision.

Given: $m_A = 2.00$ kg   **Unknowns:** $p_A, p'_A, p'_B, v'_A, v'_B$

$v_A = +5.00$ m/s   **Basic equation:** $p_A + p_B = p'_A + p'_B$

$m_B = 2.00$ kg

$v_B = 0.00$ m/s

Solution: Find the initial momenta.

$$p_A = m_A v_A = +10.0 \text{ kg} \cdot \text{m/s} \quad p_B = 0$$

Therefore, $p = p_A + p_B = +10.0$ kg $\cdot$ m/s

The vector representing the initial momentum is an arrow to the right. This vector is also the sum of the two vectors representing the final momenta. Because the angle between the final directions of ball A and ball B is 90°, the vector triangle is a right triangle with the initial momentum as the hypotenuse. The vector **p**$'_A$ is at 30.0°. We can use trigonometry to find the magnitudes of the vectors.

ball A	ball B
$\cos 30° = \dfrac{p'_A}{p_A}$	$\sin 30° = \dfrac{p'_B}{p_A}$
$p'_A = p_A \cos 30°$	$p'_B = p_A \sin 30°$
$= (1.0 \times 10^1 \text{ kg}\cdot\text{m/s})(0.87)$	$= (1.0 \times 10^1 \text{ kg}\cdot\text{m/s})(0.50)$
$= 8.7$ kg$\cdot$m/s	$= 5.0$ kg$\cdot$m/s

SUGGESTION: Have students use tracing paper to copy the momentum vectors of Figure 9–12. Then have them demonstrate that momentum is conserved.

SUGGESTION: Roll two steel balls on a smooth table and watch the collision or use an air table. Identify the momentum before and after. Let students experiment and see what the collisions look like with the same size ball but different mass and with balls of different mass and size.

Now use the definition of momentum, $p = mv$, to find the magnitudes of the velocities.

$$p'_A = m_A v'_A$$

$$v'_A = \frac{p'_A}{m_A}$$

$$= \frac{8.7 \text{ kg} \cdot \text{m/s}}{2.0 \text{ kg}}$$

$$v'_A = 4.4 \text{ m/s}$$

$$p'_B = m_B v'_B$$

$$v'_B = \frac{p'_B}{m_B}$$

$$= \frac{5.0 \text{ kg} \cdot \text{m/s}}{2.0 \text{ kg}}$$

$$v'_B = 2.5 \text{ m/s}$$

Practice Exercises

13. A pole vaulter runs toward the launch point with horizontal momentum. Where does the vertical momentum come from as the athlete vaults over the crossbar?

14. A 1325-kg car moving north at 27.0 m/s collides with a 2165-kg car moving east at 17.0 m/s. They stick together. Draw a vector diagram of the collision. In what direction and with what speed do they move after the collision?

15. A 6.0-kg object, A, moving at velocity 3.0 m/s, collides with a 6.0-kg object, B, at rest. After the collision, A moves off in a direction 40.0° to the left of its original direction. B moves off in a direction 50.0° to the right of A's original direction.

   a. Draw a vector diagram and determine the momenta of object A and object B.

   b. What is the velocity of each object after the collision?

16. A stationary billiard ball of mass 0.17 kg is struck by a second, identical ball moving at 10.0 m/s. After the collision, the second ball moves off in a direction 60.0° to the left of its original direction. The stationary ball moves off in a direction 30.0° to the right of the second ball's original direction. What is the velocity of each ball after the collision?

FIGURE 9–13. Use with Practice Exercise 16.

CHAPTER 9 REVIEW

SUMMARY

1. The momentum of an object is the product of its mass and velocity. **9:1**
2. The change in momentum of an object is equal to the impulse that acts on it. **9:1**
3. Impulse is the product of the average force and the time interval over which the force acts. **9:1**
4. Newton's third law is another statement of the law of conservation of momentum. **9:2**
5. The law of conservation of momentum states: *In a closed, isolated system, the total momentum of the system does not change.* **9:3**
6. The momentum of a system changes when it is not isolated, that is, when a net external force acts on it. **9:4**

QUESTIONS

1. What is a conservation law?
2. What approach to problem solving do you use with conservation laws?
3. **a.** Why is the momentum of a falling ball not conserved?
   b. Define a system including the falling ball in which the total momentum is conserved.
4. Can a bullet have the same momentum as a truck? Explain.
5. A spacecraft in outer space increases its velocity by firing rockets. How can the hot gases escaping from the rockets change the velocity of the craft if there is nothing in space for the gases to push against?
6. If only an external force can change the momentum of an object, how can the internal force of a car's brakes bring the car to a stop?
7. The white cue ball travels across a pool table and collides with the stationary 8-ball. The two balls have equal mass. After the collision the cue ball is at rest. What must be true of the 8-ball?
8. During a "space walk" the tether connecting an astronaut to the space capsule breaks. Using a pistol, the astronaut manages to get back to the capsule. Explain.
9. A pitcher throws a fastball to the catcher. Assuming the speed of the ball does not change appreciably in flight,
   a. which player exerts the larger impulse on the ball?
   b. which player exerts the larger force on the ball?
10. **a.** If you jump off a ledge, you bend your knees as you land. How does this reduce the shock to your body?
   b. Why are cars made with bumpers that can be pushed in during a crash?

APPLYING CONCEPTS

1. Can an object obtain a larger impulse from a smaller force than from a larger force? How?
2. You are sitting at a baseball game when a foul ball comes in your direction. You catch it barehanded. In order to catch it safely, should you move your hands toward the ball, hold them still, or move them in the same direction as the moving ball? Why?
3. Two bullets of equal mass are shot at equal speeds at blocks of wood on a smooth ice rink. One bullet, made of rubber, bounces off the wood. The other bullet, made of aluminum, burrows into the wood. Which bullet makes the wood move faster? Why?
4. Two trucks that look the same collide. One was originally at rest. The trucks stick together and move off at more than half the original speed of the moving truck. What can you say about the contents of the two trucks?
5. Jim Walewinder slides into second base. What happens to his momentum?

6. If momentum is conserved, where does the momentum go when moving objects come to rest?

7. You command Spaceship Zero, which is moving at high speed through interplanetary space. Using the law of conservation of momentum, explain how you would slow down your ship.

8. A tennis ball bounces off a wall and its momentum is reversed. How can you explain this in view of the law of conservation of momentum?

9. Which collision presents a greater possibility of danger to the passengers: (1) two cars collide and remain entangled, or (2) the two rebound off each other? Explain.

10. When you shoot a rifle for the first time, you quickly learn to put the butt of the rifle firmly against your shoulder. In terms of momentum, why is this good advice?

EXERCISES

1. A hockey player makes a slap shot, exerting a force of 30.0 N on the hockey puck for 0.16 s. What impulse is given to the puck?

2. The hockey puck shot in Exercise 1 has a mass of 0.115 kg and was at rest before the shot. With what speed does it head toward the goal?

3. A sprinter with a mass of 76 kg accelerates from 0 to 9.4 m/s in 2.8 s. Find the net force acting on the runner with the impulse-momentum theorem.

4. A fullback with mass 95 kg running at 8.2 m/s collides with a 128-kg defensive tackle moving in the opposite direction. They end up with zero speed. Calculate how fast the tackle must have been moving.

5. A car moving at 36 km/h (10 m/s) crashes into a barrier and stops in 0.25 m.

 a. Find the time required to stop the car.

 b. If a 40-kg child is to be stopped in the same time as the car, what average force must be exerted?

 c. Approximately what is the mass of an object whose weight equals the force from part **b?** Could you lift such a mass with your arm?

 d. What does your answer to part **c** say about holding an infant on your lap instead of using a special infant restraint?

6. A 10-kg lead brick falls from a height of 2 m.

 a. Find its momentum when it reaches the ground.

 b. What impulse is needed to bring the brick to rest?

 c. The brick falls on a thin carpet, 1.0 cm thick. Assuming the force stopping it is constant, find the average force the carpet exerts on the brick.

 d. If the brick falls on a 5.0-cm-thick foam rubber pad, what (constant) force is needed to bring it to rest?

7. Two students on roller skates stand face-to-face then push each other away. One student has a mass of 90 kg, the other 60 kg. Find the ratio of their velocities just after their hands lose contact. Which student has the greater speed?

8. A 2575-kg van runs into the back of a 825-kg compact car that was at rest. They move off together at 8.5 m/s. Assuming no friction with the ground, find the initial speed of the van.

9. A hockey puck, mass 0.115 kg, moving at 35 m/s, strikes an octopus thrown on the ice by a fan. The octopus has a mass of 0.465 kg. The puck and octopus slide off together. Find their velocity.

10. A 60-kg dancer leaps 0.32 m high.

 a. With what momentum does the dancer reach the ground?

 b. What impulse is needed to make a stop?

 c. As the dancer lands, the knees bend 0.12 m, lengthening the time required to stop to 0.05 s. Find the average force exerted on the body.

 d. Compare the stopping force to the performer's weight.

11. Before a collision a 25-kg mass is moving at +12 m/s. Find the impulse that acted on this mass if after the collision

 a. the mass moves at +8 m/s.

 b. the mass moves at −8 m/s.

12. A 845-kg drag race car accelerates from rest to 100 km/h in 0.9 seconds.

 a. What is the change in momentum of the car?

 b. What average force (what direction) is exerted on the car?

13. A force of 6.00 N acts on a 3.00-kg object for 10.0 s.

    a. What is the object's change in momentum?

    b. What is its change in velocity?

14. What force is needed to bring a 1.10×10^3-kg car moving at +22.0 m/s to a halt in 20.0 s?

15. The velocity of a 6.00×10^2-kg mass is changed from +10.0 m/s to +44.0 m/s in 68.0 s by an applied, constant force.

    a. What change in momentum does the force produce?

    b. What is the magnitude of the force?

16. A car with mass 1245 kg moving at 28 m/s strikes a 2175-kg car at rest. If the two cars stick together, with what speed do they move?

17. A plastic ball of mass 0.200 kg moves with a velocity of 0.30 m/s. This plastic ball collides with a second plastic ball of mass 0.100 kg that is moving along the same line at a velocity of 0.10 m/s. After the collision, the velocity of the 0.100-kg ball is 0.26 m/s. What is the new velocity of the second ball?

PROBLEMS

1. A space probe of mass 7600 kg is traveling through space at 120 m/s. Mission control determines that a change in course of 30.0° is necessary and, by electronic communication, instructs the probe to fire rockets perpendicular to its direction of motion. If the escaping gas leaves the craft's rockets at an average speed of 3200 m/s, what mass of gas should be expelled?

2. Figure 9–14 shows a brick weighing 24.5 N being released from rest on a 1.00-m, frictionless plane inclined at an angle of 30.0°. The brick slides down the incline and strikes a second brick weighing 36.8 N.

    a. If the two bricks stick together, with what initial speed will they move along the table?

    b. If the force of friction acting on the two bricks is 5.0 N, what time will elapse before the bricks come to rest?

    c. How far will the two bricks slide before coming to rest?

FIGURE 9–14. Use with Problem 2.

3. A glass ball of mass 5.0 g moves at a velocity of 20.0 m/s. The ball collides with a second glass ball of mass 10.0 g, which is moving along the same line with a velocity of 10.0 m/s. After the collision, the 5.0-g ball is still moving with a velocity of 8.0 m/s.

    a. What is the change of momentum of the 5.0-g ball?

    b. What is the change of momentum of the 10-g ball?

4. A 92-kg fullback running at 5.0 m/s is diving for a touchdown. Just as he reaches the goal line, he is met head-on in midair by two 75-kg linebackers, one moving at 2.0 m/s and the other at 4.0 m/s. If upon collision they become entangled as one mass, with what velocity do they travel? Does the fullback score?

5. A 65-kg parachutist is falling with a terminal velocity of 10.4 m/s. Upon striking the ground, she bends at the knees and her body moves a distance of 0.50 m in breaking the fall. How much force must her legs exert in bringing her to rest?

READINGS

Bernardo, Stephanie, "The Physics of the Sweet Spot." *Science Digest*, May, 1984.

Carter, W. E., "Variations in the Rotation of the Earth." *Science*, June 1, 1984.

Dewhurst, David, "Torque vs. Horsepower: You Can't Have One Without the Other." *Cycle Guide*, April, 1985.

CHAPTER 10

Work, Energy, and Simple Machines

GOALS

1. You will learn how work and power are related to energy.
2. You will be able to analyze simple machines.
3. You will gain an understanding of how machines can make a task easier without violating the law of conservation of energy.

For Your Information

In physics, *work* and *energy* have very precise meanings, which must not be confused with their everyday meanings. Robert Oppenheimer wrote, "Often the very fact that the words of science are the same as those of our common life and tongue can be more misleading than enlightening."

In Chapter 9 you learned about the conservation of momentum. Another quantity that is conserved is energy. What is energy? When you have a lot of energy you can run farther or faster; you can jump higher. Objects as well as people can have energy. A stone falling off a high ledge has enough energy to damage a car roof. Living things function by using the energy stored in chemical bonds.

One way to summarize these examples is to say that an object has energy if it is able to produce a change in itself or in its surroundings. This definition may not seem very exact, but there is no more precise definition. Because energy is an abstract concept, we will first study a more measurable quantity, work.

10:1 Work

The word work has both a common and a scientific meaning. Anyone would consider that lifting a heavy box is doing work. The task is even harder if the box is heavier or if you have to lift it higher. Thus it seems reasonable to use the quantity force times distance to measure the size of the task. In fact, we define **work** as the product of the force exerted on an object and the distance the object moves in the direction of the force. In equation form,

Work is the product of a force and the displacement of the object in the direction of the force.

$$W = Fd$$

where W is the work, F is the magnitude of force, and d is the magnitude of displacement distance in the direction of the force. Note that work is a scalar quantity. The SI unit of work is the **joule** [JOOL]. The joule is named

Work is done only if an object is moved in the direction of the force.

Uplifting Thoughts

While observing a weight lifting demonstration, Ricardo comments to Suzanne that he thinks it would be easier to lift the weight if the weight lifters spread their arms farther apart and grasped the bar bells closer to the ends. Suzanne says it would be easier to lift the weight if the lifters' hands were directly in front of them. Who is correct? Why?

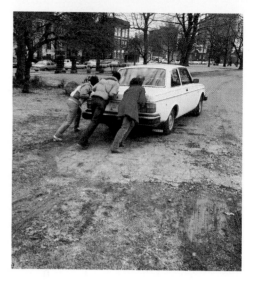

FIGURE 10–1. In order to do work on the car, the car must move. Work is done only when an object moves some distance due to an applied force.

One joule, the unit of work, is one newton-meter.

SUGGESTION: Point out that pushing on a car to keep it from rolling down a hill does not involve work.

FIGURE 10–2. Work is done on the box only when it moves in the direction of the applied force.

Direction of applied force

Direction of motion

after James Prescott Joule, a nineteenth century English physicist and brewer. If a force of one newton pushes an object one meter, one joule of work is done.

$$1 \text{ joule (J)} = 1 \text{ newton} \cdot \text{meter (N} \cdot \text{m)}$$

Work is done only if the object moves. If you hold a heavy box at the same height, you may get tired, but you do no work on the box. It is also necessary that the force and displacement be in the same direction. If you carry the box at the same height, the force you exert is upward while the motion is sideways, so you do no work on the box.

A force-displacement graph can give you a picture of the work done by a force. Figure 10–3 shows the force-displacement graph of a box weighing 20 N being lifted. A constant force of 20 N is needed to lift the box 1.5 m. The work done on the box is the product of the force and the displacement, $W = Fd = (20 \text{ N})(1.5 \text{ m}) = 30 \text{ J}$. The shaded area under the curve of Figure 10–3 is equal to 20 N × 1.5 m, or 30 J. The area under the curve of a force-displacement graph represents the work done by the force.

EXAMPLE

Calculating Work

A student lifts a box of books that weighs 185 N. The box is lifted 0.800 m. How much work does the student do?

Given: $F = 185 \text{ N}$ Unknown: work (W)
         $d = 0.800 \text{ m}$ Basic equation: $W = Fd$

Solution: $W = Fd$
          $= (185 \text{ N})(0.800 \text{ m})$
          $= 148 \text{ N} \cdot \text{m} = 148 \text{ J}$

Practice Exercises

1. A force of 825 N is needed to push a car across a lot. Two students push the car 35 m. How much work is done?
2. The force needed to push the car described above was suddenly doubled because the ground became soft. By what amount does the work done by the students change?
3. A delivery clerk carries a 34-N package from the ground to the fifth floor of an office building, a total height of 15 m. How much work is done by the clerk?
4. What work is done by a forklift raising a 583 kg box a distance of 1.2 m?

10:2 Work and Direction of Force

Only a force in the direction of motion does work. If a force is exerted perpendicular to the motion, no work is done. What if a force is exerted at some angle to the motion? For example, if you push the lawn mower in Figure 10–4a, what work do you do? You have learned that any force can be replaced by its components. The 125-N force (**F**) you exert in the direction of the handle has two components, Figure 10–4b. The horizontal component (**F_h**) is 113 N; the vertical component (**F_v**) is −53 N. The vertical component is perpendicular to the motion. It does no work. Only the horizontal component does work. The work done by a force that is exerted at an angle to a motion is equal to the component of the force in the direction of the motion times the distance moved.

The magnitude of the component of the force F acting in the direction of motion is found by multiplying the force F by the cosine of the angle between F and the direction of motion.

$$W = F(\cos \theta)d$$
$$= Fd \cos \theta$$

Force versus Displacement

FIGURE 10–3. A force-displacement graph of a box being lifted.

Only the component of force in the direction of the motion does work.

SUGGESTION: Show by diagrams and trigonometry that as the handle is lowered, the horizontal force increases.

For Your Information

Work is a scalar quantity, the dot product of two vectors, force and displacement, $\mathbf{F} \cdot \mathbf{d} = Fd \cos \theta$. Since $\cos 90° = 0$, and $\cos 0° = 1$, when the force is at right angles to the displacement, no work is done by the force; when the force is at 0°, in the same direction as the displacement, $W = Fd$.

FIGURE 10–4. If a force is applied to the mower at an angle, the net force doing the work is the component that acts in the direction of the motion.

a

b

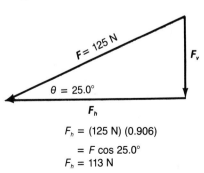

$$F_h = (125 \text{ N}) (0.906)$$
$$= F \cos 25.0°$$
$$F_h = 113 \text{ N}$$

The lawn mower has other forces acting on it, Figure 10–5a. Gravity acts downward, and the normal force of the ground acts upward. Both are perpendicular to the direction of motion. That is, the angle between the force and direction of motion is 90°. Since cos 90° = 0, neither force does work.

The grass exerts a force, friction, in the direction opposite the motion, Figure 10–5b. In fact, if the lawn mower moves at a constant speed, the horizontal component of the applied force is balanced by the force of friction, $F_{friction}$. The angle between the force of friction and the direction of motion is 180°. Since cos 180° = −1, the work done by friction is $W = -F_{friction}d$. The work done by the friction of the grass is negative. Negative work indicates work being done against the force.

FIGURE 10–5. Gravity, F_g, acts downward, while the normal of the ground, F_N, acts upward (a). The force of friction, F_f, acts in a direction opposite the direction of motion, F_x (b).

SUGGESTION: Emphasize W is for work and not weight.

EXAMPLE

Work—Force and Displacement at an Angle

A sailor pulls a boat along a dock using a rope at an angle of 60.0° with the horizontal. How much work is done by the sailor if he exerts a force of 255 N on the rope and pulls the boat 30.0 m?

Given: $\theta = 60.0°$ **Unknown:** work (W)
$F = 255$ N   **Basic equation:** $W = Fd \cos \theta$
$d = 30.0$ m

Solution: $W = Fd \cos \theta$
$$= (255 \text{ N})(30.0 \text{ m})(\cos 60.0°)$$
$$= (255 \text{ N})(30.0 \text{ m})(0.500)$$
$$= 3.83 \times 10^3 \text{ J}$$

PROBLEM SOLVING

When doing work problems, you should
a. carefully check the forces acting on the body. Draw a diagram indicating all the force vectors.
b. ask, "What is the displacement; the displacement angle?"
c. determine the sign of the work. Does the sign make sense?

Practice Exercises

5. An airplane passenger carries a 215-N suitcase up stairs a displacement of 4.20 m vertically and 4.60 m horizontally. How much work against gravity does the passenger do?

6. The same passenger carries the same suitcase back down the same stairs. How much work does the passenger do now?

7. How much work does the force of gravity do when a 25-N object falls a distance of 3.5 m?

8. A rope is used to pull a metal box 15.0 m across the floor. The rope is held at an angle of 46.0° with the floor and a force of 628 N is used. How much work does the force on the rope do?

10:3 Energy and Power

When you lift a box of books onto a shelf, you give the box a certain property. If the box falls, it can do work; it might exert forces that crush another object. You have given the box **energy**—the ability to produce a change in itself or its surroundings. By doing work on the box, you have transferred energy from your body to the box. Thus we say that **work** is the transfer of energy by mechanical means. You can think of work as energy transferred as the result of motion.

Until now, none of the discussions of work have mentioned the time it takes to move an object. The work done lifting a box of books is the same whether the box is lifted in 2 seconds or if each book is lifted separately, so that it takes 20 minutes to put them all on the shelf. The work done is the same, but the power is different. **Power** is the rate of doing work. That is, power is the rate at which energy is transferred. Power is work done divided by the time it takes. Power can be calculated using

$$P = \frac{W}{t}$$

Power is measured in **watts** (W). One watt is one joule per second. A machine that does work at a rate of one joule per second has a power of one watt. A watt is a relatively small unit of power. For example, a glass of water weighs about 2 N. If you lift it 0.5 meter to your mouth, you do 1 joule of work. If this task takes you one second, you are doing work at the rate of one watt. Because a watt is such a small unit, power is often measured in kilowatts (kW). A kilowatt is 1000 watts.

FIGURE 10–6. The power of the electric motor that moves this elevator can be calculated.

Power is the rate at which work is done.

A watt, one joule/second, is a relatively small unit. A kilowatt, 1000 watts, is more commonly used.

EXAMPLE

Power

An electric motor lifts an elevator that weighs 1.20×10^4 N a distance of 9.00 m in 15.0 s. **a.** What is the power of the motor in watts? **b.** What is the power in kilowatts?

Given: $F = 1.20 \times 10^4$ N   **Unknown:** power (P)
$\qquad\quad d = 9.00$ m
$\qquad\quad t = 15.0$ s   **Basic equation:** $P = \dfrac{W}{t}$

Solution: a. $P = \dfrac{W}{t}$

$\qquad\qquad = \dfrac{Fd}{t}$

$\qquad\qquad = (1.20 \times 10^4 \text{ N}) \dfrac{(9.00 \text{ m})}{(15.0 \text{ s})}$

$\qquad\qquad = 7.20 \times 10^3 \text{ N} \cdot \text{m/s} = 7.20 \times 10^3 \text{ J/s}$

$\qquad\qquad = 7.20 \times 10^3 \text{ W}$

$\quad$ **b.** $P = 7.20 \times 10^3 \text{ W} \dfrac{(1 \text{ kW})}{(1000 \text{ W})} = 7.20 \text{ kW}$

For Your Information

The *watt,* the SI unit of power, is named in honor of James Watt, the Scottish engineer who revolutionized industry with his vast improvements to the steam engine. As a child, Watt gave no indication that he would contribute so much to the growth of industry and automation. He was a sickly child and was even thought to be mentally retarded.

For Your Information

The English unit for power is the ft·lb/s. A more familiar unit is the *horsepower* (hp).
1 hp = 550 ft·lb/s = 746 W.

For Your Information

Practice Exercises

9. How much power can your body develop? Measure the height of a flight of stairs. Find the time needed to run up the stairs. Calculate the power.

10. A box that weighs 575 N is lifted a distance of 20.0 m straight up by a rope and a pulley system. The job is done in 10.0 s. What power is developed in watts and kilowatts?

11. A rock climber wears a 7.50-kg knapsack while scaling a cliff. After 30.0 minutes, the climber is 8.2 m above the starting point.

    a. How much work does the climber do on the knapsack?

    b. If the climber weighs 645 N, how much work does she do lifting herself and the knapsack?

    c. What is the average power developed by the climber?

12. An electric motor develops 65 kW of power as it lifts a loaded elevator 17.5 m in 35.0 s. How much force does the motor exert?

10:4 Simple Machines

Everyone uses machines in everyday life. Some are simple tools like bottle openers and screwdrivers; others are complex objects such as bicycles and automobiles. Machines, whether powered by engines or people, make the work we do easier. A machine eases the load either by changing the magnitude or the direction of the force exerted to do work. All machines are combinations of six simple machines shown in Figure 10–7. They are the lever, pulley, wheel-and-axle, inclined plane, wedge, and screw.

All machines are combinations of the simple machine: the lever, pulley, wheel and axle, inclined plane, wedge, and screw.

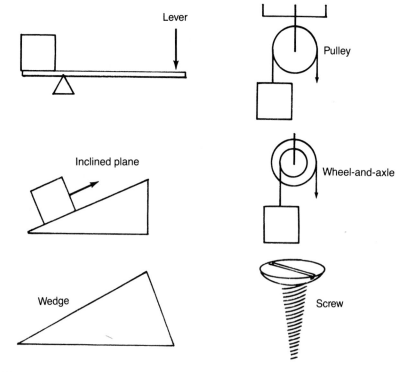

FIGURE 10–7. The six simple machines.

Consider the bottle opener in Figure 10–8. When you use the opener, you lift the handle, doing work on the opener. The opener lifts the cap, doing work on it. The work you do is called the input work, W_i. The work the machine does is called the output work, W_o.

Work, you remember, is the transfer of energy by mechanical means. You transfer energy to the bottle opener, and the opener, in turn, transfers energy to the cap. The opener is not a source of energy, so the cap cannot receive more energy than you put into the opener. Thus the output work can never be larger than the input work. The machine simply aids in the transfer of energy from you to the bottle cap.

10:5 Mechanical Advantage

The force you exert on a machine is called the **effort force,** F_e. The force exerted by the machine is called the **resistance force,** F_r. The ratio of resistance force to effort force, F_r/F_e, is called the **mechanical advantage** (*MA*) of the machine. That is,

$$MA = \frac{F_r}{F_e}$$

Many machines, like the bottle opener, have a mechanical advantage greater than one. When the mechanical advantage is greater than one, the machine increases the force you apply.

A machine can increase force, but it cannot increase energy. The input work is the product of the effort force you exert, F_e, and the displacement of your hand, d_e. In the same way, the output work is the product of the resistance force, F_r, and the displacement of the machine, d_r. An ideal machine transfers all the energy, so the output work equals the input work, or

$$W_o = W_i$$

Thus,

$$F_r d_r = F_e d_e$$

Rearranging the equation gives

$$\frac{F_r}{F_e} = \frac{d_e}{d_r}$$

The ratio of forces, F_r to F_e, is the mechanical advantage. For an ideal machine, the equation above shows that the ideal mechanical advantage, *IMA*, can be found from the ratio of displacements, or

$$IMA = \frac{d_e}{d_r}$$

In a real machine, not all of the input energy is transferred out of the machine. Some energy changes into forms that are not available as output work. The efficiency of a machine is defined as the ratio of output work to input work. That is,

$$eff = \frac{W_o}{W_i} \times 100\%$$

FIGURE 10–8. A bottle opener is a simple machine.

The mechanical advantage of a machine is the ratio of the force exerted by the machine to the force applied to the machine.

SUGGESTION: As this section is discussed, use a pulley or an inclined plane to lift a brick. Record the data and do the calculations with the class. Students often find it hard to differentiate between all the variables so it will help to do several examples in class.

Efficiency is the ratio of the work done by the machine to the work put into the machine.

FIGURE 10–9. The output work of a real machine is always less than the input work.

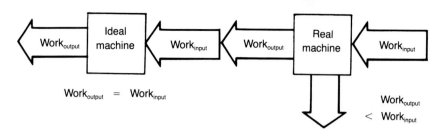

$$\text{Work}_{output} = \text{Work}_{input}$$

$$\text{Work}_{output} < \text{Work}_{input}$$

Real machines are less than 100% efficient. The work is less than the input work.

Note that an ideal machine has equal output and input work, $W_o/W_i = 1$, and the efficiency is 100%. Real machines have efficiencies less than 100%. We can express the efficiency in terms of the mechanical advantage and ideal mechanical advantage.

$$\text{efficiency} = \frac{W_o}{W_i} \times 100\%$$

$$= \frac{F_r d_r}{F_e d_e} \times 100\%$$

$$= \left(\frac{F_r}{F_e}\right)\left(\frac{d_r}{d_e}\right) \times 100\%$$

PHYSICS FOCUS

The Human Walking Machine

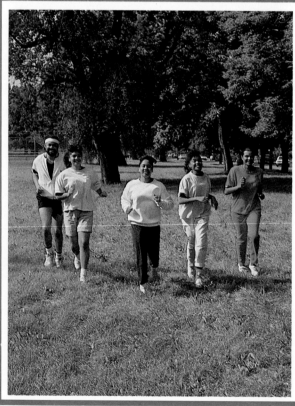

Movement of the human body is explained by the same principles of force and work used to describe all motion. Simple machines, in the form of levers, give us the ability to walk and run. Lever systems of the body are complex, but each system has four basic parts: 1) a rigid bar (bone), 2) a source of force (muscle contraction), 3) a fulcrum or pivot (movable joints between bones), and 4) a resistance (the weight of the body or an object being lifted or moved). Lever systems of the body are not very efficient and mechanical advantages are low. This is why walking and jogging require energy (burn calories) and help individuals lose weight.

When a person walks, the hip acts as a fulcrum and moves through the arc of a circle centered on the foot. The center of mass of the body moves as a resistance around the fulcrum in the same arc. The length of the radius of the circle is the length of the lever formed by the bones of the leg. Athletes in walking races increase their velocity by swinging their hips upward to increase this radius.

A tall person has a lever system with a lower *MA* than a short person. Although tall people can usually walk faster than short people, the tall person must apply a greater force to move the longer lever formed by the leg bones. Walking races are usually 20 or 50 km long. Because of the inefficiency of their lever systems and the length of a walking race, very tall people rarely have the stamina to win.

But, multiplying by d_r/d_e is the same as dividing by d_e/d_r, so

$$\text{efficiency} = \frac{F_r}{F_e} \div \frac{d_e}{d_r} \times 100\%$$

$$\boxed{\text{eff} = \frac{MA}{IMA} \times 100\%}$$

The *IMA* of most machines is fixed by the machine's construction. For example, the *IMA* of a lever depends on the length of the lever arms. An efficient machine has an *MA* almost equal to its *IMA*. A less efficient machine has a smaller *MA*. This means that a greater effort force is needed to exert the same resistance force.

EXAMPLE

Simple Machines

A student uses the bottle opener in Figure 10–8 and finds that a force of 15 N must be exerted to lift a cap 1.4 mm. The opener has an *IMA* of 16.0 and an efficiency of 90%. **a.** What is the *MA* of the opener? **b.** What force is applied to the bottle cap? **c.** How far does the handle of the opener move?

Given: effort force   **Unknowns:**
$\quad\quad\quad F_e = 15$ N   **a.** *MA*
$\quad\quad\quad IMA = 16.0$ **b.** resistance force F_r
$\quad\quad\quad$ efficiency $= 90\%$ **c.** effort displacement d_e
$\quad\quad\quad$ resistance displacement
$\quad\quad\quad d_r = 1.4$ mm

Solution: a. efficiency $= \dfrac{MA}{IMA} \times 100\%$

$$MA = \frac{IMA}{100\%}\text{eff}$$

$$= \frac{(90\%)(16.0)}{100\%} = 14$$

$\quad\quad$ **b.** $MA = \dfrac{F_r}{F_e}$

$$F_r = (MA)(F_e)$$
$$= (14)(15 \text{ N}) = 210 \text{ N}$$

$\quad\quad$ **c.** $IMA = \dfrac{d_e}{d_r}$

$$d_e = (IMA)(d_r)$$
$$= (16.0)(1.4 \text{ mm}) = 22 \text{ mm}$$

Practice Exercises

13. A sledge hammer is used to drive a wedge into a log to split it. When the wedge is driven 20 cm into the log, the log is separated a distance of 5.0 cm. A force of 1.9×10^4 N is needed to split the log, and the sledge exerts a force of 9.8×10^3 N.

    a. What is the *IMA* of the wedge?

    b. Find the *MA* of the wedge.

    c. Calculate the efficiency of the wedge as a machine.

14. A worker uses a pulley system to raise a 225 N carton 16.5 m. A force of 129 N is exerted and the rope is pulled 33.0 m.

    a. What is the mechanical advantage of the pulley system?

    b. What is the efficiency of the system?

15. A boy exerts a force of 225 N on a lever to raise a 1.25×10^3 N rock a distance of 0.13 m. If the efficiency of the lever is 88.7%, how far did the boy move his end of the lever?

CHAPTER 10 REVIEW

SUMMARY

1. Work is the product of the force exerted on an object and the distance the object moves in the direction of the force. **10:1**

2. Work is the transfer of energy by mechanical means. **10:3**

3. Power is the rate of doing work. That is, power is the rate at which energy is transferred. It is measured in watts. **10:3**

4. Machines, whether powered by engines or humans, make work easier. A machine eases the load either by changing the magnitude or the direction of the force exerted to do work. **10:4**

5. The mechanical advantage, *MA*, is the ratio of resistance force to effort force. **10:5**

6. The ideal mechanical advantage, *IMA*, is the ratio of the displacements. In all real machines, *MA* is less than *IMA*. **10:5**

QUESTIONS

1. Define work and power.

2. Two people of the same mass climb the same flight of stairs. The first person climbs the stairs in 25 seconds; the second person takes 35 seconds. Which person does more work? Explain your answer.

3. In the preceding question, which person produces more power? Explain your answer.

4. An object slides at constant speed on a frictionless surface. What forces act on the object? What work is done?

5. How are the pedals of a bicycle a simple machine?

6. A claw hammer is used to pull a nail from a piece of wood. How can you place your hand on the handle and locate the nail in the claw to make the effort force as small as possible?

7. How can one increase the ideal mechanical advantage of a machine?

8. A satellite orbits Earth in a circular orbit. Does gravity do any work on the satellite?

APPLYING CONCEPTS

1. Which requires more work, carrying a 420-N knapsack up a 200 m hill or carrying a 210-N knapsack up a 400 m hill? Why?

2. A student has an after-school job carrying cartons of new copy paper up a flight of stairs, and then carrying used paper back down the stairs. The mass of the paper does not change. The student's

physics teacher suggests that the student does no work all day, so should not be paid. In what sense is the physics teacher correct? What arrangement of payments might the student make to ensure compensation?

3. You slowly lift a box of books from the floor and put it on a table. The forces exerted on the box are the weight of the box, magnitude mg, downward, and the force you exert, magnitude mg, upward. The two forces are balanced. It appears no work is done, but you know you did work. Explain what work is done.

4. Mo and Jo have the same mass and climb the same flight of stairs. Mo climbs the stairs in 25 seconds while Jo takes 35 seconds.

    a. Who does more work, Mo or Jo? Explain.

    b. Who produces more power? Explain.

5. How could you increase the mechanical advantage of a wedge without changing the ideal mechanical advantage?

EXERCISES

1. The graph in Figure 10–10 shows the force needed to stretch a spring. Find the work needed to stretch it 0.25 m.

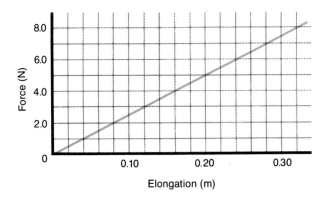

FIGURE 10–10. Use with Exercise 1 and Problem 1.

2. An 845-N sled is pulled a distance of 185 m. The task requires 1.20×10^4 J of work and is done by pulling on a rope with a force of 125 N. At what angle is the rope held?

3. A force of 462 N is needed to drag a wooden crate across a floor. The rope tied to the crate is pulled at an angle of 56.0°.

    a. How much tension is in the rope?

    b. What work is done by the force pulling the rope if the crate is moved 24.5 m?

    c. What work is done by the force of friction between the floor and the crate?

4. A student librarian picks up a 22-N book from the floor to a height of 1.25 m. He carries the book 8.0 m to the stacks and places the book on a shelf that is 0.35 m high. How much work did he do on the book?

5. A gardener pushes a wheelbarrow by exerting a 145 N force. The gardener moves it 60.0 m at a constant speed for 25.0 s.

    a. What power does the gardener develop?

    b. If the gardener moves the wheelbarrow twice as fast, how much power is developed?

6. The third floor of a house is 8.0 m above street level. How much work is needed to move a 150-kg refrigerator to the third floor?

7. A horizontal force of 805 N is needed to drag a crate across a horizontal floor. A worker drags the crate using a rope held at an angle of 32°.

    a. What force does the worker exert on the rope?

    b. How much work does the worker do on the crate when moving it 22 m?

    c. If the worker completes the job in 8.0 s, what power is developed?

8. An engine moves a boat through the water at a steady speed of 15 m/s. The engine must exert a force of 6.0×10^3 N to balance the force water exerts against the hull. What power does the engine develop?

9. A crane lifts a 2.25×10^3-N bucket that contains 1.15 m^3 of soil (density = 2.00×10^3 kg/m^3) to a height of 7.50 m. Calculate the work the crane performs.

10. A champion weightlifter raises 240 kg a distance of 2.35 m.

    a. How much work is done lifting the weights?

    b. How much work is done holding them above his head?

    c. How much work is done lowering them back to the ground?

    d. Does the weightlifter do work if the weights

are let go and fall back to the ground?

e. If the lifter completes the lift in 2.5 seconds, how much power is developed?

11. What power does a pump develop to lift 35 liters of water per minute from a depth of 110 m? (A liter of water has a mass of 1.00 kg.)

12. A lawn roller is rolled across a lawn by a force of 115 N along the direction of the handle, which is 22.5° above the horizontal. If the person pushing the roller develops 64.6 W of power for 90.0 seconds, what distance is the roller pushed?

13. A student slides a crate up a ramp at an angle of 30.0° by exerting a 225-N force parallel to the ramp. The crate moves at constant speed. The coefficient of friction is 0.28. How much work has been done when the crate is raised 1.15 m?

14. What work is required to lift a 215 kg mass a distance of 5.65 m using a machine that is 72.5% efficient?

15. A pulley system lifts a 1345 N weight a distance of 0.975 m. The person using the system pulls the rope a distance of 3.90 m, exerting a force of 375 N.

a. What is the ideal mechanical advantage of the system?

b. What is the mechanical advantage?

c. How efficient is the system?

16. A mover's dolly is used to deliver a refrigerator up a ramp into a house. The refrigerator has a mass of 115 kg. The ramp is 2.10 m long and rises 0.850 m. The mover pulls the dolly with a force of 496 N. The dolly and ramp constitute a machine.

a. What work does the mover do?

b. What is the work done on the refrigerator by the machine?

c. What is the efficiency of the machine?

PROBLEMS

1. In Figure 10–10 the magnitude of the force necessary to stretch a spring is plotted against the distance the spring is stretched.

a. Calculate the slope of the graph and show that

$$F = kd$$

where k = 25 N/m.

b. Find the amount of work done in stretching the spring from 0.00 m to 0.20 m by calculating the area under the curve from 0.00 m to 0.20 m in Figure 10–10.

c. Show that the answer to part **b** can be calculated using the formula

$$W = \tfrac{1}{2}kd^2$$

where W is the work, k = 25 N/m (the slope of the graph), and d is the distance the spring is stretched (0.20 m).

2. A complex machine is a combination of two or more simple machines arranged so that the output work of one machine becomes the input work of another. For example, a lever can be attached to a pulley system in such a way that the resistance force of the lever becomes the effort force applied to the pulley system. By attaching the lever to the pulley system, the distance the resistance moves in the lever is equal to the distance the effort moves in the pulley system. Consider an ideal complex machine consisting of a lever with an *IMA* of 3.0 and a pulley system with an *IMA* of 2.0.

a. Show that the *IMA* of this complex machine is 6.0.

b. If the complex machine is 60.0% efficient, how much effort must be applied to the lever to lift a 540-N box?

c. If the effort moves 12.0 cm when applied to the lever, how far is the box lifted?

3. In 35 s, a pump delivers 550 dm³ of oil into barrels on a platform 25 m above the pump intake pipe. The density of the oil is 0.82 g/cm³.

a. Calculate the work done by the pump.

b. Calculate the power produced by the pump.

4. The ramp in Figure 10–11 is 18 m long and 4.5 m high.

a. What force parallel to the ramp ($F_{\parallel}$) is required to slide a 25 kg box to the top of the ramp if friction is neglected?

b. What is the *IMA* of the ramp?

c. What are the real *MA* and the efficiency of the ramp if a parallel force of 75 N is actually required?

5. A 188 W motor will lift a load at the rate (speed)

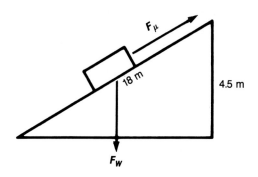

FIGURE 10–11. Use with Problem 4.

of 6.50 cm/s. How great a load can the motor lift at this speed?

6. A motor having an efficiency of 88% operates a crane having an efficiency of 42%. With what constant speed does the crane lift a 410 kg crate of machine parts if the power supplied to the motor is 5.5 kW?

READINGS

Britton, Peter, "How Canada is Tapping the Tides for Power." *Popular Science,* January, 1985.

Easton, B., "Mass Is Not Destroyed." *The Physics Teacher,* April, 1988.

Kyle, Chester, "The Aerodynamics of Human Powered Land Vehicles." *Scientific American,* December, 1983.

CHAPTER 11

Energy

GOALS

1. You will become familiar with several forms of energy.
2. You will gain an understanding of the relationship between work and energy.
3. You will gain an understanding of how to apply the law of conservation of energy.

For Your Information

Some of the most powerful laws of physics are the conservation laws. For example, the gravitational potential energy stored in a block of stone when it was lifted to the top of a pyramid 2500 years ago is still there undiminished. Making allowances for erosion, dropping the stone today could do as much work as when the stone was first put in place.

Kinetic energy is energy due to the motion of an object.

Potential energy is energy stored in an object because of its position or state.

SUGGESTION: Give examples of kinetic energy changing to thermal energy, such as rubbing two sticks together to start a fire.

We use the term "energy" in many ways. A child who runs and plays long after adults are tired is said to be full of energy. We call the rapid depletion of our oil and natural gas resource an "energy crisis."

In Chapter 10 we defined energy as the ability to change an object or its environment. Change can occur in several ways. A speeding automobile can damage itself, people, and objects in its path. The energy that causes this motion is normally stored in the chemical bonds of gasoline in the tank. Energy can be stored in many other forms. A heavy object placed high on a shelf has a potential to do damage if it falls. A stretched spring or rubber band has the ability to give an object a high velocity. In this chapter we will investigate various forms of energy and the means of converting energy from one form to another.

11:1 Forms of Energy

Suppose an archer pulls back a bowstring and bends the bow. The moment the string is released, the arrow begins to move. The moving arrow has energy. It can push deep into the target. That is, it has the ability to cause changes in itself and its environment. The form of energy possessed by moving objects is called **kinetic energy.**

The archer did work by bending the bow, but the arrow did not obtain kinetic energy until it left the string. The work done by the archer was saved or stored in the bent bow. The bent bow is said to have potential energy. Potential energy is stored in the bow as a result of changing its shape. When the bow is released, the potential energy is changed into kinetic energy.

Who-o-o-o-sh

Carlos and Jamahl waited expectantly as the roller coaster cars were slowly lifted to the crest of the first hill and then released. When the ride was over, Carlos said he felt as though his stomach had been left behind when the cars plunged down the first hill. Jamahl said he was certain the second hill had been the tallest. Carlos disagreed. How did Carlos convince Jamahl that the first hill was tallest.

If you lift a heavy stone above your head, you have done work on the stone. When you drop the stone, it will have kinetic energy. By doing work against the gravitational force between Earth and the stone, you have given the stone potential energy. The amount of the potential energy depends on the weight of the stone and how high you lift it above Earth's surface.

Work, we have said, is the transfer of energy by mechanical means. In the two examples above, a person did work, transferring energy into the potential energy of an object. From where did this energy come? The body obtains energy from food and stores it in certain chemical compounds until needed. The compounds can produce motion in muscles, transferring their stored energy to kinetic energy. Energy in both food and the body is stored in chemical bonds, and so is called chemical energy.

There are many forms of potential energy. No matter what the form, the amount of potential energy depends on the position, shape, or form of an object. Potential energy can be converted into the energy of motion, kinetic energy.

11:2 Work and Change in Kinetic Energy

A pitcher winds up and throws a baseball. During the throw, a force is exerted on the ball. As a result, the ball leaves the pitcher's hand with a high velocity and considerable kinetic energy. How can we find the amount of energy, and how is the kinetic energy related to the work done on the ball?

The kinetic energy of an object is given by the equation

$$KE = \frac{1}{2}mv^2$$

where m is the mass of the object and v is its velocity. The kinetic energy is proportional to the mass of the object. Thus a 7.3-kg shot has much

FIGURE 11-1. The archer does work in pulling back the bowstring and bending the bow. The work done by the archer in pulling back the bowstring is stored in the bent bow as potential energy.

FIGURE 11-2. Athletes do work to produce motion and hence, kinetic energy. In some events kinetic energy is changed to potential energy and back again.

more kinetic energy than a 115-g baseball going the same speed. The kinetic energy is also proportional to the square of the velocity. A car speeding at 30 m/s has four times the kinetic energy of the same car traveling at 15 m/s. Kinetic energy, like any form of energy, is measured in joules.

How can the pitcher give the ball more kinetic energy? He can either pitch the ball with greater force or exert that force over a larger distance. In other words, he can do more work on the ball. Newton's second law can be used to show the connection between work and kinetic energy. The work done on an object is given by $W = Fd$. According to Newton's second law, if a net force is exerted on an object, it accelerates with $F = ma$. Thus the work done is $W = mad$. Assume the object was originally at rest. As it accelerates,

$$v^2 = 2ad, \text{ or}$$

$$d = \frac{v^2}{2a}$$

Therefore, $W = mad$

$$= ma\left(\frac{v^2}{2a}\right)$$

$$= \frac{1}{2}mv^2$$

That is, $\quad W = KE$

Not all objects start at rest. They may already have kinetic energy when additional work is done on them. If we define initial kinetic energy (KE_i) and final kinetic energy (KE_f) as the energies the object has before and after the work is done, we can write

$$W_{net} = KE_f - KE_i = \Delta KE$$

That is, the change in the kinetic energy of a body is equal to the net work done on it. This equation represents the **work-energy theorem.** It can be stated: *The net work done on an object is equal to its change in kinetic energy.* Note that the work in the work-energy theorem is the work done on an object by a net force. It is the algebraic sum of work done by all forces.

$$Fd = \Delta KE$$

FIGURE 11-3. The increase in kinetic energy of an object is equal to the work done on it.

The work-energy theorem indicates that if the net work is positive, the kinetic energy increases. Positive net work is done when the net force acts in the same direction as the motion. For example, a pitcher exerts a net force on a baseball. The force is in the same direction as the motion of the ball. The work done by the pitcher on the ball is positive and the kinetic energy of the ball increases.

If the net work is negative, the kinetic energy decreases. A catcher also exerts a net force on the ball, but this time in the direction opposite its motion. The kinetic energy decreases to zero as the ball stops in the catcher's mitt. The catcher does negative work on the ball.

The kinetic energy of several common moving objects is shown in Table 11–1.

FIGURE 11-4. An 18-wheeler moving down the highway at 100 km/hr has 2.2 million joules of kinetic energy.

TABLE 11–1

Typical Kinetic Energies		
Item	Remarks	Kinetic Energy (J)
Aircraft carrier	91 400 tons at 30 knots	9.9×10^9
Orbiting satellite	100 kg at 300-km altitude	3.0×10^9
Trailer truck	5700 kg at 100 km/h	2.2×10^6
Compact car	750 kg at 100 km/h	2.9×10^5
Football linebacker	110 kg at 9.0 m/s	4.5×10^3
Pitched baseball	150 g at 45 m/s	1.5×10^2
Falling nickel	5 g at 50-m height	2.5
Bumblebee	2 g at 2 m/s	4×10^{-3}
Snail	5 g at 0.05 km/h	4.5×10^{-7}

EXAMPLE

Kinetic Energy and Work

A shotputter heaves a 7.26-kg shot at a velocity of 7.50 m/s. **a.** What is the kinetic energy of the shot? **b.** The shot was initially at rest. How much work was done on it to give it this kinetic energy?

Given: $m = 7.26$ kg   Unknowns: **a.** kinetic energy (KE)
$\quad\quad\quad v_i = 0$ m/s $\quad\quad\quad\quad$ **b.** work (W)
$\quad\quad\quad v_f = 7.50$ m/s

Basic equations: **a.** $KE = \frac{1}{2}mv^2$
$\quad\quad\quad\quad\quad\quad\quad$ **b.** $W = \Delta KE$

Solution: **a.** $KE = \frac{1}{2}mv^2 = \frac{1}{2}(7.26 \text{ kg})(7.50 \text{ m/s})^2$
$\quad\quad\quad\quad\quad = 204 \text{ kg} \cdot \text{m}^2/\text{s}^2$
$\quad\quad\quad KE = 204 \text{ J}$

$\quad\quad$ **b.** $W = \Delta KE = KE_f - KE_i$
$\quad\quad\quad\quad\quad = 204 \text{ J} - 0 \text{ J}$
$\quad\quad\quad W = 204 \text{ J}$

Practice Exercises

1. **a.** Verify that the compact car in Table 11–1 has the kinetic energy listed.

   b. Find the ratio of the kinetic energy of a luxury car with mass 1500 kg to that of the compact car if both are traveling at the same speed.

2. **a.** What is the kinetic energy of a compact car moving at 50 km/h?

   b. How much work must be done on the car to slow it from 100 km/h to 50 km/h?

   c. How much work must be done on the car to bring it to rest?

   d. The force that does the work slowing the car is constant. Find the ratio of the distance needed to slow the car from 100 km/h to 50 km/h to the distance needed to slow it from 50 km/h to rest. State your conclusion in a sentence.

3. A rifle can shoot a 4.20 g bullet at a speed of 965 m/s.

   a. Find the kinetic energy of the bullet.

   b. What work is done on the bullet if it starts from rest?

   c. If the work is done over a distance of 0.75 m, what is the average force on the bullet?

4. A comet with mass 7.85×10^{11} kg strikes Earth at a speed, relative to the motion of Earth, of 25 km/s.

   a. Find the kinetic energy of the comet in joules.

   b. Compare the work done on Earth with the energy released in exploding the largest nuclear weapon ever built, equivalent to 100 million tons of TNT, or 4.2×10^{15} J of energy. Such a comet collision has been suggested as having caused the extinction of the dinosaurs.

11:3 Potential Energy

If you throw a ball up into the air, you do work on it. As it leaves your hand, it has kinetic energy. As the ball rises, its speed is reduced because of the downward force of gravity. The kinetic energy of the ball becomes smaller. At the top of its flight, its speed momentarily is zero and it has no kinetic energy. By the time it returns to your hand, however, the ball has regained its original speed. Thus its kinetic energy is the same as it was when it left your hand.

The energy you give the ball is transferred to potential energy and then back into kinetic energy. It makes sense, then, to describe the total energy, E, as the sum of the kinetic energy and the potential energy.

$$E = KE + PE$$

During the flight of the ball, the sum of kinetic and potential energy is constant. At the start and end of the flight, the energy is totally kinetic. Potential energy is zero. At the top, the energy is fully potential. Kinetic energy is zero. In between, the energy is partially kinetic and partially potential.

The total energy of an object is the sum of its kinetic and potential energy.

FIGURE 11-5. A ball leaves the juggler's hand with maximum kinetic energy, which is gradually changed to maximum potential energy at the top of its flight. Then, the energy exchange reverses on its way down.

For Your Information

How does potential energy depend on height? As long as the ball is close to Earth, the gravitational acceleration, g, is constant, where $g = 9.80$ m/s^2. The velocity of the ball is given by

$$v^2 = v_i^2 - 2gh$$

In this equation h is the distance measured from the launching height of the ball. Multiplying each term in this equation by $\frac{1}{2}m$ gives the kinetic energy, $\frac{1}{2}mv^2$, at any height h

$$\frac{1}{2}mv^2 = \frac{1}{2}mv_i^2 - mgh$$

At the start of the flight $h = 0$. The energy is all kinetic, $E = \frac{1}{2}mv_i^2$. Because the total energy of the ball does not change,

$$E = \frac{1}{2}mv_i^2$$
$$= \frac{1}{2}mv^2 + mgh$$

But $E = KE + PE$, so the gravitational potential energy is

$$\boxed{PE = mgh}$$

Only changes in energy can be measured.

Only energy changes can be measured; the total amount of energy cannot be determined. This means that gravitational potential energy can be set equal to zero at any height you choose. Often potential energy is measured from the surface of Earth or from the floor of a room. That is, h is set equal to zero at the ground or floor level. Any height, called the reference level, can be used. It is important, however, that the reference level not be changed in the middle of a problem.

SUGGESTION: Point out that potential energy can also be stored in a rubber band or a spring, as it is in many toys.

The formula for gravitational potential energy, $PE = mgh$, is valid only if the gravitational force is constant. When the distance is far above Earth, the $1/r^2$ dependence shown in the equation for universal gravitation becomes important. The potential energy no longer increases linearly with the height.

Energy can be stored by bending, stretching, or deforming an object.

Energy also can be stored in the bending or stretching of an object. The work done pulling back the string of a bow is stored in the bent bow, then transferred into the kinetic energy of the arrow. The bent bow has potential energy. The stretching, squeezing, or bending of objects such as metal

FIGURE 11-6. Gravitational potential energy is arbitrarily chosen to be zero at base level.

a

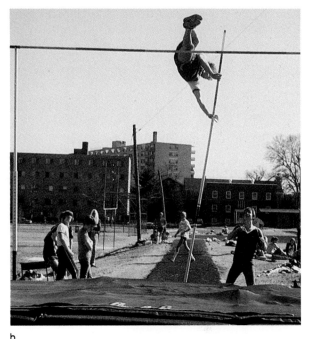

b

FIGURE 11-7. The kinetic energy of a pole vaulter is first stored in the bending of the pole (a). As the pole straightens, it is converted into gravitational potential energy as the vaulter is lifted above the ground (b).

springs, slingshots, and trampolines store potential energy. The modern fiberglass pole used in the pole vault has led to greatly increased records in competition. The pole vaulter runs with the pole, then plants the end of the pole into a socket in the ground. The kinetic energy of the runner is first stored in the bending of the pole. Then, as the pole straightens, it is converted into gravitational potential energy as the vaulter is lifted up to 6 m above the ground.

Gravitational potential energy depends on the position of an object above Earth's surface.

EXAMPLE

Gravitational Potential Energy

A 2.00-kg textbook is lifted from the floor to a shelf 2.10 m above the floor. **a.** What is its gravitational potential energy relative to the floor? **b.** What is its gravitational potential energy relative to the head of a 1.65 m tall person?

Given: $m = 2.00$ kg
heights

    a. $h = 2.10$ m $- 0$ m
        $= 2.10$ m

    b. $h = 2.10$ m $- 1.65$ m
        $= 0.45$ m

Unknown: potential
energy (PE)

Basic equation: $PE = mgh$

Solution: a. $PE = mgh = (2.00$ kg$)(9.80$ m/s$^2)(2.10$ m$) = 41.2$ J
        b. $PE = mgh = (2.00$ kg$)(9.80$ m/s$^2)(0.45$ m$) = 8.8$ J

For Your Information

For springs that obey Hooke's law, that is, where $F = -kx$, $PE = \frac{1}{2}kx^2$. The constant k is called the spring constant and x is the change in length of the spring from equilibrium.

FIGURE 11-8. The potential energy of the water above the wheel is converted to kinetic energy as the water falls (a). A pile driver does work as it falls from a higher to a lower position (b).

The law of conservation of energy states that energy can neither be created nor destroyed.

Practice Exercises

5. A weightlifter raises a 180-kg barbell to a height of 1.95 m. What is the increase in the barbell's potential energy?

6. A 90-kg rock climber first climbs 45 m upward to the edge of a quarry, then descends 85 m to the bottom. Find the potential energy of the climber at the edge and at the bottom, using the initial height as reference level.

7. A 50.0-kg shell is shot from a cannon to a height of 4.0×10^2 m.
   a. What is the gravitational potential energy of the Earth-shell system when the shell is at this height?
   b. What is the change in potential energy of the system when the shell falls to a height of 2.00×10^2 m?

8. A person weighing 630 N climbs up a ladder to a height of 5.0 m.
   a. What work does the person do?
   b. What is the increase in the gravitational potential energy of the person at this height?
   c. Where does the energy come from to cause this increase in the gravitational potential energy?

11:4 Conservation of Energy

In Chapter 9, we defined an isolated, closed system in the discussion of momentum. Such a system is a collection of objects of constant total mass with no external forces acting on it. The **law of conservation of energy** states that *within a closed, isolated system, energy can change form, but the total amount of energy is constant.* That is, energy can be neither created nor destroyed.

A ball and Earth could be an example of a closed, isolated system, as shown in Figure 11–9. The kinetic energy of the ball can change, but the sum of gravitational potential and kinetic energy is constant. The sum of potential and kinetic energy is called the **mechanical energy.** Suppose the ball has a weight of 10.00 N. If it is at rest 20.00 m above Earth's surface, it has no kinetic energy, but a potential energy given by

$$PE = mgh$$
$$= (10.00 \text{ N})(20.00 \text{ m}) = 200.0 \text{ J}$$

Assume that there are no forces on the ball other than the gravitational force of Earth, so the ball falls. When it is 10.00 m above Earth's surface, its potential energy is

$$PE = mgh$$
$$= (10.00 \text{ N})(10.00 \text{ m}) = 100.0 \text{ J}$$

The ball has lost half its potential energy falling 10.00 m. The ball is moving, however, and has gained kinetic energy. The change in kinetic energy can be found from the work-energy theorem:

$$W = \Delta KE$$
$$= KE_f - KE_i$$
$$= KE_f$$

The work was done on the falling ball by the gravitational force, mg.

$$W = Fd$$
$$= (10.00 \text{ N})(10.00 \text{ m}) = 100.0 \text{ J}$$

The work is positive because the force and motion are in the same direction. Thus the kinetic energy of the ball is

$$KE_f = 100.0 \text{ J}$$

The decrease in the potential energy of an object is equal to the increase in its kinetic energy. Thus the sum of potential and kinetic energies is not changed. The mechanical energy is constant. When the ball reaches Earth's surface, its potential energy will be zero. All its energy will be kinetic. The final kinetic energy will equal the initial potential energy. The equation describing the conservation of energy is

$$KE_i + PE_i = KE_f + PE_f$$

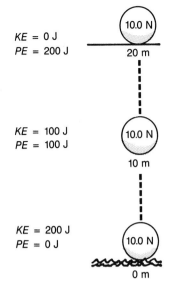

$KE = 0 \text{ J}$
$PE = 200 \text{ J}$

$KE = 100 \text{ J}$
$PE = 100 \text{ J}$

$KE = 200 \text{ J}$
$PE = 0 \text{ J}$

FIGURE 11-9. The decrease in potential energy is equal to the increase in kinetic energy.

A decrease in potential energy is accompanied by an increase in kinetic energy.

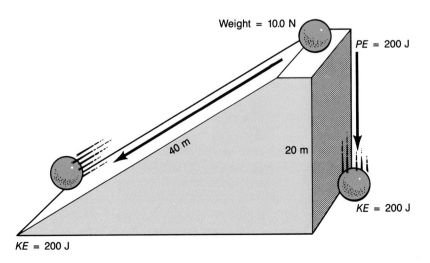

Weight = 10.0 N

$PE = 200 \text{ J}$

40 m

20 m

$KE = 200 \text{ J}$

$KE = 200 \text{ J}$

FIGURE 11-10. The path an object follows in reaching the ground does not affect the final kinetic energy.

a

A   B   C

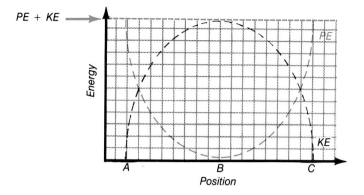

b   *PE, KE* versus Position

PE + KE

Energy

Position

FIGURE 11-11. For the simple harmonic motion of a pendulum bob (a), the sum of the potential and kinetic energies is a constant (b).

The change in the potential energy of an object does not depend on the path it takes.

For Your Information

One pound of anything, when it is completely converted into energy according to $E = mc^2$, will produce 11 400 million kilowatt-hours of energy.

The path an object follows as it falls does not change its potential energy. As shown in Figure 11–10, the 10.00 N ball might be on a frictionless inclined plane. As it slides down the plane it moves horizontally as well as vertically, but its change in height above Earth is still 20.00 m. Its potential energy depends only on its distance from Earth's surface. The kinetic energy of the ball is the same whether the ball falls vertically or slides without friction down the plane.

The simple harmonic motion of a pendulum or a mass oscillating on a spring also demonstrates the conservation of energy. Usually the gravitational potential energy is chosen to be zero at the equilibrium position of the mass. The initial gravitational potential energy of a raised pendulum bob is transferred to kinetic energy as the bob moves along its path. At the equilibrium point, the gravitational potential energy is at a minimum (zero) and kinetic energy is at a maximum. Figure 11–11b is a graph of the changing potential and kinetic energy of a pendulum bob during one period of its oscillation. The sum of potential and kinetic energies is constant.

The oscillations of a pendulum bob eventually die away, and a bouncing ball finally comes to rest. Where did the mechanical energy go? When friction is present, mechanical energy is not conserved.

If total energy is conserved, the potential and kinetic energies must have changed into other forms. When a ball hits the ground, you hear a sound. Some energy has changed into sound. If you measure the temperature of the ball or of the pendulum bob, you will find that they are slightly warmer after the motion. The energy has changed into a different form, the increased motion of the particles that make up the object. This form of energy, thermal energy, will be discussed in Chapter 12.

Albert Einstein recognized another form of potential energy, mass itself. This equivalence is expressed in his famous equation $E = mc^2$. This means that in systems where energy is conserved, a decrease in mass is accompanied by an increase in other forms of energy. According to Einstein's equation, stretching a spring or bending a bow causes them to gain mass. In these cases the change is too small to be easily detected. When the strong nuclear forces are involved, however, the energy released by changes in mass can be very large indeed.

EXAMPLE

SUGGESTION: Ask students what happens to kinetic energy when the velocity is doubled. It is quadrupled.

Conservation of Energy

A large chunk of ice with mass 15.0 kg falls from a roof 8.00 m above the ground. **a.** Find the kinetic energy of the ice when it reaches the ground. **b.** What is the speed of the ice when it reaches the ground?

Given: $m = 15.0$ kg   Unknowns: **a.** KE_f **b.** v_f

$g = 9.80$ m/s^2 Basic equation: $KE_i + PE_i = KE_f + PE_f$

$h = 8.00$ m

$KE_i = 0$

$PE_f = 0$

Solution: **a.** $KE_i + PE_i = KE_f + PE_f$

$0 + mgh = KE_f + 0$

$KE_f = mgh = (15.0$ kg$)(9.80$ m/s$^2)(8.00$ m$) = 1.18 \times 10^3$ J

b. $KE_f = \frac{1}{2}mv_f^2$

$v_f^2 = \dfrac{2KE_f}{m} = \dfrac{2(1.18 \times 10^3 \text{ J})}{(15.0 \text{ kg})} = 157$ m^2/s^2

$v_f = 12.5$ m/s

PROBLEM SOLVING

When solving conservation of energy problems, you should first carefully identify the system involved. Make sure it is closed; no objects can leave or enter it. It must also be isolated; energy can neither enter nor leave. Work must not be done by external forces. Is friction present? If it is, then mechanical energy will not be constant. However, the sum of the mechanical energy and the work done against friction will be constant. Finally, if there is no friction, find the initial and final mechanical energy and set them equal.

For Your Information

Try bending a paper clip back and forth rapidly. Then quickly put the clip against your forehead. You will notice the clip is warm. This energy came from the work you did bending the clip.

Practice Exercises

9. A bicycle rider approaches a hill with a speed of 8.5 m/s. The total mass of the bike and rider is 85 kg.
   a. Find the kinetic energy of the bike and rider.
   b. The rider coasts up the hill. Assuming there is no friction, at what height will the bike come to a stop?
   c. Does your answer depend on the mass of the bike and rider? Explain.

10. Tarzan, mass 85 kg, swings from a tree on the end of a 20 m vine. His feet touch the ground 4.0 m below the tree.
    a. How fast is Tarzan moving when he reaches the ground?
    b. Does your answer depend on Tarzan's mass?
    c. Does your answer depend on the length of the vine?

11. A skier starts from rest at the top of a 45-m hill, skis down a 30° incline into a valley, and continues up a 40-m hill. Both hill heights are measured from the valley floor. Assume you can neglect friction and the effect of ski poles.

a. How fast is the skier moving at the bottom of the valley?

b. What is the skier's speed at the top of the next hill?

12. From what height would a compact car have to be dropped to have the same kinetic energy that it has when being driven at 100 km/h?

11:5 Conservation of Energy in Collisions

During a collision between two objects, forces act that slightly change the shape of the colliding bodies. The kinetic energy of motion is changed into potential energy. If the potential energy is completely converted back into kinetic energy after the collision, the collision is called an **elastic collision.** The kinetic energy of the bodies before the collision is equal to their kinetic energy after the collision. The collision between two billiard balls or glass marbles is very nearly elastic.

a   Before collision

$v_r = 0.75$ m/s $v_w = 0.0$ m/s

b   c   After collision

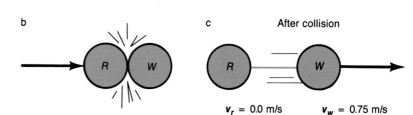

$v_r = 0.0$ m/s $v_w = 0.75$ m/s

FIGURE 11-12. In an elastic collision between two billiard balls, kinetic energy, as well as momentum, is conserved.

Momentum is conserved whenever bodies collide with no external forces present. Suppose a red billiard ball of mass $m = 95$ g moves with a speed $v = +0.75$ m/s. It collides head-on with a white billiard ball of equal mass that is at rest. The total momentum before the collision is $mv = (0.095$ kg$)(+0.75$ m/s$) = +0.071$ kg $\cdot$ m/s. What are the speeds of the two balls after the collision? Using only the momentum equation, the two speeds cannot be determined. If energy is also conserved, we have a second equation and can solve the two equations simultaneously to find the final speeds. The results show that the moving red ball must come to rest and the white ball must move with the final speed $v = +0.75$ m/s.

If, during a collision, some energy is changed into other forms, the collision is called an **inelastic collision.** In the case of the billiard balls, some energy is usually needed to do work against the surface of the table. The red ball will not stop, and the white ball will have a smaller final speed. If, instead of billiard balls, two blocks of soft clay collide and stick together, the collision is completely inelastic. The two blocks will have the same final speed. As was shown in Chapter 9, because of conservation of momentum, the final speed is half the initial speed. The momentum of the blocks is not changed: $2 \, mv/2 = (0.190$ kg$)(+0.375$ m/s$) = +0.0710$ kg $\cdot$ m/s. The energy after the collision is $\frac{1}{2}(2m)(v/2)^2 = \frac{1}{2}(0.190$ kg$)(0.375$ m/s$)^2 = 0.0130$ J. This result indicates that half the initial kinetic energy has changed into other forms.

Many collisions are neither completely elastic nor completely inelastic. The velocities can be calculated only if the amount of energy loss is known.

SUMMARY

1. Kinetic energy is the energy an object has because of its motion. **11:1**

2. Potential energy is the energy an object has because of its position, shape, or form. **11:1**

3. According to the work-energy theorem, the work done on an object by the net force acting on it is equal to the change in kinetic energy of the body. **11:2**

4. Gravitational potential energy depends on the weight of the body and its separation from Earth: $PE = mgh$. **11:3**

5. The sum of kinetic and potential energies of a system is called the mechanical energy. **11:4**

6. According to the law of conservation of energy, the total energy of a closed, isolated system is constant. Within the system energy can change form, but the total energy does not change. **11:4**

7. In an elastic collision, the total momentum and kinetic energy of the system is the same before and after the collision. **11:5**

8. In an inelastic collision, momentum is conserved; total kinetic energy is decreased. **11:5**

QUESTIONS

1. Explain how energy and forces are related.

2. What type of energy does a wound watch spring have? What form of energy does a running watch use? When a watch runs down, what has happened to the energy?

3. Name the types of energy in the Earth-sun system.

4. **a.** What is an elastic collision?

   b. What conservation laws are demonstrated in elastic collision?

   c. Which of the laws does not apply to inelastic collision?

5. A rubber ball is dropped from a height of 8 m. After striking the floor, the ball bounces to a height of 5 m.

   a. If the ball had bounced to a height of 8 m, how would you describe the collision between the ball and the floor?

   b. If the ball had not bounced at all, how would you describe the collision between the ball and the floor?

   c. What happened to the energy lost by the ball during the collision?

6. Two identical balls are thrown from the top of a cliff, each with the same velocity. One is thrown straight down, the other straight up. How do the velocities and the kinetic energies of the balls compare as they strike the ground?

7. Describe the energy transformations that occur when an athlete is pole vaulting.

8. If two identical bowling balls are raised to the same height, one on Earth and the other on the moon, which has the larger potential energy?

9. A ball is dropped from the top of a tall building and reaches terminal velocity as it falls. Will the potential energy of the ball upon release equal the kinetic energy it has when striking the ground? Explain.

10. A compact car and a semitruck are both traveling at the same velocity. Which has more kinetic energy? Which is using more fuel energy?

APPLYING CONCEPTS

1. When you pick up a box from the floor and put it on your desk, you do work on the box. The initial and final kinetic energies of the box are the same. Does this violate the work-energy theorem? Explain.

2. Does the work-energy theorem apply when a speeding car puts on its brakes and comes to a stop? Explain.

3. Roads seldom go straight up a mountain but wind around and go up slowly. Explain.

4. Earth is closer to the sun in winter than in summer in the northern hemisphere. Earth moves along

its orbit faster in winter than in summer. Assuming the mechanical energy of the Earth-sun system is constant, how does the potential energy of Earth depend on its distance from the sun?

5. According to Einstein's equation $E = mc^2$, does a rock lifted high above Earth have more or less mass than the same rock on Earth's surface?

6. A film was produced that centered around the discovery of a substance called "flubber." This substance could bounce higher than the height from which it was dropped. Explain why "flubber" is not likely to exist.

7. Two pendulums are swinging side by side. At the bottom of the swing, the speed of one pendulum bob is twice the speed of the other. Compare the heights to which the two bobs rise at the ends of their swings.

8. In a baseball game, two pop-ups are hit in succession. The second rises twice as high as the first. Compare the speeds of the two balls when they leave the bat.

EXERCISES

1. **a.** How much work is needed to hoist a 98-N sack of grain to a storage room 50 m above the ground floor of a grain elevator?
    b. What is the potential energy of the sack of grain at this height?
    c. The rope being used to lift the sack of grain breaks just as the sack reaches the storage room. What kinetic energy does the sack have just before it strikes the ground floor?

2. A 1600-kg car travels at a speed of 12.5 m/s. What is its kinetic energy?

3. A racing car has a mass of 1500 kg. What is its kinetic energy in joules if it has a speed of 108 km/h?

4. An archer puts a 0.30-kg arrow to the bowstring. An average force of 201 N is exerted to draw the string back 1.3 m.
    a. Assuming no frictional loss, with what speed does the arrow leave the bow?
    b. If the arrow is shot straight up, how high does it rise?

5. A 1200-kg car starts from rest and accelerates to 72 km/h in 20.0 s. Friction exerts an average 450-N force on the car during this time.
    a. What is the net work done on the car?
    b. How far does the car move during its acceleration?
    c. What is the net force exerted on the car during this time?
    d. What is the forward force exerted on the car as a result of the engine, power train, and wheels pushing backward on the road?

6. A net force of 410 N is applied in a direction straight up to a stone that weighs 32 N. If the force is applied through a distance of 2.0 m, to what height, from the point of release, will the stone rise?

7. **a.** A 20-kg mass is on the edge of a 100-m cliff. What potential energy does it possess?
    b. The mass falls from the cliff. What is its kinetic energy just before it strikes the ground?
    c. What speed does it have as it strikes the ground?

8. A steel ball has a mass of 4.0 kg and rolls along a smooth, level surface at 62 m/s.
    a. Find its kinetic energy.
    b. At first, the ball is at rest on the surface. A force acts on it through a distance of 22 m to give it the speed of 62 m/s. What is the magnitude of the force?

9. A railroad car with a mass of 5.0×10^5 kg collides with a stationary railroad car of equal mass. After the collision, the two cars lock together and move off at 4.0 m/s.
    a. Before the collision, the first railroad car was moving at 8.0 m/s. What was its momentum?
    b. What is the total momentum of the two cars after the collision?
    c. Find the kinetic energies of the two cars before and after the collision.
    d. Account for the loss of kinetic energy.

10. **a.** A person has a mass of 45 kg and is moving with a velocity of 10.0 m/s. Find the person's kinetic energy.
    b. The person's velocity becomes 5.0 m/s. What is the kinetic energy of the person?

c. What is the ratio of the kinetic energies in **a** and **b**? Explain the ratio.

11. A child and bicycle have a mass of 45.0 kg together. The child rides the bicycle 1.80 km in 10.0 minutes at a constant velocity. What is the kinetic energy of the system?

12. A 15.0-kg object is moving with a velocity of +7.50 m/s. A force of −10.0 N acts on the object and its velocity becomes +3.20 m/s. What is the displacement of the object while the force acts?

13. A 15.0-kg model plane flies horizontally at a speed of 12.5 m/s.

   a. Calculate its kinetic energy.

   b. The plane goes into a dive and levels off 20.4 m closer to Earth. How much potential energy does it lose during the dive?

   c. How much kinetic energy does the plane gain during the dive?

   d. What is its new kinetic energy?

   e. Neglecting frictional effects, what is its new horizontal velocity?

14. In an electronics factory, small cabinets slide down a 30.0° incline a vertical distance of 16.0 m to reach the next assembly stage. The cabinets have a mass of 10.0 kg each.

   a. Calculate the speed each cabinet would acquire if the incline were frictionless.

   b. What kinetic energy would a cabinet have under such circumstances?

15. A 10.0-kg test rocket is fired vertically from Cape Canaveral. Its fuel gives it a kinetic energy of 1960 J before it leaves the pad. How high will the rocket rise?

PROBLEMS

1. A 420-N student sits in a playground swing seat that hangs 0.40 m from the ground. A friend pulls the swing back and releases it when the seat is 1.00 m from the ground.

   a. How fast is the student on the swing moving when the swing passes through its lowest position?

   b. If the student moves through the lowest point at 2.0 m/s, how much work was done on the swing by friction?

2. A 10.0-g ball is thrown straight down from a height of 2.0 m. It strikes the floor at a speed of 7.5 m/s. What was the initial speed of the ball?

3. As everyone knows, bullets bounce from Superman's chest. Suppose Superman, mass 104 kg, while not moving is struck by a 4.2-g bullet moving with a speed of 835 m/s. If the collision is elastic, find the speed that the bullet imparts to Superman.

4. A golf ball, mass 0.046 kg, rests on a tee. It is struck by a golf club with an effective mass of 0.220 kg and a speed of 44 m/s. Assuming the collision is elastic, find the speed of the ball when it leaves the tee.

5. Show that $W = KE_f - KE_i$, using the equation relating initial and final velocity with acceleration and distance.

6. A 28-kg child climbs the 4.8-m ladder of a slide and after sliding down, reaches a velocity of 3.2 m/s at the bottom. How much work was done by friction on the child?

READINGS

Ayres, Thomas, "Thermodynamics and Economics." *Physics Today*, November, 1984.

Browne, Malcolm, "Stopping Missiles with Energy Beams." *Discover*, June, 1983.

Burns, Jack, "Centaurus A: The Nearest Active Galaxy." *Scientific American*, November, 1983.

Cleveland, C. J., "Energy and the U.S. Economy." *Science*, August 31, 1984.

Scott, David, "Gigantic Dutch Project: Sea Storage for Wind Energy." *Popular Science*, April, 1983.

CHAPTER 12

Thermal Energy

GOALS

1. You will become familiar with the concepts of thermal energy and entropy.
2. You will learn how both heat and work can change the amount of thermal energy in an object.
3. You will gain an understanding of the role of energy in changes of state.

If you rub your hands together, you are exerting a force and moving your hands. You are doing work against friction. Your hands start and end at rest, so there is no net change in kinetic energy. They remain the same distance above Earth so there is no change in potential energy. Yet, if conservation of energy is true, then the energy transferred by the work you did went somewhere. Your hands feel warm; their temperature is increased. The energy is now in the form of thermal energy. The branch of physics called thermodynamics explores the properties of thermal energy.

12:1 Theories, Hot and Cold

Although the effects of fire have been known since ancient times, only in the eighteenth century did scientists begin to understand how a warm body differs from a cold body. They proposed that when a body was warmed, an invisible fluid called "caloric" was added to the body. Hot bodies contained more caloric than cold bodies. The caloric theory could explain observations such as the expansion of objects when heated, but it could not explain why hands get warm when they are rubbed together.

In the mid-nineteenth century, scientists developed a new theory to replace caloric theory. This theory is based on the assumption that matter is made up of many tiny particles that are always in motion. In a hot body, the particles move faster, and thus have a higher energy than particles in a cold body. The theory is called the kinetic molecular theory.

194

Bottled Cloud

Janet was helping her parents prepare for a dinner party. As she popped open a bottle of sparkling grape juice, a small cloud formed around the bottle's mouth. The cloud surprised Janet's mother. What explanation for this phenomenon did Janet give her mother?

195

Internal energy   External energy

KE + PE   KE + PE

FIGURE 12-1. A baseball in flight has both internal and external energy. The internal energy is the result of the kinetic and potential energies of its particles. The external energy is the result of the position and motion of the baseball in flight.

SUGGESTION: Temperature, like density, is an intrinsic property. Thermal energy, like mass, is an extrinsic property.

FIGURE 12-2. Molecules of a solid behave as if they were held together by springs.

The kinetic theory is difficult to visualize because the motion of particles is not easily seen. A thrown baseball has a kinetic energy that depends on its velocity and a potential energy that is proportional to its height above the ground. These external properties can be seen. However, the tiny particles that make up the baseball are in constant motion within the ball. This internal motion is not readily visible.

The model of a solid in Figure 12–2 can help you understand the kinetic theory. This model pictures a solid made up of tiny spherical particles held together by massless springs. The springs represent the electromagnetic forces that bind the solid together. The particles vibrate back and forth and thus have kinetic energy. The vibrations compress and extend the springs, so the particles have potential energy as well. The sum of the kinetic and potential energies of the particles that make up an object is called the **internal** or **thermal energy** of that object.

12:2 Thermal Energy and Temperature

According to the kinetic molecular theory, a hot body has more thermal energy than a similar cold body. That is, the particles in a hot body have larger kinetic and potential energies than the particles in a cold body. This does not mean that all the particles in a body have the same kinetic energy. The particles have a range of energies, some high, others low. The average energy of particles in a hot body is higher than that of particles in a cold body. To help you understand this, consider the heights of students in a sixth-grade class. The heights vary, but you can calculate the average height. This average is likely to be larger than the average height of students in a fourth-grade class, even though some fourth-graders might be taller than some sixth-graders.

The average kinetic energy of particles in a object is measured by a property called **temperature**. The temperature of an object is proportional to the average kinetic energy of the particles in the object. Temperature does not depend on the number of particles in the body. If a one-kilogram mass of steel is at the same temperature as a two-kilogram mass, the average kinetic energy of the particles in both masses is the same. However, the total amount of kinetic energy of particles in the two-kilogram mass is twice the amount in the one-kilogram mass. The thermal energy in

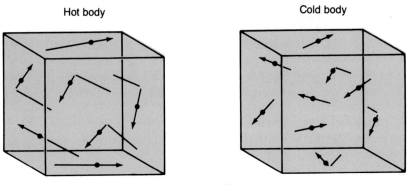

Hot body   Cold body

$$KE_{Hot} > KE_{Cold}$$

an object depends on the number of particles in it, but its temperature does not.

12:3 Equilibrium and Thermometry

You are familiar with the idea of measuring temperature. If you have a fever, you may place a thermometer in your mouth and wait two or three minutes. The thermometer then provides a measure of the temperature of your body.

The microscopic process of measuring temperature is less familiar. Your body is hot, which means the particles in your body have high thermal energy. The thermometer is made of a tube of glass. When the cold glass touches your hotter body, the particles in your body hit the particles in the glass. These collisions transfer energy to the glass particles. The thermal energy of the particles that make up the thermometer increases. As the energy of the particles in the glass increases, they are able to transfer energy back to the particles in your body. At some point, the transfer of energy between the glass and your body is equal. Your body and the thermometer are in thermal equilibrium. That is, the amount of energy that flows from your body to the glass is equal to the energy that flows from the glass to your body. The thermometer and your body are at the same temperature. Objects that are in thermal equilibrium are at the same temperature. Note that if the masses of objects are different, they may not have the same thermal energy.

DEMONSTRATION: See Teacher Guide.

SUGGESTION: Have students list other forms of thermometers, naming the property that changes with temperature.

A thermometer measures the temperature of an object with which it is in thermal equilibrium.

FIGURE 12-4. Thermal energy is transferred from a hot body to a cold body. When thermal equilibrium is reached, the transfer of energy between bodies is equal.

a   Before thermal equilibrium   b   After thermal equilibrium

Hot body   Cold body

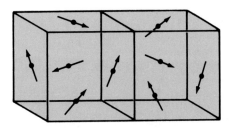

$$KE \longrightarrow$$

$$KE = KE$$

5x10⁻³ m³   1x10⁻² m³

FIGURE 12-5. Temperature does not depend on the number of particles in a body.

SUGGESTION: Celsius originally identified the boiling point as 0 and the freezing point as 100. Discuss how this scale would be better or worse than the present scale.

No temperature can be colder than absolute zero, −273.15°C.

FIGURE 12-6. Thermometers use a change in physical properties to measure temperature. A liquid crystal thermometer changes color with temperature change (a). Gas in a gas thermometer changes volume with temperature change (b).

A thermometer is a device that is placed in contact with an object and allowed to come to thermal equilibrium with that object. The operation of a thermometer depends on some property, such as volume, that changes with temperature. Most household thermometers contain colored alcohol that expands when heated. The hotter the thermometer, the larger the volume of the alcohol in it. Mercury is another liquid commonly used in thermometers.

Other properties of materials change with temperature, allowing them to be used as thermometers. In liquid crystal thermometers, the arrangement of the molecules changes at a specific temperature. As a result, the color depends on temperature. Different kinds of liquid crystals are used. Each has a different transition temperature, creating a temperature scale.

12:4 Temperature Scales

Temperature scales were developed by scientists to allow them to compare their temperature measurements with those of other scientists. A scale based on the properties of water was devised in 1741 by the Swedish astronomer and physicist Anders Celsius (1704–1744). On this scale, now called the Celsius scale, the freezing point of pure water is 0 degrees (0°C). The boiling point of pure water at sea level is 100 degrees (100°C). On the Celsius scale, the temperature of the human body is 37°C.

12:5 The Kelvin or Absolute Scale

Temperatures do not appear to have an upper limit. The interior of the sun is at least 1.5×10^7°C. Other stars are even hotter. However, temperatures do have a lower limit. Generally, materials contract as they cool. As will be discussed in Chapter 13, the contraction of any gas is such that it would have zero volume at −273°C. At this temperature, all the thermal energy would be removed from the gas. It is impossible to reduce the thermal energy any further. Therefore, there can be no lower temperature than −273°C. This temperature is called **absolute zero**.

a

b

A temperature scale based on absolute zero is named after the British physicist William Thomson, Lord Kelvin (1824–1907). Absolute zero is the zero point on the Kelvin scale. On the Kelvin scale, the freezing point of water (0°C) is 273 K and the boiling point of water is 373 K. Each interval on the Kelvin scale, called a kelvin, is equal to one Celsius degree. Thus, °C + 273 = K.

Very cold temperatures are reached by liquefying gases. Helium liquefies at 4.2 K, or −269.0°C. Even colder temperatures can be reached by using the properties of special substances when they are placed in the fields of large magnets. By these techniques, physicists have reached temperatures of only 2.0×10^{-8} K above absolute zero.

SUGGESTION: At absolute zero, no more energy can be extracted from the material. Also point out that there are no negative values on the Kelvin scale.

FIGURE 12-8. At the temperature of condensing helium, water vapor and gases in the environment condense to form a fog around the container of liquid helium.

EXAMPLE

Converting Celsius to Kelvin Temperature

Convert 25°C to kelvins.

Solution: K = °C + 273
$$= 25° + 273 = 298 \text{ K}$$

EXAMPLE

Converting Kelvin to Celsius Temperature

Convert the boiling point of helium, 4.22 K, to degrees Celsius.

Solution: °C = K − 273.15
$$= 4.22 − 273.15 = −268.93°C$$

Practice Exercises

1. Make the following conversions.
   a. 0°C to kelvins
   c. 273°C to kelvins
   b. 0 K to degrees Celsius
   d. 273 K to degrees Celsius
2. Convert these Celsius temperatures to Kelvin temperatures.
   a. 27°C
   c. −184°C
   b. 560°C
   d. −300°C
3. Convert these Kelvin temperatures to Celsius temperatures.
   a. 110 K
   c. 402 K
   b. 22 K
   d. 323 K

12:6 The First Law of Thermodynamics

One way to increase the temperature of a body is to place it in contact with a hotter body. The thermal energy of the hotter body is decreased, and the thermal energy of the cooler body is increased. Energy flows from the hotter body to the cooler body. **Heat** *is the energy that flows as a result of a difference in temperature.*

Note that this definition of heat is different from the one in everyday use. We commonly speak of a body containing heat. This description is left over from the caloric theory. In the modern theory, a hot body contains a larger amount of thermal energy than a colder body. Heat is the energy transferred because of a difference in temperature.

The thermal energy of a body can be increased in other ways. If you rub your hands together, they are warmed, yet they were not brought into contact with a hotter body. Instead, work was done on your hands by means of friction. The mechanical energy of your moving hands was changed into thermal energy.

There are other means of converting mechanical energy into thermal energy. If you use a hand pump to inflate a bicycle tire, the air and pump become warm. The mechanical energy in the moving piston is converted into thermal energy of the gas. Other forms of energy—light, sound, electrical, as well as mechanical—can be changed into thermal energy.

Thermal energy can be increased either by adding heat or by doing work on a system. Thus, *the total increase in the thermal energy of a system is the sum of the work done on it and the heat added to it.* This fact is called the **first law of thermodynamics.** Thermodynamics is the study of the changes in thermal properties of matter. The first law is merely a restatement of the law of conservation of energy.

All forms of energy are measured in joules. Work, energy transferred by mechanical means, and heat, energy transferred because of a difference in temperature, are also measured in joules. We will use the symbol Q to represent heat transferred from one body to another.

The conversion of mechanical energy to thermal energy, as when you rub your hands together, is easy. However, the reverse process, conversion of thermal to mechanical energy, is more difficult. A device able to convert thermal energy to mechanical energy is called a **heat engine.**

Heat is thermal energy transferred because of a difference in temperature. Heat always flows spontaneously from a warmer to a cooler body.

SUGGESTION: Work with students to use this definition of heat. Avoid speaking of heat as something contained within a body.

Work is energy transferred by mechanical means.

FIGURE 12-9. The flow chart diagram represents heat at high temperature transformed into mechanical energy and low temperature waste heat.

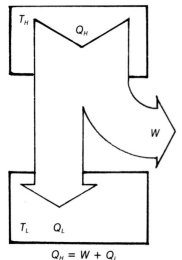

$$Q_H = W + Q_L$$

200 Thermal Energy

A Intake	B Compression	C Ignition	D Expansion (power stroke)	E Exhaust

FIGURE 12-10. The heat produced by burning gasoline causes the gases produced to expand and exert force on the cylinder.

SUGGESTION: Have students list various means of warming bodies (microwave cooking, heating over a flame, etc.). Classify each as heat or work.

Heat engines require a high temperature source from which thermal energy can be removed, and a low temperature sink into which thermal energy can be delivered. An automobile engine is an example of a heat engine. A mixture of air and gasoline vapor is ignited, producing a very high temperature flame. Heat flows from the flame to the air in the cylinder. The hot air expands and pushes on a piston, changing thermal energy into mechanical energy. In order to obtain continuous mechanical energy, the engine must be returned to its starting condition. The heated air is expelled and replaced by new air, and the piston is returned to the top of the cylinder. The entire cycle is repeated many times each minute. The heat from the burning gasoline and air is converted into mechanical energy that eventually results in the movement of the car.

However, not all the thermal energy from the very high temperature flame is converted into mechanical energy. The exhaust gases and the engine parts become warm. The exhaust comes in contact with outside air, transferring heat to it. The engine warmth is carried to a radiator. Outside air passes through the radiator and the air temperature is raised. This heat transferred out of the engine is called waste heat. All heat engines generate waste heat. In a car engine, the waste heat is at a lower temperature than the heat of the gasoline flame. The overall change in total energy of the car-air system is zero. Thus, according to the first law of thermodynamics, the heat from the flame is equal to the sum of the mechanical energy produced and the waste heat expelled.

A heat engine accepts heat from a high temperature source, performs work, and transfers heat out at a low temperature.

Heat flows spontaneously from a warm body to a cold body. It is possible to remove thermal energy from a colder body and add it to a warmer body. However, an external source of energy, usually mechanical energy, is required to accomplish this transfer. A refrigerator is a common example of such a device. Electrical energy runs a motor that does work on a gas such as Freon. Heat is transferred from the contents of the refrigerator to the Freon. Food is cooled, usually to 4.0°C, and the Freon is warmed. Outside the refrigerator, heat is transferred from the Freon to room air, cooling the Freon again. The overall change in the thermal energy of the Freon is zero. Thus, according to the first law of thermodynamics, the sum of the heat removed from the food and the work done by

The first law of thermodynamics states that the increase in thermal energy is the sum of the heat added to and the work done on a body.

FIGURE 12-11. A heat pump runs in either direction depending on whether it is used in heating or cooling. In cooling, heat is extracted from the air in the house and pumped outside. In heating, heat is extracted from the outside and pumped inside.

the motor is equal to the heat expelled to the outside at a higher temperature.

A heat pump is a refrigerator that can be run in two directions. In summer, heat is removed from the house, cooling the house. The heat is expelled into the warmer air outside. In winter, heat is removed from the cold outside air and transferred into the warmer house. In either case, mechanical energy is required to transfer heat from a cold object to a warmer one.

FIGURE 12-12. Flow chart diagram of heat transfer in a refrigerator.

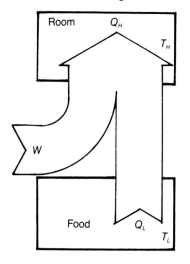

12:7 The Second Law of Thermodynamics

Many processes that do not violate the first law of thermodynamics have never been observed to occur spontaneously. For example, the first law does not prohibit heat flowing from a cold body to a hot body. Still, when a hot body is placed in contact with a cold body, the hot body has never been observed to become hotter. Heat flows spontaneously from hot to cold bodies. As another example, heat engines could convert thermal energy completely into mechanical energy with no waste heat and still obey the first law. Yet waste heat is always generated.

In the nineteenth century, the French engineer Sadi Carnot (1796–1832) studied the ability of engines to convert heat into mechanical energy. He proved that even an ideal engine would generate some waste heat. Carnot's result is best described in terms of a quantity called **entropy** (EN truh pee). Entropy, like thermal energy, is contained in an object. If heat is added to a body, entropy is increased. If heat is removed from a body, entropy is decreased. If an object does work with no change in temperature, however, the entropy does not change, as long as friction is ignored.

FIGURE 12-13. An example of the second law of thermodynamics.

On a microscopic level, **entropy** is described as the disorder in a system. When heat is added to an object, the particles move in a random way. Some move very quickly, others move slowly, many move at intermediate speeds. The greater the variety of speeds exhibited by the particles, the greater the disorder. The greater the disorder, the larger the entropy. While it is theoretically possible that all the particles could have the same speed, the random collisions and energy exchanges of the particles make the probability of this extremely unlikely.

The **second law of thermodynamics** states: *natural processes go in a direction that increases the total entropy of the universe.* Entropy and the second law can be thought of as statements of the probability of events happening. The second law describes the reason heat flows spontaneously only from a hot body to a cold body. Consider a hot iron bar and a cold cup of water. On the average, the particles in the iron will be moving very fast, whereas the particles in the water move more slowly. The bar is plunged into the water. When equilibrium is reached, the average kinetic energy of the particles in the iron and the water will be the same. This final state is less ordered than the first situation. No longer are the fast particles confined mainly in the iron and the slow particles in the water. All speeds are evenly distributed. The entropy of the final state is larger than that of the initial state.

Of course it could be possible that, as a result of collisions, all the particles in the iron would just happen to move slowly. However, the probability of this happening is so small as to be effectively impossible.

SUGGESTION: Perform the demonstration shown in Figure 12-13.

Entropy is a measure of the randomness or disorder of a body.

All natural processes proceed in the direction that leads to an increase in entropy.

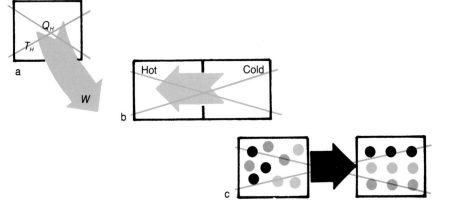

12:7 The Second Law of Thermodynamics 203

When a fuel burns, energy is not lost. Entropy is increased.

For Your Information

We take for granted many daily events that occur spontaneously, or naturally, in one direction, but that would really shock us if they happened in reverse. You are not surprised when a metal spoon, heated at one end, soon becomes uniformly hot, or when smoke from a too-hot frying pan diffuses throughout the kitchen. Consider your reaction, however, if a spoon lying on a table suddenly, on its own, became red hot at one end and icy cold at the other, or if all the smoke from the skillet collected in a 6 cm³ cube in the exact center of the kitchen. Neither of the reverse processes violates the first law of thermodynamics—they do not require external energy to occur. The events are simply examples of the countless events that are not spontaneously reversible because the reverse process would violate the second law of thermodynamics. In both examples, the reverse process decreases the total entropy.

Specific heat is the increase in thermal energy required to raise one kilogram of a material one kelvin.

The second law and entropy also give new meaning to what is commonly called the "energy crisis." When you use a resource such as natural gas to heat your home, you do not use up the energy in the gas. The potential energy contained in the molecules of the gas is converted into thermal energy of the flame, which is transferred to thermal energy in the air of your home. Even if this warm air leaks to the outside, the energy is not lost. Energy has not been used up. However, the entropy has been increased. The chemical structure of natural gas is very ordered. In contrast, the thermal motion of the warmed air is very disordered. While it is mathematically possible for the original order to be reestablished, the probability of this occurring is essentially zero. For this reason, entropy is often used as a measure of the unavailability of energy. The energy in the warmed air in a house is not as available to do mechanical work or to transfer heat to other bodies as the original gas molecules. The lack of usable energy is really a surplus of entropy.

12:8 Specific Heat

When the kinetic energy of the particles in a body increases, its temperature increases. The amount of increase depends on the size of the body. It also depends on the material from which the body is made. The **specific heat** of a material is the amount of energy that must be added to raise the temperature of a unit mass one temperature unit. In SI units, specific heat, C, is measured in J/kg · K. For example, 903 J must be added to one kilogram of aluminum to raise the temperature one kelvin. The specific heat of aluminum is 903 J/kg · K.

TABLE 12–1

Specific Heat of Common Substances			
Material	Specific heat (J/kg · K)	Material	Specific heat (J/kg · K)
alcohol	2450	ice	2060
aluminum	903	iron	450
brass	376	lead	130
carbon	710	silver	235
copper	385	steam	2020
glass	664	water	4180

Note that water has a high specific heat when compared to other substances, even ice and steam. One kilogram of water requires the addition of 4180 J of energy to increase its temperature one kelvin. By comparison, the same mass of copper requires only 385 J. The energy needed to raise the temperature of one kilogram of water 1 K would increase the temperature of the same mass of copper 11 K. The high specific heat of water is the reason water is used to remove waste heat from car engines.

Specific heat can be used to find the amount of heat that must be transferred to change the temperature of a given mass by any amount. The specific heat of water is 4180 J/kg · K. When the temperature of one kilogram of water is increased by one kelvin, the heat absorbed by the water is 4180 J. When 10 kilograms of water are heated 5.0 K, the heat absorbed, Q, is

$$Q = (10 \text{ kg})(4180 \text{ J/kg} \cdot \text{K})(5.0 \text{ K})$$
$$= 2.1 \times 10^5 \text{ J}$$

SUGGESTION: Discuss the specific heats of foods. Some cool much faster than others and thus have a lower specific heat.

The heat gained or lost by a given mass as its temperature changes depends on the mass, change in temperature, and specific heat of the substance. The relationship can be written

$$Q = mC\Delta T$$

where Q is the heat gained or lost, m is the mass of the substance, C is the specific heat, and ΔT is the change in temperature. Since one Celsius degree is equal to one kelvin, temperature changes can be measured in either kelvins or degrees Celsius.

Heat transferred is the product of specific heat, mass, and temperature change.

EXAMPLE

Heat Transfer

A 0.400-kg block of iron is heated from 22°C to 52°C. How much heat is absorbed by the iron?

Given: mass (m) = 0.400 kg   **Unknown:** Q
           specific heat (C) **Basic equation:** $Q = mC\Delta T$
             = 450 J/kg · K
           T_1 = 22°C
           T_2 = 52°C

Solution: $Q = mC\Delta T$
             $= (0.400 \text{ kg})(450 \text{ J/kg} \cdot \text{K})(52°C - 22°C)$
             $= 5.4 \times 10^3 \text{ J}$

Practice Exercises

4. How much heat is absorbed by 2.50×10^2 g of water when it is heated from 10.0°C to 85.0°C?

5. How much heat is absorbed by 60.0 g of copper when it is heated from 20.0°C to 80.0°C?

6. A 38-kg block of lead is heated from −26°C to 180°C. How much heat does it absorb during the heating?

7. The cooling system of a car engine contains 20.0 liters of water. (1 L of water has a mass of 1 kg.)

   a. What is the change in the temperature of the water if the engine operates until 836.0 kJ of heat are added?

   b. Suppose it is winter and the engine is filled with methanol having a specific heat of 2.48 kJ/kg · K. The density of methanol is 0.80 g/cm³. What would be the increase in temperature of the methanol if it absorbed 836.0 kJ of heat?

   c. Which is the better coolant, water or methanol? Explain.

Ignition wires

$O_2(g)$ inlet

$H_2O(l)$

Heavy-walled flask

$O_2(g)$

Sample holder

FIGURE 12-15. A simple calorimeter can be used to measure thermal energy transfer.

DEMONSTRATION: See Teacher Guide.

The total energy of an isolated, closed system is constant. Energy lost by one part is gained by another.

Heat flows as long as one part of a system is at a different temperature than another.

12:9 Conservation in Energy Transfer

A calorimeter is a device used to measure changes in thermal energy. A substance is heated to a known temperature and placed in the calorimeter. The calorimeter contains a known amount of cold water at a measured temperature. From the resulting increase in water temperature, the change in thermal energy of the substance is found.

The calorimeter makes use of the conservation of energy in isolated, closed systems. Energy can neither enter nor leave an isolated system. Therefore, if the energy of part of the system increases, the energy of another part must decrease by the same amount. Consider a system composed of two blocks of metal, block A and block B. The total energy of the system is constant.

$$E_A + E_B = \text{constant}$$

Suppose that the two blocks are initially separated but can be placed in contact. If the thermal energy of block A changes by an amount ΔE_A, then the change in thermal energy of block B, ΔE_B, must be related by the equation

$$\Delta E_A + \Delta E_B = 0$$

The change in energy of one block is positive, while the change in energy of the other block is negative. If the thermal energy change is positive, the temperature of that block rises. If the change is negative, the temperature falls.

Assume that the initial temperatures of the two blocks are different. When the blocks are brought together, heat flows from the hotter to the colder block. The flow continues until the blocks are in thermal equilibrium. The blocks then have the same temperature.

The change in thermal energy is equal to the heat transferred.

$$\Delta E = Q = mC\Delta T$$

The increase in thermal energy of block A is equal to the decrease in thermal energy of block B. Thus

$$m_A C_A \Delta T_A + m_B C_B \Delta T_B = 0$$

The change in temperature is the difference between the final and initial

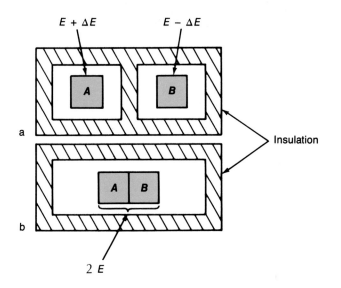

$E + \Delta E$ $E - \Delta E$

a

Insulation

b

2 E

FIGURE 12-16. The total energy for this system is constant.

temperatures, $\Delta T = T_f - T_i$. If the temperature of a block increases, $T_f > T_i$, and ΔT is positive. If the temperature of the block decreases, $T_f < T_i$, and ΔT is negative.

The final temperatures of the two blocks are equal. The equation for the transfer of energy is

$$m_A C_A (T_f - T_{A,i}) + m_B C_B (T_f - T_{B,i}) = 0$$

To solve this for T_f, expand the equation:

$$m_A C_A T_f - m_A C_A T_{A,i} + m_B C_B T_f - m_B C_B T_{B,i} = 0$$
$$T_f (m_A C_A + m_B C_B) = m_A C_A T_{A,i} + m_B C_B T_{B,i}$$
$$T_f = \frac{m_A C_A T_{A,i} + m_B C_B T_{B,i}}{m_A C_A + m_B C_B}$$

Note that either the Celsius or Kelvin temperature scale may be used with this equation.

Because 1°C = 1 K, either temperature scale may be used in this equation.

EXAMPLE

Conservation in Energy Transfer

A 0.500-kg sample of water is at 15.0°C in a calorimeter. A 0.0400-kg mass of zinc at 115°C is placed in the water. What is the final temperature of the system? The specific heat of zinc is 388 J/kg · K.

Given: zinc

$m_A = 0.0400$ kg
$T_{A,i} = 115$°C
$C_A = 388$ J/kg · K

water

$m_B = 0.500$ kg
$T_{B,i} = 15.0$°C
$C_B = 4180$ J/kg · K
1 J/kg · K = 1 J/kg · C°

Unknown: T_f

Basic equations: $\Delta E_A + \Delta E_B = 0$
$m_A C_A \Delta T_A + m_B C_B \Delta T_B = 0$

SUGGESTION: Carry out a demonstration using a piece of metal heated in boiling water and placed in cool water. Measure the final temperature. Then do the calculation and see how close you were to the calculated final temperature. Use polystyrene cups for calorimeters. They work better than the metal ones. Make a cover from a polystyrene cup.

Solution: $m_A C_A (T_f - T_{A,i}) + m_B C_B (T_f - T_{B,i}) = 0$

$$T_f = \frac{m_A C_A T_{A,i} + m_B C_B T_{B,i}}{m_A C_A + m_B C_B} =$$

$$\frac{(0.0400 \text{ kg})(388 \text{ J/kg} \cdot \text{C}°)(115°\text{C}) + (0.500 \text{ kg})(4180 \text{ J/kg} \cdot \text{C}°)(15.0°\text{C})}{(0.0400 \text{ kg})(388 \text{ J/kg} \cdot \text{C}°) + (0.500 \text{ kg})(4180 \text{ J/kg} \cdot \text{C}°)}$$

$$T_f = \frac{1.78 \times 10^3 \text{ J} + 3.14 \times 10^4 \text{ J}}{15.5 \text{ J/C}° + 2.09 \times 10^3 \text{ J/C}°}$$

$$T_f = \frac{3.32 \times 10^4 \text{ J}}{2.11 \times 10^3 \text{ J/C}°}$$

$$T_f = 15.7°\text{C}$$

Practice Exercises

8. A 2.00×10^2 g sample of water at 80.0°C is mixed with 2.00×10^2 g of water at 10.0°C. Assume no heat loss to the surroundings. What is the final temperature of the mixture?

9. A 4.00×10^2 g sample of alcohol at 16.0°C is mixed with 4.00×10^2 g of water at 85.0°C. Assume no heat loss to the surroundings. What is the final temperature of the mixture?

10. A 1.00×10^2 g mass of brass at 90.0°C is placed in a glass beaker containing 2.00×10^2 g of water at 20.0°C. Assume no heat loss to the glass or the surroundings. What is the final temperature of the mixture?

11. A 1.0×10^2 g mass of aluminum at 100.0°C is placed in 1.00×10^2 g of water at 10.0°C. The final temperature of the mixture is 25°C. What is the specific heat of the aluminum?

FIGURE 12-17. Brine solutions are evaporated in solar ponds to obtain potassium compounds. The blue dye added to the brine solutions absorbs thermal energy faster and speeds up evaporation.

12:10 Change of State

Our simplified model of a solid consists of tiny particles bonded together by springs. The springs represent the electromagnetic forces among the particles. When the thermal energy of a solid is increased, both the potential and kinetic energies of the particles increase. The temperature is a measure of the average kinetic energy of the particles.

At sufficiently high temperatures, the forces among the particles are no longer strong enough to hold them in fixed locations. The particles are still touching, but they have more freedom of movement. Eventually, the particles become free to slide past each other. At this point, the substance has changed from a solid to a liquid. The temperature at which this change occurs is called the **melting point.**

When a substance is in the process of melting, added thermal energy increases the potential energy of particles, breaking the bonds holding them together. The added thermal energy does not increase the kinetic energy of the particles. Thus, the temperature does not increase.

The amount of energy needed to melt the unit mass of a substance is called the **heat of fusion** of that substance. For example, the heat of fusion of ice is 3.34×10^5 J/kg. If 1 kg of ice at its melting point, 273 K, absorbs 3.34×10^5 J, the ice becomes 1 kg of water at the same temperature, 273 K. The added energy causes a change in state but not in temperature.

After the substance is totally melted, a further increase in thermal energy once again increases the temperature. Added thermal energy increases the kinetic and potential energies. As the temperature increases, some particles in the liquid obtain enough energy to break free from other particles. A tiny bubble of vapor is formed and rises to the surface. At a certain temperature, any added thermal energy increases the potential energy of particles and changes them from the liquid to the vapor state. This temperature is known as the **boiling point.** Water boils at 373 K at a pressure of 1 atm (101 kPa). The amount of thermal energy needed to vaporize a unit mass of liquid is called the **heat of vaporization.** For water, the heat of vaporization is 2.26×10^5 J/kg. Each substance has a characteristic heat of vaporization.

The heat, Q, required to melt a solid of mass m is given by

$$Q = mH_f$$

The value of some heats of fusion, H_f, can be found in Table 12–2.

DEMONSTRATION: See Teacher Guide.

When a substance melts, added energy does not increase temperature.

The heat of fusion is the thermal energy increase required to melt one kilogram of a substance.

The heat of vaporization is the thermal energy increase needed to boil one kilogram of a substance.

For Your Information

Blessings on Science, and her handmaid Steam
They make Utopia only half a dream.
Railways 1846
Charles Mackay

TABLE 12–2

Heats of Fusion and Vaporization of Common Substances

Material	Heat of fusion (J/kg)	Material	Heat of fusion (J/kg)	Material	Heat of vaporization (J/kg)	Material	Heat of vaporization (J/kg)
alcohol	1.09×10^5	lead	2.5×10^4	alcohol	8.78×10^5	lead	8.64×10^5
copper	2.05×10^5	mercury	1.15×10^4	copper	5.07×10^6	mercury	2.72×10^5
gold	6.30×10^4	silver	1.04×10^5	gold	1.64×10^6	silver	2.36×10^6
iron	2.66×10^5	water (ice)	3.34×10^5	iron	6.29×10^6	water	2.26×10^6

Similarly, the heat, Q, required to vaporize a mass, m, of liquid is given by

$$Q = mH_v$$

Heats of vaporization, H_v, can also be found in Table 12–2.

EXAMPLE

Heat of Fusion

If 5.00×10^3 J is added to ice at 273 K, how much ice is melted?

Given: heat added (Q)
$= 5.00 \times 10^3$ J
heat of fusion (H_f)
$= 3.34 \times 10^5$ J/kg

Unknown: mass (m)

Basic equation: $Q = mH_f$

Solution: $m = \dfrac{Q}{H_f} = \dfrac{(5.00 \times 10^3 \text{ J})}{(3.34 \times 10^5 \text{ J/kg})} = 0.0150$ kg

Figure 12–19 shows the changes in temperature as thermal energy is added to 1.0 g of H_2O at 173 K. Between points **a** and **b**, the ice is warmed

SUGGESTION: Enlarge Figure 12–19 and make an overhead transparency. Carefully go through each section explaining where you use specific heat and where you use heat of fusion.

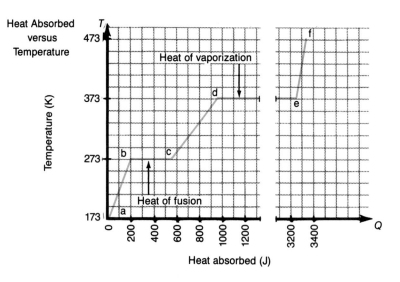

FIGURE 12-19. Graph of the temperature of 1.0 g of ice as heat is added. Notice that the slope of the graph is steeper from *a* to *b* and from *e* to *f* than it is from *c* to *d*. This is because the specific heats of ice and steam are less than the specific heat of water. The horizontal portions of the graph indicate that heat is being absorbed with no change in temperature.

to 273 K. Between points **b** and **c**, the added thermal energy melts the ice at a constant 273 K. The distance from point **c** to point **b** represents the heat of fusion. Between points **c** and **d**, the water temperature rises. The slope is larger here than between points **a** and **b**, showing that the specific heat of water is higher than that of ice. Between points **d** and **e**, the water boils, becoming water vapor. The distance, from point **d** to point **e**, represents the heat of vaporization. Between points **e** and **f**, the steam is heated to 473 K. The slope is smaller than that from point **c** to point **d**, indicating that the specific heat of steam is less than that of water.

SUGGESTION: Steam burns are worse than boiling water burns because so much heat is given off when the steam condenses compared to when water cools.

EXAMPLE

Heat of Fusion

Heat is applied to 100.0 g of ice at 0.0°C until the ice melts and the temperature of the resulting water rises to 20.0°C. How much heat is absorbed?

Given: $m = 100.0$ g   **Unknown:** Q_{total}
$T_A = 0.0°C$ **Basic equations:** $Q = mH_f$
$T_B = 20.0°C$ $Q = mC\Delta T$
$H_f = 3.34 \times 10^5$ J/kg
$C = 4180$ J/kg $\cdot$ C°

Solution:

First, find the amount of heat the ice absorbs to cause a change from solid to liquid.

$$Q = mH_f$$
$$= (0.100 \text{ kg})(3.34 \times 10^5 \text{ J/kg})$$
$$= 33\ 400 \text{ J}$$

Second, calculate the amount of heat the water absorbs to raise the temperature of the water from 0.0°C to 20.0°C.

$$Q = mC\Delta T$$
$$= (0.100 \text{ kg})(4180 \text{ J/kg} \cdot \text{C°})(20.0°C - 0.0°C)$$
$$= 8360 \text{ J}$$

Finally, add the two quantities of heat.

$$Q_{total} = 33\ 400 \text{ J} + 8360 \text{ J}$$
$$= 41\ 800 \text{ J}$$

Practice Exercises

12. How much heat is needed to change 50.0 g of water at 100.0°C to steam at 100°C?

13. How much heat is absorbed by 1.00×10^2 g of ice at $-20.0°C$ to become water at 0.0°C? The specific heat of ice is 2.06 J/g $\cdot$ C°.

14. A 2.00×10^2-g sample of water at 60.0°C is heated to steam at 140.0°C. How much heat is absorbed?

15. How much heat is needed to change 3.00×10^2 g of ice at $-30.0°C$ to steam at 130.0°C?

CHAPTER 12 REVIEW

SUMMARY

1. The thermal energy of an object is the sum of the kinetic and potential energies of the internal motion of the particles. **12:1**

2. The temperature of an object is proportional to the average kinetic energy of the particles. **12:2**

3. Thermometers use some property of a substance, such as thermal expansion, that depends on temperature. **12:3**

4. Thermometers reach thermal equilibrium with the objects they contact, and then some temperature-dependent property of the thermometer is measured. **12:3**

5. The Celsius and Kelvin temperature scales are widely used. One kelvin is equal to one degree Celsius. **12:4, 12:5**

6. At absolute zero, 0 K or −273.15°C, the average kinetic energy of the particles of matter is zero. **12:5**

7. Heat is the energy transferred because of a difference in temperature. Heat flows naturally from a hot to a cold body. **12:6**

8. The first law of thermodynamics states that the total increase in thermal energy of a system is equal to the sum of the heat added to it and the work done on it. **12:6**

9. A heat engine continuously converts thermal energy to mechanical energy. **12:6**

10. A heat pump or refrigerator uses mechanical energy to transfer heat from an area of lower temperature to an area of higher temperature. **12:6**

11. Entropy, a measure of disorder, never decreases in natural processes. **12:7**

12. Specific heat is the quantity of heat required to raise the temperature of one kilogram of a substance one kelvin. **12:8**

13. In an isolated system, the thermal energy of one part may change but the total energy of the system is constant. **12:9**

14. The heat of fusion is the quantity of heat required to melt one kilogram of a substance at its melting point. **12:10**

15. The heat of vaporization is the quantity of heat required to change one kilogram of a substance from the liquid state to the vapor state at its boiling point. **12:10**

16. The heat transferred during a change of state does not produce a change in temperature. **12:10**

QUESTIONS

1. Explain the difference between an object's external energy and its thermal energy. Give an example.

2. Distinguish between thermal energy and temperature.

3. How does heat differ from thermal energy?

4. What is the temperature of a typical winter day on the
   a. Celsius scale?   b. Kelvin scale?

5. What is the temperature of an extremely hot summer day on the
   a. Celsius scale?   b. Kelvin scale?

6. What is the normal room temperature on the
   a. Celsius scale?
   b. Kelvin scale?

7. Explain entropy to a fellow student in your physics class.

8. Which liquid would an ice cube cool faster, water or alcohol? Explain.

9. When wax freezes, is energy absorbed or released by the wax?

10. Explain why the high specific heat of water makes it desirable for use in hot water heating systems.

11. Can you add thermal energy to an object without increasing its temperature? Explain.
12. Ten grams of aluminum and ten grams of lead are heated to the same temperature. The pieces of metal are placed on a block of ice. Which metal melts more ice? Explain.

APPLYING CONCEPTS

1. An automobile is brought to a stop by applying friction brakes to the wheels. The brakes get hot; their thermal energy is increased. The decrease in kinetic energy of the car is equal to the increase in thermal energy of the brakes. According to the first law of thermodynamics, the brakes could cool and return the thermal energy to the car, causing it to resume its motion. This does not happen. Why?
2. Is your body a good judge of temperature? On a cold winter day, a metal door knob feels much colder to your hand than the wooden door. Is this true? Explain.
3. Can a temperature be assigned to a vacuum? Explain.
4. When a warmer object is in contact with a colder object, does temperature flow from one to the other? Do the two have the same temperature changes?
5. You are a physics teacher and have just told your class that the temperature of the sun is 1.5×10^7 degrees.
   a. A student asks whether you are using the Kelvin or Celsius scale. What is your answer?
   b. How would you answer if asked if you were using the Celsius or Fahrenheit scale?
   $$T_f = 9/5 \ T_c + 32$$
6. Is a human being a heat engine? Explain.
7. If you place identical uncovered pails of hot and cold water outdoors on a dry sidewalk on a very cold day, the hot water usually starts to freeze first.
   a. Explain why this might occur.
   b. What would have happened had the pails been covered?
8. Are the coils of an air conditioner that are inside the house the location of vaporization or condensation of the Freon? Explain.

9. Explain why fruit growers spray their trees with water, when frost is expected, to protect the fruit from freezing.
10. Why does water in a canteen stay cooler if it has a canvas cover that is kept wet?
11. Would opening the refrigerator door on a warm day help to cool the kitchen? Explain.

EXERCISES

1. Liquid nitrogen boils at 77 K. Find this temperature in degrees Celsius.
2. The melting point of hydrogen is $-259.14°C$. Find this temperature in kelvins.
3. How much heat in joules is needed to raise the temperature of 50.0 g of water from 4.5°C to 83°C?
4. How much heat in joules must be added to 50.0 g of aluminum at 25°C to raise its temperature to 125°C?
5. A 2.00×10^2 g sample of brass at 100.0°C is placed in a calorimeter cup that contains 261 g of water at 20.0°C. Disregard the absorption of heat by the cup and calculate the final temperature of the mixture.
6. How much heat is added to 10.0 g of ice at $-20.0°C$ to convert it to steam at 120.0°C?
7. Suppose the same amount of heat needed to raise the temperature of 50.0 g of water through $1.00 \times 10^2°C$ is applied to 50.0 g of zinc. What is the temperature change of zinc?
8. A copper wire has a mass of 165 g. An electric current runs through the wire for a short time and its temperature rises from 21°C to 39°C. What minimum quantity of heat is generated by the electric current?
9. A 1.00×10^2 g mass of tungsten at 100.0°C is placed in 2.00×10^2 g of water at 20.0°C. The mixture reaches equilibrium at 21.6°C. Calculate the specific heat of tungsten.
10. A 40.0-g sample of chloroform is condensed from a vapor at 61.6°C to a liquid at 61.6°C. It liberates 9870 joules of heat. What is the heat of vaporization of chloroform?
11. A 10.0-kg piece of zinc at 71°C is placed in a container of water. The water has a mass of 20.0 kg and has a temperature of 10.0°C before the

zinc is added. What is the final temperature of the water and zinc?

12. A 6.0×10^2 g sample of water at 90.0°C is mixed with 4.00×10^2 g of water at 22°C. Assume no heat loss to the surroundings. What is the final temperature of the mixture?

13. How much heat is removed from 60.0 g of steam at 100.0°C to change it to 60.0 g of water at 20.0°C?

14. The specific heat of mercury is 0.14 J/g · C°. Its heat of vaporization is 306 J/g. How much heat is needed to heat 1.0 kg of mercury metal from 10.0°C to its boiling point and vaporize it completely? The boiling point of mercury is 357°C.

15. Years ago, a block of ice with a mass of about 20.0 kg was used daily in a home icebox. The temperature of the ice was 0.0°C when delivered. As it melted, how much heat in joules did a block of ice this size absorb?

16. A 4.00×10^2 g glass coffee cup at room temperature, 20.0°C, is plunged into hot dishwater, 80.0°C. If the temperature of the cup reaches that of the dishwater, how much heat does the cup absorb?

17. Five kilograms of ice cubes are moved from the freezing compartment of a refrigerator into a home freezer. The refrigerator's freezing compartment is kept at −4.0°C. The home freezer is kept at −17°C. How much heat does the freezer's cooling system remove from the ice cubes?

18. A 2.50×10^2 kg cast-iron car engine contains water as a coolant. Suppose the engine's temperature is 35°C when it is shut off. The air temperature is 10.0°C. The heat given off by the engine and water in it as they cool to air temperature is 4.4×10^6 J. What mass of water is used to cool the engine?

19. An 8.00×10^2 g block of lead is heated in boiling water, 100.0°C, until its temperature is the same as that of the water. The lead is then removed from the boiling water and dropped into 2.50×10^2 g of cool water at 12.2°C. After a short time, the temperature of both lead and water is 20.0°C.
   a. How much heat is gained by the cool water?
   b. On the basis of these measurements, what is the specific heat of lead?

20. A 50.0-g sample of ice at 0.00°C is placed in a glass beaker containing 4.00×10^2 g of water at 50.0°C. All the ice melts. What is the final temperature of the mixture? Disregard heat loss to the glass.

21. A 5.00×10^2 g block of metal absorbs 5016 joules of heat when its temperature changes from 20.0°C to 30.0°C. Calculate the specific heat of the metal.

PROBLEMS

1. What temperatures on the following pairs of scales are the same? ($T_f = 9/5\ T_c + 32$)
   a. Celsius and Fahrenheit
   b. Kelvin and Fahrenheit
   c. Celsius and Kelvin

2. A 3.00×10^2-watt electric immersion heater is used to heat a cup of water. The cup is made of glass and its mass is 3.00×10^2 g. It contains 250 g of water at 15°C. How much time is needed for the heater to bring the water to the boiling point? The specific heat of glass is 664 J/kg · K. Assume the temperature of the cup to be the same as the temperature of the water at all times.

3. A nuclear power plant located on a river produces 2.00×10^2 megawatts of power, but also releases 1.0×10^{11} kJ/day of waste heat into the river. Assume that the average rate of flow of the river is 9.0×10^4 kg/s.
   a. What is the maximum temperature increase in the river water that could be caused by the plant's cooling system?
   b. The construction of four additional nuclear power plants along the river has been proposed. What is the total increase in the temperature of the river that could result if the plants are built? Could this change cause serious damage to the ecological structure of the river?

4. During a game, the metabolism of basketball players often increases by as much as 30.0 watts. How much perspiration must a player vaporize per hour to dissipate this extra thermal energy?

5. As a result of the rising cost of oil, a school converted its heating system from oil to coal. The school contains 1.70×10^4 kg of air, and the heat of combustion of coal is 3.35×10^4 kJ/kg. How many kg of coal must be burned in the school's new furnace to bring the temperature of the unheated air in the school from $-10.0°C$ to $24.0°C$? The specific heat of air is 1.1 kJ/kg · C°. Assume that 50.0% of the heat produced by the coal actually serves to heat the air in the school.

6. To get a feeling for the amount of energy needed to heat water, recall from Table 11–1 that the kinetic energy of a compact car moving at 100 km/h is 2.9×10^5 J. What volume of water (in liters) would that energy heat from room temperature (20°C) to boiling (100°C)?

7. When air is compressed in a bicycle pump, an average force of 45 N is exerted as the pump handle moves 0.24 m. During this time 2.0 J of heat leave the cylinder through the walls. What is the net change in thermal energy of the air?

8. A soft drink from Australia is labeled "Low Joule Cola." The label says "100 mL yields 1.7 kJ." The can contains 375 mL. You drink the cola and then offset this input of food energy by climbing stairs. How high would you have to climb?

9. A 750-kg car moving at 23 m/s brakes to a stop. The brakes contain about 15 kg of iron that absorbs the heat produced by the friction. What is the increase in temperature of the brakes?

10. A 4.2-g lead bullet moving at 275 m/s strikes a tank and stops. If all its kinetic energy is converted to thermal energy and none leaves the bullet, what is its temperature change?

READINGS

Brewer, Richard, "Atomic Memory." *Scientific American*, December, 1984.

Lindsley, E. F., "Stirling Auto Engine: A Lot of Progress, but. . . ." *Popular Science*, January, 1983.

Nicastro, A. J., "A Dynamic Model of a Carnot Cycle." *The Physics Teacher*, October, 1983.

Smay, Elaine, "Heat-Pipe Furnace." *Popular Science*, February, 1984.

Warren, David, "Solar Systems and Heat Pumps Combine to Cut Energy Bills." *Discover*, January, 1983.

CHAPTER 13

Gas Laws

GOALS

1. You will learn and understand the assumptions made in the kinetic theory.
2. You will gain an understanding of how the pressure, temperature, and volume of an ideal gas are related and how these relationships are explained by the kinetic theory.
3. You will learn to do calculations involving the temperature, pressure, volume, and number of particles of samples of gases.

Your first experience with the properties of gases probably came from playing with a balloon. You discovered you had to blow hard to fill it up. The air filled the entire balloon, not just one part. If you let go of the balloon, the air came rushing out with great force. You might have noticed that if you took a balloon outside on a very cold day it became smaller, but then grew bigger again when brought inside the house. You probably have had a helium-filled balloon that floated up out of reach when you let go. A balloon you blew up yourself never did that.

What kind of model of gases could you construct that would explain these observations? After studying both the physical and chemical properties of gases, scientists in the early part of the nineteenth century developed the kinetic-molecular model. Since that time the model has been used to explain the properties of liquids and solids as well as gases. It is now called the kinetic-molecular theory of matter.

13:1 Assumptions of the Kinetic-Molecular Theory

The kinetic theory of gases is based on three assumptions:

1. Gases are made of a large number of very small particles.
2. The particles are in constant, random motion. They are widely separated and make elastic collisions with one another.
3. The particles make perfectly elastic collisions with the walls of the container that holds them.

Kinetic theory is based on the assumption that all matter is made up of very small particles, in constant random motion, that experience elastic collisions.

Going Up

Scuba divers wear special inflatable vests called buoyancy compensators. Air can be added or removed to adjust buoyancy as divers change depth. A diver is seen diving 30.0 m deep. As the diver ascends, he must let air out of his vest. Why do scuba divers remove air, rather than add air, during ascents?

The kinetic theory is a microscopic theory. It pictures a volume of gas as a box filled with a large number of very small moving particles. The theory explains why the particles exert pressure on the walls of the box, how the motion of the particles accounts for temperature, and how pressure and temperature are related to the number of particles and the size of the box.

According to the kinetic theory, the collisions of the particles with the walls of the box cause a pressure. The average kinetic energy of the particles is proportional to the temperature of the gas. The kinetic theory explains the properties of a model of a real gas called an ideal gas. Except under certain conditions, real gases behave almost exactly as the ideal gas described by the kinetic theory. Later in this chapter we will discuss the conditions under which the model does not work.

13:2 Pressure

The pressure exerted by Earth's atmosphere is so well balanced by our bodies that we hardly ever notice it. You are aware of it only when your ears "pop" as a result of changes in pressure. This might occur when riding the elevator in a tall building, driving on a high mountain road, or flying in an airplane. Yet on every square centimeter of Earth's surface, the atmosphere exerts a force of approximately 10 N, about the weight of a 1-kg mass.

What is meant by the pressure exerted by a gas? **Pressure** is defined as the force on a unit surface area. That is,

$$p = \frac{F}{A}$$

A typical physics student has a weight of 700 N and wears shoes that touch the ground over an area of 400 cm², or 0.040 m². Thus the average pressure his shoes exert on the ground is

$$p = \frac{F}{A} = \frac{700 \text{ N}}{0.040 \text{ m}^2} = 1.8 \times 10^4 \text{ N/m}^2$$

In the SI system, the unit of pressure is the **pascal,** one newton per square meter. Because the pascal is a small unit of pressure, the kilopascal (kPa), equal to 1000 Pa, is more commonly used. Thus the pressure the student's shoes exert on the ground is 18 kPa. If the student were to stand on only one foot, the force would be the same, but the area would be reduced by half; the pressure would increase to 36 kPa. If a woman puts her whole weight on the heel of one high-heeled shoe, the pressure can exceed a million pascals.

Atmospheric pressure is measured with a **barometer.** There are two basic types of barometers. An aneroid (AN uh royd) barometer, Figure 13–2a, consists of a metal can, called an aneroid, from which most of the air has been removed. The atmosphere exerts pressure on the can. When air pressure changes, the shape of the aneroid changes slightly. A needle attached to the top of the can through a lever and gear system moves along a scale calibrated to read in air pressure units.

FIGURE 13–1. Pressure is the force exerted on a unit area of a surface. Similar forces may produce vastly different pressures—the pressure on the ground under a lady's high heel is far greater than that under an elephant's foot.

TABLE 13-1

Some Typical Pressures	
Location	Pressure (Pa)
Center of sun	2×10^{16}
Center of Earth	4×10^{11}
Deepest ocean trench	1.1×10^{8}
High heels on floor	1×10^{6}
Auto tire	2×10^{5}
Standard atmosphere	1×10^{5}
Blood pressure	1.6×10^{4}
Loudest sound	30
Faintest sound	3×10^{-5}
Best vacuum	1×10^{-12}

Mercury barometers are frequently used in laboratories. Figure 13—2b shows how a mercury barometer is made. A glass tube, about 80 cm long and sealed at one end, is completely filled with mercury. The filled tube is turned over and placed in a dish of mercury. Rather than emptying into the dish, the mercury only falls a little. The fact that the column of mercury does not fall farther suggests that the downward force of the weight of mercury in the tube must be balanced by an upward force. There is nothing above the mercury in the top of the tube but a few mercury atoms in the form of a gas. There is certainly nothing that can pull mercury upward. Thus, the force that balances the weight of the column is the weight of the atmosphere pressing down on the mercury in the dish. When the air pressure changes, the force on the mercury in the dish changes, changing the height of the column of mercury in the tube. For this reason, the height of the column of mercury is a direct measure of the atmospheric pressure.

The average pressure of the atmosphere measured at sea level is called the **standard atmospheric pressure.** Standard atmospheric pressure is 101.3 kPa. This pressure will support a column of mercury 760 millimeters high. For this reason, standard atmospheric pressure is sometimes

SUGGESTION: Push a suction cup dart or a plunger against the wall and explain how it works. The air is pushed out so the pressure of the atmosphere is greater than the pressure under the plunger.

SUGGESTION: Show small groups of students the detailed construction of the mercury barometer in your laboratory. Have each student individually practice reading the mercury barometer. Compare the mercury barometer to an aneroid barometer.

Standard atmospheric pressure is 101.3 kPa.

a

Top view

Side view

Pointer

Aneroid
Partial
vacuum

b

Vacuum

Glass plate

Mercury

For Your Information

It was Galileo, to whom Torricelli served as secretary and companion, who aroused Torricelli's interest and led to his experimentation and his development of the barometer.

FIGURE 13-2. An aneroid barometer measures air pressure by means of changes in the size of an evacuated chamber (a). A mercury barometer measures air pressure by using the height of a column of mercury supported by the atmosphere.

FIGURE 13–3. A pressure gauge is used to check the pressure in a tire. Most tire gauges read in pounds per square inch.

For Your Information

Boyle's law states that the product of pressure and volume is constant when the temperature is constant.

FIGURE 13–4. The force exerted per unit area by many particles of a gas randomly striking walls of the container is called pressure.

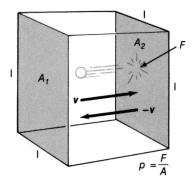

reported as 760 millimeters of mercury. The "millimeter of mercury" as a unit of pressure has been replaced by the Torr, named in honor of the Italian scientist Evangelista Torricelli (1608–1647). Torricelli studied atmospheric pressure and invented the barometer. In meteorology, an atmospheric pressure of 760 Torr or 101.3 kPa is most commonly expressed in millibars (mb). One millibar equals 0.10 kPa, so standard atmospheric pressure is 1013 mb. One atmosphere of pressure (1 atm) is equivalent to 101.3 kPa, 760 Torr, or 1013 mb. Other liquids can be used in barometers. A column of water almost ten and one-half meters high is supported by atmospheric pressure. Obviously such an instrument would not be portable! In addition, the water might freeze. Meteorologists watch barometric readings carefully because atmospheric pressure changes indicate changing weather conditions.

Pressure gauges used to measure tire pressure at service stations actually measure the amount that the pressure exceeds one atmosphere. This pressure is called gauge pressure. For example, if the pressure gauge reads 225 kPa, the total pressure in the tire is 225 kPa + 101 kPa = 326 kPa.

The kinetic theory explains how gases exert pressure on the walls of a closed container. The randomly moving gas particles in the container strike the sides of the container. Figure 13–4 shows a particle with velocity v striking the wall of the container. The collision is elastic, so the particle rebounds with velocity $-v$. The change in momentum of the particle, $m\Delta v$, exerts an outward impulse to the wall of the container, $-m\Delta v = F\Delta t$. Thus during the brief time, Δt, the particle is in contact with the wall, it exerts an outward force F. The sample of gas contains a huge number of particles, so many collisions are occurring every instant. There are so many collisions that the total force exerted by the gas is constant over any reasonable time interval. The larger the area of the wall, the larger the number of collisions, and so the greater the total force. The number of collisions per unit area is independent of the size of the wall. Thus the pressure, the force per unit area, is a constant that does not depend on the size of the wall. Because the particles are moving randomly in all directions, the pressure is the same on all walls.

13:3 Boyle's Law

Suppose a fixed amount of gas is put into a container, such as a balloon or a cylinder with a movable piston, whose size can be varied. How does the pressure of the gas depend on the volume of the container? The relationship between pressure and volume of a gas is called Boyle's law, named for Robert Boyle (1627–1691), a British chemist and physicist. Boyle's law states that *for a given sample of gas at a constant temperature, the volume of the gas (V) varies inversely with the pressure (p)*. If two variables are inversely related, then their product is a constant. That is,

$$pV = \text{constant}$$

If p_1 and V_1 are the original pressure and volume of a given mass of gas, and p_2 and V_2 are the final pressure and volume, then

$$p_1V_1 = \text{constant} = p_2V_2$$

That is, the pressure and volume of a fixed amount of gas at a constant temperature are related by the equation

$$p_1V_1 = p_2V_2$$

Real gases follow Boyle's law closely except at very high pressures or low temperatures.

The kinetic theory can be used to explain Boyle's law. Consider a gas-filled cylinder sealed with a weightless piston that is free to move up and down, Figure 13–5. The piston has an area of 0.010 m². A 100-N weight is placed on top of the piston. The piston moves down the cylinder until it comes to rest. The piston is a distance h = 10 cm (0.10 m) above the bottom of the cylinder. The piston is in equilibrium. That is, the downward force of the weight on top of the piston is balanced by the upward force of the gas on the piston. The volume of the gas is (0.010 m²)(0.10 m) = 0.0010 m³. The pressure is 100 N/0.010 m² = 10 kPa. These values are plotted on the graph in Figure 13–6.

If the weight is increased to 200 N, the piston will move downward to a new location where the gas pressure is twice the original pressure. The gas temperature is constant, so the velocity of the gas particles has not changed. The gas pressure will double only if the number of collisions with the piston each second doubles. This will occur if the vertical distance traveled by each particle is halved. Thus the piston moves down until it is a distance $h/2$ = 5 cm above the bottom. The volume of the gas is now half the original volume. This point, with p = 20 kPa and V = 0.0005 m³, is plotted on the graph.

If the weight is increased to 300 N, the pressure will be three times the original pressure. The piston will move to a position where the number of collisions per second is three times the original number. At this location, $h/3$, the volume of the gas is one-third the original. Figure 13–6 shows the three data points discussed and a smooth curve drawn through the points. The curve is a hyperbola, which shows that there is an inverse relationship between pressure and volume.

FIGURE 13–5. The volume of a gas decreases as the pressure applied to it increases.

Volume versus Pressure

FIGURE 13–6. The curve is a hyperbola, indicating an inverse relationship between pressure and volume.

EXAMPLE

Boyle's Law

A sample of gas is held in a 2.6 m³ volume at a pressure of 226 kPa. The temperature is kept constant while the volume is decreased until the pressure is 565 kPa. What is the new volume of the gas?

Given: $p_1 = 226$ kPa   Unknown: V_2

 $V_1 = 2.6$ m³   Basic equation: $p_1V_1 = p_2V_2$

 $p_2 = 565$ kPa

Solution: $p_1V_1 = p_2V_2$, or $V_2 = \dfrac{p_1V_1}{p_2}$

$$= \frac{(226\ \text{kPa})(2.6\ \text{m}^3)}{565\ \text{kPa}} = 1.0\ \text{m}^3$$

One way of exerting pressure on gas is to put it under water. Just as standard atmospheric pressure supports a column of mercury 760 mm high, it would support a column of water 10.4 m high. This means that an object at a depth of 10.4 m of water has a pressure of 2.0 atm (203 kPa) on it. One of the atmospheres of pressure is a result of the water; the other is the atmosphere pushing downward on the top of the water. Every additional 10.4 m of water exerts another atmosphere of pressure.

EXAMPLE

Boyle's Law

A balloon has a volume of 2.0 liters when 1.0 atmosphere of pressure is exerted on it. It is tied with a string, weighted with a heavy stone, and tossed into a pond. What is its volume when it reaches the bottom of a pond 20.8 m deep? A depth of 10.4 m of water produces 1 atm of pressure.

Given: Unknown: V_2

$p_1 = 1.0$ atm   Basic equation: $p_1V_1 = p_2V_2$

$V_1 = 2.0$ L

depth $= 20.8$ m

water pressure $= 1$ atm/10.4 m

Solution: $\dfrac{20.8\ \text{m}}{10.4\ \text{m/atm}} = 2.0$ atm of water pressure,

 so $p_2 = 2.0$ atm $+ 1.0$ atm $= 3.0$ atm

 $p_1V_1 = p_2V_2$, or $V_2 = \dfrac{p_1V_1}{p_2}$

$$= \frac{(1.0\ \text{atm})(2.0\ \text{L})}{3.0\ \text{atm}} = 0.67\ \text{L}$$

Practice Exercises

1. A cylinder with volume 0.063 m³ exerts a pressure of 236 kPa on air. While the temperature is held constant, the pressure is increased to 354 kPa. What is the new volume of the gas?

2. A pressure of 235 kPa holds neon gas in a cylinder 0.0500 m³ in volume. The volume increases to 0.125 m³. What pressure is now exerted on the gas?

3. A helium-filled balloon has a volume of 2.0 m³ at sea level. The balloon then rises to a height in the atmosphere where its volume is 6.0 m³. What is the pressure in kPa at this height?

4. A diver works at a depth of 52 m in fresh water. A bubble of air with a volume of 2.0 cm³ escapes from the diver's mouthpiece. What is the volume of the bubble just as it reaches the surface of the water?

13:4 Charles' Law

About one hundred years after the work of Boyle, the French scientist Jacques Charles (1746–1823) studied how the volume of a gas depends on temperature. Charles discovered that the volume of a fixed amount of gas at constant pressure depends linearly on the temperature. That is, when he increased the temperature from 0°C to 1°C, the volume increased 1/273 of the original volume. When he increased the temperature by a total of 2°C, the volume increased 2/273 of the original volume. If Charles had increased the temperature by 273°C, the volume would have doubled. He found that many gases behave the same way.

When Charles cooled a gas, the volume shrank by 1/273 of its original volume for every degree the gas was cooled. Charles could not cool gases below −20°C, so to see what lower limits might be possible, he extended the line of the graph to even lower temperatures. Extending a graph beyond measured points is called **extrapolation.** If extrapolation is based on precise data and used with care, it can provide useful information from which conclusions can be drawn. Charles' extrapolation had a startling implication. It suggested that if the temperature were reduced to −273°C,

Charles found that when the temperature of a gas at constant pressure is changed one kelvin, the volume changes 1/273 of its volume at 0°C.

DEMONSTRATION: See Teacher Guide.

FIGURE 13–7. The volume of air in the balloon expands as it is moved from an ice-water bath to a hot-water bath.

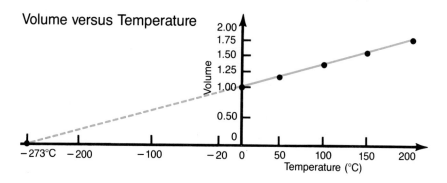

Volume versus Temperature

SUGGESTION: Blow up a balloon and place it in a refrigerator or ice bath to show change in size. Ask students if they have any experience with change in size of inflated objects with temperature.

all gases would have zero volume. The temperature at which gases would have zero volume is now called absolute zero. The zero of the Kelvin temperature scale is absolute zero.

The result of these experiments is called Charles' law: *under constant pressure, the volume of a fixed amount of gas varies directly as its kelvin temperature.*

Charles' law states that, at constant pressure, the volume of a fixed amount of gas is directly proportional to its temperature in kelvins.

$$\frac{V_1}{T_1} = constant = \frac{V_2}{T_2}$$

Charles' law is followed by real gases except at low temperatures. At temperatures below about 2 K, no substances exist as gases. Thus even though scientists can now create much lower temperatures than Charles could, they must still extrapolate their measurements of gas temperature and volume to a temperature at which the volume would be zero.

EXAMPLE

Charles' Law

A volume of 0.22 m³ of nitrogen gas at 20.0°C is heated under constant pressure to 167°C. What is its new volume?

Given: $V_1 = 0.22 \text{ m}^3$ Unknown: V_2
$\quad\quad\quad T_1 = 20.0°C$
$\quad\quad\quad T_2 = 167°C$ Basic equation: $\dfrac{V_1}{T_1} = \dfrac{V_2}{T_2}$

Solution: $T_1 = 20.0°C + 273°C = 293 \text{ K}$
$\quad\quad\quad T_2 = 167 °C + 273°C = 440 \text{ K}$
$\quad\quad\quad \dfrac{V_1}{T_1} = \dfrac{V_2}{T_2}$
$\quad\quad\quad V_2 = \dfrac{V_1 T_2}{T_1} = \dfrac{(0.22 \text{ m}^3)(440 \text{ K})}{(293 \text{ K})} = 0.33 \text{ m}^3$

Practice Exercises

5. A 30.0-m³ volume of argon gas is heated from 20.0°C to 293°C under constant pressure. What is the new volume of the gas?

6. Thirty liters of oxygen gas are cooled from 20.0°C to −146°C under constant pressure. What is the new volume?

7. A sample of krypton gas at 60.0°C has a volume of 0.21 liters. Under constant pressure, it is heated to twice its original volume. To what temperature (in degrees Celsius) is it heated?

8. A balloon of helium has a volume of 63 liters at 20.0°C. At what temperature would its volume be only 19 liters?

13:5 The Ideal Gas Law

Boyle's law and Charles' law can be combined to obtain an equation that relates the pressure, temperature, and volume of a fixed amount of gas.

$$\frac{p_1 V_1}{T_1} = \text{constant} = \frac{p_2 V_2}{T_2} \text{ or}$$

$$\boxed{\frac{p_1 V_1}{T_1} = \frac{p_2 V_2}{T_2}}$$

This equation is called the **combined gas law.** It reduces to Boyle's law if the temperature is constant. If the pressure is kept constant, it reduces to Charles' law. The law also shows that at constant volume, the pressure varies directly with the temperature.

Kinetic theory can be used to discover how the constant in the combined gas law depends on the number of particles in the sample, N. Suppose the volume and temperature are held constant. If we increase the number of particles, N, the number of collisions the particles make with the container will increase, increasing the pressure. Removing particles will decrease the number of collisions and thus decrease the pressure. We can conclude that the constant in the combined gas law equation must be proportional to N. That is,

$$\frac{pV}{T} = kN$$

We now check this result by holding other variables constant. Suppose pressure and temperature are held constant. Increasing the number of particles would increase the number of collisions. To keep the pressure constant, the volume is increased. The number of particles can be increased at constant pressure and temperature only if the volume is increased. This is consistent with the equation.

Suppose the volume and pressure are held constant. Increasing the number of particles increases the number of collisions. Therefore, the pressure can be held constant only if the impulse given by each collision is reduced. This can be done by reducing the velocity, and therefore the average kinetic energy, of the particles. Remember that temperature is proportional to the average kinetic energy of the particles. Reducing the temperature will decrease the average kinetic energy. Thus the number of

The combined gas law relates the temperature, pressure, and volume of a gas.

SUGGESTION: As a class exercise, have students predict whether the volume of a gas will increase or decrease when the pressure and temperature are changed given amounts. Then calculate to see if the prediction was correct.

particles can be increased at constant pressure and volume only if the temperature is reduced. This is also consistent with the equation written above.

The ideal gas law equation can be written in a more familiar form

$$pV = NkT$$

$k = 1.38 \times 10^{-23} \text{ L} \cdot \text{kPa/mol} \cdot \text{K}$

The constant k is called Boltzmann's constant, which has units of (pressure)(volume)/(temperature). Of course there is an extremely large number of particles in a gas. For that reason, we use a unit called the mole. One mole is equal to 6.02×10^{23} particles. The number of particles in a mole is called Avogadro's number. It is numerically equal to the number of particles in an amount of matter with mass equal to the gram formula mass of the substance. For our purposes, you might consider a mole equal to a "chemists' dozen." Thus, the ideal gas law is written using n, the number of moles in a gas sample, and the gas constant R.

$$pV = nRT$$

The value of R is 8.31 Pa $\cdot$ m³/mol $\cdot$ K.

PHYSICS FOCUS

Pressurized Fluidized-Bed Combustion

A   Dolomite feed system   D   Pressure vessel

B   Fluidized bed   E   Cyclones

C   Coal feed lines   F   Bed ash removal system

The burning of high-sulfur coal to produce electricity has been attacked as a cause of acid rain. The current method used to remove sulfur from coal combustion products uses "scrubbers." This technique is expensive and produces sludge that is an environmental problem. A promising, new, clean coal technology under research is pressurized fluidized-bed combustion (PFBC).

The PFBC process uses a pressurized combustion container. Because of its pressurized operation, the container is considerably smaller than a conventional boiler of equal generating capacity, and can operate at combustion temperatures of about half those encountered in a conventional boiler. A mixture of dolomite absorbs the sulfur dioxides that are produced. Unlike present scrubber technology, PFBC removes sulfur during combustion of the coal, not afterward. The sulfur-laden dolomite forms a dry, solid-waste product that is more manageable than the sludge that is produced by scrubbers and has some possible uses as roadbed filler.

PFBC's advantages over present conventional coal-fired power plants with scrubbers include fewer solid-waste problems, lower nitrogen oxide emissions, economic sulfur dioxide control, use of a wider range of coal types, and lower cost of electricity.

EXAMPLE

Combined Gas Law

A 20.0-L sample of argon gas at a temperature of 273 K is at atmospheric pressure, 101 kPa. The temperature is lowered to the boiling point of nitrogen, 77 K, while the pressure is increased to 145 kPa. What is the new volume of the argon sample?

Given: $V_1 = 20.0$ L   Unknown: V_2

$p_1 = 101$ kPa

$T_1 = 273$ K   Basic equation: $\dfrac{p_1 V_1}{T_1} = \dfrac{p_2 V_2}{T_2}$

$p_2 = 145$ kPa

$T_2 = 77$ K

Solution: $\dfrac{p_1 V_1}{T_1} = \dfrac{p_2 V_2}{T_2}$; so

$$V_2 = \frac{p_1 V_1 T_2}{p_2 T_1}$$

$$= \frac{(101\ \text{kPa})(20.0\ \text{L})(77\ \text{K})}{(145\ \text{kPa})(273\ \text{K})} = 3.9\ \text{L}$$

EXAMPLE

Ideal Gas Law

Find the number of moles and the mass of the argon gas sample in the example above. The mean molecular mass of argon is 39.9 g/mole.

Given: $V = 20.0$ L   Unknowns: number of moles n

$p = 101$ kPa   mass m

$T = 273$ K   Basic equation: $pV = nRT$

$R = 8.31$ Pa · m³/mol · K

Solution: $pV = nRT$ so $n = \dfrac{pV}{RT}$

$V = 20.0$ L $= (20.0\ \text{L})(1.0 \times 10^{-3}\ \text{m}^3/\text{L})$

$= 0.0200\ \text{m}^3$

$$n = \frac{(101 \times 10^3\ \text{Pa})(0.0200\ \text{m}^3)}{(8.31\ \text{Pa} \cdot \text{m}^3/\text{mol} \cdot \text{K})(273\ \text{K})}$$

$= 0.89$ mole

$m = (0.89\ \text{mole})(39.9\ \text{g/mole}) = 36$ g

Practice Exercises

9. A tank of helium gas used to inflate toy balloons is at 15.5×10^6 Pa pressure at 293 K and has a volume of 0.020 m³. How large a balloon would it fill at a pressure of 1.00 atmosphere and 323 K temperature?

FIGURE 13–9. The volume of a balloon is controlled by the temperature, mass of gas, and air pressure. As the balloon rises, changes in air pressure and temperature occur.

10. What is the mass of helium gas in Practice Exercise 9? Helium has a mass of 4.00 grams per mole.

11. Two hundred liters of hydrogen gas at 0°C are kept under a pressure of 156 kPa. The temperature is raised to 95°C and the volume is decreased to 175 L. What is the pressure of the gas?

12. Air has a molecular weight of 29 grams/mole. What is the volume of one kilogram of air at standard atmospheric pressure and 20°C temperature?

13:6 Real Gases

An ideal gas is a model. The model assumes that gas particles are infinitely small and exert no forces on each other unless they are in contact. The particles that make up real gases have a certain size and attract one another. It is perhaps surprising then that real gases obey the ideal gas law to high precision, except at very high pressures and very low temperatures. They act like ideal gases because the particles are very small in comparison to the distances between them, and because the forces among the particles are very weak.

The behavior of real gases deviates from the ideal gas law as temperatures decrease and pressures increase. Consider a gas such as oxygen. At room temperature and atmospheric pressure, the volume of the particles is very small compared to the total volume of the gas. The particles move so fast that the tiny attractive forces among the particles have practically no effect.

Now consider oxygen gas at −80°C. At this low temperature, the kinetic energy of the more slowly moving particles is almost equal to the potential energy resulting from the attractive forces. When the particles approach each other, they are drawn together. The volume shrinks faster than the equation $pV = nRT$ predicts.

Gases at normal pressures and temperatures are almost ideal gases.

a

b

FIGURE 13–10. A pressure-temperature graph shows the fusion and vaporization curves of water (a). The three phases of water are present in the chamber (b).

A second effect is seen when the pressure is high. The distance between the particles is reduced. The volume taken up by the gas particles is a considerable fraction of the total gas volume. As a result it is more and more difficult to compress the gas. Therefore, increases in pressure do not cause proportional volume decreases. Volume shrinks more slowly than predicted for an ideal gas.

An ideal gas could never change to a liquid. As a real gas is cooled and compressed, the thermal energy of the particles and the separation between them decrease. The particles collide slowly and often. As a result of the forces of attraction, particles stick together. A liquid or a solid begins to form. At some combination of temperature and pressure, determined by the properties of the gas particle, every gas changes to a liquid or a solid.

Real gases have particles that take up space and weakly attract each other over short distances.

CHAPTER 13 REVIEW

SUMMARY

1. The kinetic theory assumes that a gas is composed of tiny, perfectly elastic particles in constant random motion. **13:1**

2. An ideal gas is a model that assumes the particles have mass, but no volume and no attraction for each other. **13:1**

3. Pressure is force per unit area. It is measured in pascals (newtons per square meter). The kilopascal (kPa) is 1000 Pa. **13:2**

4. Standard atmospheric pressure is the average pressure of the atmosphere at sea level, 101.3 kPa. **13:2**

5. Boyle's law: at constant temperature, the volume of a gas varies inversely with its pressure. **13:3**

6. Charles' law: at constant pressure, the volume of a gas varies directly with its temperature in kelvins. **13:4**

7. The ideal gas law relates the pressure, volume, and temperature of a gas to the number of particles (or moles) in the sample. **13:5**

8. The particles that make up real gases have volume and attraction for one another. At moderate temperatures and pressures, however, real gases closely follow the ideal gas law. **13:6**

QUESTIONS

1. State the assumptions of the kinetic theory.
2. Which of the assumptions of the kinetic-molecular theory would be contradicted if the amount of kinetic energy were not conserved between two colliding molecules of gas?
3. How are force and pressure different?
4. What is the source of atmospheric pressure?
5. State standard atmospheric pressure in four different units.
6. If you made a barometer and filled it with a liquid one third as dense as mercury, how high would the level of the liquid be on a day of normal atmospheric pressure?
7. What happens when the pressure acting on a gas is held constant but the temperature of the gas is changed?
8. What happens when the temperature of a gas remains constant and pressure is changed?
9. Why does the air pressure in automobile tires increase when the car is driven on a hot day?
10. An air cylinder with a movable piston is placed in a refrigerator. The volume shrinks. How could you increase the volume to its original size without removing the piston?
11. Describe how a real gas differs from an ideal gas. What are some of the consequences of these differences?

APPLYING CONCEPTS

1. **a.** Explain why liquid rises in a straw when you drink a soda.
   b. What would be the longest soda straw you could use? Assume you could remove all air from the straw.
2. You lower a straw in water and place your finger over its top. Lifting the straw from the water, you notice water stays in it. Explain. Lift your finger from the top and the water runs out. Why?
3. Explain why you could not use a straw to drink a soda on the moon.
4. A tornado produces a region of extreme low pressure. If a house is hit by a tornado, is it likely to explode or implode? Why?

5. If a balloon filled with air is at rest, then the average velocity of the particles is zero. Does that mean the assumptions of the kinetic theory are not good? Explain.
6. Suppose real gas particles had volume but no attractive forces. How would this real gas differ from an ideal gas? How would it differ from other real gases?
7. Explain how Charles' experiments with gases indicate the possible location of absolute zero.
8. Suppose you are washing dishes. You place a glass, mouth downward, over the water and lower it slowly.
   a. What do you see?
   b. How deep would you have to push the glass to compress the air to one half its original volume?
   Try part **a.** Do not try part **b.**
9. Once again at the sink, you pull a filled glass above the water surface with the open end below the surface.
   a. The water does not run out. Why?
   b. How large could the glass be before water would run out?

EXERCISES

1. Weather reports often give atmospheric pressure in inches of mercury. The pressure usually ranges between 28.5 and 31.0 inches. Convert these two values to Torr, millibars, and kPa.
2. **a.** Find the force exerted by air at standard atmospheric pressure on the front cover of this book.
   b. The weight of what mass would exert the same force?
3. A tire gauge at a service station indicates a pressure of 32.0 psi (lb/in^2) in your tires. One standard atmosphere is 14.7 psi. What is the absolute pressure of air in your tires in kPa?
4. How high a column of alcohol (density 0.9 that of water) would be supported by atmospheric pressure?
5. Two cubic meters of a gas at 30.0°C are heated at constant pressure until the volume is doubled. What is the final temperature of the gas?

6. The pressure acting on a volume of 50.0 m³ of air is 1.01×10^5 N/m². The air is at a temperature of −50.0°C. The pressure acting on the air is increased to 2.02×10^5 N/m². Then the air occupies a volume of 30.0 m³. What is the temperature of the air at this new volume?

7. The pressure acting on 50.0 cm³ of a gas is reduced from 1.2 atm to 0.30 atm. What is the new volume of the gas if there is no temperature change?

8. A tank containing 30.0 m³ of natural gas at 5.0°C is heated by the sun at constant pressure to 30.0°C. What is its new volume?

9. Fifty liters of gas are cooled to 91.0 K at constant pressure. Its new volume is 30.0 liters. What was the original temperature?

10. Suppose the lungs of a scuba diver become filled to a capacity of 6.0 liters while at a depth of 8.3 m below the surface of a lake. To what volume would the diver's lungs (attempt to) expand if the diver suddenly rose to the surface?

11. A bubble of air with a volume of 0.050 cm³ escapes from a pressure hose at the bottom of a tank filled with mercury. When the bubble reaches the surface of the mercury, it has a volume of 0.500 cm³. How deep is the mercury?

12. At a temperature of 40.0 K, 0.100 m³ of helium is under 408 kPa pressure. The pressure exerted on the helium is increased to 2175 kPa while its volume is held constant. What is the temperature of the helium?

13. A 20-L sample of neon is at standard atmospheric pressure at 300°C. The sample is cooled in dry ice to −79°C at constant volume. What is its new pressure?

14. A 50.0-cm³ sample of air is at standard pressure and −45.0°C. The pressure on the gas is doubled and the temperature adjusted until the volume is 30.0 cm³. What is the temperature?

15. At 40.0 K, 10.0 m³ of nitrogen is under 4.0×10^2 kPa pressure. The pressure acting on the nitrogen is increased to 2000 kPa. Its volume stays the same. What is the temperature of the nitrogen?

PROBLEMS

1. The markings on a thermometer are worn off, so a student creates new degree markings, which she calls °S. She then measures the volume of a gas held at constant pressure at three temperatures, finding 30 L at 90°S, 45 L at 120°S, and 60 L at 150°S. What is absolute zero in °S?

2. How many particles are in one cubic centimeter of air (6.02×10^{23} particles/mole) at standard pressure at 20°C temperature?

3. Physicists can, with proper equipment, obtain vacuums with pressures of 1.0×10^{-11} Torr.
   a. What fraction of atmospheric pressure is this?
   b. Using the results from Problem 2, find the number of particles in a cubic centimeter of this vacuum.

4. Two hundred grams of argon (39.9 g/mole) are sold in a bottle at 5.0 atm pressure at 293 K. How many liters are in the bottle?

5. A 2.00-L tank of gas is designed to hold gas at 20.0 atm pressure at a temperature of 50.0°C. What is the mass of methane (16.0 gram/mole) that can be put into the tank?

6. The pressure acting on 20.0 liters of gas is 120.0 kPa. If the temperature is 23.0°C, how many molecules are present?

7. Mercury has a specific gravity of 13.6, which means that mercury is 13.6 times more dense than water. If a barometer were constructed using water rather than mercury, how high (in meters) would the water rise under normal atmospheric pressure?

READINGS

Giedd, Ronald, "Real Otto and Diesel Engine Cycles." The Physics Teacher, January, 1983.

Hollister, Charles, "The Dynamic Abyss." Scientific American, March, 1984.

Maxwell, James C., Maxwell on Molecules and Gases, Cambridge, MA: MIT Press, 1986.

Overbye, Dennis, "Mapping the Heat of Heaven." Discover, April, 1983.

Tierney, John, "Perpetual Commotion." Science 83, May, 1983.

CHAPTER 14

States of Matter

GOALS

1. You will acquire a knowledge of the properties of solids, liquids, and gases.
2. You will become familiar with some of the characteristics of static and moving fluids.
3. You will gain an understanding of how the kinetic theory explains the behavior of solids, liquids, and gases.

SUGGESTIONS: Differentiate between force and pressure. Discuss why it is not painful to lie on a bed of nails but it would be very painful to lie on one nail. Have students think of other examples of the difference between force and pressure.

For Your Information

Blaise Pascal was a man of many talents. He was a mathematician, a physicist, and a philosopher. As a child, he built a calculating machine and a slide rule. Among his other accomplishments are the invention of the mathematical (Pascal's) triangle, discovery of the properties of the cycloid, advanced differential calculus, and devising the basis for the modern theory of probabilities.

Chapter 13 discussed laws that apply only to the gaseous phase of matter. In this chapter, we will consider another aspect of gases as well as some of the characteristics and behaviors of liquids, solids, and plasmas.

We will find out how airplanes fly, how ocean liners float, and how submarines can either float or submerge. We will study why paper towels absorb spilled milk, how some insects can walk on the surface of water, and what causes the northern lights. All of these phenomena demonstrate specific principles that govern the behavior of matter.

14:1 Fluids at Rest—Hydrostatics

A **fluid** is any material that flows and offers little resistance to a change in its shape when under pressure. Both liquids and gases can be classified as fluids. To simplify our study, we will examine the behavior of an ideal fluid, one that is incompressible. In an ideal fluid there is no internal friction among the particles.

If you have ever dived deep into a swimming pool or lake, you know that fluids exert pressure. Your body is sensitive to water pressure. You probably noticed that the pressure you feel on your ears does not depend on whether your head is upright or tilted; the pressure is the same on all parts of your body. *Any change in pressure applied to an enclosed fluid at any point is transmitted undiminished throughout the fluid.* Blaise Pascal (1623–1662), a French physician, was the first to discover this principle, which became known as **Pascal's principle.** Every time you squeeze a tube of toothpaste, you use Pascal's principle.

Deep Water?

Jacqueline is enjoying a warm, lazy summer day leisurely floating on an air mattress in the swimming pool. If she were to slip into the pool to cool off, would the pool water level rise, stay the same, or drop?

FIGURE 14–1. Increased pressure is transmitted equally throughout a confined fluid.

Pascal's principle is applied in the operation of machines that use fluids to multiply forces, for example, hydraulic lifts. In a hydraulic system a fluid is confined in two connecting chambers. Each chamber has a piston that is free to move. A force, F_1, is exerted on the piston with surface area A_1. The pressure exerted on the fluid is

$$p_1 = \frac{F_1}{A_1}$$

This pressure is transmitted undiminished throughout the fluid. The pressure exerted on the piston with surface area A_2 is given by

$$p_2 = \frac{F_2}{A_2}$$

By Pascal's principle, this pressure, p_2, is the same as p_1. Therefore,

$$\boxed{\frac{F_1}{A_1} = \frac{F_2}{A_2}}$$

The force that the second piston can exert is given by

$$F_2 = F_1 \frac{A_2}{A_1}$$

For Your Information

FIGURE 14–2. Pascal's principle is the basis of a hydraulic lift and other machines that use fluids to multiply forces.

Area = 5 cm² Area = 50 cm²
100 N   1000 N

Piston A   20 N/cm²   20 N/cm²   Piston B

EXAMPLE

Hydraulic System

A 20.0-N force is exerted on the small piston of the hydraulic system in Figure 14–2. The cross-sectional area of the small piston is 0.0500 m². What is the magnitude of the weight that can be lifted by the large piston, which has a surface area of 0.100 m²?

Given: $F_1 = 20.0$ N   Unknown: F_2
$A_1 = 0.0500$ m²
$A_2 = 0.100$ m²   Basic equation: $\dfrac{F_1}{A_1} = \dfrac{F_2}{A_2}$

Solution: $\dfrac{F_1}{A_1} = \dfrac{F_2}{A_2}$

$$F_2 = \frac{F_1 A_2}{A_1}$$

$$= \frac{(20.0 \text{ N})(0.100 \text{ m}^2)}{0.0500 \text{ m}^2}$$

$$F_2 = 40.0 \text{ N}$$

You can also observe another characteristic of fluids while swimming. The deeper you swim, the greater the pressure you feel on your eardrums. The pressure of a fluid is the weight per unit area (A) of the fluid above you. The weight (W) of the water above you is

$$W = mg$$

Recall that ρ (density) $= m/V$ and $V = Ah$, therefore $W = \rho V g = \rho A h g$.

FIGURE 14–3. Breathing compressed air at a normal rate prevents the divers' lungs from compressing at increased pressure.

SUGGESTIONS: When you are swimming, the pressure you feel on your eardrums depends only on the depth and not on the size of the swimming pool.

The Greek letter rho, ρ, is used for density.

Substituting this value for W will give

$$p = \frac{W}{A} = \frac{\rho Ahg}{A} = \rho hg$$

Therefore, the pressure is proportional only to the depth of the fluid and its density. The shape of the container has no effect, as shown in Figure 14–4.

When an object of height l is placed in a fluid, force is exerted on all sides. The forces on the four sides are balanced. The forces on the top and bottom, however, are given by

$$F_{top} = p_{top}A = \rho hgA$$
$$F_{bottom} = p_{bottom}A = \rho g(h + l)A$$

The force on the bottom is larger than that on the top. The net force is

$$F_{bottom} - F_{top} = Ag\rho(h + l) - Ag\rho h$$
$$= Ag\rho l = V\rho g$$

DEMONSTRATION: See Teacher Guide.

Do you also see that the volume of the immersed object is the same as the volume of the fluid displaced? Therefore, the buoyant force, $V\rho g$, is equal to the weight of the volume of fluid displaced by the immersed object. This relationship was discovered by the Greek scientist Archimedes in 212 B.C. and is called **Archimedes' principle.** *An object immersed in a fluid is buoyed up by a force equal to the weight of the fluid displaced by the object.* It is important to note that the buoyant force *does not* depend on the weight of the submerged object, only the weight of the displaced fluid. A solid cube of aluminum, a solid cube of iron, and a hollow cube of iron, all of the same volume, would experience the same buoyant force.

Archimedes' principle applies to objects of all densities. If the density of the object is greater than that of the fluid, the buoyant force will be less than W_{object} and the object will sink. If the density of the object is equal to the density of the fluid, the buoyant force and W_{object} will be equal. The object will neither sink nor float. If the density of the object is less than

The buoyant force is equal to the weight of the fluid displaced.

FIGURE 14–4. Pascal's vases show that a container's shape has no effect on pressure.

FIGURE 14–5. Archimedes' principle can be derived from considering a volume of fluid as shown (a). If the density of an object is less than that of the fluid, the object will sink only until it displaces a volume of water with a weight equal to the weight of the object (b).

FIGURE 14–6. FLIP is a research vessel used to study waves in deep water. It is towed into position floating horizontally. Then water is pumped into its stern tanks and it flips to a vertical position, as shown.

that of the fluid, the object will submerge only until it displaces a volume of fluid with a weight equal to the weight of the object. Wearing a life jacket filled with material of very low density has the effect of decreasing the body's density.

Shipbuilders can build ships of steel (density 9.0×10^3 kg/m³) by designing them with large hollow hulls so that the overall density of the ship is less than that of water. You will notice that a ship loaded with cargo rides much lower in the water than a ship with an empty hold. Submarines take advantage of Archimedes' principle by pumping water into or out of special chambers to regulate the depth at which they operate. Fish have air sacs that allow them to adjust their density so they can swim at various depths.

EXAMPLE

Archimedes' Principle

A cubic decimeter of steel is submerged in water. **a.** What is the magnitude of the buoyant force acting on the steel? **b.** What is the net weight of the body? (The density of steel is 9.0×10^3 kg/m³.)

Given: $V = 1.00$ dm³

$\rho_{steel} = 9.0 \times 10^3$ kg/m³

$\rho_{water} = 1.00 \times 10^3$ kg/m³

Unknowns: **a.** $F_{buoyant}$
b. W_{net}

Basic equations:

a. $F_{buoyant} = V\rho_{water}g$

b. $W_{net} = mg - F_{buoyant}$

Solution:

a. $F_{buoyant} = V\rho_{water}g$

$= (1.00 \times 10^{-3} \text{ m}^3)(1.00 \times 10^3 \text{ kg/m}^3)(9.8 \text{ m/s}^2)$

$= 9.8$ N

b. $W_{net} = mg - F_{buoyant}$

$= [(1.00 \times 10^{-1} \text{ m})^3(9.0 \times 10^3 \text{ kg/m}^3)(9.8 \text{ m/s}^2)] - 9.8 \text{ N}$

$= 88.2 \text{ N} - 9.8 \text{ N} = 78.4 \text{ N}$

Practice Exercises

1. If the diameter of the larger piston in Figure 14-2 were doubled, what force would be lifted if 20.0 N were applied to the small piston?

2. Dentists' chairs are examples of hydraulic lift systems. If the chair weighs 1600 N and rests on a piston with a cross-sectional area of 1440 cm², what force must be applied to the small piston with a cross-sectional area of 72 cm² to lift the chair?

3. A teenager is floating in a freshwater lake with her head just above the water. If she weighs 600 N, what is her volume?

4. What is the tension in a wire supporting a 1250-N camera submerged in water? The volume of the camera is 8.3 × 10⁻² m³.

14:2 Fluids in Motion—Hydrodynamics

To see the effect of moving fluids, try the experiment in Figure 14-7. Hold a strip of notebook paper just under your lower lip. Now blow hard across the top surface. The strip will rise. The pressure on the top of the paper where the air is flowing fast is lower than that on the bottom where the air is not in motion. This is an example of Bernoulli's principle, named for the Swiss chemist Daniel Bernoulli (1700-1782).

Imagine a horizontal pipe completely filled with a smoothly flowing ideal fluid. If a certain volume of the fluid enters one end of the pipe, then an equal volume must come out the other end. The kinetic energy of the fluid is dependent on its velocity, and the potential energy is proportional to the pressure of the fluid. If no energy enters or leaves the system, the sum of the potential and kinetic energies must remain the same. Now consider a section of pipe where the cross section becomes narrower, as shown in Figure 14-8b. To move the required volume of fluid through the narrow section, the velocity of the fluid, and hence its kinetic energy, must increase. Since the total energy of the system is conserved, the potential energy, and therefore the pressure exerted by the fluid, will decrease. The relationship between the velocity and pressure exerted by a moving fluid is described by **Bernoulli's principle:** *As the velocity of a fluid increases, the pressure exerted by that fluid decreases.*

Most aircraft get their lift by taking advantage of Bernoulli's principle. Airplane wings are airfoils, devices designed to produce lift when moving through a fluid. The curvature of the top surface of a wing is greater than

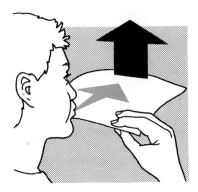

FIGURE 14-7. Blowing across the surface of a sheet of paper demonstrates Bernoulli's principle.

SUGGESTIONS: Be sure to perform the demonstrations of Bernoulli's principle. Hold a straw parallel to a candle. Blow through the straw so the air comes out next to the flame. The flame moves toward the straw.

Bernoulli's principle states that the pressure of a moving fluid decreases as the velocity of the fluid increases.

FIGURE 14-8. The spoiler on a race car is an inverted airfoil.

FIGURE 14–9. Boat docks are usually open so that a difference in water pressure does not force boats against docks.

DEMONSTRATIONS: See Teacher Guide.

In a turbulent flow, the streamlines are disrupted.

For Your Information

Daniel Bernoulli's principle explaining the relationship between the pressure and velocity of fluids is contained in his work *Hydrodynamica*, presented in 1738.

FIGURE 14–10. Smooth streamlines show the even flow of a fluid. Areas where the streamlines are crowded together indicate increased velocity.

that of the bottom. As the wing travels through the air, the air moving over the top surface travels farther, and therefore must go faster than air moving past the bottom surface. The decreased air pressure created on the top surface results in a net upward pressure producing an upward force on the wings, or lift, that holds the airplane aloft. Race cars use airfoils with a greater curvature on the bottom surface. The airfoils, called spoilers, produce a net downward pressure that holds the rear wheels of the cars on the road at high speeds.

Did you ever notice that boat docks are designed so that water can flow freely around them? Consider what would happen at a solid-walled pier as a boat approached. As the space between the boat and the pier narrowed, the velocity of the water would increase, and the pressure exerted by the water on the pier side of the boat would decrease. The boat could be pushed against the pier by the greater pressure of the water against the other side.

Figure 14–10 shows that the flow of a fluid can be represented by streamlines. Streamlines can best be illustrated by a simple demonstration. Imagine tiny drops of food coloring carefully dropped into a smoothly flowing fluid. If the colored lines that form stay thin and well defined, the flow is said to be streamlined. Notice that if the flow narrows, the streamlines move closer together. Closely spaced streamlines indicate greater velocity, and therefore reduced pressure.

If the streamlines swirl and become diffused, the flow is said to be turbulent. Bernoulli's principle does not apply to turbulent flow. Since objects require less energy to move through a streamline flow, automobile and aircraft manufacturers spend a great deal of time and money testing new designs in wind tunnels to ensure a streamlined flow of air around vehicles.

14:3 Liquids

Although liquids and gases are grouped together as fluids, liquids are different from gases in several ways.

1. A liquid has a definite volume; a gas takes the volume of any container that holds it.
2. A liquid is practically incompressible; a gas is easily compressed.
3. The particles of a liquid are very close together—the volume of the

FIGURE 14–11. Molten lava is a viscous fluid.

particles makes up almost all the volume of a liquid; the particles of a gas take up relatively little space—a volume of gas is mostly empty space.

Furthermore, although the particles of an ideal liquid are free to slide over and around one another, in real liquids the particles do exert electromagnetic forces of attraction on each other. These forces are called **cohesive forces,** and they directly affect the behavior of the liquid.

Liquids have definite volume, are practically incompressible, and the particles take up most of the room in the fluid.

14:4 Surface Tension

Have you ever noticed that dewdrops on spiderwebs and falling drops of milk or oil are nearly spherical? Perhaps you have also observed that a drop of water on a smooth surface forms a rounded shape, while a drop of alcohol tends to flatten out. All of these phenomena are examples of surface tension. It is a result of the cohesive forces among the particles of a liquid. **Surface tension** is the tendency of the surface of a liquid to contract to the smallest area.

Beneath the surface of the liquid in Figure 14–12, each particle of the liquid is attracted equally in all directions by neighboring particles. As a result, there is no net force acting on any of the particles beneath the surface. At the surface, however, the particles are attracted to the sides and downward, but not upward. Thus, there is a net downward force acting on the top layers. This net force causes the surface layer to be slightly compressed. The layer acts like a tightly stretched rubber sheet or a film. The film is strong enough to support the weight of light objects. Water bugs can stand on the surface of quiet pools of water because of surface tension. The surface tension of water also supports an object such as a steel razor blade, even though the density of steel is nine times greater than that of water.

Surface tension also accounts for the tendency of unconfined liquids to form drops. The force pulling the surface particles into the liquid causes the surface to become as small as possible. The shape that has the least surface for a given volume is a sphere. Liquid mercury has a much stronger cohesive force among its particles than water. This allows small amounts of mercury to form spherical drops, even when placed on a smooth surface. On the other hand, liquids such as alcohol or ether have weaker cohesive forces between their particles. A drop of either of these

Surface tension is a result of cohesive forces.

Surface tension makes the surface area of a fluid as small as possible.

SUGGESTION: Float some pepper on water and add detergent to break the surface tension and see the pepper sink.

FIGURE 14–12. The net downward force on molecule B draws the surface molecules together.

a

b

FIGURE 14–13. The water strider can stand on water because of surface tension (a). The dewdrops on a spider web are spherical because of surface tension (b).

Capillary action, the result of adhesion, causes some fluids to rise in small tubes.

DEMONSTRATIONS: See Teacher Guide.

liquids flattens when placed on a smooth surface.

A force similar to cohesion is adhesion. **Adhesion** is the attractive force that acts between particles of different substances. Like cohesive forces, adhesive forces are electromagnetic in nature.

If a piece of glass tubing with a small inside diameter is placed in water, the water rises inside the tube. The water rises because the adhesive force between glass and water molecules is stronger than the cohesive force between water molecules. This phenomenon is called **capillary action.** The water continues to rise until the weight of the water lifted balances the adhesive force between the glass and water molecules. If the radius of the tube increases, the volume, and therefore the weight, of the water increases proportionally faster than the surface area of the tube. For this reason, water is lifted higher in a narrow tube than in one that is wider.

As shown in Figure 14–14a, the surface of the water dips in the center of the tube. This is because the adhesive force between the glass molecules and water molecules is greater than the cohesive force between the water molecules. If the liquid in the tube were mercury, it would not rise in the tube. Furthermore, the center of the surface would bulge upward, as shown in Figure 14–14b. Both of these phenomena occur because the

FIGURE 14–14. Water climbs the wall of this capillary tube (a), while the mercury is depressed in the tube (b). The force of attraction between mercury atoms is stronger than any adhesive force between the mercury and the glass.

cohesive forces between the mercury molecules are greater than the adhesive forces between the mercury and glass.

Oil rises in the wick of a lamp because of capillary action. Paint moves up through the bristles of a brush for the same reason. It is also capillary action that causes water to move up through the soil to the roots of plants.

14:5 Evaporation and Condensation

The particles in a liquid move at random speeds. Some are moving rapidly; others are moving slowly. The temperature of a liquid is dependent on the average *KE* of its particles. Suppose a fast-moving particle is near the surface of the liquid. If it can break through the surface layers, it will escape from the liquid. Since there is a net downward cohesive force at the surface, only the more energetic particles can escape. The escape of particles is called **evaporation.**

Each time a particle with higher than average kinetic energy escapes from the liquid, the average kinetic energy of the remaining particles decreases. A decrease in kinetic energy is a decrease in temperature. The result is the cooling effect of evaporation. This effect can be demonstrated by pouring some rubbing alcohol into the palm of your hand. Alcohol molecules have weak cohesive forces (low surface tension). Alcohol molecules, therefore, evaporate easily. The cooling effect is quite noticeable. Liquids such as alcohol and ether evaporate quickly because the forces between their molecules are weak. A liquid that evaporates quickly is called a **volatile** (VAHL uht uhl) liquid.

The opposite process also exists. Water particles moving randomly in the air above the surface may strike the surface. If the particle has lost enough energy, the cohesive force will be strong enough to prevent the particle's escape. This process is called **condensation.** Each time a particle with above average kinetic energy is absorbed by the liquid, the average kinetic energy of the liquid is increased. Thus, the temperature of the liquid is increased. This results in the warming effect of condensation.

An increase in air pressure above a liquid makes it more likely that an escaping particle will have a collision and return to the liquid. Thus, increased pressure means that the particles need a higher kinetic energy (temperature) to escape.

14:6 Solid State

When the temperature of a liquid is lowered, the average kinetic energy of the particles is lowered. As the particles slow down, the cohesive forces become more effective, and the particles are no longer able to slide over one another. The particles become frozen into a fixed pattern called a crystal lattice. Despite the forces that hold the particles in place, the particles do not stop moving completely. Rather they vibrate around their fixed positions in the crystal lattice. In some solids, the particles do not form a fixed crystalline pattern. Their positions are fixed, but the pattern is variable. These substances have definite volume and shape and are called amorphous solids. Butter, paraffin, and glass do not have a crystal structure. None of these materials contains a crystal structure and are often classified as very viscous (slow-flowing) liquids.

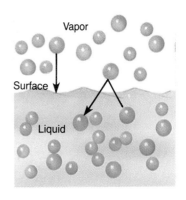

FIGURE 14–15. The vapor pressure above a liquid slows the rate of evaporation.

Evaporation results in the cooling of the remaining fluid.

SUGGESTION: Place some rubbing alcohol on a student's arm and let it evaporate to show that evaporation is a cooling process.

For Your Information

If all the water vapor in Earth's atmosphere were condensed to liquid water at the same time, there would be enough water to cover the United States with a layer of water twenty-five feet deep.

FIGURE 14–16. A pressure cooker is used to prepare foods quickly by cooking with high internal air pressure and temperature.

FIGURE 14–17. Minerals exhibit a variety of crystal structures. These structures are dependent upon the chemical composition of the minerals.

SUGGESTION: Fill a narrow glass bottle with water. Squeeze it and see the level change depending on where you squeeze it.

Particles in a solid vibrate about fixed locations.

Solids have a definite shape and volume.

Elasticity is the ability of an object to return to its original form.

FIGURE 14–18. A temperature graph of the universe points out levels above which each phase of matter no longer exists. Notice how very small the temperature range is for the human body, within the vastness of the universe.

As a liquid freezes, its particles usually fit more closely together than in the liquid state. Water is an exception. Water molecules in the solid state take up more space than they do as a liquid. Thus, water expands as it freezes, causing ice to have a lower density than liquid water and to float on the surface. If water contracted as it froze, ice would have a higher density than water and would sink. Lakes and rivers would freeze from the bottom up.

An increase in the pressure on the surface of a liquid forces the particles closer together. The cohesive force becomes stronger. For most liquids, the freezing point of a liquid increases as the pressure on the liquid increases. Again, water is the exception. Since water expands as it freezes, an increase in pressure opposes this expansion. The freezing point of water is lowered as the pressure on its surface is increased. Ice skating is possible because of this property. Increased pressure from the skate blades causes the ice under the blades to melt. The thin film of water formed acts as a lubricant and allows the skates to move across the ice with almost no friction.

14:7 Elasticity

External forces applied to a solid object may twist or bend it out of shape. The ability of an object to return to its original form when the external forces are removed is called the **elasticity** of the solid. If too much deformation occurs, the object will not return to its original shape—its elastic limit has been exceeded. Elasticity depends on the forces that hold the particles of a substance together. Malleability and ductility, the ability to be rolled into a thin sheet and drawn into a wire, respectively, are two properties that depend on the elasticity of a substance. Gold is very malleable; glass is not.

14:8 Thermal Expansion of Matter

Most materials expand when heated and contract when cooled. This property has many useful applications. For example, when air is heated it becomes less dense. Gravity pulls the denser, colder air down, pushing the warmer air upward. The motion results in the circulation of air, called a convection current. By means of convection, all the air in a room can be heated quickly.

The expansion of liquids is useful in thermometers. It also allows a liquid to be heated rapidly. When a container of liquid is heated from the bottom, convection currents form. Cold, more dense liquid falls to the bottom where it is heated and then pushed up by cooler liquid from the top. Thus all the liquid is able to come in contact with the hot surface.

The expansion of concrete and steel in highway bridges means that the structures are longer in the summer than in the winter. Temperature extremes must be considered when bridges are designed. Gaps, called expansion joints, are needed to allow for seasonal increases in length.

Some materials have been designed to have the smallest possible thermal expansion. Blocks used as standard lengths in machine shops are often made of Invar, a metal alloy. Pyrex glass is used for laboratory and cooking containers and in large telescope mirrors.

We have already seen that the kinetic theory explains the increase in volume of heated gases. Kinetic theory also explains the expansion of heated solids. Our model for a solid is a collection of particles connected by springs. The springs represent the forces that attract the particles to each other. When the particles get too close, the springs push them apart. If a solid did not have these forces of repulsion, it would collapse into a tiny sphere.

When a solid is heated, the kinetic energy of the particles increases; they vibrate more violently. The attractive force between particles in a solid is not really like the force exerted by a stretched spring. In the case of a solid, when the particles move farther apart, the force is weaker. As a result, when the particles vibrate more violently, their average separation increases. Thus the solid expands when its temperature increases.

Most liquids also expand when heated. A good model for a liquid does not exist, but it is useful to think of a liquid as a ground-up solid. Groups of two, three, or more particles move together as if they were a tiny piece of a solid. When heated, particle motion causes these groups to expand just as a solid does. As a result, the whole liquid expands. For an equal change in temperature, liquids expand considerably more than solids.

FIGURE 14–19. A hot air balloon expands and rises as the air inside it is heated.

When a solid is heated, its kinetic energy increases.

Liquids expand more than solids when heated.

FIGURE 14–20. The motion of molecules in a model of a solid (a) is less than in a liquid (b).

a

b

TABLE 14–1

Coefficients of Thermal Expansion at 20°C		
Material	Coefficient of linear expansion, α (°C^{-1})	Coefficient of volume expansion, β (°C^{-1})
Solids		
Aluminum	25×10^{-6}	75×10^{-6}
Iron, steel	12×10^{-6}	35×10^{-6}
Glass (soft)	9×10^{-6}	27×10^{-6}
Glass (Pyrex)	3×10^{-6}	9×10^{-6}
Concrete	12×10^{-6}	36×10^{-6}
Liquids		
Alcohol		1100×10^{-6}
Gasoline		950×10^{-6}
Mercury		180×10^{-6}
Water		210×10^{-6}
Gases		
Air (and most other gases)		3400×10^{-6}

FIGURE 14–21. The solid form of water, ice, has a larger volume than an equal mass of its liquid form.

The change in length of a solid is proportional to the change in temperature.

Volume expansion is three dimensional.

FIGURE 14–22. The change in length is proportional to the original length and the change in temperature.

Water expands only when its temperature is raised above 4°C. As water is heated from 0°C to 4°C, it contracts. The solid form of water, ice, has a larger volume than an equal mass of its liquid form. The forces between water molecules are strong and depend on direction. This means that the crystals that make up ice have a very open structure. Even when ice melts tiny crystals remain. Between melting and 4°C these remaining crystals melt, and the volume decreases. As a result, water is denser at 4°C than at any other temperature. The practical result is that ice floats, and that lakes, rivers, and other bodies of water freeze from the top down.

The change in length of a solid is proportional to the change in temperature. A solid will expand twice as much if heated by 20°C than if heated by 10°C. The change is also proportional to its length. A two-meter bar will expand twice as much as a one-meter bar. Thus, the length, L, of a solid at temperature T is given by

$$L = L_i + \alpha L_i(T - T_i)$$

L_i is the length at temperature T_i, and the proportionality constant, α, is called the coefficient of linear expansion. The equation can also be written

$$L - L_i = \alpha L_i(T - T_i) \text{ or } \Delta L = \alpha L_i \Delta T$$

Then

$$\frac{\Delta L}{L_i} = \alpha \Delta T$$

and

$$\boxed{\alpha = \frac{\Delta L}{L_i \Delta T}}$$

The dimensions of alpha are $\dfrac{\text{length unit}}{(\text{length unit})(\text{temperature unit})}$

Therefore, the unit for the coefficient of linear expansion is 1/°C or °C^{-1}. Volume expansion is three dimensional. The coefficient of volume expansion is approximately three times the coefficient of linear expansion.

Different materials expand at different rates. The expansion rates of gases and liquids are larger than those of solids. Engineers must consider these different expansion rates when designing structures. Steel bars are often used to reinforce concrete. The steel and concrete must have the same expansion coefficient. Otherwise, the structure may crack on a hot day. For a similar reason, a dentist must use filling materials that expand and contract at the same rate as a tooth.

Sometimes different rates of expansion are useful. Engineers have taken advantage of these differences to construct a useful device called a bimetallic strip. A bimetallic strip consists of two strips of different metals. These two metals are either welded or riveted together. Usually one strip is brass and the other is iron. When heated, brass expands more than iron. Thus, when the bimetallic strip of brass and iron is heated, the brass strip becomes longer than the iron strip. The bimetallic strip bends with the brass on the outside of the curve. If the bimetallic strip is cooled below room temperature, it bends in the opposite direction. The brass is now on the inside of the curve.

a

b

FIGURE 14–23. The properties of a bimetallic strip cause it to bend when heated (b). In this thermostat a coiled bimetallic strip controls the flow of mercury for opening and closing electrical switches (a).

Thermostats used in homes usually contain a bimetallic strip. The bimetallic strip is installed so that it bends toward an electric contact as the room cools. When the room cools below the setting on the thermostat, the bimetallic strip bends enough to make electric contact with the switch, which turns on the heater. As the room warms, the bimetallic strip bends in the other direction. The electric circuit is broken, and the heater is switched off.

EXAMPLE

Linear Expansion

A metal bar is 2.60 meters long at 21°C. The bar is heated uniformly to a temperature of 93°C and the change in length is measured to be 3.4 mm. What is the coefficient of linear expansion of this bar?

Given: $L_i = 2.60$ m   Unknown: α
$\Delta L = 3.4 \times 10^{-3}$ m
$T_i = 21°C$ Basic equation: $\dfrac{\Delta L}{L_i} = \alpha \Delta T$
$T = 93°C$

Solution: $\Delta T = T - T_i = 72°C$

$$\alpha = \frac{\Delta L}{L_i \Delta T}$$

$$= \frac{3.4 \times 10^{-3}\text{ m}}{(2.60\text{ m})(72°C)} = 1.8 \times 10^{-5}°C^{-1}$$

For Your Information

A shape-memory alloy is a metal that changes back to its original shape when heated. The alloy's crystalline structure changes from one form to another when the temperature varies. Shape-memory alloys are being used in many areas of technology—in fighter aircraft, orthodontic wires, eyeglass frames, shower heads, and heat engines to name a few.

Practice Exercises

5. A piece of aluminum siding is 3.66 m long on a cold winter day (−28°C). How much longer is it on a very hot summer day (39°C)? $\alpha_{Al} = 25 \times 10^{-6}°C^{-1}$.

6. A piece of steel ($\alpha = 11 \times 10^{-6}°C^{-1}$) is 11.5 m long at 22°C. It is heated to 1221°C, close to its melting temperature. How long is it?

7. A tank truck takes on a load of 45 725 liters of gasoline in Houston at 32.0°C. The coefficient of volume expansion (β) for gasoline is 950 ×

SUGGESTION: Make a large block of ice. Tie two 1 kg masses to the ends of a piece of copper wire and hang it over the ice. The wire will move through the ice and the ice will freeze over it.

FIGURE 14–24. A sodium vapor lamp contains glowing plasma.

A plasma can conduct electricity, a gas cannot.

$10^{-6}°C^{-1}$. The truck delivers its load in Omaha at $-18.0°C$.

a. How many liters of gasoline does the truck deliver?

b. What happened to the gasoline?

c. Who pays?

14:9 Plasma

If you heat a solid, it melts to form a liquid. Further heating results in a gas. What happens if you increase the temperature still further? Collisions between the particles become violent enough to tear the particles apart. Electrons are pulled off the atoms, producing positively-charged ions. The gaslike state of negatively-charged electrons and positively-charged ions is called a **plasma.**

A lightning bolt is in the plasma state. So is most of the sun and other stars. In addition, much of the matter between the stars is in the form of plasma. The primary difference between a gas and a plasma is that a plasma can conduct electricity and a gas cannot. A fluorescent lamp contains mercury vapor. When the lamp is turned on, the electrical forces strip electrons from the atoms, forming a mercury plasma. The plasma conducts electricity, changing electrical energy into ultraviolet light energy. Most of the light strikes chemicals coating the inner surface of the tube, causing them to glow. The glowing phosphors produce most of the visible light. Neon signs and the mercury and sodium vapor lamps used in street lighting also contain glowing plasmas.

PHYSICS FOCUS

Why Curve Balls Curve

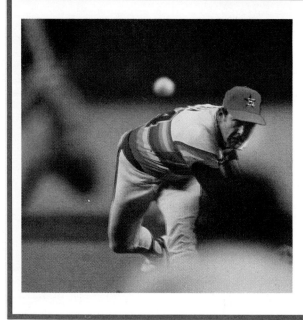

Baseball pitchers have baffled batters for years with the curve ball. When a ball curves downward, it is more difficult for the batter to time the swing of the bat.

Motion of a pitched ball can be "frozen" by strobe-light photography. A curve ball moves in a constant arc. If Earth did not get in the way, the ball would circle back to the pitcher, who could turn around and catch it.

Baseballs curve because of ball spin, aerodynamics, and gravity. A pitcher produces top spin by placing the index and middle fingers along the stitches, then snapping them over the top as the ball is released. Friction between the spinning stitches and the air pulls a thin layer of air around the ball as it spins. Throughout the ball's flight, more air flows around the bottom than around the top of the ball. Therefore, air flows faster around the bottom and less pressure is exerted there. The ball is pushed downward. Gravity accentuates the downward motion of the ball in the second half of its path. This, along with the batter's perspective, produces the optical illusion of the "break" of a curve ball.

CHAPTER 14 REVIEW

SUMMARY

1. A gas fills any container in which it is placed. A liquid has a fixed volume but takes the shape of its container. A solid has a fixed volume and fixed shape. A plasma is like a gas but electrically charged. **14:1, 14:3, 14:6, 14:9**

2. According to Pascal's principle, pressure is transmitted undiminished throughout a fluid. **14:1**

3. An object in a fluid has an upward force exerted on it called the buoyant force. **14:1**

4. According to Archimedes' principle, the buoyant force on an object is equal to the weight of the fluid displaced by that object. **14:1**

5. The pressure exerted by a fluid decreases as the velocity of the fluid increases. **14:2**

6. Cohesive forces are the attractive forces that like particles exert on one another. **14:3**

7. Adhesive forces are the attractive forces that particles of different substances exert on one an-

other. **14:4**

8. Evaporation occurs when the most energetic particles in a liquid have enough energy to escape into the gas phase. **14:5**

9. Volatile liquids are those with weak cohesive forces that evaporate quickly. **14:5**

10. As a liquid solidifies, its particles become frozen into a fixed pattern. If the pattern is regular, the solid is a crystalline solid. If the pattern is irregular, the solid is an amorphous solid. **14:6**

11. The ability of an object to return to its original form when stressed is elasticity. **14:7**

12. The increase of length of a material as the temperature increases varies directly with the temperature change and the original length. It also depends on the type of material. **14:8**

13. Plasma is an energetic state of matter made up of a mixture of positive and negative particles. **14:9**

QUESTIONS

1. Drops of mercury, water, and naphtha (lighter fluid) are placed on a smooth, flat surface. The mercury drop is almost a perfect sphere. The water drop is a flattened sphere. The naphtha, however, spreads out over the surface. What do these observations tell you about the cohesive forces in mercury, water, and naphtha?

2. Based on the observations in Question 1, which liquid would vaporize easiest? Which would have the lowest boiling point? Explain.

3. In what way are gases and plasmas similar? In what way are they different?

4. The density of carbon tetrachloride is 1.6×10^3 kg/m^3. Steel ($\beta = 9.0 \times 10^3$ kg/m^3) would sink in both water and carbon tetrachloride. Which liquid would exert a greater buoyant force? Explain.

5. A candle is made by pouring candle wax or paraffin into a mold. Unless care is taken, the top surface of the finished candle will be concave or curved inward. Explain.

6. You can easily tear a piece of aluminum foil. Describe what happens on a microscopic level when you tear the foil.

7. Equal volumes of water were heated in two narrow tubes, identical except that tube A was made of soft glass and tube B was made of Pyrex glass. As the temperature increased, the water level rose higher in tube B than in tube A. Give a possible explanation for this observation. Why are many cooking utensils made from Pyrex glass?

8. Describe how the density of water depends on temperature.

9. Some of the mercury atoms in a fluorescent lamp are in the gaseous form; others are in the form of plasma. How can you distinguish between the two?

10. Canteens are often covered with a canvas bag. If you wet the bag, the water in the canteen will be cooled. Explain.

11. Alcohol evaporates more quickly than water at the same temperature. What does this observation allow you to conclude about the properties

of the particles in the two liquids?

12. Why does high humidity make a hot day more uncomfortable?

APPLYING CONCEPTS

1. A razor blade, which has a density greater than that of water, can be made to float on water.
   a. What procedures must you follow for this to happen?
   b. Explain why it happens.
2. Suppose you use a punch to make a hole in aluminum foil. If you heat the foil, will the size of the hole decrease or increase? Explain. (Hint: Pretend you put the circle you punched out back into the hole. What happens when you heat the foil now?)
3. Suppose you pour boiling water into a glass bowl. Why would a bowl made of thick glass be more likely to break than one made of thin glass?
4. A machinist makes a steel ring that cannot quite be placed over an aluminum rod. He then heats the ring and slips it over the rod. Would he ever be able to separate the two without cutting them apart? Explain.
5. A pendulum of a grandfather clock is made of brass. At 21°C its period is 1.00 s. The house owners go on vacation for two weeks. While they are gone, the average temperature of the house is 11°C. Will the clock be fast or slow when they return? Explain.
6. Often before a thunderstorm, when the humidity is quite high, someone will say, "The air is very heavy today." Is this statement correct? Describe a possible origin for the statement.
7. Does Archimedes' principle apply in a spaceship in freefall?

EXERCISES

1. In a small machine shop, a hydraulic lift is used to raise heavy equipment for repairs and maintenance. The system has a small piston with a cross-sectional area of 7.0×10^{-2} m² and a large piston with a cross-sectional area of 2.1×10^{-1} m². An engine weighing 2.7×10^3 N is resting on the larger piston.

   a. What force must be applied to the small piston in order to lift the engine?
   b. If the engine rises 0.20 m, how far does the smaller piston move?
2. During an ecology experiment, an aquarium filled with water is placed on a scale. The scale reads 195 N.
   a. A rock weighing 8 N is added to the aquarium. If the rock sinks to the bottom of the aquarium, what will the scale read?
   b. The rock is removed from the aquarium and the amount of water is adjusted until the scale again reads 195 N. A small fish weighing 2 N is added to the aquarium. What is the scale reading while the fish is swimming in the aquarium?
3. What is the weight of a rock submerged in water if the rock weighs 54 N in air and has a volume of 2.3×10^{-3} m³?
4. If the rock in Exercise 3 is submerged in a liquid with a density exactly twice that of water, what will be its weight reading in the liquid?
5. What is the acceleration of a small metal sphere as it falls through water? The sphere weighs 2.8×10^{-1} N in air and has a volume of 13 cm³.
6. What is the maximum weight a helium-filled balloon with a volume of 1.00 m³ can lift in air? Assume the density of air is 1.20 kg/m³ and that of helium is 0.177 kg/m³.
7. What is the change in length of a 2.00-m length of copper pipe if its temperature is raised from 23°C to 978°C? The coefficient of linear expansion for copper is 1.66×10^{-5}°C^{-1}.
8. A 75-kg solid cylinder 2.5 m long and with an end radius of 5.0 cm stands on one end. How much pressure does it exert?
9. A reservoir behind a dam is 15 m deep. What is the pressure at a. the base of the dam? b. 5.0 m from the top of the dam?
10. A test tube standing vertically in a test tube rack contains 2.5 cm of oil ($\rho = 0.81$ g/cm³) and 6.5 cm of water. What is the pressure on the bottom of the tube?

PROBLEMS

1. A hydraulic jack used to lift cars is called a "3-ton

jack." The large piston is 22 mm in diameter, the small one 6.3 mm. Assume that a force of three tons is 3.0×10^4 N.

   a. What force must be exerted on the small piston to lift the three ton weight?

   b. Most jacks use a lever to reduce the force needed on the small piston. If the resistance arm is 3.0 cm, how long is the effort arm of an ideal lever to reduce the force to 100 N?

2. Bridge builders often use rivets that are larger than the rivet hole to make the joint tighter. The rivet is cooled before it is put into the hole. A builder drills a hole 1.2230 cm in diameter for a steel rivet 1.2250 cm in diameter. To what temperature must the rivet be cooled if it is to fit into the rivet hole that is at 20°C?

3. A steel tank is built to hold alcohol. The tank is 2.000 m in diameter and 5.000 m high. It is completely filled with alcohol at 10°C. If the temperature rises to 40°C, how much alcohol (in liters) will flow out of the tank? Remember that both the tank and the alcohol expand as the temperature rises.

4. An aluminum sphere is heated from 11°C to 580°C. If the volume of the sphere was 1.78 cm³ at 10°C, what is the increase in volume of the sphere at 580°C?

5. The volume of a copper sphere is 2.56 cm³ after being heated from 12°C to 984°C. What was the volume of the copper sphere at 12°C?

6. A metal object is suspended from a spring scale. The scale reads 920 N when the object is suspended in air, and 750 N when the object is completely immersed in water.

   a. Draw a diagram showing the three forces acting on the submerged object.

   b. Find the volume of the object.

   c. Find the density of the metal.

READINGS

Beasley, Malcolm, "Superconducting Materials." *Physics Today*, October, 1984.

Gosline, John, "Jet-Propelled Swimming in Liquids." *Scientific American*, January, 1985.

Overbye, Dennis, "Spacelab: Doing Science in Orbit." *Discover*, February, 1984.

White, Stuart, "Solar Design—The Last 12 Years." *Mechanix Illustrated*, September, 1984.

William, Peter, *Second Law*, Scientific American Books, New York, NY, 1984.

CHAPTER 15

Waves and Energy Transfer

GOALS

1. You will become familiar with the properties of waves.
2. You will learn how waves transfer energy.
3. You will gain an understanding of how waves can interact with each other.

For Your Information

Mach's Principle
  Every statement in physics has to state relations between observable quantities.
                              —Ernst Mach

Energy can be transferred by particles or by waves.

Mechanical waves need a medium.

Occasionally a giant storm erupts on the sun, and swarms of particles are ejected. Obeying Newton's laws of motion, some days later they reach Earth. When they bombard Earth's atmosphere, they produce beautiful displays of the Northern Lights, but they also disrupt television, radio, and even telephone signals. These particles are an example of energy transferred from sun to Earth.

How do we know the particles are coming? Scientists who observe the sun see the storms by studying sunlight. Light, as we shall see, is a type of wave. Light from the sun reaches Earth in only eight minutes. The light carries something more important than information about solar storms, it carries the energy that makes life on Earth possible. The energy causes plants to grow, produces winds and rains, and even raises waves on lakes and oceans.

Water waves, sound waves, radio waves, and light waves are very different. Yet they all carry energy, and all have many characteristics in common. In this chapter we will study the behavior of all waves. In later chapters the specific properties of sound and light waves will be explored.

15:1 Types of Waves

Water waves, sound waves, and the waves that travel along a spring or rope are mechanical waves. Mechanical wave motion requires a material medium. Water, air, and springs or ropes are the materials that carry the energy of these mechanical waves. Newton's laws govern the motion of mechanical waves.

To the Same Drummer

The following event was described recently in a local newspaper. On the way to attend a weekend football game, thousands of pedestrians jammed the Roebling suspension bridge over the Ohio River. As the close-packed crowd slowly shuffled across the bridge, it began swaying rhythmically with a displacement of about one meter. Many people feared they would be thrown from the bridge into the river below. Explain what happened on the bridge.

251

FIGURE 15–1. Electromagnetic waves, such as those producing radar images, need no medium for travel.

For Your Information

For Your Information

In a transverse wave, particles vibrate at right angles to the direction of the wave.

In a longitudinal wave, particles vibrate parallel to the wave direction.

SUGGESTION: Show that the medium does not move by putting a small piece of cork in a ripple tank and making some waves. The cork bobs up and down as a fishing bob does.

Light waves, radio waves, and X rays are examples of electromagnetic waves. No medium is needed for the motion of electromagnetic waves. They all travel through space at the speed of light, 299 792 458 m/s. The details of electromagnetic waves cannot be observed directly. Thus, we will use the easily observed mechanical waves as models for the behavior of electromagnetic waves that will be studied in later chapters.

There is a third type of wave, the matter wave. Electrons and other particles show wave-like behavior under certain conditions. Quantum mechanics is needed to describe the properties of matter waves. We will delay our study of matter waves until Chapter 28.

Mechanical waves can be classified by the way in which they displace the medium through which they travel. There are three general types of mechanical waves—transverse waves, longitudinal waves, and surface waves. A **transverse wave** causes the particles of the medium to vibrate perpendicularly to the direction of motion of the wave. Figure 15–2a shows a transverse wave. The wave moves along the spring. The spring is displaced up and down, at right angles to the motion of the wave. Waves in piano and guitar strings are examples of transverse waves.

A **longitudinal wave** causes the particles of a medium to move parallel to the direction of the wave. Figure 15–2b shows a longitudinal wave. The displacement of the spring is parallel to the motion of the wave. A sound wave is an example of a longitudinal wave. Fluids—either liquids or gases—transmit only longitudinal waves.

Although waves deep in a lake or ocean are longitudinal, at the surface of the water, the particles move both parallel and perpendicular to the direction of the wave. These are **surface waves,** a mixture of transverse and longitudinal waves.

Even though the particles of a medium move in response to a passing wave, they do not move along with the wave. For example, after a trans-

a

b

verse wave passes through the spring shown in Figure 15–2a, each coil is in the same position as before the wave arrived. Even though the huge waves may crash on a beach as the result of a distant storm, the water in the waves remains near the beach.

How are waves produced? Suppose you hold one end of a rope and tie the other end to a wall. If you suddenly jerk the rope to one side and quickly return it to the center, a pulse will travel down the rope. A **wave pulse** is a single disturbance that travels through a medium. A given point on the rope was at rest before the pulse reached it. It returned to rest after the pulse passed. If instead you move the rope from side to side in a regular manner, a **traveling wave** will move along the rope. A source that is vibrating with simple harmonic motion will produce a continuous traveling wave. Each point on the rope will vibrate regularly in response to the traveling wave.

FIGURE 15–2. Two general types of waves are the transverse wave (a) and the longitudinal wave (b).

DEMONSTRATION: See Teacher Guide.

A pulse is a single disturbance in a medium.

A wave is a series of pulses at regular intervals.

FIGURE 15–3. Water waves are examples of surface waves.

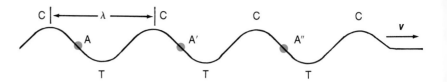

15:2 Frequency, Wavelength, and Velocity

Imagine putting a piece of tape at one spot on the rope. How does that piece of tape move in time? Figure 15–4 shows that the position of the tape repeats itself at regular time intervals. The **crests,** C, are the high points of each wave motion; the **troughs,** T, are the low points. The shortest time interval during which the motion repeats itself is called the **period,** T. The time between successive crests is one period. In the figure, the period is 2.5 seconds.

Points that are in phase move in the same direction at the same time. Two points that are a whole number of wavelengths apart are in phase.

The **frequency** of a wave, f, is the number of complete vibrations per second of any one point on a wave. Frequency is measured in hertz. One hertz (Hz) is one vibration per second. The frequency and period of a wave are related by the equation

Frequency is the number of waves that pass a given point per unit time.

SUGGESTION: The unit Hertz is named after Heinrich Hertz, who demonstrated radio waves in 1886.

$$f = \frac{1}{T} \text{ or } T = \frac{1}{f}$$

That is, they are reciprocals of each other.

The period of a wave is the reciprocal of its frequency.

EXAMPLE

Period of a Wave

This is the frequency of "middle C."

A sound wave has a frequency of 262 hertz. What is the time between successive wave crests?

Given: $f = 262$ Hz   **Unknown:** period (T)

$$\text{Basic equation: } T = \frac{1}{f}$$

Solution: $T = \dfrac{1}{f} = \dfrac{1}{262 \text{ Hz}} = 0.00382 \text{ s} = 3.82 \text{ ms}$

Wavelength is the horizontal distance between corresponding points on consecutive waves.

From Figure 15–4 you can see that the form of the wave repeats itself at regular distances. The shortest distance between points where the wave pattern repeats itself is called the **wavelength.** Each crest is one wavelength from the next crest. Troughs are also spaced by one wavelength. The Greek letter lambda, λ, represents the wavelength.

How fast does a traveling wave move? You could run alongside the wave just fast enough so that the wave appears to stand still. An easier way is to take two photographs a known time interval apart. Figure 15–5 shows two photographs taken one second apart. During the time interval, the crests moved 0.8 m to the right. The velocity of any object is the distance moved divided by the time interval. Thus the wave velocity is 0.8 m/s to the right. If the time interval were one period, the wave would

a

b

move a distance of one wavelength. Thus the velocity can be calculated from the equation

$$v = \frac{\lambda}{T}$$

This is more conveniently written as

$$\boxed{v = f\lambda}$$

EXAMPLE

Velocity of a Traveling Wave

A sound wave with frequency 262 Hz has a wavelength of 1.29 m. What is the velocity of the sound wave?

Given: frequency f = 262 Hz   **Unknown:** velocity (v)
        wavelength λ = 1.29 m   **Basic equation:** $v = f\lambda$

Solution: $v = f\lambda$
        = (262 Hz)(1.29 m) = 338 m/s

Practice Exercises

1. A sound wave produced by a clock chime 515 m away is heard 1.50 seconds later.
   a. What is the speed of sound in air?
   b. The sound wave has a frequency of 436 Hz. What is its period?
   c. What is its wavelength?
2. A hiker shouts toward a vertical cliff 685 m away. The echo is heard 4.0 s later.
   a. What is the speed of sound in air?
   b. The wavelength of the sound is 0.750 m. What is its frequency?
   c. What is the period of the wave?
3. A radio wave (a form of electromagnetic wave) has a frequency of 99.5 MHz (99.5 × 10⁶ Hz). What is its wavelength?
4. A typical light wave has a wavelength of 580 nm.
   a. What is the wavelength of the light in meters?
   b. What is the frequency of the wave?

FIGURE 15–5. The two photographs were taken 1 s apart. During that time the crest moved 0.8 m. The velocity of the wave is 0.8 m/s.

The velocity of a wave can be found from the product of its frequency and wavelength.

SUGGESTION: The basic equation $v = \lambda f$ will also be used for optics and quantum theory calculations.

SUGGESTION: Have students calculate the carrier wavelength of their favorite radio station.

The speed of sound in air depends on the temperature; not all problems or exercises use the same value.

15:3 Amplitude of a Wave

Two waves with the same frequency can differ in another way. A rope can be shaken forcefully or gently; a sound can be loud or soft. A water wave can be a giant tidal wave or a gentle ripple. The stronger the wave, the greater its amplitude. The **amplitude** of a wave is its maximum displacement from the rest or equilibrium position. The two waves in Figure 15–6 have the same frequency, velocity, and wavelength, but their amplitudes differ.

In order to produce a wave with larger amplitude, more work has to be done. For example, strong winds produce larger water waves than gentle breezes. A wave with larger amplitude transfers more energy. A small

The amplitude of a wave is its maximum displacement from rest position.

The energy content of a wave depends on its amplitude.

FIGURE 15–6. The relationship of the amplitude of a wave to the work it can perform is shown here. The greater the work done to create the wave, the greater the amplitude of the wave. The greater the amplitude of the wave, the more work it can do. Waves transfer energy.

DEMONSTRATION: See Teacher Guide.

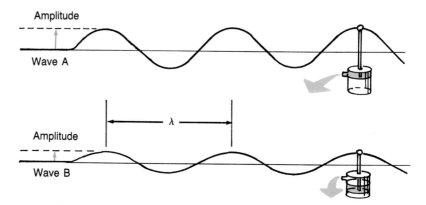

wave might move sand on a beach back and forth. When a giant wave crashes on a beach, however, it can uproot trees or move heavy boulders. It can be shown that the rate at which energy is carried by a wave is proportional to the square of the amplitude of the wave. Thus if you double the amplitude of the wave, you increase the energy it transfers per unit time by a factor of four.

SUGGESTION: A sound wave with a large amplitude is a loud sound.

For Your Information

Measurements made with wave dynamometers have shown that some breaking ocean waves strike with a force equal to a pressure of 6000 pounds per square foot. A four-foot swell moving along a hundred-mile front would supply energy to a city the size of Seattle for almost twenty-four hours.

FIGURE 15–7. Wave B has a wavelength that is one half the wavelength of A. The frequency of B is twice that of A. Waves A and B are traveling through the same medium so their speeds are the same.

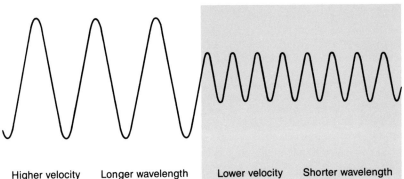

Higher velocity   Longer wavelength
Incident plus reflected waves

Lower velocity   Shorter wavelength
Transmitted wave

FIGURE 15–8. The speed and wave-length of a wave change when the wave enters a new medium. The left half of the figure shows the sum of the incident and reflected waves. The transmitted wave is on the right.

DEMONSTRATION: See Teacher Guide.

15:4 Wave Speed in a Medium

The speed of a mechanical wave does not depend on the amplitude or the frequency of the wave. It depends only on the properties of the medium. The speed of water waves depends on the depth of the water. The speed of waves in a rope depends on the tension on the rope and its mass per unit length. The speed of sound depends on the temperature of the air. Although a wave with larger amplitude transfers more energy, it moves at the same speed. A wave with higher frequency has a shorter wavelength, as given by the equation $v = f\lambda$. As long as the material is the same, the speed of high and low frequency waves is the same.

The speed of a wave depends on the medium.

The amplitude of a wave does not affect its wavelength, frequency, or velocity.

15:5 Reflection and Transmission of Waves at Boundaries

Often a wave moves from one medium to another. Light might move from air into water. In Figure 15–9, waves move in both large and small springs. The spring can end by being fastened to a rigid wall, as in Figure 15–10, or by being allowed to move freely, as in Figure 15–11. What happens to a wave when the medium changes?

Suppose a wave, called the incident wave, reaches the boundary of a medium. A wave with the same frequency continues on in the new

The velocity of a wave is higher in a more rigid medium.

FIGURE 15–9. A pulse reaching a boundary between two media (a) is partially reflected and partially transmitted (b).

a

b

a

b

FIGURE 15–10. A pulse is shown as it approaches a rigid wall (a) and as it is reflected from the wall (b). Notice that the amplitude of the reflected pulse is nearly equal to the amplitude of the incident pulse but that the reflected pulse is inverted.

SUGGESTION: Inverted reflected waves can be shown by attaching a Slinky to a rigid clamp. Erect reflected waves can be shown by attaching a short length of rubber hose to a clamp and then a Slinky to the hose.

For Your Information

In some materials the force that brings the particles displaced by a wave back to equilibrium is not proportional to the displacement (*i.e.*, the medium is not linear). In these media, the speed of a wave will depend on the frequency. Such a medium is called *dispersive*.

FIGURE 15–11. A pulse reflected from an open-ended boundary returns erect.

When a wave is reflected from a more rigid medium, the reflected portion is inverted.

medium. This wave is called the transmitted wave. In addition, a wave moves backward from the boundary in the old medium. This wave is called the reflected wave.

If the difference in the media is small, then the amplitude of the transmitted wave will be almost as large as that of the incident wave, and the amplitude of the reflected wave will be small. Most of the energy of the incident wave is transmitted. If the two materials are very different, however, most of the wave energy will be reflected.

Figure 15–10 shows a wave on a spring approaching a rigid wall. The spring and wall are very different from each other, so most of the energy of the wave is reflected. You can also see in the figure that the reflected wave

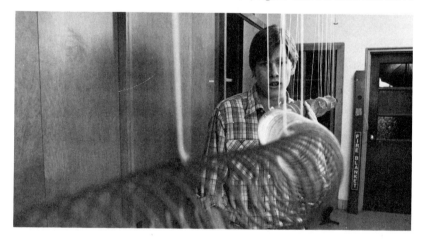

is inverted. The incident wave pulse was in the upward direction, the reflected pulse is in the downward direction. Whenever a wave passes from a less dense to a more dense medium, the reflected wave is inverted.

In Figure 15–11, the spring is supported by light threads. When a pulse reaches the end of the spring, the pulse is transmitted into another medium. The new medium is air. Because the two media are very different, most of the energy of the wave is reflected. In this case, however, the reflected wave is not inverted. When a wave passes from a more dense to a less dense medium, the reflected pulse is erect, not inverted.

Suppose a wave on a light spring is transmitted to a heavy spring. The wave in the light spring generated the wave in the heavy spring, so the frequencies of the two waves are the same. However, the speed of the wave in the heavier spring is slower. The speed, frequency, and wavelength of a wave are related by the equation $v = f\lambda$. Because the speed of the transmitted wave is different, but the frequency remains the same, the wavelength of the transmitted wave must also be different. The speed in the heavier spring is less, so the wavelength is smaller. For the same reason, if the speed of a wave increases when it passes into a new medium, then its wavelength also increases.

Although the waves in the examples are transverse waves, longitudinal waves behave in exactly the same way. Whenever a wave reaches a boundary, some of the wave energy is transmitted, some is reflected. The amount of reflected energy is larger if the two media have vastly different properties.

When a wave passes into a new medium, its speed changes.

The wave must have the same frequency in the new medium as in the old medium. Thus, the wavelength changes so that $v = f\lambda$.

When a wave travels from one medium to another, the wave is both reflected and transmitted.

Practice Exercises

5. A long spring runs across the floor of a room and out the door. A pulse is sent along the spring. After a few seconds, an inverted pulse returns. Is the spring attached to the wall in the next room or is it lying loose on the floor?

6. If you want to increase the wavelength of waves in a rope, should you shake it at a higher or lower frequency?

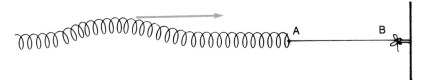

FIGURE 15–12. Use with Practice Exercise 7.

7. A pulse is sent along a spring. The spring is attached to a light thread that is tied to the wall, as in Figure 15–12.
   a. What happens when the pulse reaches point *A*?
   b. Is the pulse reflected from *A* erect or inverted?
   c. What happens when the transmitted pulse reaches *B*?
   d. Is the pulse reflected from *B* erect or inverted?

8. A pulse is sent along a thin rope that is attached to a thick rope. The thick rope is itself tied to a wall, as in Figure 15–13.
   a. What happens when the pulse reaches point *A*?
   b. Is the pulse reflected from *A* erect or inverted?
   c. What happens when the transmitted pulse reaches *B*?
   d. Is the pulse reflected from *B* erect or inverted?

FIGURE 15–13. Use with Practice Exercise 8.

15:6 Interference of Waves

What happens when two or more waves travel through a medium at the same time? Each wave affects the medium independently. As a result, we can analyze the effects of these waves using the principle of superposition. The **principle of superposition** states that *the displacement of a medium caused by two or more waves is the algebraic sum of the displacements caused by the individual waves.* The result of the superposition of two or more waves is called **interference.** A

When two or more waves meet, their displacements add. This process is called superposition.

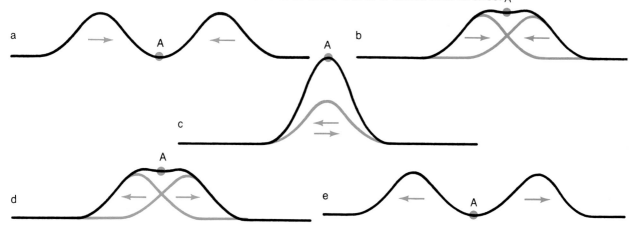

FIGURE 15–14. Constructive interference of two equal pulses. An antinode is a point of maximum displacement.

Constructive interference occurs when two pulses combine to produce a pulse of greater amplitude.

Destructive interference occurs when two pulses combine to produce a pulse with smaller amplitude than either of the original pulses.

FIGURE 15–15. Destructive interference of two equal pulses. A node is a point of the medium that remains undisturbed.

Interference can be either constructive or destructive. **Constructive interference** occurs when the wave displacements are in the same direction. The result is a wave with larger amplitude than any of the individual waves. Figure 15–14 shows the constructive interference of two equal pulses. When the two pulses meet, a larger pulse is formed. The amplitude of the larger pulse is the algebraic sum of the amplitudes of the two pulses. After the two pulses have passed through each other, they retain their original shape and size. The pulses are not changed by their interaction.

Figure 15–15 shows the **destructive interference** of two pulses with equal but opposite amplitudes. As the two pulses overlap, the displacement of the medium at each point in the overlap is reduced. When the pulses are at the same location, the displacement is zero. The pulses

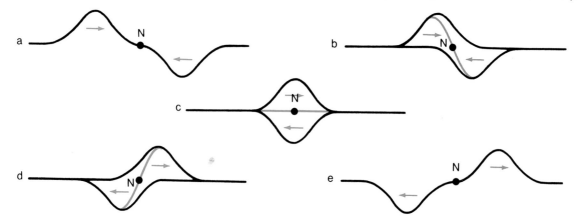

continue moving and resume their original form. An important characteristic of waves is their ability to pass through one another and not change.

If the pulses have unequal amplitudes, the destructive interference is not complete. The pulse at overlap is the algebraic sum of the two pulses. Some wave amplitude always remains.

15:7 Standing Waves

Look again at Figure 15–15. Two pulses with equal but opposite amplitudes meet. You can find one point in the medium that is completely undisturbed at all times. This point is called a **node.** At a node, the medium is never displaced. If you put your finger on the rope at the node, you would feel no motion. A node is produced by the destructive interference of waves.

In Figure 15–14, two pulses with equal amplitudes in the same direction meet. There is one point that undergoes the greatest displacement. Its maximum amplitude is equal to the sum of the amplitudes of the two pulses. This point of maximum displacement is called an **antinode.** Constructive interference of waves produces antinodes.

Imagine one end of a rope attached to a fixed point. You continuously vibrate the other end up and down. A traveling wave will leave your hand, move to the other end, be reflected, and return toward your hand. At your hand, the wave will be reflected again. At each reflection, the displacement direction will change. If the original displacement was upward, it will be downward when moving back to your hand, but be upward again after reflection from your hand.

Now, suppose you adjust the motion of your hand so that the period of the rope's vibration equals the time required for the wave to travel to the fixed point and back. The displacement your hand gives to the rope will add to the displacement of the reflected wave. The result is a very large amplitude oscillation in the rope, much larger than the motion of your hand. This large amplitude oscillation is an example of resonance. There are nodes at the ends of the rope and an antinode in the middle. The nodes and antinodes are stationary. The wave appears to be standing still. It is called a **standing wave.** If you double the frequency of vibration, you can produce additional nodes in the rope. It appears to vibrate in two segments. Further increases produce even more nodes, as in Figure 15–16.

After two pulses pass through one another, they return to their original shapes.

SUGGESTION: Point out that individual waves do not change when they pass through one another.

A node is a point in a medium that does not undergo a displacement as waves pass through each other in the medium.

An antinode is a point where the displacement caused by interfering waves is largest.

SUGGESTION: A wave machine can show nodes. A Slinky or a rope can show a standing wave. Standing waves are formed in most musical instruments. They were also produced in the Tacoma Narrows bridge, which was completed and collapsed in 1940.

A standing wave is the result of identical waves moving in opposite directions. The frequency and length of medium must be correctly chosen to make the nodes stationary.

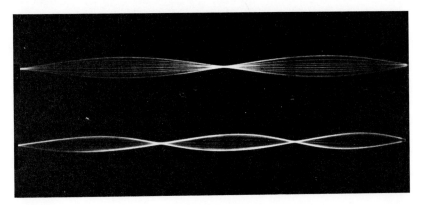

FIGURE 15–16. Interference produces standing waves in a string.

SUGGESTION: Call students'
attention to the fact that light is
reflected from mirrors and other shiny
surfaces. Sound is reflected and
produces echoes.

15:8 Reflection of Waves

The waves in the ropes and springs we have been studying move in only one dimension. Waves on the surface of water move in two dimensions, while sound and electromagnetic waves move in three dimensions. A ripple tank can be used to show the properties of two-dimensional waves. A ripple tank contains a thin layer of water. Vibrating boards produce wave pulses or traveling waves with constant frequency. A lamp above the tank produces shadows below the tank that show the locations of the waves. Figure 15–17 shows a wave pulse traveling toward a straight rigid wall, a barrier. The incident pulse moves upward. The reflected pulse moves toward the right.

FIGURE 15–17. Reflection of a plane wave pulse by a barrier (a). In (b), part of the pulse front is shown in time sequence as it approaches, and then is reflected from the barrier. The blue pulse front corresponds to the one shown in (a).

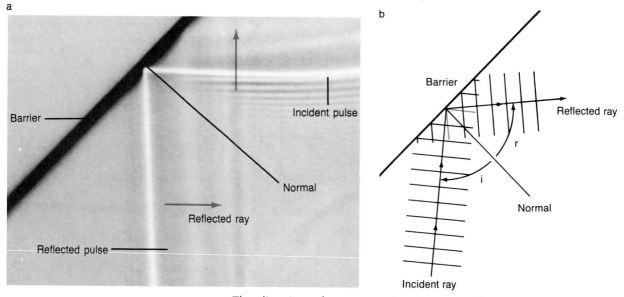

The direction of waves moving in two or three dimensions is often shown by ray diagrams. A ray is a line drawn at a right angle to the crest of the wave. A ray diagram shows only the direction of the waves, it does not show the actual waves. In Figure 15–17 the ray representing the incident ray is the arrow pointing upward. The ray representing the reflected ray points to the right.

The direction of the barrier is also shown by a line drawn at a right angle to it. This line is called the **normal.** The angle between the incident ray and the normal is called the **angle of incidence.** The angle between the normal and the reflected ray is called the **angle of reflection.**

The **law of reflection** states that *the angle of incidence is equal to the angle of reflection.*

The law of reflection states that the angle at which a wave approaches a barrier is equal to the angle at which the wave is reflected.

15:9 Refraction of Waves

A ripple tank can also be used to study the behavior of waves as they move from one medium into another. Figure 15–18 shows a glass plate placed in a ripple tank. The water above the plate is shallower than the water in the rest of the tank. The motion of water waves depends on the depth of the water, so the water above the plate acts like a different medium.

SUGGESTION: Refraction can be shown by placing a glass plate in a ripple tank so that it is at an angle to the oncoming wave.

How does the velocity of waves depend on water depth? In Figure 15–18a the edge of the plate is placed parallel to the wave fronts. The ray direction is parallel to the normal to the edge. As the waves move from deep to shallow water their wavelength decreases, but the direction of the waves does not change. Because the waves in the shallow water are generated by the waves in deep water, their frequency is not changed. From the equation $v = f\lambda$, the decrease in the wavelength of the waves means that the velocity is lower in the shallower water.

In Figure 15–18b the waves approach the glass plate at an angle. The ray direction is not parallel to the normal. Not only does the wavelength

SUGGESTION: Point out that refraction of light produces rainbows; allows vision to be corrected, and telescopes to be made.

FIGURE 15–18. Notice the change in wavelength (a) as the water waves enter a more shallow region (b). When waves enter at an angle they change direction, demonstrating refraction (c).

a Long   Transition   Short

b

c

decrease over the glass plate, but the direction of the waves changes. The change in the direction of waves at the boundary between two different media is known as **refraction.**

Refraction is the change of wave direction at the boundary between two media.

FIGURE 15–19. Waves bending around barriers demonstrate diffraction.

15:10 Diffraction and Interference of Waves

If particles are thrown at a barrier with holes in it, the particles will either reflect off the barrier or pass straight through the holes. When waves encounter a small hole in a barrier, however, they do not pass straight through. Rather, they bend around the edges of the barrier, forming circular waves that spread out, Figure 15–19. The spreading of waves around the edge of a barrier is called **diffraction.** Diffraction also occurs when waves meet a small obstacle. They can bend around the obstacle, producing waves behind it. The smaller the wavelength in comparison to the size of the obstacle, the less the diffraction.

Figure 15–20a shows the result of waves striking a barrier having two closely spaced holes. The waves are diffracted by each hole, forming circular waves. But the circular waves interfere with each other. There are regions of constructive interference where the resulting waves are large,

Diffraction is the bending of a wave around an object in its path.

and bands of destructive interference where the water remains almost undisturbed. Constructive interference occurs where wave crests or troughs from the two circular waves meet. The antinodes lie on lines called antinodal lines. These lines radiate from the barrier as shown in

FIGURE 15–20. Waves are diffracted at two openings in the barrier. At each opening, circular waves are formed. The circular waves interfere with each other, with points of constructive interference appearing as light colored dashes. Lines of constructive interference (antinodal lines) occur where crest meets crest.

Central
antinodal line

Figure 15–20. Between the antinodal lines are areas where a crest from one circular wave and a trough from the other meet. Destructive interference produces nodes where the water is undisturbed. The lines of nodes, or nodal lines, lie betwen adjacent antinodal lines.

PHYSICS FOCUS

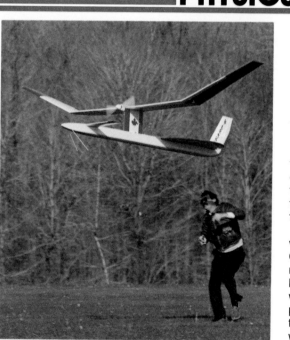

Microwave-Powered Aircraft

Imagine an aircraft that does not carry on-board fuel and can stay in flight for half a year. Or imagine spacecraft that could be placed in orbit using engines powered by microwave energy beams transmitted from Earth. This would allow large payloads to be lifted into space at a fraction of the current cost. Advances in microwave technology could bring both of these dreams to life.

Microwave energy beaming is much like radio-wave transmissions, except that it works with higher power levels. A transmitter sends out microwave energy, and a distant antenna and receiver pick it up and turn it into another form of energy, usually electricity. The waves have transferred energy without moving matter.

Research on the potential of microwave power is underway at NASA's Lewis Research Center in Cleveland, Ohio. Scientists are working on a Mars mission in which a mother ship orbiting the planet would transmit microwave beams to power a remote-controlled drone. The drone would fly down, land, and unload a rover to explore the planet's surface and collect samples. It is estimated that the drone could cover about 40 percent of Mars' surface without refueling.

SUMMARY

1. Waves transfer energy without the transfer of matter. **15:1**

2. Mechanical waves, such as sound waves and the waves on a rope, require a medium. Electromagnetic waves, such as light and radio waves, do not need a medium. **15:1**

3. In transverse waves the particles of the medium move perpendicularly to the direction of the wave. In longitudinal waves the particles move parallel to the wave direction. In surface waves the particles move both perpendicularly and parallel to the direction of the wave's motion. **15:1**

4. The frequency of a wave, f, is the number of vibrations per second of any one point on a wave. The period of a wave is the time interval between successive wave crests or troughs. **15:2**

5. The shortest distance between points where the wave pattern repeats itself is called the wavelength, λ. **15:2**

6. The velocity of a wave, the distance a point on the wave moves in a unit time interval, can be calculated from the equation $v = f\lambda$. **15:2**

7. The amplitude of a wave is its maximum displacement from the rest or equilibrium position. Energy transferred by a wave is proportional to the square of the amplitude. **15:3**

8. The speed of a wave depends on the properties of the medium through which the wave is moving. **15:4**

9. When waves reach the boundary between two media, they are partially transmitted and partially reflected. The amount reflected depends on how much the two media differ. **15:5**

10. When a wave moves from a less dense to a more dense medium, the reflected wave is inverted. When it moves from a more dense to a less dense medium, the reflected wave is erect. **15:5**

11. The principle of superposition states that the displacement of a medium due to two or more waves is the algebraic sum of the displacements caused by the individual waves. **15:6**

12. The result of the superposition of two or more waves on a medium is called interference. Interference does not affect the individual waves. **15:6**

13. Maximum destructive interference produces a node where there is no displacement. Maximum constructive interference results in an antinode, a location of the largest displacement. **15:6**

14. The nodes and antinodes of a standing wave are stationary. **15:7**

15. The law of reflection states that the angle of incidence is equal to the angle of reflection. Waves are reflected from a barrier at the same angle at which they approach it. **15:8**

16. The change in the direction of waves at the boundary between two different media is known as refraction. **15:9**

17. The spreading of waves around the edge of a barrier is called diffraction. **15:10**

QUESTIONS

1. How many general methods of energy transfer are there? Give two examples of each.

2. Distinguish between a mechanical wave and an electromagnetic wave.

3. How do transverse waves, longitudinal waves, and surface waves differ?

4. If a pulse is sent along a rope, how does the rope behave at any given point after the pulse has passed?

5. A pulse differs from a wave. How?

6. Distinguish among the wavelength, frequency, and period of a wave.

7. What is the amplitude of a wave and what does it measure?

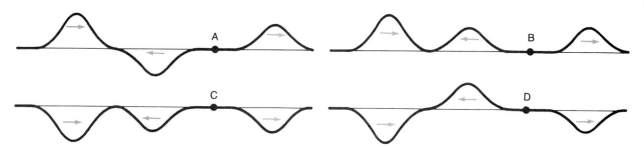

FIGURE 15–21. Use with Applying Concepts 8.

8. Waves are sent along a spring of fixed length. Can the speed of the waves in the spring be changed? How can the frequency of a wave in the spring be changed?

9. When a wave reaches the boundary of a new medium, part of the wave is reflected and part is transmitted. What determines the amount of reflection?

10. A pulse reaches the boundary of a medium more dense than the one from which it came. Is the reflected pulse erect or inverted?

11. A pulse reaches the boundary of a medium less dense than the one from which it came. Is the reflected pulse erect or inverted?

APPLYING CONCEPTS

1. How does wave frequency differ from wave velocity?

2. What is the difference between the speed of a transverse wave down a spring and the motion of one coil of the spring?

3. Suppose you hold a 1-meter metal bar in your hand. You hit its end with a hammer, first in a direction parallel to its length, second in a direction at right angles to its length. Describe the waves you produce in the two cases.

4. When a wave crosses a boundary between thin and thick rope, its wavelength and velocity change, but its frequency does not. Explain why the frequency is constant.

5. AM radio signals have wavelengths between 600 m and 200 m, while FM signals have wavelengths about 3 m. Explain why AM signals can often be heard behind hills while FM signals cannot.

6. You can make water slosh back and forth in a shallow pan only if you shake the pan with the correct frequency. Explain.

7. Is the energy lost when two waves interfere destructively? Explain.

8. In each of the four waves in Figure 15–21, the pulse on the left is moving toward the right. The center pulse is a reflected pulse; the pulse on the right is a transmitted pulse. Describe the relative rigidity of the boundaries at A and B, C and D.

9. Sonar is the detection of sound waves reflected off boundaries in water. A region of warm water in a cold lake can produce a reflection, as can the bottom of the lake. Which would you expect to produce the stronger echo? Explain.

10. If a string is vibrating in four segments, there are places it can be touched without disturbing its motion. Explain. How many places exist?

11. A metal plate is held fixed in the center and sprinkled with sugar. Using a violin bow, the plate is stroked along one edge and made to vibrate. The sugar begins to collect in certain areas and move away from others. Describe these regions in terms of standing waves.

EXERCISES

1. An ocean wave has a length of 10.0 m. A wave passes by every 2.0 s. What is the speed of the wave?

2. Water waves in a shallow dish are 6.0 cm long. At one point the water oscillates up and down at a rate of 4.8 oscillations per second.
   a. What is the speed of the water waves?
   b. What is the period of the water waves?

3. Water waves in a lake travel 4.4 m in 1.8 seconds. The period of oscillation is 1.2 seconds.

a. What is the speed of the water waves?

b. What is their wavelength?

4. The frequency of yellow light is 5.0×10^{14} Hz. Find its wavelength.

5. A sonar signal of frequency 1.00×10^6 Hz has a wavelength of 1.50 mm in water.

a. What is the speed of the signal in water?

b. What is its period in water?

c. What is its period in air?

6. The time needed for a water wave to change from the equilibrium level to the crest is 0.18 s. What is

a. the period of the wave?

b. the frequency of the wave?

7. If you slosh the water back and forth in a bathtub at the correct frequency, the water rises first at one end and then at the other. Suppose you can make a standing wave in a 150-cm-long tub with a frequency of 0.30 Hz. What is the velocity of the water wave?

8. A sound wave of wavelength 0.70 m and velocity 330 m/s is produced for 0.50 s.

a. What is the frequency of the wave?

b. How many complete waves are emitted in this time interval?

c. After 0.50 s, how far is the front wave from the source of the sound?

9. Sketch the shape of each as the two wave pulses are superpositioned.

PROBLEMS

1. A group of swimmers is resting in the sun on an off-shore raft. They estimate that 3 meters separate a trough and an adjacent crest of surface waves on the lake. They time the crests that pass by the raft and count 14 passing in 20 seconds. How fast are the waves moving?

2. AM radio signals are broadcast at frequencies between 550 kHz and 1600 kHz (kilohertz) and travel 3.0×10^8 m/s.

a. What is the range of wavelengths for these signals?

b. FM frequencies range between 88 MHz and 108 MHz (megahertz) and travel at the same speed. What is the range of FM wavelengths?

3. The speed of sound in water is 1498 m/s. A sonar signal is sent from a ship at a point just below the water surface and 1.80 s later the reflected signal is detected. How deep is the ocean beneath the ship?

4. The velocity of the transverse waves produced by an earthquake is 8.9 km/s, while that of the longitudinal waves is 5.1 km/s. A seismograph records the arrival of the transverse waves 73 seconds before that of the longitudinal waves. How far away was the earthquake?

5. The wavelength of the ripples in a certain groove 10 cm from the center of a 45 rpm phonograph record is 0.25 cm. When this part of the record is played, what will be the frequency of the sound produced?

6. Predicting the speed of a wave in a specific medium can often require complex mathematics. In general, the speed depends on the type of wave, the properties of the medium, and sometimes the frequency. The speed of a wave on a string is proportional to T, the tension in the string, and μ, the mass/unit length of the string.

$$v = \sqrt{\frac{T}{\mu}}$$

A piece of string 5.30 m long has a mass of 1.50 g. What must the tension in the string be to make the wavelength of a 125 Hz wave 60.0 cm?

READINGS

Berry, M. V., "The Geometric Phase." *Scientific American*, December, 1988.

Broad, William, "The Chaos Factor." *Science 83*, January, 1983.

Gilbert, Ray, "Springs: Distorted and Combined." *The Physics Teacher*, October, 1983.

Gilbert, S., "How a Wave Works." *Science Digest*, August, 1986.

Snow, John, "The Tornado." *Scientific American*, April, 1984.

Sound

GOALS

1. You will learn the properties of longitudinal waves.
2. You will gain a knowledge of the characteristics of sound.
3. You will gain an understanding of some of the applications of sound, including music.

For Your Information

Sound and music are important parts of the human experience. Primitive human beings made sounds not only with their voices, but also with drums, rattles, and whistles. Stringed instruments are at least 3000 years old. In the sixth century B.C., the Greek mathematician Pythagoras noted that when two strings had lengths in the ratio of small whole numbers, for example 2:1, 3:2, or 4:3, pleasing sounds resulted when the strings were plucked together. However, the physics of music did not develop until Marin Mersenne (1588–1648) and Robert Hooke (1635–1703) connected pitch with the frequency of vibration.

In the middle of the nineteenth century, a German physicist and an English physicist, Hermann Helmholtz and Lord Rayleigh, studied how the human voice as well as musical instruments produce sounds, and how the human ear detects these sounds. In the twentieth century, scientists and engineers have developed electronics that permit not only detailed study of sound, but the creation of new electronic musical instruments and recording devices that allow us to have music whenever and wherever we wish.

SUGGESTION: Emphasize that a sound wave is produced by a vibration. Show a tuning fork, a string vibrating, and a doorbell. Strike the tuning fork and put the tip in water. The water will splash because of the movement of the tuning fork.

16:1   Sound Waves

You have previously studied waves and simple harmonic motion. Sound is a longitudinal wave produced by the compression and rarefaction of matter.

Sound waves move through air because a vibrating source produces rhythmic variations in air pressure. The air molecules collide, transmitting

Bat Music

The method of navigation used by bats is called sound echolocation. Bats emit 30 to 50 sound pulses per second, each with a duration of 5 to 10 milliseconds, and then monitor the return pulses reflected off of objects in their path. Assume that a bat is approaching an insect. As the distance between them decreases, the frequency of the pulse reflected back to the bat from the insect increases. Why does this happen, and how is the echo different from the emitted sound.

FIGURE 16–1. Kepler's *Harmony of the Worlds* contained celestial music.

Saturnus   Jupiter   Mars fere   Terra

Venus   Mercurius   Hic locum habet etiam)

SUGGESTION: Have students compare the speed of sound with that of radio waves. In the same time light travels around Earth, sound travels about 42.5 m.

A sound wave is an oscillation in the pressure in the medium.

SUGGESTION: Sound travels about four times faster in water than in air and about eleven times as fast in steel. It is elasticity rather than density that affects the speed.

The speed of sound in air at room temperature is 343 m/s.

Sound cannot travel through a vacuum.

Sound waves can be reflected and diffracted, and can interfere.

In any wave, frequency, wavelength, and velocity are related by the equation $v = \lambda f$.

DEMONSTRATION: See Teacher Guide.

the pressure oscillations away from the source of the sound. The pressure of the air varies or oscillates about an average value, the mean air pressure. The frequency of the wave is the number of oscillations in pressure each second. Figure 16–2 shows the relationship between the displacement of the molecules and the air pressure in a sound wave. Sound is a longitudinal wave because the motion of the air molecules is parallel to the direction of motion of the wave.

The velocity of the sound wave depends on the temperature of the air. Sound waves move through air at a velocity of 343 m/s at room temperature (20°C). Sound can also travel through liquids and solids. In general, the velocity of sound is greater in solids and liquids than in gases. The molecules in liquids and solids are much closer together so the pressure variations are more rapidly transferred. Sound cannot travel through a vacuum because there are no particles to move and collide.

Sound waves share the properties of other waves. They can be reflected off hard objects, such as the walls of a room. Reflected sound waves are called echoes. Sound waves can also be diffracted, spreading outward after passing through narrow openings. Two sound waves can interfere, causing "dead spots" at nodes where little sound can be heard.

The wavelength of a sound wave is the distance between adjacent regions of maximum pressure. The frequency and wavelength of a wave are related to the velocity of the wave by the equation

$$v = f\lambda$$

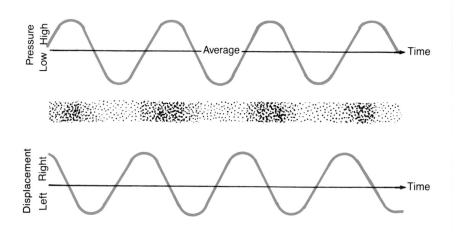

FIGURE 16–2. Graphic representation of the relationship between the displacement of molecules and the air pressure in a sound wave.

270   Sound

EXAMPLE

Determining the Wavelength of Sound

A sound wave has a frequency of 261.6 Hz. What is the wavelength of this sound traveling in air at 343 m/s?

Given: $f = 261.6$ Hz   **Unknown:** λ

$v = 343$ m/s   **Basic equation:** $v = f\lambda$

Solution: $v = f\lambda$

$$\lambda = \frac{v}{f}$$

$$\lambda = \frac{(343 \text{ m/s})}{(261.6 \text{ Hz})} = 1.31 \text{ m}$$

For Your Information

The speed of sound, known as Mach 1 after the Austrian physicist and philosopher Ernst Mach, is different at different heights. It is 760 mph at sea level, and reaches 660 mph at 36 000 feet.

Practice Exercises

1. Sound with a frequency of 261.6 Hz travels through water at a speed of 1435 m/s. Find its wavelength.

2. Find the frequency of a sound moving in air at room temperature with a wavelength of 0.667 m.

3. Sound with a frequency of 442 Hz travels through steel. A wavelength of 11.66 m is measured. Find the speed of the sound in steel.

4. The human ear can detect sounds with frequencies between 20 Hz and 16 kHz. Find the largest and smallest wavelengths the ear can detect, assuming the sound travels through air with a speed of 343 m/s at 20°C.

16:2 The Doppler Shift

Have you ever noticed the pitch of an ambulance, fire, or police siren as the vehicle sped past you? The frequency seems higher as the vehicle moves toward you, then suddenly drops and seems lower as it moves away. This effect is called the **Doppler shift.** The frequency of the sound source does not change, but when the source is moving toward the sound detector (Figure 16–3), more waves are crowded into the same space. The wavelength is shortened. Because the velocity is not changed, the frequency of the detected sound increases.

When the source is moving away from the detector, the wavelength is lengthened and the detected frequency is lower. The Doppler shift also occurs if the detector is moving and the source is stationary.

The Doppler shift occurs in all wave motion, both mechanical and electromagnetic. It has many applications. Radar detectors use the Doppler shift to measure the speed of baseballs and automobiles. Astronomers use the Doppler shift of light from distant galaxies to measure their speed and infer their distance. Physicians can detect the heartbeat of a fetus by means of the Doppler shift in ultrasound. Bats use the Doppler shift to detect and catch flying insects.

The Doppler shift is the change in the wavelength of sound emitted by a moving source.

SUGGESTION: Emphasize that the Doppler effect is a sudden drop in frequency. The frequency changes from a high pitch to a low pitch suddenly—not sliding.

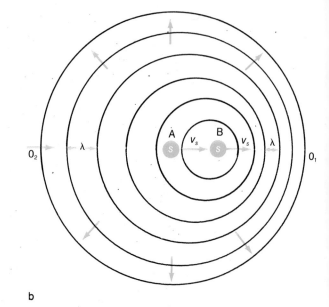

a

b

FIGURE 16–3. A point source moving across a ripple tank (a) can be used to show the Doppler Shift (b).

DEMONSTRATION: See Teacher Guide.

16:3 Pitch and Loudness

The wave characteristics of sound, such as frequency, wavelength, and amplitude, can be detected by the human ear. In this case they are described by a special set of names. **Pitch** is related to frequency. **Loudness,** or intensity, is a function of the amplitude of the wave.

While the pitch of a sound can be expressed in terms of its frequency, pitch can also be given the name of a note on a musical scale. Musical scales are based on the work of Pythagoras. Two notes with frequencies related by the ratio 2:1 are said to differ by an **octave.** For example, if one note has a frequency of 440 Hz, a note one octave higher has a frequency of 880 Hz. A note one octave lower has a frequency of 220 Hz. It is

FIGURE 16–4. The loudness heard at a concert depends on the response of our ears to sound in different frequency ranges.

important to recognize that it is the ratio of two frequencies, not the size of the interval between them, that determines the musical interval.

In other common musical intervals, the frequencies have ratios of small whole numbers. For example, the notes in an interval called a "major third" have a ratio of frequencies of 5:4. A typical major third are the notes C and E. The note C has a frequency of 262 Hz, so E has a frequency (5/4)(262 Hz) = 327 Hz. In the same way, notes in a "fourth" (C and F) have a frequency ratio of 4:3 and those in a "fifth" (C and G) have a ratio of 3:2.

The human ear is sensitive to an enormous variation in the intensity of sound. For instance, the intensity of a sound that causes pain is one trillion (10^{12}) times greater than the smallest sound that can be detected by the ear. Intensity is proportional to the square of the amplitude of the sound wave. Loudness, as measured by the human ear, is not directly proportional to the intensity of a sound. Instead, a sound with ten times the intensity of a given sound will only be perceived as twice as loud. To

For Your Information

Not all experiments are performed in a laboratory. Dutch meteorologist Cristoph H. D. Buys Ballot tested the Doppler shift for sound waves in 1845. As a moving source of sound, he used an orchestra of trumpeters standing in an open railroad car, racing back and forth through the Dutch countryside at different speeds. On the ground, musicians recorded the notes they heard as the train approached and as it left. The results supported the Doppler shift, a phenomenon explained by Christian Johann Doppler, an Austrian physicist.
—Steven Weinberg in *The First Three Minutes*

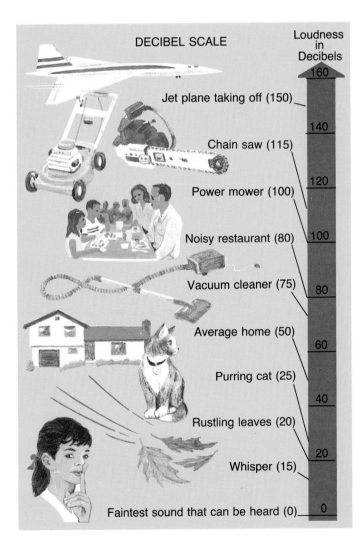

DECIBEL SCALE — Loudness in Decibels

Jet plane taking off (150)
Chain saw (115)
Power mower (100)
Noisy restaurant (80)
Vacuum cleaner (75)
Average home (50)
Purring cat (25)
Rustling leaves (20)
Whisper (15)
Faintest sound that can be heard (0)

160
140
120
100
80
60
40
20
0

FIGURE 16–5. The decibel scale measures relative loudness of sounds.

The intensity of sound waves is
measured in decibels (dB).

deal conveniently with the wide range of intensities, and the relationship between intensity and loudness, we often speak of a quantity called sound level. **Sound level** is measured in decibels (dB) and is a ratio of the intensity of a given sound wave to the intensity of the most faintly heard sound. Sound at the threshold of hearing is said to have a sound level of zero decibels (0 dB). A sound level with a 10 times larger intensity is 10 dB. An intensity 10 times larger than this, one hundred times as loud, is 20 dB. Figure 16–5 shows the sound level in decibels for a variety of sounds.

16:4 Sources of Sound

Sound is produced by a vibrating object. The vibrations of the object create molecular motions and pressure oscillations in the air. A loudspeaker has a diaphragm, or cone, that is made to vibrate by electrical currents. The cone creates the sound waves. Musical instruments such as gongs or cymbals and the surface of a drum are other examples of vibrating sources of sound.

SUGGESTION: The shape of sound
waves can be demonstrated by
attaching a microphone to an
oscilloscope.

Sound waves are produced by
vibrating objects.

The human voice is the result of vibrations of the vocal cords, two membranes located in the throat. Air from the lungs rushing through the throat starts the vocal cords vibrating. The frequency of vibration is controlled by the muscular tension placed on the cords.

Brass instruments, such as the trumpet, trombone, and tuba, produce their sounds as the result of vibrations of the lips of the performer. In this sense, the source of sound in a brass instrument is very similar to that of the voice. Reed instruments, like the clarinet, saxophone, and oboe, have a thin wooden strip, or reed, that vibrates as a result of air blown across it. In a flute, recorder, organ pipe, or whistle, air is blown across an opening in a pipe. Air moves in and out of the pipe at the frequency of the note. The vibration of the column of air in the instrument causes the sound.

The sound of a wind instrument is the
result of a vibrating column of air.

In stringed instruments, such as the piano, guitar, and violin, a wire or string is set into vibration. In the piano the wire is struck; in the guitar, it is plucked. In the violin, the friction of the bow pulls the string aside. The string is attached to a sounding board that vibrates with the string. The vibrations of the sounding board cause the pressure oscillations in the air

The sound of a stringed instrument is
the result of the vibration of a
sounding board.

FIGURE 16–6. The shapes of the mouthpieces of a brass instrument (a) and a reed instrument (b) determine the characteristics of the sound each instrument produces.

that we hear as sound. Electric guitars use electronic devices to detect and amplify the vibrations of the strings.

16:5 Resonance

If you have ever blown through the mouthpiece of a brass or reed instrument, you know that the vibration of your lips or the reed alone does not make a sound in any particular pitch. The long tube that makes up the instrument must be attached if music is to result. When the instrument is played, the air within this tube vibrates at the same frequency, or in resonance, with a particular vibration of the lips or reed. Remember that resonance is increasing the amplitude of a vibration by repeatedly applying a small external force at the same frequency. The pitch of an instrument is varied by changing the length of the resonating column of vibrating air. The length of the air column controls the resonant frequency of the vibrating air. The mouthpiece creates a mixture of different frequencies. The resonating air column acting on the vibrating lips or reed amplifies a single note.

To understand resonance in an air column, consider a tuning fork above a hollow tube. The tube is placed in water so that the bottom end of the tube is below the water surface. The length of the air column is adjusted by changing the height of the tube above the water. The tuning fork is struck with a rubber hammer. When the length of the air column is varied, the sound of the fork will alternately become louder and softer. The sound is loud when the air column is in resonance with the tuning fork. The air column has intensified the sound of the tuning fork.

Consider the effect of the vibrating tuning fork on the molecules in the air. The molecules are struck by the fork and produce a sound wave that moves down the air column. When the wave hits the water surface, it is reflected back up to the tuning fork. If the reflected wave is at the same point in its oscillation as the wave leaving the tuning fork, the motions of

FIGURE 16-8. An example showing resonance of an air column.

Hammer

Tuning fork

Air column

Water

a

¼ λ

First resonant length

¾ λ

Second resonant length

5/4 λ

Third resonant length

b

Tuning fork

Glass tube

λ/2

Saw dust

FIGURE 16–9. Standing waves are produced in closed pipes (a). Standing waves deposit tiny mounds of sawdust at half-wavelength intervals in a closed pipe or tube (b).

In a standing wave, the separation between two nodes (or antinodes) is one-half wavelength.

A closed pipe resonates when its length is λ/4, 3λ/4, 5λ/4, ...

SUGGESTION: Pieces of plastic water pipe and golf club tubes can be used to demonstrate closed and open pipes. A string vibrator is very helpful in demonstrating nodes and antinodes.

the leaving and returning waves will reinforce each other. A **standing wave** is produced.

In a standing wave, the motion of air molecules has nodes and antinodes. Nodes occur where the normal motion of the molecules is not disturbed. Antinodes occur where the molecules have their maximum forward or backward displacements. Two antinodes (or two nodes) are separated by one-half wavelength. There is an antinode at the tuning fork. The surface of the water stops the motion of the molecules, producing a node at that location.

The shortest column of air that can have a node at the bottom and an antinode at the top is one-fourth wavelength long. As the air column is lengthened, additional resonances are found. Thus columns λ/4, 3λ/4, 5λ/4, 7λ/4, and so on will all be in resonance with the tuning fork.

In practice the first resonance length is slightly longer than one-fourth wavelength. This is caused by the gap between the tuning fork and the tube. However, each additional resonance length is spaced by exactly one-half wavelength. Measurement of the spacings between resonances can be used to find the velocity of sound in air.

Have you ever put your ear to a large seashell and heard a low frequency sound? The shell acts like a closed pipe resonator. The source of the sound is the soft background noise that occurs almost everywhere. This sound contains almost all frequencies the ear can hear. The shell increases the intensity of sounds with frequency equal to the resonant frequency of the shell. The result is the almost pure tone we hear.

The small size of the vibrating string of a guitar or other stringed instrument cannot cause much vibration in the air. The instrument uses resonance to increase the sound intensity. Vibration of the string causes the sounding box to vibrate. The large size of the box produces a more intense sound in the air around it.

EXAMPLE

Measuring Sound

A tuning fork with a frequency of 392 Hz is found to cause resonances in an air column spaced by 44.3 cm. The air temperature is 27°C. Find the velocity of sound in air at that temperature.

Given: f = 392 Hz   **Unknown:** v

ℓ = 44.3 cm   **Basic equation:** $v = f\lambda$

Solution: Resonances are spaced by one-half wavelength.

$$\ell = \frac{\lambda}{2},$$

or $\lambda = 2\ell = (2)(0.443 \text{ m}) = 0.886 \text{ m}$

Thus, $v = f\lambda$

$= f(2\ell)$

$= (392 \text{ Hz})(0.886 \text{ m})$

$= 347 \text{ m/s}$

Practice Exercises

5. A 440-Hz tuning fork is held above a closed pipe. Find the spacings between the resonances when the air temperature is 20°C.

6. The 440-Hz tuning fork is used with a resonating column to determine the velocity of sound in helium gas. If the spacings between resonances are 110 cm, what is the velocity of sound in He?

7. The frequency of a tuning fork is unknown. A student uses an air column at 27°C and finds resonances spaced by 39.2 cm. What is the frequency of the tuning fork?

An open pipe will also resonate with a sound source. A sound wave will obviously reflect from the closed end of a pipe, but why does it reflect from an open end? Remember that whenever the medium through which a wave moves changes, there is some reflection and some transmission. When the wave reaches the open end of the tube, some of the wave is transmitted. We can hear the transmitted sound. The remainder is reflected to form a standing wave. Sound transmission is easier in open air, so there is an antinode at the open end of the tube. Thus the minimum length of a resonating open pipe is one-half wavelength. If open and closed pipes of the same length are used as resonators, the wavelength of the resonant sound for the open pipe will be half as long. Therefore the frequency will be twice as high for the open pipe as for the closed pipe. The resonances in the open pipe are spaced by half wavelengths just as in closed pipes. Have you ever shouted into a long tunnel or underpass? The booming sound you hear is the tube acting as a resonator. Many musical instruments are also open pipe resonators. Some examples are the saxophone and the flute.

An open pipe resonates if its length is $\lambda/2$, $2\lambda/2$, $3\lambda/2$, ...

FIGURE 16–10. The normal modes of oscillation of an open tube show the fundamental and the second harmonic.

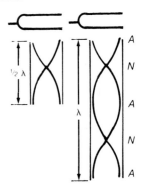

Practice Exercises

8. A bugle can by treated as an open pipe. If a bugle were straightened out, it would be 2.65 m long. If the speed of sound is 343 m/s, find the lowest frequency that is resonant in a bugle.

9. A soprano saxophone is an open pipe. If all keys are closed, it is approximately 65 cm long. Using 343 m/s as the speed of sound, find the lowest frequency that can be played on this instrument.

16:6 Detection of Sound

A sound detector converts the energy of a sound wave into a different form of energy.

Sound detectors convert sound energy—kinetic energy of the air molecules—into another form of energy. In a sound detector, a diaphragm vibrates at the frequency of the sound wave. The vibration of the diaphragm is then converted into another form of energy. A microphone is an electronic device that converts sound energy into electrical energy. It is discussed in Chapter 26.

DEMONSTRATION: See Teacher Guide.

The ear is an amazing sound detector. Not only can it detect sound waves over a very wide range of frequencies, it is also sensitive to an enormous range of sound intensities. In addition, human hearing can distinguish many different qualities of sound. The ear is a complex detector that requires knowledge of both physics and biology to understand. The interpretation of sounds by the brain is even more complex and not totally understood.

The ear consists of the outer, middle, and inner ear. In the inner ear, sound waves stimulate nerves.

The ear (Figure 16–11) is divided into three parts: the outer, middle, and inner ear. The outer ear consists of the fleshy, visible part of the ear called the pinna, which collects sound; the auditory canal; and the eardrum. Sound waves cause vibrations in the eardrum. The middle ear consists of three tiny bones in an air-filled space in the skull. The bones transmit the vibrations of the eardrum to the oval window on the inner

SUGGESTION: Try to borrow a model or a poster showing parts of the ear.

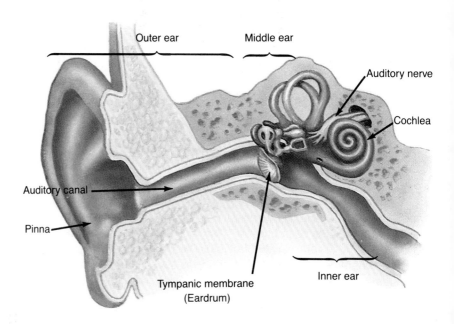

FIGURE 16–11. The human ear is a complex sense organ that translates sound vibrations into nerve impulses that are then sent to the brain for interpretation.

ear. The inner ear is filled with a watery liquid. Sound vibrations are transmitted through the liquid into sensitive portions of the spiral-shaped cochlea. In the cochlea tiny hair cells are vibrated by the waves. Vibrations of these cells stimulate nerve fibers that lead to the brain, producing the sensation of sound.

The ear is not equally sensitive to all frequencies. Most people cannot hear sounds with frequencies below 20 Hz or above 16 000 Hz. In general, people are most sensitive to sounds with frequencies between 1000 Hz and 5000 Hz. Older people are less sensitive to frequencies above 10 000 Hz than are young people. Exposure to loud sounds, either noise or music, has been shown to cause the ear to lose its sensitivity, especially to high pitched sounds.

16:7 The Quality of Sound

Musical instruments sound very different from one another, even when playing the same note. This is true because most sounds are made up of a number of frequencies. The quality of a sound depends on the relative intensities of these frequencies. In music, sound quality is called **timbre** (ᴛᴏᴍ bur) or sometimes "tone color."

The quality of sound is called timbre.

When two waves of the same frequency arrive at the ear or another sound detector, the detector senses the sum of the amplitudes of the waves. If the waves are of slightly different frequencies, the sum of the two waves has an amplitude that oscillates in intensity. A listener hears a pulsing variation in loudness. This oscillation of wave amplitude is called a **beat** (Figure 16–12). The frequency of the beat is the difference in the frequencies of the two waves. Musical instruments in an orchestra are often tuned by sounding them against a standard note, and then adjusting them until the beat disappears. This technique is also used by piano tuners.

Two waves of slightly different frequencies produce beat notes.

SUGGESTION: Have students bring in instruments to show beats, consonance, dissonance, and overtones.

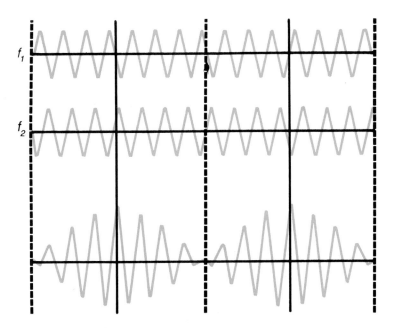

FIGURE 16–12. Beats occur as a result of the superposition of two sound waves of slightly different frequencies.

EXAMPLE

Beats

A 442-Hz tuning fork and a 444-Hz tuning fork are struck simultaneously. What beat frequency will be produced?

Solution: The beat frequency is 444 Hz − 442 Hz, or 2 Hz.

The human ear can detect beat frequencies as high as 7 Hz. When two waves differ by more than 7 Hz, the ear detects a complex wave. If the resulting sound is unpleasant, the result is called a **dissonance.** If the sound is pleasant, the result is a **consonance,** or a chord. As discovered by Pythagoras, consonances occur when the wave frequencies have ratios that are small whole numbers. Figure 16–13 shows the waves that result when sound waves have frequencies with ratios of 2:1 (octave), 3:2 (fifth), 4:3 (fourth), and 5:4 (major third).

FIGURE 16–13. Time graphs showing the superposition of two waves having the ratios of 2:1, 3:2, 4:3, and 5:4.

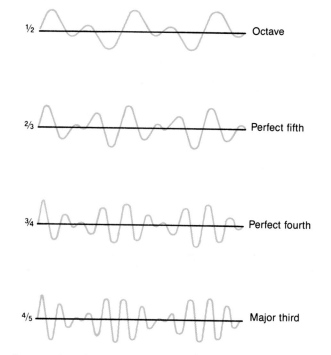

As discussed earlier, open and closed pipes resonate at more than one frequency. As a result, musical instruments using pipe resonators produce sounds that contain more than one resonant frequency. The lowest frequency making up the sound is called the **fundamental.** Waves of higher frequency are called **overtones.** Usually the intensity of the overtones is less than the intensity of the fundamental. An open pipe resonates when the length is an integral number of half wavelengths, $\lambda/2$, $2\lambda/2$, $3\lambda/2$,.... Thus the frequencies produced by an open pipe instrument with fundamental frequency f are f, $2f$, $3f$,.... The first overtone ($2f$) is one octave above the fundamental. The second overtone ($3f$) is an octave and a fifth above the fundamental. Many familiar musical instruments use

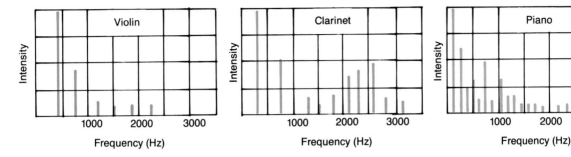

FIGURE 16–14. A violin, clarinet, and piano produce characteristic sound spectra.

·open pipe resonance. Brass instruments, flutes, oboes, and saxophones are some examples.

Sound can be transmitted through the air or changed into electrical energy and back into sound by a public address system. The air transmits different frequencies with varying efficiencies that could lead to distortion of the original sound. An electrical system can also distort the sound quality. A high-fidelity system is carefully designed to transmit all frequencies with equal efficiency. A system that has a response within 3 dB between 20 and 20 000 Hz is considered to be very good.

On the other hand, it is sometimes useful to transmit only certain frequencies. Telephone systems transmit only frequencies between 300 and 3000 Hz, where most information in spoken language exists. Words can be understood even when the high and low frequencies are missing. The distortion of musical sounds can also produce effects that are interesting and even desired by musical groups.

Noise consists of a large number of frequencies with no particular relationship. If all frequencies are present in equal amplitudes, the result is white noise. White noise has been found to have a relaxing effect, and as a result has been used by dentists to help their patients relax.

The human voice uses the throat and mouth cavity as a resonator. The number of overtones present, and thus the quality of the tone, depends on the shape of the resonator. Closing the throat, moving the tongue, and closing the teeth change the shape of the resonant cavity. Even nasal cavities, or sinuses, can affect the sound quality. The complex sound waves produced when the vowels a (as in sat) and u (as in suit) are spoken are shown in Figure 16–16.

FIGURE 16–15. This machine generates "white" sound.

Noise is a mixture of a large number of unrelated frequencies.

Vocal tract

a

Sound wave

u

FIGURE 16–16. The shape of the vocal tract determines the resonant wave forms for a as in sat (a) and u as in suit (b).

PHYSICS FOCUS

Synthetic Music

When Robert Moog introduced his electronic synthesizer in 1964, he could not have known the impact he was to make on the music industry. Musicians could not only mimic a wide variety of instruments, but, for the first time, create new sounds.

The original synthesizers were monophonic, meaning that they could play only one musical note at a time. The timbre, or color, of the tone could be changed to imitate a standard instrument, or to make an eerie, unearthly sound. These synthesizers were used to produce background music for low-budget science fiction movies in the 1960s and 1970s. With the development of polyphonic synthesizers, capable of playing musical chords, electronic music became more commercially acceptable. After synthesizers were coupled with computers and tape recorders, a composer or arranger could sit at a keyboard and orchestrate an entire horn or string section.

A synthesizer does not produce waves in the normal sense. Rather it produces a number that represents the amplitude of a wave at any instant. Any waveform can be represented by a series of these numbers. To combine various overtones, the synthesizer sums the numbers representing each of the desired waveforms. The synthesizer must provide a large number of sums each second. The human ear can detect frequencies as high as 16 000 Hz. The synthesizer must produce at least twice this many, or 32 000 numbers each second. The computer then converts these numbers to an electrical signal that produces the sound in a speaker system.

The sampler synthesizer takes this process one step further. This instrument records any sound, such as the bark of a dog or the slam of a door, then converts the sound into a sequence of numbers. When a key is pressed, the numbers are replayed at a speed determined by the pitch desired. The entire musical scale might be produced with nothing but door slams at different pitches.

Modern synthesizers can produce electronic music indistinguishable from music from traditional instruments. On the other hand, the synthesizer can make available such a wide range of sounds that composers need only be limited by their imaginations.

CHAPTER 16 REVIEW

SUMMARY

1. Sound is a longitudinal wave transmitted through a gas, liquid, or solid. **16:1**

2. A sound wave is an oscillation in the pressure of the medium. The displacement of the molecules also oscillates in time. **16:1**

3. The velocity of sound in air is 343 m/s at room temperature (20°C). **16:1**

4. The Doppler shift is the change in frequency of sound caused by the motion of either the source or detector. **16:2**

5. The frequency of a sound wave is called its pitch. **16:3**

6. Two notes that differ by one octave have pitches in the ratio of two to one. **16:3**

7. The amplitude of a sound wave is described by its intensity, or its loudness measured in decibels. **16:3**

8. Sound is produced by vibrating objects. **16:4**

9. An air column can resonate with a sound source, increasing the loudness of the source. **16:5**

10. A closed pipe resonates when its length is $\lambda/4$, $3\lambda/4$, $5\lambda/4$, and so forth. **16:5**

11. Sound detectors convert sound energy into a different form of energy. **16:6**

12. An open pipe resonates when its length is $\lambda/2$, $2\lambda/2$, $3\lambda/2$, and so forth. **16:7**

13. Two waves with almost the same frequency interfere to produce a beat note. **16:7**

14. Most sounds consist of waves with more than one frequency. The quality of the wave is called its timbre. **16:7**

15. The timbre of a musical instrument depends on the number and intensity of the overtones it produces. **16:7**

16. The shape of the throat and mouth cavity determine the vowel sounds produced by the human voice. **16:7**

QUESTIONS

1. In the last century, people put their ears to a railroad track to get an early warning of an approaching train. Why did this work?

2. If the pitch of sound is increased, what are the changes in
   a. the frequency?
   b. the wavelength?
   c. the wave velocity?
   d. the amplitude of the wave?

3. Suppose the horns of all cars emitted sound of the same pitch. What would be the change in the pitch of the horn of a car moving
   a. toward you?
   b. away from you?

4. Is a sound of 20 dB a factor of 100 (10^2) times more intense than the threshold of hearing, or a factor of 20 times more intense?

5. The speed of sound increases when the air temperature increases. For a given sound, as the temperature rises, what happens to
   a. the frequency?
   b. the wavelength?

6. The speed of sound increases with temperature. Would the pitch of a closed pipe increase or decrease when the temperature rises? Assume the length of the pipe does not change.

7. What property distinguishes notes played on both a trumpet and a clarinet if they have the same pitch and loudness?

8. Explain how the slide of a trombone changes the pitch of the sound using the idea of a trombone as a resonance tube.

9. How can a certain note sung by an opera singer cause a piece of crystal glass to shatter?

10. Why does sound travel faster in liquids and solids than in gases?

11. When a ringing bell is placed inside the jar of a vacuum pump and the air is removed, no sound is heard. Explain.

APPLYING CONCEPTS

1. In a science fiction movie, when a spaceship explodes, the vibrations from the sound nearly destroy a nearby spaceship. If you were the science consultant for the movie, how would you advise the producer?

2. A loud sound wave causes vibrations in a set of hanging ribbons. Describe how they vibrate.

3. A closed organ pipe plays a certain note. If the cover is removed to make it an open pipe, is the pitch increased or decreased?

4. If a firecracker produces a sound with intensity 90 dB, how many firecrackers would have to be exploded together to produce a 100-dB sound?

5. Sound waves with frequencies higher than can be heard, called ultrasound, can be transmitted through the human body. How could ultrasound be used to measure the speed of blood flowing in veins or arteries?

6. A bat emits short pulses of high-frequency sound and detects the echoes.
   a. In what way would the echoes from large and small insects compare?
   b. In what way would the echo from an insect flying toward the bat differ from that of an insect flying away from the bat?

7. In the military, as marching soldiers approach a bridge, the command "route step" is given. The soldiers then walk out-of-step with each other as they cross the bridge. Explain.

8. When timing the 100-m run, officials at the finish line are instructed to start their stopwatches at the sight of smoke from the starter's pistol and not on the sound of its firing. Explain. What would happen to the times for the runners if the timing started when sound was heard?

EXERCISES

Use 343 m/s as the speed of sound.

1. If you shout across a canyon and hear an echo 4.00 seconds later, how wide is the canyon?

2. A certain instant camera determines the distance to the subject by sending out a sound wave and measuring the time needed for the echo to return to the camera. How long would it take if the subject were 3.00 m away?

3. If the wavelength of a 4.40×10^2 Hz sound in fresh water is 3.30 m, what is the speed of sound in this medium?

4. A rock band plays with a 90-dB loudness. How much more intense is the sound from another rock band playing at
   a. 100 dB?
   b. 110 dB?

5. The lowest note on an organ is 16.4 Hz.
   a. What is the shortest open organ pipe that will resonate at this frequency?
   b. What would be the pitch if the same organ pipe were closed?

6. One tuning fork has a 445-Hz pitch. When a second fork is struck, beat notes occur with a frequency of 3 Hz. What are the two possible frequencies of the second fork?

7. A flute sounds a note with a 370-Hz pitch. What are the frequencies of the first, second, and third overtones of this pitch?

8. A clarinet also sounds the same note, 370 Hz. However, it only produces overtones that are odd multiples of the fundamental frequency. What are the frequencies of the lowest three overtones produced by this clarinet?

9. The sound emitted by bats has a wavelength of 3.5 mm. What is its frequency in air?

10. Ultrasound with a frequency of 4.25 MHz can be used to produce images of the human body. If the speed of sound in the body is that of sound in salt water, 1.50 km/s, what is the wavelength of the wave in the body?

11. A common method of estimating how far a lightning flash is from you is to count the seconds between the flash and the thunder and divide by

five. The result is the distance in miles.

a. Explain how this rule works.

b. How would you modify this method to find the distance in kilometers?

12. A slide whistle has a length of 27 cm. If you want to play a note one octave higher, how long should the whistle be?

13. One organ pipe has a length of 836 mm. A second pipe should have a pitch one major third higher. How long should this pipe be?

PROBLEMS

1. One closed organ pipe has a length of 2.40 m. Assume 343 m/s as the speed of sound.

a. What is the frequency of the note played by this pipe?

b. When a second pipe is played at the same time, a 1.40 Hz beat note is heard. By how much is the second pipe too long?

2. The equation for the Doppler shift of a sound wave of speed v, reaching a moving detector, is

$$f' = f\left(\frac{v - v_d}{v - v_s}\right)$$

where v_d is the speed of the detector and v_s is the speed of the source. If the detector moves toward the source, v_d is negative. A train moving toward a detector at 31 m/s blows a 305-Hz horn. What pitch is detected by a

a. stationary train?

b. train moving toward the first at 21 m/s?

3. The Doppler shift was first tested in 1845 by the French scientist B. Ballot. He had a trumpet player sound an A (440 Hz) while riding on a flatcar pulled by a locomotive. At the same time, a stationary trumpeter played the same note. Ballot heard 3.0 beats per second. How fast was the train moving toward him?

4. A student wants to repeat Ballot's experiment. She plans to have a trumpet played in a rapidly moving car. Rather than listening for beat notes, she wants to have the car move fast enough so the moving trumpet sounds a major third above a stationary trumpet. How fast would the car have to move? Should she try the experiment?

5. Two speakers emit a sound with a frequency of 550 Hz. Up to what maximum distance can the speakers be separated without destructive interference occurring?

6. An open vertical tube is filled with water and a tuning fork vibrates over its mouth. As the water level is lowered in the tube, resonance is heard when the water level has dropped 17 cm, and again after 49 cm of distance exists from the water to the top of the tube. What is the frequency of the tuning fork?

READINGS

Engel, Kenneth, "They Can See What You Can Hear." *Technology Illustrated*, August, 1983.

Fletcher, Neville, "The Physics of Organ Pipes." *Scientific American*, January, 1983.

Oster, Gerald, "Muscle Sounds." *Scientific American*, March, 1984.

Rossing, T., "106 Decibels!" *The Physics Teacher*, May, 1988.

Ruby, Daniel, "Visible Wind," *Popular Science*, August, 1984.

CHAPTER 17

Light

GOALS

1. You will become aware that light is a form of energy.
2. You will gain an understanding of the wave properties of light and the methods to determine the speed of light.
3. You will learn how colors are produced and seen.

Light and sound are the two major ways we receive information about the world. Of the two, light provides the greater variety of information. The eye can detect tiny changes in the size, brightness, and color of an object. In addition, by means of microscopes and telescopes, the worlds of the very small and the very distant are made available for scientific study.

We see objects because light is either reflected or emitted by them. Light is emitted by incandescent and fluorescent lamps, by television screens and tiny LEDs (light-emitting diodes), by flames, sparks, and even fireflies. But the major source of emitted light in the world is the sun. Light is reflected not only by mirrors and white paper, but by the moon, trees, and even dark black cloth. In fact, it is very difficult to find an object that does not reflect some light. Although light is only a small portion of the entire range of electromagnetic waves, the study of light is, in many ways, a study of all electromagnetic radiation.

17:1 The Facts of Light

Light is the form of electromagnetic waves that stimulates the retina of the eye. Light waves have wavelengths from about 400 nm (4.00×10^{-7} m) to 700 nm (7.00×10^{-7} m). The shortest wavelengths are seen as violet light. As the wavelength increases, the colors change to blue, green, yellow, orange, and finally, red. See Figure 17–1.

Light travels in a straight line. When your body blocks sunlight there is a sharp shadow. If light from the sun or a flashlight is made visible by dust particles in the air, the path of the light is seen to be a straight line. We locate objects by assuming that light travels from them to our eyes in straight lines.

Light is a form of electromagnetic radiation. It travels in a straight line.

Colors to Mix and Match

A small carving of a zebra is seen illuminated simultaneously by adjacent red, blue, and green lights. Multicolored shadows are formed. Examine the photographs and explain how each of the colors in the zebra's shadow is formed.

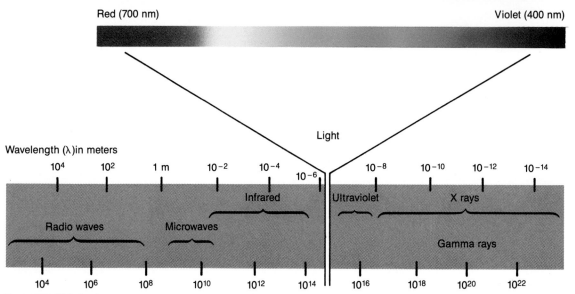

Red (700 nm)   Violet (400 nm)

Wavelength (λ) in meters

| 10^4 | 10^2 | 1 m | 10^{-2} | 10^{-4} | 10^{-6} | | 10^{-8} | 10^{-10} | 10^{-12} | 10^{-14} |

Light

Infrared   Ultraviolet   X rays

Radio waves   Microwaves

Gamma rays

| 10^4 | 10^6 | 10^8 | 10^{10} | 10^{12} | 10^{14} | 10^{16} | 10^{18} | 10^{20} | 10^{22} |

Frequency (f) in hertz

FIGURE 17–1. The visible spectrum is only a very small portion of the whole electromagnetic spectrum.

Since light travels in straight lines, the direction of light waves can be represented by rays.

DEMONSTRATION: See Teacher Guide.

Roemer made the first calculations of the speed of light using astronomical data.

For Your Information

Ole Roemer made his measurements in Paris as part of a project to improve maps by calculating the longitude of locations on Earth. The method required simultaneous observations of Io's eclipses, so it was important to compile accurate tables of Io's motion. This is an early example of the needs of technology resulting in scientific advances.

The straight-line path of light has led to the **ray model** of light. A **ray** is a straight line that represents the path of a very narrow beam of light. Using ray diagrams to study the travel of light is called **ray optics.** Even though ray optics ignores the wave nature of light, it is very useful in describing how light is reflected and refracted.

17:2 The Speed of Light

Before the seventeenth century, most people believed that light traveled instantaneously. Galileo was the first to suggest a method of measuring the speed of light, but he was forced to conclude that the speed of light was too fast to be measured accurately over a distance of a few kilometers. The Danish astronomer Ole Roemer (1644–1710) was the first to determine that light did travel with a finite speed. Between 1668 and 1674 Roemer made 70 careful measurements of the 42.5-hour orbital period of Io, one of the moons of Jupiter. He recorded the times when Io emerged from behind Jupiter and found that period varied slightly. The variation was as much as 14 seconds longer when Earth was moving away from Jupiter and 14 seconds shorter when Earth was approaching Jupiter. He concluded that as Earth moved away from Jupiter, the light from each new appearance of Io took longer to travel the increasing distance to Earth. Thus the measured period was increased. Based on these data, in 1676 Roemer announced that light took 22 minutes to cross a diameter of Earth's orbit. The speed of light had to be finite, but so fast that light took less than one second to cross the entire Earth!

Roemer was more interested in proving that light moved at a finite speed than calculating its exact speed. If we use the correct value of the diameter of Earth's orbit, 3.0×10^{11} m, Roemer's value of 22 minutes gives a speed of 2.2×10^8 m/s. Today we know that light takes 16 minutes, not 22, to cross Earth's orbit.

Although many laboratory measurements have been made, the most important was a series performed by the American physicist Albert A. Michelson (1852–1931). Between 1880 and the 1920s he used the rotating mirror method first developed by the French scientist Jean Foucault. In 1926, Michelson measured the time light required to make a round trip between two California mountains 35 km apart. Light was sent from source S, as seen in Figure 17–3, to a rapidly rotating octagonal mirror. When mirror A is in the position shown, the light reflects from A to the two mirrors 35 km away and back to the rotating mirror. If mirror B has moved into the exact position of mirror C when the light returns, the observer will see the light through a telescope. If the rotation speed is either too fast or too slow, no light will be seen. The time required for the light to make the round trip is equal to the time needed for the mirror to make one-eighth of a rotation. By measuring the rotation rate and the distance between the mirrors, the speed can be calculated. Michelson's best result was $2.997996 \pm 0.00004 \times 10^8$ m/s. For this work, he became the first American to receive the Nobel prize.

   The development of the laser in the 1960s provided new methods of measuring the speed of light. As with other electromagnetic waves, the speed of light is equal to the product of the frequency and wavelength.

Michelson made an accurate measurement of the speed of light.

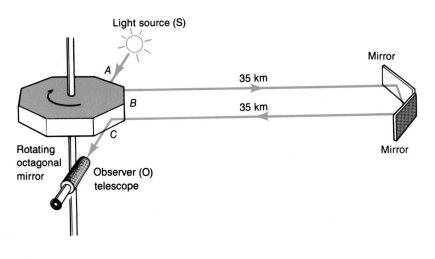

The speed of light in a vacuum is such an important and universal value that it has its own special symbol, *c*. Thus $c = f\lambda$. The frequency of light can be counted more precisely than its wavelength can be measured. As a result, in 1983 the International Committee on Weights and Measurements decided to make the speed of light a defined quantity. Length is now measured in terms of the time required by light to travel that distance. The committee defined the speed of light in a vacuum to be exactly

$$c = 299\ 792\ 458 \text{ m/s}$$

Practice Exercises

1. The octagonal mirror in Figure 17–3 makes 534 rotations per second. What time is required for one rotation?

2. **a.** What time is needed for face *B* of the mirror in Exercise 1 to move to position *C*?

   b. How far does light travel between the two reflections of the rotating mirror?

3. Use your answers to Exercise 2 to calculate the speed of light in both m/s and km/s.

4. The distance to the moon can be found with the help of mirrors left on the moon by astronauts. A pulse of light is sent to the moon and returns to Earth in 2.562 s. Using the defined velocity of light, calculate the distance to the moon.

17:3 Sources of Light

A **luminous** body emits light waves; an **illuminated** body reflects light waves. The sun is a luminous body and the moon is an illuminated body. An incandescent lamp is luminous because electrical energy heats a thin tungsten wire in the bulb and causes it to glow. An incandescent object emits light as a result of its being extremely hot.

We register the sensation of light when rays from either a luminous or an illuminated body reach our eyes. Our eyes have different sensitivities for different wavelengths. For that reason, measurements of light are not made in units such as joules, but in units based on comparisons with standard luminous bodies.

The rate at which an object emits light energy depends on the rate at which energy is put into it. A 100-W lamp uses 100 joules of electrical energy each second. It uses more electrical power and also emits more light per unit time than a 40-W lamp. Light output also depends on how efficiently the source converts the input energy to light. Only about five percent of the electrical energy put into an incandescent lamp appears in the form of light. A fluorescent lamp is about four times more efficient, converting about twenty percent of the electrical energy into light. Thus for the same amount of light, less electrical energy is needed.

The rate at which light is emitted from a source is called the **luminous flux,** *P*. The unit of luminous flux is the **lumen** (lm). A typical 100-W incandescent light bulb emits 1750 lm. A bulb emits light in almost all

The lumen is the unit for luminous flux. It is a power unit.

DEMONSTRATION: See Teacher Guide.

FIGURE 17–4. The standard light source contains glowing thoria. The brightness of all other light sources is defined in terms of light emitted by this standard.

One candela

$^1/_{60}$ cm²
Opening

Insulation

Freezing platinum

Fused thoria

directions. Imagine placing the bulb at the center of a sphere one meter in radius. The 1750 lm of luminous flux refers to all of the light that strikes the surface of the sphere.

Often we are not interested in the total amount of light emitted. We are more interested in the amount of illumination the bulb provides on a book, sheet of paper, or highway. The illumination on a surface is called the **illuminance,** E. Illuminance is measured in lumens per square meter, lm/m^2, or lux (lx). The area of the surface of a sphere is $4\pi r^2$. Thus the area of a sphere of 1-meter radius is 4π m^2. Therefore, the luminous flux striking each square meter of the sphere is $(1750/4\pi)$ lm/m^2. That is, the illumination provided by the 100-W bulb on the surface of the 1-m radius sphere is $1750/4\pi$ lux.

What happens if the sphere surrounding the lamp is larger? If the sphere had a radius of two meters, the luminous flux would still total 1750 lm, but the area of the sphere would now be $4\pi(2$ $m)^2 = 16\pi$ m^2, four times larger. The illumination on the surface would be reduced by a factor of four to $(1750/16\pi)$ lx. Thus, if the distance from a point source of light is doubled, the illumination provided by the source is one fourth as great. In the same way, if the distance is increased to three meters, the illumination would be $1/3^2$ or one ninth as large as it was when the light source was 1 meter away.

There are two ways to increase the illumination on a surface. The luminous flux of a light source can be increased or the distance between the source and surface can be decreased. Thus illuminance varies directly with the flux of the light source and inversely with the square of the distance from the source. The illuminance, E, directly under a small light source, is given by

$$E = \frac{P}{4\pi d^2}$$

P represents the luminous flux of the source and d its distance from the surface. This equation is valid only if the surface normal points toward the bulb. It is also valid only for sources that are small enough or far enough away to be considered point sources. Thus the equation does not give accurate values with long fluorescent lamps, or with incandescent bulbs in large reflectors that are close to the illuminated surface.

FIGURE 17–5. The lumen is the unit of luminous flux and is a measure of the rate of flow of light energy from a source.

Illuminance is the rate at which light falls on a surface of unit area.

For Your Information

Some light sources are specified in candle power, or candela, cd. A candela is not a measure of luminous flux but of luminous intensity, I. The luminous intensity of a point source is the luminous flux that falls on one square meter of a sphere one meter in radius. Thus luminous intensity is luminous flux divided by 4π. A bulb with 1750 lm flux has an intensity (1750 lm)/4π = 139 cd. Conversely, a flashlight bulb labeled 1.5 cd emits a flux of $4\pi(1.5$ cd) = 19 lm.

All light units are officially defined in terms of luminous intensity. One candela is the intensity emitted by 1/60 cm^2 of fused thoria (a powdery white oxide of the element thorium) maintained at the melting point of platinum, 2043 K.

SUGGESTION: Remind the students that they have had one inverse square law already, Newton's Law of Gravitation. Practice having the students predict what happens to the illumination if the distance is doubled, halved, etc.

FIGURE 17–6. The illuminance on a surface varies inversely as the square of its distance from a light source.

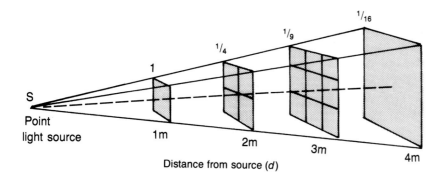

Distance from source (d)

EXAMPLE

Illumination of a Surface

A student's desktop is 2.5 m below a 1750-lm incandescent lamp. What is the illumination on the desktop?

Given: luminous flux
$P = 1750$ lm
distance
$d = 2.5$ m

Unknown: illuminance E

Basic equation: $E = \dfrac{P}{4\pi d^2}$

Solution: $E = \dfrac{(1750 \text{ lm})}{4\pi(2.5 \text{ m})^2}$

$= 22.3 \text{ lm/m}^2 = 22.3 \text{ lx}$

Practice Exercises

5. A lamp is moved from 30 cm to 90 cm above the pages of a book. Compare the illumination on the book before and after the lamp is moved.

6. What is the illumination on a surface 3.0 m below a 150-watt incandescent lamp that emits a luminous flux of 2275 lm?

7. A 64-cd point source of light is 3.0 m above the surface of a desk. What is the illumination on the desk's surface in lux?

8. The illumination on a tabletop is 2.0×10^1 lx. The lamp providing the illumination is 4.0 m above the table. What is the luminous flux of the lamp?

For a point source, the luminous intensity, I, measured in candela (cd), is related to luminous flux by $I = P/4\pi$.

17:4 Transmission and Absorption of Light

Objects can be seen clearly through air, glass, some plastics, and other materials. These materials transmit light waves and are called **transparent** materials. Other materials, such as frosted glass, transmit light but do not permit objects to be seen clearly through them. These materials are called **translucent.** Lampshades and frosted light bulbs are translucent. Materials such as brick transmit no light. They absorb or reflect all the light waves that fall on them. These materials are called **opaque.**

17:5 Color

One of the most beautiful phenomena in nature is a rainbow. People have long wondered about the source of the colors. Artificial rainbows can be produced by prisms. In 1666, the 24-year-old Isaac Newton did his first scientific experiments on the colors produced when a narrow beam of sunlight passes through a prism. Newton called the ordered arrangement of colors from violet to red a **spectrum.** He thought that some unevenness in the glass might be producing the spectrum. To test this assumption, he allowed the spectrum from one prism to fall on a second, reversed prism. If the spectrum were caused by irregularities in the glass, the second prism should have increased the spread in colors. Instead, a spot of white light was formed. After more experiments, Newton convinced himself that white light is composed of colors. We now know that

FIGURE 17–7. The transparent and translucent glass window ornament contrasts with the opaque window frame.

For Your Information

Although most people will agree that blue is light with wavelengths between 455 and 485 nm, green is between 500 and 530 nm, yellow is between 570 and 600 nm, and red is above 625 nm, color is very subjective. The color seen (perceived) depends on the amount of illumination as well as nearby colors.

each color in the spectrum is associated with a specific wavelength of light, as shown in Figure 17-1.

White light can be formed from colored light in a variety of ways. For example, if correct intensities of red, green, and blue light are projected onto a white screen, as in Figure 17-9, the screen will appear white. Thus red, green, and blue light added together form white light. This is called the additive color process. A color television tube uses the additive process. It has tiny dotlike sources of red, blue, and green light. When all have the correct intensities, the screen appears white. Therefore red light, green light, and blue light are called the **primary colors** of light. The primary colors can be mixed by pairs to form three different colors. Red and green light together produce yellow light. Blue and green light produce cyan, and red and blue light produce magenta. These three colors, yellow, cyan, and magenta, are called the **secondary light colors.**

Yellow light consists of red light and green light. If yellow light and blue light are projected onto a white screen, the surface will appear white. Thus yellow and blue light add to form white light. Yellow light is called the **complementary color** to blue light. Yellow light is made up of the two other primary colors. In the same way, cyan and red are complementary colors, as are magenta and green.

White light is composed of many colors.

Red, blue, and green are the primary colors of light. The correct mixture of red, blue, and green light will produce white light.

White light can also be produced by mixing one primary color with its complementary secondary color.

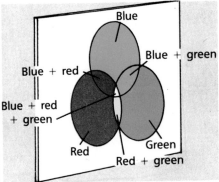

FIGURE 17-9. The additive mixture of blue, green, and red light produces white light.

FIGURE 17–10. An apple absorbs the blue and green wavelengths of white light and reflects red light (a). In red light, the apple still appears red (b). In blue light, the apple appears black since the blue light is absorbed (c).

The color of an object depends on which wavelengths of light the object reflects.

SUGGESTION: Go to a newspaper printing shop and ask for the transparencies used to make color pictures in the paper. Put these on the overhead and show how a few colors are mixed to get many colors.

The primary pigments are yellow, cyan, and magenta.

For Your Information

A dye is a material that dissolves in a liquid to form a colored solution. The dye molecule absorbs some colors of light and transmits others. Food coloring is a dye. The water can be evaporated, but the dye molecules themselves still interact with light.

An apple is red because it reflects red light to our eyes. When white light falls on the apple, molecules in the apple skin absorb the blue and green light and reflect the red. When only blue light falls on the apple, no light is reflected. The apple appears black. Black is the absence of reflected light.

A **pigment** is a colored material that absorbs certain colors and transmits or reflects others. A pigment particle is larger than a molecule and can be seen with a microscope. Often a pigment is a finely ground chemical such as titanium(IV) oxide (white), chromium(III) oxide (green), or cadmium sulfide (yellow). Pigments mix to form suspensions rather than solutions.

The absorption of light forms colors by the subtractive process. Molecules in pigments and dyes absorb certain colors from white light. A pigment that absorbs only one color from white light is called a **primary pigment.** Yellow pigment absorbs blue light and reflects red and green light. Yellow, cyan, and magenta are the primary pigments. A pigment that absorbs two primary colors and reflects one is a **secondary pigment.** The secondary pigments are red (absorbs green and blue light), green (absorbs red and blue light), and blue (absorbs red and green light). Note that the primary pigment colors are the secondary light colors. In the same way, the secondary pigment colors are the primary light colors.

The primary pigment yellow absorbs blue light. If it is mixed with the secondary pigment blue that absorbs green and red light, all light will be absorbed. No light will be reflected, so the result will be black. Yellow and blue are called complementary pigments. Cyan and red, as well as magenta and green, are also complementary pigments.

17:6 Formation of Colors in Thin Films

Have you ever seen a spectrum of colors produced by a soap bubble or by gasoline spilled on a water puddle? These colors are not the result of separation of white light by a prism or absorption of colors in a dye. They are a result of the constructive and destructive interference of light waves.

If a soap film is held vertically, as in Figure 17–11, its weight makes it thicker at the bottom than at the top. The thickness varies gradually from top to bottom. When a light wave strikes the film, part of it is reflected, as shown by R_1, and part is transmitted. The transmitted wave travels through the film to the back surface where again part is reflected, R_2. If the thickness of the film is one-quarter of the wavelength of the wave in the film ($\lambda/4$), the "round trip" path length in the film is $\lambda/2$. It would appear that the wave returning from the back surface would reach the front surface one-half wavelength out of phase with the first reflected wave and the two waves would cancel. But, as we learned in Chapter 15, when a wave is reflected from a more dense medium, it is inverted. As a result, the first reflected wave, R_1, is inverted on reflection. The second reflected wave, R_2, is reflected from a less dense medium and is not inverted. Thus, when the film has a thickness of $\lambda/4$, the wave reflected from the back surface returns to the front surface in phase with the first reflected wave. The two waves reinforce each other as they leave the film. Light with other wavelengths is partly or completely canceled. At any point on the film, the light most strongly reflected has a wavelength satisfying the requirement that the film thickness equals $\lambda/4$.

Different colors of light have different wavelengths. As the thickness of the film changes, the $\lambda/4$ requirement will be met at different locations for different colors. As the thickness increases, first blue will be most strongly reflected, then green, yellow, orange, and finally red. A rainbow of color results. Notice in Figure 17–11 that the rainbow repeats. When the thickness is $3\lambda/4$, the round trip distance is $3\lambda/2$, and constructive interference

a

FIGURE 17–11. Each color is reinforced where the soap film is 1/4, 3/4, 5/4, . . . , of the wavelength for that color. Since each color has a different wavelength, a series of color bands is seen reflected from the soap films.

b

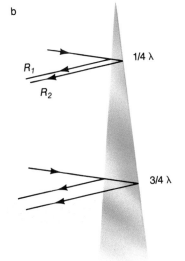

A film will have a particular color when the thickness of the film is λ/4, 3λ/4, 5λ/4, ...

The film looks black if it is so thin that no color satisfies the λ/4 thickness criterion.

occurs again. Any thickness equal to an odd multiple of quarter wavelengths, λ/4, 3λ/4, 5λ/4, 7λ/4, and so on, satisfies the conditions for reinforcement for a given color. At the top of the right-hand film there is no color; the film appears black. Here the film is too thin to produce constructive interference for any color. Shortly after the top of a film is thin enough to appear black, it breaks.

17:7 Polarization of Light

Have you ever looked at light reflected off a road through Polaroid sunglasses? As you rotate the glasses, the road first appears dark, then light, then dark again. Light from a lamp, however, changes very little as the glasses are rotated. The light reflected from the road is partially polarized. Only transverse waves can be polarized.

FIGURE 17–12. This photograph of menthol crystals was taken with a polarizing microscope. A polarizing microscope can be used to determine optical properties such as refractive index.

a

b

Polarization can be understood by considering the rope model of light waves shown in Figure 17–13. The transverse mechanical waves in the rope represent the transverse electromagnetic waves of light. The slots represent the polarizing axis of the Polaroid material. When the rope waves are parallel to the slots, they pass through. When they are perpendicular to the slots, the waves are blocked. Polaroid material contains long vibrating molecules that act like a fence. Only waves vibrating parallel to the polarizing axis of the material can pass through. The fact that the intensity of light reflected off a road varies as Polaroid sunglasses are rotated suggests that the reflected light must contain a great deal of light vibrating in only one direction. On the other hand, light from a lamp must be made up of waves vibrating equally in all directions.

Ordinary light contains electromagnetic waves vibrating in every direction perpendicular to its direction of travel. Each wave can be resolved into two perpendicular components. On the average, therefore, half the waves vibrate in one plane, the other half in a plane perpendicular to the first. If polarizing material is placed in such a beam, only those waves vibrating in one plane pass through. The polarizing material produces light that is **polarized** in a particular plane of vibration. It is said to be a "polarizer" of light and is called a polarizing filter.

Suppose a second polarizing filter is placed in the path of the polarized light. If the direction of the plane of vibration that passes through the filter is perpendicular to the plane of the polarized light, no light will pass

SUGGESTION: Have students bring in old polarizing sunglasses. Break them in half to use them as polarizing filters.

Waves oriented to a particular plane are plane polarized.

FIGURE 17–14. The arrows show that unpolarized light vibrates in many planes (a). Plane polarized light vibrates in only one plane. Polarized light from the first polarizer (b) is absorbed by the analyzer (c).

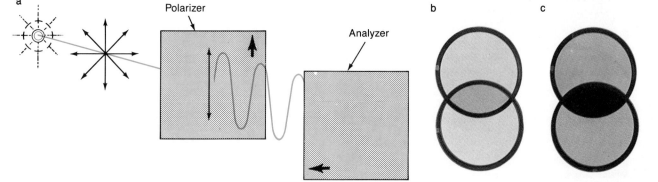

a

Polarizer

Analyzer

b

c

Light can be polarized by passing it through a Polaroid filter.

through. If it is parallel, most light will be transmitted. Thus a polarizing filter can also analyze the polarization of light. It is the "analyzer" in Figure 17–14.

Light can also be polarized by reflection. If you look through a polarizing filter at the light reflected by a sheet of glass and rotate the filter, you will see the light brighten and dim. The light was partially polarized when it was reflected. Light is also polarized when it is scattered by molecules in the air. The polarization of light reflected by roads and scattered by air is the reason polarizing sunglasses reduce glare.

FIGURE 17–15. Light becomes polarized when it is reflected from a smooth surface such as glass or water.

PHYSICS FOCUS

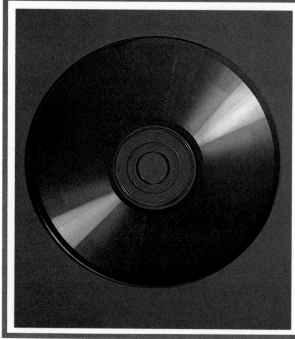

Compact Discs

The audio compact disc (CD) represents a technology that is made for no other purpose than to enhance the musical pleasure of humans. The invention of many new industrial processes involved in mass producing CDs is a major accomplishment. Now, music can be reproduced with a clarity and accuracy never before possible.

The CD is essentially a sandwich of three layers of different materials: the plastic substrate, the reflective coating, and the sealing layer. The musical information in a digital recording consists of binary numbers or strings of 1's or 0's. These digits are represented by approximately five billion tiny pits in the substrate. The reflective coating covers the surface of these tiny pits. The laser beam from the CD player reflects off these coated pits and is translated into a digital code. This code is converted into an analog (continuously changing voltage) signal that is amplified to make music.

Since the microscopic pits are smaller than most dirt particles, the entire manufacturing process must take place under stringent clean-room conditions. The "dirty" areas of a CD plant are usually cleaner than the "clean" areas of other factories.

SUMMARY

1. Light is electromagnetic radiation capable of stimulating the retina of the eye. **17:1**

2. Light travels in a straight line at a speed of 3.00×10^8 m/s in a vacuum. **17:1, 17:2**

3. The rate at which light energy is emitted by a source is called luminous flux. The unit of luminous flux is the lumen. **17:3**

4. The rate at which light energy falls on a unit area is illuminance, measured in lux. **17:3**

5. Materials may be either transparent, translucent, or opaque, depending on the amount of light they reflect, transmit, and absorb. **17:4**

6. White light is a combination of the spectrum of colors, each having a different wavelength. **17:5**

7. White light can be formed by adding together the primary light colors, red, blue, and green. **17:5**

8. The subtractive primary colors, cyan, magenta, and yellow, are used in pigments and dyes to produce a wide variety of colors. **17:5**

9. Colors in soap and oil films are caused by the interference of light reflected from the front and back surfaces of the thin film. **17:6**

10. Light is polarized if only waves vibrating in a particular plane are present. **17:7**

QUESTIONS

1. Distinguish among transparent, translucent, and opaque objects.

2. Distinguish between a luminous body and an illuminated body.

3. Of what colors does white light consist?

4. Is black a color? Why does an object appear black?

5. You put a piece of red cellophane over one flashlight and a piece of green cellophane over another. You shine the light beams on a white wall. What color will you see where the two flashlight beams overlap?

6. You now put both the red and green cellophane pieces over the same flashlight. If you shine the flashlight beam on a white wall, what color will you see? Explain.

7. What color will a yellow banana appear when illuminated by
   a. white light?
   b. green plus red light?
   c. blue light?

8. Why can sound waves not be polarized?

9. Why would a perfect polarizing filter transmit half the nonpolarized light incident on it?

10. To what is the illumination of a surface by a light source directly proportional? To what is it inversely proportional?

11. Why would the inside of binoculars and cameras be painted black?

APPLYING CONCEPTS

1. Suppose Albert Michelson replaced his 8-sided mirror with one with 12 sides. Would the mirror have to be rotated faster or slower? Explain.

2. Look carefully at an ordinary frosted incandescent bulb. Is it a luminous or an illuminated body? Explain.

3. A soap film is too thin to absorb any color. If such a film reflects blue light, what kind of light does it transmit?

4. An apple is red because it reflects red light and either absorbs or transmits blue and green. Follow these steps to decide if a piece of transparent red cellophane absorbs or transmits blue and green.
   a. Explain why it looks red in reflected light.
   b. When you hold it between your eye and a white light, it looks red. Explain.
   c. Now, what happens to the blue and green?

5. The eye is most sensitive to 550-nm wavelength light. Its sensitivity to red and blue light is less than 10% as great. Based on this knowledge, what color would you recommend fire trucks and ambulances be painted? Why?

6. Some very efficient streetlights contain sodium vapor under high pressure. They produce light that is mainly yellow with some red. Should a community having these lights buy dark blue police cars? Why or why not?

7. Consider a thin film of gasoline floating on water. The speed of light is slower in gasoline than in air, and slower in water than in gasoline. Would you expect the $\lambda/4$ rule (Section 17:6) to hold in this case? Explain.

8. Photographers often put polarizing filters over the camera lens to make clouds more visible in the sky. The clouds remain white while the sky looks darker. Explain this based on your knowledge of polarized light.

9. Suppose astronauts made a soap film in the space shuttle. Would you expect an orderly set of colored lines, such as in Figure 17–11? Explain.

EXERCISES

1. Light takes 1.28 s to travel from the moon to Earth. What is the distance between them?

2. The sun is 1.5×10^8 km from Earth. How long does it take for its light to reach us?

3. Using Albert Michelson's eight-sided mirror, light is beamed between two mountains 40 km apart. At what minimum frequency must the mirror rotate for light to be reflected into an observer's eye by each successive mirror face?

4. Find the illumination 4.0 m below a 405-lm lamp.

5. A 1.00×10^2-cd point source of light is 2.0 m from screen A and 4.0 m from screen B. How does the illumination on screen B compare with the illumination on screen A?

6. You have a small reading lamp 35 cm from the pages of a book. You decide to raise it to 70 cm. Is the illumination on the book the same? If not, how much more or less is it?

7. An observer uses a 20-sided mirror to measure the speed of light. A clear image occurs when the

mirror is rotating at 5.00×10^2 rev/s. The total path of the light pulse is 30.00 km. What is the speed of light?

8. Two lamps illuminate a screen equally. The first lamp has an intensity of 101 cd and is 5.0 m from the screen. The second lamp is 3.0 m from the screen. What is the intensity of the second lamp?

9. A 3-way bulb uses 50-100-150 watts of electrical power to deliver 665, 1620, or 2285 lumens in its three settings. The bulb is placed 80 cm above a sheet of paper. If an illumination of at least 175 lx is needed on the paper, what is the minimum setting that should be used?

10. A public school law requires a minimum illumination of 160 lx on the surface of each student's desk. An architect's specifications call for classroom lights to be located 2.0 m above the desks. What is the minimum luminous flux the lights must deliver?

11. A screen is placed between two lamps so that they illuminate the screen equally. The first lamp emits a luminous flux of 1445 lm and is 2.5 m from the screen. What is the distance of the second lamp from the screen if the luminous flux is 2375 lm?

PROBLEMS

1. Ole Roemer found that the maximum increased delay in the appearance of Io from one orbit to the next was 14 seconds.
   a. How far does light travel in 14 seconds?
   b. Each orbit of Io is 42.5 hours. Earth traveled the distance calculated above in 42.5 hours. Find the speed of Earth in km/s.
   c. See if your answer for part b is reasonable. Calculate Earth's speed in orbit using the orbital radius, 1.5×10^8 km, and the period, one year.

2. Suppose you wanted to measure the speed of light by putting a mirror on a distant mountain, setting off a camera flash, and measuring the time it takes the flash to reflect off the mirror and return to you. Without instruments, a person can detect a time interval of about 1/10 s. How many kilometers away would the mirror have to be? Compare this size with some known objects.

3. A streetlight contains two identical bulbs 3.3 m above the ground. If the community wants to save electrical energy by removing one bulb, how far from the ground should the streetlight be positioned to have the same illumination on the ground under the lamp?

4. A student wants to compare the luminous flux from a bulb with that of a 1750-lm lamp. The two bulbs equally illuminate a sheet of paper. The 1750-lm lamp is 1.25 m away; the unknown bulb is 1.08 m away. What is its luminous flux?

READINGS

Edelson, Edward, "Faster Than Light." *Popular Science,* April, 1984.

Shapiro, Alan, "Experiment and Mathematics in Newton's Theory of Color." *Physics Today,* September, 1984.

Tsang, W. T., "The C³ LASER." *Scientific American,* November, 1984.

Walker, Jearl, "Some Interesting Lessons in Optics That May Make Air Travel Easier to Endure." *Scientific American,* August, 1988.

CHAPTER 18

Reflection and Refraction

GOALS

1. You will learn how light is reflected and refracted.
2. You will gain a knowledge of several applications of light, such as fiber optics and the separation of light into colors.

SUGGESTION: An optical disk or ray box is useful in demonstrating ray optics.

DEMONSTRATION: See Teacher Guide.

In our study of the nature of light, we found that light travels in straight lines and at a very high speed. Let us now study some specific behaviors of light. What happens when light is bounced off a barrier? How does light behave when it passes from one medium into another medium?

18:1 The Law of Reflection

When a light ray strikes a reflecting surface, the angle of reflection is equal to the angle of incidence. Both of these angles are measured from a normal (perpendicular) to the surface at the point of incidence. The incident ray, the reflected ray, and the normal all lie in the same plane.

When a beam of light strikes most surfaces, it reflects in many directions. A painted wall or a page in a book may appear to be very smooth. Actually, these surfaces are rough and have many small projections. Rays of light strike different parts of these projections. Each ray reflects according to the law of reflection. The rays are reflected in many different directions, producing a **diffuse reflection,** shown in Figure 18–2a.

If a beam of light falls on a very smooth surface, the rays undergo **regular reflection.** Figure 18–2b shows a beam of parallel rays reflecting from a smooth, flat surface. Since each ray follows the law of reflection, the reflected rays are also parallel. The rays are arranged in the same order after they leave a smooth surface as they were before they approached the surface.

FIGURE 18–1. A light ray reflecting from a mirror shows that the angle of incidence equals the angle of reflection.

18:2 Refraction of Light

Light travels at different speeds in different media. Light also changes direction, or bends, as it moves from one medium to another if the angle of incidence is not zero. The change in direction or bending of light at the

Rainbows are created by a combination of refraction and reflection in raindrops. As a rainbow is viewed, violet always appears on the bottom and red on the top. Occasionally a secondary rainbow can be seen, as in this photograph. Explain the origin of the secondary rainbow and why the red band is seen on the bottom, not the top.

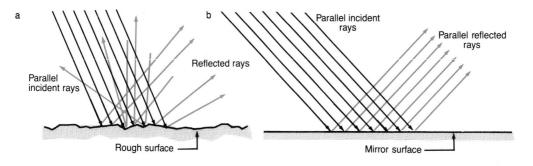

FIGURE 18–2. When parallel light rays strike a rough surface, they are randomly reflected (a). When parallel light rays strike a mirror surface, they reflect as parallel rays (b).

Refraction is the bending of light as it enters a new medium.

An angle of incidence is measured from the normal to the incident ray. The angle of refraction is measured from the normal to the refracted ray.

DEMONSTRATIONS: See Teacher Guide.

Light bends toward the normal if its speed is reduced as it enters the new medium; light bends away from the normal if its speed increases as it enters the new medium.

FIGURE 18–3. Light is refracted toward the normal as it enters a more dense medium. Compare the deflection of a set of wheels as it crosses a pavement-mud boundary.

boundary between two media is called **refraction.**

Consider an incident ray that falls on the boundary between two media. Once the ray enters a new medium, it is a refracted ray. The angle between the incident ray and a normal to the surface at the point of incidence is the angle of incidence, i. The angle between the refracted ray and the same normal is the angle of refraction, r. The incident ray, the refracted ray, and the normal lie in the same plane. Refraction occurs only when the incident ray strikes the boundary between the two media at an angle. When the angle of incidence is zero (the ray is perpendicular to the surface), the angle of refraction is also zero. The ray changes speed but passes straight into the new medium.

Figure 18–3 shows a ray of light as it passes from air into glass at different angles of incidence. Part of the ray is reflected and part is transmitted (refracted). Notice that as the ray enters a medium in which it travels more slowly, the refracted ray bends toward the normal. The angle of refraction is smaller than the angle of incidence.

In Figure 18–4, a light ray passes from glass into air. Rays that strike the surface at an angle are refracted away from the normal. When a light ray passes into a medium in which it travels faster, the light ray bends or refracts away from the normal. In other words, the angle of refraction is larger than the angle of incidence.

Figures 18–3 and 18–4 compare the refraction of light to a car entering or leaving a patch of mud. When the wheels enter the mud at an angle, as in Figure 18–3, the right wheel enters the mud before the left wheel. The

a

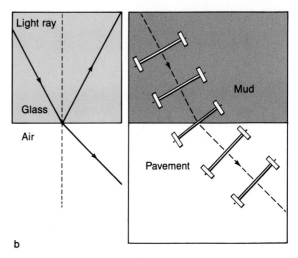

b

right wheel slows before the left wheel. As a result, the car swings to the right or toward the normal. Figure 18–4 shows the car as it leaves the mud at an angle. The right wheel leaves the mud first and speeds up. The left wheel is still held back. Therefore, the car swings to the left or away from the normal. Keep this car analogy in mind until the behavior of light at various surfaces becomes more familiar to you.

18:3 Snell's Law

Rays of light that travel from air into glass, or any other medium more optically dense than air, are refracted toward the normal. As the angle of incidence increases, the angle of refraction increases, as in Figure 18–5. Although the angle of refraction does not vary directly with the angle of incidence, the increase in the angle of refraction as the angle of incidence increases suggests that a definite relationship exists.

The relationship between the angle of incidence and the angle of refraction was discovered by the Dutch scientist Willebrord Snell (1591–1626)

FIGURE 18–4. Light is refracted away from the normal as it enters a less dense medium. Compare the deflection of a set of wheels as it crosses a mud-pavement boundary.

SUGGESTION: This analogy is often quite helpful to students in understanding the concept of refraction.

For Your Information

Optical density is the property of a medium that determines the speed of light in that medium. If a medium is optically dense, it slows light more than a medium that is less optically dense.

SUGGESTION: It is important to emphasize that refraction is a boundary phenomenon. The analogy of a car going into the mud is often quite helpful to the student in understanding the concept of refraction.

FIGURE 18–5. When light passes from one medium to another, the angle of refraction depends upon the angle of incidence. This is shown very clearly by the pencils of light leaving the glass prism.

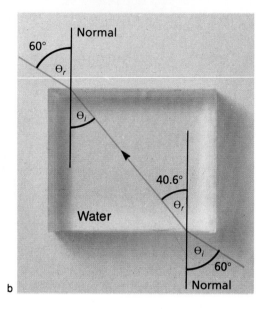

a   b

FIGURE 18–6. The index of refraction for glass is greater than that for water. If light enters both media at the same angle, the angle of refraction is greater for water. This result agrees with Snell's law.

Snell's law states that the ratio of the sine of the incident angle to the sine of the refracted angle is a constant.

and is called **Snell's law.** This law states: *a ray of light bends in such a way that the ratio of the sine of the angle of incidence to the sine of the angle of refraction is a constant.* For a light ray passing from a vacuum into a given medium, this constant (the ratio of the sines) is called the **index of refraction,** *n,* for that medium. Snell's law can be written

$$n = \frac{\sin \theta_i}{\sin \theta_r}$$

In this equation, θ_i is the angle of incidence, θ_r is the angle of refraction, and *n* is the index of refraction of the medium. Note that this equation applies only to a ray traveling from a vacuum into another medium.

In general, for a ray traveling from one medium into another medium, Snell's law can be written

$$n_i \sin \theta_i = n_r \sin \theta_r$$

In this equation, n_i is the index of refraction of the incident medium and n_r is the index of refraction of the second medium. Angles θ_i and θ_r are the angles of incidence and refraction, respectively.

A ray diagram is very useful in solving problems involving the reflection and refraction of light. Some problems can be solved, at least approximately, using a diagram. You should draw a ray diagram for all problems involving reflection or refraction to check the answer you get using a calculator.

PROBLEM SOLVING

1. Draw a diagram showing the two media. Label them, indicating the two indices of refraction, *n.*
2. Draw the incoming ray until it hits the surface. Draw a normal to the surface at that point.
3. Use a protractor to measure the angle of incidence.

4. Use Snell's law to calculate the angle of refraction.
5. Draw the refracted ray, using a protractor to find the correct angle.
6. Always make sure your answer obeys the qualitative statement of Snell's law: "Light moving from smaller n to larger n is bent toward the normal. Light moving from larger n to smaller n is bent away from the normal."

TABLE 18–1

Indices of Refraction			
Medium	**n**	**Medium**	**n**
vacuum	1.00	crown glass	1.52
air	1.00*	quartz	1.54
water	1.33	flint glass	1.61
ethanol	1.36	diamond	2.42

*Index of refraction of air is 1.0003, which is higher than that of vacuum, 1.0000. However, for practical purposes, they are the same.

EXAMPLE

Snell's Law

A ray of light traveling through air is incident upon a sheet of crown glass at an angle of 30.0°. What is the angle of refraction?

Given: incident medium (air)
second medium
(crown glass)
incident angle
$(\theta_i) = 30.0°$

Unknown: refracted angle (θ_r)

Basic equation: $n_i \sin \theta_i = n_r \sin \theta_r$

Solution: From Table 18–1, the index of refraction of crown glass is 1.52.

$$n_i \sin \theta_i = n_r \sin \theta_r$$

$$\sin \theta_r = \frac{n_i \sin \theta_i}{n_r}$$

$$= \frac{(1.00)(\sin 30.0°)}{1.52} = \frac{0.500}{1.52} = 0.329$$

$$\theta_r = 19.2°$$

Practice Exercises

1. Light is incident upon a piece of crown glass at an angle of 45.0°. What is the angle of refraction?

2. A ray of light passes from air into water at an angle of 30.0°. Find the angle of refraction.

3. Light is incident upon a piece of quartz at an angle of 45.0°. What is the angle of refraction to the nearest degree?

4. A ray of light is incident upon a diamond at 45.0°.

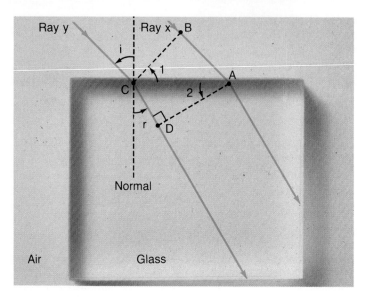

SUGGESTION: Set up a laser so the beam shines along a sheet of paper into the block of glass and out the other side along the sheet of paper. You can see the ray Y being bent as it enters and leaves the glass.

a. What is the angle of refraction?

b. Compare your answer for (a) to your answer for Practice Exercise 1. Does glass or diamond bend light more?

18:4   Index of Refraction and the Speed of Light

Refraction occurs because the speed of light depends on the medium in which the light is traveling. The index of refraction is a measure of the amount that light bends when passing into the medium from a vacuum. In this section, the relationship between the index of refraction and the speed of light in a medium will be derived.

Figure 18–7 shows the behavior of two parallel rays of light that are incident upon a glass plate from air. The rays are refracted toward the normal. Consider the wave front CB as it approaches the glass plate. After a time interval, the wave front reaches position DA. Since the speed of the wave is slower in the glass, point C on ray y travels only distance CD. Point B on ray x travels distance BA. This difference causes the wave front to turn.

During a time interval t, point B on ray x travels to A and point C on ray y travels to D. Therefore, the ratio of BA to CD is the same as the ratio of the speed of light in vacuum, c, to the speed of light in glass, v_g.

$$\frac{\frac{BA}{t}}{\frac{CD}{t}} = \frac{BA}{CD} = \frac{c}{v_g}$$

Angle θ_i in Figure 18–7 is equal to the angle of incidence of the ray. Angle θ_r is equal to the angle of refraction of the ray (corresponding sides mutually perpendicular). The sine of angle θ_i is BA/CA. The sine of angle θ_r is CD/CA. Since $n_{vacuum} = 1$, using Snell's law, the index of refraction is

$$n_g = \frac{\sin i}{\sin r} = \frac{\sin \theta_i}{\sin \theta_r} = \frac{BA/CA}{CD/CA} = \frac{BA}{CD} = \frac{c}{v_g}$$

The index of refraction for any substance is

$$n_s = \frac{c}{v_s}$$

The index of refraction of a medium is the ratio of the speed of light in a vacuum to the speed of light in the medium.

where v_s represents the speed of light in the substance.

The index of refraction of many transparent substances, such as water or glass, can be found by measurement. A small ray of light is caused to fall on the substance and the resulting angle of refraction is measured. The sine of the angle of incidence divided by the sine of the angle of refraction gives the index of refraction of the substance. The speed of light in a vacuum, 3.00×10^8 m/s, is known. Therefore, it is possible to calculate the speed of light in many substances by using the equation $v_s = c/n_s$.

EXAMPLE

Speed of Light in a Medium

The index of refraction of water is 1.33. Calculate the speed of light in water.

Given: $n_{water} = 1.33$
$ c = 3.00 \times 10^8$ m/s

Unknown: v_{water}

Basic equation: $n_s = \frac{c}{v_s}$

Solution: $n_{water} = \frac{c}{v_{water}}$

$$v_{water} = \frac{c}{n_{water}} = \frac{3.00 \times 10^8 \text{ m/s}}{1.33} = 2.26 \times 10^8 \text{ m/s}$$

Practice Exercises

5. Use Table 18–1 to find the speed of light in
   a. ethanol. **b.** quartz. **c.** flint glass.
6. The speed of light in a plastic is 2.00×10^8 m/s. What is the index of refraction of the plastic?
7. The speed of light in a glass plate is 196 890 km/s. Find the index of refraction of this material.

18:5 Total Internal Reflection

DEMONSTRATIONS: See Teacher Guide.

When a ray of light passes from a more optically dense medium into air, the light is bent away from the normal. In other words, the angle of refraction is larger than the angle of incidence. The fact that the angle of refraction is larger than the angle of incidence leads to an interesting phenomenon known as total internal reflection. **Total internal reflection** occurs when light passes from a more optically dense medium to a less optically dense medium at an angle so great that there is no refracted ray. Figure 18–8 shows such an occurrence. Ray 1 is incident upon the surface of the water at angle θ_i. Ray 1 produces the angle of refraction, θ_r. Ray 2 is incident at such a large angle, θ_i, that the refracted ray lies along the surface of the water. The angle of refraction is 90°.

In total internal reflection, no light rays are transmitted into the new medium.

SUGGESTION: Bring the optical system from a pair of binoculars to class and have students follow the path of the light through the prisms. Because there is no light lost in total internal reflection, totally reflecting prisms are used instead of mirrors in such instruments as binoculars and periscopes.

Applying Snell's law for light traveling from one medium into another, the equation is

$$n_i \sin \theta_i = n_r \sin \theta_r$$
$$(n_{water})(\sin \theta_i) = (n_{air})(\sin \theta_r)$$
$$(1.33)(\sin \theta_i) = (1.00)(\sin 90°)$$

Solving the equation for $\sin \theta_i$,

$$\sin \theta_i = \frac{(1.00)(\sin 90°)}{(1.33)}$$
$$= 0.752$$
$$\theta_i = 48.8°$$

When an incident ray of light passing from water to air makes an angle of 48.8°, the angle of refraction is 90°.

The incident angle that causes the refracted ray to lie right along the boundary of the substance, angle θ_c, is unique to the substance. It is known as the **critical angle** of the substance.

The critical angle, θ_c, of any substance may be calculated as follows.

$$n_i \sin \theta_i = n_r \sin \theta_r$$

In this situation, $\theta_i = \theta_c$; $n_r = 1.000$; and $\theta_r = 90.0°$.

$$\sin \theta_c = \frac{(1.00)(\sin 90.0°)}{n_i}$$

$$\sin \theta_c = \frac{1}{n_i}$$

FIGURE 18–9. When the submerged legs of a person sitting at the edge of a pool are observed by an underwater swimmer close to the surface of the pool (a) the swimmer will not see the upper torso of the person, but will see the submerged legs and an inverted image of the legs above the surface of the water in place of the person's torso (b).

a

b

b

a

c

Eyepiece lens

Reversing prisms

Objective lens

Light path

For crown glass, the critical angle can be calculated as follows.

$$\sin \theta_c = \frac{1}{1.52} = 0.658$$

$$\theta_c = 41.1°$$

Any ray that reaches the surface of water at an angle greater than the critical angle (ray 3) cannot be refracted. All of the light is reflected. Total internal reflection has occurred.

Total internal reflection causes some curious effects. Suppose an underwater swimmer looks at the surface of the water. The legs of a second swimmer, seated on the edge of the pool, may appear to be inverted. Likewise, if a swimmer is near the surface of a quiet pool, the swimmer may not be visible to an observer standing near the side of the pool. Total internal reflection is important in the design of binoculars. It has also given rise to the field of fiber optics.

What happens to light that enters a long, thin glass rod? Figure 18-11 shows the path of one ray. Each surface reflection is at an angle larger than the critical angle. The reflection is total, keeping the light within the rod. Light acts the same way in a thin glass fiber coated with a layer of glass with a lower index of refraction. Such an **optical fiber** can be twisted or coiled into loops.

Light passing through optical fibers can be used to transmit information. Information is carried by normal telephone, radio, and television by varying the amplitude of the signal. The amplitude of the signal can be converted into a digital signal, a series of binary bits, "0"s and "1"s. For example, a signal with amplitude 13 would be 1,1,0,1, while 3 would be 0,0,1,1. A light that is turned on (for a 1) and off (for a 0) produces a signal that is a series of light pulses that can be carried by a fiber. A solid-state laser at one end of an optical fiber is turned on and off very rapidly. The series of pulses is detected at the other end of the fiber and converted back into a signal of varying amplitude. Information equivalent to 25 000 telephone conversations can be carried by a fiber the thickness of a human hair. For this reason optical fibers are being used to transmit telephone,

FIGURE 18–10. The passage of light through the reflecting prisms in a pair of binoculars shows total internal reflection (a). The angle of the prisms changes the path of the reflected rays (b) and (c).

For Your Information

In 1880, a few years after he invented the telephone, Alexander Graham Bell created a device, called the photophone, that transmitted sound using a beam of light. However, the device was not useful because there were no wires or means of transmitting the light signals from the photophone. Today, through the technology of fiber optics, hairlike strands of glass can carry light signals.

FIGURE 18–11. Fiber optics makes it possible to use light instead of electricity to transmit voices and data. A standard 3-inch bundle of fibers can carry 14 400 telephone conversations.

Optic fiber

Coating of glass with lower index of refraction

Light ray

a

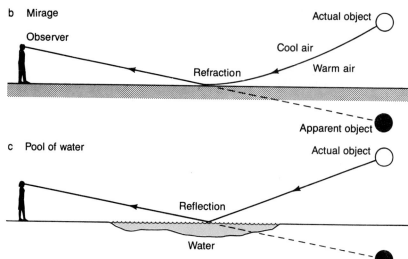

b   Mirage

Observer

Actual object

Cool air

Refraction

Warm air

Apparent object

c   Pool of water

Actual object

Reflection

Water

Apparent object

FIGURE 18–12. After the sun has actually set, it is still visible due to refraction of light over the horizon through the atmosphere (a). Refraction of light in air of different densities (b) produces an effect similar to the reflection of light off a pool of water (c).

Twilight and mirages are the result of the refraction of light.

computer, and video signals within buildings, from city to city, and even across oceans.

18:6   Effects of Refraction

Many interesting effects are caused by the refraction of light. Mirages, the apparent shift in the position of objects immersed in liquids, and the lingering daylight after the sun is below the horizon are examples.

Mirages can be observed along highways in summer. A driver looking down the road sees what looks like a puddle of water. However, the puddle disappears as the car approaches. The mirage occurs because the air next to the surface of the road is heated sooner than the air above it. This heated air expands. As the distance above the road increases, the air gradually cools. The index of refraction of the air also increases with distance above the road because of the greater optical density of cooler air. As a ray of light moves from the road, it passes through air of increas-

FIGURE 18–13. White light directed through a prism is dispersed into a band of different colors.

312   Reflection and Refraction

FIGURE 18–14. Newton's drawing showing how he used a prism to disperse sunlight into its spectrum and then a lens to recombine the colors to form white light again.

ingly higher index of refraction. The ray bends in the manner shown in Figure 18–12. To an observer, the refracted light looks like light reflected from a puddle.

An object submerged in a liquid is not where it appears to be. As a result of refraction, an object may appear to be much closer to the surface of the liquid than it really is. Refraction also makes a spoon placed in a glass of water appear bent.

Light travels at a slightly slower speed in Earth's atmosphere than it does in outer space. As a result, sunlight is refracted by the atmosphere. In the morning, this refraction causes sunlight to reach Earth before the sun is actually above the horizon. In the evening, the sunlight is bent above the horizon after the sun has actually set. Thus, daylight is extended in the morning and evening because of the refraction of light.

18:7 Dispersion of Light

Light of all wavelengths travels through the vacuum of space at 3.00×10^8 m/s. In other media, however, light waves travel more slowly. In addition, waves of different wavelengths travel at different speeds. This fact means that the index of refraction of a material depends on the wavelength of the incident light.

In glass and many other materials, red light travels fastest; it has the smallest index of refraction. Violet light, on the other hand, is slowed the

DEMONSTRATION: See Teacher Guide.

FIGURE 18–15. This rainbow is the result of dispersion of white light by water droplets in the air (a). Refraction occurs when rays pass into and out of a drop. Reflection occurs at the inside surface (b). Ray angles have been exaggerated for clarity.

a

b

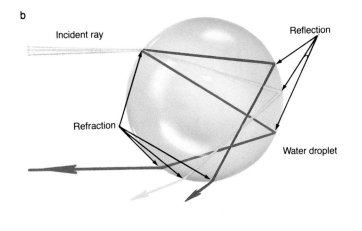

18:7 **Dispersion of Light** 313

FIGURE 18–16. The formation of the rainbow was explained by Rene Descartes about 1637.

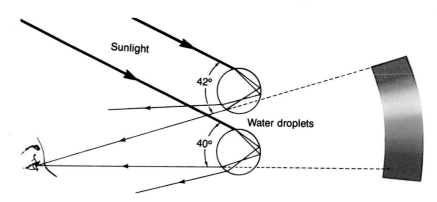

SUGGESTION: The picture in Figure 18–15 shows a faint secondary rainbow. Note that the colors are reversed in the secondary rainbow, which is produced by double reflection in the water droplets.

White light is dispersed into an array of colored light when it passes through a prism.

most; it has the largest index of refraction. As a result, when white light falls on a prism, red light is bent the least and violet light the most. The wavelengths (colors) are separated. The light leaving the prism is dispersed to form a spectrum. **Dispersion** is the separation of light into a spectrum by refraction.

PHYSICS FOCUS

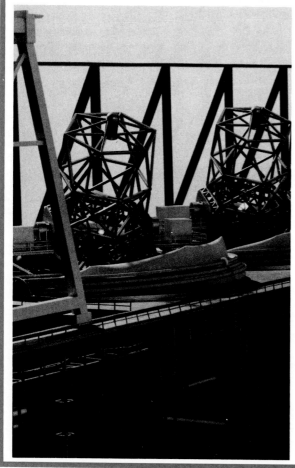

Stargazing Among the Stars

Astronomers have known for decades that to push the observational horizon farther back in space and time would require giant telescopes radically different from those existing today. Conventional technology encounters the problem of increased distortion of light as telescope mirrors become larger and more massive. Two approaches seemed possible: either build an observatory as an orbiting space station or design a new type of telescope for use on Earth.

An orbiting observatory has the important advantage of eliminating the refraction of light in Earth's atmosphere. Refraction in the atmosphere is what causes stars to "twinkle." Without this distortion, clearer images of distant objects are possible. Experiments already conducted in space have demonstrated the value of such an observatory. A powerful space telescope in orbit around Earth is one of the missions of the United States' space-shuttle program.

Ground-based telescopes are still important. New telescopes have been built with many small mirrors rather than one large mirror. These small mirrors must be continuously adjusted so they all focus light in the same place. Innovative engineering has led to changes from conventional passive telescopes (stiff mirrors with movable telescope) to active optics in which mirrors are constantly moved and kept in correct shape by computer-activated supports. A VLT (Very Large Telescope) using this technology is being constructed on a mountaintop in Chile to simulate a mirror sixteen meters in diameter. By comparison, the mirror in the largest U.S. telescope, the Hale Telescope at Mt. Palomar in California, is about five meters in diameter.

Different light sources have different spectra. Light from an incandescent lamp contains all visible wavelengths of light. When this light passes through a prism, a continuous band of color is seen. Light from a mercury street lamp emits most of its light at four individual wavelengths. Thus its spectrum is not a continuous band, but only lines at specific colors.

A rainbow is a spectrum formed when sunlight is dispersed by water droplets in the atmosphere. Sunlight that is incident on a water droplet refracts, and the light disperses (Figure 18–16). After undergoing total internal reflection at the back surface of the droplet, the light is dispersed more when it leaves the droplet. Although each droplet produces a complete spectrum, an observer will see only a certain wavelength of light from each droplet. The wavelength depends on the relative positions of sun, droplet, and observer. Because there are thousands of droplets in the sky, a complete spectrum is seen. The droplets reflecting red light make an angle of 42° with respect to the direction of the sun's rays; the droplets reflecting blue light make an angle of 40°. Note that in a droplet, the order of the spectrum is reversed. In other words, the blue wavelengths are on top and the red are on the bottom.

A visible spectrum is a display of color formed when a light beam of multiple wavelengths is bent and spread by passing through a prism.

A rainbow shows the various components of white light.

Red light has the longest wavelength and the highest speed for visible light in a medium. Violet light has the shortest wavelength and the lowest speed.

CHAPTER 18 REVIEW

SUMMARY

1. The law of reflection, the angle of reflection is equal to the angle of incidence, is obeyed by light rays. **18:1**
2. Refraction is the bending of light rays at the boundary between two media. Refraction occurs only when the incident ray strikes the boundary at an angle. **18:2**
3. Snell's law states that when light goes from a medium with small n to one with large n, it is bent toward the normal. Light going from materials with a large n to those with a small n is bent away from the normal. **18:3**
4. Total internal reflection occurs if light is incident on a boundary from the medium with the larger index of refraction. If the angle of incidence is greater than the critical angle, no light leaves; it is all reflected. **18:5**
5. Total internal reflection occurs when light passes from a more to a less dense medium at an angle greater than the critical angle. **18:5**
6. Light waves of different wavelengths have slightly different refractive indices. Thus they are refracted at different angles. Light falling on a prism is dispersed into a spectrum of colors. **18:7**

QUESTIONS

1. How does regular reflection differ from diffuse reflection?
2. If a light ray does not undergo refraction at the boundary between two transparent media, what is its angle of incidence?
3. How does the angle of incidence compare with the angle of refraction when a light ray passes from air into glass at an angle?
4. How does the angle of incidence compare with the angle of refraction when a light ray leaves glass and enters air?
5. State Snell's law.
6. Write equations for finding the index of refraction

of a medium in terms of speed and of angles.

7. What is the "critical angle" of incidence?

8. Explain mirages.

9. Which color of light travels fastest in glass—red, green, or blue?

10. What type of spectrum is provided by sunlight?

APPLYING CONCEPTS

1. Which two media, air and water, or air and glass, have the smaller critical angle?

2. Close to sunset you see a rainbow in the water from a lawn sprinkler. Carefully draw your location and the locations of the sun and the water from the sprinkler that shows the rainbow.

3. A prism bends violet light more than red light because **(a)** blue light travels slower in the prism, **(b)** red light travels slower in the prism, **(c)** blue light travels slower in the air, **(d)** red light travels slower in the air. Choose only one.

4. According to legend, Erik the Red sailed from Iceland and discovered Greenland after he had seen the land in a mirage. Draw a sketch of Iceland and Greenland and explain how the mirage might have occurred.

5. A dry road is a diffuse reflector while a wet road is not. Sketch a car with headlights illuminating the road ahead. Show why the driver would find the wet road much harder to see than the dry road.

6. Why would you never see a rainbow in the southern sky if you were in the northern hemisphere?

7. Examine Figure 18–5. Why do the three left-hand rays that enter the prism from the bottom exit vertically while the three right-hand rays exit horizontally? (If you look carefully, you will find that the fourth ray has some vertical intensity and that there is a trace of the third ray moving horizontally.)

8. If you crack the windshield in your car, you will see a silvery line along the crack. The two pieces of glass have separated at the crack, and there is air between them. The silvery line indicates light is reflecting off the crack. Draw a ray diagram to explain why this occurs. What phenomenon does this illustrate?

9. In the Example on Snell's law, a ray of light is incident upon crown glass at 30.0°. The angle of refraction is 19.2°. Assume the glass is rectangular in shape. Construct a diagram to show the incident ray, the refracted ray, and the normal. Continue the ray through the glass until it reaches the opposite edge.

a. Construct a normal at this point. What is the angle at which the refracted ray is incident upon the opposite edge of the glass?

b. Assume the material outside the opposite edge is air. What is the angle at which the ray leaves the glass?

c. As the ray leaves the glass, is it refracted away from the normal or toward the normal?

d. How is the orientation of the ray leaving the glass related to the ray entering the glass?

EXERCISES

1. A ray of light strikes a mirror at an angle of 53° to the normal.

a. What is the angle of reflection?

b. What is the angle between the incident ray and the reflected ray?

2. A ray of light incident upon a mirror makes an angle of 36.0° with the mirror. What is the angle between the incident ray and the reflected ray?

3. A ray of light is incident at an angle of 60.0° upon the surface of a piece of glass ($n = 1.5$). What is the angle of refraction?

4. A light ray strikes the surface of a pond at an angle of incidence of 36.0°. At what angle, to the nearest degree, is the ray refracted?

5. A ray of light travels from air into a liquid. The ray is incident upon the liquid at an angle of 30.0°. The angle of refraction is 22.0°.

a. What is the index of refraction of the liquid?

b. Refer to Table 18–1. What might the liquid be?

6. Light is incident at an angle of 60.0° on the surface of a diamond. Find the angle of refraction.

7. The speed of light in a clear plastic is 1.90×10^8 m/s. A ray of light enters the plastic at an angle of 22°. At what angle is the ray refracted?

8. A ray of light passes from water into crown glass at an angle of 23.2°. Find the angle of refraction.

9. A ray of light in flint glass is incident onto ethanol at an angle of 25.0°. At what angle does it enter the ethanol?

10. A thick sheet of plastic ($n = 1.500$) is used as the side of an aquarium tank. Light reflected from a fish in the water is incident onto the plastic at 35.0°. At what angle does the light enter the air?

11. A sheet of plastic ($n = 1.500$) 25 mm thick is used in a bank. A ray of light strikes the sheet at an angle of 45°. The ray leaves the sheet at 45° but at a different location. Use a ray diagram to find the distance between the ray that leaves and the one that would have left if the plastic were not there.

PROBLEMS

1. A ray of light is incident upon a 60-60-60-degree glass prism ($n = 1.5$) as shown in Figure 18–17.

   a. Using Snell's law, determine the angle θ_r to the nearest degree.

   b. Using elementary geometry, determine the values of angles A, B, and C.

FIGURE 18–17. Use with Problem 1.

   c. Angle C is actually the angle of incidence on the other side of the prism. However, the reversibility of light rays tells us that if angle D were the incident angle, angle C would be the angle of refraction. Assume this statement is true and determine angle D.

2. The index of refraction for a diamond for red light (656 nm) is 2.410, while that for blue light (434 nm) is 2.450. Suppose white light is incident on the diamond at 30.0°. Find the angles of refraction for these two colors.

3. The index of refraction for crown glass for red light is 1.514, while that for blue light is 1.528. White light is incident on the glass at 30.0°.

   a. Find the angles of refraction for these two colors.

   b. Compare the difference in angles to that for diamond.

   c. Use the results to explain why diamonds are said to have "fire."

4. The critical angle for crown glass in air is 41°. What is the critical angle if the glass is immersed in water?

5. A light ray enters a rectangle of glass as shown in Figure 18–18. Use a ray diagram to trace the path of the ray until it leaves the right-hand face of the glass.

Problem 5

FIGURE 18–18. Use with Problem 5.

6. A light source, S, is located 2.0 m below the surface of a swimming pool and 1.5 m from one edge of the pool. The pool is filled with water ($n = 1.33$) to the top.

   a. At what angle does the light reaching the edge of the pool leave the water?

   b. Does this cause the light viewed from this angle to appear deeper or shallower than it actually is?

7. A beam of light strikes the flat, glass side of a water-filled aquarium at an angle of 40° to the normal. The index of refraction for glass and water are 1.50 and 1.33, respectively.

   a. At what angle does the beam enter the glass?

   b. At what angle does the beam enter the water?

   c. What would be the entry angle if the beam struck the water directly?

8. How many more minutes would it take light from the sun to reach Earth if the space between them were filled with water rather than a vacuum? The sun is 1.5×10^8 km from Earth.

READINGS

Harris, Whitney, "The Corner Reflector." *The Mathematics Teacher,* February, 1983.

Mandolini, Dina, "Fiber Optics in Plants." *Scientific American,* August, 1984.

Millman, Anne, "The Light in the Tomb." *Science Digest,* May, 1983.

Olivastro, D., "About the Looking Glass." *Science,* June, 1988.

CHAPTER 19

Mirrors and Lenses

GOALS

1. You will become familiar with the characteristics of mirrors and lenses.
2. You will be able to locate and describe the images formed by mirrors and lenses.
3. You will gain a knowledge of instruments that use mirrors and lenses.

We are so accustomed to using mirrors and lenses that we give them little thought. We take for granted the truly wonderful phenomena they make possible. From our first look in a mirror in the morning to our last look at television in the evening, we live with applications of the laws of reflection and refraction. Eyeglasses, magnifying glasses, microscopes, and cameras use the laws of refraction. The rearview mirror in a car and the three-way mirror in a clothing store demonstrate the laws of reflection. Even more immediate, our entire view of the world is the result of the optical images formed on our retinas by the lenses in our eyes.

19:1 Objects and Their Images in Plane Mirrors

When you look at yourself in a bathroom mirror, you are seeing your image in a plane mirror. A **plane mirror** is a flat, smooth surface that reflects light in a regular way. You are the object. An **object** is a source of diverging light rays. An object may be luminous, like a candle or lamp. More often an object is illuminated and then diffusely reflects light in all directions. Figure 19–1 shows how some of the rays from point P strike the mirror and are reflected with equal angles of incidence and reflection. After reflection, the rays continue to spread. If we extend the rays backward, behind the mirror, as done with the dashed lines in Figure 19–1, we find that they intersect at a point P'. Point P', where the rays intersect, is called the **image.** To an observer, the light rays appear to meet to form an image at point P', but of course, no light is really there. For that reason, this kind of image is called a **virtual image.**

While experimenting with a lens, Leslie produced this image of a butterfly on the screen. Jerome was amazed. He said, "That must be a diverging lens, since the butterfly image is spread out and is larger than the real butterfly." Leslie replied, "Maybe, but I am not so sure." Who is correct?

FIGURE 19–1. Formation of an image in a plane mirror.

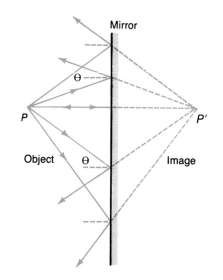

SUGGESTION: Refer to Figure 19–3a and ask students how long a mirror has to be so you can see your whole length, and at what height do you have to hang it on the wall.

DEMONSTRATIONS: See the Teacher Guide.

The image is the same size as the object and the same distance behind the mirror as the object is in front of the mirror.

FIGURE 19–2. Ray diagram for finding an image in a plane mirror is shown in (a). Two rays from the object are traced to the point behind the mirror at which they intersect. The image appears behind the mirror (b).

Where is the image located? Figure 19–2 shows two rays from object P. One strikes the mirror at B, the other at M. Both rays are reflected with equal angles of incidence and reflection. Thus the triangles BPM and BP'M are congruent. From P to B, the distance between the object and the mirror, is d_o. From P' to B, the distance between the image and the mirror, is d_i; $d_o = d_i$. The image is the same distance behind the mirror that the object is in front of it. In a similar way, as shown in Figure 19–3a, you can show that the image is the same size as the object.

In Figure 19–3b and c, the right and left ears of an image appear to be reversed. You might ask why the top and bottom are not also reversed. If you look at the figure carefully, you will see that the direction that is really reversed is the one perpendicular to the mirror. Thus it is more correct to say that the front and back of an image are reversed. Left and right are interchanged, in a way, by pushing the nose through the face in the same manner that a right-hand glove can be worn on the left hand by turning it inside out.

b

a.

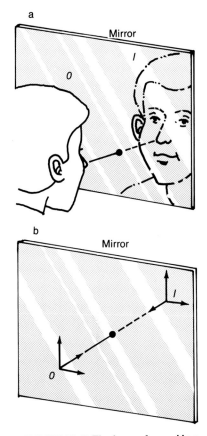

FIGURE 19–3. The image formed in a plane mirror is the same size as the object and is the same distance behind the mirror as the object is in front (a). A mirror seems to reverse right and left (b). More careful consideration shows that it interchanges front and back (c).

19:2 Concave Mirrors

Examine the inside surface of a spoon. It acts like a concave mirror. A **concave mirror** reflects light from its inner ("caved in") surface. In a spherical concave mirror, the mirror is part of the inner surface of a sphere, Figure 19–4. The sphere of radius r has a geometric center, C. Point A is the center of the mirror, and the line CA is the **principal axis,** the straight line perpendicular to the mirror at its center.

How does light reflect from a concave mirror? Think of a concave mirror as a large number of small plane mirrors arranged around the surface of a sphere. Each mirror is perpendicular to a radius of the sphere. When a ray strikes a mirror, it is reflected with equal angles of incidence and reflection. A ray parallel to the principal axis is reflected at P and crosses the principal axis at point F, as in Figure 19–4. A parallel ray an equal distance below the principal axis would, by symmetry, also cross the principal axis at F. These parallel rays would meet, or converge, at the focal point of the mirror. A concave mirror is also called a **converging mirror** because parallel rays converge at the focal point. The two sides FC and FP of the triangle CFP are equal in length. Thus for small angles, the focal point, F, is half the distance between the mirror and the center of curvature, C.

How can you find the location of the focal point of a concave mirror? The sun is far enough away that all rays from it are parallel for all practical purposes. Therefore, if you point the principal axis of a concave mirror at the sun, all the rays will be reflected through the focal point. Hold a piece

The principal axis is an imaginary line extending from the geometric center of a spherical mirror to its center of curvature, C.

FIGURE 19–4. The focus of a concave spherical mirror is located halfway between the center of curvature and the mirror surface. Rays entering parallel to the optical axis are reflected to converge at the focal point.

FIGURE 19–5. The many plane mirrors of a solar oven reflect light to one small area (a). The surface of a curved mirror reflects light to a given point (b) much like a group of plane mirrors arranged in a curve (c).

The focal length, f, is the distance from F to A.

The focal point, F, of a converging mirror is the point where parallel rays of light meet after being reflected from the mirror.

Spherical aberration occurs because rays that strike a spherical mirror along its outer edge are not reflected through F.

DEMONSTRATION: See the Teacher Guide.

of paper near the mirror and move the paper toward and away from the mirror until the smallest and sharpest image is formed. The image is at the focal point. The distance from the focal point to the mirror along the principal axis is the **focal length,** f, of the mirror. The focal length is half the radius of curvature of the mirror.

19:3 Spherical Aberration and Parabolic Mirrors

The distance FP in Figure 19–4 is equal to the focal length only if the angle of incidence is small. As seen in Figure 19–6, the two rays farthest from the principal axis are reflected to a convergence point slightly closer to the mirror than the others. The image formed by parallel rays in a large spherical mirror is not a perfect point. This effect is called **spherical aberration** (ab uh RAY shuhn).

Parabolic mirrors have no spherical aberration. They are used to focus parallel rays from distant stars to a sharp focus in telescopes. Parabolic mirrors produce the parallel beams of light needed in flashlights, car headlights, and searchlights. In these applications, the light source is placed at F and the reflected rays leave in a parallel beam.

19:4 Real vs Virtual Images

Rays of the sun or some other distant object that reflect from a concave mirror converge at the focal point of the mirror. The converging rays can be seen on a piece of paper held at that point. An image produced by rays that actually converge can be seen on a piece of paper or screen placed at the image point and is called a **real image.**

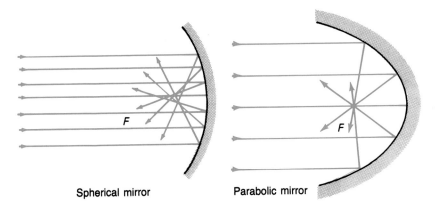

Spherical mirror   Parabolic mirror

In contrast, the image produced by a plane mirror is behind the mirror. The rays reflected from a plane mirror never actually converge but appear to diverge from a point behind the mirror. A virtual image cannot be projected on a screen or captured on a piece of paper because no light rays actually pass through a virtual image.

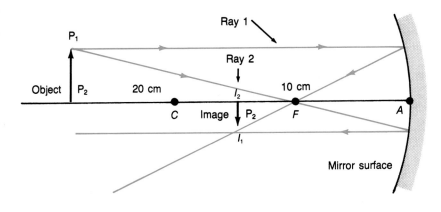

Ray 1

Ray 2

Object   P₂   20 cm I_2 10 cm

C   Image P_2 F   A

I_1

Mirror surface

19:5   Real Images Formed by Concave Mirrors

Concave mirrors can form both real and virtual images. We will use ray diagrams to show how concave mirrors form real images and how to locate these images.

Figure 19–7 shows a concave mirror with an object farther from the mirror than C. Such an object is said to be "beyond C." When light falls on it, rays are reflected in all directions. Some fall on the mirror. We will now find the image formed by those rays.

PROBLEM SOLVING

Two rules are used to find the images formed by mirrors.
A. Incident light rays parallel to the principal axis of a mirror are reflected through the focal point.
B. Incident rays that pass through the focal point are reflected parallel to the principal axis.

Ray diagrams can be used to locate images graphically.

When drawing ray diagrams of virtual images, be sure to leave room for the image to the right of the mirror.

The mirror equation can be used to locate the image.

A negative image distance indicates a virtual image.

To construct a ray diagram, follow these steps:

1. Choose a scale. Your goal is to make the drawing close to the width of your paper, about 20 cm. If the object is beyond F, the image is real. If the object is beyond 2F, the object distance is larger than the image distance. If not, the image distance is larger. Choose the scale such that the larger distance, object or image, is 15 to 20 cm. Let 1 cm equal 1, 2, 4, 5, or 10 cm, never 3, 6, or 7 cm.

2. Draw the principal axis and put the mirror at the right-hand side of the paper. Draw the mirror as a straight line. Place a dot on the axis at the location of the focal point.

3. Draw the object. Usually the object and image height have to be drawn to a different scale to be visible.

4. Select a point, P_1, to be the top of the object. Draw Ray 1 parallel to the principal axis. It is called the parallel ray and reflects through the focal point, F. Draw Ray 2 so it passes through F on its way to the mirror. Ray 2 is called the focus ray. This ray reflects parallel to the principal axis. The two rays drawn from P_1 converge at I_1, beyond F.

5. Select a second point at the bottom of the object and draw two rays. Normally you choose the second point, P_2, to be on the principal axis. In this case, both rays are along the optical axis and reflect along the principal axis. The bottom of the image is located on the principal axis at I_2.

6. Draw the image as a line between the two sets of ray crossings.

The image formed by an object beyond C is between C and F. It is a real image because the rays actually come together at this point. The image is inverted; point I_1 is below the principal axis. The image is also smaller than the object.

As an object is moved inward toward C, the image position moves outward toward C. When the object is at C, the image is also located there. The image is real, inverted, and, in this case, the same size as the object. If the object is moved between C and F, the image moves out beyond C. This can be seen by reversing the direction of the light rays in Figure 19–7. The roles of image and object are reversed. Parts a, b, and c of Figure 9–11 summarize these relationships.

An equation can also be used to locate the image and find its size. The focal length, f, the distance of the object from the mirror, d_o, and the distance of the image from the mirror, d_i, are related by the **mirror equation.**

$$\frac{1}{d_o} + \frac{1}{d_i} = \frac{1}{f}$$

The ratio of the size of the image, h_i, to the size of the object, h_o, is called the **magnification,** m. The magnification is related to the distances to the mirror by the equation

$$m = \frac{h_i}{h_o} = \frac{-d_i}{d_o}$$

Both m and h_i are negative. This means the image is inverted.

EXAMPLE

Real Image from a Concave Mirror

An object 2.0 cm high is 30.0 cm from a concave mirror. The radius of curvature of the mirror is 20.0 cm. **a.** What is the location of the image? **b.** What is the size of the image?

Given: object height
(h_o) = 2.0 cm
object location
(d_o) = 30.0 cm
radius of curvature
(r) = 20.0 cm

Unknowns: **a.** image location (d_i)
b. image height (h_i)

Basic equations:

$$f = \frac{r}{2}$$

$$\frac{1}{d_o} + \frac{1}{d_i} = \frac{1}{f}$$

$$m = \frac{h_i}{h_o}$$

$$= \frac{-d_i}{d_o}$$

Solution: **a.** $f = \frac{1}{2}(20.0 \text{ cm}) = 10.0 \text{ cm}$

$$\frac{1}{d_o} + \frac{1}{d_i} = \frac{1}{f}$$

Solving the equation for d_i yields

$$\frac{1}{d_i} = \frac{1}{f} - \frac{1}{d_o}$$

$$= \frac{d_o - f}{d_o f}$$

$$d_i = \frac{d_o f}{d_o - f}$$

$$d_i = \frac{(30.0 \text{ cm})(10.0 \text{ cm})}{30.0 \text{ cm} - 10.0 \text{ cm}}$$

$$= 15.0 \text{ cm}$$

b. $\dfrac{h_i}{h_o} = \dfrac{-d_i}{d_o}$

$$h_i = \frac{-h_o d_i}{d_o}$$

$$= \frac{-(2.0 \text{ cm})(15.0 \text{ cm})}{(30.0 \text{ cm})}$$

$$= -1.0 \text{ cm}$$

The negative sign indicates that the image is inverted.

For Your Information

A *corner reflector* consists of three plane mirrors fastened together like an inside corner of a cube. A corner reflector will reflect a beam of light directly back toward the source, no matter how the reflector is oriented. The glowing "cat's eyes" that mark the boundaries of many highways and runways are made of corner reflectors. LAGEOS, a laser geodynamic satellite, contains over four hundred corner reflectors. By bouncing laser signals off of these reflectors, geologists can measure continental drift to within two centimeters.

You can build your own corner reflector with three pocket-size plane mirrors or three mirrored wall panels. Tape the mirrors together to form one corner of a cube, or tape them to an aluminum corner brace.

SUGGESTION: Students are asked to derive the lens (and mirror) equation in Review Problem 9.

For Your Information

Practice Exercises

1. A concave mirror has a 20.0-cm radius of curvature. Find the image of an object located 15.0 cm from the mirror using
   a. a ray diagram.
   b. the mirror equation.
2. Solve the Example in Section 19:5 using a ray diagram.
3. An object 3.0 mm high is 10.0 cm in front of a concave mirror having a 6.0-cm focal length. Find the image by means of
   a. a ray diagram.
   b. the mirror equation.
   c. Find the magnification of the mirror.
   d. What is the height of the image?
4. The image of an object is 30.0 cm from a concave mirror with a 20.0-cm radius of curvature. Locate the object.

19:6 Virtual Images Formed by Concave Mirrors

We have seen that as the object approaches the focal point, F, of a mirror, the image moves farther out. If the object is at the focal point, all reflected rays are parallel. The object is said to be at infinity. What happens if the object is closer to the mirror than F? Figure 19–8 shows an object 5.0 cm in front of a mirror of 10.0 cm focal length. The two rays have been drawn to locate the image. Ray 1 approaches the mirror parallel to the principal axis and is reflected through the focal point. Ray 2 moves from the object as if it has come from the focal point. It is reflected parallel to the principal axis. The two reflected rays spread apart and will never converge. No real image exists. The dashed lines show the rays traced back behind the mirror to their apparent origin. A virtual image is located behind the mirror.

If an object is located between the focal point and a concave mirror, its image will be virtual, erect, and enlarged. Shaving and makeup mirrors are concave. If you hold the mirror close to your face, the image will be virtual, erect, and enlarged.

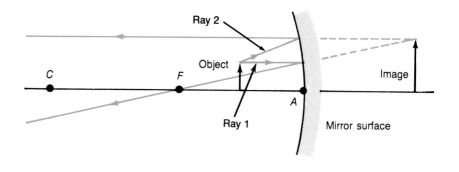

FIGURE 19–8. Finding the virtual image formed by a concave spherical mirror when the object is located between the mirror and F.

EXAMPLE

Virtual Image from a Concave Mirror

Find the location of the image in Figure 19–8 if an object 2.0 cm in height is 5.0 cm in front of a concave mirror of focal length 10.0 cm.

Given: $h_o = 2.0$ cm

$d_o = 5.0$ cm

$f = 10.0$ cm

Unknowns: a. d_i **b.** h_i

Basic equations: $\dfrac{1}{d_o} + \dfrac{1}{d_i} = \dfrac{1}{f}$

$m = \dfrac{h_i}{h_o} = \dfrac{-d_i}{d_o}$

Solution: a. $\dfrac{1}{d_o} + \dfrac{1}{d_i} = \dfrac{1}{f}$

$\dfrac{1}{d_i} = \dfrac{1}{f} - \dfrac{1}{d_o}$

$d_i = \dfrac{d_o f}{d_o - f} = \dfrac{(5.0 \text{ cm})(10.0 \text{ cm})}{5.0 \text{ cm} - 10.0 \text{ cm}}$

$= \dfrac{5.0 \times 10^1 \text{ cm}^2}{-5.0 \text{ cm}} = -1.0 \times 10^1$ cm

A negative image distance indicates a virtual image.

b. $\dfrac{h_i}{h_o} = \dfrac{-d_i}{d_o}$

$h_i = \dfrac{-h_o d_i}{d_o}$

$= \dfrac{-(2.0 \text{ cm})(-1.0 \times 10^1 \text{ cm})}{5.0 \text{ cm}} = +4.0$ cm

A positive height indicates an upright image.

The negative image distance indicates that the image is behind the mirror; it is virtual. The positive height shows that the image is erect. Notice that the image height is larger than the object height; the image is enlarged.

Practice Exercises

5. An object is 4.0 cm in front of a concave mirror having a 12.0-cm radius. Locate the image using the mirror equation.

6. A concave mirror has a focal length of 9.0 cm. A 15-mm high object is placed 6.0 cm from the mirror.
   a. Find the image using the mirror equation.
   b. How large is the image?

7. A 4.0-cm high candle is placed 10.0 cm from a concave mirror having a focal length of 16.0 cm.
   a. Where is the image located?
   b. What is the height of the candle's image?

For Your Information

Any bright object several meters or more from the mirror can be used in place of the sun to find the focal length approximately.

FIGURE 19–9. Convex spherical mir-rors cause reflected light rays to di-verge.

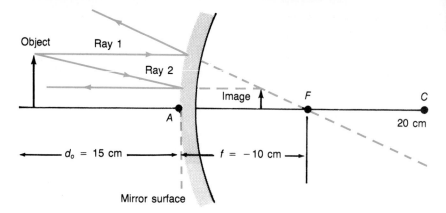

FIGURE 19–9. Convex spherical mir-rors cause reflected light rays to di-verge.

19:7 Virtual Images Formed by Convex Mirrors

A **convex mirror** is a spherical mirror that reflects light from its outer surface. The outside of a spoon is a convex mirror. Rays reflected from a convex mirror diverge. Thus, convex mirrors never form real images. The focal point, F, is behind the mirror. It is half the distance to the center of curvature. The focal length, f, of a convex mirror is negative.

A convex mirror is a diverging mirror.

The ray diagram in Figure 19–9 shows how an image is formed in a convex mirror. Ray 1 approaches the mirror parallel to the principal axis and is reflected. The path of the reflected ray is in the direction of a ray (dashed line) that comes from the focal point, F. Ray 2 approaches the mirror on a path that, if extended behind the mirror, would pass through F. The reflected part of Ray 2 is parallel to the principal axis. The two reflected rays diverge, as if coming from a point behind the mirror. The image, located at the apparent intersection behind the mirror, is virtual, erect, and reduced in size.

SUGGESTION: Obtain a curved rearview mirror and pass it around. Have the students hold it far away and close and notice that the image is always upright and smaller.

Convex mirrors are called diverging mirrors because the reflected rays spread apart. Convex mirrors form images reduced in size, but they can reflect a large field of view. Rearview mirrors used in cars are often con-vex mirrors, as are mirrors used in stores to watch for shoplifters.

Images formed by diverging mirrors are always virtual, erect, and smaller than the object.

DEMONSTRATION: See the Teacher Guide.

FIGURE 19–10. Convex mirrors are used to show a large field of view.

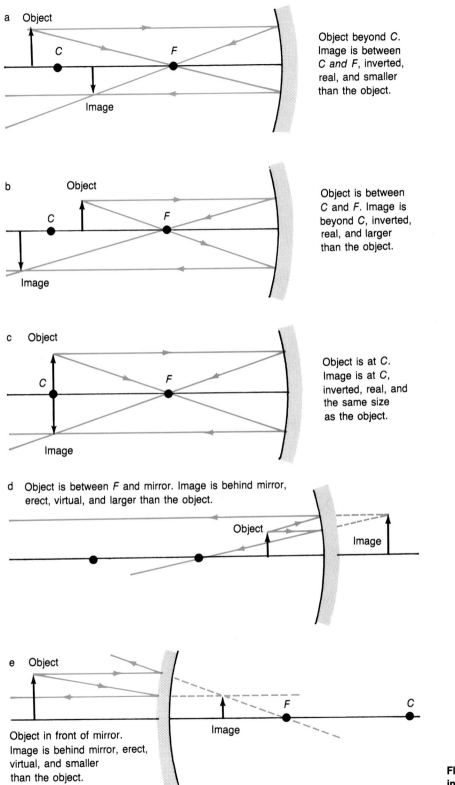

a Object beyond C. Image is between C and F, inverted, real, and smaller than the object.

b Object is between C and F. Image is beyond C, inverted, real, and larger than the object.

c Object is at C. Image is at C, inverted, real, and the same size as the object.

d Object is between F and mirror. Image is behind mirror, erect, virtual, and larger than the object.

e Object in front of mirror. Image is behind mirror, erect, virtual, and smaller than the object.

FIGURE 19–11. Formation of images in spherical mirrors.

EXAMPLE

Image from a Convex Mirror

Calculate the position of the image in Figure 19–9. Use the mirror equation.

Given: $d_o = 15$ cm $\qquad$ **Unknown:** d_i
$\qquad\quad f = -10.0$ cm

Basic equation: $\dfrac{1}{d_o} + \dfrac{1}{d_i} = \dfrac{1}{f}$

Solution: $\dfrac{1}{d_o} + \dfrac{1}{d_i} = \dfrac{1}{f}$

$$d_i = \frac{d_o f}{d_o - f}$$

$$= \frac{(15 \text{ cm})(-10.0 \text{ cm})}{15 \text{ cm} - (-10.0 \text{ cm})}$$

$$= \frac{-150 \text{ cm}}{25}$$

$$= -6.0 \text{ cm}$$

Practice Exercises

8. An object is 20.0 cm in front of a convex mirror with a −15.0-cm focal length. Find the location of the image using
   a. a ray diagram.
   b. the mirror equation.

9. A convex mirror has a focal length of −12 cm. A light bulb with a diameter of 6.0 cm is placed 60.0 cm in front of the mirror.
   a. Where is the image of the light bulb? Use the mirror equation.
   b. What is the diameter of the image?

10. In a department store, a mirror used to watch for shoplifters has a focal length of −40.0 cm. A person stands in an aisle 6.0 m from the mirror. Locate the person's image using the mirror equation.

19:8 Lenses

Eyeglasses were made from lenses as early as the thirteenth century. Around 1610, Galileo combined two lenses into a telescope. With this instrument he discovered the moons of Jupiter. Lenses have since been used in optical instruments such as microscopes and cameras. Lenses are probably the most useful and important of all optical devices.

A **lens** is made of glass or plastic with a refractive index larger than that of air. Each of its two faces is part of a sphere and can either be convex or concave. One face may also be plane, or flat. A lens is called **convex** if it is thicker at the center than at the edges. Convex lenses are converging lenses because they refract parallel light rays so that they meet. **Concave** lenses are thinner in the middle than at the edges and are called diverging lenses. Rays refracted through concave lenses spread out.

FIGURE 19–12. Light is refracted as it passes through a lens. In (a) the rays converge while in (b) they diverge.

a

b

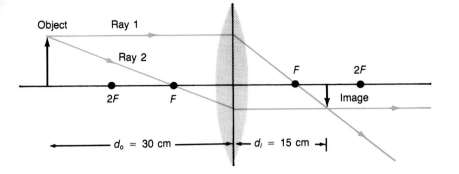

A converging lens is thick in the center and thin at the edges.

19:9 Real Images Formed by Convex Lenses

A convex lens can form an image that can be projected on a screen. In Figure 19–14, a convex lens is used to form an image of the sun on a leaf. As in the case of a mirror, the principal axis of a lens is a line perpendicular to the plane of the lens that passes through its midpoint. Light rays that approach a convex lens parallel to the principal axis, as in the case of the rays of the sun, will, upon refraction, converge to a point. This point is called the focal point, *F*, of the lens. The distance from the lens to the focal point is the focal length, *f*. The focal length of a lens depends on its shape and on the refractive index of the lens material.

Let us trace rays from an object far from a convex lens, Figure 19–13. Ray 1 is parallel to the principal axis. It refracts and passes through *F* on the other side of the lens. Ray 2 passes through *F* on its way to the lens. After refraction, its path is parallel to the principal axis. The two rays intersect beyond *F*, locating the image. Rays selected from other points on the object would converge at corresponding points on the image. Note that the image is real, inverted, and smaller than the object.

To find the image of an object that is close to the focal point, reverse the path of light through the lens in Figure 19–13. The image and object are reversed. The image is again real and inverted, but it is now larger than the object.

A diverging lens is thin in the center and thick at the edges.

A convex lens is a converging lens. A concave lens is a diverging lens.

The focal point of a converging lens is the point where rays that approach the lens parallel to the principal axis meet after being refracted by the lens.

The focal length of a lens depends on its shape and its index of refraction.

The image and object can be reversed.

FIGURE 19–14. This camper is using a converging lens to start a fire in this pile of leaves.

19:9 Real Images Formed by Convex Lenses 331

FIGURE 19–15. If an object is located at a distance greater than 2F, the image in the lens appears inverted.

If the object were placed at a distance twice the focal length from the lens, the point 2F on Figure 19–13, then the image would also be at 2F. By symmetry, the two have the same size. Thus we see that if an object is more than twice the focal length from the lens, the image is reduced in size. If it is between F and 2F, then the image is enlarged.

The lens equation can also be used to find the location of the image and the magnification equation can be used to find its size.

$$\frac{1}{d_o} + \frac{1}{d_i} = \frac{1}{f}$$

$$m = \frac{h_i}{h_o} = \frac{-d_i}{d_o}$$

The **lens equation,** as well as the equation for magnification, is the same as that used for mirrors.

EXAMPLE

Real Images from a Convex Lens

In Figure 19–13, the object is 32.0 cm from a convex lens of 8.0 cm focal length. Use the lens equation to locate the image.

Given: $d_o = 32.0$ cm   Unknown: d_i
$\quad\quad\quad f = 8.0$ cm

Basic equation: $\frac{1}{d_o} + \frac{1}{d_i} = \frac{1}{f}$

Solution: $\frac{1}{d_o} + \frac{1}{d_i} = \frac{1}{f}$

$$d_i = \frac{d_o f}{d_o - f} = \frac{(32.0 \text{ cm})(8.0 \text{ cm})}{32.0 \text{ cm} - 8.0 \text{ cm}}$$

$$= 10.7 \text{ cm}$$

Practice Exercises

11. Use a ray diagram to find the image position of an object 30 cm from a convex lens with a 10-cm focal length. (Let 1 cm on the drawing represent 2 cm.)

12. An object 12 mm high is placed in front of a convex lens of 10.0 cm focal length so that its image is 30.0 cm from the lens. Find the location of the object and the size of the image

    a. using a ray diagram.

    b. using the lens equation.

13. An object 2.25 mm high is 8.5 cm in front of a convex lens of 5.5-cm focal length. Find the image distance and height.

14. An object is placed in front of a 25-mm focal length convex lens so that its image is the same height as the object. What are the image and object distances?

For Your Information

The earliest eyeglasses were made of thick convex lenses. These lenses reminded their makers of lentils. Hence the term *lens*, from the Latin for "lentil beans."

FIGURE 19–16. Finding the virtual image formed by a converging lens when the object is placed between the lens and principal focus, *F*.

19:10 Virtual Images Formed by Convex Lenses

If an object is placed at the focal point of a convex lens, the refracted rays will emerge in a parallel beam. If the object is brought closer, the rays do not converge on the opposite side of the lens. The image appears on the same side of the lens as the object. This image is virtual, erect, and enlarged.

Figure 19–16 shows how a convex lens forms a virtual image. The object is between *F* and the lens. Ray 1, as usual, approaches the lens parallel to the principal axis and is refracted through the focal point, *F*. Ray 2 starts at the tip of the object, in the direction it would have if it had started at *F* on the object side of the lens. It leaves the lens parallel to the principal axis. Rays 1 and 2 diverge as they leave the lens. Thus no real image is possible. Tracing the two rays back to their apparent intersection locates the virtual image. It is on the same side as the object, erect, and larger than the object. A magnifying glass is a convex lens used to produce an enlarged, virtual image.

If an object is placed between a converging lens and its focal point, a virtual, enlarged image is produced.

SUGGESTION: Distribute some convex lenses. Have students hold the lens close to some printing and then move it gradually away so they can see the image change from a magnified erect image to a smaller inverted image.

EXAMPLE

Virtual Image from a Convex Lens

An object is 4.0 cm from a convex lens of 6.0-cm focal length.
a. Locate its image. **b.** What kind of image is formed?

Given: $d_o = 4.0$ cm   Unknown: d_i
$f = 6.0$ cm

Basic equation: $\dfrac{1}{d_o} + \dfrac{1}{d_i} = \dfrac{1}{f}$

Solution:

a. $\dfrac{1}{d_o} + \dfrac{1}{d_i} = \dfrac{1}{f}$ so $\dfrac{1}{d_i} = \dfrac{1}{f} - \dfrac{1}{d_o}$

$$d_i = \frac{d_o f}{d_o - f} = \frac{(4.0 \text{ cm})(6.0 \text{ cm})}{4.0 \text{ cm} - 6.0 \text{ cm}} = -12 \text{ cm}$$

b. Since the image distance is negative, the image is virtual. It is on the same side of the lens as the object.

Practice Exercises

15. A newspaper is held 6.0 cm from a convex lens of 20.0-cm focal length. Find the image distance of the newsprint image.

16. A magnifying glass has a focal length of 12 cm. A coin, 2.0 cm in diameter, is placed 3.4 cm from the lens.
    a. Locate the image of the coin.
    b. What is the diameter of the image?

17. An object is 8.0 cm from a lens. What focal length must the lens have to form a virtual, erect image 16.0 cm from the lens?

18. Suppose you are looking at a stamp through a magnifying glass and want to increase the size of the image. Should you move the glass closer to the stamp or farther away? Explain and indicate the maximum distance you should move it.

19:11 Virtual Images Formed by Concave Lenses

Image formation by a concave lens is shown in Figure 19–17. A concave lens causes all rays to diverge. Ray 1 approaches the lens parallel to the principal axis. It leaves the lens in the direction it would have if it had passed through the focal point. Ray 2 passes directly through the center of the lens. Such a ray is not bent at all. Rays 1 and 2 diverge after passing through the lens. Their apparent intersection is *I*, on the same side of the lens as the object. The image is virtual, erect, and reduced in size. This is true no matter how far from the lens the object is located. The focal length of a concave lens is negative. Concave lenses are used in eyeglasses to correct nearsightedness and in combination with convex lenses in cameras and telescopes.

SUGGESTION: Have students look through a concave lens at some printing as they move the lens away from the paper. They will see the image upright and smaller than the object.

Images formed by concave lenses are always virtual and erect.

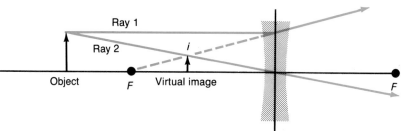

FIGURE 19–17. Formation of a virtual image by a concave lens.

19:12 Chromatic Aberration

The edges of a lens resemble a prism, and different wavelengths of light are bent at slightly different angles. Thus, the light that passes through a lens, especially near the edges, is slightly dispersed. An object viewed through a lens appears ringed with color. This effect is called **chromatic aberration.** The term chromatic comes from the Greek *chromo,* related to color.

Chromatic aberration is always present when a single lens is used. By joining a converging lens with a diverging lens that has a different index of refraction, chromatic aberration can be eliminated. Both lenses disperse the light. However, the dispersion caused by the converging lens is canceled by that caused by the diverging lens. The index of refraction of the diverging lens is chosen so that the combination lens still converges the light. A lens constructed in this way is called an achromatic lens. All precision optical instruments use achromatic lenses.

SUGGESTION: Find a lens that exhibits chromatic aberration and let the students examine it.

Chromatic aberration limits the sharpness of an image.

Newton invented the reflecting telescope because of this lens defect.

a   b

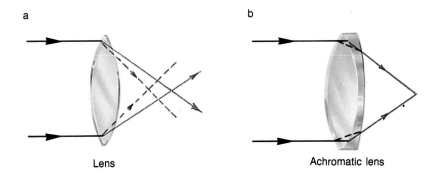

Lens   Achromatic lens

FIGURE 19–18. Chromatic aberration occurs when light passing through a lens is dispersed, causing an object to appear ringed with color (a). An achromatic lens reduces chromatic aberration (b).

19:13 Optical Instruments

Although the eye itself is a remarkable optical device, its abilities can be greatly extended by a wide variety of instruments based on lenses and mirrors. The eye is a fluid-filled, almost spherical object that focuses the image of an object on the retina. Most of the refraction occurs at the curved surface of the cornea. The eye lens is made of flexible material with a refractive index different from that of the fluid. Muscles can change the shape of the lens, thereby changing its focal length. This permits images of objects from infinitely far away to as close as 15 cm to be focused on the retina.

If the shape of the cornea or of the eye itself is distorted, external lenses, eyeglasses or contact lenses, are needed to adjust the focal length and move the image to the retina. The cause of nearsightedness (myopia) is usually a bulging cornea or an elongated eyeball. Images of distant objects are formed in front of the retina. Concave lenses correct this defect by diverging the light rays, increasing the image distance, and placing the image on the retina. Farsightedness (hyperopia) can be caused by a shortened eyeball. In people more than 45 years old, farsightedness is often caused by the lens' inability to change shape. The image of nearby objects is formed behind the retina. Convex lenses converge the light rays, reducing the image distance. The image is focused on the retina and the defect is corrected.

Corrective glasses, microscopes, and telescopes are important uses of lenses.

SUGGESTION: If a small telescope is available, bring it to class for the students to inspect the lenses.

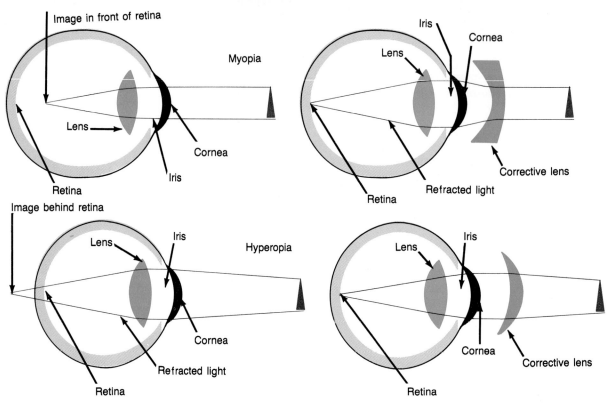

Myopia

Hyperopia

FIGURE 19–19. A person with far-sightedness (hyperopia) cannot see close objects. The image is focused behind the retina. A convex lens will correct the problem by refracting light to focus the image on the retina. A person with nearsightedness (myopia) cannot see distant objects. The image is focused in front of the retina. A concave lens will correct this defect.

Microscopes allow the eye to see extremely small objects. They use at least two convex lenses. An object is placed very close to a lens with a very short focal length, the objective lens. This lens produces a real image located between the second lens, the eyepiece lens, and its focal point. The eyepiece produces a greatly magnified virtual image of the image formed by the objective lens.

An astronomical refracting telescope uses two convex lenses. The objective lens of a telescope has a long focal length. The parallel rays from a star or other distant object come to focus in a plane at the focal point of this lens. The eyepiece lens, with a short focal length, then refracts the rays into another parallel beam. The viewer sees a virtual, enlarged, inverted image. The primary purpose of a telescope is not to magnify the image. It is to increase the angle between the rays from two different stars and to collect more light than would strike the unaided eye.

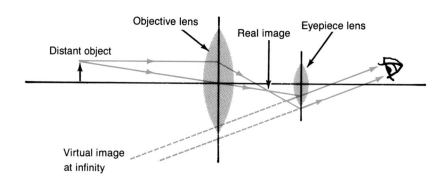

FIGURE 19–20. The lens system of an astronomical telescope has two converging lenses.

336 Mirrors and Lenses

CHAPTER 19 REVIEW

SUMMARY

1. The image in a plane mirror is the same size as the object. It is as far behind the mirror as the object is in front of the mirror. The image is virtual and erect. **19:1**

2. The focal point of a spherical mirror, concave or convex, is halfway between the center of curvature of the mirror and the mirror. **19:2**

3. The distance from the focal point to the center of the mirror is the focal length of the mirror. **19:2**

4. An imaginary line that passes from the center of the mirror through the center of curvature and beyond is called the principal axis of the mirror. **19:2**

5. The light rays that fall on the outer edges of a spherical mirror do not pass through its focal point. This defect is called spherical aberration. **19:3**

6. A real image is located where light rays converge and can be displayed on a screen. Light rays appear to converge at a virtual image. A virtual image cannot be displayed on a screen. **19:4**

7. Concave mirrors produce real, inverted images if the object is farther from the mirror than the focal point. A virtual image is formed if the object is between the mirror and the focal point. **19:5, 19:6**

8. Convex mirrors always produce virtual, upright, reduced images. **19:7**

9. Lenses that are thinner at their outer edges than at their centers are called converging or convex lenses. Lenses that are thicker at their outer edges are diverging or concave lenses. **19:8**

10. The location of an image can be found either by ray tracing or by using the lens or mirror equation, as fits the situation. The equation is the same in either case. **19:9**

11. Chromatic aberration is a lens defect caused by the dispersion of different wavelengths of light as they pass through the lens. **19:12**

QUESTIONS

1. Describe the image of a person seen in a plane mirror.

2. An object is located beyond the center of curvature of a spherical concave mirror. Locate and describe the image of the object.

3. Locate and describe the image produced by a concave mirror when the object is located at the center of curvature.

4. An object is located between the center of curvature and the focus of a concave mirror. Locate and describe the image of the object.

5. How does a virtual image differ from a real image?

6. An object produces a virtual image in a concave mirror. Where is the object located?

7. Describe the image seen in a convex mirror.

8. Describe the properties of a virtual image.

9. What factor, other than the curvature of a lens, determines the location of its focal point?

10. Locate and describe the image produced by a convex lens if an object is placed some distance beyond 2F.

11. What causes the defect that exists in all single lenses?

12. What causes the defect that all concave spherical mirrors have?

13. Convex mirrors are used as rearview mirrors on school buses. Why are convex mirrors used?

APPLYING CONCEPTS

1. List all the possible arrangements in which you can use a spherical mirror, either concave or convex, to form a real image.
2. List all the possible arrangements in which you can use a spherical mirror, either concave or convex, to form an image reduced in size.
3. The outside rearview mirrors of cars often carry the warning "Objects in the mirror are closer than they appear."
   a. What kind of a mirror would have such a warning?
   b. What advantage does this type of mirror have?
4. List all the possible arrangements in which you can use a lens, either concave or convex, to form an inverted image.
5. If you use a shaving or makeup mirror in a swimming pool, will the focal length change? Explain.
6. If you try to use a magnifying glass underwater, will its properties change? Explain.
7. Consider a plane mirror.
   a. What is its focal length?
   b. Does the mirror equation work for plane mirrors? Explain.
8. A student believes that very sensitive photographic film can detect a virtual image. The student puts photographic film at the location of the image. Does this attempt succeed? Explain.
9. To project an image from a movie camera onto a screen, the film is placed between F and 2F of a converging lens. This arrangement produces an inverted image. Why do the actors appear to be erect when the film is viewed?

EXERCISES

1. An object 15 mm in height is 16 cm from a concave mirror having a 16-cm radius of curvature. Find the location of the image using
   a. a ray diagram.
   b. the mirror equation.
   c. Find the magnification of the object.
   d. What is the height of the image?
2. The sun falls on a concave mirror and forms an image 3.0 cm from the mirror. If an object 24 mm high is placed 12.0 cm from the mirror, where

will its image be formed? Use
   a. a ray diagram.
   b. the mirror equation.
   c. How high is the image?
3. A concave mirror forms an image of the sun 8.0 cm from the mirror. It then forms an image of a candle 24.0 cm from the mirror. Where is the candle?
4. A photographer wishes to take a picture of her image in a plane mirror. If the camera is 1.2 m in front of the mirror, at what distance should the lens be focused?
5. Use a ray diagram to show that if you want to see yourself from your feet to the top of your head in a plane mirror, the mirror must be at least half your height.
6. An object is 20.0 cm from a spherical concave mirror of 8.0 cm focal length (16 cm radius). Locate the image
   a. using a ray diagram.
   b. using the mirror equation.
7. An object 3.0 cm high is placed 25 cm from a concave mirror of 15-cm focal length. Find the location and height of the image
   a. using a ray diagram.
   b. using the mirror equation.
8. An object is 30.0 cm from a concave mirror of 15-cm focal length. The object is 1.8 cm high.
   a. Locate the image.
   b. How high is the image?
9. A jeweler inspects a watch with a diameter of 3.0 cm by placing it 8.0 cm in front of a concave mirror of 12.0-cm focal length.
   a. Where will the image of the watch appear?
   b. What will be the diameter of the image?
10. A convex mirror has a focal length of −16 cm. How far behind the mirror does the image of a person 3.0 m away appear?
11. An object is 8.0 cm in front of a concave mirror having a focal length of 30.0 cm. Locate the image.
12. How far behind the surface of a convex mirror of −6.0 cm focal length does an object 10.0 m from the mirror appear?
13. The convex lens of a copy machine has a focal length of 25.0 cm. A letter to be copied is placed

40.0 cm from the lens.

a. How far from the lens is the copy paper located?

b. The machine is adjusted to give an enlarged copy of the letter. How much larger will the copy be?

14. Shiny lawn spheres placed on pedestals are convex mirrors. One such sphere has a diameter of 40 cm. A robin sits in a tree 1.5 m from the sphere.

a. Where is the image of the robin? Use the mirror equation.

b. If the robin is 12 cm long, how long is its image?

15. What is the focal length of a convex lens that forms an image 25 cm from the lens if the object distance is 20 cm?

16. A camera with a 135-mm focal length lens is used to photograph a 45-mm diameter flower that is 75.0 cm from the lens.

a. How far should the lens be from the film?

b. What is the diameter of the flower on the film?

17. If the flower in Exercise 16 is brought closer to the lens, will the image move toward or away from the lens? Explain.

18. Suppose you want the image formed on the film to be larger than the image you got with the lens of Exercise 16. If you keep the flower the same distance from the lens,

a. should you use a lens with a longer or shorter focal length?

b. What other adjustment will be necessary? Explain.

PROBLEMS

1. A microscope slide with an onion cell is placed 12 mm from the objective lens of a microscope. The focal length of the objective lens is 10.0 mm.

a. How far from the lens is the image formed?

b. What is the magnification of this image?

c. The real image formed is located 10.0 mm beneath the eyepiece lens of the microscope. If the focal length of the eyepiece is 20.0 mm, where does the final image appear?

d. What is the final magnification of this compound system?

2. A dentist uses a small mirror of radius 40 mm to locate a cavity in a patient's tooth. If the mirror is concave and is held 16 mm from the tooth, what is the magnification of the resulting image?

3. Camera lenses are described in terms of their focal length. A 50.0-mm lens has a focal length of 50.0 mm.

a. A camera is focused on an object 3.0 m away using a 50.0 mm lens. Locate the position of the image.

b. A 1.00×10^3 mm lens is focused on an object 125 m away. Locate the position of the image.

4. The 50.0 mm lens in Problem 3 is focused on a dog 0.50 m high. What is the size of the image?

5. Two plane mirrors are set at right angles. Use a ray diagram to show that your image in this mirror is not reversed as in a single plane mirror.

6. Draw a set of two mirrors that would allow you to see the back of your head. Find the distance from the image to your eyes.

7. A production line inspector wants a mirror that produces an upright image with magnification of 7.5 when it is located 14.0 mm from a machine part. What kind of mirror would do this job? What is its radius of curvature?

8. Solve Problem 7 using a lens rather than a mirror.

9. Using algebra and geometry, derive the lens equation geometrically, using Figure 19–21.

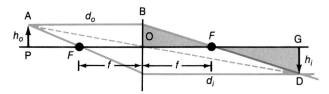

FIGURE 19–21. Use with Problem 9.

READINGS

Conery, Christopher, "The Reality of a Real Image." *The Physics Teacher*, December, 1984.

Noran, Paul, "The Physics of Medical Imaging." *Physics Today*, July, 1983.

Yulsman, T., "The Ultimate Zoom: A Revolution in Glassmaking Design Could Lead to Lighter, Smaller Lenses." *Discover*, August, 1988.

CHAPTER 20

Diffraction and Interference of Light

For Your Information

SUGGESTION: Have students hold up a sheet of paper to the light or toward the window and look at the edge. They will see a fringe along the edge due to diffraction.

SUGGESTION: Suggest that your students look at street lights at night through a handkerchief or a piece of sheer woven cloth to see the diffraction patterns.

Diffraction is the bending of light around the edges of barriers.

GOALS

1. You will gain an understanding of how the wave nature of light results in diffraction and interference.
2. You will learn how these phenomena may be used to measure the wavelength of light.

As you are leaving school, you walk by the open door of the band's rehearsal room. You hear the music long before you can see players through the door. Sound seems to have bent around the corner, while light has traveled only in a straight line. Yet, if they are both waves, why do they not act the same? The Italian Francesco Maria Grimaldi (1618–1663) first noted that the edges of shadows are not perfectly sharp. He named the slight spreading of light waves **diffraction.** Almost two hundred years later this effect was used to prove that light was in fact a wave. The wave properties of light create some of nature's most beautiful spectacles. The colors in peacock tails, mother-of-pearl shells, and soap films are due to interference by thin films discussed in Chapter 17. The colors in beetles and butterfly wings, however, come from diffraction, which we will study in this chapter.

20:1 The Two-Slit Interference Pattern

An English physician, Thomas Young (1773–1829), became interested in optics when he studied the human eye. Young's medical studies of the human voice led him to the study of waves, which he applied to the understanding of wave interference in oceans and lakes. He read Newton's book and became convinced that Newton's experiments could be explained if light were a wave of almost unimaginably small wavelength. In 1801 he developed an experiment that would allow him to make a precise measurement of that wavelength. Diffraction is the bending of waves around the edges of barriers. Young allowed light to fall on two closely spaced narrow slits. The light passing through each slit was spread

All in the Eyes of the Beholder

The South American Morpho butterfly, shown in this photograph, has a unique and beautiful coloration. In daylight its wings appear to be a brilliant, metallic, iridescent blue. What characteristic of light could provide an explanation for this unusual coloration?

341

FIGURE 20–1. The beautiful colors of this opal, a form of quartz, are produced by diffraction from ridges in the surface of the gem.

out, or diffracted. The spreading light from the two slits overlapped. When the light fell on an observing screen, the overlap did not produce extra light, but a pattern of light and dark bands called **interference fringes.** Young explained that these bands were the result of constructive and destructive interference of the light waves from the two slits.

Young used a **monochromatic** (mahn uh croh MAT ik) light source, one that emits light of only one wavelength. He placed a narrow slit in front of the source. This slit allowed light from only a small part of the source to pass through. As a result the waves were not only the same wavelength, but all were in step. That is, they were **coherent.** The waves spread after passing through the single slit and fell on the double slit. The double slit acted as two sources of new circular waves. In Figure 20–2a, the semi-circles represent wave crests moving outward from the slits. Midway between the crests are the troughs. The waves from the two sources interfere constructively at points where two crests overlap. They interfere destructively where a crest and a trough meet. The solid lines on the diagram are antinodal lines, passing through points of constructive inter-

b

c

a

Bright

Dark

Bright
Dark
Bright
Dark
Central bright
Dark
Bright
Dark

Bright

Dark

Bright

FIGURE 20–2. The diffraction of a monochromatic light source produces an interference pattern on the screen (a) resulting in a pattern, such as the one shown for blue light (b). The diffraction of white light produces bands of colors (c).

Single slit   Double slit   Screen

342   **Diffraction and Interference of Light**

ference. The dotted lines are nodal lines, passing through points of destructive interference.

Bright bands of light appear at points where the antinodal lines fall on the screen. One bright band appears at the center of the screen. On either side of the central band are bright bands corresponding to the other anti-nodal lines. Between the bright bands are dark areas located where nodal lines fall on the screen.

When white light is used in a double-slit experiment, colored spectra are seen instead of light and dark bands. The positions of the nodal and antinodal lines depend on the wavelength of the light. All wavelengths interfere constructively in the central bright band, so that band is white. The positions of the other bands depend on the wavelength, so the light is separated by diffraction into a spectrum of color at each band.

Antinodal lines pass through points where waves interfere constructively.

Nodal lines pass through points where waves interfere destructively.

20:2 Measuring the Wavelength of a Light Wave

Young used the double-slit experiment to make the first precise measurement of the wavelength of light. The central bright band that falls on the screen at point P_0 in Figure 20–3 does not depend on the wavelength, so another bright band is used. The first bright band on either side of the central band is called the **first-order line.** It falls on the screen at point P. The band is bright because light from the two slits interferes constructively. The two path lengths differ by one wavelength. That is, the distance PS_1 is one wavelength longer than PS_2.

To follow Young's experiment using Figure 20–3, you must understand that the drawing is not to scale. The length PO (L) is really very much greater than S_1S_2 (d). It is necessary to distort the diagram so the details close to the slit can be shown. To measure the wavelength, Young first measured the distance between P_0 and P, labeled x in the diagram. The distance between the screen and the slits is L, and the separation of the two slits is d. In the right triangle NS_1S_2 the side S_1N is the length difference of the two paths. S_1N is one wavelength, λ, long. The lines from the slits to the screen are almost parallel because length L is so much larger than d. Thus the lines NS_2 and OP are perpendicular. The triangle NS_1S_2 is similar to triangle PP_0O. Therefore the ratio of the corresponding sides of

When white light passes through a double slit, a continuous spectrum is formed.

Lines appear on each side of the central bright line. The first lines, which are one wavelength farther from one slit than the other, are called first-order lines.

Each antinodal line is a whole number of wavelengths farther from one slit than the other.

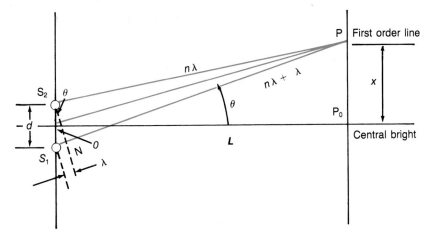

FIGURE 20–3. Schematic diagram for analysis of double-slit interference. The diagram is not to scale. Typically L is about 10^5 times the slit separation, d.

DEMONSTRATION: See the Teacher Guide.

these similar triangles is the same. That is,

$$\frac{x}{L} = \frac{\lambda}{d}$$

Solving this equation for λ gives

$$\boxed{\lambda = \frac{xd}{L}}$$

The wavelengths of light waves can be measured with considerable precision using double-slit interference patterns. It is not unusual for wavelength measurements to be precise to four digits.

The wavelength of light can be determined by using interference patterns.

EXAMPLE

Wavelength of Light

Red light falls on two narrow slits 1.90×10^{-5} m apart. A first-order bright line is 21.1 mm from the central bright line on a screen 0.600 m from the slits. What is the wavelength of the red light?

Given: $d = 1.90 \times 10^{-5}$ m   Unknown: λ
$x = 21.1 \times 10^{-3}$ m
$L = 0.600$ m   Basic equation: $\lambda = \frac{xd}{L}$

Each wavelength of light produces an interference pattern that is independent of other wavelengths.

Solution: $\lambda = \dfrac{xd}{L} = \dfrac{(21.1 \times 10^{-3} \text{ m})(1.90 \times 10^{-5} \text{ m})}{(0.600 \text{ m})}$

$= 6.68 \times 10^{-7}$ m $= 668$ nm

Practice Exercises

1. Violet light falls on two slits separated by 1.90×10^{-5} m. A first-order line appears 13.2 mm from the central bright line on a screen 0.600 m from the slits. What is the wavelength of the violet light?

2. Yellow light from a sodium lamp of wavelength 596 nm is used instead of the violet light of Exercise 1. The slit separation and distance to the screen are not changed. What is the distance from the central line to the first-order yellow line?

3. A physics class uses a laser with a known wavelength of 632.8 nm in a double-slit experiment. The slit separation is unknown. A student places the screen 1.000 m from the slits and finds the first-order line 65.5 mm from the central line. What is the slit separation?

4. Using the double-slit apparatus of Exercise 3, the student now measures the wavelength of an unknown green light. The first-order line is 55.8 mm from the central line. What is the wavelength of the light?

SUGGESTION: Show students that diffraction is greatest when the wavelength and the opening are about equal in size. This can be done using a ripple tank on an overhead projector.

20:3   Single-Slit Diffraction

The wave nature of light can be seen when light passes through a single opening. Grimaldi had noted the effects of light bending around the edge of an obstruction. When the opening is small, the two edges are close together and a series of bright and dark interference bands appears.

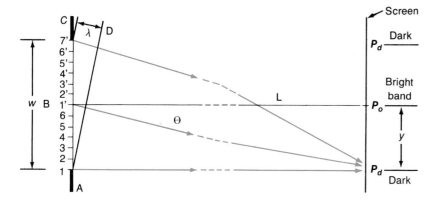

FIGURE 20-4. Schematic diagram for analysis of single-slit diffraction. The diagram is not to scale. Typically L is about 10^4 times the slit width.

For Your Information

You can produce single-slit diffraction by holding the index and middle fingers of one hand together and looking at a bright light through the space between them. Then press the fingers together to change the opening size and observe how the diffraction pattern changes.

Instead of the equally spaced bright bands produced by two slits, the pattern from a single slit has a wide, bright central band with dimmer bright bands on either side.

To observe single-slit diffraction, fold a small piece of paper and cut a slit along its folded edge. Unfold the paper and look through the slit at a light source. You will see an interference pattern. You can vary the width of the slit by pulling on the opposite edges of the paper. Observe the effect the change in slit width has on the pattern.

What causes the diffraction pattern? Figure 20-4 shows monochromatic light falling on a slit of width w. All points of the wave along the slit are in phase. Light falls on a screen placed a distance L from the slit. The wide central band, P_0, has dark bands, P, on either side. The letter P stands for all of the dark bands that form; P_d, however, refers to specific dark bands. What waves contribute to the central band? Because L is so much larger than w, all rays falling on the slit are, in effect, the same distance from P_0. The distances AP_0, BP_0, CP_0, and L are equal, and all waves arriving at P_0 are in phase. Thus, the central band is bright. As you move away from the center, the distance CP becomes larger than AP. The band becomes darker. For this discussion we have divided the width of the slit into twelve parts. When you reach point P_d, $CD = \lambda$, so the distance CP_d is exactly one wavelength longer than AP_d. Therefore waves from point 1' travel one-half wavelength longer than those from point 1. They destructively interfere and there is a dark band. The same is true for points 2' and 2, 3' and 3, and so on down the slit. A wave from one point of the slit is canceled by a wave from another. The result is darkness.

If you go farther away from the center, the distance CP is more than one wavelength longer and some waves no longer cancel. Thus light once again appears. When CP is 2λ larger than AP, there is a second dark band. Third, fourth, and higher bands are reached when the difference in path length is 3λ, 4λ, and so forth. What is the distance from P_0 to the first dark band (P_d)? If angle θ is very small, triangles CDA and BP_dP_0 are similar. From triangle CDA

A diffraction pattern is the result of light passing through a single narrow slit.

Diffraction is a maximum when the width of the opening is equal to the wavelength of light.

$$\sin \theta = \frac{\lambda}{w}$$

In the same way, consider triangle BP_dP_0. Because BP_d and L are nearly equal, we can say

FIGURE 20–5. These diffraction patterns for red light (a), blue light (b), and white light (c) were produced with a slit of width 0.02 cm.

a

d

c

$$\sin \theta = \frac{y}{BP_d} = \frac{y}{L}$$

Therefore

$$\frac{\lambda}{w} = \frac{y}{L}$$

$$y = \frac{\lambda L}{w}$$

Notice that the smaller the slit width, w, the larger the distance y. That is, the smaller the slit, the wider the central band. As a model, imagine a beam of light shining through an open door. The beam has sharp edges because the interference fringes are very close together and almost unnoticeable. As you close the door, the beam becomes smaller. If the opening is reduced to a few wavelengths wide, the edges of the beam become less well defined. The interference fringes become more widely spaced and more visible, making the edges appear fuzzy. Thus sharp shadows are cast only by large openings.

EXAMPLE

Single-Slit Diffraction

Monochromatic orange light of wavelength 605 nm falls on a single slit of width 0.095 mm. The slit is located 85 cm from a screen. How far from the center of the central band is the first dark band?

Given: $w = 0.095$ mm   Unknown: y
$\qquad L = 85$ cm
$\qquad \lambda = 605$ nm   Basic equation: $y = \lambda\dfrac{L}{w}$
$\qquad = 6.05 \times 10^{-7}$ m

Solution: $y = \lambda\dfrac{L}{w} = \dfrac{(6.05 \times 10^{-7} \text{ m})(0.85 \text{ m})}{(9.5 \times 10^{-5} \text{ m})} = 5.4 \times 10^{-3}$ m

Practice Exercises

5. Monochromatic green light of wavelength 546 nm falls on a single slit of width 0.095 mm. The slit is located 75 cm from a screen. How far from the center of the central band is the first dark band?

6. Light from a He-Ne laser (λ = 632.8 nm) falls on a slit of unknown width. A pattern is formed on a screen 1.15 m away where the first dark band is 7.5 mm from the center of the central bright band. How wide is the slit?

7. Yellow light falls on a single slit 0.0295 mm wide. On a screen 60.0 cm away there is a dark band 12.0 mm from the center of the bright central band. What is the wavelength of the light?

8. White light falls on a single slit 0.050 mm wide. A screen is placed 1.00 m away. A student first puts a blue filter (λ = 441 nm) over the slit, then a red filter (λ = 622 nm). The student measures the width of the central peak, that is, the distance between the two dark bands.

   a. Will the band be wider with the blue or the red filter?

   b. Find the width for the two filters.

For Your Information

Joseph von Fraunhofer was a German optical craftsman. He was the first person to designate and map the dark lines that cross the solar spectrum. Some 25 000 Fraunhofer lines have been mapped using the concept of diffraction.

SUGGESTION: Pass around diffraction gratings to the students and let them look at the spectral lines from several different gas discharge tubes. Point out that these patterns of lines are like a "fingerprint" of the gas.

20:4 Diffraction Gratings

Although single- or double-slit diffraction can be used to measure the wavelength of light, in practice a diffraction grating is used. **Diffraction gratings** are made by scratching very fine lines with a diamond point on glass. The clear spaces between the lines serve as slits. Gratings can have as many as 10 000 lines per centimeter. That is, the spacing between the lines is 10^{-6} m, or 1000 nm. Inexpensive *replica gratings* are made by pressing a thin plastic sheet onto a glass grating. When the plastic is pulled away, it contains an accurate imprint of the scratches. Jewelry is often made from replica gratings.

Gratings form interference patterns in the same way a double slit does. The bright bands are in the same location, but they are narrower, and the dark regions are broader. As a result, light colors are not smeared out and can be distinguished more easily. This means that wavelengths can be measured more precisely than with double slits.

In Section 20:2 the equation used to calculate the wavelength of light using double-slit interference was given as

$$\lambda = \frac{xd}{L}$$

DEMONSTRATIONS: See the Teacher Guide.

The same equation holds for a diffraction grating where d is the distance between the lines. Instead of measuring the distance from the central band to the first bright band, x, most laboratory instruments measure the angle between these bright bands. As seen in Figure 20–3, $\sin \theta = x/L$. Therefore the wavelength can be found by measuring the angle between the central bright band and the first-order line and using the equation

$$\boxed{\lambda = \frac{xd}{L} = d \sin \theta}$$

FIGURE 20–6. This diffraction grating can be used to create an interference pattern.

Keep fingerprints off film

Transmission Diffraction Grating Replica

13,400 Grooves per inch

Best Results Observe Sunlight, Moon, Fluorescent Light

a

b

Spectrometers are used to measure the wavelength of light.

Resolving power indicates a lens' ability to distinguish between the images of two points.

FIGURE 20-8. The resolving power of a lens is increased if the diameter of the lens is increased.

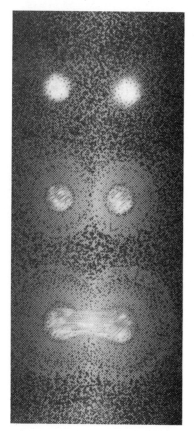

The instrument used to measure light wavelengths with a diffraction grating is called a grating spectrometer, Figure 20-7. The source emits light that falls on a slit and then passes through a diffraction grating. When monochromatic red light is used, Figure 20-7b, a series of bright bands appears to the left and right of the central bright line, O. When white light falls on the instrument, each red band is replaced by a spectrum. The red band in the spectrum is at the same location as when monochromatic light is used. The telescope is moved until the desired line appears in the middle of the viewer. The angle θ is then read directly from the calibrated base of the spectrometer. Because d is known, λ can be calculated.

20:5 Resolving Power of Lenses

When light passes through the lens of a telescope, it passes through a circular hole. The lens diffracts the light just as a slit does. The smaller the lens, the wider the diffraction pattern. If the light comes from a star, the star will appear spread out. If two stars are close enough together, the images will be so blurred that a viewer cannot tell whether there are two stars or only one. The telescope can no longer resolve the images of the two stars. Lord Rayleigh set the **Rayleigh criterion** for resolution. If the central bright band of one star falls on the first dark band of the second, the two stars are just resolved. That is, a viewer can tell that there are two stars and not one star.

The effects of diffraction on the resolving power of the instrument can be reduced by increasing the size of the lens. Diffraction also limits the resolving power of microscopes. The objective lens of a microscope cannot be enlarged, but the wavelength of light can be reduced. The diffraction pattern formed by blue light is narrower than that of red light. Thus biologists often use blue or violet light to illuminate microscopes.

PHYSICS FOCUS

Holograms

Interference properties of light are used to produce three-dimensional images called holograms. Developed by Dennis Gabor, who won the 1971 Nobel Prize in physics for his work, holograms record both the intensity and phase of light. The key difference between a photograph and a hologram is the recording of constructive and destructive interference patterns on the hologram.

To make a hologram, laser light is split by a mirror into two parts. One part is directed to the object and then reflected off the object onto film. The other part goes directly to the film. The result is complex interference patterns. The film will not look like the object at all and may, in fact, look like a series of overlapping fingerprints. When the film is illuminated by laser light, the emerging light is an exact duplicate of the light reflected originally by the object. The image appears three-dimensional. You can look around it. A holographic image of a magnifying glass will also magnify.

Because holograms are exceptionally difficult to counterfeit, holography is being used in security identification and credit cards. There is speculation that holograms may be used as part of a future design of United States currency. Research is being conducted to apply the use of holograms in microscopic work, medicine, and information storage. In addition to technological applications, the production of holograms has become an art form. Although confined to still pictures at present, holography may someday be used to produce truly three-dimensional motion pictures.

CHAPTER 20 REVIEW

SUMMARY

1. Light passing through a narrow hole or slit is diffracted, or bent from a straight-line path. **20:1**

2. Interference between light diffracted from two closely spaced narrow slits causes an interference pattern to appear on a distant screen. **20:1**

3. The wavelength of light can be measured by analyzing the double-slit interference pattern. **20:2**

4. When light passes through a narrow opening, diffraction causes a pattern of light and dark bands to form. **20:3**

5. Single slits produce diffraction patterns that are less well defined than those formed by double slits. **20:3**

6. Diffraction gratings with large numbers of evenly spaced slits produce interference patterns that are used to measure the wavelength of light precisely. **20:4**

7. Diffraction limits the resolving power of lenses. **20:5**

QUESTIONS

1. Explain why the central bright line produced when light is diffracted by a double slit cannot be used to measure the wavelength of the light waves.

2. Suppose you are using a double slit to measure light wavelength precisely. It is easier to measure a larger than a smaller distance precisely. Given that

$$\lambda = \frac{xd}{L}$$

   how can the value of x be increased?

3. How can you tell whether an interference pattern is from a single or a double slit?

4. Describe the changes in a single-slit pattern as slit width is decreased.

5. What is the difference between the interference patterns formed by a diffraction grating containing 10^4 lines/cm and one having 10^5 lines/cm?

6. For a given grating, which color of light produces the bright line closest to the central bright line?

7. As monochromatic light passes through a diffraction grating, what difference in path length exists between two adjacent slits and a dark area on the screen?

8. When white light is passed through a grating, what is seen on the screen? Why are no dark areas seen?

9. How does diffraction aid in radio reception?

10. Why do diffraction gratings have a large number of slits? Why are the slits so close together?

11. Describe how you could use light of a known wavelength to find the distance between two slits.

APPLYING CONCEPTS

1. Why is the diffraction of sound waves more familiar in everyday experience than the diffraction of light?

2. In each of the following examples, state whether the color is produced by diffraction, refraction, or the presence of pigments: (a) soap bubbles (b) peacock tails (c) rose petals (d) mother of pearl (e) oil films (f) blue jeans (g) the halo around the moon on a night when there is a high, thin cloud cover.

3. Why would a small telescope not be able to resolve the images of two closely spaced stars?

4. The ridges in the *Morpho* butterfly wing in the chapter opening photograph are spaced about 2.2×10^{-7} m apart. Explain how they could cause the wing to appear iridescent blue.

5. Using Figure 17–1 or Table 27–1, decide for which part of the electromagnetic spectrum a picket fence possibly could be used as a diffraction grating.

6. Two loudspeakers are placed 1 m apart on the edge of a stage. They emit two wavelengths of sound, 1 m long and 2 m long.

   a. If you are sitting 3 m from the stage, directly in front of the speakers, do you hear loud or quiet sounds for each of the wavelengths? Explain.

   b. If you sit on the edge of the stage, 0.5 m from one speaker and 1.5 m from the other, what do you hear? Explain.

EXERCISES

1. Using a compass and ruler, construct a diagram of the interference pattern that results when waves 1 cm in length fall on two slits 2 cm apart. The slits may be represented by two dots spaced 2 cm apart and kept to one side of the paper. Draw a line through the central and all other lines of reinforcement. Draw dotted lines where crests meet troughs and produce nodal lines.

2. Light falls on a pair of slits 1.90×10^{-3} cm apart. The slits are 80.0 cm from the screen. The first-order bright line is 1.90 cm from the central bright line. What is the wavelength of the light?

3. Light of wavelength 542 nm falls on a double slit. First-order bright bands appear 4.00 cm from the central bright line. The screen is 1.20 m from the slits. How far apart are the slits?

4. A good diffraction grating has 2.50×10^3 lines per centimeter. What is the distance between two lines in the grating?

5. Using the grating of Exercise 4, a red line appears 16.5 cm from the central line on a screen. The screen is 1.00 m from the grating. What is the wavelength of the red light?

PROBLEMS

1. Sound waves of frequency 550 Hz enter a window 1.2 m wide. The window is in the exact center of one wall of a theater 24 m × 12 m. The window is 12 m from the opposite wall, along which is a row of seats occupied by people. The theater is acoustically prepared to prevent the reflection of sound waves, and the speed of sound is 330 m/s. Two people in the row along the wall hear no sound. Where are they sitting?

2. A radio station uses two antennas and broadcasts at 600 kHz.
   a. What is the wavelength of the signals emitted by the station?
   b. The occupants of a home that is located 17 500 m from one antenna and 19 500 m from the other antenna have their receiver tuned to the station. Is the reception good or poor?

3. A camera with a 50-mm lens set at f/8 aperture has an opening 6.25 mm in diameter. Suppose this lens acts like a slit 6.25 mm wide. For light with λ = 550 nm, what is the resolution of the lens, the distance from the middle of the central bright band to the first-order dark band? The film is 50 mm from the lens.

4. The owner of the camera in Problem 3 tries to decide which film to buy for it. The expensive one, called fine-grain film, has 200 grains per millimeter. The less costly coarse-grain film has only 50 grains per millimeter. If the owner wants a grain to be no smaller than the width of the central bright band calculated above, which film should be purchased?

5. The image formed on the retina of the eye shows the effect of diffraction. The diameter of the iris opening in bright light is 3.0 mm. For yellow light, 545 nm wavelength, find the resolution of the eye. That is, find the distance from the center of the central band to the dark band. Assume the distance from iris to retina is 2.5 cm.

6. Cone cells in the retina are about 1.5 μm apart. On how many cone cells does the image found in Problem 5 fall? Would the eye's resolution be better if the iris were much larger, like the 10 mm diameter of the eagle? Explain.

7. Suppose the Hubble Space Telescope, 2.4 m in diameter, is in orbit 100 km above Earth and is turned to look at Earth. If you ignore the effect of the atmosphere, what is the resolution of this telescope? Use λ = 500 nm.

8. A student uses a 33-1/3 rpm record as a diffraction grating. She shines a laser, λ = 632.8 nm, on the grating. On a screen 4.0 m from the record, a series of red dots 21 mm apart are seen.
   a. How many grooves are there in a centimeter on the record?
   b. She checks her result by noting that the grooves came from a song that lasted 4.01 minutes and took up 16 mm on the record. How many grooves should there be in a centimeter?

9. A lecturer is demonstrating two-slit interference with sound waves. Two speakers are used, 4.0 m apart. The sound frequency is 325 Hz. (The speed of sound is 343 m/s.) Students sit in seats 4.5 m away. What is the spacing between the locations where no sound is heard because of destructive interference?

10. A spectrometer uses a grating with 12 000 lines per centimeter. Find the angles at which red (632 nm) and blue (421 nm) light have the first-order bright bands.

READINGS

Altman, T. C., "Pre-Newtonian Holograms or How to Make Holograms Without All the Bother of Inertia and Vibrations." *The Physics Teacher*, April, 1988.

Edelson, Ed., "Holography—Out of the Lab at Last." *Popular Science*, March, 1984.

Hecht, Jeff, "Store It with Light." *Computers and Electronics*, July, 1984.

Ronada, David, "Compact Disc Digital Audio Systems." *Computers and Electronics*, August, 1983.

CHAPTER 21

Static Electricity

For Your Information

A single lightning bolt may give off 3.750 million J of electrical energy. It also generates temperatures five times hotter than the 6000°C found at the surface of the sun.

For Your Information

Benjamin Franklin was cautious while performing his famous kite experiment, in which he charged a Leyden jar with electricity drawn from the clouds. The first two men who tried to repeat the experiment were electrocuted.
—*Isaac Asimov's Book of Facts*

GOALS

1. You will become familiar with the nature of electric charges.
2. You will learn how an object can acquire an electric charge.
3. You will learn what forces are produced by electric charges.

Nature provides few more awesome displays than lightning. Benjamin Franklin, colonial America's foremost scientist, showed that lightning is the result of electric charges. Starting in 1740, Franklin studied electricity produced by friction, such as the result of shoes rubbed on the carpet. He proposed that rubbing transferred an "electrical fluid" from one body to the other. He wrote that a body with excess fluid was "positively" charged, while one with too little fluid was "negatively" charged. Franklin proposed his famous kite experiment in 1750, and two years later showed that "electrical fire" could be drawn from a cloud. Franklin became famous as a scientist throughout Europe. This fame probably helped assure his diplomatic successes in France during the American revolution.

In this chapter we will investigate static electricity, or electrostatics, the study of electrical charges that can be collected and held in one place. Current electricity, produced by batteries and generators, will be explored in later chapters.

21:1 The Electrical Atom

Electric charges exist because of the structure of the atom. In 1890 J. J. Thomson discovered that all materials contain light, negatively-charged particles he called electrons. Between 1909 and 1911, Ernest Rutherford, a New Zealander, discovered that atoms have a massive, positively-charged nucleus, or center. The electrons surround the nucleus. The positive charge of the nucleus is exactly balanced by the negative charge of the electrons.

The nucleus is made up of protons and neutrons. A proton has a charge equal in size to that of the electron, but positive rather than negative.

About the nucleus is a "cloud" of electrons (negatively charged).

A neutral object has the same number of electrons as protons.

The nucleus of an atom contains protons (positively charged) and neutrons (no charge).

Sky Light

During a thunderstorm, Jody and Dion were curiously watching lightning bolts as they lit up the sky. Dion was amazed at the power and beauty of a single bolt. The electricity appeared to flow from the clouds to the ground. Jody asked Dion, "Why do you suppose lightning jumps from a cloud to Earth?" What explanation did Dion give?

Neutrons have no net charge. The proton and the neutron have nearly the same mass, which is about 1830 times the mass of the electron.

One or more electrons can be removed from an atom by adding energy. Energy is released when a negative ion is formed. Electrons move from one atom to another if the creation of a positive ion and a negative ion releases energy. Rubbing the atoms in your shoes against the atoms in the carpet brings the two kinds of atoms into close contact. When an electron is removed, an atom is left with a net positive charge and is called a positive ion. Adding electrons will create a negative ion, an atom with a net negative charge. You cannot, by ordinary means, remove protons from the atom. The protons and neutrons are held together in the nucleus by the strong nuclear force and can be separated only by supplying very large amounts of energy.

21:2 Transferring Electrons

How can you give an object an electrical charge? In the same way that mass cannot be created or destroyed, charge cannot be created or destroyed. As Franklin first proposed in 1750, charge is conserved. You can only transfer charge from one object to another one. Charge is transferred by moving electrons from one place to another, separating positive and negative charges. If a glass rod is rubbed with a piece of silk, electrons will move from the glass rod to the silk. The glass rod is left with some positive ions, atoms with fewer electrons than protons. The glass rod has a positive charge. Rubbing a hard rubber rod with fur also separates charges. However, in this case, electrons move from the fur to the rubber rod. The rubber rod gains electrons and becomes negatively charged. The glass rod and the rubber rod became charged when electrons were transferred from one body to another. The energy needed to transfer the electrons was supplied by rubbing two bodies together. Individual charges are never created or destroyed. The separation of positive and negative charges always means that electrons have been transferred.

21:3 Conductors, Insulators, and Semiconductors

If you add electrons to one part of a rubber rod, they will stay on that part. If you add electrons to one end of a metal rod, however, they will flow to all parts of the rod. Materials through which electrons will not

Electron movements cause electric phenomena.

SUGGESTION: Be very consistent when explaining how an object acquires charge by saying it loses or gains electrons, not protons.

When a neutral object loses electrons, it has a net positive charge.

When a neutral object gains electrons, it has a net negative charge.

An electrically-charged object has a static charge.

SUGGESTION: Charge a rubber rod with fur and bring it near an electroscope. Try to charge a metal rod. Show that it does not hold charge because it is a good conductor.

FIGURE 21–1. A rubber object can be charged when rubbed with fur.

Hard rubber rod

Fur

move easily are called electrical **insulators.** Electrons removed from one area on an insulator are not replaced by electrons from another area. Glass, dry wood, most plastics, cloth, and dry air are good insulators.

Extra electrons added to one end of a piece of metal will spread very quickly over the entire piece. Materials such as metals that allow electrons to move about easily are called electrical **conductors.** Electrons carry, or conduct, electric charges through the material. Metals are good conductors because at least one electron on each atom can be removed easily. These electrons act as if they no longer belong to any one atom, but to the metal as a whole. They are free to move throughout the metal in the same way atoms in a gas move about a container. They are said to form an electron gas. Copper and aluminum are both excellent conductors and are used commercially to carry electricity. Graphite, the form of carbon used in pencils, also is a good conductor.

Even though air is an insulator, forces produced by very strong charges can rip electrons off atoms in the air, producing a plasma. Plasmas are electrical conductors. Lightning and other forms of sparks are plasmas created by electrical forces.

Semiconductors are materials, such as silicon and germanium, with a conductivity between that of conductors and insulators. Only a few electrons are free to move within a semiconductor. The number of free electrons in a semiconductor can be greatly increased by adding small amounts of other elements. By adding the correct amount, a scientist can create a semiconductor with a specific conductivity. Transistors and the integrated circuits used in computers are made from silicon treated by this method. Light can also produce free electrons in semiconductors,

Materials that do not conduct electricity well are insulators.

Metals are good conductors.

DEMONSTRATION: See the Teacher Guide.

a

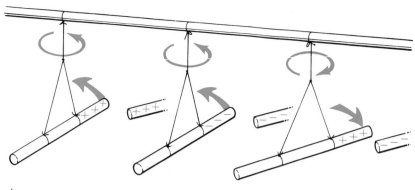

b

FIGURE 21–3. A charged rod, when brought close to another suspended rod, will attract or repel the suspended rod.

SUGGESTION: It is very important to do many of these demonstrations and to explain electron flow as you go along. Have the students make observations, then give explanations in terms of electron flow.

DEMONSTRATION: See the Teacher Guide.

For Your Information

Victor Hess won the Nobel Prize for physics in 1936 for his discovery of cosmic radiation. He performed research by sending up balloons carrying electroscopes into the atmosphere.

Electroscopes are used to detect the presence of static charge.

FIGURE 21–4. Electroscope with accompanying diagrams of possible charge distributions.

increasing their conductivity. Electric eyes, solar cells that generate electricity directly from sunlight, and photocopy machines use semiconductors that are sensitive to light.

21:4 Forces on Charged Bodies

When you pull woolen socks out of the dryer they stick to other pieces of clothing. "Static cling" is a common wash-day problem. The forces exerted by charged bodies are an important result of static electricity. These forces can be demonstrated by suspending a negatively-charged rubber rod so that it turns easily, as in Figure 21–3. If you bring a similarly-charged rod near the suspended rod, it will turn away. The negative charges on the rods repel each other. It is not necessary to bring the rods very close; the force, called the electric force, acts over a distance. If a positively-charged glass rod is suspended and a similarly-charged glass rod is brought close, the two positively-charged rods will also repel. If a negatively-charged rod is brought near the positively-charged rod, however, the two will attract each other, and the suspended rod will turn toward the oppositely-charged rod. These observations can be summarized in this way:

1. There are two kinds of electrical charges, positive and negative.
2. Charges exert force on other charges over a distance.
3. Like charges repel; opposite charges attract.

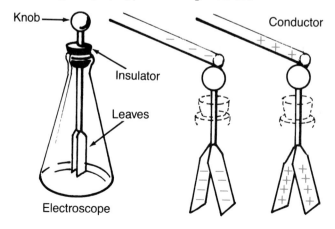

A large rod hanging in open air is not a very sensitive or convenient way of determining charge. Instead, a device called an electroscope is used. An electroscope consists of a metal knob connected by a metal stem to two thin, lightweight pieces of metal foil called leaves, as in Figure 21–4. Note that the leaves are enclosed to eliminate stray air currents.

When a negatively-charged rod is touched to the knob, negative charges (electrons) are added to the knob. The charges spread over all the metal surfaces. The two leaves are charged negatively and repel each other, causing them to spread apart. The electroscope has been given a net charge. Charging a neutral body this way, by touching it with a charged body, is called **charging by conduction.**

The leaves will also spread if the electroscope is charged positively. How then can you find out whether the electroscope is charged positively or negatively? The type of charge can be determined by observing what happens to the spread leaves if a rod of known charge is brought close to the knob. The leaves will spread farther apart if the electroscope has the same charge as that of the rod. The leaves will fall slightly if the electroscope has a charge opposite to that of the rod.

21:5 Charging by Induction

Forces exerted on charges can be used to charge an object without touching it. If a charged rod is brought close to, but does not touch, the knob of an uncharged electroscope, the leaves will spread apart. The spreading indicates the leaves have been charged. Electrons could not have been transferred from the rod to the knob because air is an insulator. Therefore the electroscope must still be neutral. To understand what happened, assume the rod was charged negatively. When the rod was brought near the knob, it repelled the negative charges from the knob down the stem onto the leaves. The knob was left positively charged. The leaves became negatively charged and spread apart. When the charged rod is removed, however, the separation of charge ends and the leaves fall.

Separation of charge can be used to give a body a net charge. Suppose a negatively-charged rod is brought close to one of two identical metal spheres that are touching, as in Figure 21–6. Electrons from the first sphere will be pushed onto the sphere farther from the rod. The closer sphere is now positively charged. If the spheres are separated while the rod is nearby, the two spheres will have equal but opposite charges. This process is called **charging by induction.**

FIGURE 21–5. A negatively-charged rod repels electrons from the electroscope down to the leaves (a); a positively-charged rod attracts electrons from the leaves to the top of the electroscope (b).

Neutral conductors can be charged by conduction if they come in contact with charged objects.

Charges can be separated on a neutral conductor by induction.

SUGGESTION: Obtain the metal spheres on insulated rods and do the demonstration in Figure 21–6.

FIGURE 21–6. The negative rod is brought near the touching spheres and the electrons are repelled to the right-hand sphere. The spheres are separated to show that they are charged.

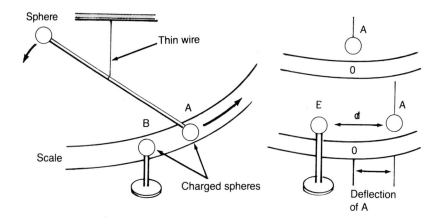

21:6 Coulomb's Law

How does the electric force depend on the size of the charges and their separation? In 1785, a French physicist named Charles Coulomb (1736–1806) measured the force between two charged spheres, shown in Figure 21–7. An insulating rod with small conducting spheres at each end was suspended by a thin wire. A third sphere, B, was placed in contact with sphere A. Both were then charged. They received the same charge, so they repelled each other and sphere A moved away from B.

Coulomb found how the force between the two charged spheres depended on the distance. First, he carefully measured the amount of force needed to twist the suspending wire through a given angle. He then placed equal charges on spheres A and B and varied the distance, d, between them. The electric force moved A from its rest position, twisting the suspending wire. By measuring the deflection of A, Coulomb could calculate the force of repulsion. He made many measurements with spheres charged both positively and negatively. He showed that the force, F, varied inversely with the square of the distance between the spheres.

The electric force varies inversely with the square of the distance between two charged objects.

$$F \propto \frac{1}{d^2}$$

Next, Coulomb investigated the way the force depended on the amount of charge. He had to change the charges on the spheres in a known way. Coulomb first charged spheres A and B as before. Then he selected an extra uncharged sphere, C, the same size as sphere B. When C was placed in contact with B, the spheres shared the charge that had been on B alone. Because the two were the same size, B now had only half its original charge. Therefore, the charge on B was only one half the charge on A. The extra sphere was then removed. After Coulomb adjusted the position of B so that the distance, d, between A and B was the same as before, he found that the force between A and B was half of its former value. That is, he found that the electric force varied directly with the charge of one of the bodies.

The electric force between two charged objects varies directly with the product of their charges.

$$F \propto qq'$$

After many similar measurements, Coulomb summarized the results in a

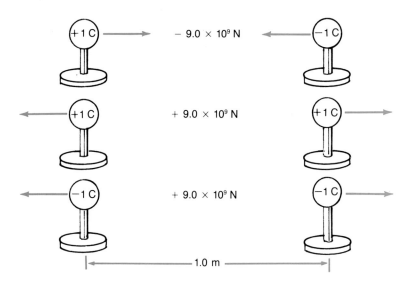

+1 C → — 9.0 × 10⁹ N ← −1 C

← +1 C + 9.0 × 10⁹ N +1 C →

← −1 C + 9.0 × 10⁹ N −1 C →

|— 1.0 m —|

law now known as Coulomb's law. *The magnitude of the force that a sphere with charge q exerts on a second sphere with charge q', separated a distance d, is*

Coulomb's law describes the force between two charged objects.

$$F = \frac{Kqq'}{d^2}$$

This equation gives the force that the charge q exerts on q' and also the force that q' exerts on q. These two forces are equal in magnitude but opposite in direction. They are examples of action-reaction forces described by Newton's third law of motion. In this equation, K is a constant that depends on the units used to measure charge, force, and distance. Coulomb's law works at all distances. It has even been found to be true for individual electrons separated by less than 10^{-18} m. This is a separation one ten-millionth as large as the size of the atom.

DEMONSTRATION: See the Teacher Guide.

21:7 The Unit of Charge: The Coulomb

Just as matter is made up of tiny units called atoms, charge also comes in unit "packages." Any charge that can be measured is an integer multiple of the **elementary charge.** The elementary charge is the charge of an electron. It is so tiny that a much larger value has been established as the unit of charge. The standard unit of charge is called the coulomb (C). The charge that produces a large lightning bolt is about ten coulombs, while the charge of an electron is 1.60×10^{-19} C. One coulomb is the charge on 6.25×10^{18} electrons. Thus, as we will calculate in Problem 7, even small pieces of matter, like the coins in your pocket, contain up to one million coulombs of charge. This enormous amount of charge shows almost no external effects because it is balanced by an equal amount of opposite charge. A charge as small as 10^{-9} C can result in large forces.

The force on a body with charge q caused by a body with charge q' a distance d away can be written

$$F = \frac{Kqq'}{d^2}$$

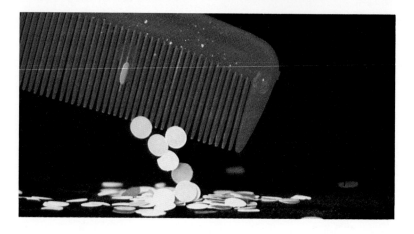

When charges are measured in coulombs, the distance in meters, and the force in newtons, the constant K is 9.0×10^9 N $\cdot$ m²/C².

The electric force, like all other forces, is a vector quantity. Coulomb's law in this form does not indicate the direction of the force. It does tell us that a positive force indicates a force of repulsion and a negative force indicates attraction. It is important to include the positive or negative signs for q and q' when using Coulomb's law.

EXAMPLE

Coulomb's Law—Two Charges

A positive charge of 6.0×10^{-6} C is 0.030 m from a second positive charge of 3.0×10^{-6} C.

a. Calculate the force between the charges.
b. What would be the force if the second charge were negative?

Given: $q = +6.0 \times 10^{-6}$ C   **Unknown:** F
$q' = +3.0 \times 10^{-6}$ C
$d = 0.030$ m   **Basic equation:** $F = K\dfrac{qq'}{d^2}$

Solution:

a. $F = K\dfrac{qq'}{d^2}$

$$= \frac{(9.0 \times 10^9 \text{ N} \cdot \text{m}^2/\text{C}^2)(+6.0 \times 10^{-6} \text{ C})(+3.0 \times 10^{-6} \text{ C})}{(0.030 \text{ m})^2}$$

$$= \frac{(9.0 \times 10^9 \text{ N} \cdot \text{m}^2/\text{C}^2)(18 \times 10^{-12} \text{ C}^2)}{(9.0 \times 10^{-4} \text{ m}^2)}$$

$$= +1.8 \times 10^2 \text{ N}$$

The positive sign of the force indicates repulsion between the charges.
b. If the second charge were negative, the sign of the force would be negative, which indicates attraction.

SUGGESTION: Do some oral exercises emphasizing the inverse square law. If you double the distance, the force decreases by 1/4; if you halve the distance, F increases by 4. This is the same as the gravitational force, but gravitational force is only an attractive force.

A positive force between charges indicates repulsion.

A negative force indicates attraction.

EXAMPLE

Coulomb's Law—Three Charges

A positive charge of 6.0×10^{-6} C has two other charges nearby. One, -3.00×10^{-6} C, is 0.040 m located at 90.0°. The other, $+1.5 \times 10^{-6}$ C, is 0.030 m at 0.0°. What is the total force on the 6.0×10^{-6} C charge?

Solution:

A sketch of the problem is shown in Figure 21–10. Force F_1, due to the charge at 90.0°, is attractive. That is, its direction is toward 90°. Force F_2, due to the charge at 0°, is repulsive, or toward 180°.

First, the magnitudes of the two forces are calculated.

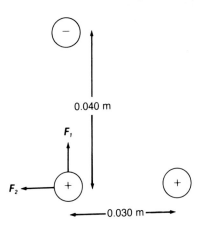

FIGURE 21–10. Use with Example.

$$F_1 = K\frac{qq'}{d^2}$$

$$= \frac{(9.0 \times 10^9 \text{ N} \cdot \text{m}^2/\text{C}^2)(+6.0 \times 10^{-6} \text{ C})(-3.0 \times 10^{-6} \text{ C})}{(4.0 \times 10^{-2} \text{ m})^2}$$

$$F_1 = -1.0 \times 10^2 \text{ N at } 90°$$

$$F_2 = \frac{(9.0 \times 10^9 \text{ N} \cdot \text{m}^2/\text{C}^2)(+6.0 \times 10^{-6} \text{ C})(+1.5 \times 10^{-6} \text{ C})}{(3.0 \times 10^{-2} \text{ m})^2}$$

$$F_2 = 9.0 \times 10^1 \text{ N at } 180°$$

Next, the forces are added vectorially to find the resultant force.

$$F^2 = F_1{}^2 + F_2{}^2$$
$$= 1.8 \times 10^4 \text{ N}^2$$
$$F = 1.3 \times 10^2 \text{ N}$$

The angle can be found by $\tan \theta = (9.0 \times 10^1 \text{ N})/(1.0 \times 10^2 \text{ N}) = 0.90$

$$\theta = 42°$$
$$\theta + 90° = 132°$$
$$F = 1.3 \times 10^2 \text{ N at } 132°$$

Practice Exercises

1. Two positive charges of 6.0×10^{-6} C are separated by 0.50 m. What force exists between the charges?

2. A negative charge of -2.0×10^{-4} C and a positive charge of 8.0×10^{-4} C are separated by 0.30 m. What is the force between the two charges?

3. A negative charge of -6.0×10^{-6} C exerts an attractive force of 65 N on a second charge 0.050 m away. What is the magnitude of the second charge?

4. The electrostatic force can be either attractive or repulsive, while the gravitational force is always attractive. What significance does this have for the formation of the universe?

21:8 Forces on Neutral Bodies

A charged body may either attract or repel another charged body. However, a charged body always attracts a neutral (uncharged) body. A charged rod brought near a neutral body separates the charges in the neutral body by induction. The charge separation occurs in conductors and even to some extent in insulators as well. The opposite charges are pulled closer to the rod; the like charges are pushed away from the rod. According to Coulomb's law, the force that charges exert on each other is inversely proportional to the square of the separation distance. Therefore the force on the closer, opposite charges will be stronger than the force on the like charges that are farther away. The neutral body will have a net force of attraction to the rod. The force of attraction on neutral bodies explains how a small piece of paper is attracted to a charged body. Forces on both charged and uncharged bodies are important in the operation of photocopiers. A typical copier has a drum made of a conductor, aluminum, coated with a thin layer of the semiconductor selenium. Suppose you want to copy a page from a book. The selenium layer is first charged by a spray of charged air molecules. In the dark, selenium is a poor conductor, and the charges stay where they are put. Light is reflected from the page to be copied, passed through a lens, and focused on the drum. In the places where light hits the selenium, the semiconductor becomes a conductor, letting the charges flow away from the surface to the aluminum drum. Where there was a black area on the page, however, there will be a dark area on the drum, and the charge will remain on the selenium layer. The drum is then rotated through a container of toner. Toner consists of tiny charged plastic beads coated with carbon grains. The coated beads are attracted to the charged areas of the selenium layer on the drum but not to the areas where the charge has flowed away. A sheet of paper is pressed against the drum and the coated beads are transferred to the paper. The paper is heated and the beads melt, attaching the carbon to the paper. The carbon makes a copy of the original page. Thus, electrostatics and semiconductors allow everyone to have inexpensive and quick copies of important documents.

In other applications, electric forces on neutral particles can be used to collect soot in smokestacks, reducing air pollution. Tiny paint droplets with induced charges can be used to paint automobiles and other objects very uniformly.

FIGURE 21-11. Photocopier drums utilize electric forces.

a

b

a

b

FIGURE 21–12. Electronic precipitators are used to reduce the fly ash released into the environment. An electric field exerts a force on charged particles, deflecting them sideways. In (a) the device is off, in (b) it is on.

PHYSICS FOCUS

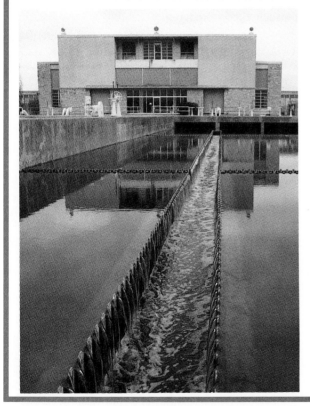

Purification with Electricity

The use of electric charge is being studied to help solve one of our most important ecological problems: the disposal of sewage sludge without pollution of land or water. Untreated sludge contains bacteria, protozoans, and parasites that can be agents of disease. Chemical treatment of this sludge is the most common method of killing disease organisms. The chemicals used are primarily forms of chlorine, which can become ecological hazards over a period of time. Recent studies have shown that the injection of accelerated electrons into sludge is an effective method of decontamination that does not create an environmental hazard.

A stream of sludge is disinfected in less than a second when subjected to a beam of electrons accelerated to 94% of the speed of light. In addition to killing microorganisms, electron treatment can destroy potentially toxic trace organic substances such as polychlorinated biphenyls (PCBs) and diminish the water soluble fraction of metals such as cadmium, chromium, copper, and lead. The treated sludge is so "clean" that it can be recycled and used as fertilizer with no adverse effects to either the soil or ground water.

The initial cost of an electron accelerator with beam scanner is high, but once in place, the operational cost is less than that of chemical water treatment methods being used today. The use of electric charge is part of a continuing search for better alternatives for waste management.

SUMMARY

1. There are two kinds of electrical charges, positive and negative. Electrons have a negative charge. **21:1**

2. An electrical charge is conserved; it cannot be created or destroyed. **21:2**

3. Bodies can be charged negatively or positively by transferring electrons. An object is charged negatively by adding electrons to it. An object is charged positively by removing electrons from it. **21:2**

4. Charges added to one part of an insulator remain on that part. **21:3**

5. Charges added to a conductor very quickly spread over the surface of the body. This is called electrical conduction. **21:3**

6. Semiconductors have a conductivity between conductors and insulators. The amount of conduction can be changed by exposing them to light or by adding other elements. **21:3**

7. Charges exert forces on other charges. Like charges repel; unlike charges attract. **21:4**

8. An electroscope indicates electrical charge. In an electroscope, forces on charges cause thin metal leaves to spread. **21:4**

9. A charged rod can charge an electroscope by induction by causing a separation of charges. **21:5**

10. Coulomb's law states that *the force between two charged objects varies directly with the product of the two charges and inversely with the square of the distance between them.* **21:6**

11. The unit of charge is the coulomb. One coulomb (C) is the charge on 6.25×10^{18} electrons or protons. The elementary charge, the charge on the proton or electron, is 1.60×10^{-19} C. **21:7**

12. A charged body of either sign can produce separation of charge in a neutral body. Thus a charged body attracts a neutral body. **21:8**

QUESTIONS

1. If you comb your hair on a dry day, the comb can become charged positively. Can your hair remain neutral? Explain.

2. Using a charged rod and an electroscope, how can you find if an object is a conductor?

3. List some insulators, conductors, and semiconductors.

4. Explain what happens to the leaves of a positively-charged electroscope when it is nearby but not touching
   a. a positive rod.
   b. a negative rod.

5. Explain how Coulomb made sure that the pair of spheres (*A* and *B* in Figure 21–7) had equal charges of the same sign.

6. Coulomb's law and Newton's law of universal gravitation appear similar. In what ways are the electrical and gravitational forces similar? How are they different?

7. The constant *K* in Coulomb's equation is much larger than the constant *G* in the Universal Gravitation equation. Of what significance is this?

8. Why does a wool sock taken from a clothes dryer sometimes cling to other clothes?

9. Name three methods to charge an object.

10. What property makes a metal a good conductor and rubber a good insulator?

APPLYING CONCEPTS

1. If you wipe a phonograph record with a clean cloth, why does the record now attract dust?

2. The combined charge of all electrons in a nickel coin is hundreds of thousands of coulombs. Does that imply anything about the net charge on the coin? Explain.

3. A rod-shaped insulator is suspended so it can rotate. A negatively-charged comb held nearby attracts the rod.
   a. Does this mean the rod is positively charged? Explain.
   b. If the comb repelled the rod, what could you conclude, if anything, about the charge on the rod?

4. Explain how to charge a conductor negatively if you have only a positively-charged rod.

5. Lightning usually occurs when a negative charge in a cloud is transported to Earth. If Earth is neutral, how can there be an attractive force that pulls the electrons toward Earth?

6. Section 21:6 describes Coulomb's method for obtaining two charged spheres, A and B, so that the charge on B was exactly half the charge on A. Suggest a way Coulomb could have placed a charge on sphere B exactly one third the charge on sphere A.

7. Coulomb measured the deflection of sphere A when A and B had equal charges and were a distance d apart. He then made the charge on B one third the charge on A. How far apart would the two spheres have to be now for A to have the same deflection it had before?

8. Explain why an insulator that is charged can be discharged by passing it above a flame.

9. A charged rod is brought near a pile of tiny plastic spheres. Some of the spheres are attracted to the rod, but as soon as they touch the rod, they fly away in different directions. Explain.

EXERCISES

1. Two objects, one with positive charge 1.8×10^{-6} C and the other with negative charge -1.0×10^{-6} C, are 0.014 m apart. What is the force between the two charged bodies?

2. Two charges, q_1 and q_2, are separated by a distance d and exert a force f on each other. What new force will exist if
   a. q_1 is doubled?
   b. q_1 and q_2 are cut in half?
   c. d is tripled?
   d. d is cut in half?
   e. q_1 is tripled and d is doubled?

3. Two electrons in an atom, each with charge -1.6×10^{-19} C, are separated by 1.5×10^{-10} m. What is the force between them?

4. Charges of 4.5×10^{-6} C exist on the three spheres in Figure 21–10, page 361. Find the magnitude of the total force on the top sphere.

5. Two charged bodies exert a force of 0.145 N on each other. If they are now moved so they are one fourth as far apart, what force is exerted?

6. How far apart are two protons if they exert a force of repulsion of 1 N?

7. A positive and a negative charge, each of magnitude 1.5×10^{-5} C, are separated by a distance of 15 cm. Find the force between the particles.

8. Two identical positive charges exert a repulsive force of 6.4×10^{-9} N when separated by a distance of 3.8×10^{-10} m. Calculate the charge of each.

9. How many excess electrons are on a particle charged -4.0×10^{-17} C?

10. A force of -4.4×10^3 N exists between a positive charge of 8.0×10^{-4} C and a negative charge of -3.0×10^{-4} C. What distance separates the charges?

11. Two negatively-charged bodies with -5.0×0^{-5} C are 0.20 m from each other. What force acts on each particle?

12. A positive charge of 3.0×10^{-6} C is pulled on by two negative charges. One, -2.0×10^{-6} C, is 0.050 m to the north and the other, -4.0×10^{-6} C, is 0.030 m to the south. What total force is exerted on the positive charge?

13. Two negative charges of -3.0×10^{-6} C exert a repulsive force of 2.0 N on each other. By what distance are they separated?

PROBLEMS

1. Two pith balls shown in Figure 21–13 have a mass of 1.0 g each and have equal charges. One pith ball is suspended by an insulating thread. The other is brought to 3.0 cm from the suspended ball. The suspended ball is now hanging with the thread forming an angle of 30.0° with the vertical. The ball is in equilibrium with F_E, mg and T adding vectorially to yield zero. Calculate
   a. mg.   b. F_E.
   c. the charge on the balls.

FIGURE 21–13. Use with Problem 1.

2. Benjamin Franklin once wrote that he had "erected an iron rod to draw the lightning down into my house, in order to make some experiment on it, with two bells to give notice when the rod should be electrify'd...." The chime had two small bells mounted side by side. One bell was connected to the iron rod for a charge; the other bell was attached to Earth. Between the two bells, a small metal ball was suspended on a silk thread so it could swing back and forth, striking the two bells. Explain why, when the one bell was charged, the ball would keep swinging, hitting first one bell then the other.

3. Water drips slowly from a narrow dropper inside a negatively-charged metal ring, as seen in Figure 21–14.
   a. Will the drops be charged?
   b. If they are charged, are they positive or negative?

   The drops fall into a can that is on an insulating platform.
   c. Will the can be charged?
   d. What will be the sign of the charge on the can?

4. What is the total charge on the electrons in one liter (1.0 kg) of water?

5. Three particles are placed in a line. The left particle has a charge of -67 μC, the middle $+45$ μC, the right -83 μC. The middle particle is 72 cm from each of the others.
   a. Find the net force on the middle particle.
   b. Find the net force on the right particle.

6. A strong lightning bolt transfers about 25 C to Earth.
   a. How many electrons are transferred?
   b. If each water molecule donates one electron, what mass of water lost an electron to the lightning?

7. How many coulombs of electrical charge are on the electrons in a nickel coin? Follow this method to find the answer.
   a. Find the number of atoms in a nickel. A nickel coin has a mass of about 5 g. Each mole (6.02×10^{23} atoms) has a mass of about 58 g. Find the number of atoms in a nickel coin.
   b. Find the number of electrons in the coin. Each nickel atom has 28 electrons.
   c. Find how many coulombs of charge are on 28 electrons.

8. Two charges, q_1 and q_2, are at rest near a positive test charge, q, of 7.2×10^{-6} C. q_1 is a positive charge of 3.6×10^{-6} C, located 0.025 m away at 35°; q_2 is a negative charge of 6.6×10^{-6} C, located 0.068 m away at 125°.
   a. Determine the magnitude of each of the forces acting on q.
   b. Sketch a force diagram.
   c. Determine the resultant force acting on q.

FIGURE 21–14. Use with Problem 3.

9. The hydrogen atom contains a proton, mass 1.67×10^{-27} kg, and an electron, mass 9.11×10^{-31} kg. The average distance between them is 5.3×10^{-11} m.

    a. What is the magnitude of the average electrostatic attraction between them?

    b. What is the magnitude of the average gravitational attraction between them?

    c. How do the magnitudes of the two forces compare?

READINGS

Bier, M., "Electrophoresis: Mathematical Modeling and Computer Simulation." *Science,* March, 1983.

Eskow, Dennis, "Striking Back at Lightning." *Popular Mechanics,* August, 1983.

Fincher, J., "Summer's Light and Sound Show; A Deadly Delight." *Smithsonian,* July, 1988.

Stern, Marc, "Zapping Static." *Popular Mechanics,* October, 1985.

CHAPTER 22

The Electric Field

GOALS

1. You will gain a knowledge of the development of the concept of electric fields and potential.
2. You will gain an understanding of work done by electric fields.
3. You will be able to apply these concepts to explain the motion of electric charges.

For Your Information

Even if I could be Shakespeare, I think I should still choose to be Faraday.
—Aldous Huxley (1925)

The electric force, like the gravitational force, varies inversely as the square of the distance between the two bodies. Both forces can act at a great distance. How can a force be exerted across what seems to be empty space? Our usual idea of a force is something that acts when two bodies touch each other. In trying to understand the electric force, Michael Faraday (1791–1867) invented the concept of an electric field. According to Faraday, a charge creates an electric field about it in all directions. If a second charge is placed at some point in the field, that charge interacts with the field at that point. The force it feels is the result of a local interaction. Interaction between particles separated by some distance is no longer required. Just as both electrical and gravitational forces depend on distance in the same way, so do their fields. In this chapter, we will describe the electric field concept and discuss its uses.

22:1 Electric Fields

It is easy to say that a charge produces an electric field. But how can the field be detected and measured? We will describe a method that can be used to measure the field produced by an electric charge q. A small positive test charge is placed at A, near the charge. The force that q exerts on the test charge at this location is measured. The test charge is then moved to another location, and the force on it is measured again. This process is repeated again and again until every location in space has a measurement of the electric force on the test charge associated with it. The measured forces are vector quantities.

High-Energy Halo

Research into ultra-high-voltage—to 2 million volts—transmission of electricity is essential for development of future power technology. At a special test facility, this ultra-high-voltage test line demonstrates a man-made corona effect. Why is the corona visible around this power line when the effect is not seen in electric wires in our homes?

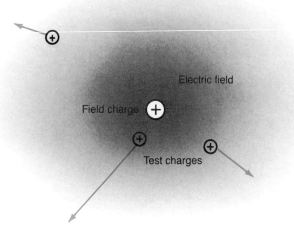

An electric field exists around charged objects. The electric field exerts a force on charged objects.

The collection of these vector quantities is called an **electric field.** A charge placed in this electric field experiences a force on it due to the electric field at that location. The strength of the force depends on the magnitude of the field. The direction of the force depends on the direction of the field. A picture of an electric field can be made by using arrows to represent the force vectors at various locations, as in Figure 22–1. The length of the arrow shows the magnitude of the force; the direction of the arrow shows the direction of the force.

Electric field lines produce a picture of the electric field.

The collection of arrows is not a very useful picture. A better picture of an electric field is shown in Figure 22–2. The lines are called **electric field lines.** The direction of the field at any point is the tangent drawn to the field line at that point. The strength of the electric field is indicated by the spacing between the lines. The field is strong where the lines are close together. It is weaker where the lines are spaced farther apart. Remember that electric fields exist in three dimensions. Our drawings are only two-dimensional models.

If electric field lines are close together, the field is strong.

The direction of an electric field is away from positive charges and toward negative charges.

The direction of the force on the positive test charge near a positive charge is away from the charge. The field lines extend radially outward like the spokes of a wheel, as in Figure 22–2a. Near a negative charge the direction of the force on the positive test charge is toward the charge, so the field lines point radially inward, shown in Figure 22–2b.

a   b   c

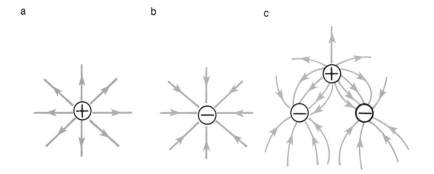

FIGURE 22–2. Lines of force are drawn perpendicularly away from the positive object (a) and perpendicularly into the negative object (b). Electric field lines between oppositely-charged objects are shown in (c).

370 The Electric Field

For Your Information

Robert Van de Graaff devised the high-voltage electrostatic generator in the 1930s. This model is capable of slowly building up giant potentials that can accelerate particles to high energies.

When there are two or more charges, the force on a test charge is the vector sum of the forces due to the individual charges. The field lines become bent and the pattern complex, as in Figure 22–2c. Note that field lines always leave a positive charge and enter a negative charge.

When a person receives an electric charge, as in Figure 22–3, the person's hair follows the field lines. Another method of visualizing field lines is to use grass seed in an insulating liquid such as mineral oil. The electric forces cause a separation of charge in the long, thin grass seed. The seeds turn so they line up along the direction of the electric force. Therefore, the seeds form a pattern of the electric field lines. The patterns in Figure 22–4 were made this way.

Field lines do not really exist. They are just a means of providing a picture of an electric field. Electric fields, on the other hand, do exist. An

Electric fields are real. Field lines are imaginary, but useful in making a picture of a field.

FIGURE 22–4. Lines of force between unlike charges (a) and between like charges (b) describe the behavior of a positively-charged object in a field. The top photographs are computer tracings of electric field lines.

a

b

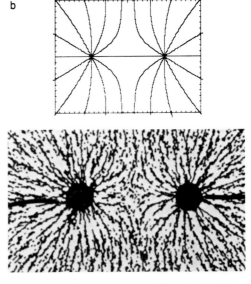

electric field is produced by one or more charges and is independent of the existence of the test charge that is used to measure it. The field provides a method of calculating the force on a charged body. It does not explain, however, why charged bodies exert forces on each other. That question is still unanswered.

22:2 Electric Field Intensity

Electric field lines show the direction of the electric force. How does the field strength depend on the force? According to Coulomb's law, the electric force acting on a charge is proportional to the magnitude of that charge. If the magnitude of the charge is doubled, the force is doubled. Thus the ratio of force to charge is independent of the size of the charge. The ratio is called the **electric field intensity.** That is, if F is the force on test charge q',

Electric field intensity is force per unit charge.

$$E = \frac{F_{on\ test\ charge\ q'}}{q'}$$

The magnitude of the electric field intensity is measured in newtons per coulomb, N/C. The direction of the electric field intensity is indicated by the field lines—away from positive charges—toward negative charges.

Some typical electric field intensities are shown in Table 22–1.

SUGGESTION: Make the analogy between the electric field and the gravitational field. The gravitational field is the force on a unit mass, $g = F/m$. The electric field is the force on a unit charge, $E = F/q$.

DEMONSTRATION: See the Teacher Guide.

TABLE 22–1

Approximate Values of Typical Electric Fields	
Field	**Value (N/C)**
Inside wire in 120 V AC circuits	10^{-2}
At surface of Earth	10^2
Near charged hard rubber rod	10^3
In television picture tube	10^5
Needed to create spark in air	3×10^6
At electron orbit in hydrogen atom	5×10^{11}

The electric field caused by a single charge is proportional to the magnitude of the charge and inversely proportional to the square of the distance from the charge.

The magnitude of the force on a charge q' due to a single charge q, a distance d away, is given by the equation

$$F = \frac{Kqq'}{d^2}$$

Therefore, the electric field intensity due to a single charge is given by the equation

$$E = \frac{1}{q'}F$$
$$= \frac{1}{q'}\left(\frac{Kqq'}{d^2}\right)$$
$$= \frac{Kq}{d^2}$$

This equation indicates that E, the electric field intensity, does not depend on the test charge.

We said that an electric field should be measured by a small test charge. The reason is that the test charge also produces an electric field that exerts a force on other charges. The size of the test charge should be so small that the field it produces is very weak in comparison to the field of the charge being measured.

EXAMPLE

Electric Field Intensity

A positive test charge of 4.0×10^{-5} C is placed in an electric field. The force acting on it is 0.60 N at 10°. What is the electric field intensity and direction at the location of the test charge?

Given: charge $(q') = 4.0 \times 10^{-5}$ C
$F = 0.60$ N at 10°

Unknown: electric field intensity (E)

Basic equation: $E = \dfrac{F}{q'}$

Solution: $E = \dfrac{F}{q'}$

$E = \dfrac{0.60 \text{ N}}{4.0 \times 10^{-5} \text{ C}}$

$= 1.5 \times 10^4$ N/C at 10°

If the force were negative, the field at the test charge would have the opposite direction, that is, $E = 1.5 \times 10^4$ N/C at 190°.

Practice Exercises

1. A negative charge of 2.0×10^{-8} C experiences a force of 0.060 N in an electric field. What is the field intensity?

2. A positive test charge of 5.0×10^{-4} C is in an electric field that exerts a force of 2.5×10^{-4} N on it. What is the electric field intensity at the location of the test charge?

3. Suppose the electric field in Practice Exercise 2 were caused by a point charge. The test charge is moved to a distance twice as far from the charge. What force does the field now exert on the test charge?

4. You are probing the field of a charge of unknown magnitude and sign. You first map the field with a 1.0×10^{-6} C test charge, then repeat your work with a 2.0×10^{-6} C charge.
   a. Would you measure the same forces with the two test charges? Explain.
   b. Would you find the same fields? Explain.

a

g

Ball

Earth

Increase in gravitational potential energy

b

E

B

A

Increase in electric potential energy

FIGURE 22–5. Work is needed to move an object against the force of gravity (a) and against the electric force (b). In both cases the potential energy of the object is increased.

For Your Information

For Your Information

22:3 Energy and the Electric Potential

The concept of energy is extremely useful in mechanics. The law of conservation of energy allows us to solve problems without knowing the forces in detail. For example, gravity attracts a ball toward Earth. Both the gravitational force, F, and the gravitational field, $g = F/m$, point toward Earth. If you lift a ball against the force of gravity, you do work on it, and thus its potential energy is increased.

The energy concept is also useful in electricity. The force, F, exerted on a positive test charge, q', by a negative charge is toward the negative charge. The vector describing the field intensity, $E = F/q'$, also points toward the negative charge. To move the test charge away from the negative charge, you have to do work on the test charge. Thus the potential energy of the test charge is increased. The amount of change in potential energy depends on the size of the test charge. The larger the test charge, the greater the energy change. In fact, the change in PE is proportional to the size of the test charge. Therefore, a much more useful value is the potential energy per unit charge, the electric potential. The potential energy of two test charges at the same point in an electric field will be different if the size of the test charges is different. The electric potential of the two charges at the same point in the field will be the same, regardless of the size of the charges. We define the **electric potential**, V, to be the potential energy divided by the charge, $V = PE/q'$. The unit of electric potential is joule per coulomb. One joule per coulomb is called a **volt** (J/C = V).

Work must be done on the test charge to move it from point A to point B. Therefore, the potential energy of the positive test charge at point B, farther from the negative charge, is larger than the potential energy at point A. Thus the electric potential at point B,

$$V_B = \frac{PE}{q'}$$

is larger than the potential at point A, V_A. The change in potential between points A and B will be negative.

As the positive test charge is returned to point A, its potential energy decreases. Therefore, the change in potential between points B and A will be negative. The change in potential energy when moving from B to A will be equal and opposite to the change when moving from A to B. Thus, the potential of point A depends only on its location, not on the path taken to get there.

As already discussed, only differences in potential energy can be measured. The same is true of electric potential. Thus only differences in electric potential are important. We define the potential difference $V = V_B - V_A$. Potential differences are measured with a voltmeter. Sometimes the potential difference is simply called the *voltage*.

As described in Chapter 11, the potential energy of a system can be defined to be zero at any convenient reference point. In the same way, the potential of any point, for example point A, can be defined to be zero. If

$V_A = 0$, then $V_B = V$. If instead, $V_B = 0$, then $V_A = -V$. No matter what reference point is chosen, the potential difference between points A and B will always be the same.

We have seen that electric potential increases when two unlike charges are separated. Between two like charges, however, there is a repulsive force. Potential energy decreases when two like charges are moved farther apart. Therefore, the potential is smaller at a point where the two like charges are far apart, as shown in Figure 22–6.

22:4 The Electric Potential in a Uniform Field

How does the potential difference depend on the electric field? In the gravitational case, near the surface of Earth the gravitational force and field are constant. It is also possible to create an electric force and field that are constant. To make a constant, or uniform, field, two flat conducting plates are placed parallel to each other. One is charged positively and the other negatively. The electric field between the plates is constant, except at the edges of the plates. Figure 22–7 shows a grass seed representation of the field between parallel plates.

In a constant gravitational field, the change in potential energy when a body of mass m is raised a distance h is given by $\Delta PE = mgh$. Remember that g, the gravitational field intensity near Earth, is given by $g = F/m = 9.80$ (N/kg). The gravitational potential, or potential energy per unit of mass, could be written as $mgh/m = gh$.

In a uniform electric field, the change in potential energy in moving a charge a distance d is given by $\Delta PE = -Fd$. The negative sign indicates that motion opposite to the force increases the potential energy. Thus, the potential difference, the change in potential energy per unit charge, is given by the equation $V = -Fd/q = -(F/q)d$. The force per charge is the electric field intensity, $E = F/q$. Therefore, $V = -Ed$. Normally the direction of the electric field is not considered, and the negative sign is

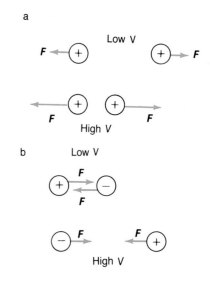

FIGURE 22–6. Electric potential energy is larger when two like charges are closer together (a) and smaller when two unlike charges are closer together (b).

For Your Information

Gravitational potential energy is discussed in Chapter 11.

A uniform electric field exists between two parallel metal plates that have opposite charges.

FIGURE 22–7. An electric field between parallel plates.

ignored. Therefore, the potential difference, V, between two points a distance d apart in a uniform field of intensity E is given by

$$V = Ed$$

By unit analysis, the product of the units of E and d is $(N/C) \cdot m$. This is equivalent to a J/C, the definition of a volt.

For Your Information

Section 11:3 introduces the idea that work done on an object can be considered negative.

EXAMPLE

Potential Difference Between Two Parallel Plates

Two parallel plates are 0.500 m apart. The electric field intensity between them is 6.00×10^3 N/C.

a. What is the potential difference between the plates?

b. What work is done moving a charge equal to that on one electron from one plate to another?

Given: $d = 0.500$ m   Unknowns: V, W
       $E = 6.00 \times 10^3$ N/C   Basic equation: $V = Ed$

Solution: **a.** $V = Ed$
            $= (6.00 \times 10^3$ N/C$)(0.500$ m$)$
            $= 3.00 \times 10^3$ N $\cdot$ m/C
            $= 3.00 \times 10^3$ J/C $= 3.00 \times 10^3$ V

          b. $W = qV$
            $= (1.6 \times 10^{-19}$ C$)(3.00 \times 10^3$ V$)$
            $= 4.8 \times 10^{-16}$ CV
            $= 4.8 \times 10^{-16}$ J

EXAMPLE

Electric Field Intensity Between Two Parallel Plates

A voltmeter measures the potential difference between two parallel plates to be 60.0 V. The plates are 0.030 m apart. What is the magnitude of the electric field intensity?

Given: $V = 60.0$ V   Unknown: E
       $d = 0.030$ m   Basic equation: $V = Ed$

Solution: $V = Ed$, so $E = \dfrac{V}{d}$

$$= \frac{(60.0 \text{ V})}{(0.030 \text{ m})}$$

$$= \frac{(60.0 \text{ J/C})}{(0.030 \text{ m})}$$

$$= 2.0 \times 10^3 \text{ N/C}$$

Practice Exercises

5. The electric field intensity between two charged metal plates is 8000 N/C. The plates are 0.05 m apart. What is the potential difference between them?

6. A voltmeter reads 500 V when placed across two parallel plates. The plates are 0.020 m apart. What is the field intensity between them?

7. What voltage is applied to two metal plates 0.500 m apart if the field intensity between them is 2.50×10^3 N/C?

8. What work is done when 5.0 C is raised in potential by 1.5 V?

22:5 Millikan's Oil Drop Experiment

DEMONSTRATION: See the Teacher Guide.

One important application of the uniform electric field between two parallel plates was the measurement of the charge of an electron. This was made by American physicist Robert A. Millikan (1868–1953) in 1909.

The charge of an electron was found by Millikan in his oil drop experiment.

Figure 22–8 shows the method used by Millikan to measure the charge carried by a single electron. Fine oil drops were sprayed from an atomizer into the air. These drops were often charged by friction with the atomizer. Gravity acting on the drops caused them to fall. A few entered the hole in the top plate of the apparatus. A potential difference was placed across the two plates. The resulting electric field between the plates exerted a force on the charged drops. When the top plate was made positive enough, the electric force caused negatively-charged drops to rise. The potential difference between the plates was adjusted to suspend a charged drop between the plates. At this point, the downward force of the weight and the upward force of the electric field were equal in magnitude.

The intensity of the electric field, E, was determined from the potential difference between the plates. A second measurement had to be made to find the weight of the drop, mg, which was too tiny to measure by ordinary methods. To make this measurement, a drop was first suspended. Then the electric field was turned off and the rate of the fall of the drop

When the electric force balances the gravitational force, the drop is suspended.

a

Atomizer

Electric force

Light source

Metal plate

Charged oil drop

Metal plate

Gravitational force

Calibrated telescope

FIGURE 22–8. This apparatus, (a) and (b), can be used to determine the charge on an oil drop.

b

measured. Because of friction with the air molecules, the oil drop quickly reached terminal velocity. This velocity was related to the mass of the drop by a complex equation. Using the measured terminal velocity to calculate mg, and knowing E, the charge q could be calculated. When Millikan used X rays to add or remove electrons from the drops, he noted that the drops had a large variety of charges. He found, however, that the *changes* in the charge were always a multiple of -1.6×10^{-19} C. The changes were caused by different numbers of electrons being added to or removed from the drops. As a result, the smallest change in charge that could occur was the amount of charge of one electron. Therefore, Millikan said that each electron always carried the same charge, -1.6×10^{-19} C. Millikan's experiment showed that charge is quantized. This means that an object can have only a charge with a magnitude that is some integral multiple of the charge of the electron.

The presently accepted theory of matter says that protons are made up of fundamental particles called quarks. The charge on a quark is either $+1/3$ or $-2/3$ the charge on an electron. A theory of quarks that agrees with experimental evidence states that quarks can never be isolated. In an attempt to test this theory, William Fairbank (1917–   ) of Stanford University used an updated Millikan apparatus to look for fractional charges on tiny metal spheres. He reported finding fractional charges on several spheres. No other experimenters have been able to duplicate his work. Thus the discovery of an isolated quark with a fraction of the electron's charge has not been confirmed.

EXAMPLE

Finding the Charge on an Oil Drop

An oil drop weighs 1.9×10^{-14} N. It is suspended in an electric field of intensity 4.0×10^4 N/C.

a. What is the charge on the oil drop?

b. If the drop is attracted toward the positive plate, how many excess electrons does it have?

Given: $W = mg$
$\qquad = 1.9 \times 10^{-14}$ N
$\qquad E = 4.0 \times 10^4$ N/C

Unknown: excess charge (q)

Basic equation: $Eq = mg$

Solution: a. $Eq = mg$

$$\text{Thus } q = \frac{mg}{E} = \frac{1.9 \times 10^{-14} \text{ N}}{4.0 \times 10^4 \text{ N/C}}$$

$$= 4.8 \times 10^{-19} \text{ C}$$

b. number of electrons $= \dfrac{\text{total charge on drop}}{\text{charge per electron}}$

$$= \frac{4.8 \times 10^{-19} \text{ C}}{1.6 \times 10^{-19} \text{ C/e}^-} = 3 \text{ e}^-$$

There are three extra electrons because a negatively-charged drop is attracted toward a positively-charged plate.

Practice Exercises

9. An oil drop weighs 1.9×10^{-15} N. It is suspended in an electric field intensity of 6.0×10^3 N/C.

   a. What is the charge on the drop?

   b. How many excess electrons does it carry?

10. A positively-charged oil drop weighs 6.4×10^{-13} N. An electric field intensity of 4.0×10^6 N/C suspends the drop.

    a. What is the charge on the drop?

    b. How many electrons is the drop missing?

11. If three more electrons were removed from the drop in Practice Exercise 10, what field would be needed to balance the drop?

22:6 Sharing of Charge

All systems, both mechanical and electrical, come to equilibrium when the energy of the system is at a minimum. For example, if a ball is put on a hill, it will finally come to rest in a valley where its potential energy is least. This principle explains what happens when an insulated, negatively-charged metal sphere, as seen in Figure 22–9, touches a second, uncharged sphere.

The added electrons on the charged sphere, A, repel each other. Thus the potential on sphere A is high. We can set the potential of the neutral sphere, B, to be zero. When one electron is transferred from sphere A to sphere B, the potential of sphere A is reduced because it has fewer excess electrons. The potential of sphere B does not change because no work is done adding the first extra electron to this neutral sphere. As more electrons are transferred, however, work must be done to overcome the growing repulsive force between the electrons on sphere B. Therefore, the potential of sphere B increases as the potential of sphere A decreases. Electrons continue to flow from sphere A to sphere B until the work done adding an electron to sphere B is equal to the work gained in removing the electron from sphere A. The potential of sphere A now equals the potential of sphere B. Thus electrons flow until all parts of a conducting body, the two touching spheres in this case, are at the same potential.

Consider a large sphere and a small sphere that have the same charge. The larger sphere has a larger surface area, so electrons can spread farther apart than they can on the smaller sphere. With the electrons farther apart, the repulsive force between them is reduced. Therefore, the potential on the larger sphere is lower than the potential on the smaller sphere.

DEMONSTRATION: See the Teacher Guide.

Charges are shared in a way that gives a system the minimum amount of energy.

If a large and a small sphere have the same charge, the large sphere will have a lower potential.

Metal spheres of equal size

Charged sphere

Neutral sphere

a   b

FIGURE 22–9. A charged sphere shares charge equally with a neutral sphere of equal size.

22:6 Sharing of Charge   379

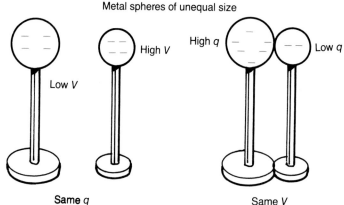

Metal spheres of unequal size

If the two spheres are now touched together, electrons will move to the sphere with the lower potential. Electrons will move from the smaller to the larger sphere. For this reason, when two spheres are at equal potentials, the larger sphere has a greater charge than the smaller sphere.

Earth is a very large sphere. If a charged body is touched to Earth, almost any amount of charge can flow without changing Earth's potential. When all the excess charge on the body flows to Earth, the body becomes neutral. Touching an object to Earth to eliminate excess charge is called **grounding.** If a computer or other sensitive instrument were not grounded, static charges could accumulate, raising the potential of the computer. A person touching the computer could suddenly lower the potential of the computer. The charges flowing through the computer to the person could damage it or hurt the person.

22:7 Electric Fields Near Conductors

The charges on a conductor are spread as far apart as they can be to make the energy of the system as low as possible. The result is that all charges are on the surface of a solid conductor. If the conductor is hollow, excess charges will move to the outer surface. If a closed tin can is charged, there will be no charges on the inside surfaces of the can.

The electric field around a conducting body depends on the shape of the body as well as the charge on it. The field is strongest near sharp points on the body. The field there can become so strong that nearby air mole-

If a large and a small sphere have the same potential, the large sphere will have a greater charge.

Grounding removes excess charges from an object.

SUGGESTION: An object is grounded if it is touching Earth. If you are doing an electrostatic demonstration and need to ground, connect the thing you want to ground to a faucet.

All charges are on the outside of a closed conductor.

Electric fields are largest in the region around sharp edges.

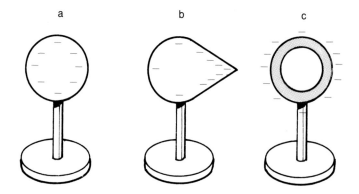

FIGURE 22–11. The electric field around a conducting body depends on the structure and shape of the body.

Negatively charged cloud

Positive ions in atmosphere

FIGURE 22-12. A lightning rod allows charges from the clouds to be grounded, rather than conducted into a house.

FIGURE 22-12. A lightning rod allows charges from the clouds to be grounded, rather than conducted into a house.

For Your Information

You know that wherever you go, with the proper instrument, you can measure a value for the acceleration given to a body at that point by Earth's gravitational attraction. Such a continuous map of values is called a map of Earth's gravitational field. In the same manner, it is possible to measure the effect of an electric charge on a test charge placed at any point in the space surrounding the first charge. This set of values describes or maps the electric field around the charge.

cules are separated into electrons and positive ions. The electrons and ions are accelerated by the field. They hit other molecules, producing more ions and electrons. The stream of ions and electrons that results is a plasma, a conductor. As the electrons and ions recombine, energy is released and light is produced. The result is a spark. Conductors that are highly charged or operate at high potentials are carefully grounded to reduce the electric fields and prevent sparking. On the other hand, lightning rods are pointed so that the electric field will be strong near the rod and produce a conducting path from the rod to the clouds. The sharply pointed shape allows the static charges in the clouds to spark to the rod rather than to a chimney or other high point on a house. From the rod, a conductor takes the charges safely to ground.

SUGGESTION: Have students find articles on lightning to share with the class.

FIGURE 22-13. Ground wire on a fuel truck.

FIGURE 22–14. Various types of capacitors.

DEMONSTRATION: See the Teacher Guide.

For Your Information

Work is done to add charges to a capacitor. Thus the capacitor stores electric energy. The energy is stored in the electric field.

For Your Information

Even if the inner surface of a hollow solid is pitted or bumpy, giving it a larger surface area than the outer surface, the charge will still be entirely on the outside.

22:8 Storing Charges—The Capacitor

You can "store" energy in a gravitational field. For example, you can increase the PE of a book by lifting it. You can also store potential energy in an electric field. In 1746 the Dutch physician and physicist Pieter Van Musschenbroek invented a device that could store electric charge. In honor of the city in which he worked, it was called a Leyden jar. The Leyden jar was used by Benjamin Franklin to store the charge from lightning and in many other experiments.

As described previously, as charge is added to a body, the potential of that body increases. For a given body, the ratio of charge to potential, q/V, is a constant. The constant is called the capacitance, C, of the body. For a small sphere, even a small amount of added charge will increase the potential. Thus C is small. The larger the sphere, the greater the charge that can be added for the same increase in potential. Thus the larger the capacitance. Van Musschenbroek found a way of producing a large capacitance in a small device. A device that is specifically designed to have a given capacitance is called a **capacitor.** In the most general sense, a capacitor is made up of two conductors, separated by an insulator. Capacitors are used in electrical circuits to store charge.

The capacitance of a body is independent of the charge on it. Capacitance can be measured by placing a specific charge on a body and measuring the potential that results. The capacitance is then found by using the equation

$$C = \frac{q}{V}$$

Capacitance is measured in farads, F, named after Michael Faraday. One farad is one coulomb per volt. Just as one coulomb is a large amount of charge, one farad is an enormous capacitance. Commercial capacitors are usually between 10 picofarads (10×10^{-12} F) and 500 microfarads (500×10^{-6} F).

Capacitors often are made of parallel conductors, or plates, separated by air or another insulator. Commercial capacitors contain strips of aluminum foil separated by thin plastic and are tightly rolled up to save room.

EXAMPLE

Finding the Capacitance from Charge and Potential

A sphere has a potential of 60.0 V when charged with 3.0×10^{-6} C. What is its capacitance?

Given: $V = 60.0$ V
$\qquad\quad q = 3.0 \times 10^{-6}$ C

Unknown: capacitance (C)

Basic equation: $C = \frac{q}{V}$

Solution: $C = \dfrac{q}{V} = \dfrac{3.0 \times 10^{-6} \text{ C}}{60.0 \text{ V}} = 5.0 \times 10^{-8}$ C/V

$\qquad\qquad = 5.0 \times 10^{-8}$ F $\times$ 1 μF/10^{-6} F $= 5.0 \times 10^{-2}$ μF

EXAMPLE

Finding the Charge on a Capacitor

A commercial 4.0×10^1 μF capacitor has a potential difference of 25 V across it. What is the charge on this capacitor?

Given: $C = 4.0 \times 10^1$ μF   **Unknown:** q
$\quad\quad\quad V = 25$ V

Basic equation: $C = \dfrac{q}{V}$

Solution: $C = \dfrac{q}{V}$

$q = CV = (4.0 \times 10^1 \text{ μF} \times 10^{-6} \text{ F/μF})(25 \text{ V})$

$\quad\quad = (4.0 \times 10^{-5} \text{ F})(25 \text{ V}) = 1.0 \times 10^{-3}$ C

CHAPTER 22 REVIEW

SUMMARY

1. An electric field exists around any charged object. The field produces forces on other charged bodies. **22:1**

2. The electric field intensity is the force per unit charge. The direction of the electric field is the direction of the force on a tiny positive test charge. **22:1**

3. Electric field lines provide a picture of the electric field. They are directed away from positive charges and toward negative charges. **22:1**

4. Electric potential is the change in potential energy of a unit charge in an electric field. Potential differences are measured in volts. **22:3**

5. The electric field intensity between two parallel plates is uniform between the plates except near the edges. **22:4**

6. Robert Millikan's experiments showed that electric charge is quantized and that the charge carried by an electron is 1.6×10^{-19} C. **22:5**

7. Electrons flow in conductors until the electric potential is the same everywhere on the conductor. **22:6**

8. A charged object can have its charge removed by touching it to Earth or to an object touching Earth. This is called grounding. **22:6**

9. Electric fields are strongest near sharply pointed conductors. **22:7**

10. Capacitance is the ratio of the charge on a body to its potential. The capacitance of a body is independent of the charge on the body. **22:8**

QUESTIONS

1. Draw the electric field lines between
   a. two like charges.
   b. two unlike charges.
   c. two parallel plates of opposite charge.
2. How is the direction of an electric field defined?
3. Define the volt in terms of the change in potential energy of a charge in an electric field.
4. If 120 joules of work are done to move one coulomb of charge from a positive plate to a negative plate, what voltage difference exists between the plates?

5. Why does a charged object lose its charge when it is touched to the ground?

6. A charged rubber rod placed on a table maintains its charge for some time. Why does the charged rod not ground immediately?

7. Describe in your own words what a capacitor is.

8. Which has a larger capacitance, a 1-cm diameter or a 10-cm diameter aluminum sphere?

9. What SI unit is used to measure electric potential energy? How about electric potential?

10. A metal box is charged. Compare the concentration of charge at the corners of the box to the charge concentration on the sides.

11. You find two capacitors with different capacitances. How could you store more charge in the smaller capacitor?

APPLYING CONCEPTS

1. Carefully sketch
   a. the electric field produced by a +1.0 μC charge.
   b. the electric field due to a +2.0 μC charge. Make the number of field lines proportional to the charge.
   c. Place a $+5 \times 10^{-3}$ C test charge near the two charges drawn in parts **a** and **b** and draw an arrow showing the force on the test charge.
   d. Now put a -2.5×10^{-3} C charge near the charges in **a** and **b** and again draw an arrow showing the force on this charge.

2. Figure 22–15 shows three spheres with charges of equal magnitude, but with signs as shown. Spheres y and z are held in place but sphere x is free to move. Initially sphere x is equidistant from spheres y and z. Choose which path sphere x will follow, assuming no other forces are acting.

3. When doing a Millikan oil drop experiment, it is best to work with drops that have small charges. When the electric field is turned on, should you try to find drops that are moving fast or slow? Explain.

4. If two oil drops can be held motionless in a Millikan oil drop experiment,
   a. can you be sure that the charges are the same?
   b. The ratios of what two properties of the drops would have to be equal?

EXERCISES

1. A test charge of 2.0×10^{-4} C is placed in the electric field produced by a negative charge. The force that is acting on the positive charge is 8.0×10^{-4} N.
   a. What is the electric field intensity at the test charge?
   b. Is the field direction toward or away from the negative charge?

2. What charge exists on a test charge that experiences a force of 1.4×10^{-8} N at a point where the electric field intensity is 2.0×10^{-4} N/C?

3. The electric field intensity between two charged plates is 1.5×10^3 N/C. The plates are 0.080 m apart. What is the potential difference between the plates in volts?

4. A voltmeter indicates that the difference in potential between two plates is 50.0 V. The plates are 0.020 m apart. What field intensity exists between them?

5. How much work is done to transfer 0.15 C of charge through a potential difference of 9.0 V?

6. A 12-V battery does 1200 J of work transferring charge. How much charge is transferred?

7. A negatively-charged oil drop weighs 8.5×10^{-15} N. The drop is suspended in an electric field intensity of 5.3×10^3 N/C.
   a. What is the charge on the drop?
   b. How many electrons does it carry?

8. A 6.8-μF capacitor has a 15 V potential difference across it. What charge does it hold?

9. Two spheres near each other form a capacitor. One is given a +75 μC charge, the other a −75 μC charge. A potential difference of 15 volts is measured between them.
   a. What is the capacitance of the spheres?

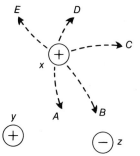

FIGURE 22–15. Use with Applying Concepts 2.

b. If the charges are now increased to $+150 \; \mu C$ and $-150 \; \mu C$, what is the capacitance?

c. What is the potential difference between the two spheres?

10. A 5.4-μF capacitor is charged with 2.7×10^{-3} C. What potential difference exists across it?

PROBLEMS

1. The energy stored in a capacitor with capacitance C having a potential difference V is given by $W = \frac{1}{2}CV^2$. One application is in the electronic photoflash or strobe light. In such a unit, a capacitor of 10.0 μF is charged to 3.00×10^2 V. Find the energy stored.

2. a. Suppose it took 30 s to charge the capacitor in Problem 1. Find the power required to charge it in this time.

b. When this capacitor is discharged through the strobe lamp, it transfers all its energy in 1.0×10^{-4} s. Find the power delivered to the lamp.

c. How is such a large amount of power possible?

3. Lasers are used to try to produce controlled fusion reactions that might supply large amounts of electrical energy. The lasers require brief pulses of energy that are stored in large rooms filled with capacitors. One such room contains a capacitance of 61×10^{-3} F charged to a potential difference of 10 kV.

a. Find the energy stored in the capacitors.

b. The capacitors are discharged in 10 ns (1.0×10^{-8} s). What power is produced?

c. If the capacitors are charged by a generator with a power capacity of 1.0 kW, how many seconds will be required to charge the capacitors?

4. In an early run (1911), Millikan observed that the following measured charges, among others, appeared at different times on a single oil drop.

What value of elementary charge can be deduced from this data?

a. 6.563×10^{-19} C   **f.** 18.08×10^{-19} C

b. 8.204×10^{-19} C   **g.** 19.71×10^{-19} C

c. 11.50×10^{-19} C   **h.** 22.89×10^{-19} C

d. 13.13×10^{-19} C   **i.** 26.13×10^{-19} C

e. 16.48×10^{-19} C

5. A positive test charge of 8.0×10^{-5} C is placed in an electric field of 50.0 N/C intensity. What is the strength of the force exerted on the test charge?

6. The electric field in the atmosphere is about 150 N/C (downward).

a. Find the electric force on a proton with charge $+1.6 \times 10^{-19}$ C.

b. Compare the force in **a** with the force of gravity on the same proton that has a mass of 1.7×10^{-27} kg.

7. Electrons are accelerated by the electric field (Table 1) in a television picture tube.

a. Find the force on an electron ($q = -1.6 \times 10^{-19}$ C).

b. If the field is constant, find the acceleration of the electron (mass = 9.11×10^{-31} kg).

8. A lead nucleus carries the charge of 82 protons.

a. What are the direction and magnitude of the electric field 10^{-10} m from the nucleus?

b. What is the direction and magnitude of the force exerted on an electron located at this distance?

READINGS

Conway, John, "Personal Robots." *Computers and Electronics*, December, 1984.

Forsyth, E. B., "The Brookhaven Superconducting Power Transmission System." *The Physics Teacher*, May, 1983.

Kowalski, L., "A Myth About Capacitors in Series." *The Physics Teacher*, May, 1988.

Parrot, Mary, "Electrography: A Metal Detective Story." *Science Teacher*, May, 1983.

Patterson, David A., "Microprogramming." *Scientific American*, March, 1984.

CHAPTER 23

Current Electricity

SUGGESTION: Have examples of devices to produce electrical energy available to show students. Hand-held generators are available.

FIGURE 23-1. Electrons flow from the negative to the positive plate (a). A generator (b) pumps electrons back to the negative plate, allowing current to continue to flow.

GOALS

1. You will gain an understanding of electric current and electric circuits.
2. You will learn how energy is transferred by means of an electric current.

The most important aspects of electrical energy are its ability to be transferred efficiently over long distances and to be changed into other forms of energy. The large amounts of natural potential and kinetic energy possessed by resources such as Niagara Falls are of little use to an industrial complex one hundred kilometers away unless that energy can be transferred efficiently. Electrical energy provides the means to transfer large quantities of energy great distances with little loss.

At an industrial site, electrical energy can be converted into other forms of energy, such as kinetic, sound, light, and thermal energy. Devices that make these conversions are very important in our everyday lives. Motors, loudspeakers, lamps, television sets, heaters, and air conditioners are examples of common devices that convert electric energy into another form of energy.

23:1 Producing Electric Current

In Chapter 22 we considered two conducting objects at different potentials. When they touched, electrons flowed from the object at a higher potential to the one at a lower potential. The flow continued until the potentials were equal.

A flow of electrons is called an **electric current.** In Figure 23-1a two conductors, A and B, are at different potentials and connected by a wire conductor, C. Electrons flow from B to A through C. The flow stops when the potentials of A, B, and C are equal. How could you keep the flow going? You would have to maintain a potential difference between B and A. This could be done by pumping electrons from conductor A back to conductor B. Such an electron pump requires external energy to run

More for Less?

High-voltage power transmission lines, such as this 765 000-volt line, crisscross our country. It would seem to be more economical if utility companies transmitted electric power to our homes at the voltage we use, rather than going to the expense of installing transformers to first increase the voltage and then decrease it at our homes. Is this a reasonable statement? Why or why not?

FIGURE 23-2. Sources of electric energy include chemical, solar, hydrodynamic, wind, and nuclear energies.

For Your Information

Electrons flow around a closed loop called a circuit.

Current is produced by an electron pump that increases the potential of electrons. Batteries, generators, and photovoltaic cells are electron pumps.

because it increases the electrical potential energy of the electrons. The electric energy can come from one of several other forms of energy. A voltaic or galvanic cell (a common dry cell) converts chemical energy to electric energy. Several cells connected together are called a **battery.** A **photovoltaic cell,** or solar cell, changes light energy into electric energy. A generator converts kinetic energy into electric energy.

23:2 Electric Circuits

The electrons in Figure 23–1b move around a closed loop from the pump through B to C, to A, and back to the pump. Such a closed loop is called an **electric circuit.** A circuit consists of an electron pump that increases the potential energy of electrons connected to a device that reduces the potential energy of the electrons. The change in potential energy of the electric charge (qV) can be converted into some other form of energy. A motor converts electric energy to kinetic energy. A lamp changes electric energy into light. A heater converts electric energy into thermal energy.

Electrons flowing through any of these energy conversion devices lose electric potential energy, and thus potential. Any device that reduces the potential of electrons flowing through it is said to have resistance.

The electron pump creates the flow of electrons, or current. Consider a generator driven by a waterwheel (Figure 23–3). The potential energy of the water is converted to kinetic energy as the water falls. This energy is converted to electric energy within the generator. The generator removes electrons from wire B and adds them to wire A, increasing the electric potential difference, V, between B and A. We say that wire A has been made negative with respect to wire B, or that wire A is negative and wire B is positive. Energy in the amount qV is needed to raise the potential of the electrons. This energy comes from the loss of potential energy of the water. No generator, however, is 100% efficient. Only 98% of the kinetic

Generator

Electron flow

SUGGESTION: Be careful to use the words *electron flow*, *charge flow*, or *current*, but not *current flow*, which is redundant.

energy put into most generators is converted into electric energy. The remainder is turned into thermal energy; the generator gets hot.

If wires A and B are connected to a motor, the excess electrons in wire A flow through the wires in the motor. The electron flow continues through wire B back to the generator. A motor converts electric energy to kinetic energy. Like generators, motors are not 100% efficient. Perhaps 90% of the electric energy is changed into kinetic energy.

The drop in potential energy of electrons in a motor creates kinetic energy.

Both charge and energy are conserved quantities. The total amount of charge (number of electrons) in the circuit does not change. If one coulomb flows through the generator in one second, one coulomb will also flow through the motor in one second. Change in electric energy, E, equals qV. Since q is conserved, the net change in potential energy of the electrons going completely around the circuit must be zero. The potential increase produced by the generator equals the potential drop across the motor.

The net change in potential around a circuit is zero. Current is the same everywhere in a circuit.

If the difference in potential between the two wires is 120 V, the generator must do 120 J of work on each coulomb of charge that it transfers from the positive wire to the negative wire. Every coulomb of charge that moves from the negative wire through the motor and back to the positive wire delivers 120 J of energy to the motor. Thus electric energy serves as a

FIGURE 23–4. The production and use of electric current is not 100 percent efficient. Some heat energy is produced by the splashing water, friction, and electrical resistance.

way to transfer the initial potential energy of falling water to the kinetic energy of a turning motor.

23:3 Rates of Energy Transfer

The rate at which energy is transferred is power. Thus if the generator converts one joule of kinetic energy to electric energy each second, it is producing electric energy at the rate of one joule per second, or one watt.

The energy carried by an electric current depends on the charge transferred and the potential difference across which it moves. The unit used for quantity of electric charge is the coulomb. Thus the rate of flow of electric charge, or electric current (I), is measured in coulombs per second. A flow of one coulomb per second is called an **ampere**, A.

$$1 \text{ C/s} = 1 \text{ A}$$

The ampere is named for the French scientist Andre Marie Ampere (1775–1836). A device that measures current is called an ammeter.

Suppose that the current through the motor of Figure 23–3 is 3.0 C/s (3.0 A). Since the potential difference is 120 V, each coulomb of charge supplies the motor with 120 J of energy. The power, or energy delivered to the motor per second, is

$$(120 \text{ J/C})(3.0 \text{ C/s}) = 360 \text{ J/s} = 360 \text{ watts}$$

The power rating of an electric device is found by multiplying the voltage, V, by the current, I.

EXAMPLE

Electric Power

A 6-V battery delivers 0.5 A of current to an electric motor connected across its terminals. **a.** What is the power rating of the motor? **b.** How much energy does the motor use in 5.0 min?

Given: $V = 6$ V $\qquad\qquad$ Unknowns: **a.** P **b.** E
$\quad\quad\quad I = 0.5$ A $\qquad\qquad$ Basic equations: **a.** $P = VI$
$\quad\quad\quad t = 5.0$ min (300 s) $\qquad\qquad\qquad\qquad$ **b.** $P = \dfrac{E}{t}$

Solution: **a.** $P = VI$
$\qquad\qquad\quad = (6 \text{ V})(0.5 \text{ A})$
$\qquad\qquad\quad = (6 \text{ J/c})(0.5 \text{ C/s}) = 3 \text{ J/s} = 3 \text{ W}$

$\qquad\quad$ **b.** $P = \dfrac{E}{t}$
$\qquad\qquad\quad E = Pt$
$\qquad\qquad\qquad = (3 \text{ W})(300 \text{ s})$
$\qquad\qquad\qquad = 900 \text{ J}$

For Your Information

Practice Exercises

1. The current through a light bulb connected across the terminals of a 120-V outlet is 0.5 A. At what rate does the bulb convert electric energy to light?

2. A 12-V car battery causes a current of 2.0 A to flow through a lamp. What is the power used by the lamp?

3. What current flows through a 75-W light bulb connected to a 120-V outlet?

4. The current through the starter motor of a car having a 12-V battery is 210 A. What electric energy is delivered to the starter in 10.0 s?

23:4 Resistance and Ohm's Law

Suppose two conductors have a potential difference between them. If you connect them with a copper rod, a large current will flow. If, on the other hand, you put a similar glass rod between them, almost no current will flow. The property that determines how much current will flow is called the **resistance.** Resistance is measured by placing a potential difference across two points on a conductor and measuring the current that flows. The resistance is defined to be the ratio of the potential difference, V, to the current, I.

$$R = \frac{V}{I}$$

The electric current, I, is in amperes. The potential difference, V, is in volts. The resistance of the conductor, R, is given in ohms. One ohm, $1\ \Omega$, is the resistance that permits a current of 1 A to flow through a potential difference of 1 V.

The German scientist Georg Simon Ohm (1787–1854) measured the resistance of many conductors. He found that *the resistance for most conductors does not depend on size or direction of the potential difference across it.* A device that has a constant resistance as long as the temperature does not change obeys Ohm's law.

Most conductors obey Ohm's law, at least over a limited range of voltages. Many important devices, however, do not. A transistor radio or pocket calculator contains many devices, such as transistors and diodes, that do not obey Ohm's law. Even a light bulb has a resistance that depends on the voltage and does not obey Ohm's law.

Wires used to connect electric devices have very small resistances. One meter of a typical wire used in physics labs has a resistance of about $0.03\ \Omega$. Wires used in house wiring offer as little as $0.004\ \Omega$ resistance for each meter of length. However, a device that is designed to have a specific resistance is called a **resistor.** Resistors are made of long, thin wires, graphite, or semiconductors.

The larger the potential difference, or voltage, placed across a resistor, the larger the current that passes through it. If the current through a resistor is doubled, the drop in potential is also doubled. It follows that the voltage applied across the resistor would have to be doubled to obtain the increased current.

Superconductors are materials that have zero resistance. There is no potential drop across a superconductor. Since the power dissipated in a conductor is given by the product IV, a superconductor can conduct elec-

For Your Information

$V = IR$ is often taken as a statement of Ohm's law, but this is not true. The equation simply defines resistance and applies to all resistances whether they obey Ohm's law or not.

For a device that obeys Ohm's law, the resistance, R, is independent of the current.

FIGURE 23–5. Ohm's law is illustrated in calculating the current between a potential difference of 30 volts and a resistance of 10 ohms.

$$I = \frac{V}{R}$$
$$= \frac{30\ V}{10\ \Omega}$$
$$= 3\ A$$

tricity without loss of energy. The development of superconductors that can be cooled by relatively inexpensive liquid nitrogen may lead to more efficient transfer of energy by electricity.

EXAMPLE

Current Flow Through a Resistor

What is the current through a 30-Ω resistance that has a potential difference of 120 V?

Given: $V = 120$ V   Unknown: I
$\quad\quad\quad R = 30\ \Omega$

Basic equation: $I = \dfrac{V}{R}$

Solution: $I = \dfrac{V}{R}$

$\quad\quad = \dfrac{120\ V}{30\ \Omega}$

$\quad\quad = 4$ A

Practice Exercises

5. An automobile headlight with a resistance of 30 Ω is placed across a 12-V battery. What is the current through the circuit?
6. A lamp draws a current of 0.5 A when it is connected to a 120-V source.
   a. What is the resistance of the lamp?
   b. What is the power rating of the lamp?
7. A motor with an operating resistance of 32 Ω is connected to a voltage source. The current in the circuit is 3.8 A. What is the voltage of the source?
8. A transistor radio uses 2×10^{-4} A of current when it is operated by a 3-V battery. What is the resistance of the radio circuit?

DEMONSTRATION: See the Teacher Guide.

A schematic diagram uses symbols for components rather than pictures.

23:5 Diagramming Electric Circuits

A simple circuit can be described in words. You could also use photographs or an artist's drawings of the parts. Instead, a diagram of an electric circuit often is drawn using symbols for the circuit elements. Such a diagram is called a circuit **schematic.** Some of the symbols are shown in Figure 23–6. Both an artist's drawing and a schematic of the same circuit are shown in Figure 23–7.

Notice that in both the artist's drawing and the schematic, current is shown flowing out of the positive terminal of the battery. As we have seen, negative charge carriers, electrons, actually leave the negative terminal of a battery or other source of electric energy. In drawing electric circuits we follow a convention. Current arrows are drawn in the direction that positive charge carriers would move. Often this is called **conventional current.** The convention works because the effect of a negative

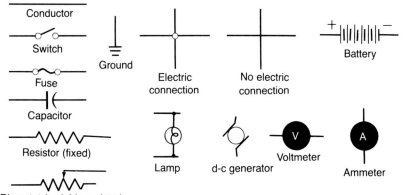

FIGURE 23–6. Electric circuit symbols.

Conductor

Switch

Fuse

Capacitor

Resistor (fixed)

Rheostat (variable resistor)

Ground

Electric connection

No electric connection

Battery

Lamp

d-c generator

Voltmeter

Ammeter

charge moving from left to right is the same as that of a positive charge moving from right to left.

PROBLEM SOLVING

Drawing Schematic Diagrams

When drawing schematic diagrams, follow these steps.

1. Draw the symbol for the battery or other source of electric energy at the left side of the page. Put the positive terminal at the top.
2. Draw a wire following the conventional current out of the positive terminal. When you reach a resistor or other device, draw the symbol for it.
3. If you reach a point where there are two current paths, such as at a voltmeter, draw a † on the diagram and follow one path until the two paths join again. Then draw the second path.
4. Follow the path until you reach the negative terminal of the battery.
5. Check your work to see that you have included all parts and that there are complete paths for current to follow.

Often instruments that measure current and voltage are connected into circuits. They must be connected in specific ways. An ammeter, which measures current, must be connected so that all of the current can flow

FIGURE 23–7. A simple electric circuit is represented both pictorially (a) and schematically (b).

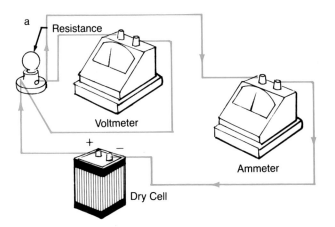

a Resistance

Voltmeter

Ammeter

Dry Cell

b

V

15 Ω

2 A A

30 V

through the ammeter. Such a connection is called a **series connection.** A voltmeter measures the potential difference across a circuit element. One voltmeter terminal is connected to one side of the element. The other terminal is connected to the other side. This connection is called a **parallel connection.** The potential difference across the element is equal to the potential difference across the voltmeter.

Practice Exercises

9. Draw a circuit diagram to include a 60-V battery, an ammeter, and a resistance of 12.5 Ω in series. Indicate the ammeter reading and the direction of current flow.

10. Draw a series circuit diagram showing a 4.5-V battery, a resistor, and an ammeter reading 90 mA. Label the size of the resistor. Choose a direction for the current and indicate the positive terminal of the battery.

23:6 Controlling Current in a Circuit

There are two ways to control the current in a circuit. Since $I = V/R$, I can be changed by varying either V or R, or both. Figure 23–8a shows a simple circuit. When V is 60 V and R is 30 Ω, the current flow is 2.0 A.

If the current is to be reduced to 1.0 A, the 60-V battery could be replaced by a 30-V battery, Figure 23–8b. Or the resistance could be increased to 60-Ω by adding a 30-Ω resistor to the circuit, Figure 23–8c. Both of these methods will reduce the current to 1.0 A. Resistors are often used to control the current in circuits or parts of circuits.

Sometimes a smooth, continuous control of the current is desired. A lamp dimmer allows continuous rather than step-by-step control of light intensity. To achieve this kind of control, a variable resistor, called a rheostat or **potentiometer,** is used (Figure 23–9). A variable resistor consists of a coil of resistance wire and a sliding contact point. By moving the contact point to various positions along the coil, the amount of wire added to the circuit is varied. As more wire is placed in the circuit, the resistance of the circuit increases; thus the current decreases in accordance with the equation $I = V/R$. In this way the light output of a lamp can be adjusted. The same type of device controls the speed of electric fans,

FIGURE 23–8. The current flow through a simple circuit (a) can be regulated by removing some of the dry cells (b) or increasing the resistance of the circuit (c).

a

b

c

a

Motor

Switch

Variable
resistor

+ −

Dry cell

b

Motor

+

−

Variable resistor

electric mixers, and other appliances. To save space, the coil of wire is often bent into a circular shape and the slide is replaced by a knob, as shown in Figure 23–10.

Practice Exercises

11. A 75-W lamp is connected to 120 V.

    a. How much current flows through the lamp?

    b. What is the resistance of the lamp?

12. A resistor is now added in series with the lamp to reduce the current to half its original value.

    a. What is the potential difference across the lamp? Assume the lamp resistance is constant.

    b. How much resistance was added to the circuit?

    c. How much power is now dissipated in the lamp?

23:7 Heating Effect of Electric Currents

Power is the energy per unit time converted by an electric circuit into another form of energy. Power is equal to the voltage multiplied by the current, $P = VI$. By the definition of resistance we know that $V = IR$. Substituting this expression into the equation for electric power, we obtain

$$P = I^2R$$

The power dissipated in a resistor is proportional to the square of the current that passes through it and to the resistance. The energy is changed from electrical to thermal energy.

The energy supplied to a circuit can be used in different ways. A motor converts electric energy into mechanical energy. An electric lamp changes electric energy into light. However, not all of the electric energy delivered to a motor or to an electric light ends up in a useful form of energy. Some energy is always converted into thermal energy. Certain devices, such as space heaters, are designed to convert all of the electric energy into thermal energy. Some electric energy, as in Figure 23–11, is also converted into light.

DEMONSTRATION: See the Teacher Guide.

FIGURE 23–10. An inside view of a rheostat.

FIGURE 23–11. The coils of this space heater are an example of the conversion of electric energy to thermal energy.

SUGGESTION: Demonstrate the heating effect of wires of different diameters.

The power varies directly with the resistance.

The power used by a resistor varies directly with the square of current flowing through the resistor.

The total energy supplied to any device is the product of power and time.

The electric energy transferred to a resistor in a time interval t is equal to I^2Rt. If all the electric energy is converted into thermal energy of the resistor, the increase in thermal energy is

$$E = I^2Rt$$

The temperature of the resistor increases, allowing heat to flow into its colder surroundings. For example, in an immersion heater, a resistor placed in a cup of water can bring the water to the boiling point in a few minutes.

EXAMPLE

Thermal Energy Produced by an Electric Current

A heater has a resistance of 10.0 Ω. It operates on 120.0 V.

a. What is the current through the resistance?

b. What thermal energy in joules is supplied by the heater in 10.0 s?

Given: $R = 10.0\ \Omega$ Unknowns: **a.** I **b.** E
        $V = 120.0$ V
        $t = 10.0$ s   Basic equations: **a.** $I = \dfrac{V}{R}$

                                      b. $E = I^2Rt$

Solution: **a.** $I = \dfrac{V}{R} = \dfrac{120.0\text{ V}}{10.0\ \Omega} = 12.0$ A

           b. $E = I^2Rt$

                $= (12.0\text{ A})^2(10.0\ \Omega)(10.0\text{ s}) = 14\ 400$ J or 14.4 kJ

Practice Exercises

13. A 15-Ω electric heater operates on a 120-V outlet.

     a. What is the current through the heater?

     b. How much energy is used by the heater in 30.0 seconds?

     c. How much thermal energy is liberated by the heater in this time?

14. A 30-Ω resistor is connected to a 60-V battery.
   a. What is the current in the circuit?
   b. How much energy is used by the resistor in 5 minutes?
15. A 100.0-W light bulb is 20.0% efficient. That means 20.0% of the electric energy is converted to light energy.
   a. How many joules does the light bulb convert into light each minute it is in operation?
   b. How many joules of thermal energy does the light bulb produce each minute?
16. The resistance of an electric stove element at operating temperature is 11 Ω.
   a. 220 V are applied across it. What is the current through the stove element?
   b. How much energy does the element convert to thermal energy in 30.0 s?
   c. The element is being used to heat a kettle containing 1.20 kg of water. Assume that 70% of the heat is absorbed by the water. What is its increase in temperature during the 30.0 s?

23:8 Transmission of Electric Energy

Niagara Falls and Hoover Dam can produce electric energy with little pollution. The energy often must be transmitted long distances to reach homes and industries. How can the transmission be done with as little loss of useful energy as possible? Thermal energy is produced at a rate given by $P = I^2R$. This loss is called the "I^2R" loss by electrical engineers. To reduce this loss, one must reduce either the current, I, or the resistance, R.

All wires have some resistance, even though it is small. For example, one kilometer of the large wire used to carry electric current into a home has a resistance of 0.2 Ω. Suppose a farmhouse were connected directly to a power plant 3.5 km away (Figure 23–12). The resistance in wires needed to carry current to the home and back to the plant is 3.5 km × 2 × 0.2 Ω/km = 1.4 Ω. An operating electric stove might cause a 41-A current through the wires. The power lost in the wires is given by $P = I^2R =$ (41 A)^2 × 1.4 Ω = 2400 W. All this power is wasted.

SUGGESTION: See what kinds of teaching materials might be available from your local power company.

FIGURE 23–12. All wires possess resistance to carrying an electric current.

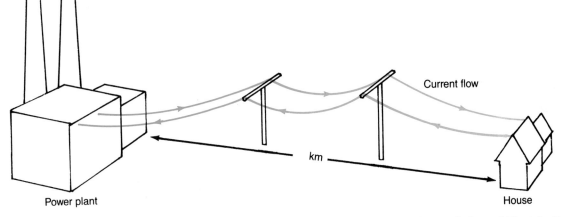

Current flow

km

Power plant

House

FIGURE 23–13. High voltage transmission lines carry electricity over
long distances.

This loss could be reduced by reducing the resistance. Cables of high
conductivity and large diameter should be used. Such cables are expensive and heavy. Since the loss is also proportional to the square of the
current in the conductors, it is even more important to keep the current in
the lines low.

The electrical energy per second (power) transferred over a long-
distance transmission line follows the relationship $P = VI$. The current can
be reduced without reducing the power by increasing the voltage. Some
long-distance lines use voltages over one-half million volts. Lower current
reduces the I^2R loss in the lines by keeping the I^2 factor low. Long-
distance transmission lines always operate at high voltage to reduce I^2R
loss.

High voltage lines are needed to
transmit electric power over long
distances with minimum energy loss.

23:9   The Kilowatt Hour

While electric companies often are called "power" companies, they
really provide energy. When you pay your home electric bill, you may be
paying for electric energy, not power.

The electric energy used by any device is its rate of energy consumption
in joules per second (watts) times the number of seconds it is operated.
Joules per second times seconds (J/s · s) equals total joules of energy.

The joule, a watt-second, is a relatively small amount of energy. For
that reason, electric companies measure their energy sales in a large number of joules called a kilowatt hour, kWh. A **kilowatt hour** is equal to
1000 watts delivered continuously for 3600 seconds (one hour). It is

A kilowatt hour is an energy unit. It is
the rate of energy use (power)
multiplied by a time, one hour.

$$1 \text{ kWh} = (1000 \text{ J/s})(3600 \text{ s}) = 3.6 \times 10^6 \text{ J}$$

Not many devices in the home other than hot-water heaters, stoves, heaters, and hair dryers require more than 1000 watts. Ten 100-watt light
bulbs operating all at once would use one kilowatt hour of energy if left on
for a full hour.

EXAMPLE

The Cost of Operating an Electric Device

A modern color television set draws 2.0 A when operated on 120 V. **a.** How much power does the set use? **b.** If the set is operated for an average of 7.0 hours per day, what energy in kWh does it consume per month (30 days)? **c.** At $0.08 per kWh, what is the cost of operating the set per month?

Given: $I = 2.0$ A   **Unknowns: a.** P **b.** E
        $V = 120$ V
        $t = 2.1 \times 10^2$ h (7.0 h/d × 30 d)   **Basic equation:** $P = VI$
                                                $P = E/t$

Solution:

a. $P = VI$ **b.** $E = Pt$
     $= (120 \text{ V})(2.0 \text{ A})$ $= (2.4 \times 10^2 \text{ W})(2.1 \times 10^2 \text{ h})$
     $= 2.4 \times 10^2$ W $= 5.0 \times 10^4$ Wh $= 5.0 \times 10^1$ kWh

c. cost $= (5.0 \times 10^1 \text{ kWh})(\$0.08/\text{kWh}) = \$4.00$

Practice Exercises

17. An electric space heater draws 15.0 A from a 120-V source. It is operated, on the average, for 5.0 h each day.

    a. How much power does the heater use?

    b. How much energy in kWh does it consume in 30 days?

    c. At $0.11 per kWh, what does it cost to operate the heater for 30 days?

18. A digital clock has an operating resistance of 12 000 Ω and is plugged into a 115-V outlet.

    a. How much current does it draw?

    b. How much power does it use?

    c. If the owner of the clock pays $0.09 per kWh, what does it cost to operate the clock for 30 days?

For Your Information

Eliha Thomson, an English-American inventor, devised a high-frequency electrical generator, among his 700 patented inventions. You are probably familiar with the company that he and Thomas Edison formed—General Electric.

For Your Information

Some electric companies still only charge for energy, but only for residential customers. Institutional customers, including schools, all commercial customers, and all industrial customers pay separate charges for power (kW) and energy (kWh). The directive of the 1978 Energy Act states that eventually all customers will be billed separately for power and energy.

Electric companies do, in fact, sell two separate products, power and energy, and charge for them separately.

a

b

FIGURE 23–14. Watthour meters (a) measure the amount of electric energy used by a consumer. The more current being used at a given time, the faster the horizontal disk in the center of the meter turns. Meter readings are then used in calculating the cost of energy (b).

CHAPTER 23 REVIEW

SUMMARY

1. Batteries, generators, and solar cells convert various forms of energy to electric energy. **23:1**
2. In an electric circuit, electric energy is transmitted from a device that produces electric energy to a resistor or other device that uses electric energy. **23:2**
3. As a charge moves through resistors in a circuit, its potential energy is reduced. The energy released when the charge moves completely around the circuit equals the work done to give the charge its initial potential energy. **23:2**
4. One ampere is a current flow of one coulomb per second. **23:3**
5. Electric power is found by multiplying voltage by current. **23:3**
6. The resistance of a device is the ratio of the voltage across it divided by the current through it. **23:4**
7. In a device that obeys Ohm's law, the resistance does not depend on the current through it. **23:4**
8. In a circuit diagram, conventional current, the direction in which a positive current carrier would move, is used. **23:5**
9. The current in a circuit can be varied by varying either the voltage or the resistance, or both. **23:6**
10. The thermal energy produced in a circuit from electric energy is equal to I^2Rt. **23:7**
11. In long-distance transmission lines, current is reduced without reducing power by increasing the voltage. **23:8**
12. A kilowatt hour, kWh, is an energy unit. It is equal to 3.6×10^6 J. **23:9**

QUESTIONS

1. Describe the energy conversions that occur in each of these devices.
   a. incandescent light bulb
   b. clothes dryer
   c. digital clock radio
2. You can buy several different designs of electric space heaters. Suppose you want to buy a space heater to heat a certain area. What information about the heater should you know to make a wise buying decision?
3. Using the equation $I = V/R$, describe two ways of increasing a circuit's current.
4. What quantities must be kept small to transmit electric energy over long distances economically?
5. Utility companies sell electrical energy in units of kWh while physicists measure energy in joules. 1 kWh is equivalent to how many joules?
6. Draw a schematic to show a circuit that includes a 90-V battery, an ammeter, and a resistance of 45 Ω connected in series. What is the ammeter reading? Draw arrows showing the direction of conventional current flow.
7. Draw a series circuit diagram to include a 16-Ω resistor, a battery, and an ammeter that reads 1.75 A. Current flows through the meter from left to right. Indicate the positive terminal and the voltage of the battery.
8. a. How must an ammeter be connected in a circuit to correctly read the current?
   b. How must a voltmeter be connected to a resistor in order to read the potential difference across it?
9. How many electrons flow past a cross section of wire each second if the wire has a current of 1 A?
10. Why can birds perch on high voltage lines without being injured?
11. Which wire conducts electricity with the least resistance: one with large cross-sectional diameter or one with small cross-sectional diameter?
12. If the voltage across a circuit is kept constant and the resistance is doubled, what effect does this have on the circuit's current?

APPLYING CONCEPTS

1. Two wires can be placed across the terminals of a 6-V battery. One has a high resistance, one low. Which wire will produce thermal energy at the faster rate?

2. Two bulbs work on a 120-V circuit. One is 50 watts, the other 100 watts. Which has a higher resistance? Explain.

3. Why do light bulbs burn out more frequently when they are initially switched on compared to while the bulbs are operating?

4. As the temperature of wire increases, its resistance also increases. Explain.

5. Explain why a cow that touches an electric fence experiences a mild shock.

6. A student finds a device that looks like a resistor. When she connects it to a 1.5 V battery, only 45×10^{-6} A flows, but when a 3.0-V battery is used, 25×10^{-3} A flows. Does the device obey Ohm's law?

7. When a battery is connected to a complete circuit, electrons flow almost instantaneously. Explain.

8. Why is it dangerous to replace a 15 A fuse in a circuit with one of 30 A?

9. Why does a wire become warmer as electricity flows through it?

EXERCISES

1. The current through a toaster connected to a 120-V source is 8.0 A. What is the power rating of the toaster?

2. A current of 1.2 A flows through a light bulb when it is connected across a 120-V source. What is the power rating of the bulb?

3. A flashlight bulb is connected across a 3.0-V difference in potential. The current through the lamp is 1.5 A.
   a. What is the power rating of the lamp?
   b. How much electric energy does the lamp convert in 11 min?

4. A voltage of 75 V is placed across a 15-Ω resistor. What is the current through the resistor?

5. A resistance of 60 Ω has a current of 0.4 A through it when it is connected to the terminals of a battery. What is the voltage of the battery?

6. A 12-V battery is connected to a device and 24 mA of current flows through it. If the device obeys Ohm's law, how much current will flow when a 24-V battery is used?

7. A lamp draws a 66 mA current when connected to a 6.0 V battery. When a 9.0 V battery is used, the lamp draws 75 mA.
   a. Does the lamp obey Ohm's law?
   b. How much power does the lamp dissipate at 6.0 V?
   c. How much power does it dissipate at 9.0 V?

8. The current through a lamp connected across 120 V is 0.4 A when the lamp is on.
   a. What is its resistance when on?
   b. When the lamp is cold, its resistance is one fifth as large as when the lamp is hot. What is its cold resistance?
   c. What is the current through the lamp as it is turned on if it is connected to a potential difference of 120 V?

9. How much energy does a 60.0-W light bulb use in half an hour? If the light bulb is 12% efficient, how much thermal energy does it generate during the half hour?

10. A lamp draws 0.50 A from a 120-V generator.
    a. How much power does the generator deliver?
    b. How much energy does the lamp convert in five minutes?

11. A 12-V automobile battery is connected to an electric starter motor. The current through the motor is 210 A.
    a. How many joules of energy does the battery deliver to the motor each second?
    b. What power does the motor use in watts?

12. A 20.0-Ω resistor is connected to a 30.0-V battery. What is the current in the resistor?

13. What voltage is applied to a 4-Ω resistor if the current is 1.5 A?

14. What voltage is placed across a motor of 15 Ω operating resistance to deliver 8.0 A of current?

15. A 6-Ω resistor is connected to a 15-V battery.
    a. What is the current in the circuit?
    b. How much thermal energy is produced in ten minutes?

16. A lamp consumes 30.0 W when connected to 120 V.

  a. What is the current in the lamp?

  b. What is the resistance of the lamp?

PROBLEMS

1. A heating coil has a resistance of 4.0 Ω and operates on 120 V.

  a. What is the current in the coil while it is operating?

  b. What energy is supplied to the coil in 5.0 min?

  c. If the coil is immersed in an insulated container holding 20.0 kg of water, what will be the increase in the temperature of the water? Assume that 100% of the heat is absorbed by the water.

  d. At $0.08 per kWh, what does it cost to operate the heating coil 30 minutes per day for 30 days?

2. An electric heater is rated at 500 W.

  a. How much energy is delivered to the heater in half an hour?

  b. The heater is being used to heat a room containing 50.0 kg of air. If the specific heat of air is 1.10 kJ/kg · C° (1100 J/kg · C°) and 50% of the thermal energy heats the air in the room, what is the change in air temperature?

  c. At $0.08 per kWh, what does it cost to run the heater 6 hours per day for 30 days?

3. An electric motor operates a pump that irrigates a farmer's crop by pumping 10 000 L of water a vertical distance of 8.0 m into a field each hour. The motor has an operating resistance of 22.0 Ω and is connected across a 110-V source.

  a. What current does it draw?

  b. How efficient is the motor?

4. A transistor radio operates by means of a 9.0-V battery that supplies it with a 50 mA (0.050 A) current.

  a. If the cost of the battery is $0.90 and it lasts for 300 h, what is the cost per kWh to operate the radio in this manner?

  b. The same radio, by means of a converter, is plugged into a household circuit by a home owner who pays $0.08 per kWh. What does

it now cost to operate the radio for 300 hours?

5. The damage caused by electric shock depends on the current flowing through the body. One mA (1×10^{-3} A) can be felt. Five mA are painful. Above 15 mA, a person loses muscle control; 70 mA can be fatal.

  A person with dry skin has a resistance from one arm to the other of about 10^5 Ω. When skin is wet, the resistance drops to about 5×10^3 Ω.

  a. What is the minimum voltage placed across the arms that would produce a current that could be felt by a person with dry skin?

  b. What effect would the same voltage have if the person had wet skin?

  c. What would be the minimum voltage that would produce a current that could be felt when the skin is wet?

6. The graph in Figure 23–15 shows the current that flows through a device called a silicon diode.

  a. A student places +0.70 V across the diode, measures the current, and calculates the resistance. What resistance would be calculated?

FIGURE 23–15. Use with Problem 6.

  b. If the same student used +0.60 V, what resistance would be calculated?

  c. Does the diode obey Ohm's law?

7. Table 23–1 shows data taken by students. They connected a length of nichrome wire to a "power supply" that could put a voltage from 0 V to 10 V across the wire. They then measured the current through the wire for several voltages. They used both positive and negative potential differences. The data table shows the voltages used and currents measured.

TABLE 23–1

Voltage and Current Measurements for Nichrome Wire		
Voltage V (volts)	**Current** I (amps)	**Resistance** R (ohms)
2.00	0.014	
4.00	0.027	
6.00	0.040	
8.00	0.052	
10.00	0.065	
−2.00	−0.014	
−4.00	−0.028	
−6.00	−0.039	
−8.00	−0.051	
−10.00	−0.064	

a. For each measurement, calculate the resistance. Also graph the data.

b. Does the nichrome wire obey Ohm's law? If not for all the voltages, specify the voltage range for which Ohm's law holds.

READINGS

Brown, Stuart, "Can Brainy New Cars Outwit Car Thieves?" *Popular Science,* January, 1985.

Henry, Richard, "Superconducting Microelectronics." *The Physics Teacher,* February, 1984.

Triestly, Harry, "All About Thermistors." *Radio Electronics,* January, 1985.

Yulsman, Tom, "Light at the End of the Tunnel." *Discover,* November, 1988.

CHAPTER 24

Series and Parallel Circuits

GOALS

1. You will learn how resistors can be used in series and parallel circuits.
2. You will become familiar with several applications of these circuits.

For Your Information

Henry Cavendish used the direct approach to measure the strength of an electric current. Lacking the appropriate instruments, he instead shocked himself with the current and then estimated the pain.

SUGGESTION: Have a student make the circuit board shown in the TRB demonstration 24–2.

In a series circuit, the current is the same at all points along the wire.

In a series circuit, the sum of the voltage drops equals the voltage drop across the entire circuit.

The electric circuits introduced in Chapter 23 had one source of electric energy and one device that used energy. Often many devices must be connected to one source. In this chapter, you will explore the ways in which devices can be connected in electric circuits.

An electric circuit in which all of the current travels through each device is called a **series circuit.** A **parallel circuit** allows the current to split and travel through several devices at once. A closer look will show how these circuits work and how they can be used.

24:1 Series Circuits

When resistors are connected in series, all current travels through each resistor. It moves through one resistor after another. Consider the flow of water in a river as a model of an electric current. At the river's source, the gravitational potential of the water is highest. Rapids are like resistors. A river having one rapid after another is like a series circuit. All the water in the river passes through each of the rapids but loses some potential energy at each one. In Figure 24–1, current passes through the generator, the ammeter, and each lamp in succession. The current is the same in each device and in the generator. To find the current we first find the potential drops around the circuit. The increase in potential across the generator is equal to the sum of the potential drops around the remainder of the circuit. The total distance the river drops is the sum of the vertical drops through each of the rapids. In the electrical circuit, there is almost no drop across the ammeter or the wires. The potential difference across the gen-

404

Which Light Lights the Lightest?

A 60-watt light bulb and a 100-watt light bulb are connected in series with a 120-volt potential difference. If the circuit is closed, which bulb will glow brighter?

FIGURE 24–1. A series circuit can be represented both pictorially and schematically. The total resistance of a series circuit is equal to the sum of the individual resistances.

Lamps

Ammeter

Generator

R_1 R_2 R_3

$30\ \Omega$ $15\ \Omega$ $15\ \Omega$

$$R = R_1 + R_2 + R_3$$
$$= 30\ \Omega + 15\ \Omega + 15\ \Omega$$
$$= 60\ \Omega$$

2 A

120 V

SUGGESTION: Use large demonstration ammeters and voltmeters to set up the circuits discussed in this chapter.

For Your Information

The net change in potential going around a circuit must be zero. A battery or generator raises the potential. While passing through the resistors, the potential drops an equal amount. The net change is zero.

An effective resistance is the resistance of a single resistor that could replace all the resistors in a circuit.

The effective resistance in a series circuit is the sum of the individual resistances.

erator, V, is equal to the sum of the voltage drops across the individual lamps.

$$V = V_1 + V_2 + V_3$$

The resistance of each lamp is defined as $R = V/I$. Thus the potential drop across the first lamp is $V_1 = IR_1$. Therefore

$$V = IR_1 + IR_2 + IR_3$$
$$V = I(R_1 + R_2 + R_3)$$

The current is given by

$$I = \frac{V}{R_1 + R_2 + R_3}$$

The same current would exist in a circuit with a single resistor, R, that has a resistance equal to the sum of the three lamp resistances. Such a resistance is called the **effective resistance** of the circuit. For resistors in series, the effective resistance is the sum of all the resistances.

$$R = R_1 + R_2 + R_3$$

Notice that the effective resistance is larger than any single resistance.

The current through a series circuit is most easily found by first calculating the effective resistance, R, and then using the equation $I = V/R$.

EXAMPLE

Current in a Series Circuit

Four 15-Ω resistors are connected in series to a 45-V battery. What is the current in the circuit?

$$R = R_1 + R_2 + R_3 + R_4$$
$$= 15\ \Omega + 15\ \Omega + 15\ \Omega + 15\ \Omega = 60\ \Omega$$

Using the definition of resistance in the form $I = V/R$ gives

$$I = \frac{V}{R} = \frac{(45\ V)}{(60\ \Omega)} = 0.75\ A$$

FIGURE 24–2. Use with the Example.

15 Ω 15 Ω

15 Ω 15 Ω

45 V

Practice Exercises

1. There are three 20-Ω resistors connected in series across a 120-V generator.
   a. What is the effective resistance of the circuit?
   b. What is the current in the circuit?

2. A 10-Ω resistor, a 15-Ω resistor, and a 5-Ω resistor are connected in series across a 90-V battery.
   a. What is the effective resistance of the circuit?
   b. What is the current in the circuit?

3. Consider a 9-V battery in a circuit with three resistors connected in series.
   a. If the resistance of one of the devices increases, how will the series resistance change?
   b. What will happen to the current?
   c. Will there be any change in the battery voltage?

4. Ten Christmas tree bulbs connected in series have equal resistances. When connected to a 120-V outlet, the current through the bulbs is 0.06 A.
   a. What is the effective resistance of the circuit?
   b. What is the resistance of each bulb?

24:2 Voltage Drops in a Series Circuit

The voltage drop across each device in a series circuit can be calculated by rewriting the equation that defines resistance, $R = V/I$, as $V = IR$. First find the effective resistance, R, in the circuit. Then use the effective resistance to find the current. Find $I = V/R$, where V is the battery voltage. Once the current in the circuit has been determined, multiply I by the resistance of the individual device to find the voltage drop across that device.

SUGGESTION: Open up the back of a small portable radio and see if you can find some resistors. Pass the radio around for students to look at the circuitry.

EXAMPLE

Voltage Drops in a Series Circuit

A 5.0-Ω resistor and a 10.0-Ω resistor are connected in series and placed across a 45.0-V potential difference. **a.** What is the effective resistance of the circuit? **b.** What is the current through the circuit? **c.** What is the voltage drop across each resistor? **d.** What is the total voltage drop across the circuit?

FIGURE 24–3. Use with the Example.

Given: $R_1 = 5.0 \ \Omega$ Unknowns: R, I, V_1, V_2
$\quad\quad\quad R_2 = 10.0 \ \Omega$ Basic equation: $V = IR$
$\quad\quad\quad V = 45.0 \ V$

Solution:
a. $R = R_1 + R_2$
$\quad = 5.0 \ \Omega + 10.0 \ \Omega = 15.0 \ \Omega$

b. $I = \dfrac{V}{R} = \dfrac{45.0 \text{ V}}{15.0 \text{ }\Omega} = 3.00 \text{ A}$

c. The voltage drop across R_1 is

$V_1 = IR_1 = (3.00 \text{ A})(5.0 \text{ }\Omega) = 15 \text{ V}$

The voltage drop across R_2 is

$V_2 = IR_2$

$= (3.00 \text{ A})(10.0 \text{ }\Omega) = 30.0 \text{ V}$

d. $V = V_1 + V_2$

$= 15 \text{ V} + 30.0 \text{ V} = 45 \text{ V}$

An important application of series resistors is the **voltage divider.** Suppose you have a 9-V battery but need a 5-V potential source. A voltage divider can supply this voltage. Consider the circuit in Figure 24–4. Two resistors, R_1 and R_2, are connected in series across a battery of voltage V. The effective resistance of the circuit is $R = R_1 + R_2$. The current, I, is given by $I = V/R = V/(R_1 + R_2)$. The desired voltage, 5 V, is the voltage drop, V_2, across resistor R_2.

$$V_2 = IR_2$$

Replacing I by the equation above gives

$$V_2 = IR_2 = \left(\frac{V}{R_1 + R_2}\right) \cdot R_2$$

$$= \frac{VR_2}{R_1 + R_2}$$

EXAMPLE

Voltage Divider

A 9.0-V battery and two resistors, $R_1 = 400 \text{ }\Omega$ and $R_2 = 500 \text{ }\Omega$, are connected as a voltage divider. What is the voltage across R_2?

Given: $V = 9.0$ V   Unknown: V_2

$R_1 = 400 \text{ }\Omega$

$R_2 = 500 \text{ }\Omega$ Basic equation: $V_2 = \dfrac{VR_2}{R_1 + R_2}$

Solution:

$$V_2 = \frac{VR_2}{R_1 + R_2} = \frac{(9 \text{ V})(500 \text{ }\Omega)}{400 \text{ }\Omega + 500 \text{ }\Omega} = 5 \text{ V}$$

Voltage dividers are often used with sensors like photoresistors. The resistance of a photoresistor depends on the amount of light that strikes it. Photoresistors are made of semiconductors like selenium or cadmium sulfide. A typical photoresistor can have a resistance of 400 Ω when light strikes it but a resistance of 400 000 Ω when it is in the dark. The output voltage of a voltage divider that uses a photoresistor depends on the amount of light striking the photoresistor sensor. This circuit can be used as a light meter or a switch that turns lights on when the sun sets.

A voltage divider is a pair of resistors used to obtain a desired voltage from a battery that supplies a higher voltage.

FIGURE 24–4. Use with the Example.

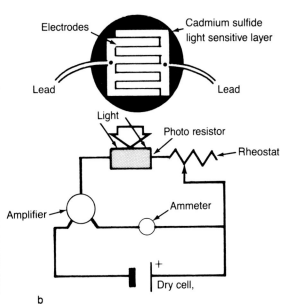

FIGURE 24–5. A light meter (a) and
schematic diagram (b).

Practice Exercises

5. A 20.0-Ω resistor and a 30.0-Ω resistor are connected in series and placed across a 120-V potential difference.
   a. What is the effective resistance of the circuit?
   b. What is the current in the circuit?
   c. What is the voltage drop across each resistor?
   d. What is the voltage drop across the two resistors together?
6. Three resistors of 3.0 kΩ (3.0×10^3 Ω), 5.0 kΩ, and 4.0 kΩ are connected in series across a 12-V battery.
   a. What is the effective resistance?
   b. What is the current through the resistors?
   c. What is the voltage drop across each resistor?
   d. Find the total voltage drop across the three resistors.
7. A student makes a voltage divider from a 45-V battery, a 475-kΩ (475×10^3 Ω) resistor, and a 235-kΩ resistor. The output voltage is taken across the smaller resistor. What is it?
8. A photoresistor is used in a voltage divider as R_2. $V = 9.0$ V and $R_1 = 500$ Ω.
   a. What is the output voltage, V_2, across R_2 when a bright light strikes the photoresistor and $R_2 = 475$ Ω?
   b. When the light is dim, $R_2 = 4.0$ kΩ. What is V_2?
   c. When the photoresistor is in total darkness, $R_2 = 0.40$ MΩ (0.40×10^6 Ω). What is V_2?

24:3 Parallel Circuits

A typical parallel circuit is shown in Figure 24–6. The circuit contains a voltage source and three resistors. The three resistors are connected in

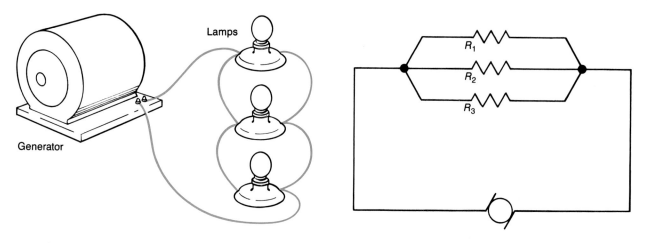

FIGURE 24–6. A typical parallel circuit is shown using both its pictorial and schematic representations. The total resistance of a parallel circuit is smaller than any of its individual resistances.

In a parallel circuit, each resistor provides a new path for electrons to flow.

parallel; their left-hand and right-hand ends are connected together. The current flows through three paths in this parallel circuit. Rapids in a wide river can illustrate a parallel circuit. The water going through rapids often divides into several channels. Some channels may have a large flow of water, others a small flow. The sum of the flows, however, is equal to the total flow of water in the river. In addition, no matter which channel the water follows, the loss in gravitational potential will be the same. All the water started at the same level and comes together again at the same level below the rapids. In the same way, in a parallel electrical circuit, the total current is the sum of the currents through each current path, and the potential difference across each path is the same.

A schematic diagram of three resistors connected in parallel is shown in Figure 24–7. The 120-V generator provides the source of potential difference for the circuit. Each current path from A to B is part of a complete circuit including the generator, resistors, and ammeters. Each path acts as if the other paths were not present. What is the current through one resistor? There is a 120-V potential difference across each resistor. The current through a 60-Ω resistor across a 120-V potential difference is

$$I = \frac{V}{R} = \frac{120 \text{ V}}{60 \text{ }\Omega} = 2 \text{ A}$$

The current flow through each path from A to B is 2 A. The total current between the two points is 6 A. The potential difference across the two points is 120 V. A single resistor that would permit 6 A current with 120 V potential difference has a resistance given by

$$R = \frac{V}{I} = \frac{120 \text{ V}}{6 \text{ A}} = 20 \text{ }\Omega$$

The total resistance of a parallel circuit decreases as each new resistor is added.

This single resistor is the effective resistance. Placing resistors in parallel always decreases the effective resistance of the circuit. The resistance decreases because each new resistor provides an additional path for current to flow between points A and B. Notice that the effective resistance of the circuit is less than the resistance of any resistor in the circuit.

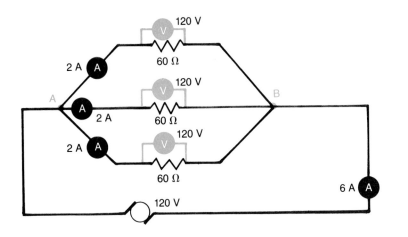

The effective resistance of a parallel circuit can be found by applying the fact that the total current in the circuit is the sum of the currents through the branches of the circuit. If I is the total current, and I_1, I_2, and I_3 are the currents through each of the branches, then

$$I = I_1 + I_2 + I_3$$

The current through each resistor, for example R_1, can be found from $I_1 = V/R_1$. The total current through the effective resistance, R, of the circuit is given by $I = V/R$, but all voltage drops in a parallel circuit are the same.

$$\frac{V}{R} = \frac{V}{R_1} + \frac{V}{R_2} + \frac{V}{R_3}$$

Dividing both sides of the equation by V gives an equation for the effective resistance of three parallel resistors.

$$\boxed{\frac{1}{R} = \frac{1}{R_1} + \frac{1}{R_2} + \frac{1}{R_3}}$$

EXAMPLE

Total Resistance and Current in a Parallel Circuit

Three resistors of 60.0 Ω, 30.0 Ω, and 20.0 Ω are connected in parallel across a 90.0-V difference in potential, Figure 24–8.

a. Find the effective resistance of the circuit.

b. Find the current in the entire circuit.

c. Find the current through each branch of the circuit.

Given: $R_1 = 60.0\ \Omega$ Unknowns: R, I, I_1, I_2, I_3
$\quad\quad\quad R_2 = 30.0\ \Omega$ Basic equation: $V = IR$
$\quad\quad\quad R_3 = 20.0\ \Omega$
$\quad\quad\quad V = 90.0\ \text{V}$

FIGURE 24–8. Use with the Example.

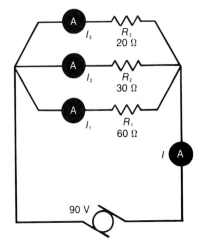

Solution:

a. $\dfrac{1}{R} = \dfrac{1}{60.0\ \Omega} + \dfrac{1}{30.0\ \Omega} + \dfrac{1}{20.0\ \Omega}$

$\dfrac{1}{R} = \dfrac{6}{60.0\ \Omega}$

$R = 10.0\ \Omega$

b. $I = \dfrac{V}{R} = \dfrac{90.0\ V}{10.0\ \Omega} = 9.00\ A$

c. The voltage drop across each resistor is 90.0 V.

$$\text{(for } R_1) \ I_1 = \dfrac{V}{R_1} = \dfrac{90.0\ V}{60.0\ \Omega}$$
$$= 1.50\ A$$

$$\text{(for } R_2) \ I_2 = \dfrac{V}{R_2} = \dfrac{90.0\ V}{30.0\ \Omega}$$
$$= 3.00\ A$$

$$\text{(for } R_3) \ I_3 = \dfrac{V}{R_3} = \dfrac{90.0\ V}{20.0\ \Omega}$$
$$= 4.50\ A$$

Practice Exercises

9. Three 15.0-Ω resistors are connected in parallel and placed across a 30-V potential difference.
   a. What is the effective resistance of the parallel circuit?
   b. What is the current through the entire circuit?
   c. What is the current through each branch of the parallel circuit?

10. A 12.0-Ω resistor and a 15.0-Ω resistor are connected in parallel and placed across the terminals of a 15-V battery.
   a. What is the effective resistance of the parallel circuit?
   b. What is the current through the entire circuit?
   c. What is the current through each branch of the parallel circuit?

11. Suppose the 12.0-Ω resistor in Exercise 10 is replaced by a 10.0-Ω resistor.
   a. Does the effective resistance become smaller, become larger, or remain the same?
   b. Does the amount of current through the entire circuit change? In which direction?
   c. Does the amount of current through the 15.0-Ω resistor change? In which direction?

12. A 120.0-Ω resistor, a 60.0-Ω resistor, and a 40.0-Ω resistor are connected in parallel and placed across a potential difference of 12.0 V.
   a. What is the effective resistance of the parallel circuit?
   b. What is the current through the entire circuit?
   c. What is the current through each branch of the parallel circuit?

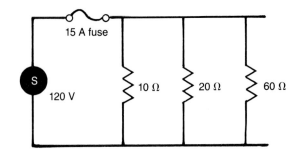

24:4 Applications of Parallel Circuits

Fuses and circuit breakers are switches in an electric circuit that act as safety devices. They prevent circuit overloads that can occur when too many appliances are turned on at the same time. When appliances are connected in parallel, each additional appliance placed in operation reduces the effective resistance in the circuit and causes more current to flow through the wires. The additional current may produce enough thermal energy (at the rate $P = I^2R$) to melt insulation on the wires, causing a short circuit or even a fire.

A **fuse** is a short piece of metal that melts from the heating effect of the current. The thickness of the metal is adjusted to set the current needed to melt the fuse. A circuit breaker is an automatic switch that opens when the current reaches some set value. If more than 15 A flows in the circuit in Figure 24–9, the circuit will be overloaded. The fuse will melt, stopping all current flow. A house is often wired with one parallel circuit for the outlets on each floor, or even each room. Such an arrangement helps to prevent an overload in any single circuit.

Electric wiring in a home uses parallel circuits so that the current in any one circuit does not depend on the current in the other circuits. The current in a device that dissipates power P when connected to a voltage source V is given by $I = P/V$. Figure 24–9 shows a schematic diagram of the circuit. Suppose first a 240-W television is plugged into a 120-V outlet. The current that flows is given by $I = (240 \text{ W})/(120 \text{ V}) = 2$ A. Then a 720-W curling iron is plugged in. The current through the iron is $I = (720 \text{ W})/(120 \text{ V}) = 6$ A. Finally, a 1440-W hair dryer is added. The current through the hair dryer is $I = (1440 \text{ W})/(120 \text{ V}) = 12$ A. The total current in the circuit is the sum of the three currents, $I = 2 \text{ A} + 6 \text{ A} + 12 \text{ A} = 20$ A. The 15-A fuse is connected in series with the power source, so the entire current flows through it. The 20 A exceeds the rating of the 15-A fuse. This will cause the fuse to melt, or "blow," cutting off current to the entire circuit.

Fuses and circuit breakers are safety devices that prevent too much current from flowing in a circuit.

SUGGESTION: Discuss circuit breaker construction again when dealing with electromagnetism in Chapter 25.

FIGURE 24–10. When the current in a circuit is too great, the metal bar in this circuit breaker is pulled away from its contact points. The current stops flowing.

a

Switch-operating electromagnet

Spring

Iron bar

Current

b

a

120 V

Appliance

Appliance

Appliance

FIGURE 24–11. The wiring diagram for this house (a) indicates the parallel nature of the circuit. This wiring arrangement will permit the use of one or more appliances (b).

In a parallel circuit, each resistor can be operated independently.

b

The current through these three appliances can be found by considering them as a parallel circuit. Each resistor represents an appliance. The value of the resistance is found by first calculating the current the appliance draws as above and then using the equation $R = V/I$. The effective resistance of the three appliances is

$$\frac{1}{R} = \frac{1}{10\ \Omega} + \frac{1}{20\ \Omega} + \frac{1}{60\ \Omega} = \frac{10}{60\ \Omega} = \frac{1}{6\ \Omega}$$

$$R = 6\ \Omega$$

The current flowing through the fuse is

$$I = \frac{V}{R} = \frac{120\ V}{6\ \Omega} = 20\ A$$

as was found by adding the currents in the three separate circuits.

A **short circuit** occurs when a circuit is formed that has a very low resistance. The low resistance causes the current to be very large. If there were no fuse or circuit breaker, such a large current could easily start a fire. A short circuit can occur if the insulation on a lamp cord becomes old and brittle. The two wires in the cord could accidentally touch. The resistance of the wire might be only 0.010 Ω. When placed across 120 V, this resistance would result in a current of

$$I = \frac{V}{R} = \frac{120\ V}{0.010\ \Omega} = 12\ 000\ A$$

Such a current would cause the fuse to blow or the circuit breaker to open the circuit immediately. Thus, the wire would be prevented from becoming hot and starting a fire.

FIGURE 24–12. The metal wire in a fuse melts when the circuit is overloaded. The fuse must then be replaced.

24:5 Series-Parallel Circuits

Circuits often consist of combinations of series and parallel circuits. They can be understood by simplifying them in steps.

1. If any resistors are connected in parallel, replace them with a single effective resistance.
2. If any effective resistances are now connected in series, replace them with a single new effective resistance.
3. By repeating steps 1 and 2, you can reduce the circuit to a single resistance. The current can now be found. The voltage drops and currents through individual resistors can then be calculated.

In analyzing series-parallel circuits, first combine parallel resistors. Then combine series resistors.

$I = V/R$ can be used on each separate part of a series-parallel circuit.

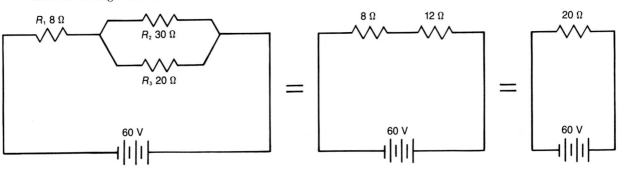

FIGURE 24–13. Use with the Example.

EXAMPLE

Series-Parallel Circuit

In Figure 24–13, a 30.0-Ω resistor is connected in parallel with a 20.0-Ω resistor. The parallel connection is placed in series with an 8.0-Ω resistor, and the entire circuit is placed across a 60.0-V difference of potential. **a.** What is the effective resistance of the parallel portion of the circuit? **b.** What is the effective resistance of the entire circuit? **c.** What is the current in the entire circuit? **d.** What is the voltage drop across the 8.0-Ω resistor? **e.** What is the voltage drop across the parallel portion of the circuit? **f.** What is the current in each line of the parallel portion of the circuit?

Given: See Figure 24–13.

Unknowns:
$$R_{2,3}, R, I, V_1, V_p, I_2, I_3$$

Basic equations:
$$V = IR$$
$$R = R_1 + R_2 + \ldots$$
$$1/R = 1/R_1 + 1/R_2 + \ldots$$

Solution:

a. R_2 and R_3 are connected in parallel. Their effective resistance is

$$\frac{1}{R_{2,3}} = \frac{1}{R_2} + \frac{1}{R_3}$$

$$= \frac{1}{30.0\ \Omega} + \frac{1}{20.0\ \Omega} = \frac{5}{60.0\ \Omega}$$

$$R_{2,3} = 12.0\ \Omega$$

b. The circuit is equivalent to a series circuit with an 8.0-Ω resistor and a 12.0-Ω resistor in series, Figure 24–13.

$$R = R_1 + R_{2,3}$$
$$= 8.0\ \Omega + 12.0\ \Omega = 20.0\ \Omega$$

c. The current in the circuit is

$$I = \frac{V}{R}$$
$$= \frac{60.0\ V}{20.0\ \Omega} = 3.00\ A$$

d. The voltage drop across the 8.0-Ω resistor is

$$V_1 = IR_1$$
$$= (3.00\ A)(8.0\ \Omega) = 24\ V$$

e. The parallel branch (R_2 and R_3) behaves like a 12.0-Ω resistor. Therefore, the voltage drop across it is

$$V_p = IR_{2,3}$$
$$= (3.00\ A)(12.0\ \Omega) = 36.0\ V$$

f. The 36.0-V drop across the parallel portion of the circuit is the same across all parts of the parallel circuit. Therefore, the current through the 30.0-Ω resistor is

$$I_2 = \frac{V}{R_2} = \frac{36.0\ V}{30.0\ \Omega}$$
$$= 1.20\ A$$

The current through the 20.0-Ω resistor is

$$I_3 = \frac{V}{R_3}$$
$$= \frac{36.0\ V}{20.0\ \Omega} = 1.80\ A$$

The current through the parallel part of the circuit is

$$1.20\ A + 1.80\ A,\ \text{or } 3.00\ A$$

This value agrees with the value for current calculated in part **c.**

Practice Exercises

13. Two 60-Ω resistors are connected in parallel. This parallel arrangement is connected in series with a 30-Ω resistor. The entire circuit is then placed across a 120-V potential difference.

    a. Draw a diagram of the circuit.

    b. What is the effective resistance of the parallel portion of the circuit?

    c. What is the effective resistance of the entire circuit?

    d. What is the current in the circuit?

    e. What is the voltage drop across the 30-Ω resistor?

    f. What is the voltage drop across the parallel portion of the circuit?

For Your Information

How do you figure out which resistors are in series? Remember that a series circuit has only one current path. Resistors are in series only if there is one and only one current path through them.* Resistors are in parallel only if they have the same potential difference across them. {See diagrams showing resistors in series and parallel.}

g. What is the current in each branch of the parallel portion of the circuit?

14. Three 15-Ω resistors are connected in parallel. This arrangement is connected in series with a 10-Ω resistor. The entire circuit is then placed across a 45-V difference in potential.

    a. Draw a diagram of the circuit.

    b. What is the effective resistance of the parallel portion of the circuit?

    c. What is the effective resistance of the entire circuit?

    d. What is the current in the entire circuit?

    e. What is the voltage drop across the 10-Ω resistor?

15. Suppose you are given three 68-Ω resistors. You can use them in a series, parallel, or series-parallel circuit. Find the three resistances you can get.

24:6 Ammeters and Voltmeters

An **ammeter** is used to measure the current in a circuit. An ammeter is always placed in series with the resistance. This requires opening a current path and inserting an ammeter. The use of an ammeter should not change the current in the circuit. Because current would decrease if the ammeter increased the resistance in the circuit, the resistance of an ammeter should be as low as possible. In Figure 24–15c, the ammeter resistance is much smaller than the values of the resistors. The current decrease would be from 1.0 A to 0.9995 A, too small to notice.

A **voltmeter** is used to measure the voltage drop across any part of a circuit. To measure the potential drop across a resistor, connect the voltmeter in parallel with the resistor. To change currents or voltages in the circuit the least, a voltmeter should have a very high resistance. Consider

An ammeter measures current in a circuit.

An ammeter should have as low a resistance as possible.

A voltmeter measures voltage drop across a circuit.

A voltmeter should have as high a resistance as possible.

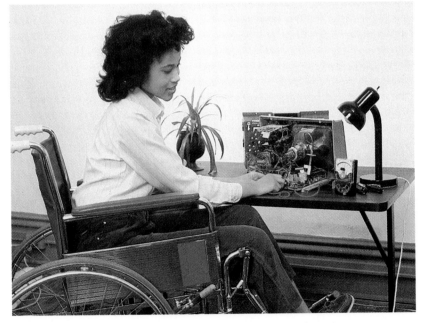

SUGGESTION: Many multimeters have clear plastic bottoms. Point out the parts of a meter and pass one around so students can see the construction, or take apart a broken meter for inspection.

FIGURE 24–14. Electric meters are used to troubleshoot problems in electric appliances.

a

b

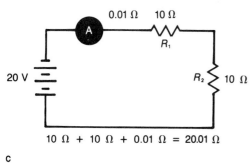

0.01 Ω   10 Ω
(A) ⌇⌇⌇ R_1
20 V ⎓
R_2 ⌇ 10 Ω

$10\ \Omega + 10\ \Omega + 0.01\ \Omega = 20.01\ \Omega$

c

10 Ω
⌇⌇⌇ R_1
10 000 Ω
20 V ⎓
10 Ω ⌇ R_2
(V)

$$\frac{1}{10\ \Omega} + \frac{1}{10\ 000\ \Omega} = \frac{1}{9.995\ \Omega}$$

d

FIGURE 24–15. A battery tester (a) and a standard laboratory voltmeter (b) measure potential differences. Ammeters are always placed in series within a circuit (c) and voltmeters are placed in parallel (d).

the circuit in Figure 24–15d. When a voltmeter is connected in parallel with R_2, the effective resistance of the combination is smaller than R_2 alone. Thus the total resistance of the circuit decreases. As a result, the current increases. R_1 has not changed, but the current through it has increased. Therefore the potential drop across it increases. The battery, however, holds the potential drop across the two resistors constant. Thus the potential drop across R_2 must decrease. The result of connecting a voltmeter across a resistor is to lower the potential drop across it. The change is smallest if the resistance of the voltmeter is very high. Using a voltmeter with a 10,000 Ω resistance changes the voltage across R_2 from 10 V to 9.9975 V, too small a change to detect. Modern electronic voltmeters have even higher resistances, 10^7 Ω.

FIGURE 24–16. A modern digital multimeter can be used to measure a wide range of curents, voltages, and resistances in electric circuits.

418   Series and Parallel Circuits

SUMMARY

1. The current is the same everywhere in a series circuit. **24:1**

2. The effective resistance of a series circuit is the sum of the resistances of its parts. **24:1**

3. The sum of the voltage drops across the resistors in a series circuit is equal to the potential difference across the voltage source. **24:2**

4. A voltage divider is a series circuit used to produce a voltage source from a higher voltage battery. **24:2**

5. The voltage drops across all branches of a parallel circuit are the same. **24:3**

6. In a parallel circuit, the total current is equal to the sum of the currents in the branches. **24:3**

7. The reciprocal of the effective resistance of a parallel circuit is equal to the sum of the reciprocals of the individual resistances. **24:3**

8. If any branch of a parallel circuit is opened, there is no current in that branch. The current in the other branches is unchanged. **24:4**

9. A complex circuit is often a combination of series and parallel circuits. Any parallel circuit is first reduced to a single resistance. Then any series circuit is replaced by a single equivalent resistance. **24:5**

10. An ammeter is used to measure the current in a circuit or in a part of a circuit. An ammeter always has a low resistance and is connected in series. **24:6**

11. A voltmeter measures the potential difference (voltage) across any part or combination of parts of a circuit. A voltmeter always has a high resistance and is connected in parallel with the part of the circuit being measured. **24:6**

QUESTIONS

1. Circuit A contains three 60-Ω resistors in series. Circuit B contains three 60-Ω resistors in parallel. How does the current in the second 60-Ω resistor change if a switch cuts off the current to the first 60-Ω resistor in
   a. circuit A?
   b. circuit B?

2. Why is there a difference in total resistance between three 60-Ω resistors connected in series and three 60-Ω resistors connected in parallel?

3. An engineer needs a 10-Ω resistor or a 15-Ω resistor. But, there are only 30-Ω resistors in stock. Must new resistors be purchased? Explain.

4. For each part of this question, write the form that applies: series circuit or parallel circuit.
   a. The current is the same throughout.
   b. The total resistance is equal to the sum of the individual resistances.
   c. The voltage drop is the same across each resistor.
   d. The voltage drop is proportional to the resistance.
   e. Adding a resistor decreases the total resistance.
   f. Adding a resistor increases the total resistance.
   g. If one resistor is turned off or broken, there is no current in the entire circuit.
   h. If one resistor is turned off, the current through all other resistors remains the same.
   i. This form is suitable for house wiring.

5. Explain the function of a fuse in an electric circuit.

6. What is a short circuit? Why is a short circuit dangerous?

7. Why does an ammeter have a very low resistance?

8. Why does a voltmeter have a very high resistance?

9. If several resistors with different values are connected in parallel, the equivalent resistance will be less than which one?

10. Why is it frustrating when one bulb burns out on a string of Christmas tree lights connected in series?

APPLYING CONCEPTS

1. Two lamps have different resistances, one larger than the other.
   a. If they are connected in parallel, which is brighter (dissipates more power)?
   b. When connected in series, which is brighter?

2. If you have a 6-V battery and a stock of 1.5-V bulbs, how could you connect them so they light but do not burn out?

3. Two 100-watt light bulbs are connected in series to a 12-V battery and another two 100-watt light bulbs are connected in parallel to a separate 12-V battery. Which battery will run out of energy first? Why?

4. Compare the amount of current entering a junction in a parallel circuit with that leaving the junction.

5. Why does the equivalent resistance decrease as more resistors are added to a parallel circuit?

6. Why is household wiring done in parallel instead of in series?

EXERCISES

1. A 20.0-Ω lamp and a 5.0-Ω lamp are connected in series and placed across a difference in potential of 50.0 V.
   a. What is the effective resistance of the circuit?
   b. What is the current in the circuit?
   c. What is the voltage drop across each lamp?
   d. What is the power used in each lamp?

2. A 20.0-Ω lamp and a 50.0-Ω lamp are connected in parallel and placed across a difference in potential of 50.0 V.

   a. What is the effective resistance of the circuit?
   b. What is the current in the circuit?
   c. What is the current through each resistor?
   d. What is the voltage drop across each resistor?
   e. What is the power used by each lamp?
   f. Compare this result to the result of the preceding exercise.

3. A 16.0-Ω and a 20.0-Ω resistor are connected in parallel. A difference in potential of 40.0 V is applied to the combination.
   a. Compute the effective resistance of the parallel circuit.
   b. What is the current in the circuit?
   c. How large is the current through the 16.0-Ω resistor?

4. A household circuit contains six 240-Ω lamps (60-W bulbs) and a 10.0-Ω heater. The voltage across the circuit is 120 V.
   a. What is the current in the circuit when four lamps are on?
   b. What is the current when all six lamps are lighted?
   c. What is the current in the circuit if all six lamps and the heater are operating?

5. A 75.0-W bulb is connected to a 120-V source.
   a. What is the current through the bulb?
   b. What is the resistance of the bulb?
   c. A lamp dimmer puts a resistance in series with the bulb. What resistance would be needed to reduce the current to 0.30 A?

6. In Exercise 5, you found the resistance of a lamp and a dimmer resistor.
   a. Assuming the resistances are constant, find the voltage drops across the lamp and the resistor.
   b. Find the power dissipated by the lamp.
   c. Find the power dissipated by the dimmer resistor.

7. A student is designing a voltage divider using a 12-V battery and a 100.0-Ω resistor as R_2. What resistor should be used as R_1 if the output voltage is to be 4.0 V?

8. The student who designed the circuit for Exercise 7 now wants an output voltage of 4.75 V. Should resistor R_1 be increased or decreased?

9. A string of eighteen identical Christmas tree lights are connected in series and to a 120-V source. The string dissipates 64 W.
   a. What is the effective resistance of the light string?
   b. What is the resistance of a single light?
   c. What power is dissipated by each lamp?

10. One of the bulbs on the light string in Exercise 9 burns out. The lamp has a wire that shorts out the lamp filament when it burns out. This drops the resistance of the lamp to zero.
   a. What is the resistance of the light string now?
   b. Find the power dissipated by the string.
   c. Did the power go up or down when the bulb burned out?

11. A 60.0-W lamp and a 40.0-W lamp are connected in parallel to a 120-V source. What is the effective resistance of the two lamps?

12. A 75-Ω heater and a 150-Ω lamp are connected in parallel across a potential difference of 150 V.
   a. What is the current through the 75-Ω heater?
   b. What is the current through the 150-Ω lamp?
   c. What is the current through the entire circuit?
   d. What is the effective resistance of the entire circuit?
   e. Divide the voltage by the effective resistance. Does the result agree with the solution to part c?

13. A typical television dissipates 275 W when connected to 120 V.
   a. Find the resistance of the television.
   b. The television is connected to a circuit with wires that have a resistance of 2.5 Ω. The television and wire resistance form a series circuit that works like a voltage divider. Find the voltage drop across the television.
   c. A hair dryer is now plugged into the same circuit. The hair dryer, with a resistance of 12 Ω, is in parallel with the television. Find the effective resistance of the two appliances.
   d. Find the voltage drop across the television and hair dryer combination. The lower voltage explains why the television picture sometimes shrinks when another appliance is turned on.

14. A lamp having a resistance of 10 Ω is connected across a 15-V battery.
   a. What is the current through the lamp?
   b. What resistance must be connected in series with the lamp to reduce the current to 0.5 A?

PROBLEMS

1. An ohmmeter is made by connecting a 6.0-V battery in series with an adjustable resistor and an ideal ammeter. The ammeter deflects full-scale with a current of 1.0 mA (1.0×10^{-3} A). The two leads are touched together and the resistance is adjusted so that 1.0 mA flows.
   a. What is the resistance of the adjustable resistor?
   b. The leads are now connected to an unknown resistance. What resistance would produce a current of half full-scale (0.5 mA)?
   c. What resistance would produce a reading of quarter full-scale (0.25 mA)?
   d. What resistance would produce a reading of three-quarters full-scale (0.75 mA)?
   e. To make a usable ohmmeter, a scale reading in ohms is now attached to the ammeter. From your answers above, show what resistances would appear at various places on the ammeter dial.

2. A student needs 5.0 V for some integrated circuit experiments. She uses a 6.0-V battery and two resistors to make a voltage divider. One resistor is 330 Ω. She decides to make the other resistor smaller. What should it be?

3. Determine the reading of each ammeter and each voltmeter in Figure 24–17.

4. Determine the power in watts used by each resistance shown in Figure 24–17.

FIGURE 24–17. Use with Problems 3 and 4.

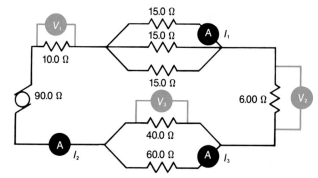

FIGURE 24–18. Use with Problem 5.

5. Find the reading of each ammeter and each voltmeter in Figure 24–18.

6. A typical home circuit is diagrammed in Figure 24–19. Note that the lead lines to the kitchen lamp have very low resistances. The lamp contains a typical 60-W incandescent bulb of resistance 240.0 Ω. Although the circuit is a parallel circuit, the lead lines are in series with each of the components of the circuit.

   a. Compute the effective resistance of the circuit consisting of just the light and the lead lines to and from the light. We will assume that neither the power saw nor the wall outlets are in use.

   b. Show that the current to the bulb is essentially 0.5 amperes and that the bulb is a 60-W device.

   c. Since the current in the bulb is 0.5 A, the current in the lead lines must also be 0.5 A. Calculate the voltage drop due to the two leads.

FIGURE 24–19. Use with Problem 6.

7. A power saw is operated by an electric motor. When electric motors are first turned on, they have very low resistances. In Chapter 26 we will study why the resistance is low. Suppose that the kitchen light discussed in Problem 6 is on and the power saw is suddenly turned on. The saw plus

the lead lines between the saw and the light have an initial total resistance of 6.0 Ω.

   a. Compute the effective resistance of the light-saw parallel circuit.

   b. What current flows through the two leads to the light?

   c. What is the total voltage drop across the two leads to the light?

   d. What voltage remains to operate the light? Will this voltage cause the light to dim temporarily? (You may have noticed this effect before.)

8. During a laboratory exercise, you are supplied with the following apparatus:
   —a battery of potential difference V,
   —two heating elements of low resistance that can be placed in water,
   —an ammeter of negligible resistance,
   —a voltmeter of extremely high resistance,
   —wires of negligible resistance,
   —a beaker that is well-insulated and has negligible heat capacity,
   —100.0 g of water at 25°C.

   a. By means of a diagram using standard symbols, show how these components should be connected to heat the water as rapidly as possible.

   b. If the voltmeter reading holds steady at 50.0 V and the ammeter reading holds steady at 5.0 A, estimate the time in seconds required to completely vaporize the water in the beaker. Use 4200 J/kg · C° as the specific heat of water and 2300 J/kg as the heat of vaporization of water.

9. A current of 2 A flows through a wire, Figure 24–20. What is the change in potential between

   a. A and B?

   b. A and C?

   c. A and D?

FIGURE 24–20. Use with Problem 9.

READINGS

Boyd, J. N., "Parallel Circuits and Probability." *The Physics Teacher*, February, 1988.

Hughes, Thomas, "The Inventive Continuum." *Science*, November, 1984.

Loper, Orla E., and Edgar Tedsen, *Direct Current Fundamentals*. Albany, NY: Delmar, 1986.

Ong, P. P., "A Short-Circuit Method for Networks." *The Physics Teacher*, October, 1983.

Owen, Bill, "Energy Miser for Air Conditioners." *Radio Electronics*, July, 1984.

Rosenberg, Robert, "American Physics and the Origins of Electrical Engineering." *Physics Today*, October, 1983.

Stanley, Leon, *Easy-to-Make Electric Gadgets*. New York, 1980: Harvey.

CHAPTER 25

Magnetic Fields

For Your Information

Fritz Zwicky, an astronomer, and a minister were discussing the origin of the universe. The minister said that the universe began when God said, "Let there be light." Zwicky replied that he could buy this explanation only if God had said "Let there be light and a magnetic field."

—Letter from Emil Herzog

For Your Information

William Gilbert (1544–1603) was an English physician known for his early studies of electricity and magnetism. In his work *De magnete*, written in 1600, Gilbert proposed the theory that Earth has north and south magnetic poles and that Earth exerts a magnetic force throughout the solar system. He also explained the function of a lodestone compass.

GOALS

1. You will gain a knowledge of magnetic fields and how they are produced.
2. You will become aware of the properties and effects of magnetic fields.
3. You will become familiar with some devices that use magnetic fields.

Why does the disk float? What force opposes the force of gravity? The floating disk is a magnet. The larger disk below is a superconductor. The superconductor conducts electricity without resistance. As a result, it permits none of the magnetic field produced by the magnet to pass through it. The resulting forces lift the magnet. Perhaps soon high speed trains will be lifted above their rails by superconducting magnets. Even today superconducting magnets curve the paths of high-speed particles in particle accelerators like those in Fermilab and the proposed Superconducting Super Collider (SSC).

Magnets are not new. The properties of naturally occurring magnetic rocks (lodestones) have been known for over 2000 years. The Chinese were using magnets as compasses when the first European explorers reached China in the 1500s. In 1600 the English physician William Gilbert wrote the first European book describing their properties. Today ordinary magnets are used in all generators that supply us with electricity. In addition, motors, television sets, and tape recorders depend on the magnetic effects of electric currents. Thus the study of magnetism is an important part of our investigation of electricity.

25:1 General Properties of Magnets

It is impossible to study electricity without investigating magnetism. The two are inseparable. Magnetic effects appear only in the presence of a moving electric charge. Conversely, a moving charge always creates a magnetic field. The properties of magnets can be summarized in these ways.

Magnetic Personalities

In a demonstration of the Meissner Effect, a magnet made of one of the lanthanoid metals is seen floating in the air above a superconductive disc. The superconductor has been cooled by immersing it in −196°C liquid nitrogen. Why is a lanthanoid magnet used instead of an ordinary ALNICO magnet? How is the magnet repelled from the superconductor material?

For Your Information

Iron, nickel, and cobalt are called *ferromagnetic*, from the Latin word for iron, *ferrous*.

For Your Information

Materials that are slightly repelled by magnets are called *diamagnetic*.

For Your Information

Dysprosium and gadolinium are also ferromagnetic.

DEMONSTRATION: See the Teacher Guide.

Unlike poles attract, like poles repel.

SUGGESTION: Many students think all metals are magnetic. Demonstrate that they are not by showing that a magnet will not pick up aluminum cans and many other metals.

SUGGESTION: Demonstrate magnetizing an iron nail by rubbing it with a magnet many times in the same direction.

SUGGESTION: Tie a thread to a paper clip. Put the paper clip near a bar magnet and move it all around the magnet to show direction of force. The magnet shows little or no force in the middle of the bar.

1. A magnet has polarity. The poles, called the north and south poles, always come in pairs. A single pole has never been found.

2. Like magnetic poles repel one another; unlike poles attract one another.

3. A compass is a small, suspended, needle-shaped magnet. The end that points north is the north-seeking pole (N-pole) of the magnet. The end that points south is its south-seeking pole (S-pole). A compass needle points toward the magnetic north pole, which is near but not at the geographic north pole.

4. Permanent magnets retain their magnetism for a long time. Most permanent magnets are made of ALNICO, an alloy of ALuminum, NIckel, and CObalt.

5. Iron, cobalt, and nickel may be magnetized by induction. When a piece of iron, for example, touches a permanent magnet, the iron becomes a magnet itself. The iron is a temporary magnet; as soon as it is removed from the permanent magnet, the iron ceases to be a magnet.

25:2 Magnetic Fields Around Permanent Magnets

Just as electric charges exert forces on each other, magnets exert forces on other magnets at a distance. In the same way the electric forces can be explained by an electric field, the magnetic forces can be explained by the existence of **magnetic fields** around a magnet. The symmetry between electricity and magnetism would be stronger if there were single magnetic poles or charges, just as there are positive and negative electric charges. The problem is, no one has been able to find these *monopoles*. Many scientists are searching for them, but so far none has been discovered.

The presence of a magnetic field around a magnet can be shown by covering the magnet with a piece of paper and sprinkling iron filings onto the paper. Each long, thin iron filing becomes a small magnet by induction. The filings arrange themselves in lines running from pole to pole, as shown in Figure 25–2a. These lines help you to visualize magnetic field lines.

Note that the magnetic field lines, like the electric field lines, are imaginary. You can, however, use field lines to picture how magnets affect one another. The number of magnetic field lines in any given region is called the **magnetic flux.** The flux per unit area is proportional to the strength of the magnetic field. As shown in Figure 25–2a, the flux lines are most concentrated at the poles, where the flux per unit area, that is, the magnetic field, is the greatest.

The direction of the magnetic field lines is the direction to which the N-pole of a compass points when it is placed in the magnetic field. Outside the magnet, the field lines come out of the magnet at its N-pole and enter the magnet at its S-pole. Note that the lines continue through the inside of the magnet. Field lines always form closed loops.

What are the magnetic fields produced by pairs of poles? You can again visualize the fields by placing a sheet of paper over the poles of two magnets. Sprinkle the paper with iron filings. Figure 25–3a shows the field lines between two like poles. By contrast, two unlike poles (N and S) placed close together show the pattern in Figure 25–3b. The filings show that the field lines between two unlike poles run directly from one magnet to the other.

Magnetic fields exert forces on other magnetic poles. The field produced by the N-pole of a magnet pushes another N-pole in the direction of the field line. The second N-pole is pushed away from the N-pole of the magnet producing the field and toward its S-pole. The force exerted by the

FIGURE 25–2. Magnetic flux lines extend from the N-pole to the S-pole outside a magnet (a). The magnetic flux in any region is proportional to the number of magnetic field lines in that region (b).

Magnetic field lines are imaginary lines that indicate the direction and magnitude of the field about a magnet.

Magnetic flux density is magnetic flux per unit area.

DEMONSTRATION: See the Teacher Guide.

Magnetic poles always occur in pairs.

Magnetic fields outside a magnet run from north pole to south pole.

a

b
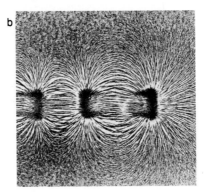

FIGURE 25–3. The field lines for like poles (a) and unlike poles (b).

same field on an S-pole is in a direction opposite the field lines. The force on an S-pole is toward the N-pole and away from the S-pole of the magnet producing the field. Forces can cause a magnet either to rotate, like a compass needle, or to move toward or away from the other magnet. In summary, unlike poles of magnets attract one another; like poles repel.

Practice Exercises

1. An iron filing is placed in the magnetic field shown in Figure 25–2. Which end of the filing has the induced N-pole?

2. A student holds a bar magnet in each hand. If both hands are brought close together, will the force be attractive or repulsive if the magnets are held so that

   a. the two N-poles are brought close together?

   b. an N-pole and an S-pole are brought together?

25:3 Electromagnetism

In 1820, the Danish physicist Hans Christian Oersted (1777–1851) was experimenting with electric currents in wires. Oersted laid one of his wires across the tip of a small compass. He observed that each time he sent a current through the wire, the compass needle moved. Oersted knew a magnetic field exerted a force on another magnet. He reasoned that in some way the electric current in the wire caused a magnetic field around the wire. Oersted was able to show that any wire carrying an electric current has a magnetic field around it. That is, electric currents produce magnetic fields.

The magnetic field around a current-carrying wire can easily be shown by placing a wire vertically through a piece of cardboard on which iron filings are sprinkled. When a current is flowing, tap the cardboard. The filings form a pattern of concentric circles around the wire. The center of each circle is the wire itself.

The circular lines indicate that magnetic field lines form closed loops just like field lines about permanent magnets. The strength of the magnetic field around the wire varies directly with the magnitude of the cur-

DEMONSTRATION: See the Teacher Guide.

FIGURE 25–4. This train is magnetically levitated. Moving along on a magnetic cushion allows the train to reach extremely high speeds.

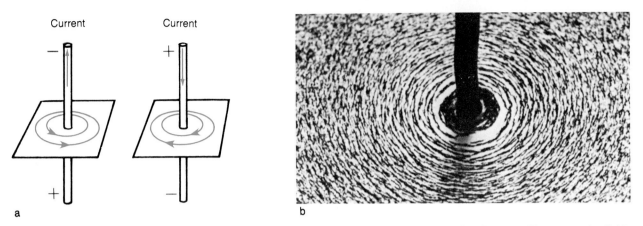

a

b

rent flowing in the wire. The strength also varies inversely with the distance from the wire. The **right-hand rule** can be used to find the direction of the magnetic field around a current-bearing straight wire. Grasp the wire with the right hand. Keep the thumb of that hand pointed in the direction of conventional (positive) current flow. The fingers of the hand circle the wire and point in the direction of the magnetic field.

The first right-hand rule gives the direction of the magnetic field around a current-carrying wire.

Practice Exercises

3. A current-carrying wire runs from north to south.
   a. A compass needle placed above the wire points with its N-pole toward the east. In what direction is the current flowing?
   b. If a compass is put underneath the wire, in which direction will it point?
4. Suppose you measure the strength of the magnetic field 1 cm from a current-carrying wire.
   a. Compare the strength of the field 2 cm away.
   b. Now compare the strength of the field 3 cm from the wire.

25:4 Magnetic Field Near a Coil

When an electric current flows through a single circular loop of wire, a magnetic field appears all around the loop. By applying the right-hand rule as in Figure 25–7b to any part of the wire loop, it can be shown that the direction of the field inside the loop is always the same. In the case shown in the diagram, the field is always up, out of the page. Outside the loop, it is always down, into the page.

Suppose wire is looped several times to form a coil. When a current flows through the coil, the field around all loops will be in the same direction. The field inside the coil is up, out of the page. The field outside the coil is in the opposite direction, into the page.

When an electric current flows through a coil of wire, the coil has a field like that of a permanent magnet. When this current-carrying coil is brought close to a suspended bar magnet, one end of the coil repels the north pole of the magnet. Thus, the current-carrying coil has a north and a south pole and is itself a magnet. This type of magnet is called an **electromagnet**.

FIGURE 25–6. The right-hand rule for a current-bearing straight wire shows the direction of the magnetic field.

Current

Right hand

Direction of magnetic field

a

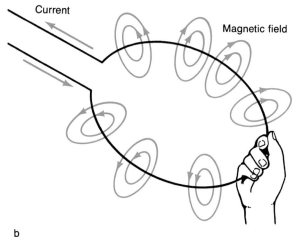

Current

Magnetic field

b

FIGURE 25–7. The magnetic field about a circular loop of current-bearing wire is shown.

The direction of the field produced by an electromagnet may be found by using a **second right-hand rule.** Grasp the coil with the right hand. Curl the fingers around the loops in the direction of conventional (positive) current flow. The thumb points toward the N-pole of the electromagnet.

The strength of an electromagnet can be increased by placing an iron rod or core inside the coil. The field inside the coil magnetizes the core by induction. The magnetic strength of the core adds to that of the coil to produce a much stronger magnet.

The strength of the magnetic field around a current-carrying wire is proportional to the current in the wire. The strength of the field of an electromagnet is also proportional to the current flowing through the coil. The magnetic field produced by each loop of a coil is the same as that produced by any other loop. These fields are in the same direction, and thus all contribute to the total field. Therefore, increasing the number of loops in an electromagnet increases the strength of the magnetic field. The strength of the field of an electromagnet is proportional to the current and to the number of loops, and depends on the nature of the core.

FIGURE 25–8. The second right-hand rule can be used to determine the polarity of an electromagnet.

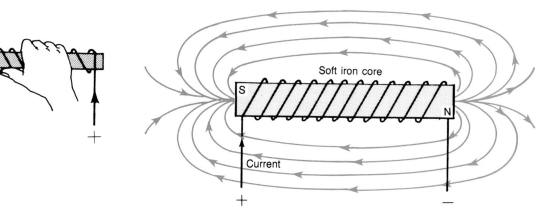

Soft iron core

S

N

Current

430   Magnetic Fields

Practice Exercises

5. The loop in Figure 25–7 has current running in a counterclockwise direction (from left to right above the cardboard). If a compass is placed on the cardboard beneath the loop, in which direction will the N-pole point?

6. A student makes a magnet by winding wire around a large nail as in Figure 25–9. The magnet is connected to the battery as shown. Which end of the nail, pointed end or head, will be the N-pole?

25:5 Magnetic Materials

If you put a sample containing iron, nickel, or cobalt in a magnetic field, the sample will become magnetic. That is, north and south poles will be created. The polarity created depends on the direction of the external field. When you take away the external field, the sample will lose its magnetism.

Iron, nickel, and cobalt, three ferromagnetic elements, behave in many ways like an electromagnet. In the early 19th century, a theory of magnetism in iron was proposed by Andre Marie Ampere to explain this behavior. Ampere knew that the magnetic effects of an electromagnetic coil result when an electric current flows through its loops. He reasoned that the effects of a bar magnet must result from tiny "loops" of current within the bar. In essence, Ampere's reasoning was correct.

Each electron in an atom acts like a tiny electromagnet. The magnetic fields of electrons in a group of neighboring atoms can add together. Such a group is called a **domain.** Although domains may contain 10^{20} individual atoms, they are still very small. Thus, even a small sample of iron contains a huge number of domains.

When a piece of iron is not in a magnetic field, the domains do not all point in the same direction. Their magnetic fields cancel one another. However, if the iron is placed in a magnetic field, the domains tend to align with the external field, as in Figure 25–10. In a temporary magnet, after the external field is removed, the domains return to their random arrangement. In permanent magnets, the iron has been alloyed with other substances that keep the domains aligned after the external magnetic field is removed.

Sound or video tape recorders use electronic devices to create electric signals representing the sounds or pictures being recorded. The electric signals produce currents in an electromagnet called a recording head. Magnetic recording tape passes directly over the recording head. The tape has many very tiny pieces of magnetic material bonded to thin plastic. When these pieces pass over the recording head, their domains are aligned by the magnetic fields of the head. The direction of the alignment depends on the direction of the current in the recording head. The directions of the magnetic fields of the tiny pieces become a magnetic record of the sounds or pictures being recorded. The material on the tape is chosen so that the domains keep their alignment permanently. In Chapter 26, the method of playing back the sound or picture will be described. "Floppy disks" used in computers are magnetically-coated disks that record computer data in the same way.

FIGURE 25–9. Use with Practice Exercise 6.

The field about an electromagnet also varies directly with the number of loops in the coil.

DEMONSTRATION: See the Teacher Guide.

All the domains can be lined up in the same direction.

FIGURE 25–10. A piece of iron becomes a magnet only when its domains align.

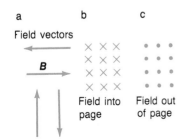

DEMONSTRATION: See the Teacher Guide.

FIGURE 25–11. A representation of forces on currents in magnetic fields.

For Your Information

Earth's magnetic field has flipflopped, north and south, at least 171 times.

FIGURE 25–12. Directions of magnetic fields are indicated by directional arrows (a) when the field is in the same plane as the page, by crosses (b) when the field is into the page, and by dots (c) when the field is out of the page toward you.

Rocks that contain iron have made a "tape recording" of the direction of Earth's magnetic field. The rocks were produced when molten rock poured out of cracks in the bottom of the oceans. As they cooled, they were magnetized in the direction of Earth's field. The seafloor spread, so rocks farther from the crack are older than those near the crack. When scientists examined these rocks, they were surprised to find the direction of the magnetization varied. They concluded that the north and south magnetic poles of Earth have exchanged places many times in Earth's history. The origin of Earth's magnetic field is not well understood. How this field might reverse direction periodically is even less well understood.

Not all elements act like iron. In superconductors, for example, the electrons in the materials move without resistance in response to an applied magnetic field. The motion of the electrons generates a magnetic field inside the superconductor that exactly cancels the applied field. There is no magnetic field inside the superconductor. As a result, there is a force that pushes the superconductor away from the applied field. This force is now used as a test to see if a sample material is superconducting. A possible future application for superconductivity is the levitation of heavy objects, such as trains.

25:6 Forces on Currents in Magnetic Fields

Ampere predicted that there would be a force on a current-carrying wire placed in a magnetic field. He based this prediction on the fact that electric currents produce magnetic fields similar to the fields of permanent magnets. So, Ampere reasoned, a magnetic field should cause a force on a current-carrying wire in the same way the field exerts a force on a permanent magnet.

We described the force exerted by an electric field in terms of its effect on a stationary electric charge placed in the field. No magnetic charge

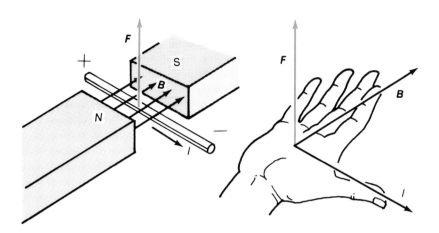

The force on a wire is at right angles to the wire and to the magnetic field.

A third right-hand rule is used to determine the direction of force on a current-carrying wire placed in a magnetic field.

SUGGESTION: It is helpful to stick three wood ice cream sticks or splints into a plastic foam ball and label them F, B, and I as shown in Figure 25–13. Use this in demonstrating the third right-hand rule.

FIGURE 25–14. Two current-bearing conductors (a) are attracted when the currents are in the same direction, and (b) are repelled when the currents are in opposite directions.

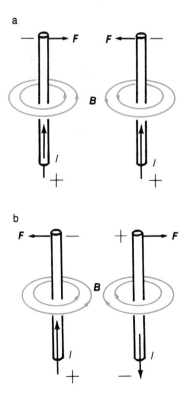

exists, so the force produced by a magnetic field cannot be described in a similar way. Therefore, we will use a moving electric charge. The strength and direction of the force exerted by a magnetic field are defined in terms of the field's effect on a moving electric charge.

The force on a wire in a magnetic field can be demonstrated using the arrangement shown in Figure 25–11. The cross on the wire in Figure 25–11a indicates that the conventional current is flowing down, into the page. The dot on the wire in Figure 25–11b shows that the current is flowing out of the page. Think of the current as an arrow. The cross represents the tail feathers of the arrow as it moves away from the reader; the dot represents the point of the arrow.

The strength of a magnetic field is called **magnetic induction.** The symbol for magnetic induction is **B.** Magnetic induction is a vector quantity, which can be indicated by an arrow. Several vectors are shown in Figure 25–12. Vectors pointing into or out of the page follow the same convention as that used for current flow.

Michael Faraday (1791–1867) found that the force on the wire is at right angles to the direction of the magnetic field. The force is also at right angles to the direction of the current. The direction of the force on a current-carrying wire in a magnetic field can be found by using a **third right-hand rule,** shown in Figure 25–13. Point the fingers of your right hand in the direction of the magnetic field. Point your thumb in the direction of the conventional (positive) current flow in the wire. The palm of your hand then faces in the direction of the force acting on the wire.

Figure 25–14 shows that the direction of the magnetic field around each of the current-carrying wires follows the first right-hand rule. In Figure 25–14a, we see that the fields between the wires are in opposite directions. Since magnetic fields add vectorially, the field between the wires is weak while the field outside the wires is stronger. By applying the right-hand rule you can show that the wires are forced together, or attract each other. In Figure 25–14b, we see the opposite situation. Here, the fields between the wires act in the same direction. Thus, the field between the wires is strengthened. Outside the wires, the fields are at normal strength. Thus, the wires are forced apart by the stronger field between them.

FIGURE 25-15. Earth's magnetic field lines run from the south magnetic pole to the north magnetic pole.

For Your Information

Magnetic domains also lose their alignment if the sample is heated above the Curie temperature. For example, if you touch a nickel coin to a strong permanent magnet, it will become magnetized and stick to the permanent magnet. If you use a propane torch to heat the nickel above its Curie temperature (1043 K), the nickel will lose its magnetism and drop off the magnet. If you try this, be careful! The nickel will be very hot.

Magnetic induction is measured in teslas (T). One tesla is one newton per ampere-meter (N/A·m).

25:7 Measuring the Force on a Wire

Imagine a current-carrying wire passing through a magnetic field at right angles to the wire. The magnitude of the force on the wire is proportional to three factors:

1. the magnetic induction or strength, B, of the field,

2. the current, I, in the wire, and

3. the length, L, of the wire that lies in the magnetic field.

The magnitude of the force is given by the expression

$$F = BIL$$

We can measure force, current, and length, but not B. By rewriting the equation above, the strength of the field, B, can be calculated.

$$B = \frac{F}{IL}$$

The SI unit that measures the induction or strength of a magnetic field is the tesla, T. One tesla is equivalent to one newton per ampere-meter, N/A · m. The strength of a magnetic field is measured in terms of the force on a wire one meter long carrying one ampere of current.

TABLE 25-1

Typical Magnetic Fields	
Source and location	**Strength (T)**
surface of neutron star (calculated)	10^8
laboratory magnet	1
small bar magnet	0.01
surface of Earth	10^{-4}

A magnetic field of 1 T (N/A · m) field strength is a very strong field, found only in powerful electromagnets. The magnetic fields of most magnets found in the laboratory are closer to 0.01 T. Earth's magnetic field has a strength of approximately 5×10^{-5} T. The direction of Earth's field is toward the north magnetic pole, which is in arctic Canada. The field does not point along the surface of Earth, but mostly down into Earth, as shown in Figure 25–15.

EXAMPLE

Magnetic Induction

A wire 1.0 m long carries a current of 5.0 A. The wire is at right angles to a uniform magnetic field. The force on the wire is 0.2 N. What is the size of the magnetic induction, B, of the field?

Given: $F = 0.2$ N   **Unknown:** magnetic induction B
$I = 5.0$ A   **Basic equation:** $B = F/IL$
$L = 1.0$ m

Solution: $B = \dfrac{F}{IL} = \dfrac{0.2 \text{ N}}{(5.0 \text{ A})(1.0 \text{ m})} = 0.04$ N/A $\cdot$ m $= 0.04$ T

FIGURE 25–16. A loudspeaker (a) can be represented as a schematic diagram (b).

a

EXAMPLE

Force on a Current-Carrying Wire in a Magnetic Field

A wire 115 m long is at right angles to a uniform magnetic field. The field has a magnetic field strength of 0.060 T. The current through the wire is 4.0 A. Find the magnitude of the force.

Given: $L = 115$ m   **Unknown:** F
$B = 0.060$ T   **Basic equation:** $B = F/IL$
$I = 4.0$ A

Solution: $F = BIL$
$= (0.060 \text{ T})(4.0 \text{ A})(115 \text{ m})$
$= (0.060 \text{ N/A} \cdot \text{m})(4.0 \text{ A})(115 \text{ m})$
$= 28$ N

b

A loudspeaker changes electrical energy to sound energy using the force on a current-carrying wire in a magnetic field. A loudspeaker consists of a coil of fine wire mounted on a paper cone and placed in a magnetic field, as shown in Figure 25–16. The amplifier driving the loudspeaker sends a current through the coil. A force is exerted on the coil because it is in a magnetic field. The force pushes the coil either into or out of the magnetic field, depending on the direction of the current. The motion of the coil causes the cone to vibrate, creating sound waves in the air. An electric signal that represents a musical tone consists of a current that changes direction between 20 and 20 000 times each second, depending on the pitch of the tone.

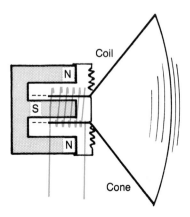

Coil

N

S

N

Cone

Practice Exercises

7. A wire 0.10 m long carrying a current of 2.0 A is at right angles to a magnetic field. The force on the wire is 0.04 N. What is the strength of the magnetic field?

8. A wire 0.5 m long carrying a current of 8.0 A is at right angles to a 0.40 T magnetic field. How strong a force acts on the wire?

9. A wire 75 cm long carrying a current of 6.0 A is at right angles to a uniform magnetic field. The magnitude of the force acting on the wire is 0.60 N. How strong is the magnetic field?

10. A copper wire 40 cm long carries a current of 6.0 A and weighs 0.35 N. A certain magnetic field is strong enough to balance the force of gravity on the wire. What is the strength of the magnetic field?

25:8 Galvanometers

A galvanometer, a sensitive current meter, consists of a coil of wire in a magnetic field.

The **galvanometer** is a device used to measure very small currents and is used in most voltmeters and ammeters.

A galvanometer consists of a small coil of wire placed in the strong magnetic field of a permanent magnet. Each turn of wire in the coil is a wire loop. The current passing through such a loop in a magnetic field goes in one side of the loop and out the other side. Applying the third right-hand rule to each side of the loop, we find that one side of the loop is forced down while the other side of the loop is forced up. As a result, the loop rotates.

The magnitude of the force acting on the coil is proportional to the magnitude of the current. Figure 25–17 shows how the force exerted on a loop of wire in a magnetic field can be used to measure current. The force due to the current is opposed by the force exerted by a small spring. Thus the amount of rotation is proportional to the current. The meter is calibrated by finding out how much the coil turns when a known current is sent through it. The galvanometer can then be used to measure unknown currents.

FIGURE 25–17. If a wire loop is placed in a magnetic field, the loop will rotate when current flows.

436   Magnetic Fields

Many galvanometers produce a full-scale deflection with as little as 50 μA (50×10^{-6} A) current. The resistance of the coil of wire in a sensitive galvanometer is about 1000 Ω. Such a galvanometer can be converted into an ammeter by placing a resistor with resistance smaller than that of the galvanometer in parallel with the meter. Most of the current flows through the resistor, called the shunt, because the current is inversely proportional to resistance. A galvanometer can also be connected as a voltmeter. To make a voltmeter, a resistor, called the multiplier, is placed in series with the meter. The galvanometer measures the current through the multiplier. The current is given by $I = V/R$, where V is the voltage across the voltmeter and R is the effective resistance of the galvanometer and the multiplier resistor. Suppose you want a meter that reads full scale when 10 volts are placed across it. The resistor is chosen so that at 10 V, the meter is deflected full scale by the current through meter and resistor.

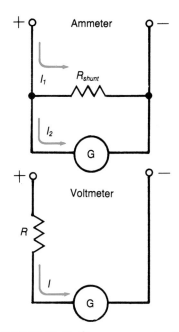

FIGURE 25–18. The components of an electric meter are shown.

25:9 Electric Motors

The simple loop of wire used in a galvanometer cannot rotate more than 180°. As shown in Figure 25–17, the force acting upward on the right side of the loop pushes the loop up. At the same time, the force acting downward on the left side of the loop pushes that side down. The loop turns until it reaches the vertical position. The loop will not continue to turn because the force acting on the right side of the loop is still directed up. It cannot move down through the field. Similarly, the left side of the loop will not move up through the field because the force acting on it is still directed down.

For the loop to rotate 360° in the field, the current running through the loop must reverse direction just as the loop reaches its vertical position. This reversal allows the loop to continue rotating (Figure 25–19). To reverse current direction, a split-ring commutator is used. Brushes, pieces of graphite that make a rubbing or brushing contact with the commutator, allow current to flow into the loop. The split ring is arranged so that each half of the commutator changes brushes just as the loop reaches the ver-

An electric motor consists of a loop of wire in a magnetic field. When current flows in the loop, the loop rotates.

A split-ring commutator enables the loop in a motor to rotate 360°.

DEMONSTRATION: See the Teacher Guide.

SUGGESTION: Show students the parts of a motor using a St. Louis motor. Try to have other motors from appliances to show different types of armatures, commutators, and brushes.

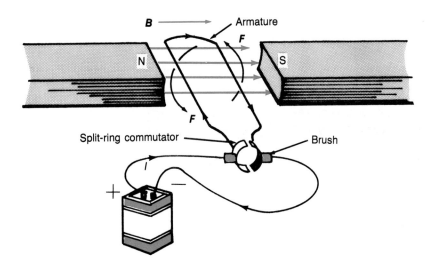

FIGURE 25–19. In an electric motor, split-ring commutators allow the wire loops in the motor to rotate 360°.

In a television picture tube, magnetic fields are used to exert forces on a beam of electrons.

The force acting on a single charged particle as it moves through a magnetic field is Bqv.

SUGGESTION: If an old TV set is available, show how the picture is affected by bringing a magnet near it. You can also use a demonstration cathode-ray tube. (Observe safety precautions.) Students can actually see that the force is at right angles to the field.

tical position. Changing brushes reverses the current in the loop. As a result, the direction of the force on each side of the loop is reversed and the loop continues to rotate. This process is repeated each half-turn. Thus, the loop spins in the magnetic field.

In practice, electric motors have several rotating loops of wire. Together they make up the armature of the motor. The total force acting on the armature is proportional to $nBIL$, where n is the total number of loops on the armature and L is the length of wire in each loop that moves through the magnetic field. The magnetic field can be produced either by permanent magnets or by an electromagnet called a field coil. The force on the armature, and as a result the speed of the motor, is controlled by varying the current flowing through the motor.

25:10   The Force on a Single Charged Particle

The force exerted by a magnetic field on a current-carrying wire is a result of the forces on the individual electrons that make up the current flow. The electrons do not have to be confined to a wire, but can move across any region as long as the air has been removed to prevent collisions between the electrons and air molecules.

The picture tube, or cathode-ray tube, in a television set uses electrons deflected by magnetic fields to form the pictures to be viewed. In the tube, electrons are pulled off atoms by electric fields at the negative electrode, or cathode. Other electric fields gather, accelerate, and focus the electrons into a narrow beam. Magnetic fields are used to deflect the beam back and forth and up and down across the screen of the tube. The screen is coated with a phosphor that glows when struck by the electrons, producing the picture.

The force produced by a magnetic field on a single electron depends on the velocity of the electron, the strength of the field, and the angle between directions of the velocity and the field. It can be found by starting with the force on a current-carrying wire in a magnetic field, $F = BIL$. Consider a single electron moving in a wire of length L. The electron is moving perpendicular to the magnetic field. The current, I, is equal to the charge per unit time entering the wire, $I = q/t$. In this case, q is the charge of the electron and t is the time it takes to move the length of the wire, L. The time required for a particle with velocity v to travel a distance L is

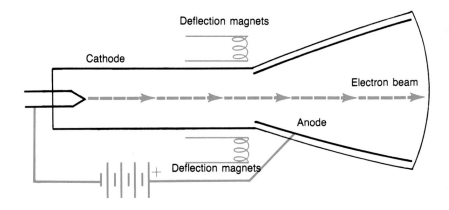

FIGURE 25–20. A television uses a cathode-ray tube to form pictures for viewing.

found by using the equation of motion, $d = vt$, or here, $t = L/v$. As a result, the equation for the current, $I = q/t$, can be replaced by $I = qv/L$. Therefore, the force on a single electron moving through a magnetic field of strength B is

$$F = BIL = B\left(\frac{qv}{L}\right)L = Bqv$$

The particle charge is measured in coulombs, the velocity in m/s, and the magnetic induction in teslas (T).

The direction of the force is perpendicular to both the velocity of the particle and the magnetic field. It is *opposite* that given by the third right-hand rule with the thumb pointed along the velocity of the particle. It is opposite because the electron has a negative charge and "conventional current" has a positive charge.

The path of a charged particle in a uniform magnetic field is circular because the force is always perpendicular to its velocity, just like a centripetal force. The circular motion allows charged particles to be trapped and held in magnetic fields. High energy nuclear particle accelerators, such as the one at Fermilab and the proposed SSC, use magnets to force the particles to travel in circular paths. Electrons trapped in the magnetic field of Earth, shown in Figure 25–21, form the Van Allen radiation belts. A disturbance on the sun can disturb Earth's magnetic field. The disturbance can cause particles to leave the belts and enter Earth's atmosphere at the magnetic poles, producing the northern and southern auroras. Strong magnetic fields will be used in a magnetic confinement fusion device that is under development. The fields confine protons and other nuclei. The nuclei collide at high speed, producing large amounts of energy. The details are discussed in Chapter 31.

FIGURE 25–21. A representation of the Van Allen radiation belts around Earth.

A charged particle moves in a circular path in a magnetic field.

EXAMPLE

Force on a Charged Particle in a Magnetic Field

A beam of electrons travels at 3.0×10^6 m/s through a 4.0×10^{-2}-T uniform magnetic field.

a. The beam is at right angles to the magnetic field. What is the magnitude of the force acting on each electron?

b. Compare the force acting on a proton moving at the same speed and in the same direction to the force acting on the electron in part a.

Given: $v = 3.0 \times 10^6$ m/s   Unknown: F

$B = 4.0 \times 10^{-2}$ T   Basic equation: $F = Bqv$

$q = 1.6 \times 10^{-19}$ C

Solution:

a. $F = Bqv$

$= (4.0 \times 10^{-2}$ T$)(1.6 \times 10^{-19}$ C$)(3.0 \times 10^6$ m/s$)$

$= (4.0 \times 10^{-2}$ N/A $\cdot$ m$)(1.6 \times 10^{-19}$ C$)(3.0 \times 10^6$ m/s$)$

$= 1.9 \times 10^{-14}$ N

b. The magnitude of the force is exactly the same on a proton as it is on an electron. The proton and the electron have exactly the same charge. However, because the proton has the opposite charge, it is deflected in the opposite direction.

Practice Exercises

11. An electron passes through a magnetic field at right angles to the field at a velocity of 4.0×10^6 m/s. The strength of the magnetic field is 0.50 T. What is the magnitude of the force acting on the electron?

12. A stream of doubly-ionized particles (missing two electrons and thus carrying a net charge of two elementary charges) moves at a velocity of 3.0×10^4 m/s perpendicular to a magnetic field of 9.0×10^{-2} T. What is the magnitude of the force acting on each ion?

13. Triply-ionized particles in a beam carry a net positive charge of three elementary charge units. The beam enters a 4.0×10^{-2}-T magnetic field. The particles have a velocity of 9.0×10^6 m/s. What is the magnitude of the force acting on each particle?

14. Doubly-ionized helium atoms (alpha particles) are traveling at right angles to a magnetic field at a speed of 4.0×10^{-2} m/s. The induction of the field is 5.0×10^{-2} T. What force acts on each particle?

CHAPTER 25 REVIEW

SUMMARY

1. Like magnetic poles repel; unlike magnetic poles attract. **25:1**

2. Magnetic fields run out from the north pole of a magnet and enter its south pole. **25:2**

3. Magnetic field lines always form closed loops. **25:2**

4. A magnetic field exists around any wire that carries current. **25:3**

5. A coil of wire through which a current flows also has a magnetic field. The field about the coil is like the field about a permanent magnet. **25:4**

6. When a current-carrying wire is placed in a magnetic field, there is a force on the wire that is perpendicular to the field and also to the wire. Galvanometers are based on this principle. **25:6, 25:7, 25:8**

7. The intensity of a magnetic field is called magnetic induction. The unit of magnetic induction is the tesla (newton per ampere-meter). **25:7**

8. An electric motor consists of a coil of wire placed in a magnetic field. When current flows in the coil, the coil rotates due to the force on the wire in the magnetic field. **25:9**

9. The force a magnetic field exerts on a charged particle depends on the velocity and charge of the particle and the strength of the field. **25:10**

QUESTIONS

1. State the principle of magnetic attraction and repulsion.
2. Name the three most important magnetic chemical elements.
3. How does a temporary magnet differ from a permanent magnet?
4. A piece of metal is attracted to one pole of a large magnet. How could you tell whether the metal is a temporary or permanent magnet?
5. Draw a small bar magnet and show the magnetic field lines as they appear around a magnet. Use arrows to show the direction of the field lines.
6. Draw the field between two like magnetic poles and between two unlike magnetic poles. Show the directions of the fields.
7. Draw the field around a straight current-carrying wire. Show its direction.
8. Explain the right-hand rule used to determine the direction of a magnetic field around a straight current-carrying wire.
9. Explain the right-hand rule used to determine the polarity of an electromagnet.
10. Explain the right-hand rule used to determine the direction of force on a current-carrying wire placed in a magnetic field.
11. A wire is carrying current toward you. Describe the magnetic field it produces.
12. Two wires carry equal currents and run parallel to each other.
    a. If the two currents are in the opposite direction, where will the magnetic field from the two wires be larger than the field from either wire alone?
    b. Where will the magnetic field be exactly twice as large?
    c. If the two currents are in the same direction, where will the magnetic field be exactly zero?
13. In what direction with respect to a magnetic field would you run a wire so that the force on it due to the field is minimized?
14. A beam of protons is moving from the back to the front of a room. It is deflected upward. What is the direction of the magnetic field causing the deflection?

APPLYING CONCEPTS

1. A small bar magnet is hidden inside a tennis ball. Describe the experiments you could do to find the location of the N-pole and the S-pole of the magnet.
2. A room contains a strong, uniform magnetic field. A loop of fine wire in the room has current flowing through it. You rotate the loop until there is no tendency for it to rotate as a result of the field. What is the direction of the magnetic field relative to the plane of the coil?
3. Iron, nickel, and cobalt are electrical conductors. So are superconductors. Do they behave the same way in magnetic fields?
4. A magnet can attract a piece of iron that is not a permanent magnet. A charged rubber rod can attract an uncharged insulator. Describe the microscopic effects that make these two similar.
5. A magnetic field can exert a force on a charged particle. Can it change the particle's kinetic energy? Explain.
6. Is the magnetic force Earth exerts on a compass needle less than, equal to, or greater than the force the compass needle exerts on Earth? Explain.
7. As shown by the spacing of the field lines in Figure 25–15, Earth's magnetic field in space is stronger near the poles than over the equator. At what location would the circular paths followed by the charged particles have larger radii? Explain.
8. If you broke a magnet in two, could you have isolated north and south poles? Explain.
9. You are lost in the woods but have a compass with you. Unfortunately, the red paint marking the N-pole has worn off. You do have a flashlight with a battery and a length of wire. How could you identify the N-pole?
10. Each electron in a piece of iron is like a tiny magnet. The iron, however, is not a magnet. Explain.
11. A strong current is suddenly switched on in a wire. No force acts on it. Can you conclude that there is no magnetic field at the location of the wire? Explain.

EXERCISES

1. A wire 0.50 m long carrying a current of 8.0 A is at right angles to a uniform magnetic field. The force on the wire is 0.40 N. What is the strength of the magnetic field?

2. A wire 25 cm long is at right angles to a 0.30 T uniform magnetic field. The current through the wire is 6.0 A. What force acts on the wire?

3. A wire 1.50 m long carrying a current of 10.0 A is at right angles to a uniform magnetic field. The force acting on the wire is 0.60 N. What is the induction of the magnetic field?

4. The current through a wire 0.80 m long is 5.0 A. The wire is perpendicular to a 0.60 T magnetic field. What force acts on the wire?

5. The force on a wire 0.80 m long that is perpendicular to Earth's magnetic field is 0.12 N. What current flows through the wire?

6. The force acting on a wire at right angles to a 0.80 T magnetic field is 3.6 N. The current flowing through the wire is 7.5 A. How long is the wire?

7. A singly-ionized particle experiences a force of 4.1×10^{-13} N when it travels at right angles through a 0.61 T magnetic field. What is the velocity of the particle?

8. A force of 5.78×10^{-16} N acts on an unknown particle traveling at a 90° angle through a magnetic field. If the velocity of the particle is 5.65×10^4 m/s and the field is 3.20×10^{-2} T, how many elementary charges does the particle carry?

9. A muon (a particle with the same charge as an electron) is traveling at 4.21×10^7 m/s at right angles to a magnetic field. The muon experiences a force of 5.00×10^{-12} N. How strong is the field?

10. The mass of a muon is 1.88×10^{-28} kg. What acceleration does the muon described in Exercise 9 experience?

11. A beta particle (high-speed electron) is traveling at right angles to a 0.60-T magnetic field. It has a speed of 2.5×10^7 m/s. What force acts on the particle?

12. The mass of an electron is 9.11×10^{-31} kg. What is the acceleration of the beta particle described in Exercise 11?

13. A beam of electrons moves at right angles to a 6.0×10^{-2} T magnetic field. The electrons have a velocity of 2.5×10^6 m/s. What is the magnitude of the force acting on each electron?

14. A wire 625 m long is in a 0.40-T magnetic field. A 1.8 N force acts on the wire. What current is in the wire?

15. A power line carries a 225-A current from east to west parallel to the surface of Earth.
    a. What is the magnitude of the force acting on each meter of the wire due to Earth's magnetic field?
    b. What is the direction of the force?
    c. In your judgment, would this force be important in designing towers to hold these power lines?

16. The magnetic field in a loudspeaker is 0.15 T. The wire consists of 250 turns wound on a 2.5 cm diameter cylindrical form. The resistance of the wire is 8.0 ohms. Find the force exerted on the wire when 15 V is placed across the wire.

PROBLEMS

1. In a nuclear research laboratory, a proton moves in a particle accelerator through a magnetic field of intensity 0.10 T at a speed of 3.0×10^7 m/s.
    a. If the proton is moving perpendicular to the field, what force acts on it?
    b. If the proton continues to move in a direction that is consistently perpendicular to the field, what is the radius of curvature of its path? (mass of proton $= 1.67 \times 10^{-27}$ kg)

2. An electron is accelerated from rest through a potential difference of 20 000 V, which exists between the plates P_1 and P_2, Figure 25–22. The electron then passes through a small opening into a magnetic field of uniform field strength B. As indicated, the magnetic field is directed into the page.

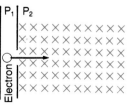

FIGURE 25–22. Use with Problem 2.

a. State the direction of the electric field between the plates as either P_1 to P_2 or P_2 to P_1.

b. In terms of the information given, calculate the electron's speed at plate P_2.

c. Describe the motion of the electron through the magnetic field.

FIGURE 25–23. Use with Problem 3.

Spring

Mercury

3. A current is sent through a vertical spring as shown in Figure 25–23. The end of the spring is in a cup filled with mercury. What will happen? Why?

4. A galvanometer deflects full scale for 50 microamps current.

a. What must be the total resistance of the series resistor and the galvanometer to make a voltmeter with 10-volt full-scale deflection?

b. If the galvanometer has a resistance of 1.0 kΩ, what should be the resistance of the series (multiplier) resistor?

5. The galvanometer in Problem 4 is used to make an ammeter that deflects full scale for 10 mA.

a. What is the potential difference across the galvanometer (1.0 kΩ resistance) when 50×10^{-6} A flows through it?

b. What is the effective resistance of parallel resistors that have the potential difference calculated in part **a** for a circuit with a total of 10 mA current?

c. What resistor should be placed in parallel with the galvanometer to make the resistance calculated in part **b?**

6. A magnetic field of 16 T acts in a direction of due west. An electron is traveling due south at 8.1×10^5 m/s. What is the magnitude and direction of the force acting on the electron?

7. A wire carrying 15 A of current has a length of 25 cm between a magnetic field of 0.85 T. Find the force on the wire if it makes an angle with the magnetic field lines of

a. 90°.   **b.** 45°.   **c.** 0°.

READINGS

Faucher, G., "Ferromagnetism and the Secret Agent." *The Physics Teacher*, January, 1988.

Kryder, Mark, "Magnetic Information Technology." *Physics Today*, December, 1984.

Monforte, John, "The Digital Reproduction of Sound." *Scientific American*, December, 1984.

Rubin, Laurence, "High Magnetic Fields for Physics." *Physics Today*, August, 1984.

Sponseller, Michael, "Magnetic Train." *Popular Science*, December, 1988.

Timmons, D. L., "Finding Magnetic North the Hard Way." *The Physics Teacher*, May, 1988.

CHAPTER 26

Electromagnetic Induction

GOALS

1. You will learn how induced electric currents were discovered.
2. You will learn how electric currents are induced and what effect they have.
3. You will become familiar with some of the applications of these effects.

Think of all the ways you use electricity. It produces light and warmth. Electric motors start our cars and move air through our furnaces. We are entertained by television, radio, tape players, and motion pictures. None of this would be possible without generators and transformers, two devices that are based on the discoveries of Michael Faraday and Joseph Henry.

In 1822, Michael Faraday wrote a goal in his notebook: "Convert Magnetism into Electricity." After nearly ten years of unsuccessful experiments, he was able to show that a changing magnetic field could produce electric current. In the same year, Joseph Henry, an American high school teacher, made the same discovery.

26:1 Faraday's Discovery

Oersted had discovered that an electric current produces a magnetic field. Faraday experimented with a moving wire in a magnetic field. He found that he could induce a current to flow in a wire by moving the wire across the magnetic field. Figure 26–1 shows one of Faraday's experiments. A wire loop that is part of a closed circuit is placed in a magnetic field. When the wire is moved through the field, current flows in the wire, as shown by the meter. If the wire moves up through the field, the current moves in one direction. When the wire moves down through the field, the current moves in the opposite direction. If the wire is held stationary or is moved parallel to the field, no current flows. An electric current is generated in a wire only when the wire cuts through magnetic field lines.

When a wire is moved through a magnetic field, a current is generated in the wire.

DEMONSTRATION: See the Teacher Guide.

444

Go with the Flow

Aluminum is classified as a non-magnetic substance. Two aluminum rings, one with a slit and one a continuous ring, are placed over a magnetic field generator that is producing a constantly changing magnetic flux. What causes one ring to float and the other not to float?

FIGURE 26–1. When a wire is moved in a magnetic field, an electric current flows in the wire, but only while the wire is moving. The direction of the current flow depends on the direction the wire is moving through the field. The arrows indicate the direction of conventional current flow.

SUGGESTION: Demonstrate that to induce a current the magnet and the wire must move with respect to one another. It does not matter which one moves. Also move the wire parallel to the field to show no current is generated.

Electromagnetic induction is the process of generating a current by the relative motion between a wire and a magnetic field.

To generate current, either the conductor can move through a field, or the field can move past a conductor. It is the relative motion between the wire and the magnetic field that produces the current. The process of generating a current in this way is called **electromagnetic induction.**

In what direction does the current move? Use the right-hand rule described in Chapter 25. Hold your right hand so that your thumb points in the direction in which the wire is moving and your fingers point in the direction of the magnetic field. The palm of your hand will point in the direction of the conventional (positive) current flow (Figure 26–2).

26:2 Electromotive Force

When we studied electric circuits, we learned that an electron pump is needed to produce a continuous current flow. The potential difference, or voltage, given to the electrons by the pump is sometimes called the **electromotive force,** or *EMF. Electromotive force, however, is not a force; it is a potential difference and is measured in volts.* Thus the term *EMF* is misleading. Like many other historical terms, it originated before electricity was well understood and is still used.

EMF is the energy per charge, or potential.

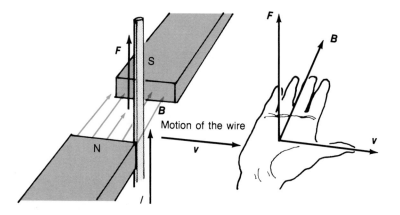

FIGURE 26–2. The right-hand rule can be used to find the direction of a conventional current flowing through a conductor that is moving in a magnetic field.

446 Electromagnetic Induction

a   b

FIGURE 26–3. A microphone (a) and construction details (b).

What creates the potential difference that causes an induced current to flow? When a wire is moved through a magnetic field, a force acts on the electrons and they move in the direction of the force. Work is done on the electrons. Their energy, and thus their potential, is increased. The difference in potential is called the induced *EMF*. The *EMF*, measured in volts, depends on the magnetic induction, *B*, the length of the wire in the magnetic field, *L*, and the velocity of the wire in the field, *v*. If *B*, *v*, and the direction of the wire are mutually perpendicular,

Induced *EMF* is the energy given to electrons when a wire moves through a magnetic field.

EMF is the product of magnetic induction, wire length, and velocity of the wire.

$$\boxed{EMF = BLv}$$

If the moving wire is part of a closed circuit, a current will flow in the circuit.

If a wire moves through a magnetic field at an angle to the field, only the component of the wire's velocity that is perpendicular to the direction of the field generates *EMF*.

A microphone is a simple application of induced *EMF*. The "dynamic" microphone is similar to a loudspeaker. The microphone in Figure 26–3 has a diaphragm attached to a coil of wire that is free to move in a magnetic field. Sound waves vibrate the diaphragm, which moves the coil in the magnetic field. The motion of the coil in turn induces an *EMF* across the ends of the coil. The voltage generated is small, typically 10^{-3} V, but it can be increased, or amplified, by electronic devices.

SUGGESTION: Compare the loudspeaker and the microphone. The loudspeaker changes electrical energy to sound energy, and the microphone converts sound energy to electrical energy.

EXAMPLE

Induced EMF

A wire 0.20 m long moves perpendicularly through a magnetic field of magnetic strength 8.0×10^{-2} T at a speed of 7.0 m/s. **a.** What *EMF* is induced in the wire? **b.** The wire is part of a circuit that has a resistance of 0.50 Ω. What current flows in the circuit?

Given: $L = 0.20$ m   Unknowns: **a.** *EMF* **b.** *I*

$B = 8.0 \times 10^{-2}$ T   Basic equations: **a.** $EMF = BLv$

$v = 7.0$ m/s   **b.** $I = V/R$

$R = 0.50$ Ω

Solution: a. $EMF = BLv$

$$= (8.0 \times 10^{-2}\ \text{T})(0.20\ \text{m})(7.0\ \text{m/s})$$

$$= (8.0 \times 10^{-2}\ \text{N/A} \cdot \text{m})(0.20\ \text{m})(7.0\ \text{m/s})$$

$$= 0.11 \left(\frac{\text{N}}{\text{A} \cdot \text{m}}\right)(\text{m})\left(\frac{\text{m}}{\text{s}}\right) = 0.11\ \frac{\text{W}}{\text{A}} = 0.11\ \text{V}$$

b. $I = \dfrac{V}{R} = \dfrac{0.11\ \text{V}}{0.50\ \Omega} = 0.22\ \text{A}$

Practice Exercises

1. A wire 0.5 m long cuts straight up through a 0.4 T magnetic field at a speed of 20 m/s.
   a. What *EMF* is induced in the wire?
   b. The wire is part of a circuit of total resistance 6.0 Ω. What is the current in the circuit?

2. A wire 25 m long is mounted on an airplane flying at 125 m/s. The wire moves perpendicularly through Earth's magnetic field ($B = 5.0 \times 10^{-5}$ T).
   a. What *EMF* is induced in the wire? ·
   b. If the wire is part of a circuit with a total resistance of 315 Ω, what current will flow?

3. A permanent magnet is mounted with the field lines vertical. If a student passes a wire between the poles and pulls it toward herself, the current flow through the wire is from right to left. Which is the N-pole of the magnet?

4. A wire 30.0 m long moves at 2.0 m/s perpendicularly through a 1.0 T magnetic field.
   a. What *EMF* is induced in the wire?
   b. The total resistance of the circuit of which the wire is a part is 15.0 Ω. What is the current?

26:3 Electric Generators

The **electric generator** was invented by Michael Faraday. It converts mechanical energy to electric energy. An electric generator consists of a number of wire loops placed in a strong magnetic field. The wire is wound around an iron form to increase the strength of the field. The iron and wires are called the armature, similar to that of an electric motor.

The wire loops are mounted so that they can rotate freely in the field. As the loops turn, they cut through magnetic field lines, inducing an *EMF*. In Section 26:2, we found that *EMF* = *BLv*. Thus, the *EMF* (voltage) developed by the generator depends upon the magnetic induction, *B*, the length of wire rotating in the field, *L*, and *v*, the rate at which the loops move through the field. Increasing the number of loops in the armature increases the wire length, *L*, increasing the induced *EMF*.

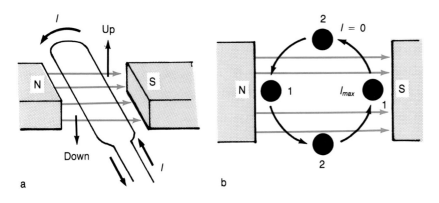

Current flows when a generator is connected in a closed circuit. The current is proportional to the induced *EMF*. Figure 26–4 shows a single loop generator. The direction of the induced current can be found from the right-hand rule. As the loop rotates, the size and direction of the current changes. The current is greatest when the motion of the loop is perpendicular to the magnetic field. Then the velocity of the loop perpendicular to the field is largest. This occurs when the loop is in the horizontal position. As the loop moves from the horizontal to the vertical position, it moves through the magnetic field lines at an ever-increasing angle. Thus, it cuts through fewer magnetic field lines per unit time, and the current decreases. When the loop is in the vertical position, the segments move parallel to the field and the current is zero. As the loop continues to turn, the segment that was moving up begins to move down, reversing the direction of the current in the loop. This change in direction takes place each time the loop turns through 180°. The current changes smoothly from zero to some maximum value and back to zero during each half-turn of the loop. Then it reverses direction. The graph of current versus time is shown in Figure 26–5.

Generators and motors are identical in construction but convert energy in opposite directions. A generator converts mechanical energy to electric energy. A motor converts electric energy to mechanical energy.

In a generator, mechanical energy turns an armature in a magnetic field. The induced voltage causes current to flow. In a motor, a voltage is placed across an armature coil in a magnetic field. The voltage causes current to flow in the coil and the armature turns, producing mechanical energy.

DEMONSTRATION: See the Teacher Guide.

Maximum current and voltage are produced when the loops move at right angles to the field.

Zero current and voltage are produced when the loops move parallel to the field.

The current induced in a wire loop changes direction each time the loop rotates 180°

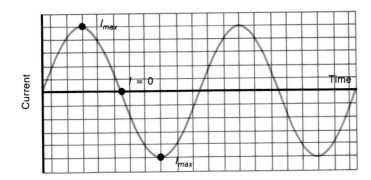

FIGURE 26–5. This graph shows the variation of current with time as a loop rotates. The variation of *EMF* with time is given by a similar graph.

FIGURE 26-6. Alternating current generators transmit current to an external circuit by way of a brush-slip-ring arrangement.

Permanent magnet

Armature

Slip rings

Brush

SUGGESTION: Emphasize that the current generated in the armature is always alternating current. The type of current transmitted to the external circuit depends on whether it is transmitted by a commutator (DC) or slip rings (AC).

The effective current is 0.707 × maximum current.

The effective voltage is 0.707 × maximum voltage.

26:4 Alternating Current Generator

An energy source turns the armature of a generator in a magnetic field at a fixed number of revolutions per second. Commercially, in the United States, this frequency is 60 Hz. The current changes direction, or alternates, 120 times a second.

In Figure 26-6, an alternating current in an armature is transmitted to the rest of the circuit. The brush, slip-ring arrangement permits the armature to turn freely while still allowing the current to pass into the external circuit. As the armature turns, the alternating current varies between some maximum value and zero. If the armature is turning rapidly, the light in the circuit does not appear to dim or brighten because the changes are too fast for the eye to detect.

The power produced by a generator is the product of the current and the voltage. Power is always positive because either I and V are both positive or I and V are both negative. However, because I and V vary, the power delivered by alternating current is less than the power supplied by direct current with the same I_{max} and V_{max}. In fact,

$$P_{AC} = \frac{1}{2}P_{DC}$$

Since alternating currents and voltages are constantly changing with time, it is common to describe these quantities in terms of effective currents and voltages. Recall that $P = I^2R$. Thus, power can be written in terms of the effective current, $P_{AC} = I^2_{eff}R$.

$$P_{AC} = \frac{1}{2}P_{DC}$$
$$I^2_{eff}R = \frac{1}{2}(I^2_{max})R$$
$$I_{eff} = \sqrt{\frac{1}{2}I^2_{max}}$$

$$\boxed{I_{eff} = 0.707I_{max}}$$
$$\boxed{V_{eff} = 0.707V_{max}}$$

The 120-V AC voltage, generally available at wall outlets, is the value of the effective voltage, not the maximum voltage.

EXAMPLE

Effective Voltage and Effective Current

An AC generator develops a maximum voltage of 34 V and delivers a maximum current of 0.17 A to a circuit. **a.** What is the effective voltage of the generator? **b.** What effective current is delivered to the circuit? **c.** What is the resistance of the circuit?

Given: $V_{max} = 34$ V   **Unknowns: a.** V_{eff} **b.** I_{eff} **c.** R

$I_{max} = 0.17$ A   **Basic equations: a.** $V_{eff} = 0.707 V_{max}$

b. $I_{eff} = 0.707 I_{max}$

Solution: a. $V_{eff} = 0.707(V_{max})$

$= 0.707(34$ V$) = 24$ V

b. $I_{eff} = 0.707(I_{max})$

$= 0.707(0.17$ A$) = 0.12$ A

c. $R = \dfrac{V_{eff}}{I_{eff}} = \dfrac{24 \text{ V}}{0.12 \text{ A}} = 200 \ \Omega$

Practice Exercises

5. A generator in a power plant develops a maximum voltage of 170 V.
   a. What is the effective voltage?
   b. A 60-W light bulb is placed across the generator. A maximum current of 0.70 A flows through the bulb. What effective current flows through the bulb?
6. The effective voltage of an AC household outlet is 117 V.
   a. What is the maximum voltage across a lamp connected to the outlet?
   b. The effective current through the lamp is 5.5 A. What is the maximum current in the lamp?
7. An AC generator delivers a peak voltage of 425 V.
   a. What is the effective voltage in a circuit placed across the generator?
   b. The resistance of the circuit is $5.0 \times 10^2 \ \Omega$. What is the effective current?
8. If the effective power dissipated by an electric light is 100 W, what is the peak power?

26:5 Lenz's Law

In a generator, current flows when the armature turns through a magnetic field. We learned in Chapter 25 that when current flows through a wire in a magnetic field, a force is exerted on the wire. Thus, a force is exerted on the wires in the armature. The direction of the force on the

A motor produces a back-*EMF* as it rotates. The generated current opposes the current operating the motor, reducing the current flow.

DEMONSTRATION: See the Teacher Guide.

For Your Information

Many modern automobiles have an electronic ignition system that varies the magnetic field. An aluminum armature with 4, 6, or 8 protrusions (depending on the number of spark plugs) spins. Each protrusion in turn passes through the magnetic field, causing it to vary.

FIGURE 26–7. The magnet approaching the coil causes an induced current to flow. Lenz's law predicts the direction of flow shown.

wires opposes the original motion of the wires. That is, the force acts to slow down the rotation of the armature. The direction of the force was first determined in 1834 by H. F. E. Lenz and is called Lenz's law.

Lenz's law states: *The direction of the induced current is such that the magnetic effects produced by the current oppose the change in flux that caused the current.* Note that it is the *change* in flux and not the flux itself that is opposed by the induced magnetic effects.

Figure 26–7 is a simple example of how Lenz's law works. The N-pole of a magnet is moved toward the right end of a coil. To oppose the approach of the N-pole, the right end of the coil must also become an N-pole. In other words, the magnetic field lines must emerge from the right end of the coil. Use the second right-hand rule you learned in Section 25:4. You will see that if Lenz's law is correct, the induced current must flow in a counterclockwise direction. Experiments have shown that this is so. If the magnet is turned so an S-pole approaches the coil, the induced current will be in the opposite direction.

If a generator supplies a small current, then the opposing force will be small, and the armature will be easy to turn. If the generator supplies a larger current, the force will be larger, and the armature will be more difficult to turn. A generator supplying a large current is producing a large amount of electrical energy. The opposing force on the armature means that a large amount of mechanical energy must be supplied to the generator to produce the electrical energy.

Lenz's law also applies to motors. When a current-carrying wire moves in a magnetic field, an *EMF* is generated. The *EMF*, called the back-*EMF*, is in a direction that opposes the current flow. When a motor is first turned on, a large current flows because of the low resistance of the motor. As the motor begins to turn, the motion of the wires across the magnetic field induces the back-*EMF* that opposes the current flow. Therefore, the net current flowing through the motor is reduced. If a mechanical load is placed on the motor, slowing it down, the back-*EMF* is reduced and more current flows. If the load stops the motor, current flow can be so high that wires overheat.

The heavy current required when a motor is started can cause voltage drops across the resistance of the wires that carry current to the motor. The voltage drop across the wires reduces the voltage across the motor. If a second device, such as a light bulb, is in a parallel circuit with the motor, the voltage at the bulb will also drop when the motor is started.

Induced current

The bulb will dim. As the motor picks up speed, the voltage will rise again and the bulb will brighten.

When the current to the motor is interrupted by turning off a switch in the circuit or by pulling the motor's plug from a wall outlet, the sudden change in the magnetic field generates a back-*EMF* that can be large enough to cause a spark across the switch or between the plug and the wall outlet.

A sensitive balance, such as the kind used in chemistry laboratories, uses Lenz's law to stop its oscillation after an object is placed on the pan. A piece of metal attached to the balance arm is located between the poles of a horseshoe magnet. When the balance arm swings, the metal moves through the magnetic field. Currents are generated in the metal. The currents produce a magnetic field that acts to oppose the motion that caused the currents. Thus the metal piece is slowed down. The force opposes the motion of the metal in either direction, but does not act if the metal is still. Thus it does not change the mass read by the balance. This effect is called "eddy-current damping."

For Your Information

Heinrich Lenz (1804–1865), a Russian physicist, was third in the field of electrical induction, behind Faraday and Henry. Lenz's law must be considered when designing electrical equipment.

26:6 Self-Inductance

Back-*EMF* can be explained another way. As Faraday showed, *EMF* is induced whenever a wire cuts lines of magnetic flux. Consider the coil of wire shown in Figure 26–9. When no current flows through the wire, there are no magnetic flux lines in the coil. When a steady current flows, a constant number of lines pass through the coil. Flux lines are always closed loops. If the magnetic field increases, new flux lines are created. The flux lines expand and cut through the coil wires, generating an *EMF* to oppose the current changes. This effect is called **self-inductance.** The size of the *EMF* is proportional to the rate at which flux lines cut through the wires. The direction of the *EMF* opposes the increase in current. The result of the opposing *EMF* is that the current through the coil does not reach its maximum value instantaneously, but gradually, over a short period of time. When the current is once again steady, the magnetic flux is constant

As current in a coil changes, an induced *EMF* appears in that same coil. The effect is called self-inductance.

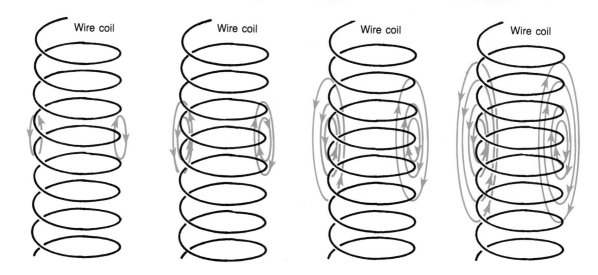

FIGURE 26–9. *EMF* **is generated as a current increases in a coil.**

and the *EMF* is zero. When the current is decreased, an *EMF* is generated that tends to prevent the reduction in magnetic flux and current.

Because of self inductance, work has to be done to increase the current flowing through the coil. As a result, a coil can store electric energy. The energy is actually stored in the magnetic field. This is similar to the way energy is stored in a charged capacitor in an electric field.

26:7 Transformers

Inductance is the basis for the operation of a transformer. A **transformer** is a device that is used to increase or decrease AC voltages. Transformers are widely used because they change the voltage with essentially no loss of energy.

Self-inductance produces an *EMF* when current changes in a single coil. A transformer has two coils, electrically insulated from each other, wound around the same iron core. One coil is called the **primary coil.** The other coil is called the **secondary coil.** When the primary coil is connected to a source of AC voltage, the changing current flow creates a varying magnetic field. The varying magnetic flux is carried by the core to the secondary coil. In the secondary coil, the varying flux induces a varying *EMF*. This effect is called **mutual inductance.**

The *EMF* induced in the secondary coil, called the secondary voltage, is proportional to the primary voltage. The secondary voltage also depends on the ratio of turns on the secondary to turns on the primary.

$$\frac{\text{secondary voltage}}{\text{primary voltage}} = \frac{\text{number of turns on secondary}}{\text{number of turns on primary}}$$

$$\boxed{\frac{V_s}{V_p} = \frac{N_s}{N_p}}$$

$$V_s = \frac{N_s}{N_p} V_p$$

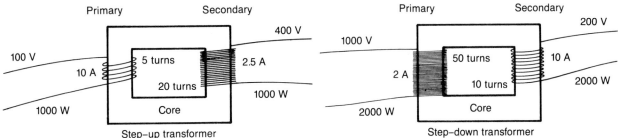

Primary   Secondary

100 V

10 A

5 turns

20 turns

Core

400 V

2.5 A

1000 W

1000 W

Step–up transformer

Primary   Secondary

1000 V

2 A

50 turns

10 turns

Core

200 V

10 A

2000 W

2000 W

Step–down transformer

If the secondary voltage is larger than the primary voltage, the transformer is called a **step-up transformer.** If the voltage out of the transformer is smaller than the voltage put in, then it is called a **step-down transformer.**

In an ideal transformer, the electric power delivered to the secondary circuit equals the power used by the primary. An ideal transformer dissipates no power itself. Since $P = VI$,

$$V_p I_p = V_s I_s$$

The current that flows in the primary depends on how much current is required in the secondary circuit. A step-up transformer increases voltage; the current in the primary circuit is greater than that in the secondary. In a step-down transformer, the current is greater in the secondary circuit than it is in the primary.

As was discussed in Chapter 23, long-distance transmission of electric energy is economical only if low currents and very high voltages are used. Step-up transformers are used at power sources to develop voltages as high as 480 000 V. The high voltage reduces the current flow required in the transmission lines, keeping I^2R losses low. When the energy reaches the consumer, step-down transformers provide appropriately low voltages for consumer use.

FIGURE 26–10. For a transformer, the ratio of input voltage to output voltage depends upon the ratio of the number of turns on the primary to the number of turns on the secondary.

DEMONSTRATION: See the Teacher Guide.

In an ideal transformer, the power delivered to the secondary circuit is equal to the power consumed in the primary.

SUGGESTION: Demonstrate with induction coils that a current is produced in the secondary coil only when it is changing in the primary coil.

FIGURE 26–11. Transformers are used at power stations to increase voltages to transmission line levels. They are used to reduce voltages to consumer levels at the points of use.

a

b

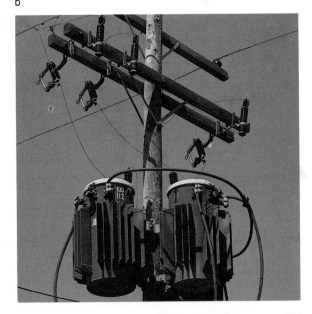

There are many other important uses of transformers. Television picture tubes require up to 25 kV, developed by a transformer within the set. The spark or ignition coil in an automobile is a transformer designed to step up the 12 V from the battery to thousands of volts. The "points" interrupt the DC current from the battery to produce the changing magnetic field needed to induce *EMF* in the secondary coil. Arc welders require currents of 10^4 A. Large step-down transformers are used to provide these currents, which can heat metals to 3000°C or more.

For Your Information

Either effective voltages or maximum voltages may be used in transformer calculations.

EXAMPLE

Step-Up Transformer

A step-up transformer has 2.00×10^2 turns on its primary coil and 3.00×10^3 turns on its secondary coil. **a.** The primary coil is supplied with an alternating current at 90.0 V. What is the voltage in the secondary circuit? **b.** The current flowing in the secondary circuit is 2.00 A. What current flows in the primary circuit? **c.** What is the power in the primary circuit? In the secondary circuit?

Given: $N_p = 2.00 \times 10^2$ Unknowns: **a.** V_s **b.** I_p **c.** P
$\qquad\quad N_s = 3.00 \times 10^3$
$\qquad\quad V_p = 90.0$ V   Basic equations: **a.** $\dfrac{V_p}{V_s} = \dfrac{N_p}{N_s}$
$\qquad\quad I_s = 2.00$ A
$\qquad\qquad\qquad\qquad\qquad\qquad\qquad\quad$ **b.** $V_p I_p = V_s I_s$

Solution:

a. $\dfrac{V_p}{V_s} = \dfrac{N_p}{N_s}$ or $V_s = \dfrac{V_p N_s}{N_p}$

$\qquad = \dfrac{(90.0 \text{ V})(3.00 \times 10^3)}{2.00 \times 10^2} = 1350$ V

b. $V_p I_p = V_s I_s$ or $I_p = \dfrac{V_s I_s}{V_p}$

$\qquad I_p = \dfrac{(1350 \text{ V})(2.00 \text{ A})}{90.0 \text{ V}} = 30.0$ A

c. $V_p I_p = (90.0 \text{ V})(30.0 \text{ A})$
$\qquad\quad = 2.70 \times 10^3$ W
$\quad V_s I_s = (1350 \text{ V})(2.00 \text{ A})$
$\qquad\quad = 2.70 \times 10^3$ W

Practice Exercises

9. A step-down transformer has 7500 turns on its primary and 125 turns on its secondary. The voltage across the primary is 7200 V.

    a. What voltage is across the secondary?

    b. The current in the secondary is 36 A. What current flows in the primary?

10. An ideal step-up transformer's primary circuit has 50 turns. Its secondary circuit has 1500 turns. The primary is connected to an AC generator having an *EMF* of 120 V.
    a. Calculate the *EMF* of the secondary.
    b. Find the current in the primary if the current in the secondary is 3.0 A.
    c. What power is drawn by the primary? What power is supplied by the secondary?

11. The secondary of a step-down transformer has 50 turns. The primary has 1500 turns.
    a. The *EMF* of the primary is 3600 V. What is the *EMF* of the secondary?
    b. The current in the primary is 3.0 A. What current flows in the secondary?

12. A step-up transformer has 300 turns on its primary and 90 000 (9.000 $\times 10^4$) turns on its secondary. The *EMF* of the generator to which the primary is attached is 60.0 V.
    a. What is the *EMF* in the secondary?
    b. The current flowing in the secondary is 0.50 A. What current flows in the primary?

CHAPTER 26 REVIEW

SUMMARY

1. Michael Faraday and Joseph Henry discovered that if a wire moves through a magnetic field, an electric current will be induced in the wire. **26:1**

2. The direction that current flows in a wire moving through a magnetic field depends upon the direction of the motion of the wire and the direction of the magnetic field. **26:1**

3. The current produced depends upon the angle between the velocity of the wire and the magnetic field. Maximum current occurs when the wire is moving at right angles to the field. **26:2**

4. Electromotive force, *EMF*, is the energy imparted to each unit of charge by the energy source. *EMF* is measured in volts. **26:2**

5. *EMF* is the product of the magnetic induction, *B*, the length of the wire in the field, *L*, and the component of the velocity of the moving wire, *v*, perpendicular to the field. **26:2**

6. An electric generator consists of a number of wire loops placed in a magnetic field. Because each side of the coil moves alternately up and down through the field, the current alternates direction in the loops. The generator develops alternating voltage and current. **26:3, 26:4**

7. A generator and a motor are similar devices. A generator converts mechanical energy to electric energy; a motor converts electric energy to mechanical energy. **26:4**

8. Lenz's law states: *An induced current always acts in opposition to the change in flux that is causing the current.* **26:5, 26:6**

9. A transformer has two coils wound about the same core. An AC voltage across the primary coil induces an alternating *EMF* in the secondary coil. The voltages in alternating current circuits may be increased or decreased by transformers. **26:7**

QUESTIONS

1. How are Oersted's and Faraday's results similar? How are they different?
2. What is *EMF*? Why is the name inaccurate?
3. Substitute units to show that the unit of *BLv* works out to be volts.
4. Sketch and describe an AC generator.
5. What is the armature of an electric generator?
6. Why is iron used in an armature?
7. What is the difference between a generator and a motor?
8. Why is the effective value of an AC current less than the maximum value?
9. State Lenz's law.
10. When a wire is moved through a magnetic field, what depends on the resistance of the closed circuit: the *EMF*, the current, both, or neither?
11. Suppose a magnetic field is in the downward direction. You move a wire at the same speed, first horizontally, then at 45°, then downward.
    a. Will the induced *EMF* be different for the three motions? Explain.
    b. If it depends on direction, which direction generates the largest voltage? Explain.
12. You have a coil of wire and a bar magnet. Describe how you could use them to generate an electric current.
13. What is the difference between the current generated in a wire when the wire is moved up through a horizontal magnetic field and the current generated when the wire is moved down through the same field?
14. If the strength of a magnetic field is fixed, in what three ways could you vary the size of the *EMF* you could generate?
15. You make an electromagnet by winding wire around a large nail. If you connect the magnet to a battery, is the current larger just after you make the connection or a long time after the connection is made? Or is it always the same? Explain.
16. What causes the back-*EMF* of an electric motor?
17. Why is the self-inductance of a coil a major factor when the coil is in an AC circuit and a minor factor when the coil is in a DC circuit?
18. Upon what does the ratio of the *EMF* in the primary of a transformer to the *EMF* in the secondary of the transformer depend?

APPLYING CONCEPTS

1. The direction of AC voltage changes 120 times each second. Does that mean a device connected to an AC voltage alternately delivers and accepts energy?
2. A transformer is connected to a battery through a switch. The secondary circuit contains a light bulb. Which of these statements best describes when the lamp will be lighted?
    a. as long as the switch is closed
    b. only the moment the switch is closed
    c. only the moment the switch is opened
    Explain.
3. Thomas Edison proposed distributing electrical energy using constant voltages (DC). George Westinghouse proposed using the present AC system. What are the reasons the Westinghouse system was adopted?
4. Explain why the word "change" appears so often in this chapter.
5. Explain why a spark jumps when you pull the plug on a vacuum cleaner but not when you do the same on an electric lamp.
6. A physics instructor drops a magnet through a copper pipe, Figure 26–12. The class sees that the magnet falls very slowly. The class concludes that there must be some force opposing gravity to reduce the acceleration of the magnet. The instructor suggests that the class explain how this occurs and notes that the magnet has its S-pole at the bottom.

FIGURE 26–12. Use with Applying Concepts 6.

a. What is the direction of the current induced in the pipe by the falling magnet?

b. The current produces a magnetic field. What is the direction of the field?

c. How does this field reduce the acceleration of the falling magnet?

7. Water trapped behind Hoover dam turns turbines that rotate generators. List the forms of energy between the stored water and the final electricity produced.

8. An inventor claims that a very efficient transformer will step up power as well as voltage. Should we believe this? Explain.

9. A bicycle's headlamp is powered by a generator that rubs against a wheel. Is the bike harder to pedal when the generator is lighting the lamp? Why?

10. Suppose an "anti-Lenz's law" existed that meant a force was exerted to increase the change in magnetic flux. Thus when more electrical energy was demanded from a generator, the force needed to turn it would be reduced. What conservation law would be violated by this new "law"? Explain.

11. The direction of Earth's magnetic field in the northern hemisphere is downward and to the north. If a wire moves from north to south, in which direction does the current flow?

EXERCISES

1. A wire segment 31 m long moves straight up through a 4.0×10^{-2} T magnetic field at a speed of 15.0 m/s. What *EMF* is induced in the wire?

2. A straight wire 0.75 m long moves upward through a horizontal 0.30 T magnetic field at a speed of 16 m/s.

    a. What *EMF* is induced in the wire?

    b. The wire is part of a circuit with a total resistance of 11 Ω. What current flows in the circuit?

3. A wire 20.0 m long moves at 4.0 m/s perpendicularly through a 0.50 T magnetic field. What *EMF* is induced in the wire?

4. An AC generator develops a maximum voltage of 150 V. It delivers a maximum current of 30.0 A to an external circuit.

    a. What is the effective voltage of the generator?

    b. What effective current does it deliver to the external circuit?

    c. What is the effective power dissipated in the circuit?

5. An electric stove is connected to a 220-V AC source.

    a. What is the maximum voltage across one of the stove's elements when it is operating?

    b. The resistance of the operating element is 11 Ω. What effective current flows through it?

6. A 0.045 T magnetic field is at an angle of 60° above the horizontal. A wire 2.5 m long moves horizontally at 2.4 m/s. What *EMF* is induced in the wire?

7. An AC generator develops a maximum *EMF* of 565 V. What effective *EMF* does the generator deliver to an external circuit?

8. A step-up transformer has 80 turns on its primary coil. It has 1200 turns on its secondary coil. The primary coil is supplied with an alternating current at 120 V.

    a. What voltage is across the secondary coil?

    b. The current in the secondary coil is 2.0 A. What current flows in the primary circuit?

    c. What is the power input and output of the transformer?

9. A portable computer requires an effective voltage of 9.0 volts from the 120 V line.

    a. If the primary of the transformer has 475 turns, how many does the secondary have?

    b. A 125 mA current flows through the computer. What current flows through the transformer's primary?

10. In a hydroelectric plant, electric energy is generated at 1200 V. It is transmitted at 240 000 V.

    a. What is the ratio of the turns on the primary to the turns on the secondary of a transformer connected to one of the generators?

    b. One of the plant generators can deliver 40.0 A to the primary of its transformer. What current is flowing in the secondary?

11. The primary of a transformer has 150 turns. It is connected to a 120-V source. Calculate the number of turns on the secondary needed to supply these voltages.

    a. 6.0×10^2 V

    b. 3.0×10^1 V

    c. 6.0 V

12. A student connects a transformer to a 24 V source and measures 8.0 V at the secondary. If the primary and secondary were reversed, what would the output voltage be?

13. A hair dryer uses 10 A at 120 V. It is used with a transformer in England, where the line voltage is 240 V.

    a. What should be the turns ratio of the transformer?

    b. What current will it draw from the 240 V line?

14. An instructor connects both ends of a copper wire of total resistance 0.10 Ω to the terminals of a galvanometer. The galvanometer has a resistance of 875 Ω. The instructor then holds part of the wire in a 2.0×10^{-2} T magnetic field. The length of the wire between the magnetic poles is 10.0 cm. If the instructor moves the wire up through the field at 1.0 m/s, what current will the galvanometer indicate?

15. A step-up transformer is connected to a generator that is delivering 1.20×10^2 V and 1.00×10^2 A. The ratio of the turns on the secondary to the turns on the primary is 1000 to 1.

    a. What voltage is across the secondary?

    b. What current flows in the secondary?

PROBLEMS

1. An instructor is moving a loop of copper wire down through a magnetic field B, as shown in Figure 26–13.

    a. Will the induced current move to the right or left in the wire segment in the diagram?

    b. As soon as the wire is moved in the field, a current appears in it. Thus, the wire segment is a current-carrying wire located in a magnetic field. A force must act on the wire. What will be the direction of the force acting on the wire due to the induced current?

Down

FIGURE 26–13. Use with Problem 1.

2. An inventor proposes that a considerable amount of gasoline could be conserved each year by mounting antenna-like wire segments on the roofs of cars. When the cars move perpendicular to or at some angle with Earth's magnetic field, a current would be generated in the wires that could be used to charge storage batteries. The batteries could, in turn, power the car.

    a. Earth's magnetic field in the United States has an average strength of about 5.0×10^{-5} T. If a car were moving 72.0 km/h perpendicular to that field (east-west), what would have to be the total length of the wire segments on its roof to develop an *EMF* of 12 V?

    b. If, because of its low weight, aluminum wire of resistance 2.6×10^{-4} Ω per meter is used for the wire segments, what maximum current could be developed?

3. A generator at Hoover dam can supply 375 MW (375×10^6 W) of electrical power. Assume that the turbine and generator are 85% efficient.

    a. Find the rate at which falling water must supply energy to the turbine.

    b. The energy of the water comes from a change in potential energy, *mgh*. What is the needed change in potential energy each second?

    c. If the water falls 22 m, what is the mass of water that must pass through the turbine each second to supply this power?

4. An airplane traveling at 950 km/h passes over a region where Earth's magnetic field is 4.5×10^{-5} T and nearly vertical. What voltage is induced between the plane's wing tips, which are 75 m apart?

5. A 40 cm wire is moved perpendicular with a velocity of 1.3 m/s through a magnetic field of 0.32 T. If this wire is connected across a circuit of 10 Ω resistance, how much current is flowing?

6. A 150 W transformer has an input voltage of 9 V and an output current of 5 A.

    a. Is this a step-up or step-down transformer?

    b. By what factor is the output voltage multiplied?

7. A transformer has input voltage and current of 12 V and 3.0 A respectively, and an output current of 0.75 A. If there are 1200 turns on the secondary side of the transformer, how many turns are on the primary side?

READINGS

Gutnik, Martin J., *Electricity From Faraday to Solar Generators*. New York: Franklin Watts, 1986.

Parker, E. N., "Magnetic Fields in the COSMOS." *Scientific American*, August, 1983.

Patterson, Walt, "A New Way to Burn." *Science 83*, April, 1983.

Pool, R., "A New Standard Volt." *Science*, April 29, 1988.

Reid, T. R., "The Chip." *Science 85*, January, 1985.

CHAPTER 27

Electric and Magnetic Fields

GOALS

1. You will gain an understanding of the use of separated electric and magnetic fields to study the properties of charged particles.
2. You will gain a knowledge of the properties of electromagnetic waves produced by coupled electric and magnetic fields.

For Your Information

Sir Joseph John Thomson was awarded the Nobel Prize in physics in 1906 for his work on the electron. Eventually, seven of his research assistants won Nobel Prizes. In 1908 he was knighted.

The huge dishes of the Very Large Array (VLA) detect radio waves from space. They are used to receive information sent from satellites reaching Uranus and Neptune and signals from distant galaxies. They are only more complicated versions of television antennas on the roofs of homes.

Signals from galaxies, satellites, and television stations are electromagnetic waves. The properties of electric and magnetic fields were studied over most of the last century. In 1820, Hans Christian Oersted published his findings that current-carrying wires produced magnetic fields. In 1831, Michael Faraday and Joseph Henry discovered that changing magnetic fields produced electric currents. James Clerk Maxwell, a Scottish physicist, was born in the year Faraday demonstrated electromagnetic induction. In the 1860s, Maxwell predicted that even without wires, changing electric fields cause magnetic fields, and the changing magnetic fields produce electric fields. The result of this coupling is energy transmitted across empty space in the form of electromagnetic waves. Maxwell's theory, soon tested experimentally by Heinrich Hertz, led to a complete description of electricity and magnetism. It also gave us radio, television, and many other devices important to our lives.

27:1 Mass of the Electron

Electrons are not only a part of every atom, they are also the source of electric fields and currents. Therefore it is important to know the properties of electrons. The force of an electric field on a charge was used in the Millikan oil drop experiment to measure the charge of the electron. The

Big Ears

These parabolic-dish antennas are used to detect radio-frequency radiation having short wavelengths. Of what benefit is this dish-style antenna rather than one similar to your television antenna or automobile radio antenna?

FIGURE 27–1. The Thomson *m/q* tube (a) is diagrammed in (b). The electromagnets have been moved forward to show the deflection plates. When the tube is in use, the electromagnets and the deflection plates lie in the same plane.

Thomson observed the deflection of electrons in both electric and magnetic fields. The electric field, the magnetic field, and the electron beam are all perpendicular to one another.

To find the velocity of the electrons, the fields are adjusted until electrons follow an undeflected path.

mass is too small to measure on an ordinary balance. It is possible, however, to find the ratio of the mass to the charge, *m/q*, by balancing the forces of an electric and a magnetic field acting on an electron.

The ratio of mass to charge of the electron was first measured in 1897 by the British physicist J. J. Thomson (1856–1940). He used a cathode-ray tube similar to the one in Figure 27–1. All air is removed from the glass tube. An electric field pulls electrons out of the negatively-charged cathode and accelerates them toward the positively-charged anode. Some of the electrons pass through a hole in the anode and travel in a tiny beam toward a fluorescent screen. The screen glows at the point where the electrons hit.

In the middle of the tube, the forces caused by the electric and magnetic fields are balanced. Parallel plates form a uniform electric field perpendicular to the beam. The electric field intensity, *E*, produces a force, *qE*, that deflects the beam upward. Two coils produce a magnetic field at right angles to both the beam and the electric field. Remember that the force exerted by a magnetic field is perpendicular to the field and to the direction of motion of the particles. The force exerted by the magnetic field is equal to *Bqv*. Here, *B* is the magnetic induction and *v* is the electron velocity. The magnetic force acts downward.

The electric and magnetic fields are adjusted until the beam of electrons follows a straight, or undeflected, path. Then the forces due to the two fields are equal in magnitude and opposite in direction.

$$Bqv = Eq$$

Solving this equation for *v*, we obtain the expression

$$v = \frac{Eq}{Bq}$$

$$= \frac{E}{B}$$

If the electric field is turned off, only the force due to the magnetic field remains. The magnetic force acts perpendicular to the direction of motion of the electrons, causing a centripetal acceleration. The electrons follow a circular path with radius r. Newton's second law gives

$$Bqv = m\frac{v^2}{r}$$

Solving for $\frac{m}{q}$ gives

$$\boxed{\frac{m}{q} = \frac{Br}{v}}$$

When electrons move through a magnetic field, they follow a circular path.

Thomson calculated the velocity, v, using the measured values of E and B. Next, he measured the distance between the undeflected spot and the position of the spot when only the magnetic field acted on the electrons. Using this distance and the size of the field region, he calculated the radius of the circular path of the electron, r. This allowed Thomson to calculate m/q. The average of many experimental trials gave the value m/q = 5.686 × 10⁻¹² kg/C. Using Millikan's value of q = 1.602 × 10⁻¹⁹ C gives the mass of the electron, m.

SUGGESTION: Thomson actually used the value of the charge on the electron found from electrochemistry experiments. We can use Millikan's value.

$$\frac{m}{q} = 5.686 \times 10^{-12} \text{ kg/C}$$

$$\begin{aligned}
m &= (5.686 \times 10^{-12} \text{ kg/C})(q)\\
&= (5.686 \times 10^{-12} \text{ kg/C})(1.602 \times 10^{-19} \text{ C})\\
&= 9.109 \times 10^{-31} \text{ kg}\\
&= 9.11 \times 10^{-31} \text{ kg}
\end{aligned}$$

Thomson used a related method to find m/q for positive ions. A positive ion is produced by removing one or more electrons from an atom. To accelerate positively-charged particles into the deflection region, he reversed the direction of the field between the cathode and anode. A small amount of a gas, such as hydrogen, was put into the tube. The field pulled the electrons off the hydrogen atoms and accelerated the positively-charged protons through a tiny hole in the negatively-charged electrode.

The mass of a proton can be measured by the same method.

FIGURE 27–2. This photograph shows the circular tracks of two electrons (e⁻) and a positron (e⁺) moving through the magnetic field in a bubble chamber. Note that the electrons and positron curve in opposite directions.

The proton beam then passed through the electric and magnetic deflecting fields to the fluorescent screen of the Thomson m/q tube. The mass of the proton was determined in the same manner as was the mass of the electron. The mass of the proton is 1.67×10^{-27} kg. Heavier ions produced by stripping an electron from gases such as helium, neon, or argon were measured by a similar method.

EXAMPLE

Balancing Electric and Magnetic Fields in an m/q Tube

A beam of electrons travels an undeflected path in a tube. E is 7.0×10^3 N/C. B is 3.5×10^{-2} T. What is the speed of the electrons as they travel through the tube?

Given: $E = 7.0 \times 10^3$ N/C   **Unknown:** v
$\quad\quad\quad B = 3.5 \times 10^{-2}$ T

$\quad\quad\quad\quad\quad\quad\quad\quad\quad\quad\quad$ **Basic equation:** $v = \dfrac{E}{B}$

Solution: $v = \dfrac{E}{B}$

$\quad\quad\quad = \dfrac{7.0 \times 10^3 \text{ N/C}}{3.5 \times 10^{-2} \text{ N/A} \cdot \text{m}}$

$\quad\quad\quad = 2.0 \times 10^5$ m/s

EXAMPLE

Path of an Electron in a Magnetic Field

An electron of mass 9.11×10^{-31} kg moves with a speed 2.0×10^5 m/s across an 8.0×10^{-4} T magnetic field. What is the radius of the circular path followed by the electrons?

Given: $m = 9.11 \times 10^{-31}$ kg   **Unknown:** r
$\quad\quad\quad v = 2.0 \times 10^5$ m/s
$\quad\quad\quad B = 8.0 \times 10^{-4}$ T   **Basic equation:** $Bqv = \dfrac{mv^2}{r}$
$\quad\quad\quad q = 1.6 \times 10^{-19}$ C

Solution:

$Bqv = \dfrac{mv^2}{r}$

$\quad r = \dfrac{mv}{Bq} = \dfrac{(9.11 \times 10^{-31} \text{ kg})(2.0 \times 10^5 \text{ m/s})}{(8.0 \times 10^{-4} \text{ N/A} \cdot \text{m})(1.6 \times 10^{-19} \text{ C})}$

$\quad r = 1.4 \times 10^{-3}$ m

Practice Exercises

Assume the direction of all moving charged particles is perpendicular to the magnetic field.

1. Protons passing without deflection through a 0.6 T magnetic field are balanced by a 4.5×10^3 N/C electric field. What is the speed of the moving protons?

2. A proton moves at a speed of 7.5×10^3 m/s as it passes through a 0.6 T magnetic field. Find the radius of the circular path. The mass of a proton is 1.7×10^{-27} kg. The charge carried by the proton is equal to that of the electron, but it is positive.

3. Electrons move through a 6.0×10^{-2} T magnetic field balanced by a 3.0×10^3 N/C electric field. What is the speed of the electrons?

4. Calculate the radius of the circular path the electrons in Practice Exercise 3 follow in the absence of the electric field. The mass of an electron is 9.11×10^{-31} kg.

27:2 The Mass Spectrograph

When Thomson put neon gas into his tube, he found two values of *m/q*. This meant that atoms could have the same chemical properties but have different masses. Thus Thomson had shown the existence of isotopes, a possibility first proposed by the chemist Frederick Soddy.

The masses of positive ions can be measured precisely using a **mass spectrograph,** an adaptation of the Thomson tube. The type used by K. T. Bainbridge is shown in Figure 27–3. It uses either a gas or a material that can be heated to form a gas. Accelerated electrons strike the gas atoms, knocking off electrons to form positive gas ions. A potential difference, *V*, between the electrodes, S_1 and S_2, produces an electric field that accelerates the ions.

Ion source

Accelerating field

Electric and magnetic deflecting fields

Film

Uniform magnetic field into paper

FIGURE 27–3. Diagram of early Bainbridge mass spectrograph.

FIGURE 27–4. Marks left on the film in a mass spectrograph by isotopes of chromium.

In a mass spectrograph, the beam of ions is first accelerated in an electric field so that only ions of the same energy continue through the magnetic field.

SUGGESTION: Point out that the equation $KE = \frac{1}{2}mv^2$ is used here in connection with electric effects. This is another example of the universality of physical laws.

The ions then pass through electric and magnetic deflecting fields as in the Thomson tube. As explained in Section 27:1, only ions with a certain velocity follow an undeflected path through the fields. They move into a region with a uniform magnetic field. There they are deflected into a circular path. The radius of the path is found from Newton's second law, $Bqv = mv^2/r$. Solving for r yields

$$r = \frac{mv}{qB}$$

The velocity of the ion can be found from the equation for the kinetic energy of ions accelerated through a known potential difference V.

$$KE = \frac{1}{2}mv^2 = qV$$

$$v = \sqrt{\frac{2Vq}{m}}$$

Substituting this expression for v in the previous equation gives the radius of the circular path.

$$r = \frac{1}{B}\sqrt{\frac{2Vm}{q}}$$

From this equation, the mass to charge ratio of the ion is found to be

$$\frac{m}{q} = \frac{B^2r^2}{2V}$$

The ions hit a photographic film where they leave a mark. The radius, r, is found by measuring the distance between the mark and the hole in the electrode. This distance is twice the radius of the circular path.

The place that the ion hits depends linearly on the ratio of mass to charge of the ion. For example, Figure 27–4 shows marks on film from the isotopes of the element chromium. The isotope with mass number 52 makes the darkest mark, showing that most chromium atoms have this mass. All of these ions have the same charge. The charge depends on how many electrons were removed in the ion source. It takes more-energetic electrons to remove a second electron from the gas atoms. For low electron energies, only one electron is removed from an atom. When the energy is increased, however, both singly- and doubly-charged ions are produced. The operator of the mass spectrograph can choose the charge on the ion.

Mass spectrographs can be used to separate isotopes of atoms, such as uranium. Instead of film, cups are used to collect the separated isotopes. A mass spectrograph (often called an MS) is used by chemists as a very sensitive tool to find small amounts of molecules in samples. Amounts as small as one molecule in 10 billion molecules can be identified. Investigators detect the ions using electronic devices and are able to separate ions with mass differences of one ten-thousandth of one percent. Many dangerous contaminants in the environment have been detected with this device.

EXAMPLE

The Mass of a Neon Atom

The operator of a mass spectrograph produces a beam of doubly-ionized neon atoms (charge $q = 2(1.60 \times 10^{-19}$ C). The accelerating voltage is $V = 34$ V. In a 0.050 T magnetic field, the radius of the path of the ions is $r = 0.053$ m. **a.** Calculate the mass of a neon atom. **b.** How many proton masses are in the neon atom mass? (The mass of a proton is 1.67×10^{-27} kg.)

Given: $V = 34$ V   Unknown: m

$\quad\quad B = 0.050$ N/A·m

$\quad\quad r = 0.053$ m   Basic equation: $\dfrac{m}{q} = \dfrac{B^2 r^2}{2V}$

$\quad\quad q = 3.2 \times 10^{-19}$ C

Solution: **a.** $m = \dfrac{qB^2 r^2}{2V}$

$$= \frac{(3.2 \times 10^{-19} \text{ C})}{2(34 \text{ V})}(0.050 \text{ T})^2(0.053 \text{ m})^2$$

$$= 3.3 \times 10^{-26} \text{ kg}$$

b. proton masses $= \dfrac{3.3 \times 10^{-26} \text{ kg}}{1.67 \times 10^{-27} \text{ kg/proton}}$

$$= 20 \text{ proton masses}$$

DEMONSTRATION: See the Teacher Guide

Practice Exercises

5. A stream of singly-ionized lithium atoms is not deflected as it passes through a 1.5×10^{-3} T magnetic field perpendicular to a 6.0×10^2 V/m electric field.

   a. What is the speed of the lithium atoms as they pass through the crossed fields?

   b. The lithium atoms move into a 0.18 T magnetic field. They follow a circular path of radius 0.165 m. What is the mass of a lithium atom?

6. A mass spectrograph gives data for a beam of doubly-ionized argon atoms. The values are $B = 5.0 \times 10^{-2}$ T, $q = 2(1.6 \times 10^{-19}$ C), $r = 0.106$ m, and $V = 66.0$ V. Find the mass of an argon atom.

7. A beam of singly-ionized oxygen atoms is sent through a mass spectrograph. The values are $B = 7.2 \times 10^{-2}$ T, $q = 1.6 \times 10^{-19}$ C, $r = 0.085$ m, and $V = 110$ V. Find the mass of an oxygen atom.

27:3 Electromagnetic Waves

Oersted found that an electric current in a conductor produced a magnetic field. Changing the current changed the magnetic field. Faraday discovered that a changing magnetic field can induce an electric current in a wire. Furthermore, even if the wire is not there, the electric fields that

A changing magnetic field generates a changing electric field.

For Your Information

In the course of his experiments, Hertz first observed the photoelectric effect. However, he did not follow up his observation. Einstein later explained this phenomenon, earning a Nobel Prize.

FIGURE 27–5. Representation of an induced electric field (a), magnetic field (b), and both electric and magnetic fields (c).

produce the current exist (Figure 27–5a). Thus *a changing magnetic field produces a changing electric field.* The field lines of the induced electric field will be closed loops because without a conductor, there are no charges on which the lines can begin or end.

In 1860 James Clerk Maxwell postulated that the opposite is also true. *A changing electric field produces a changing magnetic field* (Figure 27–5b). Oersted had shown that a changing magnetic field could come from accelerating electric charges. Maxwell, however, suggested that the electric charges were not necessary; the changing electric field alone would produce the magnetic field.

Maxwell then predicted that either accelerating charges or changing magnetic fields would produce electric and magnetic fields that move through space. The combined fields are called an **electromagnetic wave.** The speed at which the wave moves, calculated Maxwell, was the speed of light, 3.00×10^8 m/s as measured by Fizeau in 1849. Not only were electricity and magnetism linked, but optics, the study of light, became a branch of the study of electricity and magnetism. Heinrich Hertz (1857–1894), a German physicist, demonstrated in 1887 that Maxwell's theory was correct.

Figure 27–6 shows the formation of an electromagnetic wave. A wire, called an **antenna,** is connected to an alternating current (AC) source. The source creates an electric field that accelerates electrons in the antenna. The field, and the acceleration of the electrons, alternates in direction at the frequency of the AC source. The moving charges generate a changing magnetic field, which in turn generates a changing electric field, and so on, as suggested in Figure 27–5c. The fields move away from the source and are replaced by new fields. The fields continue to spread through space at the speed of light.

A view of part of the fields at an instant in time (Figure 27–7) shows that the fields form a transverse wave in space. The electric field oscillates. It alternates, first up, then down. The magnetic field also oscillates at right angles to the electric field. The two fields are at right angles to the direction of the motion of the wave. An electromagnetic wave produced by the antenna in Figure 27–6 is polarized. That is, the electric fields are all in one direction, the direction of the antenna.

a

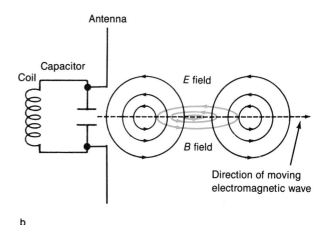

b

27:4 Production of Electromagnetic Waves

One method of creating the oscillating fields in the antenna has already been described, the AC generator. In fact, all alternating current transmission lines create electromagnetic waves. The frequency of the waves is the same as the frequency of the current. Frequency can be changed by varying the speed at which the generator is rotated. The highest frequency that can be generated in this way is about 1000 Hz.

The most common method of generating higher frequencies is to use a coil and capacitor connected in a series circuit. If the capacitor is charged by a battery, the potential difference across the capacitor creates an electric field. When the battery is removed, the capacitor discharges, and the stored electrons flow through the coil, creating a magnetic field. After the capacitor has discharged, the magnetic field of the coil collapses. A back-*EMF* develops that recharges the capacitor, this time in the opposite direction. The capacitor again discharges, and so on. One complete oscillation cycle is seen in Figure 27–8. The number of oscillations each second is called the frequency, which depends on the size of the capacitor and the coil. The antenna extends the fields of the capacitor into space.

A pendulum is a good analogy to help understand the coil and capacitor circuit. The electrons in the coil and capacitor are represented by the pendulum bob. The mass of a pendulum moves fastest at the lowest point

FIGURE 27–7. A look at portions of the fields at an instant in time.

E field strongest

B field strongest

B field strongest

E field strongest

FIGURE 27–8. Production of electro-magnetic waves.

There is energy in both electric fields and magnetic fields.

A system readily absorbs energy that is offered at the natural frequency of the system.

SUGGESTION: The magnetic fields circle around an electric current or a changing electric field.

of the swing. This is similar to the largest current flowing in the coil when the charge on the capacitor is zero. When the pendulum mass is at its greatest angle, its displacement from the vertical is largest, and it has a zero velocity. This position is like the moment when the capacitor holds the largest charge and the current through the coil is zero.

The analogy also holds when considering energy. The potential energy of the pendulum is largest when its displacement is greatest. The kinetic energy is largest when the velocity is greatest. The sum of the potential and kinetic energy, the total energy, is constant. Both the magnetic field produced by the coil and the electric field in the capacitor contain energy. When the current is largest, the energy stored in the magnetic field is greatest. When the current is zero, the electric field of the capacitor is largest and all the energy is in the electric field. The total energy, the sum of magnetic field energy and electric field energy, is constant.

Just as the pendulum will stop swinging if left alone, the oscillations in a coil and capacitor will also die out if energy is not added to the circuit. Gentle pushes, applied at the correct times, will keep a pendulum moving. The largest amplitude swing occurs when the frequency of pushing is the same as the frequency of swinging. This is the condition of resonance discussed in Chapter 7. Voltage pulses applied to the coil-capacitor circuit at the right frequency keep the oscillations going. One way of doing this is to add a second coil to form a transformer. The AC induced in the secondary coil is increased by an amplifier and added back to the coil and capacitor. This type of circuit can produce frequencies up to approximately 10 MHz.

Coils and capacitors are not the only method of generating oscillation voltages. Quartz crystals have a property called **piezoelectricity.** They bend or deform when a voltage is applied across them. Just as a piece of

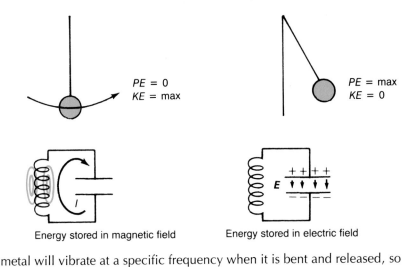

PE = 0
KE = max

PE = max
KE = 0

Energy stored in magnetic field

Energy stored in electric field

Crystals are used to generate high-frequency waves.

metal will vibrate at a specific frequency when it is bent and released, so will a quartz crystal. A crystal can be cut so that it will vibrate at a specific desired frequency. An applied voltage will start it vibrating. The piezoelectric property also generates an *EMF* when the crystal is bent. Since this *EMF* is produced at the vibrating frequency of the crystal, it can be amplified and returned to the crystal to keep it vibrating. Quartz crystals are used in wristwatches because the frequency of vibration is so constant. Frequencies in the range from 1 kHz to 10 MHz can be generated in this way.

To increase the oscillation frequency, the size of the coil and capacitor must be made smaller. Above 1000 MHz, individual coils and capacitors will not work. For these electromagnetic waves, called microwaves, a rectangular box, called a resonant cavity, acts as both a coil and a capacitor. The size of the box determines the frequency of oscillation. Such a cavity is in every microwave oven.

At frequencies of infrared waves, the size of resonant cavities would have to be reduced to the size of molecules. The oscillating electrons that produce infrared waves are in fact within the molecules. Visible and ultraviolet waves are generated by electrons within atoms.

X rays can be generated by electrons in heavy atoms. **Gamma rays** are the result of accelerating charges in the nucleus of an atom. All electromagnetic waves arise from accelerated charges and travel at the speed of light.

The natural frequency of a crystal depends on its size and shape.

SUGGESTION: Tanning requires a source of ultraviolet light. Warn students of the danger from too much exposure to UV radiation.

Light waves are electromagnetic waves generated by the acceleration of electrons within an atom.

SUGGESTION: Spend time discussing the electromagnetic spectrum, Table 27-1. Refer back to Figure 17–1, which clearly shows that the visible portion of the spectrum is very small.

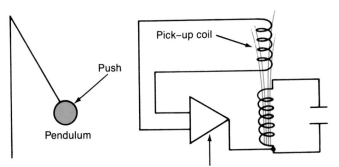

Pick–up coil

Push

Pendulum

FIGURE 27–10. Resonance in the pendulum analogy.

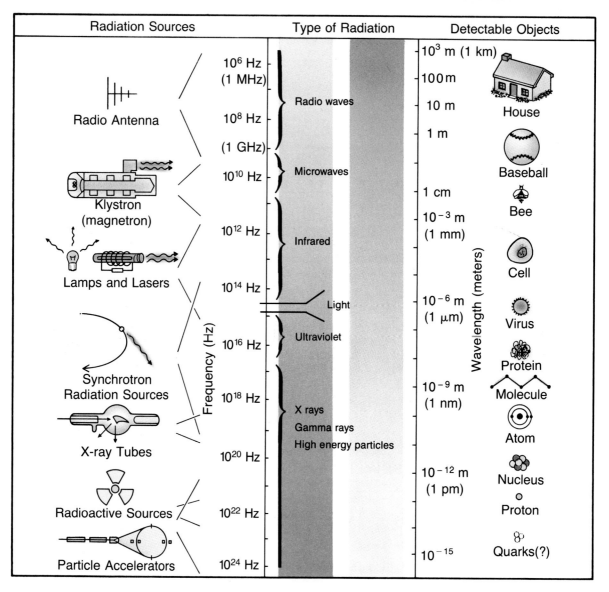

Radiation Sources	Type of Radiation		Detectable Objects

Radio Antenna

10^6 Hz
(1 MHz)

10^8 Hz

(1 GHz)

10^{10} Hz

10^{12} Hz

10^{14} Hz

10^{16} Hz

10^{18} Hz

10^{20} Hz

10^{22} Hz

10^{24} Hz

Frequency (Hz)

Klystron
(magnetron)

Lamps and Lasers

Synchrotron
Radiation Sources

X-ray Tubes

Radioactive Sources

Particle Accelerators

Radio waves

Microwaves

Infrared

Light

Ultraviolet

X rays

Gamma rays

High energy particles

Wavelength (meters)

10^3 m (1 km)

100 m

10 m

1 m

1 cm

10^{-3} m
(1 mm)

10^{-6} m
(1 μm)

10^{-9} m
(1 nm)

10^{-12} m
(1 pm)

10^{-15}

House

Baseball

Bee

Cell

Virus

Protein

Molecule

Atom

Nucleus

Proton

Quarks(?)

Electromagnetic waves can be generated over a wide range of frequencies. Table 27–1 lists the electromagnetic spectrum.

27:5 Reception of Electromagnetic Waves

Electromagnetic waves are caused by the acceleration of electrons in an antenna. When the electric fields in these electromagnetic waves strike another antenna, they accelerate the electrons in it. This acceleration is largest when the antenna is turned in the direction of the polarization of the wave. That is, it must be parallel to the direction of the electric fields in the wave. An *EMF* is produced across the terminals of the antenna. The *EMF* oscillates at the frequency of the electromagnetic wave that produced it. The *EMF* is largest if the length of the antenna is one half the wavelength of the wave. The antenna then resonates in the same way an open pipe one-half wavelength long resonates with sound waves. For that reason, an antenna designed to receive radio waves is much longer than one designed to receive microwaves.

While a simple wire antenna can detect electromagnetic waves, several wires can be used to increase the detected *EMF*. A television antenna often consists of two or more wires spaced about one-quarter wavelength apart. Electric fields generated in the individual wires form constructive interference patterns that increase the strength of the signal. At very short wavelengths parabolic dishes reflect the waves just as parabolic mirrors reflect light waves. The giant dishes of the Very Large Array (VLA) concentrate the waves with 2 to 6 cm wavelength on the antennas at the center of the dish.

Radio and television waves are used to transmit information across space. There are many different radio and television stations producing electromagnetic waves at the same time. If the information being broadcast is to be understood, it must be possible to select the waves of a particular station. To select waves of a particular frequency and reject the others, a coil and capacitor circuit is connected to the antenna. The capacitance is adjusted until the oscillation frequency of the circuit equals the frequency of the desired wave. Only this frequency can cause the oscillations of the electrons in the circuit. The information carried by the oscillations is then amplified and ultimately drives a loudspeaker. The combination of antenna, coil and capacitor circuit, and amplifier is called a **receiver.**

At microwave and infrared frequencies, the electromagnetic waves accelerate electrons in molecules. The energy of the electromagnetic waves is converted to thermal energy in the molecules. Microwaves cook foods in this way. Infrared waves from the sun produce the warmth we feel.

Light waves can transfer energy to electrons in atoms. In photographic film, this energy causes a chemical reaction. The result is a permanent record of the light reaching the camera from the subject. In the eye, the energy produces a chemical reaction that stimulates a nerve, resulting in a response in our brain that we call vision.

27:6 X Rays

In 1895 in Germany, Wilhelm Roentgen (1845–1923) sent electrons through an evacuated discharge tube. Roentgen used a very high voltage across the tube to give the electrons a large kinetic energy. The electrons struck the metal anode of the tube. When this happened, Roentgen noted a glow on a phosphorescent screen a short distance away. The glow continued even if a piece of wood was placed between the tube and the screen. He concluded that some kind of highly-penetrating rays were coming from the discharge tube.

Because Roentgen did not know what these strange rays were, he called them X rays. A few weeks later, Roentgen found that photographic plates were darkened by X rays. He also discovered that while soft body tissue was transparent to the rays, bone blocked them. He produced an X-ray picture of his wife's hand. Within months, doctors recognized the medical uses of this phenomenon.

FIGURE 27–11. Schematic diagram of a receiver.

E

Antenna

Amplifier

FIGURE 27–12. This apparatus is used in producing X rays.

X rays are high-frequency electromagnetic waves generated when electrons strike an anode.

SUGGESTION: X-ray images were originally called "skiagraphs" from the Greek meaning "shadow graphs."

It is now known that X rays are high frequency electromagnetic waves. They pass through most matter, but are blocked more by heavier atoms. X rays are produced when high speed electrons crash into matter and their kinetic energies are converted into electromagnetic waves. As a result of these collisions, X rays are emitted. The electrons are accelerated to high speeds by means of potential differences of 20 000 volts or more. Electrons are accelerated to these speeds in cathode-ray tubes, such as the picture tube in a television. X rays are produced when these electrons hit the faceplate and cause the colored phosphors to glow. The faceplate glass contains lead to stop the X rays and protect viewers.

PHYSICS FOCUS

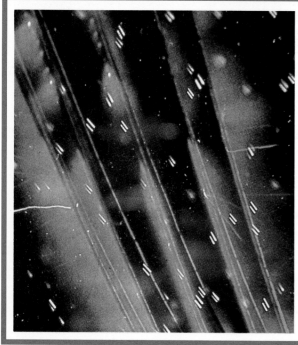

Ultra-High Voltage Electric Power Transmission

In the past, the electric utility industry in the United States has had to double its available power capacity approximately every 10 years. Long-term projections still indicate an increased use of electric energy. This means that electric generation and transmission capacity must keep pace.

Transmission levels greater than the current extra-high voltage (EHV) levels of 345, 500, and 765 kilovolts will be needed in the years ahead. The new levels of transmission now being researched are called ultra-high voltage (UHV). UHV transmission levels of more than 2000 kilovolts are being tested. UHV lines would allow electrical power to be delivered at a lower cost per kilowatt than electrical power delivered by EHV lines.

Research on the environmental aspects of EHV transmission will be even more important with the advent of UHV. Research generally falls into three areas: possible ozone emission by transmission lines, audible noise and radio- and television-frequency interference, and the biological effects of electrostatic and electromagnetic fields on living organisms.

SUMMARY

1. The ratio of mass to charge of the electron was measured by J. J. Thomson using balanced electric and magnetic fields. **27:1**

2. The mass of the electron can be found by combining Thomson's result with Millikan's measurement of the electron charge. **27:1**

3. The mass spectrograph uses both electric and magnetic fields to measure the masses of atoms and molecules. **27:2**

4. A changing electric field in space generates a changing magnetic field. **27:3**

5. A changing magnetic field generates a changing electric field in space. **27:3**

6. Electromagnetic waves are coupled changing electric and magnetic fields that move through space. **27:3**

7. Oscillating electrons in an antenna generate electromagnetic waves. **27:4**

8. The frequency of oscillating currents can be selected by a resonating coil and capacitor circuit. **27:4**

9. Electromagnetic waves can be detected by the *EMF* they produce in an antenna. The length of the most efficient antenna is one-half wavelength. **27:5**

10. Microwave and infrared waves can accelerate electrons in molecules, producing thermal energy. **27:5**

11. When high-energy electrons strike an anode in an evacuated tube, their kinetic energies are converted to electromagnetic waves of very high energy called X rays. **27:6**

QUESTIONS

1. The electrons in a Thomson tube, like the one in Figure 27–1, travel from left to right. Which deflection plate should be charged positively to bend the electron beam up?

2. The electron beam of Question 1 has a magnetic field to make the beam path straight. What would be the direction of the magnetic field needed to bend the beam down?

3. A mass spectrograph operates on neon ions. What is the direction of the magnetic field needed to bend the beam in a clockwise semicircle?

4. Car radio antennas are vertical. What is the direction of the electric fields they detect?

5. The frequency of television waves broadcast on channel 2 is about 58 MHz. The waves on channel 7 are about 180 MHz. Which channel requires a longer antenna?

6. Which television channel, 2 or 7, requires a larger capacitor in the resonant circuit in the television set?

7. The direction of an induced magnetic field is always at what angle to the changing electric field?

8. Of radio waves, light, or X rays, which has the largest
   a. wavelength?   b. frequency?   c. velocity?

9. What happens to quartz crystals when a voltage is placed across them?

10. What are isotopes?

APPLYING CONCEPTS

1. The radio waves detected by the VLA receiver dishes are 2 cm long. How long is the antenna that detects the waves?

2. Suppose the eyes of an alien being are sensitive to microwaves (1 cm wavelength). Would you expect such a being to have larger or smaller eyes than ours? Explain.

3. A vertical antenna wire transmits radio waves. Sketch the antenna and the electric and magnetic fields it produces.

4. Charged particles are moving through an electric field and a magnetic field that are perpendicular to each other. Suppose you adjust the fields so that one ion with the correct velocity passes without deflection. Now another ion with the same velocity, but a different mass, enters the fields. Does it pass without deflection?

5. If the sign of the charge on the particle mentioned above is changed from positive to negative, do the directions of either or both of the two fields have to be changed to keep the particle undeflected? Explain.

6. How does an antenna receiving circuit select electromagnetic radio waves of a certain frequency and reject all others?

7. Why must an AC generator be used to propagate electromagnetic waves? If a DC generator were used, when would it create electromagnetic waves?

8. Like all waves, microwaves can be transmitted, reflected, and absorbed. Why can soup be warmed in a ceramic mug in a microwave but not in a metal pan? Why does the handle of the mug not get as hot as the soup?

EXERCISES

1. A proton enters a magnetic field of induction 6.4 $\times$ 10^{-2} T with a velocity of 4.5×10^4 m/s. What is the circumference of the circular path that it follows?

2. Electrons moving at 3.6×10^4 m/s pass through an electric field of intensity 5.8×10^3 N/C. How large of a magnetic field must the electrons also experience for their path to be undeflected?

3. A proton moves across a 0.36 T magnetic field in a circular path of radius 0.2 m. What is the speed of the proton?

4. Electrons move across a 4.0 mT magnetic field. They follow a circular path of radius 2.0 cm.
   a. What is their speed?

b. An electric field is applied perpendicularly to the magnetic field. The electrons then follow a straight-line path. Find the magnitude of the electric field.

5. A mass spectrograph yields data for a beam of doubly-ionized sodium atoms. These values are $B = 8.0 \times 10^{-2}$ T, $q = 2(1.60 \times 10^{-19}$ C), $r = 0.077$ m, and $V = 156$ V. Calculate the mass of a sodium atom.

6. If an atomic mass unit is equal to 1.67×10^{-27} kg, how many units are in the sodium atom in Exercise 5?

7. Television channel 6 broadcasts on a frequency of 85 MHz.
   a. What is the wavelength of the electromagnetic wave broadcast on channel 6?
   b. What is the length of an antenna that will detect channel 6 most easily?

8. What energy is given to an electron to transfer it across a difference in potential of 4.0×10^5 V?

9. A proton enters a 6.0×10^{-2} T magnetic field with a speed of 5.4×10^4 m/s. What is the radius of the circular path it follows?

PROBLEMS

1. An alpha particle has a mass of approximately 6.6×10^{-27} kg and bears a double elementary positive charge. Such a particle is observed to move through a 2.0 T magnetic field along a path of radius 0.15 m.
   a. What speed does it have?
   b. What is its kinetic energy?
   c. What potential difference would be required to give it this kinetic energy?

2. The difference in potential between the cathode and anode of a spark plug is 1.0×10^4 V.
   a. What energy does an electron give up as it passes between the electrodes?
   b. One fourth of the energy given up by the electron is converted to electromagnetic radiation. The frequency of the wave is related to the energy by the equation $E = hf$, where h is Planck's constant, 6.6×10^{-34} J/Hz. What is the frequency of the waves?

3. A mass spectrograph is used to analyze a molecule with a mass of 175×10^3 proton masses. The operator wants to know whether the carbon in the molecule has mass 12 or 13 proton masses. What percent differentiation is needed?

4. An electron is accelerated by 4.5 KV of potential difference. How strong of a magnetic field must be experienced by the electron if its path is a circle of radius 5.0 cm?

5. An alpha particle, a doubly-ionized helium atom, has a mass of 6.7×10^{-27} kg and is accelerated by a voltage of 1.0 KV. If a uniform magnetic field of 6.5×10^{-2} T is maintained on the alpha particle, what will be the particle's radius of curvature?

6. In a mass spectrograph, silicon atoms have radii of curvature of 16.23 cm and 17.97 cm. If the smaller radius corresponds to an atomic mass of 28 units, what is the atomic mass of the other silicon isotope?

READINGS

Bertsch, George, "Vibrations of the Atomic Nucleus." *Scientific American,* May, 1983.

Foster, Kenneth R., and Arthur Guy, "The Microwave Problem." *Scientific American,* September, 1986; *Scientific American,* December, 1986.

Fox, B., "High Frequencies Relieve Radio Traffic Jams." *New Scientist,* April 21, 1988.

Lachenbruch, David, *Television.* Milwaukee: Raintree, 1985.

Langone, John, "X-Raying Egyptian Mummies." *Discover,* November, 1984.

CHAPTER 28

Quantum Theory

For Your Information

GOALS

1. You will become aware of how the quantum nature of matter was discovered.
2. You will gain an understanding of the particle nature of light and the wave properties of particles.
3. You will learn of some of the applications of the dual nature of waves and matter.

A body heated until it emits light is called incandescent.

Light is made up of discrete bundles of energy called photons.

In 1887 the experiments of Heinrich Hertz confirmed the predictions of Maxwell's theory. All of optics seemed to be explainable by electromagnetic theory. Only two small problems remained. Wave theory could not describe the spectrum of light emitted by a hot body, such as the lava. Also, as discovered by Hertz himself, ultraviolet light discharged electrically-charged metal plates. This effect, called the photoelectric effect, could not be explained by Maxwell's wave theory.

The solution of these two problems required a total change in our understanding of the structure of matter, and of electromagnetic energy as well. It was shown that the energy of particles was quantized. That is, particles could not have a continuous range of energies, but only a few specific values. Electromagnetic energy was also shown to be quantized. It must consist of discrete bundles of energy called light quanta or photons. Quantum theory is the name given to the explanation of the discrete properties of matter and electromagnetic energy. The development of this theory and its experimental confirmation is one of the highlights of the history of the twentieth century.

28:1 Radiation from Incandescent Bodies

If you look through a prism at the light coming from an incandescent light bulb, you will see all the colors of the rainbow. The bulb also emits

Red Hot or Not

Jean's family toured a steel mill during vacation. They saw a large vat of molten steel. Jean pointed out that the molten red steel was very hot, but not as hot as the yellowish-white steel. Her younger brother disagreed saying, ''Everyone knows that red hot is supposed to be the hottest.'' How did Jean defend her statement.

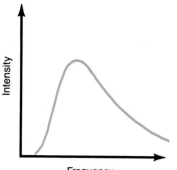

FIGURE 28–1. This graph shows the spectrum of an incandescent body.

An incandescent body emits a broad spectrum of light.

The energy emitted by an incandescent body increases very rapidly with temperature.

The spectrum of an incandescent body can be explained only if energy is quantized.

A property is quantized if it occurs only in certain distinct values.

infrared radiation, which you cannot see. Figure 28–1 shows the spectrum of an incandescent body. A spectrum indicates the light intensity emitted at various frequencies. Light and infrared radiation are produced by the vibration of the charged particles within the atoms of a hot, or incandescent, body.

Suppose you put the light bulb on a dimmer control. You gradually turn up the voltage, increasing the temperature of the glowing filament. The color of the incandescent body changes from deep red through orange to yellow and finally to white. The higher the temperature, the "whiter" the body appears. The color you see depends on the relative amounts of emission at various frequencies. Spectra of incandescent bodies at various temperatures are shown in Figure 28–2. The frequency at which the maximum amount of light is emitted is proportional to the temperature measured in kelvins.

The energy emitted also increases with temperature. The amount of energy emitted in electromagnetic waves is proportional to the absolute temperature raised to the fourth power, T^4. Thus, as the figure shows, hotter sources radiate considerably more energy than cooler bodies. The sun, for example, is a dense ball of gases heated to incandescence by the energy produced within it. It has a surface temperature of 5800 K and a yellow color. The sun radiates 4×10^{26} W, a truly enormous amount of power. Each square meter on Earth receives about one thousand joules of energy each second.

Why does the spectrum have the shape shown in Figure 28–2? Between 1887 and 1900, many physicists tried to predict the shape of this spectrum using existing physical theories, but all failed. In 1900, the German physicist Max Planck (1858–1947) found that he could calculate the spectrum only if he introduced a revolutionary hypothesis. Planck assumed that the energy of vibration of the atoms in a solid could have only the specific frequencies given by the equation

$$E = nhf$$

Here f is the frequency of vibration of the atom, h is a constant, and n is an integer like 0, 1, 2, or 3. The energy, E, could have the values hf, $2hf$, $3hf$, and so on, but never, for example, $\frac{2}{3}hf$. This means that energy is quantized. Energy only comes in packages of a certain size.

Intensity of Blackbody Radiation versus Frequency

FIGURE 28–2. This graph shows spectra of incandescent bodies at various temperatures.

Further, Planck proposed that atoms did not radiate electromagnetic waves all the time they were vibrating, as predicted by Maxwell. Instead, they could emit radiation *only when their vibration energy changed.* For example, when the energy changed from $3hf$ to $2hf$, the atom emitted radiation. The energy radiated was equal to the change in energy of the atom, hf.

Planck found that the constant h was extremely small, about 7×10^{-34} J/Hz. This meant that the energy-changing steps were too small to be noticeable in ordinary bodies. Still, the introduction of quantized energy was extremely troubling to physicists, especially Planck himself. It was the first hint that the physics of Newton and Maxwell might be valid only under certain conditions.

SUGGESTION: Objects that are good absorbers are also good radiators of thermal energy. Black objects are good absorbers.

Practice Exercise

1. Suppose a 5.0-g object, such as a nickel, vibrates while connected to a spring. Its maximum velocity is 1.0 cm/s.
   a. Find the maximum kinetic energy of the vibrating object.
   b. The object emits energy in the form of light of frequency 5×10^{14} Hz and its energy is reduced by one step. Find the energy lost by the object.
   c. How many step reductions would this object have to make to lose all its energy?

28:2 Photoelectric Effect

The second troubling experimental result was that a negatively-charged zinc plate was discharged when ultraviolet light but not visible light fell on it. A positively-charged plate did not discharge when either ultraviolet or visible light fell on it. Further study showed that zinc was discharged because it emitted electrons when ultraviolet light fell on it. The emission of electrons when light falls on a body is called the **photoelectric effect.**

FIGURE 28–3. A diagram of a photocell circuit (a) shows the ejection of electrons from a metal. Photocells are used in the automatic control of street lights (b).

a

Light source

Light

Anode

Cathode

Photocell

b

The photoelectric effect can be studied in a photocell like that in Figure 28–3. The cell contains two metal electrodes sealed in an evacuated tube. It is evacuated to keep the metal surface clean and to keep electrons from being stopped by air molecules. The large electrode is usually cesium or another alkali metal. It is called the cathode. The second electrode, the anode, is a thin wire so it does not block any light. The tube is made of quartz to permit ultraviolet light to pass through. A potential difference is placed across the electrodes.

When no light falls on the cathode, current does not flow in the circuit. When light falls on the cathode, however, a current, shown by the meter, flows in the circuit. Current is the result of electrons, called photoelectrons, being ejected from the cathode by the light. The electrons travel to the positive electrode, the anode.

Photoelectrons are electrons ejected from metal as a result of light hitting it.

Not all light results in current flow. Electrons are ejected only if the frequency of the light is above a certain minimum value, called the threshold frequency, f_0. The threshold frequency varies with the metal. Light of a frequency below f_0 does not eject any electrons from the metal, no matter how bright the light. Even if it is very dim, light at or above the threshold frequency causes electrons to leave the metal immediately. The greater the intensity of light, the larger the flow of photoelectrons.

The threshold frequency is the minimum frequency of light needed to eject a photoelectron.

The electromagnetic wave theory of light cannot explain these facts. In the wave theory, a more intense light has stronger electric and magnetic fields. According to wave theory, the electric field accelerates and ejects the electrons from the metal. With very faint light shining on the metal, electrons would require a very long time before they gained enough energy to be ejected.

In 1905, Albert Einstein published a revolutionary theory that explained the photoelectric effect. According to Einstein, light consists of discrete bundles of energy, which were later called photons. The energy of each photon depends on the frequency of the light. The energy is given by the equation $E = hf$, where h is Planck's constant, 6.626×10^{-34} J/Hz.

Einstein explained the photoelectric effect by proposing that light consists of photons.

It is important to note that Einstein's theory of the photon goes further than Planck's theory of hot bodies. While Planck proposed that the vibrat-

SUGGESTION: Make a display of photocells and devices operated by them. Photocells are used in circuits to count people coming into buildings and in automatic door opening circuits.

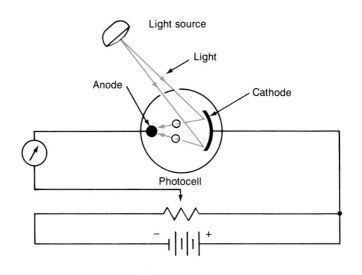

FIGURE 28–4. The kinetic energy of the ejected electrons can be measured with this device. An ammeter is used to measure the current flowing through the circuit.

484 Quantum Theory

ing atoms emitted radiation with energy hf, he did not suggest that light and other forms of radiation acted like particles. Einstein's theory of the photon reinterpreted and extended Planck's theory of hot bodies.

DEMONSTRATION: See the Teacher Guide.

Einstein's photoelectric-effect theory explains the existence of a threshold frequency. A photon with a minimum energy, hf_0, is needed to eject an electron from the metal. Further, an electron cannot accumulate photons until it has enough energy; only one photon interacts with one electron. If the photon has a frequency below f_0, it does not have the energy needed to eject an electron.

Light with a frequency greater than f_0 has more energy than needed to eject an electron. The excess energy, $hf - hf_0$, becomes the kinetic energy of the electron. The kinetic energy of the ejected electrons can be measured by a device like the one pictured in Figure 28–4. A variable potential difference is placed across the tube until the anode is made slightly negative. Then the potential difference opposes the movement of ejected electrons to the anode. Light of the chosen frequency illuminates the cathode. An ammeter measures the current flowing through the circuit. The experimenter increases the opposing potential difference, making the anode more negative. Electrons need higher and higher kinetic energies to reach the anode. At some voltage, called the stopping potential, no electrons have enough energy to reach the anode, and the current is zero. The work done by the stopping potential equals the maximum kinetic energy of the electrons,

Light with frequency above the threshold frequency gives kinetic energy to the electron.

The kinetic energy of ejected electrons can be found by determining the work needed to bring them to rest.

$$\boxed{KE_{max} = -qV_0}$$

Here, V_0 is the stopping potential in volts (J/C) and q is the charge of the electron (-1.60×10^{-19} C).

The joule is not a convenient unit of energy to use with atomic systems. A more convenient energy unit is the electron volt (eV). One electron volt is the energy of an electron accelerated across a potential difference of one volt. That is,

An electron volt is the energy of an electron accelerated through a potential difference of one volt.

$$1 \text{ eV} = 1.60 \times 10^{-19} \text{ J}$$

EXAMPLE

Maximum Kinetic Energy of a Photoelectron

The stopping potential that prevents electrons from flowing across a photocell is 4.0 V. What is the maximum kinetic energy given to the electrons by the incident light? Give the answer in both J and eV.

Given: stopping potential   **Unknown:** KE_{max}
$V_0 = 4.0$ V   **Basic equation:** $KE_{max} = -qV_0$

Solution: $KE_{max} = -qV_0$
$$= -(-1.60 \times 10^{-19} \text{ C})(4.0 \text{ J/C})$$
$$= +(6.4 \times 10^{-19} \text{ J})\left(\frac{1 \text{ eV}}{1.6 \times 10^{-19} \text{ J}}\right)$$
$$= 4.0 \text{ eV}$$

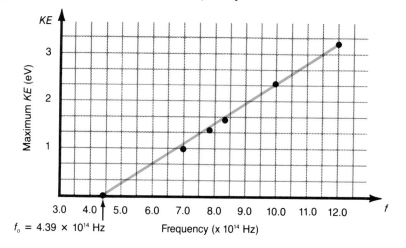

KE$_{max}$ of Photoelectrons versus Frequency

A graph of the maximum kinetic energies of the electrons ejected from a metal versus the frequencies of the incident photons is a straight line (Figure 28-5). All metals have similar graphs with the same slope. The slope of the line is Planck's constant, h.

The graphs differ only in the threshold frequency that is needed to free electrons.

$$h = \frac{\Delta KE}{\Delta f} = \frac{\text{change in maximum kinetic energy of ejected electrons}}{\text{change in frequency of incident light}}$$

The work function of a metal is the energy needed to free an electron from the metal.

The energy needed to free the most weakly-bound electron from a metal is called the work function of the metal. The work function is the product of the threshold frequency and Planck's constant, hf_0. The maximum kinetic energy of the emitted electron is then the total energy given the electron by the photon, hf, less the work function, hf_0. That is,

$$\boxed{KE_{max} = hf - hf_0}$$

This equation is called the photoelectric equation.

Robert A. Millikan did the experiments that proved Einstein's photoelectric theory to be correct. Einstein won the Nobel prize in 1921 for his work on the photoelectric effect.

EXAMPLE

Photoelectric Equation

The threshold frequency of sodium is 5.6×10^{14} Hz. **a.** What is the work function of sodium in J and eV? **b.** Sodium is illuminated by light of frequency 8.6×10^{14} Hz. What is the maximum kinetic energy of the ejected electrons in eV?

Given: threshold frequency
$f_0 = 5.6 \times 10^{14}$ Hz
illumination frequency
$f = 8.6 \times 10^{14}$ Hz

Unknown: KE_{max}

Basic equation:
$KE_{max} = hf - hf_0$

Solution:

a. work function $= hf_0$

$$= (6.6 \times 10^{-34} \text{ J/Hz})(5.6 \times 10^{14} \text{ Hz})$$

$$= 3.7 \times 10^{-19} \text{ J}$$

$$= \frac{(3.7 \times 10^{-19} \text{ J})}{(1.6 \times 10^{-19} \text{ J/eV})}$$

$$= 2.3 \text{ eV}$$

b. $hf = (6.6 \times 10^{-34} \text{ J/Hz})(8.6 \times 10^{14} \text{ Hz})(1 \text{ eV}/1.6 \times 10^{-19} \text{ J})$

$$= 3.5 \text{ eV}$$

$KE_{max} = hf - hf_0 = 3.5 \text{ eV} - 2.3 \text{ eV} = 1.2 \text{ eV}$

The wavelength of light is more easily measured than its frequency. If the wavelength is given in a problem, the frequency may be found using the equation $\lambda = c/f$. The energy (in eV) of a photon with wavelength λ is given by the formula

$$E = hf = \frac{hc}{\lambda}$$

$$E = \frac{(6.62 \times 10^{-34} \text{ J/Hz})(3.00 \times 10^8 \text{ m/s})(1 \text{ eV}/1.6 \times 10^{-19} \text{ J})}{\lambda(10^{-9} \text{ m/nm})}$$

$$= \frac{1240}{\lambda} \text{ eV} \cdot \text{nm}$$

In this equation the value of λ must be in nanometers.

Practice Exercises

2. The stopping potential to prevent current through a photocell is 3.2 V. Calculate the maximum kinetic energy in joules of the photoelectrons within the cell.

3. The stopping potential for a photoelectric cell is 5.7 V. Calculate the maximum kinetic energy in electron volts of the photoelectrons within the cell.

4. The threshold wavelength of zinc is 310 nm (310×10^{-9} m).
   a. Find the threshold frequency of zinc.
   b. What is the work function in eV of zinc?
   c. Zinc in a photocell is irradiated by ultraviolet light of 240 nm wavelength. What is the maximum kinetic energy of the photoelectrons in eV?

5. The work function for cesium is 1.96 eV.
   a. Find the threshold wavelength for cesium.
   b. What is the maximum kinetic energy in eV of photoelectrons ejected when 425 nm blue light falls on the cesium?

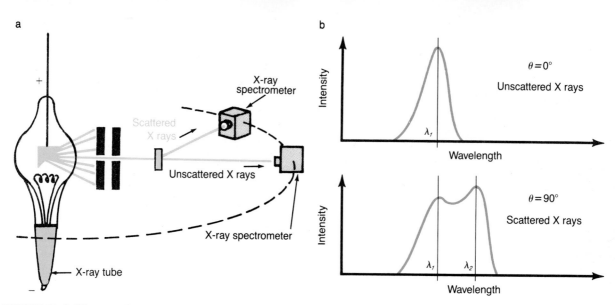

b

X-ray
spectrometer

Scattered
X rays

Unscattered X rays

X-ray spectrometer

X-ray tube

Intensity

Wavelength

$\theta = 0°$

Unscattered X rays

λ_1

Intensity

Wavelength

$\theta = 90°$

Scattered X rays

λ_1 λ_2

FIGURE 28–6. Diagram of apparatus used by Compton to study the nature of photons (a). An increased wavelength denotes that the X-ray photons have lost energy (b).

Einstein predicted that a photon has momentum.

SUGGESTION: Compton was one of the top scientists on the Manhattan Project, which developed the atomic bomb. He directed the research on the methods of producing plutonium.

The Compton effect shows that photons have the particlelike properties of energy and momentum.

28:3 The Compton Effect

The photoelectric effect demonstrates that although a photon has no mass, it has kinetic energy just as a particle does. In 1916, Einstein predicted that the photon should have another property of a particle, momentum. He showed that the momentum of a photon should be hf/c. Since $f/c = 1/\lambda$, the photon's momentum is

$$p = \frac{hf}{c} = \frac{h}{\lambda}$$

The American Arthur Holly Compton tested Einstein's theory in 1922.

Compton directed X rays of known wavelength at a graphite target and measured the wavelengths of the X rays scattered by the target. He found that some of the X rays were scattered without change in wavelength. Other scattered X rays, however, had a longer wavelength, as shown in Figure 28–6b. The energy of a photon is hf, given by

$$E = \frac{hc}{\lambda}$$

Thus, an increased wavelength meant that the X-ray photons had lost energy. In later experiments Compton observed that electrons were ejected from the graphite block during the experiment. He concluded that the X-ray photons collided with electrons in the graphite target and transferred energy and momentum. These collisions were similar to the elastic collisions experienced by two billiard balls. Compton also measured the energy of the ejected electrons and found that the energy and momentum gained by the electrons just equaled the energy and momentum lost by the photons. Photons obeyed the laws of conservation of momentum and energy.

Compton's experiments further verified Einstein's theory. A photon is a particle that has energy and momentum. Unlike matter, however, a photon has no mass and travels at the speed of light.

Before

After

FIGURE 28-7. The energy and momentum gained by electrons equals the energy and momentum lost by photons.

Photon

Energy = hf

Electron

Momentum = $\frac{hf}{c}$

Photon

Energy = hf'

Momentum = $\frac{hf'}{c}$

ϕ

Energy = $E_{electron}$

Electron

Momentum = mv

28:4 Matter Waves

The photoelectric effect and Compton scattering showed that electromagnetic waves had particle properties. The French physicist Louis-Victor de Broglie (di-BROY-lee) (1892–1987) suggested in 1923 that material particles have wave properties. By analogy with the momentum of the photon, h/λ, the momentum of a particle is given by the equation

$$mv = \frac{h}{\lambda}$$

Thus, the wavelength of the particle is given by

$$\lambda = \frac{h}{mv}$$

According to de Broglie, particles such as electrons or protons should show wavelike properties. Effects like diffraction and interference had never been observed, so de Broglie's work was greeted with considerable doubt. Einstein read de Broglie's papers, however, and supported his ideas. In 1927, the results of two different experiments showed the diffraction of electrons. One experiment was conducted by the Englishman G. P. Thomson, the son of J. J. Thomson, and the other by two Americans, C. J. Davisson and L. H. Germer. The experiments used a beam of electrons with a small crystal as a target. The atoms in the crystal formed a meshlike pattern that acted as a diffraction grating. Electrons diffracted from the crystal formed the same patterns that X rays of a similar wavelength formed (Figure 28–8). The two experiments proved that material particles have wave properties.

The wave nature of ordinary matter is not obvious because the wavelengths are so extremely short that wavelike behaviors such as diffraction and interference are not observed. Consider the de Broglie wavelength of a 0.25-kg baseball when it leaves a bat with a speed of 20 m/s.

De Broglie proposed that particles have wave properties.

The wavelength of a particle is inversely proportional to its momentum.

SUGGESTION: This particle-wave duality is similar to the wave-particle duality for the photon proposed by Compton.

The wavelength of microscopic bodies is too small to be detected.

FIGURE 28-8. In the apparatus of Davisson and Germer, a beam of electrons from a hot cathode is directed at a crystal, and the angles of the scattered electrons are detected (a). Electron diffraction patterns of aluminum demonstrate the wave characteristic of particles (b).

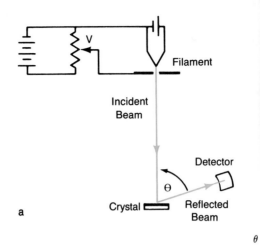

Filament

Incident
Beam

Detector

Crystal

Reflected
Beam

a

θ

b

θ

$$\lambda = \frac{h}{mv} = \frac{6.6 \times 10^{-34} \text{ J} \cdot \text{s}}{(0.25 \text{ kg})(20 \text{ m/s})} = 1.3 \times 10^{-34} \text{ m}$$

The wavelength is far too small to have effects that can be observed. On the other hand, consider an electron moving with a velocity of 7.3×10^6 m/s, which it would obtain from an acceleration through a potential difference of 150 V. The de Broglie wavelength of the electron is

$$\lambda = \frac{h}{mv} = \frac{6.6 \times 10^{-34} \text{ J} \cdot \text{s}}{(9.11 \times 10^{-31} \text{ kg})(7.3 \times 10^6 \text{ m/s})} = 9.9 \times 10^{-11} \text{ m}$$

This wavelength is approximately the distance between the atoms in a crystal. For this reason, a crystal used as a grating produces diffraction and interference effects, making the wave properties of very small particles of matter observable.

Practice Exercises

6. **a.** Find the speed of an electron accelerated by a potential difference of 250 V.
   b. What is the de Broglie wavelength of this electron?
7. A 7.0-kg bowling ball rolls down the alley with a velocity of 8.5 m/s.
   a. What is the de Broglie wavelength of the bowling ball?
   b. Why does the bowling ball show little wave behavior?
8. An X ray of wavelength 5.0×10^{-12} m is traveling in a vacuum.
   a. Calculate the momentum associated with this X ray.
   b. Why does the X ray show little particle behavior?
9. **a.** In what ways are electrons and photons the same?
   b. In what ways are they different?

28:5 Particles and Waves

When you think of a particle, you think of properties like mass, size, kinetic energy, and momentum. You can locate a particle at one point in space. You do not think of particles showing diffraction and interference effects.

The properties of a wave, on the other hand, are frequency, wavelength, and amplitude. A wave travels with a given velocity. A wave cannot be located at one point in space because it must be at least one wavelength long. Thus a wave must be spread out in space. It produces effects like diffraction and interference.

In this chapter, however, we have shown, as another example of the symmetry of the natural world, that light and other electromagnetic waves also have particlelike properties. We have also shown that matter, which is normally considered to be made of particles, can behave like a wave.

Is light a particle or a wave? In the years since the work of Einstein, de Broglie, and others, many physicists and philosophers have tried to work out a satisfactory answer to this question. Some have suggested that the nature of light depends on the experiment. In the Compton effect, for example, the X ray acts like a particle when it is scattered from the graphite target. It is considered a wave when its wavelength is measured by diffraction from a crystal. Most physicists share a belief that the particle and wave aspects of light show complementary views of the true nature of light. They must be taken together. Either picture alone, particle or wave, is incomplete.

The German physicist Werner Heisenberg suggested that the properties of an object can only be defined by thinking of an experiment that can measure them. One cannot simply say that a particle is at a certain location moving with a specific speed. Rather, an experiment must be described that will locate the particle and measure its speed.

How can you find the location of a particle? You must touch it or reflect light from it. The reflected light then must be collected by an instrument or the human eye. Because of diffraction effects, light spreads out, making it impossible to locate the particle exactly. You can reduce the spreading by decreasing the wavelength of the light. Thus the shorter the wavelength, the more precisely you can measure the location.

The Compton effect, however, proves that when light of short wavelengths strikes a particle, the velocity, and hence the momentum, of the particle is changed. Therefore, the act of making a measurement of the location of an object disturbs its momentum.

In the same way, if the momentum of the particle is measured, the position of the particle will be changed. *The position and momentum of a particle cannot both be precisely known at the same time.* This fact is called the **Heisenberg uncertainty principle.** It is the result of the dual wave and particle description of light and matter.

SUGGESTION: The uncertainty principle applies to photons as well. The narrower the slit used to determine the location of a photon, the wider the diffraction pattern becomes. This is due to a spread in photon momenta.

Particles have wavelike properties and waves have particlelike properties.

The Heisenberg uncertainty principle describes the inability to measure precisely both the position and momentum of a particle at the same time.

FIGURE 28–9. If an electron were in a fixed position and a photon collided with it, the velocity of the electron would change. Thus, there is always some uncertainty as to the position and momentum of the electron.

CHAPTER 28 REVIEW

SUMMARY

1. Hot, or incandescent, bodies emit light because of the vibrations of the charged particles inside their atoms. **28:1**

2. The spectrum of incandescent bodies covers a wide range of wavelengths. The spectrum depends on their temperature. **28:1**

3. Planck explained the spectrum by supposing that a particle can have only certain energies that are multiples of a small constant called Planck's constant. **28:1**

4. Certain metals emit electrons when exposed to light, the photoelectric effect. **28:2**

5. Einstein explained the photoelectric effect by postulating that light came in bundles of energy, called photons. **28:2**

6. The photoelectric effect allows the measurement of Planck's constant, h. **28:2**

7. The work function of metals, the energy with which electrons are held inside metals, is measured by the threshold frequency in the photoelectric effect. **28:2**

8. The Compton effect demonstrates the momentum of photons, first predicted by Einstein. **28:3**

9. Photons, or light quanta, are massless and always travel at the speed of light. Yet they have energy, hf, and momentum, h/λ. **28:3**

10. The wave nature of material particles was suggested by de Broglie and verified experimentally by diffracting electrons off crystals. **28:4**

11. The particle and wave aspects of matter and light show complementary parts of the complete nature of matter and light. **28:5**

12. The Heisenberg uncertainty principle states that the position and momentum of a particle (light or matter) cannot both be known precisely at the same time. **28:5**

QUESTIONS

1. Two iron rods are held in a fire. One glows dark red while the other is glowing bright orange.
   a. Which rod is hotter?
   b. Which rod is radiating more energy?

2. Define the word "quantized."

3. What is quantized in Planck's blackbody radiation theory?

4. Potassium in a photocell emits photoelectrons when struck by blue light. Tungsten emits them only when ultraviolet light is used.
   a. Which has a higher threshold frequency?
   b. Which metal has a larger work function?

5. Light above the threshold frequency shines on a metal in a photocell. How does Einstein's theory explain that as the light intensity is increased the current of photoelectrons increases?

6. Explain how Einstein's theory accounts for the fact that light below the threshold frequency produces no photoelectrons, no matter how intense it is.

7. How does the Compton effect demonstrate that photons have momentum as well as energy?

APPLYING CONCEPTS

1. Certain types of black-and-white film are not sensitive to red light. They can be developed with a red "safelight" on. Explain this on the basis of the photon theory of light.

2. The momentum of a material particle is mv. Can ycu calculate the momentum of a photon using mv? Explain.

3. Compare the de Broglie wavelength of a baseball moving 20 m/s with the size of the baseball.

4. What types of experiments could be done to demonstrate the wave nature of particles?

5. Explain how the following properties of the electron could be measured. Explain in each case what is to be done.
   a. charge   b. mass   c. wavelength

6. Explain how the following properties of a photon

could be measured. Explain in each case what is to be done.

a. energy **b.** momentum **c.** wavelength

EXERCISES

1. To block the current in a photocell, a stopping potential of 3.8 V is used. Find the maximum *KE* of the photoelectrons in the cell in J.
2. The threshold frequency of tin is 1.2×10^{15} Hz.
   a. What is the threshold wavelength?
   b. What is the work function of tin in eV?
   c. Light of 167-nm wavelength falls on tin. What is the maximum kinetic energy of the ejected electrons in eV?
3. The work function of iron is 4.7 eV.
   a. What is the threshold wavelength of iron?
   b. Iron is exposed to radiation of wavelength 150 nm. What is the kinetic energy of the ejected electrons in eV?
4. Find the de Broglie wavelength of a deuteron of mass 3.3×10^{-27} kg that moves with a speed of 2.5×10^4 m/s.
5. An electron is accelerated across a potential difference of 54 V.
   a. Find the velocity of the electron.
   b. Calculate the de Broglie wavelength of the electron.
6. A neutron is held in a trap with a kinetic energy of only 0.025 eV.
   a. What is the velocity of the neutron?
   b. Find the de Broglie wavelength of the neutron.
7. What is the de Broglie wavelength of a proton moving with a speed of 1.00×10^6 m/s? The mass of a proton is 1.67×10^{-27} kg.
8. A photocell is used by a photographer to measure the light falling on the subject to be photographed. What should be the work function of the cathode if the photocell is to be sensitive to red light ($\lambda = 680$ nm) as well as the other colors?

PROBLEMS

1. A home uses about 4×10^{11} J of energy each year. In many parts of the United States, there are about 3000 h of sunlight each year.

   a. How much energy from the sun falls on one square meter each year?
   b. If the solar energy can be converted to useful energy with an efficiency of 20%, how large an area of converters would produce the energy needed by the house?
2. The energy of the hydrogen atom electron is 13.65 eV.
   a. Find the velocity of the electron.
   b. Calculate the de Broglie wavelength of this electron.
   c. Compare your answer with the radius of the hydrogen atom, 5.19 nm.
3. **a.** Find the velocity of an electron with a de Broglie wavelength of 400 nm, the shortest wavelength of visible light.
   b. Calculate the energy of this electron in eV.
   c. An electron microscope is useful because the de Broglie wavelength of electrons can be made smaller than the wavelength of visible light. What energy (in eV) has to be given to an electron for it to have a de Broglie wavelength of 20 nm?
4. Barium has a work function of 2.48 eV. What is the longest wavelength of light that will emit electrons from barium?
5. The threshold frequency of a given metal is 6.7×10^{14} Hz. Calculate the maximum kinetic energy (in eV) of the electrons ejected when the surface is illuminated with light of wavelength
   a. 3.5×10^{-7} m. **b.** 5.5×10^{-7} m.
6. **a.** How large of a potential difference did an electron experience if it has a de Broglie wavelength of 0.18 nm?
   b. If a proton has a de Broglie wavelength of 0.18 nm, how large of a potential difference did it experience?

READINGS

"Interviews [John Bell]." *Omni*, May, 1988.

Rohrlich, F., "Facing Quantum Mechanical Reality." *Science*, September 23, 1983.

Wheaton, Bruce, "Louis de Broglie and the Origins of Wave Mechanics." *The Physics Teacher*, May, 1984.

CHAPTER 29

The Atom

GOALS

1. You will learn how the structure of the atom was discovered.
2. You will gain an understanding of how the quantum theory explains the structure.
3. You will learn how light interacts with atoms in lasers.

As you have learned, a diffraction grating separates white light into its component colors. Different sources of light look very different through diffraction gratings. While some sources emit continuous spectra, others give off only certain colors. Why is this so? How can the light emitted by atoms be used to help unravel their structure? Today the answers are known, but at the end of the last century these important questions were unsolved.

29:1 The Nuclear Model

By the end of the nineteenth century most scientists agreed that atoms exist. The successful kinetic theory of gases required the existence of atoms. Chemical reactions could be understood only if atoms existed. The discovery of the electron by J. J. Thomson (1856–1940), however, showed that an atom is not a single, indivisible particle. All the atoms Thomson tested contained electrons. Yet atoms were known to be electrically neutral and much more massive than electrons. Therefore, atoms must contain not only electrons, but a massive, positively-charged part as well.

Discovering the nature of the massive part of the atom and the arrangement of the electrons was a major challenge to scientists. Physicists and chemists from many countries cooperated and competed in searching for the solution to this puzzle. The result provided not only knowledge of the structure of the atom, but a totally new approach to both physics and chemistry. The story of this work is one of the most exciting stories of the twentieth century.

Mineral Magic

A variety of mineral specimens, which are shades of grays, whites, and browns in daylight, appear as in this photograph when illuminated by ultraviolet light. Why would ultraviolet light cause brilliant colors in these minerals when daylight or infrared light does not?

J. J. Thomson believed that a massive, positively-charged substance filled the atom. The electrons were arranged within this substance like raisins in a muffin. Ernest Rutherford, then working in England, performed a series of brilliant experiments that showed that the atom was very different.

Rutherford's experiments used the findings of French physicist Henri Becquerel (1852–1908) as a tool. In 1896 Becquerel was studying compounds containing the element uranium. To his surprise, he found that covered photographic plates became fogged, or partially exposed, when uranium compounds were anywhere near the plates. This fogging suggested that some kind of ray from the uranium had passed through the plate coverings. Several materials other than uranium and its compounds were also found to emit penetrating rays. Materials that emit this type of radiation are called **radioactive materials.**

Further studies of radioactive materials showed that some of the radiation was composed of massive, positively-charged particles moving at high speed. These were called alpha (α) particles. The α particles could be detected by a small fluorescent screen that emitted a small flash of light, or **scintillation** (sint uhl AY shuhn), each time an α particle hit it.

Rutherford directed a beam of α particles at a thin sheet of metal only a few atoms thick. He noticed that while most of the α particles passed through the sheet, the beam was spread slightly by the metal. In 1910 two members of Rutherford's team, Hans Geiger and Ernest Marsden, further studied the deflection of α particles by metal sheets. They found that while most of the particles passed through the sheet without deflection, some were deflected at large angles, even larger than 90° (Figure 29–2). Rutherford was amazed. He had assumed that the mass was spread throughout the atom. He commented that it was as surprising as if you had fired a 15-inch cannon shell at tissue paper and the shell had come back and hit you.

Becquerel discovered that radiation was being emitted from uranium compounds.

Radiation causes some materials to scintillate, or emit brief flashes of light.

Rutherford's group studied atomic structure by bombarding metal foils with alpha particles.

FIGURE 29–1. After bombarding metal foil with alpha particles, Rutherford's team concluded that most of the mass of the atom was concentrated in the nucleus.

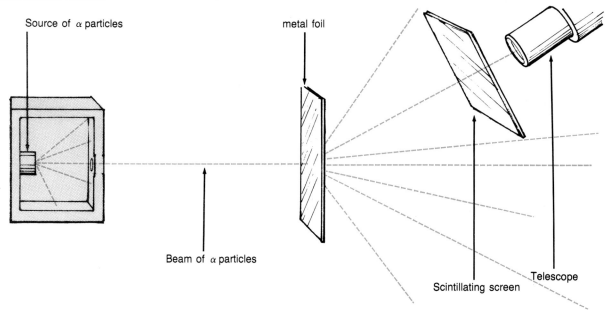

Source of α particles

metal foil

Beam of α particles

Scintillating screen

Telescope

Rutherford analyzed the experimental results using Coulomb's force law and Newton's laws of motion. He found that the large angle deflections could be explained only if all the positive charge of the atom were concentrated in a tiny, massive central core, now called the nucleus. Rutherford's model is, therefore, called a nuclear model of the atom. All the positive charge is in the nucleus, which also contains essentially all the mass of the atom. Electrons are outside the nucleus and do not contribute a significant amount of mass. The electrons are far away from the nucleus; the atom is 10 000 times larger than the nucleus. So the atom is mostly empty space. Rutherford, however, assumed incorrectly that the electrons would circle the nucleus like planets circle the sun.

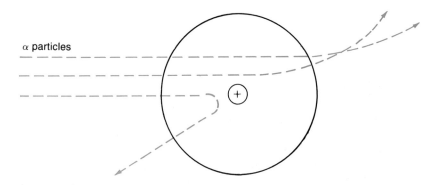

α particles

Rutherford's analysis predicted that, for any atom, the number of α particles deflected through a given angle should be proportional to the square of the charge of the nucleus. At that time only the mass of an atom was known. The number of electrons, and thus the charge of the nucleus, was not known. For many of the lighter elements, the mass of the atom is almost exactly the mass of the hydrogen atom multiplied by some whole number. That whole number is called the atomic mass number.

Rutherford and his co-workers experimented with sheets of carbon, aluminum, and gold. In each case the charge of the nucleus was found to be roughly half the atomic mass number times the elementary unit of charge. Thus the number of electrons in an atom is also roughly half the atomic mass number. The carbon nucleus has a charge of 6, so the carbon atom must contain 6 electrons. Using a similar argument, aluminum contains 13 electrons and gold 79 electrons.

29:2 The Proton and the Neutron

The proton is the name given to the nucleus of the hydrogen atom. The proton is positively charged with one unit of elementary charge. Its mass is one **atomic mass unit.** Assuming that protons are the charged particles that make up all nuclei, carbon must have 6 protons and aluminum 13. The mass of the carbon atom is that of 12 protons, however, not 6. To account for the excess mass in the nucleus, Rutherford postulated the existence of a neutral particle with a mass of a proton. In 1932 James Chadwick, a student of Rutherford's, demonstrated the existence of this particle, called the neutron. A neutron is a particle with no charge and with a mass almost equal to that of the proton.

For Your Information

The mass of the nucleus is actually slightly less than the sum of the masses of the particles that make it up. As is described in Einstein's famous formula, $E = mc^2$, the smaller mass means that the nucleus has less energy than the sum of its parts. That is, it takes energy to pull the nucleus apart.

The nucleus of every atom except hydrogen contains both neutrons and
protons. The mass of the nucleus is the sum of the masses of the protons
and neutrons. The total number of neutrons and protons is the atomic
mass number. The mass of the nucleus in atomic mass units is approximately equal to the atomic mass number. The mass number of carbon is
12, while that of aluminum is 27.

The charge of the nucleus is equal to the sum of the charges of the
protons. The number of protons in the nucleus is called the atomic number (Z). The atomic number of carbon is 6 and that of aluminum is 13.

29:3 Atomic Spectra

How are the electrons arranged around the nucleus of the atom? Are
they really like planets circling a star? One of the clues to the answer to
this question came from studying the light emitted by atoms. The set of
wavelengths of light emitted by an atom is called the **emission spectrum**
of that atom.

When a solid is heated, it becomes incandescent. The light given off
comes from the atoms. All incandescent solids, however, emit the same
spectrum. The properties of individual atoms become apparent only
when they are not tightly packed together into a solid. Many substances
can be vaporized by heating them in a flame. Then they can emit light that
is characteristic of the elements making up the substance. For example, if
sodium chloride is put on a wire and held in a flame, the sodium atoms
will emit a bright yellow light. Similarly, lithium salts emit red light, and
barium salts, green light.

Gas atoms can be made to emit their characteristic colors by a method
shown in Figure 29–3. A glass tube containing neon gas at low pressure
has metal electrodes at each end. When a high voltage is applied across

**FIGURE 29–3. A gas discharge tube
apparatus (a). Neon (b), helium (c),
molecular hydrogen (d) gases glow
when high voltage is applied.**

a

b   c   d

a

b

c

d

FIGURE 29–4. A prism spectroscope (a) can be used to observe emission spectra (b). The emission spectra of neon (c) and molecular hydrogen (d) show characteristic lines.

Prism

Slit

Gas discharge tube

the tube, electrons pass through the gas. The electrons collide with the neon atoms, transferring energy to them. The atoms then give up this extra energy, emitting it in the form of light. The light emitted by neon is red. Nitrogen and argon emit a bluish color, and mercury, a greenish blue.

The emission spectrum of an atom can be studied in greater detail using the instrument shown in Figure 29–4b. In this **spectroscope** the light passes through a slit and is then dispersed passing through a prism. A lens system focuses the dispersed light for viewing through a telescope or onto a photographic plate. Each wavelength of light forms an image of the slit. The spectrum of an incandescent solid is a continuous band of colors from red through violet. The spectrum of a gas, however, is a series of lines of different colors. Each line corresponds to a particular wavelength of light emitted by the atoms. Suppose an unidentified gas such as mercury, argon, or nitrogen is contained in a tube. The gas will emit light at wavelengths characteristic of the atoms of that gas. Thus, the gas can be identified by comparing its wavelengths with the lines present in the spectrum of a known sample. Some emission spectra are shown in Figure 29–4c, d.

When the emission spectrum of a combination of elements is photographed, analysis of the lines on the photograph can indicate both the elements present and their relative amounts. If the substance being examined contains a large amount of any particular element, the lines for that element are more intense on the photograph. By comparing the intensities of the lines, the percentage composition of the substance can be determined. An emission spectrum is a useful analytic tool.

A gas that is cool and does not emit light will absorb light at characteristic wavelengths. This set of wavelengths is called an **absorption spectrum.** To obtain an absorption spectrum, white light is sent through a

SUGGESTION: Have the students look through a diffraction grating at the spectra of several different gas discharge tubes.

Gaseous atoms can also absorb light. The wavelength absorbed is the same as that emitted by excited, hot atoms.

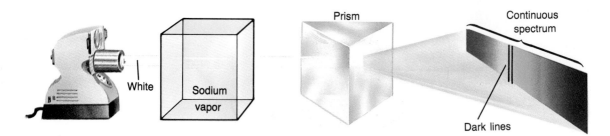

White Sodium vapor Prism Continuous spectrum Dark lines

FIGURE 29–5. This apparatus is used to produce the absorption spectrum of sodium.

SUGGESTION: Do the lab to find the wavelength of light using a diffraction grating if it has not been done.

sample of gas and into a prism. The normally continuous spectrum of the white light now has dark lines in it. These lines show that light of some wavelengths has been absorbed. It has been found that the bright lines of the emission spectrum of a gas and the dark lines of the absorption spectrum occur at the same wavelengths. Thus, cool gaseous elements absorb the same wavelengths that they emit when excited. Suppose white light shines through a cool gas. The spectrum will be continuous, but there will be a few dark lines in it. Analysis of the wavelengths of the missing lines can indicate the composition of the gas.

FIGURE 29–6. The emission spectrum (a) and the absorption spectrum (b) of sodium.

Helium was found on the sun, by means of spectroscopy, before it was found on Earth.

While examining the spectrum of sunlight in 1814, Josef von Fraunhofer (1787–1826) noticed some dark lines. The dark lines he found in the sun's spectrum are now called Fraunhofer lines. To account for these lines, he assumed that the sun has a relatively cool atmosphere of gaseous elements. As light leaves the sun, it passes through these gases. The gases absorb light at their characteristic wavelengths. As a result, these wavelengths are missing from the sun's absorption spectrum. By comparing the missing lines with the known lines of the various elements, the composition of the atmosphere of the sun was determined. In this manner the element helium was discovered in the sun before it was found on Earth. Spectrographic analysis has made it possible to determine the composition of stars.

FIGURE 29–7. Fraunhofer lines appear in the absorption spectrum of the sun.

Both emission and absorption spectra are valuable scientific tools. As a result of the characteristic spectrum emitted by each element, chemists are able to analyze unknown materials by observing the spectra they emit. Not only is this an important research tool, it is important in industry as well. For example, steel mills reprocess large quantities of scrap iron of varying compositions. The exact composition of a sample of scrap can be determined in minutes by spectrographic analysis. The composition of the

Analysis of spectra allows the identification of the elements that make up a compound or mixture.

steel can then be adjusted to suit commercial specifications. Aluminum, zinc, and other metal processing plants employ the same method.

The study of spectra is a branch of science known as spectroscopy. Spectroscopists are employed throughout the research and industrial communities.

29:4 The Bohr Model of the Atom

In the nineteenth century many physicists tried to use the spectra of atoms to determine the structure of the atom. Hydrogen was studied extensively because it is the lightest element and has the simplest structure. The visible spectrum of hydrogen consists of four lines: red, green, blue, and violet. The Swedish scientist A. J. Ångstrom (1814–1874) made very careful measurements of the wavelengths of these lines. Any theory that explained the structure of the atom would have to account for those wavelengths.

Any valid theory of the structure of the atom would also have to fit Rutherford's results. Rutherford's nuclear model of the atom proposed a tiny, massive nucleus at the center of the atom, surrounded by negatively-charged electrons. By analogy with the solar system, the electrons orbited the nucleus much as the planets orbit the sun. There was, however, a problem with this planetary model. An electron in an orbit undergoes centripetal acceleration. As discussed in Chapter 27, accelerated electrons radiate energy by emitting electromagnetic waves. As the electron lost energy, it would spiral into the nucleus in only 10^{-9} second. The universe would have self-destructed billions of years ago. Atoms are known to be stable, however, and to last for long times. Thus, the planetary model was not consistent with the laws of electromagnetism. In addition, if the planetary theory were true, the accelerated electron should radiate energy at all wavelengths. But, as we have seen, the light emitted by different atoms is radiated only at specific wavelengths.

Rutherford's model did not account for (1) the lack of emission of radiation as electrons move about the nucleus and (2) the unique spectrum of each element.

FIGURE 29–8. A spectrograph is used in research to measure particle momenta in a subatomic reaction (a) as well as in industry in laser absorption in gas (b).

a

b

The Danish physicist Niels Bohr (1885–1962) went to England in 1911 and soon joined Rutherford's group. Bohr worked on the problem of the atom. He tried to unite the nuclear model with Einstein's quantum theory of light. Remember that in 1911 Einstein's revolutionary theory of the photoelectric effect had not yet been confirmed by experiment and was not widely believed.

Bohr accepted the planetary arrangement of electrons, but made the bold hypothesis that the laws of electromagnetism do not operate inside atoms. He postulated that an electron in a stable orbit does not radiate energy, even though it is accelerating. Therefore, the electron does not spiral into the nucleus, destroying the atom.

Bohr assumed that a hydrogen atom emits light only when the energy of the electrons changes. He believed that the specific wavelengths in an atomic spectrum meant an atomic electron cannot absorb or emit just any wavelength of light. According to Einstein, the energy of a photon of light is given by the equation $E = hf$. Thus, an electron can emit or absorb only specific amounts of energy. Bohr theorized that this means that the atomic electrons can have only certain amounts of energy. That is, the energy of an electron in an atom is **quantized.**

The quantization of energy in atoms is unlike everyday experience. For example, if the energy of a pendulum were quantized, if could oscillate only with certain amplitudes, such as 10 cm or 20 cm, but not, for example, 11.3 cm.

The different amounts of energy that an atomic electron is allowed are called **energy levels.** When an electron has the smallest allowable amount of energy, it is in the lowest energy level. This level is also called the **ground state.** If an electron absorbs energy, it can make a transition to a higher energy level, called an **excited state.** Atomic electrons usually remain in excited states only a very small fraction of a second before returning to the ground state and emitting light.

According to Bohr, the energy of an orbiting electron in an atom is the sum of the kinetic energy of the electron and the potential energy resulting from the attractive force between the electron and the nucleus. Work must be done to move an electron from an orbit near the nucleus to one farther away. Therefore, the energy of an electron in an orbit near the nucleus is less than that of an electron in an orbit farther away. The electrons in excited states have larger orbits and correspondingly higher energies.

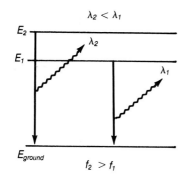

$\lambda_2 < \lambda_1$

E_2

λ_2

E_1

λ_1

E_{ground}

$f_2 > f_1$

FIGURE 29–10. The energy of the emitted photon is equal to the difference between the excited and the ground state energies.

Einstein's theory says the light photon has an energy hf. Bohr postulated that the change in the energy of an atomic electron when a photon is absorbed is equal to the energy of the photon. That is,

$$hf = E_{excited} - E_{ground}$$

When the electron makes the return transition to the ground state, a photon is emitted. The energy of the photon is equal to the energy difference between the excited and ground states. Molecules have additional discrete energy levels. For example, they can rotate and vibrate, which individual atoms cannot do. As a result, molecules can emit a much wider variety of light frequencies than can atoms (Figure 29–4d).

According to Bohr, the energy of the photon emitted or absorbed by an atom is equal to the change in energy of the atom.

Practice Exercises

1. Which of these quantities are quantized: your height, number of siblings, mass of a sample of gas?
2. What does it mean to say that the energy levels of an atom are quantized?
3. The difference between two energy levels in an atom is 3.4 eV.
   a. Find the frequency of the light emitted by this atom.
   b. Find its wavelength.
   c. In what part of the electromagnetic spectrum is this radiation?

29:5 Fluorescence and Phosphorescence

So far we have discussed two ways in which atoms can be excited, thermal excitation and electron collision.

Consider a fluorescent lamp that contains mercury vapor. When a high voltage is applied across the tube, electrons collide with the Hg atoms, causing them to emit invisible ultraviolet photons. These photons strike a material called a phosphor that coats the inner surface of the glass tube. The ultraviolet photons are absorbed by the atoms in the phosphor, exciting them to higher energy levels. The phosphor atoms then lose this energy by emitting several photons of visible rather than ultraviolet light. Collision with photons, then, is another method of exciting atoms.

Both fluorescent and phosphorescent materials contain atoms that are easily excited. The two types of substances differ in the time it takes

SUGGESTION: Bring in samples of fluorescent and phosphorescent materials to demonstrate.

a

b

High-speed
electrons

Gas

High voltage

Photons

c

Photons

Photons   Atom

Molecules

Photon

FIGURE 29–11. Photons can be emitted by excited atoms in three ways: thermal excitation (a), electron excitation (b), and photon excitation (c).

For Your Information

their excited atoms to return to their ground states. When an atom of a **fluorescent** material is in the excited state the atoms return to their normal energy levels at once. The atoms have no stability in the higher energy levels. A **phosphorescent** material contains atoms that, once excited, can remain in higher than normal energy levels for some time. Thus, a fluorescent bumper sticker on a car will glow only while it is being irradiated by the photons from the headlights of another car. The coating on a fluorescent lamp emits light only when current flows through the tube. "Glow-in-the-dark" toys, on the other hand, emit energy for some time after the light source has been removed.

The screen of a television picture tube is coated with a phosphor that emits light when electrons strike it. In a color television the screen is coated with dots of phosphors that glow red, blue, or green. The correct colors are produced by aiming electrons at the correct dot (or dots).

A doctor's fluoroscope works in the same way as a television picture tube, with one exception. In the fluoroscope, X rays are used instead of electrons to bombard the screen and excite atoms. If a picture of an organ is required, a heavy atom is introduced into the body to block the X rays. For example, if a patient swallows a barium solution, the stomach and

FIGURE 29–12. In a luminescent organism, enzymatic chemical reactions cause the excitation of molecules to a high energy state. The return to the ground state results in the emission of visible light. The color of light produced is determined by the enzyme protein.

504   The Atom

intestines then block the X rays and thus produce a shadow on the screen of the fluoroscope.

Phosphorescence is a matter of degree. Some phosphors are nearly fluorescent. Their atoms remain in higher energy levels only a bit longer than those in fluorescent substances. There is no sharp dividing line between fluorescence and phosphorescence. Generally, if the atom of a substance remains in a higher energy level for 10^{-3} second or longer, the substance is a phosphor.

Different substances produce different colors of light as they fluoresce. These colors are due to the different allowable transitions as atoms move from higher to lower energy levels, as will be explained in the next section. Many posters appear drab in white light but become very colorful when exposed to violet light. This is because the violet light is more energetic and produces many more excited atoms in the poster inks than do the lower energy red and green wavelengths.

29:6 Predictions of the Bohr Model

A scientific theory must do more than present postulates; it must allow predictions to be made that can be checked against experimental data. A good theory can also be applied to many different problems and ultimately provides a simple, unified explanation of some part of the physical world.

DEMONSTRATION: See the Teacher Guide.

Bohr was able to show that his two postulates could be used with the known laws of physics to calculate the wavelengths of light emitted by hydrogen. The calculations were in excellent agreement with the values measured by Ångstrom. As a result, Bohr's model was widely accepted. Unfortunately, the model could not predict the spectrum of the next simplest element, helium. In addition, the postulates could not be explained, and not even Bohr believed that his model was a complete theory of the structure of the atom.

Despite its shortcomings, the Bohr model describes hydrogen and hydrogenlike atoms remarkably well. We will outline the method used by Bohr to calculate the wavelengths of light emitted by an atom. Bohr's calculations start with Newton's law, $F = ma$, applied to an electron of

Frequency and wavelength of emitted photons can be calculated with the Bohr theory.

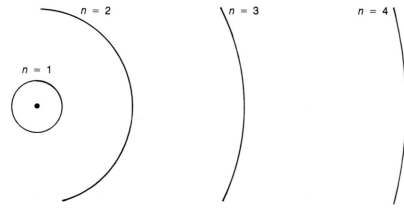

$n = 2$ $n = 3$ $n = 4$

$n = 1$

FIGURE 29–13. Radii of electron orbits for the first four energy levels of hydrogen according to the Bohr model.

mass m and charge $-q$, in circular orbit of radius r about a massive proton of charge q.

$$\frac{Kq^2}{r^2} = \frac{mv^2}{r}$$

K is the constant 9.0×10^9 N $\cdot$ m²/C² from Coulomb's law.

Bohr proposed a third postulate. The product of the momentum of the electron and the radius of its orbit, mvr, can have only certain values. These values are given by the equation $mvr = nh/2\pi$, where h is Planck's constant and n is an integer. Because the quantity mvr can have only certain values, it is said to be quantized.

The result of combining Newton's law with the quantization of mvr together with simple algebra gives the radius of the orbit.

$$r = \frac{h^2}{4\pi^2 Kmq^2} n^2$$

If we substitute SI values for the quantities into the equation, we can calculate the radius of the innermost orbit of the hydrogen atom.

$$r = \frac{(6.626 \times 10^{-34} \text{ J·s})^2(1)^2}{(4)(3.14)^2(9.00 \times 10^9 \text{ N·m}^2/\text{C}^2)(9.11 \times 10^{-31} \text{ kg})(1.60 \times 10^{-19} \text{ C})^2}$$

$$r = 5.3 \times 10^{-11} \frac{\text{J}^2 \cdot \text{s}^2}{\text{N} \cdot \text{m}^2 \cdot \text{kg}}$$

$$r = 5.3 \times 10^{-11} \text{ m, or } 0.053 \text{ nm}$$

A little more algebra shows that the total energy of the electron in its orbit, the sum of the potential and kinetic energy of the electron, is given by

$$E = \frac{-2\pi^2 K^2 mq^4}{h^2} \times \frac{1}{n^2}$$

A numerical value of the energy can be found by using the values of the constants above:

$$E = -2.17 \times 10^{-18} \text{ J}(1/n^2)$$

or, using the electron volt as the unit of energy,

$$E = -13.6 \text{ eV}(1/n^2)$$

Both the radius of an orbit and the energy of the electron can have only certain values. That is, both are quantized. The integer n is called the principal **quantum number**. The number n determines the values of r and E. The radius increases as the square of n, as shown in Figure 29–13. The energy depends on $1/n^2$. The energy is negative because the energy has to be added to the electron to free it from the attractive force of the nucleus. The energy levels of hydrogen are shown in Figure 29–14.

Bohr's theory requires that the quantity mvr is quantized.

The Bohr theory predicts the radius of the electron orbit.

The orbital energy of electrons in the hydrogen atom can be calculated with the Bohr theory.

The quantum number, n, determines the value of the orbital radius and energy level.

506   The Atom

EXAMPLE

Orbital Energy of Electrons in the Hydrogen Atom

For the hydrogen atom, determine **a.** the energy of the innermost energy level ($n = 1$) **b.** the energy of the second energy level **c.** the energy difference between the first and second energy levels.

Given: $n = 1$, $n = 2$ **Unknowns:** E_1, E_2, ΔE

Basic equation: $E = -13.6 \text{ eV}(1/n^2)$

Solution:

a. $E_1 = \dfrac{-13.6 \text{ eV}}{(1)^2} = -13.6 \text{ eV}$

b. $E_2 = \dfrac{-13.6 \text{ eV}}{(2)^2} = -3.4 \text{ eV}$

c. $\Delta E = E_f - E_i = E_2 - E_1$
$= -3.4 \text{ eV} - (-13.6 \text{ eV}) = 10.2 \text{ eV}$

EXAMPLE

Frequency and Wavelength of Emitted Photons

An electron drops from the second energy level to the first energy level within an excited hydrogen atom. **a.** Determine the energy of the photon emitted. **b.** Calculate the frequency of the photon emitted. **c.** Calculate the wavelength of the photon emitted.

Given: $n = 2$, $n = 1$ **Unknowns:** hf, f, λ

Basic equation: $hf = E_i - E_f$

Solution:

a. $hf = E_i - E_f = E_2 - E_1$
$= -3.4 \text{ eV} - (-13.6 \text{ eV})$
$= 10.2 \text{ eV}$

b. $f = \dfrac{(10.2 \text{ eV})(1.60 \times 10^{-19} \text{ J/eV})}{6.64 \times 10^{-34} \text{ J/Hz}} = 2.46 \times 10^{15} \text{ Hz}$

c. $\lambda = \dfrac{c}{f} = \dfrac{3.00 \times 10^8 \text{ m/s}}{2.46 \times 10^{15} \text{ Hz}} = 1.22 \times 10^{-7} \text{ m}$

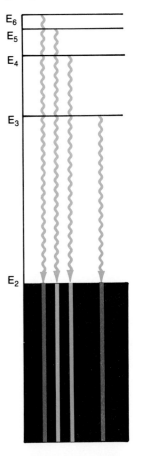

FIGURE 29–14. Bohr's model of the hydrogen atom showed that a definite amount of energy is released when an electron moves from a higher to a lower energy level. The energy released in each transition corresponds to a definite line in the hydrogen spectrum.

Practice Exercises

4. How many times larger is the orbit of hydrogen in the second level than in the first?

5. The discussion on page 506 shows how to calculate the radius of the innermost orbit of the hydrogen atom. Note that all factors in the equation are constants with the exception of n^2. Use the solution to the Example to find the radius of the orbit of the second, third, and fourth allowable energy levels in the hydrogen atom.

6. Calculate the energies of the second, third, and fourth energy levels in the hydrogen atom.
7. Calculate the energy difference between E_3 and E_2 in the hydrogen atom. Do the same for E_4 and E_3.

29:7 Present Theory of the Atom

The Bohr model of the atom was a major contribution to the understanding of the structure of the atom. Using the spectra of the elements, Bohr and his students were able to determine the energy levels of many elements. They were also able to calculate the ionization energy of a hydrogen atom. The ionization energy of an atom is the energy needed to free an electron completely from an atom. The calculated value was in good agreement with experimental data. The Bohr model also provided an explanation of some of the chemical properties of the elements. The idea that atoms have electron arrangements unique to each element is the foundation of much of our knowledge of chemical reactions and bonding.

The postulates Bohr made, however, could not be explained on the basis of known physics. Electromagnetism required that accelerated particles radiate energy. This radiation would cause the rapid collapse of all atoms, and thus the universe. In addition, the reason for the quantized values of the quantity mvr was not known.

The first hint to the solution of these problems was provided by de Broglie. As you recall from Section 28:4, he proposed that particles have wave properties just as light waves have particle properties. The wavelength of a particle with momentum mv is given by $\lambda = h/mv$. Therefore, the quantity $mvr = hr/\lambda$. The Bohr quantization condition, $mvr = nh/2\pi$ can be written as

$$\frac{hr}{\lambda} = mvr = \frac{nh}{2\pi}$$

Thus

$$\frac{hr}{\lambda} = \frac{nh}{2\pi}$$

or

$$n\lambda = 2\pi r$$

Note that the circumference of the Bohr orbit ($2\pi r$) is equal to a whole number multiple (n) of the wavelength of the electron (λ).

In 1926 the German physicist Erwin Schroedinger (1887–1961) used de Broglie's wave model to create a quantum theory of the atom based on waves. Further work by Werner Heisenberg, Wolfgang Pauli, Max Born, and others developed this theory into a complete description of the atom. The theory does not provide a simple planetary picture of an atom as in the Bohr model. In particular, the radius of the electron orbit is not like the radius of the orbit of a planet about the sun. The wave-particle nature of matter means that it is impossible to know both the position and momen-

High probability of finding an electron

$n = 1$

$n = 2$

FIGURE 29–15. The electron cloud model of the atom shows regions of high and low probability.

tum of an electron at the same time. Thus, the modern **quantum model** of the atom predicts only the probability that an electron is at a specific location. The most probable distance of the electron from the nucleus is the same as the radius of the Bohr orbit. The probability that the electron is at any radius can be calculated, and a three-dimensional shape can be constructed that shows regions of equal probability. The region in which there is a high probability of finding the electron is called the **electron cloud** (Figure 29–15).

Even though the quantum model of the atom is difficult to visualize, **quantum mechanics,** which uses this model, has been extremely successful in predicting many details of the structure of the atom. These details are very difficult to calculate exactly for all but the simplest atoms. It takes large computers to make highly accurate approximations for the heavier atoms. Quantum mechanics also allows the structure of many molecules to be calculated, allowing chemists to determine the arrangement of atoms in the molecules. Guided by quantum mechanics, chemists have been able to create new and useful molecules not otherwise available.

Quantum mechanics also allows calculations of the details of the emission and absorption of light by atoms. As a result of this theory, a new source of light has been developed.

The present model of the atom is a mathematical model. It gives the probability of finding an electron at any given location.

29:8 Lasers

Light is emitted by an incandescent source at many wavelengths and in all directions. Light produced by an atomic gas consists of only a few different wavelengths, but is also emitted in all directions. The light waves emitted by atoms at one end of a discharge tube are not necessarily in phase with the waves from the other end. That is, the waves are not necessarily all at the same point in their cycle (Figure 29–16). Such light is called incoherent.

Consider an atom in an excited state. After a very short time, it normally returns to the ground state, giving off a photon of the same energy that it

DEMONSTRATION: See the Teacher Guide.

Photons emitted by ordinary light sources are not in phase. They are incoherent.

29:8 Lasers 509

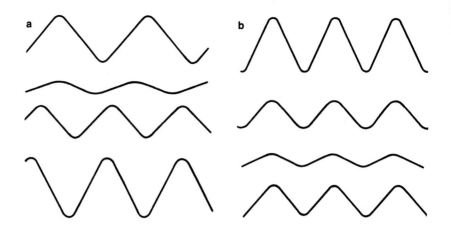

a
b

FIGURE 29–16. Waves of incoherent light (a) and coherent light (b).

Einstein predicted that an atom in an excited state struck by a photon with the correct energy could be stimulated to emit another photon and return to the ground state.

had absorbed. This is called spontaneous emission. In 1917, Einstein considered what would happen to an atom already in an excited state that is struck by another photon of the same energy as the original photon. He showed that the atom will return to the ground state, emitting the striking photon and a second photon. This is called **stimulated emission.** The two photons leaving the atom will not only have the same wavelength, they will also be in phase (Figure 29–17b).

Either of the two photons can now strike other excited atoms, producing additional photons that are in phase with the original photons. This process can continue, producing an avalanche of photons, all in phase. If this is to happen, certain conditions must be met. First, of course, there must be other atoms in the excited state. Second, the photons must be collected so that they strike the excited atoms. A device that can do this was invented in 1959 and is called a **laser.** The word laser is an acronym. It stands for **L**ight **A**mplification by **S**timulated **E**mission of **R**adiation.

FIGURE 29–17. An atom in an excited state is struck by a photon (a) and returns to ground state by emitting a photon in phase with the stimulating photon (b).

The atoms in a laser can be put into the excited state, or pumped, in different ways. An intense flash of light with wavelength shorter (more energetic) than that of the laser can pump the atoms. The more energetic photons produced by the flash collide with and excite the lasing atoms. As a result, a brief flash or pulse of laser light is emitted. Alternatively, an electric discharge can be used to put atoms in the excited state. The resulting laser light is continuous rather than pulsed. The lasers often seen in science classrooms are continuous lasers in which neon gas atoms lase. An electric discharge excites the helium atoms. They collide with the neon atoms, pumping them to an excited state.

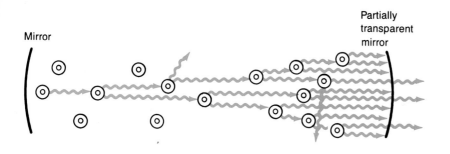

FIGURE 29–18. A photon striking an atom in the excited state stimulates it to make a transition to a lower state and emit a second coherent photon.

The photons emitted by the atoms are collected by placing the glass tube containing the atoms between two parallel mirrors. One mirror reflects all the light hitting it while the other allows about 1% to pass through. When a photon strikes an atom in the excited state it stimulates the atom to make a transition to the lower state. Thus, two photons leave the atom. These photons can strike other atoms and produce more photons. Photons that are directed toward the ends will be reflected back into the gas by the mirrors. Some of the photons pass through the partially reflecting mirror, producing the laser beam.

Laser light is highly directional because of the parallel mirrors. The light beam is very small, about 1/2 mm in diameter, so the light is very intense. The light is all one wavelength, or monochromatic, because only one pair of energy levels in one type of atom is involved. Finally, laser light is coherent because all the stimulated photons are emitted in phase with the photons that struck the atoms.

Many substances, including solids, liquids, and gases, can be made to "lase." Most produce laser light at only one wavelength. For example, red is produced by a neon laser, blue by argon, and green by helium-cadmium. The light from liquid lasers, on the other hand, can be tuned, or adjusted, over a range of wavelengths.

A laser contains atoms in excited states. It has mirrors that confine the emitted photons to the location of the atoms.

Laser light is directional, monochromatic, intense, and coherent.

FIGURE 29–19. A laser produces a beam of coherent light.

TABLE 29-1

Common Lasers		
Medium	**Wavelength (nm)**	**Type**
Nitrogen	337 (uv)	Pulsed
Helium-cadmium	441.6	Continuous
Argon ion	476.5, 488.0, 524.5	Continuous
Krypton ion	476.2, 520.8, 568.2, 647.1	Continuous
Neon	632.8	Continuous
Ruby	694.3	Pulsed
Gallium arsenide*	840–904 (IR)	Continuous
Neodymium	1060 (IR)	Pulsed
Carbon dioxide	10 600 (IR)	Continuous

*The wavelength of gallium arsenide depends on temperature.

SUGGESTION: Collect holograms from magazines or science museum stores to show students and talk about how they are made.

FIGURE 29-20. (a) When a hologram is made on film, a laser beam is split in two parts by a half-silvered mirror. Interference occurs on the film as the direct laser light meets laser light reflected off an object. The interference of both beams of light allows the film to record both intensity and phase of light from the object (b).

All lasers are very inefficient. No more than 1% of the electrical energy delivered to the laser is converted to light energy. Despite this inefficiency, the unique properties of laser light have led to many applications. The laser beam is narrow and highly directional. It does not spread out over long distances. Surveyors use laser beams for this reason. Laser light shows are dramatic examples of this property.

Laser light can be directed into a tiny glass fiber. The fiber is designed to transmit light over many kilometers with little loss. The laser is modulated, or switched on and off, rapidly. By this means, it transmits information over the fiber. In many cities, glass fibers are replacing copper wires for the transmission of telephone calls, computer data, and even television pictures.

The single wavelength of light emitted by lasers makes lasers valuable in spectroscopy. The laser light is used to excite other atoms. The atoms then return to the ground state, emitting characteristic spectra. Samples with extremely small numbers of atoms can be analyzed in this way. In fact, the presence of single atoms has been detected by means of laser excitation!

Holograms are made possible by the coherent nature of laser light. A hologram is a photographic recording of the phase as well as the intensity of the light. Holograms form realistic three-dimensional images and can be used in industry to study the vibration of sensitive parts.

The concentrated power of laser light is used in a variety of ways. In medicine, lasers can be used to repair the retina in an eye. Lasers can also be used in surgery in place of a knife to cut flesh with little loss of blood. In industry, lasers are used to cut steel and to weld materials together. In the future lasers may produce nuclear fusion for an inexhaustible energy source.

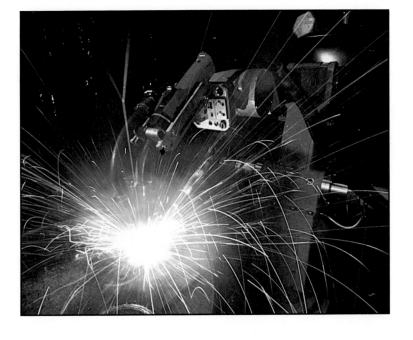

FIGURE 29–21. Laser light is used for precision welding.

PHYSICS FOCUS

Scanning Tunneling Microscope

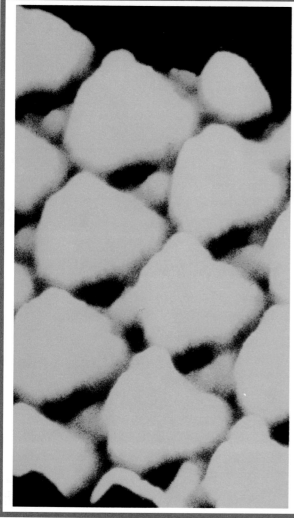

Scientists have powerful new tools that enable them to study materials at molecular and atomic levels. A new instrument, the scanning tunneling microscope (STM), produces pictures of the arrangements of atoms on solid surfaces. With it, scientists can even see bonds between atoms.

The STM views a surface much as a blind person reads braille. A blind person rubs his or her fingers over a page to find patterns in raised dots. An STM uses a very sharp metal "finger" that is brought near, but not touching, the surface to be studied. Because the point of the finger and the surface are not touching, they are insulated from each other. Still, electrons flow across the gap between the surface and the point as a result of the wave nature of electrons. The number of electrons that cross the gap depends on how close the point is to the surface. In this way the STM maps out the "hills and valleys" of a surface. Each hill is a single atom and the valley is the space between neighboring atoms.

The use of the STM has already led to new understanding of chemical reactions such as those that occur in the catalytic converter of a car. An STM has been used to find the shape of a virus and a DNA molecule in water. The STM may be useful in learning more about the roles of viruses and DNA in diseases.

A new variation of the STM is the Atomic Force Microscope, or AFM. The point is mounted on a thin arm that bends when the point is attracted to the surface. A force as small as 10^{-8} N can be measured. The AFM has shown how friction between two metal surfaces comes about. In another application, the magnetic fields of materials used in floppy disks have been explored. An important advantage of the AFM is that it can be used on insulators, unlike the STM, which can be used only on conductors.

CHAPTER 29 REVIEW

SUMMARY

1. In 1896 Becquerel discovered that uranium compounds are radioactive. They emit highly penetrating radiation. **29:1**

2. One kind of radiation is α particles, which are massive, positively-charged, high-speed particles. **29:1**

3. Ernest Rutherford directed alpha particles at thin metal sheets. By studying the paths of the reflected particles, he theorized that atoms are mostly empty space with a tiny, massive, positively-charged nucleus at the center. **29:1**

4. The nucleus contains positively-charged protons and uncharged neutrons. **29:2**

5. The spectra produced by atoms of an element can be used to identify that element. **29:3**

6. If white light passes through a gas, the gas absorbs the same wavelengths it would emit if excited. If light leaving the gas goes through a prism, an absorption spectrum is seen. **29:3**

7. In the model of the atom developed by Niels Bohr, the electrons are allowed to have only certain energy levels. **29:4**

8. In the Bohr model, electrons can make transitions between energy levels. As they do, they emit or absorb electromagnetic radiation. **29:4**

9. The frequency and wavelength of the absorbed and emitted radiation can be calculated using the Bohr model. The calculations agree with experiments. **29:6**

10. The quantum mechanical model of the atom cannot be visualized easily. Only the probability that an electron is at a specific location can be calculated. **29:7**

11. Quantum mechanics is extremely successful in calculating the properties of atoms, molecules, and solids. **29:7**

12. Lasers produce light that is directional, powerful, monochromatic, and coherent. Each property gives the laser useful applications. **29:8**

QUESTIONS

1. How did Rutherford determine that the positive charge in an atom is concentrated in a tiny region rather than spread throughout the atom?

2. Compare and contrast the properties of the neutron and proton.

3. What are the problems with a planetary model of the atom?

4. What three assumptions did Bohr make in developing his model of the atom?

5. How does the Bohr model account for the spectra emitted by atoms?

6. A certain atom has energy levels as shown in Figure 29–22. If an electron can make transitions between any two levels, how many spectral lines can the atom emit? Which transition gives the photon with the highest energy?

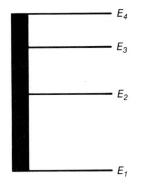

FIGURE 29–22. Use with Question 6.

7. Compare the quantum mechanical theory of the atom with the Bohr model.

8. **a.** What properties of the laser led to its use in laser light shows?

   b. Does a laser that emits red light, green light, or blue light produce photons with the highest energy?

9. How would you distinguish between a fluorescent substance and a phosphorescent substance?

10. A device like a laser that emits microwave radiation is called a maser. What words make up this acronym?

APPLYING CONCEPTS

1. Suppose you wanted to explain quantization to a younger brother or sister. Would you use money or water as an example? Explain.

2. The northern lights are the result of high energy particles coming from the sun striking atoms high in Earth's atmosphere. If you looked at the light through a spectrometer, would you expect to see a continuous or line spectrum? Explain.

3. The periodic table, as developed by Mendeleev, listed the atoms according to their mass. It is now ordered by charge. Look at the elements potas-

sium and argon. How does the discovery of a means of finding the charge on the nucleus change the ordering of the periodic table?

4. Could infrared radiation cause a substance to fluoresce in the visible part of the spectrum? Explain.

5. A laboratory laser has a power of only 0.8 mW (8×10^{-4} W). Why does it seem stronger than the light of a 100 W lamp?

6. A photon is formed by an electron dropping through energy levels within an excited hydrogen atom. What is the maximum energy the photon can have? If this same amount of energy were given to an electron in ground state in a hydrogen atom, what would happen?

7. When electrons fall from higher energy levels to the third energy level within hydrogen atoms, are the photons emitted infrared, visible, or ultraviolet light? Explain.

8. If white light were emitted from Earth's surface and observed by someone in space, would its spectrum be continuous? Explain.

9. If laser light is passed through a diffraction grating, how many spectra lines are seen in the first order?

6. Use Exercise 5 solutions to determine the wavelengths of the photons having the frequencies listed.

Use Figure 29–23 to answer Exercises 7 and 8.

7. A mercury atom is in an excited state when its energy level is 6.67 eV above the ground state. A photon of energy 2.15 eV strikes the mercury atom and is absorbed by it. To what energy level is the mercury atom raised?

8. A mercury atom drops from 8.81 eV above its ground state to 6.67 eV above its ground state. What is the energy of the photon emitted by the mercury atom?

9. The carbon dioxide laser emits very high power infrared radiation. What is the energy difference (in eV) between the two lasing energy levels?

10. Determine the frequency and wavelength of the photon emitted when an electron drops from
   a. E_3 to E_2 in an excited hydrogen atom.
   b. E_4 to E_3 in an excited hydrogen atom.

11. What is the difference between the energies of the E_4 and E_1 energy levels of the hydrogen atom?

12. Determine the frequency and wavelength of the photon emitted when an electron drops from E_4 to E_1 in an excited hydrogen atom.

EXERCISES

1. A hydrogen nucleus is 2.5×10^{-15} m in diameter, while the distance between the nucleus and the first electron is about 5×10^{-9} m. Suppose you used a baseball to represent the nucleus. How far away would the electron be?

2. Calculate the radius of the orbital associated with the energy levels E_5 and E_6 of the hydrogen atom.

3. What energy is associated with the hydrogen atom energy levels E_2, E_3, E_4, E_5, and E_6?

4. Calculate these values for the hydrogen atom.
   a. $E_6 - E_5$
   b. $E_6 - E_3$
   c. $E_4 - E_2$
   d. $E_5 - E_2$
   e. $E_5 - E_3$

5. Use Exercise 4 solutions to determine the frequencies of the photons emitted when the hydrogen atom passes through the energy differences.

PROBLEMS

1. For a hydrogen atom in the $n = 3$ Bohr orbital, find
   a. the radius of the orbital.
   b. the electric force acting on the electron.
   c. the centripetal acceleration of the electron.
   d. the orbital speed of the electron. Compare this speed with the speed of light.

2. A hydrogen atom has the electron in the $n = 2$ level.
   a. If a photon with a wavelength of 332 nm strikes the atom, will the atom be ionized?
   b. If the atom is ionized, assume the electron receives the excess energy from the ionization. What will be the kinetic energy of the electron in joules?

3. Gallium arsenide lasers are used in CD (compact disk) players. If the temperature is chosen so the

laser emits at 840 nm, what is the difference (in eV) between the two lasing energy levels?

4. By what amount does the mass of a hydrogen atom decrease when its electron makes a down transition from the fourth energy level to the first?

5. How many orders of magnitude larger is the electrical force between the electron and proton in a hydrogen atom than the gravitational force between them?

6. From what energy level did an electron fall if it emits a photon of 9.38×10^{-8} m wavelength when it reaches ground state within a hydrogen atom?

READINGS

Berger, Melvin, *Atom, Molecules, and Quarks.* New York: Putnam, 1986.

Boraiko, Allen, "A Splendid Light." *National Geographic,* March, 1984.

Jones, Edwin, "Observational Evidence for Atoms." *The Physics Teacher,* September, 1984.

Peltz, James F., "Bright Lights, Big Money." *Discover,* March, 1988.

Wheaton, Bruce, "Louis de Broglie and the Origins of Wave Mechanics." *The Physics Teacher,* May, 1984.

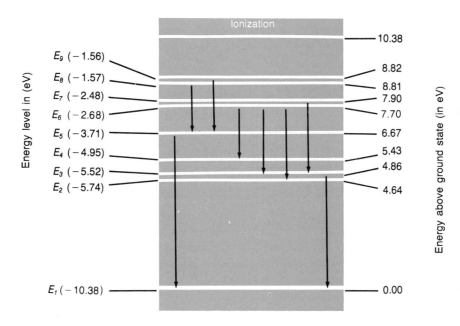

FIGURE 29–23. Use with Exercises 7 and 8.

CHAPTER 30

The Nucleus

GOALS

1. You will gain a knowledge of the structure of the nucleus.
2. You will gain an understanding of radioactive decay and the interaction of particles within the nucleus.
3. You will learn the present theory that explains the results of these interactions, and the instruments used to test the theory.

For Your Information

Idealists maintain that all nations should share the atomic bomb. Pessimists maintain they will.

—Punch

The nucleus, composed of protons and neutrons, is an extremely tiny, massive body at the center of the atom.

The atomic number of an element is represented by the letter Z.

The atomic mass of an element is represented by the letter A.

After the discovery of radioactivity by Becquerel in 1896, many scientists studied this new phenomenon. In Canada, Ernest Rutherford and Frederick Soddy discovered that uranium atoms were changed, or transmuted, to other atoms. The French scientists Marie and Pierre Curie discovered the new elements polonium and radium in samples of radioactive uranium. Further study of radioactivity has led to an understanding of the structure of the nucleus and to many useful applications. Artificially produced radioactive isotopes have been widely used in medicine and other fields. Electricity produced from the energy of the nucleus may reduce our reliance on fossil fuels.

Studies of nuclei have also led to an understanding of the structure of the particles found in the nucleus, the proton and the neutron, and the nature of the forces that hold the nucleus together.

30:1 Description of the Nucleus

Rutherford had found that the nucleus is a very small body in the center of the atom. Today it is known that the nucleus is almost spherical and has a radius between 1.3 fm (1.3×10^{-15} m) in hydrogen and 8.1 fm in uranium. The nucleus is composed of protons and neutrons. The number of protons, which is equal to the number of electrons surrounding the nucleus of a neutral atom, is given by the **atomic number,** Z. All atoms of a given element contain the same number of protons. The sum of the numbers of protons and neutrons is equal to the **mass number,** A. Elements with twenty or fewer protons have roughly equal numbers of pro-

Phantom Tracks

This computer-enhanced photograph shows the trails of subatomic particles in a bubble chamber. A magnetic field has been applied to aid in determining the sign and energy of charged particles. About 3 cm from the bottom left side of the photograph, as well as in other areas of the photograph, is a small pair of symmetric blue spirals. Since the two tracks are nearly identical in shape, the particles' masses must be similar. What might cause this pair of paths.

519

tons and neutrons. Heavier elements, however, contain more neutrons than protons.

The mass of the nucleus is approximately equal to the mass number, A, multiplied by the atomic mass unit (u), 1.66×10^{-27} kg.

30:2 Isotopes

Careful measurements of the mass of the boron atom consistently yielded 10.8 u. If, as was thought, the nucleus is made up of protons and neutrons each with a mass of approximately 1 u, then the total mass of any atom should be near a whole number.

The problem of atomic masses that were not integral numbers of the atomic mass unit, u, was solved with the mass spectrometer. The mass spectrometer demonstrated that an element could have atoms with different masses. For example, when analyzing a pure sample of neon, not one, but two spots appeared on the film of the spectrometer. The two spots were produced by neon atoms of different masses. One variety of neon atom was found to have a mass of 20 u; the second type has a mass of 22 u. All neon atoms have ten protons in the nucleus and ten electrons in the atom. One kind of neon atom, however, has ten neutrons in its nucleus, while the other has twelve neutrons. The two kinds of atoms are called **isotopes** of neon. The nucleus of an isotope is called a **nuclide.** All nuclides of an element have the same number of protons, but different numbers of neutrons. All isotopes of an element have the same number of electrons around the nucleus and behave the same chemically.

The measured mass of neon gas is 20.183 u. This figure is now understood to be the average mass of the naturally occurring isotopes of neon.

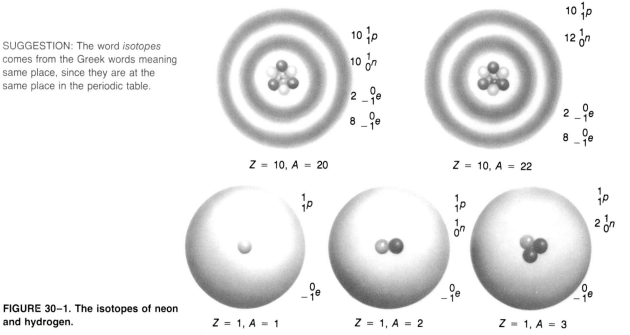

$10\ {}^{1}_{1}p$
$10\ {}^{1}_{0}n$
$2\ {}^{0}_{-1}e$
$8\ {}^{0}_{-1}e$

$Z = 10,\ A = 20$

$10\ {}^{1}_{1}p$
$12\ {}^{1}_{0}n$
$2\ {}^{0}_{-1}e$
$8\ {}^{0}_{-1}e$

$Z = 10,\ A = 22$

${}^{1}_{1}p$
${}^{0}_{-1}e$

$Z = 1,\ A = 1$

${}^{1}_{1}p$
${}^{1}_{0}n$
${}^{0}_{-1}e$

$Z = 1,\ A = 2$

${}^{1}_{1}p$
$2\ {}^{1}_{0}n$
${}^{0}_{-1}e$

$Z = 1,\ A = 3$

FIGURE 30–1. The isotopes of neon and hydrogen.

Thus, while the mass of an individual atom of neon is close to a whole number of mass units, the atomic mass of an average sample of neon atoms is not. Most elements have many isotopic forms that occur naturally. The mass of the isotope of carbon, $^{12}_{6}C$, is used to define the mass unit. One u is $^{1}/_{12}$ the mass of the $^{12}_{6}C$ isotope.

A special method of notation is used to describe an isotope. A subscript for the atomic number, Z, is written to the lower left of the symbol for the element. A superscript written to the upper left of the symbol is the mass number, A. This notation takes the form $^{A}_{Z}E$. For example, the two isotopes of neon, with atomic number 10, are written as $^{20}_{10}Ne$ and $^{22}_{10}Ne$.

The atomic mass unit is defined as 1/12 of the mass of a $^{12}_{6}C$ atom.

The general form for the symbol of an isotope is $^{A}_{Z}E$, where E represents the symbol for the element.

Practice Exercises

1. An isotope of oxygen has a mass number of 15. The atomic number of oxygen is 8. How many neutrons are in the nuclei of this isotope?
2. Three isotopes of uranium have mass numbers of 234, 235, and 238 respectively. The atomic number of uranium is 92. How many neutrons are in the nuclei of each of these isotopes?
3. How many neutrons are in an atom of the mercury isotope $^{200}_{80}Hg$?
4. Write the symbols for the three isotopes of hydrogen in Figure 30–1 with 0, 1, and 2 neutrons in the nucleus.

30:3 Radioactive Decay

In 1896 Henri Becquerel was working with compounds containing the element uranium. To his surprise, he found that covered photographic plates became fogged, or partially exposed, when these uranium compounds were anywhere near the plates. This fogging suggested that some kind of ray had passed through the plate coverings. Several materials other than uranium or its compounds were also found to emit these penetrating rays. Materials that emit this kind of radiation are said to be **radioactive** and to undergo **radioactive decay.**

In 1899 Rutherford discovered that uranium compounds produce three different kinds of radiation. He separated the radiations according to their penetrating ability and named them α (alpha), β (beta), and γ (gamma) radiation.

The α radiation can be stopped by a thick sheet of paper (Figure 30–2). Rutherford later showed that an α particle is the nucleus of a helium atom, $^{4}_{2}He$. Beta particles were later identified as high speed electrons. Six millimeters of aluminum are needed to stop most β particles. Several centimeters of lead are required to stop γ rays, which proved to be high energy photons. Alpha particles and γ rays are emitted with a specific energy that depends on the radioactive isotope. Beta particles, however, are emitted with a wide range of energies.

The emission of an α particle is a process called α **decay.** Since α particles contain protons and neutrons, they must come from the nucleus of an atom. The nucleus that results from α decay will have a mass and charge different from those of the original nucleus. A change in nuclear charge means that the element has been changed, or transmuted, into a different element. The mass number, A, of an α particle, $^{4}_{2}He$, is four, so the mass number, A, of the decaying nucleus is reduced by four. The

SUGGESTION: Marie Curie named the phenomenon radioactivity. For a while the rays were called Becquerel rays.

Rutherford found that naturally radioactive materials emit three types of radiation. Alpha particles are doubly-ionized helium nuclei. Beta particles are high-speed electrons. Gamma rays are high-frequency photons.

The nucleus resulting from α decay has an atomic number reduced by 2 and a mass number reduced by 4.

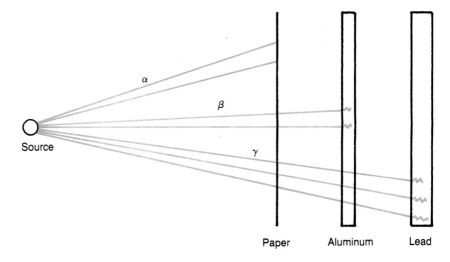

FIGURE 30–2. Alpha, beta, and gamma radiation have different penetrating properties.

Source

Paper   Aluminum   Lead

atomic number, Z, of $^4_2$He is two, and therefore the atomic number of the nucleus, the number of protons, is reduced by two. For example, when $^{238}_{92}$U emits an α particle, the atomic number, Z, changes from 92 to 90. From Table C–5 of the Appendix, we find that $Z = 90$ is thorium. The mass number of the nucleus is $A = 238 - 4 = 234$. A thorium isotope, $^{234}_{90}$Th, has been formed. The uranium isotope has been transmuted into thorium.

Beta particles are negative electrons emitted by the nucleus. Since the mass of an electron is a tiny fraction of an atomic mass unit, the atomic mass of a nucleus that undergoes β decay is changed only a tiny amount. The mass number is unchanged. Within the nucleus, when the electron is emitted, a neutron is changed to a proton. The number of protons, and thus the atomic number, is increased by one. For example, the isotope $^{234}_{90}$Th, produced by the decay of $^{238}_{92}$U, is unstable and emits a β particle. $^{234}_{90}$Th becomes a protactinium isotope, $^{234}_{91}$Pa.

Gamma radiation results from the redistribution of the charge within the nucleus. The γ ray is a high energy photon. Neither the mass number nor the atomic number is changed in γ decay.

Radioactive elements often go through a series of successive decays, or **transmutations,** until they form a stable nucleus. For example, $^{238}_{92}$U undergoes fourteen separate transmutations before the stable lead isotope $^{206}_{82}$Pb is produced.

30:4 Nuclear Reactions and Equations

A **nuclear reaction** occurs whenever the number of neutrons or protons in a nucleus changes. Some nuclear reactions occur with a release of energy; others occur only when energy is added to a nucleus.

One form of nuclear reaction is the emission of particles by radioactive nuclei. The reaction releases excess energy in the form of the kinetic energy of the emitted particles.

While nuclear reactions can be described in words, they can be written more easily in equation form. Nuclear equations use symbols for the

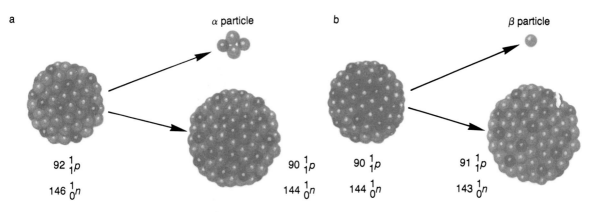

a
α particle

b
β particle

$92\ {}^{1}_{1}p$

$146\ {}^{1}_{0}n$

$90\ {}^{1}_{1}p$

$144\ {}^{1}_{0}n$

$90\ {}^{1}_{1}p$

$144\ {}^{1}_{0}n$

$91\ {}^{1}_{1}p$

$143\ {}^{1}_{0}n$

FIGURE 30–3. The emission of an alpha particle (a) by uranium-238 results in the formation of thorium-234. The emission of a beta particle (b) by thorium-234 results in the formation of protactinium-234.

nuclei that make the calculation of atomic number and mass number in nuclear reactions simpler. For example, the word equation for the change of uranium to thorium due to α decay is

$$\text{uranium } 238 \rightarrow \text{thorium } 234 + \alpha \text{ particle}$$

The nuclear equation for this reaction is

$$^{238}_{92}\text{U} \rightarrow {}^{234}_{90}\text{Th} + {}^{4}_{2}\text{He}$$

No nuclear particles are destroyed during the nuclear reaction. Thus, the sum of the superscripts on the right side of the equation must equal the sum of the superscripts on the left side of the equation. The sum of the superscripts on both sides of the equation is 238. Electric charge is also conserved. Thus, the sum of the subscripts on the right is equal to the sum of the subscripts on the left.

The symbol for an alpha particle is ${}^{4}_{2}\text{He}$.

In a nuclear equation, the sum of the superscripts on the right side must be equal to the sum of the superscripts on the left side.

EXAMPLE

Nuclear Equations—Alpha Decay

Write the nuclear equation for the transmutation of a radioactive radium isotope, ${}^{226}_{88}\text{Ra}$, into a radon isotope, ${}^{222}_{86}\text{Rn}$, by the emission of an α particle.

Solution: ${}^{226}_{88}\text{Ra} \rightarrow {}^{222}_{86}\text{Rn} + {}^{4}_{2}\text{He}$

A β particle is represented by the symbol ${}^{0}_{-1}e$. This indicates that the electron has one negative charge and an atomic mass number of zero. The equation for the transmutation of a thorium atom by the emission of a β particle is

The symbol for a beta particle is ${}^{0}_{-1}e$.

$$^{234}_{90}\text{Th} \rightarrow {}^{234}_{91}\text{Pa} + {}^{0}_{-1}e$$

The sum of the superscripts on the right side of the equation equals the sum of the superscripts on the left side of the equation. Also, the sum of the subscripts on the right side of the equation equals the sum of the subscripts on the left side of the equation.

In a nuclear equation, the sum of the subscripts on the right side must be equal to the sum of the subscripts on the left side.

EXAMPLE

Nuclear Equations—Beta Decay

Write the nuclear equation for the transmutation of a radioactive lead isotope, $^{209}_{82}\text{Pb}$, into a bismuth isotope, $^{209}_{83}\text{Bi}$, by the emission of a β particle.

Solution: $^{209}_{82}\text{Pb} \rightarrow {}^{209}_{83}\text{Bi} + {}^{0}_{-1}\text{e}$

Practice Exercises

5. Write the nuclear equation for the transmutation of a radioactive uranium isotope, $^{234}_{92}\text{U}$, into a thorium isotope, $^{230}_{90}\text{Th}$, by the emission of an α particle.

6. Write the nuclear equation for the transmutation of a radioactive thorium isotope, $^{230}_{90}\text{Th}$, into a radioactive radium isotope, $^{226}_{88}\text{Ra}$, by the emission of an α particle.

7. Write the nuclear equation for the transmutation of a radioactive radium isotope, $^{226}_{88}\text{Ra}$, into a radon isotope, $^{222}_{86}\text{Ra}$, by the emission of an α particle.

8. A radioactive lead isotope, $^{214}_{82}\text{Pb}$, can change to a radioactive bismuth isotope, $^{214}_{83}\text{Bi}$, by the emission of a β particle. Write the nuclear equation.

30:5 Half-Life

The time required for half of the atoms in any given quantity of a radioactive element to disintegrate is the **half-life** of that element. Each particular isotope has its own half-life. For example, the half-life of radium

DEMONSTRATION: See the Teacher Guide.

The half-life of an element is the time required for half of the radioactive nuclei to decay.

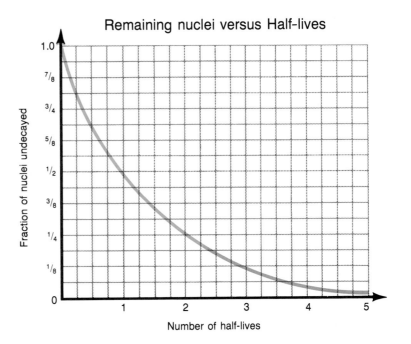

FIGURE 30–4. Use this half-life graph with Practice Exercises 9 through 12 on page 525.

isotope $^{226}_{88}$Ra is 1600 years. That is, in 1600 years, half of a given quantity of $^{226}_{88}$Ra will disintegrate into another element. In a second 1600 years, half of the remaining sample will have disintegrated. Only one fourth of the original amount will remain after 3200 years.

The decay rate, or number of decays per second, of a radioactive substance is called its **activity.** Activity is proportional to the number of radioactive atoms present. Therefore, the activity of a particular sample is reduced by one half in one half-life. Consider $^{131}_{53}$I with a half-life of 8.07 days. If the activity of a certain sample is 8×10^5 decays per second when the $^{131}_{53}$I is produced, 8.07 days later its activity will be 4×10^5 decays per second. After another 8.07 days, its activity will be 2×10^5 decays per second.

The half-lives of radioactive isotopes differ widely.

TABLE 30–1

Half-Life of Selected Isotopes			
Element	**Isotope**	**Half-Life**	**Radiation Produced**
hydrogen	$^3_1$H	12.3 years	β
carbon	$^{14}_6$C	5730 years	β
iodine	$^{131}_{53}$I	8.07 days	β, γ
lead	$^{212}_{82}$Pb	10.6 hours	β, γ
polonium	$^{194}_{84}$Po	0.7 second	α
polonium	$^{210}_{84}$Po	138 days	α
uranium	$^{227}_{92}$U	1.1 minutes	α
uranium	$^{235}_{92}$U	7.1×10^8 years	α, γ
uranium	$^{238}_{92}$U	4.51×10^9 years	α, γ
plutonium	$^{236}_{94}$Pu	2.85 years	α, γ
plutonium	$^{242}_{94}$Pu	3.79×10^5 years	α

SUGGESTION: Rutherford named the time for half the material to decay the half-life.

Practice Exercises

These problems require the use of Figure 30–4 and Table 30–1.

9. A sample of 1.0 g of tritium, $^3_1$H, is produced. What will be the mass of tritium remaining after 24.6 years?

10. The isotope $^{238}_{93}$Np has a half-life of 2.0 days. If 4.0 g are produced on Monday, what will be the mass remaining on Tuesday of the next week?

11. A sample of $^{210}_{94}$Po is purchased for a physics class on September 1. Its activity is 2×10^6 decays per second. The sample is used in an experiment on June 1. What activity can be expected?

12. Tritium, $^3_1$H, is used in some watches to produce a fluorescent glow so the watch can be read in the dark. If the brightness of the glow is proportional to the activity of the tritium, what will be the brightness of the watch, in comparison to its original brightness, when the watch is six years old?

30:6 Nuclear Bombardment

Rutherford bombarded many elements with α particles. He used the α particles to cause a nuclear reaction. When nitrogen gas was bom-

FIGURE 30-5. Production of oxygen-
17 from the artificial transmutation of
nitrogen.

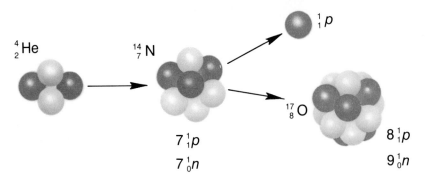

barded, Rutherford noted that high energy hydrogen nuclei, or protons, were emitted from the gas. A proton has a charge of one, while an α particle has a charge of two. Rutherford hypothesized that the nitrogen had been artificially transmuted by the α particles. The unknown results of the transmutation can be written $_Z^A E$, and the nuclear reaction can be written

$$_2^4 He + _7^{14} N \rightarrow _1^1 H + _Z^A E$$

Simple arithmetic shows that the atomic number of the unknown isotope is $Z = 2 + 7 - 1 = 8$. The mass number is $A = 4 + 14 - 1 = 17$. From Appendix Table C-5, the isotope must be $_8^{17} O$. The identity of the $_8^{17} O$ isotope was confirmed with a mass spectrograph several years later.

Bombarding $_4^9 Be$ with α particles produced a radiation more penetrating than any previously discovered. In 1932 Irene Curie (daughter of Marie and Pierre Curie) and her husband, Frederic Joliot, discovered that high speed protons were expelled from paraffin wax that was exposed to this new radiation from beryllium. In 1932 James Chadwick showed that the particles emitted from beryllium were uncharged, but had approximately the same mass as protons. That is, the beryllium emitted the particle Rutherford had theorized must be in the nucleus, the neutron. The reaction can be written using the symbol for the neutron, $_0^1 n$.

$$_2^4 He + _4^9 Be \rightarrow _6^{12} C + _0^1 n$$

Neutrons, being uncharged, are not repelled by the nucleus. As a result, neutrons are often used to bombard nuclei.

Alpha particles are useful in producing nuclear reactions. Alphas from radioactive materials, however, have fixed energies. In addition, sources that emit a large number of particles per second are difficult to produce. Thus methods of artificially accelerating particles to high energies are needed. Energies of several million electron volts are required to produce nuclear reactions. Several types of particle accelerators have been developed. The linear accelerator and the synchrotron are the two accelerators in greatest use today.

30:7 Linear Accelerators

A linear accelerator consists of a series of hollow tubes within a long evacuated chamber. The tubes are connected to a source of high frequency alternating voltage, Figure 30-6. Protons are produced in an ion source similar to that described in Chapter 27. When the first tube has a

If a particle (α, proton, electron, neutron, or γ) strikes a nucleus with enough energy, it can cause a nuclear reaction.

Particle accelerators have been developed to give particles very high energy in order to study the structure of the nucleus.

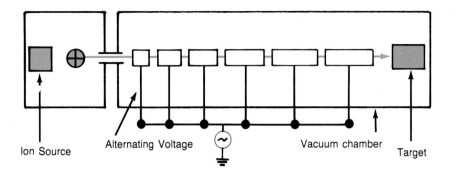

Ion Source

Alternating Voltage

Vacuum chamber

Target

negative potential, protons are accelerated into it. There is no electric field within the tube, so the proton moves at constant velocity. The length of the tube and the frequency of the voltage are adjusted so that when the protons have reached the far end of the tube, the potential of the second tube is negative with respect to that of the first. The resulting electric field in the gap between the tubes accelerates the protons into the second tube. This process continues, with the protons receiving an acceleration between each pair of tubes. The energy of the protons is increased by 10^5 eV by each acceleration. The proton rides along the crest of an electric field wave much as a surfboard moves on the ocean. At the end of the accelerator, the protons can have energies of many millions of electron volts.

Linear accelerators can be used with both electrons and protons. One of the largest linear accelerators is at Stanford University in California. It is 3.3 km long and accelerates electrons to energies of 20 GeV (2.0×10^{10} eV).

30:8   The Synchrotron

An accelerator may be made smaller by using a magnetic field to bend the path of the particles into a circle. In a device known as a **synchrotron,** the bending magnets are separated by accelerating regions. In the straight regions, high frequency alternating voltage accelerates the particles. The strength of the magnetic field and the length of the path are chosen so that the particles reach the location of the alternating electric field precisely when the field's polarity will accelerate them. One of the largest synchrotrons in operation is at the Fermi National Accelerator Laboratory near Chicago. Protons there reach energies of 1 TeV (1.0×10^{12} eV).

30:9   Particle Detectors

Photographic films become "fogged," or exposed, when α particles, β particles, or γ rays strike them. Thus, photographic film can be used to detect these particles and rays. Many other devices are used to detect charged particles and γ rays. Most of these devices make use of the fact that a collision with a high speed particle will remove electrons from atoms. That is, the high speed particles ionize the matter that they bombard. In addition, some substances fluoresce when exposed to certain types of radiation. Thus, fluorescent substances can be used to detect radiation.

Linear accelerators use potential differences to accelerate charged particles.

Synchrotrons use magnetic fields to bend particle paths into a circle and electric fields to accelerate the particles.

SUGGESTION: The linear accelerator became inconveniently long because the particle was accelerating and there was a longer and longer distance between "kicks."

Photographic plates can be used to detect particles emitted in radioactive decay.

Some fluorescent substances can be used to detect radiation.

FIGURE 30–7. Fermi Laboratory's synchrotron has a diameter of 2 km.

A Geiger-Muller tube is a sensitive detector of radioactive emissions.

SUGGESTION: Demonstrate the Geiger counter and the cloud chamber if possible.

In the **Geiger-Mueller tube** particles ionize gas atoms, Figure 30–8. The tube contains a gas at low pressure (10 kPa). At one end of the tube is a very thin "window" through which charged particles or gamma rays pass. Inside the tube is a copper cylinder with a negative charge. A rigid wire with a positive charge runs down the center of this cylinder. The voltage across the wire and cylinder is kept just below the point at which a spontaneous discharge, or spark, occurs. When a charged particle or gamma ray enters the tube, it ionizes a gas atom between the copper cylinder and the wire. The positive ion produced is accelerated toward the copper cylinder by the potential difference. The electron is accelerated toward the positive wire. As these new particles move toward the electrodes, they strike other atoms and form even more ions in their path.

Thus an avalanche of charged particles is created and a pulse of current flows through the tube. The current causes a potential difference across a resistor in the circuit. The voltage is amplified and registers the arrival of a particle by advancing a counter or producing an audible signal, such as a click. The potential difference across the resistor lowers the voltage across the tube so that the current flow stops. Thus the tube is ready for the beginning of a new avalanche when another particle or gamma ray enters it.

Another device used to detect particles is the **Wilson cloud chamber.** The chamber contains an area supersaturated with water vapor or ethanol

FIGURE 30–8. A Geiger counter can be used to detect gamma rays.

FIGURE 30–9. In a bubble chamber, charged particles produce trails of tiny vapor bubbles in liquid hydrogen as they pass through the chamber.

vapor. When charged particles travel through the chamber, leaving a trail of ions in their paths, the vapor tends to condense into small droplets on the ions. In this way, visible trails of droplets, or fog, are formed. The **bubble chamber** is similar, except that trails of small vapor droplets form in a liquid held just above the boiling point.

Modern experiments use **spark chambers** that are like giant Geiger-Mueller tubes. Plates several meters in size are separated by a few centimeters. The gap is filled with a low-pressure gas. A discharge is produced in the path of a particle passing through the chamber. Phototubes collect light from the discharge. The amount of light depends on the energy of the particle. Neutral particles do not leave tracks. However, the laws of conservation of energy and momentum in collisions are used to tell if any neutrals were produced. Detectors used to analyze particles produced by accelerators can be many meters in size, weigh 10 tons or more, and cost tens of millions of dollars.

Cloud and bubble chambers produce records of the paths of charged particles.

30:10 The Fundamental Particles

The atom was once thought to be the smallest particle into which matter could be divided. Then Rutherford found that the atom had a nucleus surrounded by electrons. After the proton was discovered, it was also thought to be indivisible. Experiments have been done that bombard protons with other protons accelerated by synchrotrons to very high energies. The results of these experiments show that the proton is composed of yet smaller bodies. The neutron also appears to be composed of smaller bodies. The structure of the proton and neutron is closely related to the strong nuclear forces that act between neutrons and protons.

Physicists now believe that the particles out of which all matter is made are grouped into two families, quarks and leptons. Quarks make up protons and neutrons. Leptons are particles with little or no mass, the electron and neutrino. There are also particles that carry, or transmit, forces between particles. The photon is the carrier of the electromagnetic force. Eight particles, called gluons, carry the strong force that binds quarks into protons and the protons and neutrons into nuclei. Three particles, the

For Your Information

The atom is still the smallest amount of an element that retains the properties of that element.

All matter is believed to be made up of two families of particles, quarks and leptons.

weak bosons, are involved in the weak interaction, which operates in beta decay. The graviton is the name given to the yet-undetected carrier of the gravitational force. These particles are summarized in Tables 30–2 and 30–3. Charges are given in units of the electron charge and masses are stated as energy equivalents.

TABLE 30–2

Quarks				Leptons			
Name	Symbol	Mass	Charge	Name	Symbol	Mass	Charge
down	d	330 Mev	−1/3	electron	e	0.511 Mev	−1
up	u	330 Mev	2/3	neutrino	$\bar{\nu}_e$	0	0

TABLE 30–3

Force Carriers				
Force	Name	Symbol	Mass	Charge
Electromagnetic	photon	γ	0	0
Weak	weak bosons	W^+	82 Gev	1
		W^-	82 Gev	−1
		Z^0	93 Gev	0
Strong	gluons (8)	g	0	0
Gravitational	graviton	G	0	0

There is an antiparticle for every particle.

Annihilation occurs when a particle meets an antiparticle.

Each quark and each lepton also has its antiparticle. The antiparticles are identical with the particles except they have the opposite charge. When a particle and its antiparticle collide, they annihilate each other and are transformed into energy. The total number of quarks and the total number of leptons in the universe is constant. That is, quarks and leptons are created or destroyed only in particle-antiparticle pairs. The number of charge carriers is not conserved; the total charge, however, is conserved. Gravitons, photons, gluons, and weak bosons can be created or destroyed if there is enough energy. After exploring the production and annihilation of antiparticles, we will return to the quark and lepton theory of matter.

FIGURE 30–10. The collision of a positron and an electron results in gamma ray production.

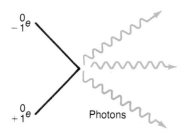

Photons

30:11 Particles and Antiparticles

The α particles and γ rays emitted by radioactive nuclei have single energies that depend on the decaying nucleus. For example, the energy of the α particle emitted by $^{234}_{90}$Th is always 4.2 MeV. Beta particles, however, are emitted with a wide range of energies. One might expect the energy of the β particle to be equal to the difference between the energy of the nucleus before decay and the energy of the nucleus produced by the decay. In fact, the wide range of energies of electrons emitted during β decay suggested to Niels Bohr that energy might not be conserved in nuclear reactions. Wolfgang Pauli in 1931 and Enrico Fermi in 1934 suggested that an unseen neutral particle was emitted with the β particle.

Named the **neutrino** ("little neutral one" in Italian) by Fermi, the particle (actually an antineutrino) was not directly observed until 1956.

In a stable nucleus the neutron does not decay. In an unstable nucleus, however, the neutron can decay by emitting a β particle. Sharing the energy with the β particle is an antineutrino ($_0^0\bar{\nu}$). The antineutrino has zero mass and is uncharged, but like the photon, it carries momentum and energy. The neutron decay equation is written

$$_0^1n \rightarrow {}_1^1p + {}_{-1}^0e + {}_0^0\bar{\nu}$$

When an isotope decays by emission of a **positron** (antielectron), the inverse of a β decay occurs. A proton within the nucleus changes into a neutron with the emission of a positron and a neutrino ($_0^0\nu$). The decay reaction is written

$$_1^1p \rightarrow {}_0^1n + {}_1^0e + {}_0^0\nu$$

The decay of neutrons into protons and protons into neutrons cannot occur as a result of the strong force. The existence of β decay indicates there must be another force or interaction, called the weak interaction, acting in the nucleus.

The positron is an example of an antiparticle, or a particle of antimatter. When a positron and an electron collide, the two annihilate each other,

Experiments showing that beta particles are emitted with a wide range of energies suggested the existence of the neutrino.

A neutrino has no mass and no charge.

A positron has one positive charge. Like an electron, it has little mass.

Neutron → Electron +
  Proton + Antineutrino
Proton → Positron +
  Neutrino + Neutron

FIGURE 30–11. Scientists identify the particles produced in high-energy collisions by the tracks they produce.

resulting in energy in the form of γ rays. Matter is converted directly into energy.

The amount of energy can be calculated using Einstein's equation for the energy equivalent of mass

$$E = mc^2$$

The mass of the electron is 9.11×10^{-31} kg. The mass of the positron is the same. Therefore, the energy equivalent of the positron and the electron together is

$$E = 2(9.11 \times 10^{-31} \text{ kg})(3.00 \times 10^8 \text{ m/s})^2$$
$$= (1.64 \times 10^{-13} \text{ J})(1 \text{ eV}/1.60 \times 10^{-19} \text{ J})$$
$$= 1.02 \times 10^6 \text{ eV or } 1.02 \text{ MeV}$$

When a positron and an electron annihilate each other, the sum of the energies of the γ rays emitted is 1.02 MeV.

The inverse of annihilation can also occur. That is, energy can be converted directly into matter. If a γ ray with at least 1.02 MeV energy passes close by a nucleus, a positron and electron pair can be produced. Individual positrons or electrons, however, cannot be produced alone because such an event would violate the law of conservation of charge. Matter and antimatter particles must always be produced in pairs.

The production of a positron-electron pair is shown in the bubble chamber photograph of Figure 30–11. A magnetic field around the bubble chamber causes the oppositely-charged particles to curve in opposite directions. The γ ray that produced the pair disappears. If the energy of the γ ray is larger than 1.02 MeV, the excess energy goes into kinetic energy of the positron and electron. The positron soon collides with another electron and they are both annihilated, resulting in the production of two or three γ rays with a total energy of 1.02 MeV.

Antiprotons also exist. An antiproton has a mass equal to that of the proton but is negatively charged. Protons have 1836 times as much mass as electrons. The energy needed to create proton-antiproton pairs is comparably larger. The first proton-antiproton pair was produced and observed at Berkeley, California, in 1955.

Practice Exercise

13. The mass of a proton is 1.67×10^{-27} kg.
   a. Find the energy equivalent of the proton's mass in joules.
   b. Convert this value to eV.
   c. Find the lowest energy γ ray that could produce a proton-antiproton pair.

30:12 The Quark Model of Nucleons

The quark model describes the proton and the neutron as an assembly of quarks. The nucleons are each made up of three quarks. The proton has two up quarks and one down quark. A proton is described as $p = (uud)$. The charge on the proton is the sum of the charges of the three quarks, $2/3 + 2/3 + -1/3 = 1$. The neutron is made up of one up quark and

For Your Information

The electromagnetic attraction of an electron and a positron is 42×10^{41} as strong as their gravitational attraction.
—*Isaac Asimov's Book of Facts*

Photons with energies in excess of 1.02 MeV are capable of causing pair production.

two down quarks, $n = (udd)$. The charge of the neutron is $2/3 + -1/3 + -1/3 = 0$.

Individual quarks cannot be observed because the strong force that holds them together becomes larger as the quarks are pulled farther apart. In this sense the strong force acts like the force of a spring. It is unlike the electric force, which becomes weaker as charged particles are moved farther apart. In the quark model, the strong force is the result of the emission and absorption of gluons that carry the force.

TABLE 30–4

Additional Quarks			
Name	**Symbol**	**Mass**	**Charge**
strange	s	510 MeV	−1/3
charm	c	1.6 GeV	2/3
bottom	b	5.2 GeV	−1/3
top	t	>40 GeV	2/3

TABLE 30–5

Additional Leptons			
Name	**Symbol**	**Mass**	**Charge**
muon	μ	105 MeV	−1
muon neutrino	ν_μ	0	0
tau	τ	1.8 GeV	−1
tau neutrino	ν_τ	0	0

According to the present theory, the weak interaction involves three charge carriers: W^+, W^-, and Z^0 bosons. Beta decay, the decay of a neutron into a proton, electron, and antineutrino, occurs in two steps. As was shown before, the neutron and the proton differ by one quark. In β decay, one d quark in a neutron changes to a u quark with the emission of a W^- boson.

$$d \rightarrow u + W^-$$

The W^- boson then decays into an electron and an antineutrino.

$$W^- \rightarrow e^- + \bar{\nu}$$

Similarly, the inverse β decay of a proton involves the emission of a W^+ boson. This decays into a positron and a neutrino.

The emission of a Z^0 boson is not accompanied by a change from one quark to another. The Z^0 boson produces an interaction between the nucleons and the electrons in atoms. This interaction is much weaker than the electromagnetic force holding the atom together. The interaction was first detected in 1979. The W^+, W^-, and Z^0 bosons were first observed directly in 1983.

The force between charged particles, the electromagnetic interaction, is carried by photons in much the same way as weak bosons carry the weak force. The electric force acts over a long range because the photon

In the quark model, beta decay involves the change of a d quark into a u quark. This changes the neutron into a proton.

The quark change is accompanied by emission of a W particle. The W produces the electron and antineutrino.

has zero mass, while the weak force acts over short distances because the W and Z bosons are so relatively massive. The mathematical structures of the theories of the weak interaction and electromagnetic interaction, however, are similar. In the high energy collisions produced in accelerators, the electromagnetic and weak interactions have the same strength and range.

Astrophysical theories of supernovae indicate that during massive stellar explosions, the two interactions are identical. Present theories of the origin of the universe suggest that the two forces were identical during the early moments in the life of the cosmos as well. For this reason, the electromagnetic and weak forces are said to be unified by this theory into a single force, called the electroweak force.

The electromagnetic and weak interactions are unified into the electroweak interaction.

Bombardment of particles at high energies creates many particles of medium and large mass that have very short lifetimes. Some of these particles are combinations of two or three u or d quarks. Particles composed of two quarks are called **mesons;** those composed of three quarks are called **baryons.** Combinations of the u and d quarks, however, cannot account for all the particles produced. Combinations of three other quarks are necessary to form all known baryons and mesons. The fourth quark, the top quark, has not been found, but the theories that work very well predict its existence. Two additional pairs of leptons are also produced in high energy collisions. The additional quarks and leptons are listed in Tables 30–4 and 30–5. No one knows why there are six quarks and six leptons or if there are still other undiscovered particles. One of the reasons for building the Superconducting Super Collider is to attempt to answer this question.

Baryons are made up of a combination of three quarks. Mesons are made up of a quark and an antiquark.

In addition to the quarks and leptons found in ordinary matter, at high energies four more quarks and four more leptons are needed.

In the same way that the electromagnetic and weak forces were unified into the electroweak force during the 1970s, physicists are presently trying to create a Grand Unified Theory that includes the strong force as well. Work is still incomplete. One prediction of current theories is that the proton should not exist forever, but decay into leptons and photons. The proton half-life should be 10^{31} years. After three years, experiments to test this prediction on a large number of protons showed no decays. Theories are being revised and new experiments planned. A fully unified theory that includes gravitation requires even more work.

In Grand Unified Theories, the strong and electroweak forces are unified.

The field of physics that studies these particles is called high energy or elementary particle physics. The field is very exciting because new discoveries occur almost every week. Each new discovery seems to raise as many questions as it answers. The question of what makes up the universe does not yet have a complete answer.

CHAPTER 30 REVIEW

SUMMARY

1. The number of protons in a nucleus is given by the atomic number. **30:1**

2. The sum of the numbers of protons and neutrons in a nucleus is equal to the mass number. **30:1**

3. Atoms having nuclei with the same number of protons but different numbers of neutrons are called isotopes. **30:2**

4. An unstable nucleus undergoes radioactive decay, changing, or transmuting, into another element. **30:3**

5. Radioactive decay produces three kinds of particles. Alpha (α) particles are helium nuclei; beta (β) particles are high speed electrons; and gamma (γ) rays are high energy photons. **30:3**

6. Nuclear reactions do not change the sum of the mass numbers (A) or atomic numbers (Z) of the nuclei involved. **30:4**

7. The half-life of a radioactive isotope is the time required for half of the nuclei to decay. **30:5**

8. The rate of radioactive decay, the activity, is also reduced by a factor of two in a time equal to the half-life. **30:5**

9. Bombardment of nuclei by protons, neutrons, alpha particles, electrons, or gamma rays can produce a nuclear reaction. **30:6**

10. Linear accelerators are used to produce very high energy protons and electrons. **30:7**

11. Synchrotrons are circular accelerators that produce the highest energy protons. **30:8**

12. The Geiger counter and other particle detectors use the ionization of charged particles passing through matter. **30:9**

13. In beta decay, an uncharged, massless antineutrino is emitted with the electron. **30:11**

14. A positron (antimatter electron) and a neutrino are emitted by radioactive nuclei in a process called inverse beta decay. **30:11**

15. When antimatter and matter combine, all mass is converted into energy. **30:11**

16. By pair production, energy is transformed into a matter-antimatter particle pair. **30:11**

17. The weak interaction, or weak force, operates in beta decay. The strong force binds the nucleus together. **30:11**

18. Protons and neutrons, together called nucleons, are composed of still smaller particles called quarks. **30:10, 30:12**

19. When matter and antimatter particles collide, they annihilate each other, converting mass into energy. Conversely, it is possible to convert energy into a matter-antimatter pair. **30:10, 30:12**

20. All matter appears to be made up of two families of particles, quarks and leptons. **30:10, 30:12**

QUESTIONS

1. Define the term *transmutation* in nuclear physics and give an example.
2. What happens to the atomic number and mass number of a nucleus that emits an alpha particle?
3. What happens to the atomic number and mass number of a nucleus that emits a beta particle?
4. What happens to the atomic number and mass number of a nucleus that emits a positron?
5. Give the symbol, mass, and charge of the following particles.
   a. proton
   b. neutron
   c. positron
   d. electron
   e. α particle
6. If the half-life of an isotope is two years, what fraction of the isotope remains after six years?
7. In which of the four interactions (strong, weak, electromagnetic, gravitational) do the following particles take part?
   a. electron
   b. proton
   c. neutrino
8. Which is most like an X ray: alpha, beta, or gamma radiation?
9. Find the elements that are shown by the following symbols, where X replaces the symbol for the element.
   a. $^{18}_{9}X$
   b. $^{241}_{95}X$
   c. $^{21}_{10}X$
   d. $^{7}_{3}X$
10. Why would a linear accelerator have no effect on a neutron?

APPLYING CONCEPTS

1. What would happen if a meteorite made of antiprotons, antineutrons, and positrons landed on Earth?
2. What would be the charge of a particle composed of three *u* quarks?
3. The charge of an antiquark is opposite that of a quark. A pion is composed of a *u* quark and an anti-*d* quark. What would be the charge of this pion?
4. Find the charges of the following pions made of
   a. *u* and anti-*u* quark pair.
   b. *d* and anti-*u* quarks.
   c. *d* and anti-*d* quarks.
5. Could a deuteron, $^{2}_{1}H$, decay via alpha decay? Explain.
6. In an accident in a research laboratory, a radioactive isotope with a half-life of three days is spilled. As a result, the radiation is eight times the maximum permissible amount. How long must workers wait before they can enter the room?
7. Why is carbon dating useful in establishing the age of skeletons but not the age of a set of knight's armor?
8. Which are generally more unstable, small or large nuclei? Why?

EXERCISES

1. An atom of an isotope of magnesium has an atomic mass of about 24 u. The atomic number of magnesium is 12. How many neutrons are in the nucleus of this atom?
2. An atom of an isotope of nitrogen has an atomic mass of about 15 u. The atomic number of nitrogen is 7. How many neutrons are in the nucleus of this isotope?
3. List the number of neutrons in an atom of each of these isotopes.
   a. $^{112}_{48}Cd$
   b. $^{209}_{83}Bi$
   c. $^{208}_{83}Bi$
   d. $^{80}_{35}Br$
   e. $^{1}_{1}H$
   f. $^{40}_{18}Ar$
   g. $^{132}_{54}Xe$
4. An aluminum isotope, $^{25}_{13}Al$, when bombarded by α particles absorbs an alpha particle and then emits a neutron. Write a nuclear equation for this transmutation.
5. During a reaction, two deuterons combine to form a helium isotope, $^{3}_{2}He$. (The symbol for a deuteron is $^{2}_{1}H$.) What other particle is produced?

6. On the sun, the nuclei of four ordinary hydrogen atoms combine to form a helium isotope, $^4_2$He. What type of particle is missing from the following equation for this reaction?

$$4^1_1\text{H} \rightarrow\ ^4_2\text{He} +\ ?$$

7. A radioactive bismuth isotope, $^{214}_{83}$Bi, emits a β particle. Use Table C–5 of the Appendix to determine the element formed. Write the nuclear equation.

8. A radioactive polonium isotope, $^{210}_{84}$Po, emits an α particle. Use Table C–5 of the Appendix to determine the element formed. Write the nuclear equation.

9. An unstable chromium isotope, $^{56}_{24}$Cr, emits a β particle. Write a complete equation and show the element formed.

10. Write a complete nuclear equation for the transmutation of a uranium isotope, $^{227}_{92}$U, into a thorium isotope, $^{223}_{90}$Th.

PROBLEMS

1. The half-life of strontium-90 is 28 years. After 280 years, how would the intensity of a sample of strontium-90 compare to the original intensity of the sample?

2. A 1.00-μg sample of a radioactive material contains 6.0×10^{14} nuclei. After 48 hours 0.25 μg of the material remains.

   a. What is the half-life of the material?

   b. How could one determine the activity of the sample at 24 hours using this information?

3. The synchrotron at FermiLab has a diameter of 2.0 km. Protons circling in it move at approximately the speed of light.

   a. How long does it take a proton to complete one revolution?

   b. The protons enter the ring at an energy of 8.0 GeV. They gain 2.5 MeV each revolution. How many revolutions must they travel before they reach 400 GeV energy?

   c. How long does it take the protons to be accelerated to 400 GeV?

   d. How far do the protons travel during this acceleration?

4. A Geiger counter registers an initial reading of 3200 counts for a radioactive substance and 100 counts 30 hours later. What is the half-life of this substance?

5. $^{238}_{92}$U decays by α emission and two successive β emissions back into uranium again. Show the three nuclear decay equations and predict the atomic mass number of the uranium formed.

6. 14 g of $^{14}_{6}$C contains Avogadro's number, 6.02×10^{23}, nuclei. A 5 g sample of $^{14}_{6}$C will have how many nondecayed nuclei after 11 460 years?

READINGS

Brown, Gerald, "The Structure of the Nucleon." *Physics Today,* February, 1983.

"Elements Rise Up From Dying Stars." *New Scientist,* August 11, 1988.

Guillen, Michael, "The Paradox of Antimatter." *Science Digest,* February, 1985.

McGeachy, Frank, "Radioactive Decay—An Analog." *The Physics Teacher,* January, 1988.

Palmer, Robert I., "What's a Quark?" *Science '85,* November, 1985.

CHAPTER 31

Nuclear Applications

GOALS

1. You will gain a knowledge of the forces that hold the nucleus together.
2. You will become familiar with some of the applications of nuclear physics.

For Your Information

Whatever nature has in store for mankind, unpleasant as it may be, men must accept, for ignorance is never better than knowledge.

—Enrico Fermi

The strong force acts the same between neutrons and protons as it does between protons and protons or neutrons and neutrons.

SUGGESTION: The strong force acts when the particles are closer than about 10^{-14} meter.

Neutrons and protons are forms of nucleons.

In no other area of physics has basic knowledge led to applications as quickly as in the field of nuclear physics. The medical use of the radioactive element radium began within 20 years of its discovery. Proton accelerators were tested for medical applications less than one year after being invented. In the case of nuclear fission, the military application was under development before the basic physics was even known. Peaceful applications followed in less than 10 years. The question of the uses of nuclear reactors in our society is an important one for all citizens today. In this chapter we will explore some applications of nuclear physics.

31:1 Forces Within the Nucleus

The electrons that surround the positively-charged nucleus of an atom are held in place by the attractive electric force. The nucleus consists of positively-charged protons and neutral neutrons. The repulsive electric force between the protons might be expected to cause them to fly apart. This does not happen because an even stronger attractive force exists within the nucleus. This force is called the **strong nuclear force.** The strong force acts between protons and neutrons that are very close together, as they are in a nucleus. The strong force is always attractive and is of the same strength between protons and protons, protons and neutrons, and neutrons and neutrons. As a result of this equivalence, both neutrons and protons are called **nucleons.**

Shock Waves

Part of the core of a nuclear reactor is the fuel assembly. Each fuel assembly is made of a number of fuel rods containing enriched uranium. A fuel assembly submerged in water is shown here. What is a possible explanation for the blue glow surrounding the fuel assembly?

The strong force holds the nucleons in the nucleus. If a nucleon were to be pulled out of a nucleus, work would have to be done to overcome the attractive force. Doing work adds energy to the nucleus. The amount of energy needed to pull a nucleus apart into separate protons and neutrons is the **binding energy** of the nucleus.

The binding energy of a nucleus is the energy that would have to be added to separate it into separate nucleons.

31:2   Binding Energy of the Nucleus

Binding energy can be expressed in the form of an equivalent amount of mass, according to the equation $E = mc^2$. Because energy has to be added to take a nucleus apart, the mass of the assembled nucleus is less than the sum of the masses of the nucleons that compose it. For example, the helium nucleus, ^4_2He, consists of 2 protons and 2 neutrons. The mass of a proton is 1.007825 u. The mass of a neutron is 1.008665 u. The mass of the nucleons that make up the helium nucleus is equal to the sum of the masses of the two protons and the two neutrons. Thus the mass of the nucleus should be 4.032980 u. Careful measurement, however, shows the mass of a helium nucleus is only 4.002603 u. The mass of the helium nucleus is less than the mass of its constituent parts. This difference is called the **mass defect.** The binding energy can be calculated from the experimentally determined mass defect by using $E = mc^2$ to compute the energy equivalent of the missing mass.

The binding energy of a nucleus is expressed in the reduced mass of the nucleus. $E = mc^2$ shows the equivalence.

The energy equivalent of one atomic mass unit is 931.5 MeV.

Binding energy versus *A*

Average binding energy per nucleon (MeV)

Number of nucleons (A)

FIGURE 31–1. A graph of the binding energy per nucleon.

SUGGESTION: 1 eV = 1.6 × 10⁻¹⁹ J.

Masses are normally measured in atomic mass units. It will be useful, then, to determine the energy equivalent of 1 u (1.66 × 10⁻²⁷ kg). The most convenient unit of energy to use is the electron volt.

$$
\begin{aligned}
E &= mc^2 \\
&= (1.66 \times 10^{-27} \text{ kg})(3.00 \times 10^8 \text{ m/s})^2 \\
&= (14.9 \times 10^{-11} \text{ J})(1 \text{ eV}/1.60 \times 10^{-19} \text{ J}) \\
&= 9.31 \times 10^8 \text{ eV} \\
E &= 931 \text{ MeV}
\end{aligned}
$$

EXAMPLE

Mass Defect and Nuclear Binding Energy

The mass of a proton is 1.007825 u. The mass of a neutron is 1.008665 u. The mass of the nucleus of the radioactive hydrogen isotope tritium, ^3_1H, is 3.016049 u. **a.** What is the nuclear mass defect of this isotope? **b.** What is the binding energy of tritium?

Solution:

a. As indicated by the superscript and subscript in the symbol for tritium, its nucleus contains 1 proton and 2 neutrons.

$$\text{mass of 1 proton} = 1.007825 \text{ u}$$
$$\text{mass of 2 neutrons} = (2)(1.008665 \text{ u}) = \underline{2.017330 \text{ u}}$$
$$\text{total} = 3.025155 \text{ u}$$
$$\text{mass of tritium nucleus} = \underline{3.016049 \text{ u}}$$
$$\text{mass defect} = 0.009106 \text{ u}$$

b. Since 1 u is equivalent to 931 MeV, the binding energy of the tritium nucleus can be calculated.

$$\text{binding energy of } ^3_1H \text{ nucleus} = (0.009106 \text{ u})(931 \text{ MeV/u})$$
$$= 8.48 \text{ MeV}$$

Practice Exercises

Use these values in the following problems: mass of proton = 1.007825 u; mass of neutron = 1.008665 u; 1 u = 931 MeV.

1. The carbon isotope, $^{12}_6C$, has a nuclear mass of 12.0000 u.
   a. Calculate its mass defect.
   b. Calculate its binding energy in MeV.

2. The isotope of hydrogen that contains 1 proton and 1 neutron is called deuterium. The mass of its nucleus is 2.0140 u.
   a. What is its mass defect?
   b. What is the binding energy of deuterium in MeV?

3. A nitrogen isotope, $^{15}_7N$, has 7 protons and 8 neutrons. Its nucleus has a mass of 15.00011 u.
   a. Calculate the mass defect of this nucleus.
   b. Calculate the binding energy of the nucleus.

4. An oxygen isotope, $^{16}_8O$, has a nuclear mass of 15.99491 u.
   a. What is the mass defect of this isotope?
   b. What is the binding energy of its nucleus?

When you worked the Practice Exercises, you found that heavier nuclei are bound more strongly than lighter nuclei. A useful relationship is shown by the graph of binding energy per nucleon in Figure 31–1.

Except for a few nuclei, the binding energy per nucleon increases as A increases to a value of 56, iron, Fe. $^{56}_{26}Fe$ is the most tightly bound nucleus. Nuclei larger than iron are less strongly bound.

The binding energy per nucleon is largest for iron-56.

A nuclear reaction will occur naturally if energy is released by the reaction. Energy will be released if the nucleus that results from the reaction is more tightly bound than the original nucleus. When a heavy nucleus, such as $^{238}_{92}U$, decays by releasing an alpha particle, the binding energy per nucleon of the resulting $^{234}_{90}Th$ is larger than that of the uranium. The excess energy of the $^{238}_{92}U$ nucleus is transferred into the kinetic energy of the alpha particle. At low atomic numbers, reactions that add nucleons to a nucleus increase the binding energy of the nucleus and are energetically favored. In the sun and other stars, the production of heavier nuclei like helium and carbon from hydrogen releases energy that eventually becomes the electromagnetic radiation by which we see the stars.

31:3 Artificial Radioactivity

Marie and Pierre Curie had noted as early as 1899 that substances placed close to radioactive uranium became radioactive themselves. In 1934 Irene Joliot-Curie and Frederic Joliot bombarded aluminum with alpha particles, producing neutrons by the reaction

$$^4_2He + ^{27}_{13}Al \rightarrow ^{30}_{15}P + ^1_0n$$

In addition to neutrons, the Curies found another particle coming from the aluminum, a positively-charged electron, or positron. The positron, a particle with the same mass as the electron but with a positive charge, had been discovered two years earlier by American Carl Anderson. The most interesting result of the Curies' experiment was that positrons continued to be emitted after the alpha bombardment stopped. The positrons were found to come from the phosphorus isotope $^{30}_{15}P$. The Curies had produced a radioactive isotope not previously known.

Radioactive isotopes can be formed from stable isotopes by bombardment with alpha particles, protons, neutrons, electrons, or gamma rays. The resulting unstable nuclei emit radiation until they are transmuted into stable isotopes. The radioactive nuclei may emit alpha, beta, and gamma radiation as well as positrons.

Artificially produced radioactive isotopes have many uses, especially in medicine. In many medical applications, patients are given radioactive isotopes that are absorbed by specific parts of the body. The detection of the decay products of these isotopes allows doctors to trace the movement of the isotopes, and of the molecules to which they are attached, through the body. For that reason, these isotopes are called tracer isotopes. Iodine, for example, is primarily used in the thyroid gland. A patient is given an iodine compound containing radioactive $^{131}_{53}I$. The iodine concentrates in the thyroid gland. A physician uses a Geiger-Mueller counter to monitor the activity of $^{131}_{53}I$ in the region of the thyroid. The amount of iodine taken up by this gland is a measure of its ability to function.

A recently invented instrument, the Positron Emission Tomography Scanner, or PET scanner, uses isotopes that emit positrons. The positron annihilates an electron, emitting two gamma rays. The PET scanner detects the gammas and pinpoints the location of the positron-emitting isotope. A computer is then used to make a three-dimensional map of the isotope distribution. By this means details such as the use of nutrients in particular regions of the brain can be traced. For example, if a person in a

Bombardment of nuclei can produce radioactive isotopes not otherwise found in nature.

SUGGESTION: Unfortunately, there are few good radioisotopes available for the elements most common in tissue, C, H, O, and N.

Tracer isotopes allow doctors to follow the path of molecules through the body.

The PET scanner makes a three-dimensional map of the distribution of decaying nuclei in the body.

a

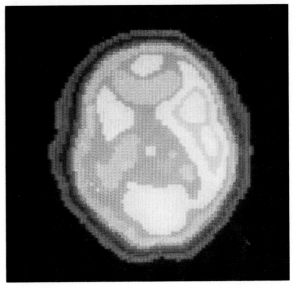

b

PET scanner were solving a physics problem, more nutrients would flow to the part of the brain being used to solve the problem. The decay of the positrons in this part of the brain would increase, and the PET scanner could map this area.

Another use of radioactivity in medicine is the destruction of cells. Often gamma rays from the isotope $^{60}_{27}$Co are used to treat cancer patients. The ionizing radiation produced by radioactive iodine can be used to destroy cells in a diseased thyroid gland, with minimal harm to the rest of the body. Another method of reducing damage to healthy cells is to use unstable particles produced by particle accelerators like the synchrotron. These unstable particles pass through body tissue without doing damage. When they decay, however, the emitted particles destroy cells. The physician adjusts the accelerator so the particles decay only in the cancerous tissue.

FIGURE 31–2. PET scanner and results.

Ionizing radiation can destroy cancerous cells.

Practice Exercises

5. Use Table C–5 of the Appendix to complete the following nuclear equations.

   a. $^{14}_{6}C \rightarrow ? + ^{0}_{-1}e$

   b. $^{55}_{24}Cr \rightarrow ? + ^{0}_{-1}e$

6. Write the nuclear equation for the transmutation of a uranium isotope, $^{238}_{92}U$, into a thorium isotope, $^{234}_{90}Th$, by emission of an alpha particle.

7. A radioactive polonium isotope, $^{214}_{84}Po$, undergoes alpha decay and becomes lead. Write the nuclear equation.

8. Write the nuclear equations for the beta decay of these isotopes.

   a. $^{210}_{82}Pb$ c. $^{234}_{90}Th$

   b. $^{210}_{83}Bi$ d. $^{239}_{93}Np$

DEMONSTRATION: See the Teacher Guide.

31:4   Nuclear Fission

The possibility of obtaining useful forms of energy from nuclear reactions was discussed in the 1930s. The most promising results came from bombarding substances with neutrons. In Italy, in 1934, Enrico Fermi and Emilio Segré produced many new radioactive isotopes by bombarding uranium with neutrons. They believed they had formed new elements with atomic numbers larger than 92, that of uranium.

German chemists Otto Hahn and Fritz Strassmann made careful chemical studies of the results of bombardment of uranium by neutrons. In 1939 their analyses showed that the resulting atoms acted chemically like barium. The two chemists could not understand how barium, with an atomic number of 56, could be produced from uranium. One week later Lise Meitner and Otto Frisch proposed that the neutrons had caused an "explosion" of the uranium into two smaller nuclei, with a large release of energy. A division of a nucleus into two or more fragments is called **fission.** The possibility that fission could be not only a source of energy, but an explosive weapon, was immediately realized by many scientists.

> Fission is the splitting of a nucleus into two or more fragments of almost equal size. Fission is accompanied by the release of large amounts of energy.

The uranium isotope $^{235}_{92}U$ undergoes fission when bombarded with neutrons. The elements barium and krypton are common results of fission, as shown in Figure 31–3. The reaction is

$$^1_0n + ^{235}_{92}U \rightarrow ^{92}_{36}Kr + ^{141}_{56}Ba + 3\ ^1_0n + 200\ \text{MeV}$$

The energy released by each fission can be found by calculating the masses of the atoms on each side of the equation. In the uranium-235 reaction, the total mass on the right side of the equation is 0.215 u smaller than that on the left. The energy equivalent of this mass is 3.21×10^{-11} J, or 200 MeV.

For Your Information

> The energy produced by the breaking down of the atom is a very poor kind of thing. Anyone who expects a source of power from the transformation of these atoms is talking moonshine.
> –Ernest Rutherford
> *Physics Today*, 1970

SUGGESTION: Some say the chain reaction was the beginning of the "atomic age."

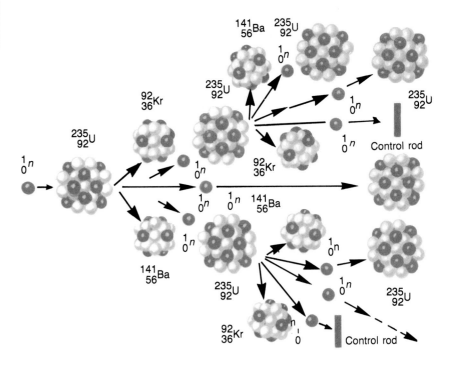

FIGURE 31–3. The nuclear fission chain of uranium-235 takes place in the core of a nuclear reactor.

Once the fission process is started, the neutron needed to cause the fission of additional $^{235}_{92}U$ nuclei can be one of the three neutrons produced by an earlier fission. If one or more of the neutrons causes a fission, that fission releases three more neutrons, each of which can cause more fission. This process is called a **chain reaction.**

In a chain reaction, the neutrons released by one fissioning nucleus induce other fissions.

31:5 Nuclear Reactors

Most of the neutrons released by the fission of $^{235}_{92}U$ atoms are moving at high speed and are unable to cause the fission of another $^{235}_{92}U$ atom. In addition, naturally occurring uranium consists of less than 1% $^{235}_{92}U$ and more than 99% $^{238}_{92}U$. When a $^{238}_{92}U$ nucleus absorbs a fast neutron it does not undergo fission, but becomes a new isotope, $^{239}_{92}U$. The absorption of neutrons by $^{238}_{92}U$ keeps most of the neutrons from reaching the fissionable $^{235}_{92}U$ atoms.

A slow neutron is a more effective bombarding particle than a fast neutron.

Fermi suggested that a chain reaction would occur if the uranium were broken up into small pieces and placed in a material that can slow down, or moderate, the fast neutrons. When a neutron collides with a light atom, it transfers momentum and energy to the atom. In this way the neutron loses energy. The **moderator** creates many slow neutrons, which are more likely to be absorbed by $^{235}_{92}U$ than by $^{238}_{92}U$. The larger number of slow neutrons greatly increases the probability that a neutron released by a fissioning $^{235}_{92}U$ nucleus will cause another $^{235}_{92}U$ nucleus to fission. If there is enough $^{235}_{92}U$ in the sample, a chain reaction can occur.

The lightest atom, hydrogen, would be an ideal moderator. Fast neutrons, however, cause a nuclear reaction with normal hydrogen nuclei, ^1_1H. For this reason, when Fermi produced the first controlled chain reaction on December 2, 1942, he used graphite (carbon) as a moderator. Heavy water, in which the hydrogen, ^1_1H, is replaced by the isotope deuterium, ^2_1H, does not absorb fast neutrons. As a result, heavy water is used as a moderator with natural uranium in the Canadian CANDU reactors.

Ordinary water can be used as a moderator if the number of $^{235}_{92}U$ nuclei in the uranium sample is increased. The process that increases the number of fissionable nuclei is called enrichment. Enrichment of uranium is difficult and requires large, expensive equipment. The United States government operates the plants that produce enriched uranium for most of the nuclear reactors in the western world.

A nuclear reactor consists of about 200 metric tons of uranium sealed in hundreds of metal rods. The rods are immersed in water. Water not only is the moderator, but also transfers thermal energy from the fissioning uranium. Between the uranium rods are rods of cadmium metal. Cadmium absorbs neutrons easily. The cadmium rods are moved in and out of the reactor to control the rate of the chain reaction. Thus the rods are called **control rods.** When the control rods are inserted completely into the reactor they absorb enough neutrons to prevent the chain reaction. As they are removed from the reactor the rate of energy release increases.

Energy released by the fission heats the water surrounding the uranium rods. As shown in Figure 31−5, this water is pumped to a heat exchanger, where it causes other water to boil. The steam produced turns turbines. The turbines are connected to generators that produce electrical energy.

FIGURE 31−4. Diagram of a carbon-moderated nuclear reactor indicating graphite block moderators, the cadmium control rods, and the uranium-235 fuel cylinders (a). Photograph of a water-moderated reactor. The blue glow in the water surrounding the reactor core is called the Cerenkov effect (b).

a

Uranium fuel rods

Cadmium control rods

Carbon (graphite) blocks

b

For Your Information

SUGGESTION: Have the students make reports on Three Mile Island and Chernobyl.

SUGGESTION: France gets a very large percent of its electric energy from nuclear power plants.

SUGGESTION: Hot springs are warmed by nuclear power plants in Earth's interior. Natural radioactive decay of atomic nuclei in Earth's interior gives off heat.

FIGURE 31–5. In a nuclear power plant, the thermal energy released in nuclear reactions is converted to electric energy.

A breeder reactor produces more atoms of fissionable material than it originally contained.

Fusion is the union of small nuclei to form larger nuclei.

At present about 10% of the electricity used in the United States is produced by nuclear energy.

Fission of $^{235}_{92}$U nuclei produces Kr, Ba, and other atoms in the fuel rods. Most of these atoms are radioactive. About once a year some of the uranium fuel rods must be replaced. The old rods can no longer be used in the reactor, but they are still extremely radioactive and must be stored in safe locations. Research is now being done on methods of safe, permanent storage of these radioactive waste products. Among the waste products is an isotope of plutonium, $^{239}_{94}$Pu. This isotope is extremely toxic and can also be used in nuclear weapons. There is hope that in the future this fissionable isotope might be removed from radioactive waste and recycled to fuel other reactors.

The world's supply of uranium is limited. If nuclear reactors are used to supply a large fraction of the world's energy, uranium will become scarce. In order to extend the supply of uranium, **breeder reactors** are being developed. When a reactor contains both plutonium and $^{238}_{92}$U, the plutonium will undergo fission just as $^{235}_{92}$U does. Many of the free neutrons from the fission are absorbed by the $^{238}_{92}$U to produce additional $^{239}_{94}$Pu. For every two plutonium atoms that undergo fission, three new ones are formed. More fissionable fuel can be recovered from this reactor than was originally present. Thus the reactor "breeds" plutonium. Research on breeder reactors is underway in France, the United States, and the Soviet Union.

31:6 Nuclear Fusion

In nuclear fusion, nuclei with small masses combine to form a nucleus with a larger mass. In the process energy is released. The larger nucleus is more tightly bound (Figure 31–1) so its mass is less than the sum of the masses of the smaller nuclei. A typical example of fusion is the process

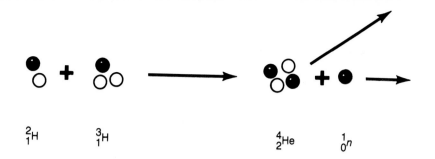

$$\begin{matrix} {}^{2}_{1}\text{H} & {}^{3}_{1}\text{H} & {}^{4}_{2}\text{He} & {}^{1}_{0}n \end{matrix}$$

FIGURE 31–6. The fusion of deuterium and tritium produces helium.

Fusion reactions release even larger quantities of energy per mass of matter than fission reactions.

that occurs in the sun. Four hydrogen nuclei (protons) fuse in several steps to form one helium nucleus. The mass of the four protons is greater than the mass of the helium nucleus that is produced. The energy equivalent of this mass difference is transferred to the kinetic energy of the resultant particles. The energy released by the fusion of one helium nucleus is 25 MeV. In comparison, the energy released when one dynamite molecule reacts chemically is about 20 eV, almost one million times smaller.

Fusion in the sun occurs in steps. The most important process is called the proton-proton chain.

$$\begin{aligned} {}^{1}_{1}\text{H} + {}^{1}_{1}\text{H} &\rightarrow {}^{2}_{1}\text{H} + {}^{0}_{+1}e + {}^{0}_{0}\nu \\ {}^{1}_{1}\text{H} + {}^{2}_{1}\text{H} &\rightarrow {}^{3}_{2}\text{He} \\ {}^{3}_{2}\text{He} + {}^{3}_{2}\text{He} &\rightarrow {}^{4}_{2}\text{He} + 2\,{}^{1}_{1}\text{H} \end{aligned}$$

The first two reactions must occur twice in order to produce the two ${}^{3}_{2}\text{He}$ particles needed for the final reaction. The net result is that four protons produce one ${}^{4}_{2}\text{He}$, two positrons, and two neutrinos.

Fusion reactions take place only when the nuclei have large amounts of thermal energy. The thermal energy must be large enough to overcome the electrical repulsion between the nuclei. For this reason fusion reactions are often called **thermonuclear reactions.** The proton-proton chain requires temperatures of about 2×10^{7} K, temperatures found in the center of the sun. Fusion reactions also occur in a "hydrogen," or thermonuclear, bomb. In this device, the high temperature necessary to produce the fusion reaction is produced by exploding a uranium, or "atomic," bomb.

31:7 Controlled Fusion

Could the huge energy available from fusion be used safely on Earth? Safe energy requires control of the fusion reaction. One reaction that might produce controlled fusion is

$$ {}^{2}_{1}\text{H} + {}^{3}_{1}\text{H} \rightarrow {}^{4}_{2}\text{He} + {}^{1}_{0}n + 17.6 \text{ MeV} $$

Deuterium, ${}^{2}_{1}\text{H}$, is available in large quantities in seawater, and tritium, ${}^{3}_{1}\text{H}$, is easily produced from deuterium. Therefore controlled fusion would give the world an almost limitless source of energy. In order to control fusion, however, some very difficult problems must be solved.

Fusion reactions require that the atoms be raised to temperatures of millions of degrees. No material we now have can withstand temperatures even as high as 5000 K. In addition, the atoms would be cooled if they touched confining material. Magnetic fields, however, can confine

The Tokamak reactor is a device for studying controlled fusion reactions.

Laser beams are used to implode tiny glass spheres containing liquefied deuterium and tritium. The compression creates temperatures high enough to produce fusion.

$^2_1 H = 2.014102 \text{ u}$
$^3_1 H = 3.016049 \text{ u}$

charged particles. Energy is added to the atoms, stripping away electrons and forming separated plasmas of electrons and ions. A sudden increase in the magnetic field will compress the plasma, raising its temperature. Electromagnetic fields and fast moving neutral atoms can also increase the energy of the plasma. Using this technique, hydrogen nuclei have been fused into helium. The energy released by the reaction becomes the kinetic energy of the neutron and helium ion. This energy would be used to heat some other material, possibly liquified lithium. The lithium, in turn, would boil water, producing steam to turn electric generators.

A useful reactor must produce more energy than it consumes. So far the energy produced by fusion has been only a tiny fraction of the energy required to create and hold the plasma. The confinement of plasma is a very difficult problem because instabilities in the magnetic field allow the plasma to escape. One of the most promising fusion reactors under development is the Tokamak reactor. The Tokamak provides a doughnut-shaped magnetic field in which the plasma is confined. Research has led to the confinement of larger amounts of plasma for longer periods of time. The next large Tokamak built should produce as much energy as it consumes.

A second approach to controlled fusion is called inertial confinement. Deuterium and tritium are liquefied under high pressure and confined in tiny glass spheres. Multiple laser beams are directed at the spheres. The energy deposited by the lasers causes the pellets to implode, or burst inward. The resulting tremendous compression of the hydrogen raises the temperature to levels needed for fusion.

Practice Exercise

9. **a.** Calculate the mass defect for the deuterium-tritium fusion reaction used in the Tokamak, $^2_1 H + ^3_1 H \rightarrow ^4_2 He + ^1_0 n$.

    b. Find the energy equivalent of the mass defect.

SUMMARY

1. The strong force binds the nucleus together. **31:1**

2. The energy released in a nuclear reaction can be calculated by finding the difference in mass of the particles before and after the reaction. $E = mc^2$ is then used to find the energy equivalent of the mass. The energy equivalent of 1 u is 931 MeV. **31:2**

3. Bombardment can produce radioactive isotopes not found in nature. These are called artificial radioactive nuclei and are often used in medicine. **31:3**

4. In nuclear fission the uranium nucleus is split into two smaller nuclei with a release of neutrons and energy. **31:4**

5. Nuclear reactors use the energy released in fission to generate electrical energy. **31:5**

6. The fusion of hydrogen nuclei into a helium nucleus releases the energy that causes stars to shine. **31:6**

7. Development of a process for controlling fusion for use on Earth might safely provide large amounts of energy. **31:7**

QUESTIONS

1. What is the mass defect of a nucleus? To what is it related?

2. Use the graph of binding energy per nucleon to determine if the reaction $_1^2H + _1^1H = _2^3He$ is energetically possible.

3. A newspaper claims that scientists have been able to cause iron nuclei to undergo fission. Why or why not could this report be true?

4. Give examples of naturally and artificially produced radioactive isotopes. Explain the difference.

5. What two processes are being studied to control the fusion process?

6. Fission and fusion are opposite processes. How can each release energy?

7. List three medical uses of radioactivity.

8. What critical process must occur for a chain reaction to take place?

9. What role does a moderator play in a fission reactor?

10. What is the main difference between the fission process in an atomic bomb and in a reactor?

APPLYING CONCEPTS

1. In a nuclear reactor, the water that passes through the core of the reactor flows through one loop while the water that produces steam for the turbines flows through a second loop. Why are there two loops?

2. Breeder reactors generate more fuel than they consume. Is this a violation of the law of conservation of energy? Explain.

3. In a fission reaction, binding energy is converted into thermal energy. Objects with thermal energy have random kinetic energy. What objects have kinetic energy after a fission reaction?

4. Scientists think Jupiter might have become a star, but the temperatures inside the planet are too low. Why must a star have a very high internal temperature?

5. The reactor at the Chernobyl power station that exploded and burned used blocks of graphite. What was the purpose of the graphite?

6. Why might a fusion reactor be safer than a fission reactor?

7. Explain how it might be possible for a fission reactor to produce more fissionable fuel than it consumes. What are such reactors called?

8. **a.** Does the fission of a uranium nucleus or the fusion of four hydrogen nuclei produce more energy?

   b. Does the fission of a kilogram of uranium nuclei or the fusion of a gram of deuterium produce more energy?

   c. Why are your answers to parts **a** and **b** different?

EXERCISES

1. A mercury isotope, $^{200}_{80}Hg$, is bombarded with deuterons (^2_1H). The mercury nucleus absorbs the deuteron and then emits an alpha particle.

   a. What element is formed by this reaction?

   b. Write the nuclear equation for the reaction.

2. A nitrogen isotope, $^{14}_7N$, has a nuclear mass of approximately 14.00307 u.

   a. Calculate the mass defect of the nucleus.

   b. What is the binding energy of this nucleus?

3. Assume that each nucleon shares equally in the binding energy of the nucleus. Calculate the energy needed to eject a neutron from the nucleus of a nitrogen isotope, $^{14}_7N$.

4. A carbon isotope, $^{13}_6C$, has a nuclear mass of 13.00335 u.

   a. What is the mass defect of this isotope?

   b. What is the binding energy of its nucleus?

5. The two positively-charged protons in a helium nucleus are separated by about 2.0×10^{-15} m. Find the electric force of repulsion between the two protons. The result will give you an indication of the strength of the strong nuclear force.

6. When bombarded by protons, a lithium isotope, ^7_3Li, absorbs a proton and then ejects two alpha particles. Write the nuclear equation for this reaction.

7. Complete the nuclear equations for these transmutations.

   a. $^{30}_{15}P \rightarrow ? + ^0_{+1}e$

   b. $^{205}_{82}Pb \rightarrow ? + ^0_{+1}e$

8. The radioactive nucleus indicated in each equation disintegrates by emitting a positron. Complete each nuclear equation.

   a. $^{21}_{11}Na \rightarrow ? + ^0_{+1}e$

   b. $^{49}_{24}Cr \rightarrow ? + ^0_{+1}e$

9. Each of the nuclei given below can absorb an alpha particle. Complete the equations. Assume that no secondary particles are emitted by the nucleus that absorb the alpha particle.

   a. $^{14}_7N + ^4_2He \rightarrow ?$

   b. $^{27}_{13}Al + ^4_2He \rightarrow ?$

10. In each of these reactions, a neutron is absorbed by a nucleus. The nucleus then emits a proton. Complete the equations.

   a. $^{65}_{29}Cu + ^1_0n \rightarrow ? + ^1_1H$

   b. $^{14}_7N + ^1_0n \rightarrow ? + ^1_1H$

11. When a boron isotope, $^{10}_5B$, is bombarded with neutrons, it absorbs a neutron and then emits an alpha particle.

   a. What element is also formed?

   b. Write the nuclear equation for this reaction.

12. When a boron isotope, $^{11}_5B$, is bombarded with protons, it absorbs a proton and emits a neutron.

   a. What element is formed?

   b. Write the nuclear equation for this reaction.

   c. The isotope formed is radioactive, decaying by emitting a positron. Write the nuclear equation for this reaction.

PROBLEMS

1. The isotope most commonly used in PET scanners is $^{18}_9F$.

   a. What element is formed by the positron emission of this element?

   b. Write the equation for this reaction.

   c. The half-life of $^{18}_9F$ is 110 min. A solution containing 10.0 mg of this isotope is injected into a patient at 8:00 a.m. How much remains at 4:00 p.m.?

2. One fusion reaction is $^2_1H + ^2_1H \rightarrow ^4_2He$.

   a. What energy is released in this reaction?

   b. Deuterium exists as a diatomic (two atom) molecule. One mole of deuterium contains 6.02×10^{23} molecules. Find the amount of energy released, in joules, in the fusion of one mole of deuterium molecules.

   c. When 6.02×10^{23} molecules of deuterium burn, they release 2.9×10^6 J. How many moles of deuterium molecules would have to burn to release just the energy released by the fusion of one mole of deuterium molecules?

3. The energy released in the fission of one atom of $^{235}_{92}U$ is 2.00×10^2 MeV. One mole of uranium atoms (6.02×10^{23} atoms) has a mass of 0.235 kg.

   a. How many atoms are in 1.00 kg $^{235}_{92}U$?

   b. How much energy would be released if all of the atoms in 1.00 kg of $^{235}_{92}U$ underwent fission?

c. A typical large nuclear reactor produces fission energy at a rate of 3600 MW (3.0×10^9 J/s). How many kilograms of $^{235}_{92}U$ are used each second?

d. How much $^{235}_{92}U$ would be used in one year?

4. The first atomic bomb released an energy equivalent of 20 kilotons of TNT. One kiloton of TNT is the equivalent of 5.0×10^{12} J. What was the mass of the uranium-235 that was fissioned to produce this energy?

5. The basements of many homes contain the rock granite. Granite contains small amounts of radioactive uranium and thorium. Uranium-238 goes through a series of decays before reaching a stable lead isotope. $^{238}_{92}U$ emits an alpha, leaving an isotope that decays by emitting a beta. The next decay is again a β, followed by three α decays. The result is the gas radon. Write the equations for these decays.

6. A $^{232}_{92}U$ nucleus (mass = 232.0372 u) decays to $^{228}_{90}Th$ (mass = 228.0287 u) by emitting an α particle (mass = 4.0026 u) with *K.E.* of 5.3 MeV. What must be the *K.E.* of the recoiling thorium nucleus?

7. The binding energy for ^4_2He is 28.3 MeV. Calculate the mass of a helium nucleus in atomic mass units to 4 decimal places.

READINGS

Boyd, Derek A., "Taking the Temperature of a Tokamak." *The Physics Teacher,* January, 1987.

Aldersey-Williams, H., "Sharpest Look Yet Inside the Body." *Popular Science,* June, 1988.

Eliot, Marshall, "Hanford's Radioactive Tumbleweed." *Science,* June 26, 1987.

Greiner, Walter, "Hot Nuclear Matter." *Scientific American,* January, 1985.

Lightman, Alan, "To Cleave an Atom." *Science 84,* November, 1984.

APPENDIX A

Chapter 1

1. a. 5.8×10^3 m   **c.** 3.02×10^8 m
   b. 4.5×10^5 m   **d.** 8.6×10^{10} m

2. a. 5.08×10^{-4} kg   **c.** 3.600×10^{-3} kg
   b. 4.5×10^{-7} kg   **d.** 4×10^{-3} kg

3. a. 3×10^8 s
   b. 1.86×10^5 s
   c. 9.3×10^7 s

4. a. $(1.1 \text{ cm})\dfrac{(1 \times 10^{-2} \text{ m})}{(1 \text{ cm})} = 1.1 \times 10^{-2}$ m

   b. $(76.2 \text{ pm})\dfrac{(1 \times 10^{-12} \text{ m})}{(1 \text{ pm})} = 76.2 \times 10^{-12}$ m
   $= 7.62 \times 10^{-11}$ m

   c. $(2.1 \text{ km})\dfrac{(1 \times 10^3 \text{ m})}{(1 \text{ km})} = 2.1 \times 10^3$ m

   d. $(0.123 \text{ Mm})\dfrac{(1 \times 10^6 \text{ m})}{(1 \text{ Mm})} = 0.123 \times 10^6$ m
   $= 1.23 \times 10^5$ m

5. a. 1.47×10^{-3} kg
   b. 1.1×10^{-8} kg
   c. 7.23×10^3 kg
   d. 4.78×10^{-4} kg

6. a. 8×10^{-7} kg
   b. 7×10^{-3} kg
   c. 3.96×10^{-19} kg
   d. 4.6×10^{-12} kg

7. a. 2×10^{-8} m^2
   b. -1.52×10^{-11} m^2
   c. 3.0×10^{-9} m^2
   d. 0.46×10^{-18} m$^2 = 4.6 \times 10^{-19}$ m^2

8. a. 5.0×10^{-7} mg $+ 4 \times 10^{-8}$ mg
   $= 5.0 \times 10^{-7}$ mg $+ 0.4 \times 10^{-7}$ mg $= 5.4 \times 10^{-7}$ mg
   b. 6.0×10^{-3} mg $+ 2 \times 10^{-4}$ mg
   $= 6.0 \times 10^{-3}$ mg $+ 0.2 \times 10^{-3}$ mg $= 6.2 \times 10^{-3}$ mg
   c. 3.0×10^{-14} mg $+ 2 \times 10^{-15}$ mg
   $= 3.0 \times 10^{-14}$ mg $+ 0.2 \times 10^{-14}$ mg
   $= 3.2 \times 10^{-14}$ mg
   d. 4.0×10^{-12} mg $+ 6.0 \times 10^{-13}$ mg $= 4.6 \times 10^{-12}$ mg

9. a. 4.6×10^{-7} m
   b. 5.8×10^{-3} m
   c. 1.0×10^{-14} g
   d. 7.9×10^3 m

10. a. $(2 \times 10^4 \text{ m})(4 \times 10^8 \text{ m}) = 8 \times 10^{4+8}$ m^2
   $= 8 \times 10^{12}$ m^2
   b. $(3 \times 10^4 \text{ m})(2 \times 10^6 \text{ m}) = 6 \times 10^{4+6}$ m^2
   $= 6 \times 10^{10}$ m^2
   c. $(6 \times 10^{-4} \text{ m})(5 \times 10^{-8} \text{ m}) = 30 \times 10^{-4-8}$ m^2
   $= 3 \times 10^{-11}$ m^2
   d. $(2.50 \times 10^{-7} \text{ m})(2.50 \times 10^{16} \text{ m})$
   $= 6.25 \times 10^{-7+16}$ m$^2 = 6.25 \times 10^9$ m^2

11. a. $\dfrac{6 \times 10^8 \text{ kg}}{2 \times 10^4 \text{ m}^3} = 3 \times 10^{8-4}$ kg/m$^3 = 3 \times 10^4$ kg/m^3

   b. $\dfrac{6 \times 10^8 \text{ kg}}{2 \times 10^{-4} \text{ m}^3} = 3 \times 10^{8-(-4)}$ kg/m$^3 = 3 \times 10^{12}$ kg/m^3

   c. $\dfrac{6 \times 10^{-8} \text{ m}}{2 \times 10^4 \text{ s}} = 3 \times 10^{-8-4}$ m/s $= 3 \times 10^{-12}$ m/s

   d. $\dfrac{6 \times 10^{-8} \text{ m}}{2 \times 10^{-4} \text{ s}} = 3 \times 10^{-8-(-4)}$ m/s $= 3 \times 10^{-4}$ m/s

12. a. $\dfrac{(3 \times 10^4 \text{ kg})(4 \times 10^4 \text{ m})}{6 \times 10^4 \text{ s}} = \dfrac{12 \times 10^{4+4} \text{ kg} \cdot \text{m}}{6 \times 10^4 \text{ s}}$
   $= 2 \times 10^{8-4}$ kg $\cdot$ m/s $= 2 \times 10^4$ kg $\cdot$ m/s
   The evaluation may be done in several other ways.
   For example
   $\dfrac{(3 \times 10^4 \text{ kg})(4 \times 10^4 \text{ m})}{6 \times 10^4 \text{ s}}$
   $= (0.5 \times 10^{4-4} \text{ kg/s}) \ (4 \times 10^4 \text{ m})$
   $= (0.5 \text{ kg/s})(4 \times 10^4 \text{ m}) = 2 \times 10^4$ kg $\cdot$ m/s
   b. $\dfrac{(2.5 \times 10^6 \text{ kg})(6 \times 10^4 \text{ m})}{5 \times 10^{-2} \text{ s}^2} = \dfrac{15 \times 10^{6+4} \text{ kg} \cdot \text{m}}{5 \times 10^{-2} \text{ s}^2}$
   $= 3 \times 10^{10-(-2)}$ kg $\cdot$ m/s$^2 = 3 \times 10^{12}$ kg $\cdot$ m/s^2

13. a. 4   **c.** 2   **e.** 2
   b. 3   **d.** 4   **f.** 3

14. a. 2 **b.** 4 **c.** 4 **d.** 3 **e.** 4 **f.** 3

15. 26.3 cm (rounded from 26.281 cm)

16. a. 2.5 g (rounded from 2.536 g)
   b. 475 m (rounded from 474.5832 m)

17. a. 3.0×10^2 cm^2 (the result 301.3 cm^2 expressed to two significant digits. Note that the expression in the form 300 cm^2 would not indicate how many of the digits are significant.)
   b. 13.6 km^2 (the result 13.597335 expressed to three significant digits)

18. a. 2.73 cm/s (the result 2.726045 . . . cm/s expressed to three significant figures)
   b. 0.253 cm/s (the result 0.253354 . . . cm/s expressed to three significant figures)

c. 400 m (the result 428 expressed to 1 significant digit)

d. 6.6 cm (the result 6.567 . . . expressed to 2 significant digits)

Chapter 2

1. $mx + b = y$, $b = y - mx$

2. a. $vt = d$, $v = d/t$

   b. $t = d/v$, $tv = d$, $v = d/t$

   c. $v^2/2d = a$, $v^2 = 2ad$, $v = \pm\sqrt{2ad}$

   d. $v/a = b/c$, $v = ab/c$

3. a. $E/s = f$, $E = fs$

   b. $2E/v^2 = m$, $2E = mv^2$, $E = mv^2/2$

   c. $E/c^2 = m$, $E = mc^2$

4. $v_o^2 + 2ad = v^2$, $2ad = v^2 - v_o^2$, $d = (v^2 - v_o^2)/2a$

5. a. $v_o + at = v$, $at = v - v_o$, $a = (v - v_o)/t$

   b. $v_ot + (1/2)at^2 = y$, $(1/2)at^2 = y - v_ot$, $at^2 = 2(y - v_ot)$, $a = 2(y - v_ot)/t^2$

   c. $v_o^2 + 2ay = v^2$, $2ay = v^2 - v_o^2$, $a = (v^2 - v_o^2)/2y$

   d. $\sqrt{2as} = v$, $2as = v^2$, $a = v^2/2s$

6. a. $fx = w$, $x = w/f$

   b. $gx = f$, $x = f/g$

   c. $x/y - m = n$, $x/y = n + m$, $x = (n + m)y$

   d. $ax^2 - d_o = d$, $ax^2 = d + d_o$, $x^2 = (d + d_o)/a$, $x = \pm\sqrt{(d + d_o)a}$

7. a. $A = (0.2 \text{ cm})(30 \text{ cm}) = 6 \text{ cm}^2$

   b. $P = 0.25 \text{ m} + 0.25 \text{ m} + 2.00 \text{ m} + 2.00 \text{ m} = 4.50 \text{ m}$

8. a. incorrect; area has units m^2 and (length)(width)(height) has units m^3

   b. correct since distance/speed has units $m/(m/s) = s$

   c. incorrect since (speed)(time)^2 has units $(m/s)(s)^2 = m \cdot s$

Chapter 3

1. $\bar{v} = d/t = (13 \text{ km})/(2.0 \text{ h})$
= 6.5 km/h; (6.5 km/h)(1 h/3600 s)(1000 m/1 km)
= 1.8 m/s or
(6.5 km/h)(1000 m/km)/(3600 s/h) = 1.8 m/s

2. $\bar{v} = d/t = (1.00 \times 10^2 \text{ m})/(12.20 \text{ s})$
= 8.20 m/s; (8.20 m/s)(1 km/1000 m)(3600 s/1 h)
= 29.5 km/h or
(8.20 m/s)(3600 s/h)/(1000 m/km)
= 29.5 km/h

3. $d = vt = (3.00 \times 10^8 \text{ m/s})(8.3 \text{ min})(60 \text{ s/min})$
= 1.5×10^{11} m = 1.5×10^8 km

4. Using $d = vt$ with $v = 10$ m/s:

t	d
1 h = 3600 s	36 000 m
1 min = 60 s	600 m
1 s	10 m
1 ms = 10^{-3} s	10×10^{-3} m = 0 mm
1 μs = 10^{-6} s	10×10^{-6} m = 10 μm
1 ns = 10^{-9} s	10×10^{-9} m = 10 nm

5. average speed = (distance traveled during time interval)/(time) = (5.0 km + 5.0 km)/(40 min) = (0.25 km/min)(60 min/h) = 15 km/h, average velocity = (displacement during time interval)/(time) = (+5.0 km − 5.0 km)/(40 min) = 0

6. a. $t = d/v = (324 \text{ m})/(720.0 \text{ m/s}) = 0.450$ s

   b. $v = (720.0 \text{ m/s})(3600 \text{ s/h})/(1000 \text{ m/km})$
= 2592 km/h

7. a. $v = (+20 \text{ m/s}) + (+3 \text{ m/s}) = +23$ m/s

   b. $v = (+20 \text{ m/s}) + (-2 \text{ m/s}) = +18$ m/s

8. $v = 105 \text{ km/h} - 90 \text{ km/h} = 15$ km/h

9. $a = (v_f - v_i)/t = (36 \text{ m/s} - 4.0 \text{ m/s})/4.0 \text{ s}$
= +8.0 m/s^2

10. $a = (v_f - v_i)/t = (15 \text{ m/s} - 36 \text{ m/s})/3.0 \text{ s} = -7.0$ m/s^2

11. $a = (v_f - v_i)/t = (+4.5 \text{ m/s} - (-3.0 \text{ m/s}))/2.5 \text{ s}$
= +3.0 m/s^2

12. $a = (v_f - v_i)/t = (0 - 25 \text{ m/s})/3.0 \text{ s} = -8.3$ m/s^2

13. Since acceleration varies inversely with time, the acceleration would be one-half that found above.

14. $v_f = v_i + at = 0 + (7.5 \text{ m/s}^2)(4.5 \text{ s}) = 34$ m/s

15. a. $v_f = v_i + at = +2.0 \text{ m/s} + (-0.5 \text{ m/s}^2)(2.0 \text{ s})$
= +1.0 m/s

   b. $v_f = v_i + at = +2.0 \text{ m/s} + (-0.5 \text{ m/s}^2)(6.0 \text{ s})$
= −1.0 m/s

   c. From $v_f = v_i + at$, the effect of a negative acceleration is to add a negative velocity to the initial velocity. This is seen in the motion of the ball. The velocity of the ball decreases with time as it rolls up the hill, passes through zero, and becomes more and more negative as the ball rolls with increasing speed back down the hill.

16. 30 km/h = 8.3 m/s, $v_f = v_i + at$
= +8.3 m/s + (+3.5 m/s^2)(6.8 s) = 32 m/s = 120 km/h

17. $d = (v_f + v_i)t/2 = (41 \text{ m/s} + 0)(8.0 \text{ s})/2 = 160$ m

18. $d = (v_f + v_i)t/2 = (22 \text{ m/s} + 44 \text{ m/s})(11 \text{ s})/2 = 360$ m

19. $d = (v_f + v_i)t/2 = (88 \text{ m/s} + 132 \text{ m/s})(15 \text{ s})/2$
= $+1.7 \times 10^3$ m

20. a. $a = (v_f - v_i)/t$, $t = (v_f - v_i)/a$
= (61 m/s − 0)/(2.5 m/s^2) = 24 s

   b. $d = (v_f + v_i)t/2 = (61 \text{ m/s} + 0)(24 \text{ s})/2 = 730$ m

21. $d = v_it + 1/2at^2 = 0 + (1/2)(+3.00 \text{ m/s}^2)(30.0 \text{ s})^2$
= 1.35×10^3 m

22. $d = v_it + \frac{1}{2}at^2$ with $v_i = 0$, $a = 2d/t^2$
$= 2(110\text{m})/(5.0 \text{ s})^2 = 8.8 \text{ m/s}^2$

23. a. $a = (v_f - v_i)/t = (0 - 88 \text{ m/s})/(11 \text{ s}) = -8.0 \text{ m/s}^2$
  b. $d = v_it + \frac{1}{2}at^2$
  $= (88 \text{ m/s})(11 \text{ s}) + (\frac{1}{2})(-8.0 \text{ m/s}^2)(11 \text{ s})^2 = 480 \text{ m}$

24. a. $a = (v_f - v_i)/t = (0 - 22 \text{ m/s})/(2.0 \text{ s}) = -11 \text{ m/s}^2$
  b. $d = v_it + \frac{1}{2}at^2$
  $= (22 \text{ m/s})(2.0 \text{ s}) + (\frac{1}{2})(-11 \text{ m/s}^2)(2.0 \text{ s})^2 = 22 \text{ m}$

25. $d = v_it + \frac{1}{2}at^2$
  $= +(4.5 \text{ m/s})(12 \text{ s}) + (\frac{1}{2})(+0.40 \text{ m/s}^2)(12 \text{ s})^2 = 83 \text{ m}$

26. a. $d = v_it + \frac{1}{2}at^2$
  $= (+12 \text{ m/s})(6.0 \text{ s}) + \frac{1}{2}(-1.6 \text{ m/s}^2)(6.0 \text{ s})^2 = 43 \text{ m}$
  b. $d = v_it + \frac{1}{2}at^2$
  $= (+12 \text{ m/s})(9.0 \text{ s}) + \frac{1}{2}(-1.6 \text{ m/s}^2)(9.0 \text{ s})^2 = 43 \text{ m}$
  c. The displacements are the same because between these two time intervals, at 7.5 s, the car reached its maximum displacement and began to roll back down the hill.

27. $v_f^2 = v_i^2 + 2ad = (20 \text{ m/s})^2 + 2(3.0 \text{ m/s}^2)(530 \text{ m})$
  $= 3580 \text{ m}^2/\text{s}^2$, so $v_f = 60 \text{ m/s}$

28. $v_f^2 = v_i^2 + 2ad$. Since $v_f = 0$, $v_i^2 = -2ad$
  $= -2(-8.0 \text{ m/s}^2)(484 \text{ m}) = 7744 \text{ m}^2/\text{s}^2$, $v_i = 88 \text{ m/s}$.

29. $v_f^2 = v_i^2 + 2ad$. Since $v_f = 0$, $v_i^2 = -2ad$
  $= -2(-10 \text{ m/s}^2)(60 \text{ m}) = 1200 \text{ m}^2/\text{s}^2$, $v_i = 35 \text{ m/s}$
  $= 130 \text{ km/h}$.
  Yes, the car was exceeding the speed limit.

30. $v_f = v_i + at = 1210 \text{ m/s} + (-150 \text{ m/s}^2)(8.68 \text{ s})$
  $= -92 \text{ m/s}$
  The negative acceleration has reversed the spacecraft's direction of motion.

e. $d = \bar{v}t = (50 \text{ m/s})(3 \text{ s}) = 150 \text{ m}$

2. a. 400 m   **b.** 0 m   **c.** 200 m

3. a. $\bar{v} = \dfrac{\Delta d}{\Delta t} = \dfrac{400 \text{ m}}{40 \text{ s}} = 10 \text{ m/s}$

  b. $\bar{v} = \dfrac{\Delta d}{\Delta t} = \dfrac{0 \text{ m}}{30 \text{ s}} = 0 \text{ m/s}$

  c. $\bar{v} = \dfrac{\Delta d}{\Delta t} = \dfrac{-200 \text{ m}}{20 \text{ s}} = -10 \text{ m/s}$

  d. $\bar{v} = \dfrac{\Delta d}{\Delta t} = \dfrac{-200 \text{ m}}{10 \text{ s}} = -20 \text{ m/s}$

4.

Time Interval (s)	$\bar{v}$ (m/s)
0–10	10
10–20	10
20–30	10
30–40	10
40–50	0
50–60	0
60–70	0
70–80	-10
80–90	-10
90–100	-20

5.

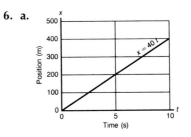

Chapter 4

1. a.

t(s)	d(m)
0	0
1	50
2	100
3	150
4	200
....	.....
10	500

b.

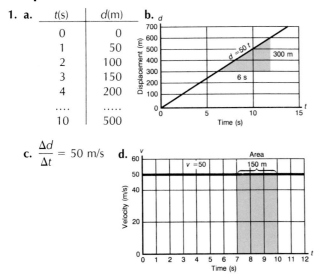

c. $\dfrac{\Delta d}{\Delta t} = 50 \text{ m/s}$ **d.**

6. a.

b. $\dfrac{\Delta x}{\Delta t} = 40 \text{ m/s}$

c.

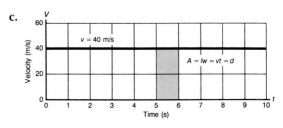

The area under the line is vt and thus represents total distance traveled during a given time interval.

   d. $A = lw = vt = (40\text{ m/s})(1\text{ s}) = 40\text{ m}$

7. a.

   b. 5.0×10^1 m south of location A.

   c. 3.0×10^2 m, south

8. a.

   b.

Chapter 5

1. $F = ma = (275\text{ kg})(-4.50\text{ m/s}^2) = -1.24 \times 10^3$ N
   The force opposes the velocity.

2. $m = F/a = (+140\text{ N})/(+19\text{ m/s}^2) = 7.4$ kg

3. $a = F/m = (+19\text{ N})/(7.3\text{ kg}) = +2.6$ m/s^2

4. $a = F/m = (+1.2 \times 10^{-4}\text{ N})/(7.0 \times 10^{-5}\text{ kg})$
   $= +1.7$ m/s^2

It is moving downward ever slower.

5. a. $W = mg = (2.00\text{ kg})(9.80\text{ m/s}^2) = 19.6$ N
   b. $W = mg = (108\text{ kg})(9.80\text{ m/s}^2) = 1.06 \times 10^3$ N
   c. $W = mg = (870\text{ kg})(9.80\text{ m/s}^2) = 8.53 \times 10^3$ N

6. a. $m = \dfrac{W}{g} = \dfrac{98\text{ N}}{9.80\text{ m/s}^2} = 10$ kg
   b. $m = \dfrac{W}{g} = \dfrac{80\text{ N}}{9.80\text{ m/s}^2} = 8.2$ kg
   c. $m = \dfrac{W}{g} = \dfrac{0.98\text{ N}}{9.80\text{ m/s}^2} = 0.10$ kg

7. 20 N upward

8. a. $W = mg = (75\text{ kg})(9.80\text{ m/s}^2) = 7.4 \times 10^2$ N
   b. $W = mg = (75\text{ kg})(3.8\text{ m/s}^2) = 2.9 \times 10^2$ N
   c. $W = mg = 0$ since $g = 0$

9. $F_f = \mu F_N$, so $\mu = F_f/F_N = (36\text{ N})/(52\text{ N}) = 0.69$

10. $F_f = \mu F_N = (0.12)(52\text{ N} + 650\text{ N}) = 84$ N

11. a. Direction: backwards.
    Size: $F_f = \mu F_N$ where $F_N = W = mg$, so
    $F_f = -(0.50)(750\text{ kg})(9.80\text{ m/s}^2) = -3.7 \times 10^3$ N

    b. Direction: backwards.
    Size: $a = F_f/m = (-3.7 \times 10^3\text{N})/(750\text{ kg})$
    $= -4.9$ m/s^2

    c. $v_f^2 = v_i^2 + 2\,ad$, so
    $d = (v_f^2 - v_i^2)/2a = (0 - (30\text{ m/s})^2)/(-9.8\text{ m/s}^2)$
    $= 92$ m

12. larger since F_f is proportional to μ; shorter distance since, from the solution to Practice Exercise 11, d is inversely proportional to a, and a is proportional to F_f

13. a. $m = W/g = (49\text{ N})/(9.80\text{ m/s}^2) = 5.0$ kg
    b. $ma = F_{net} = F_{appl} + W = 69\text{ N} + (-49\text{ N})$
    $= 20$ N. So $a = F_{net}/m = (20\text{ N})/(5.0\text{ kg}) = 4.0$ m/s^2.

14. a. $m = W/g = (14.7\text{ N})/(9.80\text{ m/s}^2) = 1.5$ kg
    b. $ma = F_{net} = F_{appl} + W = 10.2\text{ N} + (-14.7\text{ N})$
    $= -4.5$ N.
    Thus, $a = F_{net}/m = (-4.5\text{ N})/(1.5\text{ kg}) = -3.0$ m/s^2.

15. a. $W = m/g = (2 \times 10^6\text{ kg})(9.80\text{ m/s}^2) = 20 \times 10^6$ N
    b. $ma = F_{net} = F_{appl} + W$
    $= 30 \times 10^6\text{ N} + (-20 \times 10^6\text{ N}) = 10 \times 10^6$ N.
    Thus, $a = F_{net}/m = (10 \times 10^6\text{ N})/(2 \times 10^6\text{ kg})$
    $= 5.0$ m/s^2
    c. $v = at = (13\text{ m/s}^2)(600\text{ s}) = 7.8$ km/s
    d. It would increase. $a = F/m$. F is constant, m decreases, so a increases.

16. $F_{net} = ma = (1354\text{ kg})(3.0\text{ m/s}^2) = 4.1 \times 10^3$ N.
    $F_{net} = F_{appl} - F_f$, so
    $F_{appl} = F_{net} + F_f = 4.1 \times 10^3\text{ N} + 280$ N
    $= 4.4 \times 10^3$ N

Chapter 6

1. a. 11 km + 11 km = 22 km

   b.

Resultant = 16 km

2.

Resultant = 112 m/s

3. a. By construction:

   b. $t = d/\bar{v} = (136\ m)/(16\ m/s) = 8.5\ s$

   c. $d = \bar{v}t = (9.0\ m/s)(8.5\ s) = 77\ m$

4. By construction:

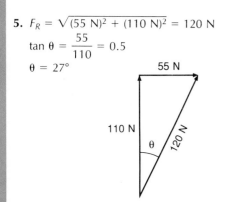

5. $F_R = \sqrt{(55\ N)^2 + (110\ N)^2} = 120\ N$

   $\tan \theta = \dfrac{55}{110} = 0.5$

   $\theta = 27°$

6. a. $v_R = \sqrt{(8.5\ m/s)^2 + (3.8\ m/s)^2} = 9.3\ m/s$

   $\tan \theta = \dfrac{3.8}{8.5} = 0.45,\ \theta = 24°$

   $v_R = 9.3\ m/s$ at 24°

   b. $t = d/\bar{v} = (110\ m)/(8.5\ m/s) = 13\ s$

7. a. $v_R = \sqrt{(3.8\ m/s)^2 + (2.2\ m/s)^2} = 4.4\ m/s$

   $\tan \theta = \dfrac{2.2}{3.8} = 0.58,\ \theta = 30°$

   $v_R = 4.4\ m/s$ at 30°

   b. $t = d/\bar{v} = (41\ m)/(3.8\ m/s) = 11\ s$

   c. $d = \bar{v}t = (2.2\ m/s)(11\ s) = 24\ m$

8. $v_R = \sqrt{(152\ km/h)^2 + (42\ km/h)^2} = 160\ km/h$

   $\tan \theta = \dfrac{42}{152} = 0.276$

   $\theta = 15°$

   $\theta_R = 1.25° + 15° = 140°$

   $v_R = 160\ km/h$ at 140°

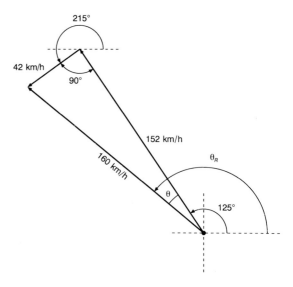

9. 55 N, due east

10. a. $R = \sqrt{(80 \text{ N})^2 + (60 \text{ N})^2} = 100 \text{ N}$

$\tan \theta = \dfrac{60}{80} = 0.75$

$\theta = 37°$

$\theta_R = 90° - 37° = 53°$ $\qquad F_R = 100 \text{ N at } 53°$

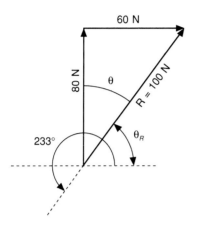

b. $F_E = 100 \text{ N at } 180° + 53° = 233°$

11. a. Vector addition is most easily carried out by using the method of addition by components. The first step in this method is the resolution of the given vectors into their horizontal and vertical components.

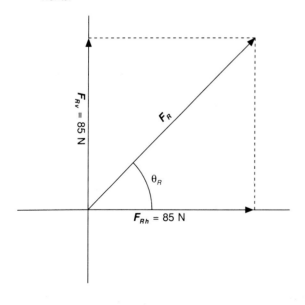

$F_{1h} = F_1 \cos \theta_1 = (62 \text{ N}) \cos 30° = 54 \text{ N}$

$F_{1v} = F_1 \sin \theta_1 = (62 \text{ N}) \sin 30° = 31 \text{ N}$

$F_{2h} = F_2 \cos \theta_2 = (62 \text{ N}) \cos 60° = 31 \text{ N}$

$F_{2v} = F_2 \sin \theta_2 = (62 \text{ N}) \sin 60° = 54 \text{ N}$

At this point the two original vectors have been replaced by four component, vectors which are much easier to add. The horizontal and vertical components of the resultant vector are found by simple addition.

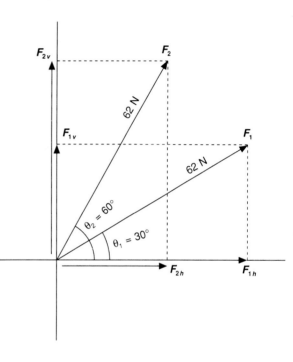

$F_{Rh} = F_{1r} + F_{2h} = 54 \text{ N} + 31 \text{ N} = 85 \text{ N}$

$F_{Rv} = F_{1v} + F_{2v} = 31 \text{ N} + 54 \text{ N} = 85 \text{ N}$

The magnitude and direction of the resultant vector are found by the usual method.

$F_R = \sqrt{(F_{Rh})^2 + (F_{Rv})^2}$

$\quad = \sqrt{(85 \text{ N})^2 + (85 \text{ N})^2}$

$\quad = 120 \text{ N}$

$\tan \theta_R = \dfrac{F_{Rv}}{F_{Rh}} = \dfrac{85 \text{ N}}{85 \text{ N}} = 1, \ \theta_R = 45°$

$F_R = 120 \text{ N at } 45°$

b. $F_E = 120 \text{ N}, 225°$

12. $R = \sqrt{(36 \text{ N})^2 + (48 \text{ N})^2} = 60 \text{ N}$

$\tan \theta = \dfrac{48}{36} = 1.33, \ \theta = 53°$

$\theta_R = 225° + 53° = 278°$

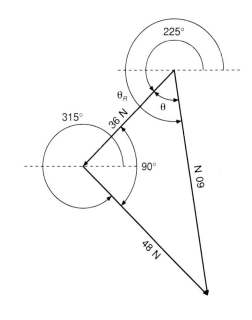

225°

θ_R

315°

36 N

θ

90°

60 N

48 N

Equilibrant: 60 N at 98°

13. $F_h = (80\ N)\cos 60° = 40\ N$

14. $\theta = 180° - 149° = 31°$

   a. $v_{90} = v \sin \theta = (500\ km/h)\sin 31° = 260\ km/h$

   b. $v_{180} = v \cos \theta = (500\ km/h)\cos 31° = 430\ km/h$

15. **a.** $F_h = (72\ N)\cos 60° = 36\ N$

   b. $F_h = (72\ N)\cos 40° = 55\ N$

   c. $F_h = (72\ N)\cos 30° = 62\ N$

16. $F_T - (350\ N)(\cos 55°) = 200\ N$

17. **a.** $F_\perp = (562\ N)\cos 66° = 229\ N$
      $F_\| = (562\ N)\sin 66° = 513\ N$

   b. The perpendicular force is less and the parallel force is greater than in the case of the 30° incline.

18. **a.** $F_\| = (1.2 \times 10^4\ N)\sin 36° = 7.1 \times 10^3\ N$

   b. $F_\perp = (1.2 \times 10^4\ N)\cos 36° = 9.7 \times 10^3\ N$

Chapter 7

1. **a.** $y = -78.4\ m$,
      $y = (1/2)gt^2$,
      so $t^2 = 2y/g =$
      $2(-78.4\ m)/(-9.80\ m/s^2)$
      $= 16.0\ s^2$;
      $t = 4.0\ s$

   b. $x = v_x t$
      $= (+5.0\ m/s)(4.0\ s)$
      $= +20.0\ m$

   c. $v_x = +5.0\ m/s$,
      $v_y = gt$

$= (-9.80\ m/s^2)(4.0\ s)$
$= -39\ m/s$ (down)

2. **a.** **a.** The time of fall would not change since it is determined by the vertical motion only.

   b. The stone would strike 40 m from the base of the cliff because the horizontal velocity has been doubled while the time of flight remains the same.

   c. v_x would double since it is always equal to the initial horizontal velocity. v_y would not change since the vertical motion does not change.

  b. **a.** The time of fall would increase by the factor $\sqrt{2} = 1.41$ since this time varies directly with the square root of the cliff height.

   b. The stone would strike 1.41 times as far from the cliff since $x = v_x t$ and t has increased by a factor of 1.41.

   c. v_x would not change since it always equals the initial horizontal velocity. $v_y = gt$ would increase by a factor of 1.41 since t has so increased.

3. We need to know how long it takes the ball to hit the ground in order to use $x = v_x t$ to calculate v_x. This time is determined by the vertical motion $y = v_y t + 1/2gt^2$, $v_y = 0$. $t^2 = 2y/g = 2(-0.950\ m)/(-9.80\ m/s^2) = 0.194\ s^2$, $t = 0.44\ s$, so that $v_x = x/t = (0.352\ m)/(0.44\ s) = 0.80\ m/s$.

4. We need to know how long it takes the ball to hit the water in order to use $y = v_y t + 1/2gt^2$, $v_y = 0$, to calculate pier height. This time is determined by the horizontal motion $x = v_x t$. $t = x/v_x = (0.75\ m)/(1.27\ m/s) = 0.59\ s$. This gives a vertical displacement $y = 1/2gt^2 = (1/2)(-9.80\ m/s^2)(0.59\ s)^2 = -1.7\ m$ and hence a pier height of 1.7 m.

5. **a.** $v_x = v_i \cos \theta = (24.5\ m/s)(0.819) = 20.1\ m/s$
      $v_y = v_i \sin \theta = (24.5\ m/s)(0.574)$
      $= 14.1\ m/s$. When $y = 0$,
      $t = -2v_y/g = -2(14.1\ m/s)/(-9.80\ m/s^2)$
      $= 2.88\ s$, so $x = v_x t = 57.9\ m$

   b. In half the flight time, $(1/2)(2.88\ s)$, it falls $y = (1/2)gt^2 = (1/2)(-9.80\ m/s^2)(1.44\ s)^2 = -10.2\ m$, so its maximum height is 10.2 m.

6. **a.** $v_x = v_i \cos \theta = 23.4\ m/s$, $v_y = v_i \sin \theta = 13.5\ m/s$. When $y = 0$, $t = -2v_y/g$
      $= -2(13.5\ m/s)/(-9.80\ m/s^2) = 2.76\ s$

   b. $x = v_x t = (23.4\ m/s)(2.76\ s) = 64.6\ m$

   c. In half the flight time, $(1/2)(2.76\ s)$, it falls
      $y = (1/2)gt^2 = (1/2)(-9.80\ m/s^2)(1.38\ s)^2$
      $= -9.33\ m$, so its maximum height is 9.33 m.

7. **a.** $v_x = v_i \cos \theta = 13.5\ m/s$, $v_y = v_i \sin \theta = 23.4\ m/s$.
      When $y = 0$, $t = -2v_y/g$
      $= -2(23.4\ m/s)/(-9.80\ m/s^2) = 4.78\ s$.

b. $x = v_x t = 64.5$ m

c. In half the flight time, $(1/2)(4.78$ s),
it falls $y = (1/2)gt^2 = (1/2)(-9.80$ m/s$^2)(2.39$ s$)^2$
$= -28.0$ m,
so its maximum height is 28.0 m.

8. High trajectories have long flight times and heights, but equal ranges when compared with low trajectories.

9. Velocity and acceleration remain the same because they do not depend upon the mass. The force is doubled because it varies directly with mass.

0. The velocity would double since the distance around the circle doubles while the time for one revolution remains the same. The acceleration doubles since it varies directly with the radius for fixed T. This is most easily seen by writing the acceleration in the form $a_c = 4\pi^2 r/T^2$. Since the force varies directly with acceleration, the force also doubles.

1. The velocity doubles since it varies inversely with the period T. The acceleration and force become four times as large because they both vary directly with the square of velocity.

2. a. $a_c = v^2/r = (8.8$ m/s$)^2/(25$ m$) = 3.1$ m/s^2

  b. The friction between the track and the shoes of the runner.

3. $T = 2\pi \sqrt{\ell/g}$, $\ell = gT^2/4\pi^2 = (9.80$ m/s$^2)(1.00$ s$)^2/4\pi^2$
$= 0.25$ m

4. $f = (1/2\pi) \sqrt{g/\ell}$

5. $f = (1/2\pi) \sqrt{g/\ell}$
$= (1/2\pi) \sqrt{(9.80 \text{ m/s}^2)/(0.40 \text{ m})} = 0.79$ s^{-1}

6. $T = 1/f = 1/(0.79$ s$^{-1}) = 1.3$ s

Chapter 8

. Since Earth moves more slowly in its orbit during summer, by Kepler's second law it must be farther from the sun. Therefore, Earth is closer to the sun in winter.

. $(T_a/T_E)^2 = (r_a/r_E)^3$, with $r_a = 2r_E$. Thus $T_a^2 = (r_a/r_E)^3 T_E^2 = (2r_E/r_E)^3 (1 \text{ yr})^2 = 8$ yr^2, $T_a = 2.8$ yr

. $(T_M/T_E)^2 = (r_M/r_E)^3$, with $r_M = 1.52r_E$. Thus $T_M^2 = (r_M/r_E)^3 T_E^2 = (1.52r_E/r_E)^3 (365 \text{ days})^2 = 4.679 \times 10^5$ days^2, $T_M = 684$ days

. $(T_s/T_m)^2 = (r_s/r_m)^3$, $T_s^2 = (r_s/r_m)^3 T_m^2 = (6.70 \times 10^3 \text{ km}/3.90 \times 10^5 \text{ km})^3 (27.3 \text{ days})^2 = 3.779 \times 10^{-3}$ days^2, $T_s = 6.15 \times 10^{-2}$ day $= 88.5$ min

. $v = R_e \sqrt{g/r}$. Take the satellite's height above Earth to be small compared to R_e so that $r \doteq R_e$.
Then $v = R_e \sqrt{g/R_e}$
$= \sqrt{gR_e}$
$= \sqrt{(9.80 \text{ m/s}^2)(6.37 \times 10^6 \text{ m})}$
$= 7.90 \times 10^3$ m/s

. a. $v = R_m \sqrt{g_m/r}$ where $R_m = (3570$ km$)/2 = 1785$ km. Since the command module orbits close to the

moon's surface, $r \doteq R_m$ and $v = R_m \sqrt{g_m/R_m}$
$= \sqrt{g_m R_m} = \sqrt{(1.60 \text{ m/s}^2)(1.785 \times 10^6 \text{ m})}$
$= 1.69 \times 10^3$ m/s.

  b. $T = 2\pi R_m/v = 2\pi(1.785 \times 10^6 \text{ m})/(1.69 \times 10^3 \text{ m/s})$
$= 6.64 \times 10^3$ s $= 111$ min

7. a. $v = R_M \sqrt{g_m/r}$ where $r = 2440$ km $+ 265$ km
$= 2705$ km
$v = (2.44 \times 10^6 \text{ m}) \sqrt{(3.78 \text{ m/s}^2)/(2.705 \times 10^6 \text{ m})}$
$= 2.88 \times 10^3$ m/s

  b. $T = 2\pi r/v = 2\pi(2.705 \times 10^6 \text{ m})/(2.88 \times 10^3 \text{ m/s})$
$= 5.90 \times 10^3$ s $= 98.4$ min

8. a. The required centripetal force $F = M_s v^2/r = 4\pi^2 M_s r/T^2$ is supplied by the gravitational force of attraction between galaxy and sun, $F = GM_g M_s/r^2$. Equating and solving for the mass of the galaxy, $M_g = 4\pi^2 r^3/GT^2$. Using this with $T = 2.5 \times 10^8$ yr $= 7.9 \times 10^{15}$ s gives $M_g = 4\pi^2(2.2 \times 10^{20} \text{ m})^3/(6.67 \times 10^{-11} \text{ N} \cdot \text{m}^2/\text{kg}^2)(7.9 \times 10^{15} \text{ s})^2 = 1.0 \times 10^{41}$ kg

  b. number of stars = (total galaxy mass)/(mass per star)
$= (1.0 \times 10^{41} \text{ kg})/(2.0 \times 10^{30} \text{ kg})$
$= 5.0 \times 10^{10}$

  c. $v = 2\pi r/T = 2\pi(2.2 \times 10^{20} \text{ m})/(7.9 \times 10^{15} \text{ s})$
$= 1.8 \times 10^5$ m/s
$= 6.5 \times 10^5$ km/h

Chapter 9

1. a. 100 km/h $= 27.8$ m/s,
$p = mv = (725 \text{ kg})(27.8 \text{ m/s}) = 2.02 \times 10^4$ kg $\cdot$ m/s

  b. $v = p/m = (2.02 \times 10^4 \text{ kg} \cdot \text{m/s})/(2175 \text{ kg})$
$= 9.29$ m/s $= 33.4$ km/h

2. a. Take the direction of the pitch to be the positive direction $\Delta p = mv_f - mv_i = m(v_f - v_i) = (0.145 \text{ kg})(-58 \text{ m/s} - (+42 \text{ m/s})) = -15$ kg $\cdot$ m/s

  b. $F\Delta t = \Delta p$, $F = \Delta p/\Delta t = (-15 \text{ kg} \cdot \text{m/s})/(4.6 \times 10^{-4} \text{ s})$
$= -3.3 \times 10^4$ N

3. a. $\Delta p = m(v_f - v_i) = (250 \text{ kg})(28.0 \text{ m/s} - 6.0 \text{ m/s})$
$= 5.50 \times 10^3$ kg $\cdot$ m/s

  b. $F = \Delta p/\Delta t = (5.50 \times 10^3 \text{ kg} \cdot \text{m/s})/(60.0 \text{ s})$
$= 91.7$ N

4. a. $m = W/g = (15\ 680 \text{ N})/(9.80 \text{ m/s}^2) = 1600$ kg

  b. $p_i = mv_i = (1600 \text{ kg})(20.0 \text{ m/s})$
$= 3.20 \times 10^4$ kg $\cdot$ m/s

  c. $\Delta p = p_f - p_i = 0 - 3.20 \times 10^4$ kg $\cdot$ m/s
$= -3.20 \times 10^4$ kg $\cdot$ m/s

  d. $F\Delta t = \Delta p$, $\Delta t = \Delta p/F$
$= (-3.20 \times 10^4 \text{ kg} \cdot \text{m/s})/(6.40 \times 10^2 \text{ N})$
$= 50.0$ s

5. $p_h + p_g = p_h' + p_g'$ or $m_h v_h + m_g v_g = m_h v_h' + m_g v_g'$. Since $v_g = 0$, $m_h v_h = (m_h + m_g) v'$ where $v' = v_h' = v_g'$ is the common final speed of goalie and puck.

$v' = m_h v_h/(m_h + m_g)$
$= (0.105 \text{ kg})(48 \text{ m/s})/(0.105 \text{ kg} + 75 \text{ kg})$
$= 0.067 \text{ m/s}$

6. $m_b \boldsymbol{v_b} + m_w \boldsymbol{v_w} = (m_b + m_w)\boldsymbol{v'}$ where $\boldsymbol{v'}$ is the common final velocity of bullet and wooden block.
Since $\boldsymbol{v_w} = 0$, $\boldsymbol{v_b} = (m_b + m_w)\boldsymbol{v'}/m_b$
$= (0.035 \text{ kg} + 5.0 \text{ kg})(8.6 \text{ m/s})/(0.035 \text{ kg})$
$= 1.2 \times 10^3 \text{ m/s}.$

7. $m_b v_b + m_w v_w = m_b v_b' + m_w v_w'$ with $v_w = 0$.
$v_w' = (m_b v_b - m_b v_b')/m_w = m_b(v_b - v_b')/m_w$
$= (0.035 \text{ kg})(475 \text{ m/s} - 275 \text{ m/s})/(2.5 \text{ kg})$
$= 2.8 \text{ m/s}.$

8. $m_A \boldsymbol{v_A} + m_B \boldsymbol{v_B} = m_A \boldsymbol{v'_A} + m_B \boldsymbol{v'_B}$, so $\boldsymbol{v'_B} = (m_A \boldsymbol{v_A} + m_B \boldsymbol{v_B} - m_A \boldsymbol{v'_A})/m_B = [(0.50 \text{ kg})(6.0 \text{ m/s}) + (1.00 \text{ kg})(-12.0 \text{ m/s}) - (0.50 \text{ kg})(-14 \text{ m/s})]/(1.00 \text{ kg}) = -2 \text{ m/s}$

9. $\boldsymbol{p_r} + \boldsymbol{p_f} = \boldsymbol{p'_r} + \boldsymbol{p'_f}$ where $\boldsymbol{p_r} + \boldsymbol{p_f} = 0$.

If the initial mass of the rocket (including fuel) is $m_r = 4.00 \text{ kg}$, then the final mass of the rocket is m'_r

$= 4.00 \text{ kg} - 0.050 \text{ kg} = 3.95 \text{ kg}.$
$0 = m'_r v'_r + m_f v'_f,$
$v'_r = -m_f v'_f/m'_r$
$= - (0.050 \text{ kg})(-625 \text{ m/s})/(3.95 \text{ kg})$
$= 7.91 \text{ m/s}.$

10. $\boldsymbol{p_A} + \boldsymbol{p_B} = \boldsymbol{p'_A} + \boldsymbol{p'_B}$ with $\boldsymbol{p_A} + \boldsymbol{p_B} = 0$,
$m_A \boldsymbol{v'_A} = -m_B \boldsymbol{v'_B}$, so $\boldsymbol{v'_B} = - m_A \boldsymbol{v'_A}/m_B$
$= -(80.0 \text{ kg})(4.0 \text{ m/s})/(110 \text{ kg})$
$= -2.9 \text{ m/s, or } 2.9 \text{ m/s in the opposite direction.}$

11. $\boldsymbol{p_A} + \boldsymbol{p_B} = \boldsymbol{p'_A} + \boldsymbol{p'_B}$ with $\boldsymbol{p_A} + \boldsymbol{p_B} = 0$,
$m_B \boldsymbol{v'_B} = -m_A \boldsymbol{v'_A}$,
so $\boldsymbol{v'_B} = - m_A \boldsymbol{v'_A}/m_B = -(1.5 \text{ kg})(-27 \text{ cm/s})/(4.5 \text{ kg})$
$= 9.0 \text{ cm/s, or } 9.0 \text{ cm/s to the right}$

12. $\boldsymbol{p_A} + \boldsymbol{p_B} = \boldsymbol{p'_A} + \boldsymbol{p'_B}$,
$m_A v_A + m_B v_B = m_A v'_A + m_B v'_B$,
so $v'_B = (m_A v_A + m_B v_B - m_A v'_A)/m_B.$

Assuming projectile (A) is launched in direction of launcher (B) motion,

$v'_B = \dfrac{(0.05 \text{ kg})(2.00 \text{ m/s}) + (4.65 \text{ kg})(2.00 \text{ m/s}) - (0.05 \text{ kg})(647 \text{ m/s})}{(4.65 \text{ kg})}$

$v'_B = -4.94 \text{ m/s, or } 4.94 \text{ m/s backwards}$

13. From the impulsive force of Earth against the pole. Earth acquires an equal and opposite vertical momentum.

14. $\boldsymbol{p_N} + \boldsymbol{p_E} = \boldsymbol{p'}$ (vector sum)
$p_N = m_N v_N = (1325 \text{ kg})(27.0 \text{ m/s})$
$= 3.58 \times 10^4 \text{ kg} \cdot \text{m/s}$
$p_E = m_E v_E = (2165 \text{ kg})(17.0 \text{ m/s})$
$= 3.68 \times 10^4 \text{ kg} \cdot \text{m/s}$

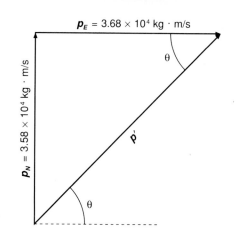

$\tan \theta = \dfrac{p_N}{p_E} = \dfrac{3.58 \times 10^4 \text{ kg} \cdot \text{m/s}}{3.68 \times 10^4 \text{ kg} \cdot \text{m/s}} = 0.973,$
$\theta = 44.2°$, north of east
$(p')^2 = (p_N)^2 + (p_E)^2$
$= (3.58 \times 10^4 \text{ kg} \cdot \text{m/s})^2 + (3.68 \times 10^4 \text{ kg} \cdot \text{m/s})^2$
$= 2.64 \times 10^9 \text{ kg}^2 \text{ m}^2/\text{s}^2),$
$p' = 5.13 \times 10^4 \text{ kg} \cdot \text{m/s}$
$p' = m'v' = (m_N + m_E) v',$
$v' = p'/(m_N + m_E)$
$= (5.13 \times 10^4 \text{ kg} \cdot \text{m/s})/(1325 \text{ kg} + 2165 \text{ kg})$
$= 14.7 \text{ m/s}$

15. a. $\boldsymbol{p_A} + \boldsymbol{p_B} = \boldsymbol{p'_A} + \boldsymbol{p'_B}$ (vector sum) with $\boldsymbol{p_B} = 0$

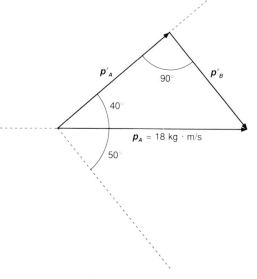

$p_A = m_A v_A = (6.0 \text{ kg})(3.0 \text{ m/s}) = 18 \text{ kg} \cdot \text{m/s}$
$p'_A = p_A \cos 40° = (18 \text{ kg} \cdot \text{m/s}) \cos 40°$
$= 14 \text{ kg} \cdot \text{m/s}$
$p'_B = p_A \sin 40° = (18 \text{ kg} \cdot \text{m/s}) \sin 40°$

$= 12 \text{ kg} \cdot \text{m/s}$

b. $p'_A = m_A v'_A, \; v'_A = p_A/m_A$
$= (14 \text{ kg} \cdot \text{m/s})/(6.0 \text{ kg})$
$v'_a = 2.3 \text{ m/s, } 40° \text{ to left}$
$p'_B = m_B v'_B, \; v'_B = p'_B/m_B$
$= (12 \text{ kg} \cdot \text{m/s})/(6.0 \text{ kg})$
$v'_B = 2.0 \text{ m/s, } 50° \text{ to right}$

16. $p_1 + p_2 = p'_1 + p'_2$ (vector sum) with $p_1 = 0$

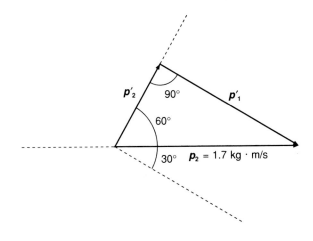

$p_2 = m_2 v_2 = (0.17 \text{ kg})(10.0 \text{ m/s}) = 1.7 \text{ kg} \cdot \text{m/s}$
$p'_1 = p_2 \sin 60° = (1.7 \text{ kg} \cdot \text{m/s}) \sin 60°$
$= 1.5 \text{ kg} \cdot \text{m/s, } v'_1 = p'_1/m_1$
$= (1.5 \text{ kg} \cdot \text{m/s})/(0.17 \text{ kg})$
$= 8.8 \text{ m/s, } 30° \text{ to right}$
$p'_2 = p_2 \cos 60° = (1.7 \text{ kg} \cdot \text{m/s}) \cos 60°$
$= 0.85 \text{ kg} \cdot \text{m/s, } v'_2 = p'_2/m_2$
$= (0.85 \text{ kg} \cdot \text{m/s})/(0.17 \text{ kg})$
$= 5.0 \text{ m/s, } 60° \text{ to left}$

Chapter 10

1. $W = Fd = (825 \text{ N})(35 \text{ m}) = 2.9 \times 10^4 \text{ J}$.
2. The work doubles because work varies directly with force.
3. $W = Fd = (34 \text{ N})(15 \text{ m}) = 510 \text{ J}$.
4. $W = Fd = (583 \text{ kg})(9.80 \text{ m/s}^2)(1.2 \text{ m}) = 6.9 \times 10^3 \text{ J}$.
5. Since gravity acts vertically, only the vertical displacement need be considered.
$W = Fd = (215 \text{ N})(4.20 \text{ m})$
$= 903 \text{ J}$.
6. Force is upward, but vertical displacement is downward, so

$W = Fd \cos \theta = Fd \cos 180° = (215 \text{ N})(4.20 \text{ m})(-1)$
$= -903 \text{ J}$.
7. Both the force and displacement are in the same direction, so
$W = Fd = (25 \text{ N})(3.5 \text{ m}) = 88 \text{ J}$.
8. $W = Fd \cos \theta = (628 \text{ N})(15.0 \text{ m}) (\cos 46.0°)$
$= 6.54 \times 10^3 \text{ J}$.
9. Since $F = mg$, $P = mgd/t$. The result will depend upon your physical fitness and the stairs chosen.
10. $P = W/t = Fd/t = (575 \text{ N})(20.0 \text{ m})/(10.0 \text{ s})$
$= 1.15 \times 10^3 \text{ W} = 1.15 \text{ kW}$.
11. a. $W = mgd = (7.50 \text{ kg})(9.80 \text{ m/s}^2)(8.2 \text{ m})$
$= 6.0 \times 10^2 \text{ J}$.
b. $W = Fd + 6.0 \times 10^2 \text{ J}$
$= (645 \text{ N})(8.2 \text{ m}) + 6.0 \times 10^2 \text{ J}$
$= 5.9 \times 10^3 \text{ J}$.
c. $P = \dfrac{W}{t} = (5.9 \times 10^3 \text{ J})/(30 \text{ min})(60 \text{ s/min})$
$= 3.3 \text{ W}$.
12. $P = W/t$, and $W = Fd$,
so $F = Pt/d = (65 \times 10^3 \text{ W})(35.0 \text{ s})/(17.5 \text{ m})$
$= 1.3 \times 10^5 \text{ N}$
13. a. $IMA = d_e/d_r = (20 \text{ cm})/(5.0 \text{ cm}) = 4.0$
b. $MA = F_r/F_e = (1.9 \times 10^4 \text{ N})/(9.8 \times 10^3 \text{ N}) = 1.9$
c. $Efficiency = (MA/IMA) \times 100\%$
$= (1.9/4.0) \times 100\% = 48\%$
14. a. $MA = F_r/F_e = (225 \text{ N})/(129 \text{ N}) = 1.74$.
b. $Efficiency = (MA/IMA) \times 100\%$ where
$IMA = d_e/d_r = (33.0 \text{ m})/(16.5 \text{ m}) = 2.00$ so
$Efficiency = (1.74/2.00) \times 100\% = 87\%$.
15. $eff = (MA/IMA) \times 100\%$ where
$MA = F_r/F_e$
$= (1.25 \times 10^3 \text{ N})/(225 \text{ N})$
$= 5.56$.
Therefore,
$IMA = (MA)(100\%)/(eff)$
$= (5.56)(100\%)/(88.7\%)$
$= 6.27$
Since $IMA = d_e/d_r$,
$d_e = (IMA)(d_r) = (6.27)(0.13 \text{ m}) = 0.81 \text{ m}$

Chapter 11

1. a. $100 \text{ km/h} = (100 \text{ km/h})/(3.6 \text{ km/h/m/s}) = 28 \text{ m/s}$.
$KE = \frac{1}{2}mv^2 = \frac{1}{2}(750 \text{ kg})(28 \text{ m/s})^2$
$= 2.9 \times 10^5 \text{ J}$

b. $KE = \frac{1}{2}mv^2$, so if v is the same, KE is proportional to mass.
Thus, the ratio is 1500 kg/750 kg = 2

2. a. 50 km/h is 14 m/s, so $KE = \frac{1}{2}mv^2$
$= \frac{1}{2}(750 \text{ kg})(14 \text{ m/s})^2 = 7.4 \times 10^4$ J

b. $W = \Delta KE = 7.4 \times 10^4$ J $- 2.9 \times 10^5$ J
$= -2.2 \times 10^5$ J

c. $W = \Delta KE = 0 - 7.4 \times 10^4$ J $= -7.4 \times 10^4$ J.

d. $W = Fd$, so distance is proportional to work. The ratio is $(-2.2 \times 10^5$ J$)/(-7.4 \times 10^4$ J$) = 3$.
It takes three times the distance to slow it to half its speed as to slow it the rest of the way to a complete stop.

3. a. $KE = \frac{1}{2}mv^2 = \frac{1}{2}(0.0042 \text{ kg})(965 \text{ m/s})^2$
$= 1.96 \times 10^3$ J

b. $W = \Delta KE = 1.96 \times 10^3$ J

c. $W = Fd$, so
$F = W/d = (1.96 \times 10^3$ J$)/(0.75 \text{ m})$
$= 2.6 \times 10^3$ N

4. a. $KE = \frac{1}{2}mv^2 = \frac{1}{2}(7.85 \times 10^{11} \text{ kg})(2.5 \times 10^4 \text{ m/s})^2$
$= 2.5 \times 10^{20}$ J

b. The work is that of 60 000 100 megaton bombs.

5. $PE = mgh = (180 \text{ kg})(9.80 \text{ m/s}^2)(1.95 \text{ m})$
$= 3.44 \times 10^3$ J

6. $PE = mgh$. At the edge, $PE = (90 \text{ kg})(9.8 \text{ m/s}^2)(+45 \text{ m})$
$= +4.0 \times 10^4$ J. At bottom,
$PE = (90 \text{ kg})(9.8 \text{ m/s}^2)(+45 \text{ m} - 85 \text{ m})$
$= -3.5 \times 10^4$ J.

7. a. $PE = mgh = (50.0 \text{ kg})(9.80 \text{ m/s}^2)(400 \text{ m})$
$= 1.96 \times 10^5$ J.

b. $\Delta PE = mgh_f - mgh_i = mg(h_f - h_i)$
$= (50.0 \text{ kg})(9.80 \text{ m/s}^2)(200 \text{ m} - 400 \text{ m})$
$= -9.8 \times 10^4$ J.

8. a. $W = Fd = Fh = (630 \text{ N})(5.0 \text{ m}) = 3200$ J

b. $\Delta PE = (mg)h = (630 \text{ N})(5.0 \text{ m}) = 3200$ J.
The increase in gravitational potential energy is equal to the work done.

c. Chemical energy stored in the person's body.

9. a. $KE = \frac{1}{2}mv^2 = \frac{1}{2}(85 \text{ kg})(8.5 \text{ m/s})^2 = 3.1 \times 10^3$ J

b. $KE_i + PE_i = KE_f + PE_f$,
$\frac{1}{2}mv^2 + 0 = 0 + mgh$,
$h = v^2/2g = (8.5 \text{ m/s})^2/(2)(9.8 \text{ m/s}^2)$
$= 3.7$ m

c. No. It cancels because both KE and PE are proportional to m.

10. a. $KE_i + PE_i = KE_f + PE_f$,
$0 + mgh = \frac{1}{2}mv^2 + 0$, $v^2 = 2gh$
$= 2(9.8 \text{ m/s}^2)(4.0 \text{ m}) = 78.4 \text{ m}^2/\text{s}^2$,
$v = 8.9$ m/s

b. No

c. No

11. a. $KE_i + PE_i = KE_f + PE_f$,
$0 + mgh = \frac{1}{2}mv^2 + 0$, $v^2 = 2gh$
$= 2(9.8 \text{ m/s}^2)(45 \text{ m}) = 880 \text{ m}^2/\text{s}^2$, $v = 30$ m/s

b. $KE_i + PE_i = KE_f + PE_f$,
$0 + mgh_i = \frac{1}{2}mv^2 + mgh_f$,
$v^2 = 2g(h_i - h_f) = 2(9.8 \text{ m/s}^2)(45 \text{ m} - 40 \text{ m})$
$= 98 \text{ m}^2/\text{s}^2$, $v = 9.9$ m/s

12. $PE = KE$,
$mgh = \frac{1}{2}mv^2$ where
$v = 100$ km/h $= 27.8$ m/s.
$h = v^2/2g = (27.8 \text{ m/s})^2/(2)(9.80 \text{ m/s}^2) = 39.4$ m

Chapter 12

1. a. K = °C + 273 = 0 + 273 = 273 K

b. °C = K $-$ 273 = 0 $-$ 273 = $-$ 273 °C

c. K = °C + 273 = 273 + 273 = 546 K

d. °C = K $-$ 273 = 273 $-$ 273 = 0 °C

2. a. K = 27°C + 273 = 300 K

b. K = 560°C + 273 = 833 K

c. K = $-$184°C + 273 = 89 K

d. impossible temperature—below absolute zero.

3. a. °C = 110 $-$ 273 = $-$163°C

b. °C = 22 $-$ 273 = $-$251°C

c. °C = 402 $-$ 273 = 129°C

d. °C = 323 $-$ 273 = 50°C

4. $Q = mC\Delta T$
$= (0.250 \text{ kg})(4180 \text{ J/kg} \cdot \text{K})(85.0 \text{ °C} - 10.0°C)$
$= 7.84 \times 10^4$ J

5. $Q = mC\Delta T$
$= (0.0600 \text{ kg})(385 \text{ J/kg} \cdot \text{K})(80.0 \text{ °C} - 20.0°C)$
$= 1390$ J

6. $Q = mC\Delta T$
$= (38 \text{ kg})(130 \text{ J/kg} \cdot \text{K})(180 \text{ °C} - (-26°C))$
$= 1.0 \times 10^6$ J

7. a. $Q = mC\Delta T$,
$\Delta T = Q/mC$
$= (836 \times 10^3 \text{ J})/(20.0 \text{ kg})(4180 \text{ J/kg} \cdot \text{K})$
$= 10.0°C$

b. Using 1L = 1000 cm^3, the mass of methanol required is
$DV = (0.80 \text{ g/cm}^3)(20 \text{ L})(1000 \text{ cm}^3/\text{L})$
$= 16\ 000$ g or 16 kg.
$\Delta T = Q/mC = (836 \times 10^3 \text{ J})/(16 \text{ kg})(2480 \text{ J/kg} \cdot \text{K})$
$= 21°C$

c. Water is the better coolant since its temperature increase is less than half that of methanol when absorbing the same amount of heat.

8. $m_A C_A(T_f - T_{A,i}) + m_B C_B(T_f - T_{B,i}) = 0$
Since $m_A = m_B$ and $C_A = C_B$ there is cancellation in this particular case so that $T_f = (T_{A,i} + T_{B,i})/2$
$= (80.0°C + 10.0°C)/2 = 45.0°C$

9. $m_a C_a(T_f - T_{a,i}) + m_w C_w(T_f - T_{w,i}) = 0$
Since in this particular case $m_a = m_w$ the masses cancel and

$$T_f = \frac{C_a T_{a,i} + C_w T_{w,i}}{C_a + C_w}$$

$$= \frac{(2456 \text{ J/kg} \cdot \text{C°})(16.0°C) + (4180 \text{ J/kg} \cdot \text{C°})(85.0°C)}{2456 \text{ J/kg} \cdot \text{C°} + 4180 \text{ J/kg} \cdot \text{C°}}$$

$$= 59.5°C$$

10. $m_b C_b(T_f - T_{b,i}) + m_w C_w(T_f - T_{w,i}) = 0,$

$$T_f = \frac{m_b C_b T_{b,i} + m_w C_w T_{w,i}}{m_b C_b + m_w C_w}$$

$$= \frac{(0.100 \text{ kg})(376 \text{ J/kg} \cdot \text{C°})(90.0°C) + (0.200 \text{ kg})(4180 \text{ J/kg} \cdot \text{C°})(20.0°C)}{(0.100 \text{ kg})(376 \text{ J/kg} \cdot \text{C°}) + (0.200 \text{ kg})(4180 \text{ J/kg} \cdot \text{C°})} = 23.0°C$$

11. $m_a C_a(T_f - T_{a,i}) + m_w C_w(T_f - T_{w,i}) = 0$
Since $m_a = m_w$ the masses cancel and
$C_a = - C_w(T_f - T_{w,i})/(T_f - T_{a,i})$
$= - (4180 \text{ J/kg} \cdot \text{K})(25°C - 10°C)/(25°C - 100°C)$
$= 840 \text{ J/kg} \cdot \text{K}$

12. $Q = m H_v = (0.0500 \text{ kg})(2.26 \times 10^6 \text{ J/kg})$
$= 1.13 \times 10^5 \text{ J}$

13. To warm the ice to 0°C, $Q_w = mC\Delta T$
$= (100 \text{ g})(2.06 \text{ J/g} \cdot \text{C°})(0 - (-20.0°C)) = 4120 \text{ J}$
To melt the ice, $Q_m = m H_f$
$= (0.100 \text{ kg})(3.34 \times 10^5 \text{ J/kg}) = 3.34 \times 10^4 \text{ J}$.
Total heat required
$= Q_w + Q_m = 0.41 \times 10^4 \text{ J} + 3.34 \times 10^4 \text{ J}$
$= 3.75 \times 10^4 \text{ J}$.

14. To heat the water from 60°C to 100°C:
$Q = mC\Delta T = (0.200 \text{ kg})(4180 \text{ J/kg} \cdot \text{C°})(40°C)$
$= 0.334 \times 10^5 \text{ J}$
To change the water to steam:
$Q = m H_v = (0.200 \text{ kg})(2.26 \times 10^6 \text{ J/kg})$
$= 4.52 \times 10^5 \text{ J}$
To heat the steam from 100°C to 140°C:
$Q = mC\Delta T = (0.200 \text{ kg})(2020 \text{ J/kg} \cdot \text{C°})(40°C)$
$= \underline{0.162 \times 10^5 \text{ J}}$
$Q_{total} = 5.02 \times 10^5 \text{ J}$

15. Warm ice from −30°C to 0°C:
$Q = mC\Delta T = (0.300 \text{ kg})(2060 \text{ J/kg} \cdot \text{C°})(30.0°C)$
$= 0.185 \times 10^5 \text{ J}$
Melt ice:
$Q = m H_f = (0.300 \text{ kg})(3.34 \times 10^5 \text{ J/kg})$
$= 1.00 \times 10^5 \text{ J}$

Heat water 0°C to 100°C:
$Q = mC\Delta T = (0.300 \text{ kg})(4180 \text{ J/kg} \cdot \text{C°})(100°C)$
$= 1.25 \times 10^5 \text{ J}$
Vaporize water:
$Q = m H_v = (0.300 \text{ kg})(2.26 \times 10^6 \text{ J/kg}) = 6.78 \times 10^5 \text{ J}$
Heat steam 100°C to 130°C:
$Q = mC\Delta T = (0.300 \text{ kg}) (2020 \text{ J/kg} \cdot \text{C}) (30°C)$
$= 0.18 \times 10^5 \text{ J}$
$Q_{total} = 9.40 \times 10^5 \text{ J}$

Chapter 13

1. $p_1 V_1 = p_2 V_2$
$V_2 = p_1 V_1/p_2 = (236 \text{ kPa})(0.063 \text{ m}^3)/(354 \text{ kPa})$
$= 0.042 \text{ m}^3$

2. $p_1 V_1 = p_2 V_2, p_2 = p_1 V_1/V_2 =$
$(235 \text{ kPa})(0.0500 \text{ m}^3)/(0.125 \text{ m}^3) = 94.0 \text{ kPa}$

3. $p_1 V_1 = p_2 V_2$ where $P_1 = 101.3 \text{ kPa}$, the atmospheric pressure at sea level.
$p_2 = p_1 V_1/V_2 = (101.3 \text{ kPa})(2.0 \text{ m}^3)/(6.0 \text{ m}^3) = 34 \text{ kPa}$

4. From the preceding text Example each 10.4 m of water depth exerts 1 atm of pressure so that the pressure at the diver's depth is
$p_1 = 1.0 \text{ atm} + (52 \text{ m})/(10.4 \text{ m/atm}) = 6.0 \text{ atm}$
$p_1 V_1 = p_2 V_2, V_2 = p_1 V_1/p_2$
$= (6.0 \text{ atm})(2.0 \text{ cm}^3)/(1.0 \text{ atm}) = 12 \text{ cm}^3$

5. $V_1/T_1 = V_2/T_2$ with $T_1 = 20.0° + 273 = 293 \text{ K}$
$T_2 = 293° + 273 = 566 \text{ K}.$
$V_2 = T_2 V_1/T_1 = (566 \text{ K})(30.0 \text{ m}^3)/(293 \text{ K}) = 58.0 \text{ m}^3.$

6. $V_1/T_1 = V_2/T_2$ with
$T_1 = 20° + 273 = 293 \text{ K}$
$T_2 = -146° + 273 = 127 \text{ K}$
$V_2 = T_2 V_1/T_1 = (127 \text{ K})(30 \text{ L})/(293 \text{ K}) = 13 \text{ L}$

7. $V_1/T_1 = V_2/T_2$ with $T_1 = 60.0° + 273 = 333 \text{ K}$,
$V_2 = 2 V_1$
$T_2 = V_2 T_1/V_1 = (2 V_1)(333 \text{ K})/V_1 = 666 \text{ K}, °C$
$= 666 \text{ K} - 273 = 393°C$

8. $V_1/T_1 = V_2/T_2$ with $T_1 = 293 \text{ K}$ so $T_2 = V_2 T_1/V_1$
$= (19 \text{ L}) (293 \text{ K})/(63 \text{ L}) = 88 \text{ K or } -185°C$

9. $p_1 V_1/T_1 = p_2 V_2/T_2,$ so $V_2 = p_1 V_1 T_2/p_2 T_1 = (15.5 \times 10^6 \text{ Pa})$
$(0.020 \text{ m}^3)(323 \text{ K})/(101 \times 10^3 \text{ Pa})(293 \text{ K})$
$= 3.4 \text{ m}^3$

10. $pV = nRT,$
$n = pV/RT =$
$(15.5 \times 10^6 \text{ Pa})(0.020 \text{ m}^3)/(8.31 \text{ Pa} \cdot \text{ m}^3/\text{mol K})(293 \text{ K})$
$= 127.3 \text{ mole}, m = (127.3 \text{ mole})(4.00 \text{ g/mole})$
$= 509 \text{ grams}$

11. $p_1 V_1/T_1 = p_2 V_2/T_2,$ so $p_2 = p_1 V_1 T_2/V_2 T_1$
$= (156 \text{ kPa})(200 \text{ L})(368 \text{ K})/(175 \text{ L})(273 \text{ K}) = 240 \text{ kPa}$

12. $pV = nRT$, so $V = nRT/p$, where $n = (1000\text{ g})/(29\text{ g/mole}) = 35$ mole; $V = (35\text{ mole})(8.31\text{ Pa} \cdot \text{m}^3/\text{mole} \cdot \text{K})(293\text{ K})/(101.3 \times 10^3\text{ Pa}) = 0.84\text{ m}^3$

Chapter 14

1. $F_1/A_1 = F_2/A_2$ with $A_2 = 0.400\text{ m}^2$, since circular area is proportional to diameter squared and the original diameter has been doubled.
$F_2 = A_2F_1/A_1 = (0.400\text{ m}^2)(20.0\text{ N})/(0.0500\text{ m}^2) = 160\text{ N}$

2. $F_1/A_1 = F_2/A_2$, $F_1 = F_2A_1/A_2$
$= (1600\text{ N})(72\text{ cm}^2)/1440\text{ cm}^2) = 80\text{ N}$

3. $F_{weight} = F_{buoyant} = \rho_{water}Vg$, $V = F_{weight}/\rho_{water}g$
$= (600\text{ N})/(1000\text{ kg/m}^3)(9.80\text{ m/s}^2) = 0.061\text{ m}^3$.
This volume does not include that portion of her head that is above the water.

4. $T + F_{buoyant} = W$ where W is the air weight of the camera.
$T = W - F_{buoyant} = W - \rho_{water}Vg = 1250\text{ N} - (1000\text{ kg/m}^3)(0.083\text{ m}^3)(9.80\text{ m/s}^2) = 440\text{ N}$

5. $\Delta L = \alpha L_i\Delta T = (25 \times 10^{-6}\text{°C}^{-1})(3.66\text{ m})(67\text{°C})$
$= 6.1 \times 10^{-3}\text{ m}$, or 6.1 mm

6. $L_f = L_i + \alpha L_i(T - T_i) =$
$(11.5\text{ m}) + (11 \times 10^{-6}\text{°C}^{-1})(11.5\text{ m})(1221\text{°C} - 22\text{°C})$
$= 11.7\text{ m}$.

7. a. $V = V_i + \beta V_i(T - T_i) = 45\ 725\text{ L} + (950 \times 10^{-6}\text{°C}^{-1})(45\ 725\text{ L})(-18.0\text{°C} - 32.0\text{°C})$
$= 45\ 725\text{ L} - 2170\text{ L} = 43\ 555\text{ L} = 43\ 600\text{ L}$

b. Its volume has decreased because of temperature change.

c. The person who charges by volume rather than mass.

Chapter 15

1. a. $v = d/t = (515\text{ m})/(1.5\text{ s}) = 343\text{ m/s}$

b. $T = 1/f = 1/(436\text{ Hz}) = 2.29 \times 10^{-3}\text{ s} = 2.29\text{ ms}$

c. $\lambda = v/f = (343\text{ m/s})/(436\text{ Hz}) = 0.787\text{ m}$

2. a. $v = d/t = (685\text{ m})/(2.0\text{ s}) = 342\text{ m/s}$

b. $f = v/\lambda = (342\text{ m/s})/(0.750\text{ m}) = 456\text{ Hz}$

c. $T = 1/f = 1/(456\text{ Hz}) = 2.19 \times 10^{-3}\text{ s} = 2.19\text{ ms}$

3. $\lambda = v/f = (3.00 \times 10^8\text{ m/s})/(99.5 \times 10^6\text{ Hz}) = 3.02\text{ m}$

4. a. $\lambda = (580\text{ nm})(1 \times 10^{-9}\text{ m/nm}) = 5.8 \times 10^{-7}\text{ m}$

b. $f = v/\lambda = (3.0 \times 10^8\text{ m/s})/(5.8 \times 10^{-7}\text{ m})$
$= 5.2 \times 10^{14}\text{ Hz}$

5. Pulse inversion means rigid boundary: attached to wall.

6. at a lower frequency because wavelength varies inversely with frequency

7. a. The pulse is partially reflected, partially transmitted.

b. Erect, since reflection is from a less dense medium.

c. It is almost totally reflected from the wall.

d. Inverted, since reflection is from a more dense medium.

8. a. The pulse is partially reflected, partially transmitted.

b. Inverted, since reflection is from a more dense medium.

c. It is almost totally reflected from the wall.

d. Inverted, since reflection is from a more dense medium.

Chapter 16

1. $v = f\lambda$, so $\lambda = v/f = 1435\text{ m/s}/261.6\text{ Hz} = 5.485\text{ m}$.

2. $v = f\lambda$, so $f = v/\lambda = 343\text{ m/s}/0.667\text{ m} = 514\text{ Hz}$.

3. $v = f\lambda = (442\text{ Hz})(11.66\text{ m}) = 5150\text{ m/s}$.

4. $\lambda_{max} = v/f_{min} = (343\text{ m/s})/(20\text{ Hz}) = 17\text{ m}$
$\lambda_{min} = v/f_{max} = (343\text{ m/s})/(16\ 000\text{ Hz}) = 0.021\text{ m}$

5. Since $v = 343\text{ m/s}$ at 20°C, $\lambda = v/f = (343\text{ m/s})/(440\text{ Hz})$
$= 0.780\text{ m}$.
The resonances are spaced by $\lambda/2 = 0.390\text{ m}$.

6. Since resonances are spaced by $\lambda/2 = 1.10\text{ m}$,
$\lambda = 2.20\text{ m}$. $v = f\lambda = (440\text{ Hz})(2.20\text{ m}) = 968\text{ m/s}$

7. From the preceding text Example, the speed of sound in air at 27°C is 347 m/s and since resonances are spaced $\lambda/2 = 0.392\text{ m}$, $\lambda = 0.784\text{ m}$.
$f = v/\lambda = (347\text{ m/s})/(0.784\text{ m}) = 443\text{ Hz}$

8. The lowest resonant frequency corresponds to the longest possible resonant wavelength, which, for an open pipe, is twice the length of the pipe,
or $2(2.65\text{ m}) = 5.30\text{ m}$ in the present case.
$f_{min} = v/\lambda_{max} = (343\text{ m/s})/(5.30\text{ m}) = 64.7\text{ Hz}$

9. Since the saxophone is an open pipe,
$\lambda_{max} = 2 \times (\text{pipe length}) = 2(0.65\text{ m}) = 1.30\text{ m}$.
$f_{min} = v/\lambda_{max} = (343\text{ m/s})/(1.30\text{ m}) = 260\text{ Hz}$

Chapter 17

1. $T = 1/f = 1/(534\text{ s}^{-1}) = 1.87 \times 10^{-3}\text{ s}$

2. a. $t = (1.87 \times 10^{-3}\text{ s/rev})(1/8\text{ rev}) = 2.34 \times 10^{-4}\text{ s}$

b. $d = 2(35\text{ km}) = 70\text{ km}$

3. $v = d/t = (70.0\text{ km})/(2.34 \times 10^{-4}\text{ s}) = 2.99 \times 10^5\text{ km/s}$.
$(2.99 \times 10^5\text{ km/s})(10^3\text{ m/km}) = 2.99 \times 10^8\text{ m/s}$.

4. Round trip distance $d = vt = (299\ 792\ 458\text{ m/s})(2.562\text{ s})$
$= 7.681 \times 10^8\text{ m}$, so distance is $3.840 \times 10^8\text{ m}$.

5. $E_f/E_i = (P/4\pi d_f^2)/(P/4\pi d_i^2) = (d_i/d_f)^2 = (30\text{ cm}/90\text{ cm})^2 = 1/9$

6. $E = P/4\pi d^2 = (2275\text{ lm})/4\pi(3.0\text{ m})^2 = 20\text{ lm/m}^2$

7. Since $P/4\pi = I$, $E = P/4\pi d^2 = I/d^2$
$= (64\text{ cd})/(3.0\text{ m})^2 = 7.1\text{ lx}$

8. $E = P/4\pi d^2$, $P = 4\pi d^2E = 4\pi(4.0\text{ m})^2(20\text{ lm/m}^2)$
$= 4000\text{ lm}$

Chapter 18

1. $n_i \sin \theta_i = n_r \sin \theta_r$, $\sin \theta_r = n_i \sin \theta_i/n_r$
= (1.00)(sin 45.0°)/(1.52) = 0.465, $\theta_r = 27.7°$

2. $n_i \sin \theta_i = n_r \sin \theta_r$, $\sin \theta_r = n_i \sin \theta_i/n_r$
= (1.00)(sin 30.0°)/(1.33) = 0.376, $\theta_r = 22.1°$

3. $n_i \sin \theta_i = n_r \sin \theta_r$, $\sin \theta_r = n_i \sin \theta_i/n_r$
= (1.00)(sin 45.0°)/(1.54) = 0.459, $\theta_r = 27°$

4. a. $n_i \sin \theta_i = n_r \sin \theta_r$, $\sin \theta_r = n_i \sin \theta_i/n_r$
= (1.00)(sin 45.0°)/(2.42) = 0.292, $\theta_r = 17.0°$

  b. Diamond bends light more than glass does.

5. $n_s = c/v_s$, so $v_s = c/n_s$

  a. $v_{ethanol} = c/n_{ethanol} = (3.00 \times 10^8 \text{ m/s})/1.36$
  $= 2.21 \times 10^8$ m/s

  b. $v_{quartz} = c/n_{quartz} = (3.00 \times 10^8 \text{ m/s})/1.54$
  $= 1.95 \times 10^8$ m/s

  c. $v_{flint\ glass} = c/n_{flint\ glass} = (3.00 \times 10^8 \text{ m/s})/1.61$
  $= 1.86 \times 10^8$ m/s

6. $n_{plastic} = c/v_{plastic} = (3.00 \times 10^8 \text{ m/s})/(2.00 \times 10^8 \text{ m/s})$
$= 1.50$.

7. $n_{glass\ plate} = c/v_{glass\ plate}$
$= (3.00 \times 10^8 \text{ m/s})/(1.9689 \times 10^8 \text{ m/s}) = 1.52$.

Chapter 19

1. a.

  b. $f = r/2 = (20.0 \text{ cm})/2 = 10.0 \text{ cm}$, $1/d_o + 1/d_i = 1/f$,
  so $d_i = d_o f/(d_o - f)$
  = (15.0 cm)(10.0 cm)/(15.0 cm − 10.0 cm)
  = 30.0 cm.

2.

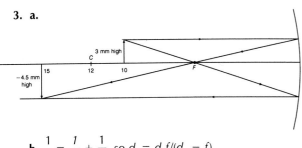

3. a.

  b. $\dfrac{1}{f} = \dfrac{1}{d_o} + \dfrac{1}{d_i}$, so $d_i = d_o f/(d_o - f)$
  = (10 cm)(6.0 cm)/(10 cm − 6.0 cm) = 15 cm.

c. $m = -d_i/d_o = -(15.0 \text{ cm})/(10.0 \text{ cm}) = -1.5$

d. $m = h_i/h_o$, so $h_i = m h_o = (-1.5)(3.0 \text{ mm})$
$= -4.5$ mm

4. $f = r/2 = (20.0 \text{ cm})/2 = 10.0 \text{ cm}$, $1/d_o + 1/d_i = 1/f$, so
$d_o = fd_i/(d_i - f)$
= (10.0 cm)(30.0 cm)/(30.0 cm − 10.0 cm)
= 15.0 cm

5. $f = r/2 = (12.0 \text{ cm})/2 = 6.0 \text{ cm}$, $1/d_o + 1/d_i = 1/f$, so
$d_i = fd_o/(d_o - f)$
= (6.0 cm)(4.0 cm)/(4.0 cm − 6.0 cm) = −12 cm

6. a. $1/d_o + 1/d_i = 1/f$, so
  $d_i = fd_o/(d_o - f)$
  = (9.0 cm)(6.0 cm)/(6.0 cm − 9.0 cm)
  = −18 cm

  b. $m = h_i/h_o = -d_i/d_o = -(-18 \text{ cm})/(6.0 \text{ cm}) = +3.0$,
  so $h_i = mh_o = (3.0)(15 \text{ mm}) = 45$ mm

7. a. $1/d_o + 1/d_i = 1/f$, so
  $d_i = fd_o/(d_o - f)$
  = (16.0 cm)(10.0 cm)/(10.0 cm − 16.0 cm)
  = −27 cm

  b. $m = h_i/h_o = -d_i/d_o = -(-27 \text{ cm})/(10.0 \text{ cm})$
  = +2.7, so $h_i = mh_o = (2.7)(4.0 \text{ cm}) = 11$ cm

8. a.

  b. $1/d_o + 1/d_i = 1/f$,
  so $d_i = fd_o/(d_o - f)$
  = (−15.0 cm)(20.0 cm)/(20.0 cm − (−15.0 cm))
  = −8.6 cm

9. a. $1/d_o + 1/d_i = 1/f$, so
  $d_i = fd_o/(d_o - f)$
  = (−12.0 cm)(60.0 cm)/(60.0 cm − (−12.0 cm))
  = −10.0 cm

  b. $m = h_i/h_o = -d_i/d_o = -(-10.0 \text{ cm})/(60.0 \text{ cm})$
  = +0.17, so
  $h_i = mh_o = (0.17)(6.0 \text{ cm}) = 1.0$ cm

10. $1/d_o + 1/d_i = 1/f$, so
$d_i = fd_o/(d_o - f)$
= (−0.40 m)(6.0 m)/(6.0 m − (−0.40 m))
= −0.38 m

11.

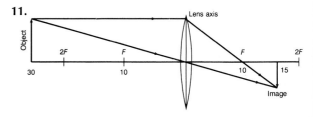

12. a. Since the direction of light in an optical system is reversible, the ray diagram can be constructed by considering, for construction purposes, the given image to be a given object.

b. $1/d_o + 1/d_i = 1/f$, so
$d_o = fd_i/(d_i - f)$
= (10.0 cm)(30.0 cm)/(30.0 cm − 10.0 cm)
= 15.0 cm,
$h_i = -d_ih_o/d_o$
= −(30.0 cm)(12 mm)/(15.0 cm) = −24 mm

13. $1/d_o + 1/d_i = 1/f$, so
$d_i = fd_o/(d_o - f)$ = (5.5 cm)(8.5 cm)/(8.5 cm − 5.5 cm)
= 16 cm
$h_i = -d_ih_o/d_o$ = −(16 cm)(2.25 mm)/(8.5 cm)
= −4.2 mm

14. $1/d_o + 1/d_i = 1/f$ with $d_o = d_i$ since $m = -d_i/d_o$ and $m = -1$. Therefore,
$2/d_o = 1/f$, $d_o = d_i = 2f = 50$ mm

15. $1/d_o + 1/d_i = 1/f$, so $d_i = fd_o/(d_o - f)$
= (20.0 cm)(6.0 cm)/(6.0 cm − 20.0 cm)
= −8.6 cm

16. a. $1/d_o + 1/d_i = 1/f$, so $d_i = fd_o/(d_o - f)$
= (12 cm)(3.4 cm)/(3.4 cm − 12 cm) = −4.7 cm
b. $h_i = -h_od_i/d_o$ = −(2.0 cm)(−4.7 cm)/(3.4 cm)
= 2.8 cm

17. $1/d_o + 1/d_i = 1/f = 1/(8.0$ cm$) + 1/(-16.0$ cm$)$
= 1/(16.0 cm)
so $f = 16.0$ cm

18. From Figure 19-15, you can increase image size by making ($d_o - f$) as small as possible. Thus, increase d_o until it is almost f, which is the limit.

Chapter 20

1. $\lambda = xd/L$ = (13.2 × 10⁻³ m)(1.90 × 10⁻⁵ m)/(0.600 m)
= 4.18 × 10⁻⁷ m = 418 nm

2. $x = \lambda L/d$ = (5.96 × 10⁻⁷ m)(0.600 m)/(1.90 × 10⁻⁵ m)
= 0.0188 m = 18.8 mm

3. $d = \lambda L/x$ = (6.328 × 10⁻⁷ m)(1.000 m)/(65.5 × 10⁻³ m)
= 9.66 × 10⁻⁶ m

4. $\lambda = xd/L$ = (55.8 × 10⁻³ m)(9.66 × 10⁻⁶ m)/(1.000 m)
= 5.39 × 10⁻⁷ m = 539 nm

5. $y = \lambda L/w$ = (5.46 × 10⁻⁷ m)(0.75 m)/(9.5 × 10⁻⁵ m)
= 4.3 × 10⁻³ m = 4.3 mm

6. $w = \lambda L/y$ = (6.328 × 10⁻⁷ m)(1.15 m)/(7.5 × 10⁻³ m)
= 9.7 × 10⁻⁵ m

7. $\lambda = wy/L$ = (2.95 × 10⁻⁵ m)(1.20 × 10⁻² m)/(0.600 m)
= 5.90 × 10⁻⁷ m = 590 nm

8. a. Red, because central peak width is proportional to wavelength.
b. Width = $2y = 2\lambda L/w$. For blue
$2y$ = 2(4.41 × 10⁻⁷ m)(1.00 m)/(5.0 × 10⁻⁵ m)
= 18 mm, for red $2y$
= 2(6.22 × 10⁻⁷ m)(1.00 m)/(5.0 × 10⁻⁵ m)
= 25 mm.

Chapter 21

1. $F = \dfrac{Kqq'}{d^2}$

$= \dfrac{(9.0 \times 10^9 \text{ N} \cdot \text{m}^2/\text{C}^2)(6.0 \times 10^{-6} \text{ C})(6.0 \times 10^{-6} \text{ C})}{(0.50 \text{ m})^2}$

= 1.3 N

2. $F = \dfrac{Kqq'}{d^2}$

$= \dfrac{(9.0 \times 10^9 \text{ N} \cdot \text{m}^2/\text{C}^2)(-2.0 \times 10^{-4} \text{ C})(8.0 \times 10^{-4} \text{ C})}{(0.30 \text{ m})^2}$

= −1.6 × 10⁴ N

3. $F = \dfrac{Kqq'}{d^2}$ $q' = \dfrac{Fd^2}{Kq} =$

$\dfrac{(65 \text{ N})(0.05 \text{ m})^2}{(9.0 \times 10^9 \text{ N} \cdot \text{m}^2/\text{C}^2)(6.0 \times 10^{-6} \text{ C})}$ = 3.0 × 10⁻⁶ C

4. Since like charges repel, large concentrations of like charge are not stable and bulk matter builds up from approximately equal numbers of positive and negative charges. Such bulk matter, even if the size of a planet or star, is electrically neutral and provides no net electrical force on other matter in the universe. The gravitational force, on the other hand, is always attractive and it can build up large masses such as planets and stars. These develop the huge gravitational forces that are effective in shaping the universe.

Chapter 22

1. $E = \dfrac{F}{q'} = \dfrac{0.060 \text{ N}}{2.0 \times 10^{-8} \text{ C}}$ = 3.0 × 10⁶ N/C

2. $E = \dfrac{F}{q'} = \dfrac{2.5 \times 10^{-4} \text{ N}}{5.0 \times 10^{-4} \text{ C}}$ = 0.50 N/C

3. $F_2/F_1 = (Kqq'/d_2^2)/(Kqq'/d_1^2) = (d_1/d_2)^2$ with $d_2 = 2d_1$
$F_2 = (d_1/d_2)^2F_1 = (d_1/2d_1)^2(2.5 \times 10^{-4} \text{ N})$
= 6.3 × 10⁻⁵ N

4. a. No. The force on the 2.0 μC charge would be twice that on the 1.0 μC charge.

b. Yes. You would divide the force by the strength of the test charge, so the results would be the same.

5. $V = Ed = (8000 \text{ N/C})(0.05 \text{ m}) = 400 \text{ J/C} = 400 \text{ V}$

6. $V = Ed$

$$E = \frac{V}{d} = \frac{500 \text{ V}}{0.02 \text{ m}} = 25\ 000 \text{ N/C} = 2.5 \times 10^4 \text{ N/C}$$

7. $V = Ed = (2.50 \times 10^3 \text{ N/C})(0.500 \text{ m}) = 1250 \text{ V}$

8. $W = qV = (5.0 \text{ C})(1.5 \text{ V}) = 7.5 \text{ J}$

9. a. $F = mg$ and $F = Eq$

$$q = \frac{F}{E} = \frac{1.9 \times 10^{-15} \text{ N}}{6.0 \times 10^3 \text{ N/C}} = 3.2 \times 10^{-19} \text{ C}$$

b. # electrons $= \dfrac{q}{q_e} = \dfrac{3.2 \times 10^{-19} \text{ C}}{1.6 \times 10^{-19} \text{ C/electron}}$

$= 2$ electrons

10. a. $F = Eq$

$$q = \frac{F}{E} = \frac{6.4 \times 10^{-13} \text{ N}}{4.0 \times 10^6 \text{ N/C}} = 1.6 \times 10^{-19} \text{ C}$$

b. # electrons $= \dfrac{q}{1.6 \times 10^{-19} \text{ C/electron}} = 1$ electron

11. $E = \dfrac{F}{q} = \dfrac{6.4 \times 10^{-13} \text{ N}}{(4)(1.6 \times 10^{-19} \text{ C})} = 1.0 \times 10^6 \text{ N/C}$

Chapter 23

1. $P = VI = (120 \text{ V})(0.5 \text{ A}) = 60 \text{ J/s} = 60 \text{ W}$

2. $P = VI = (12 \text{ V})(2.0 \text{ A}) = 24 \text{ W}$

3. $P = VI, I = \dfrac{P}{V} = \dfrac{75 \text{ W}}{120 \text{ V}} = 0.63 \text{ A}$

4. $P = VI = (12 \text{ V})(210 \text{ A}) = 2500 \text{ W}$
In 10 s, $E = Pt = (2500 \text{ J/s})(10 \text{ s})$
$= 25000 \text{ J} = 2.5 \times 10^4 \text{ J}$

5. $I = \dfrac{V}{R} = \dfrac{12 \text{ V}}{30 \text{ Ω}} = 0.40 \text{ A}$

6. a. $R = \dfrac{V}{I} = \dfrac{120 \text{ V}}{0.5 \text{ A}} = 240 \text{ Ω} = 200 \text{ Ω}$

b. $P = VI = (120 \text{ V})(0.5 \text{ A}) = 60 \text{ W}$

7. $V = IR = (3.8 \text{ A})(32 \text{ Ω}) = 120 \text{ V}$

8. $R = \dfrac{V}{I} = \dfrac{3 \text{ V}}{2 \times 10^{-4} \text{ A}} = 1.5 \times 10^4 \text{ Ω} = 2 \times 10^4 \text{ Ω}$

9. $I = \dfrac{V}{R} = \dfrac{60 \text{ V}}{12.5 \text{ Ω}} = 4.8 \text{ A}$

10. $R = V/I = (4.5\text{V})/(0.090 \text{ A}) = 50 \text{ Ω}$

11. a. $I = P/V = (75 \text{ W})/(120 \text{ V}) = 0.63 \text{ A}$

b. $R = V/I = 120 \text{ V}/0.63 \text{ A} = 190 \text{ Ω}$

12. a. The new value of the current is $0.63 \text{ A}/2 = 0.315 \text{ A}$, so $V = IR = (0.315 \text{ A})(190 \text{ Ω}) = 60 \text{ V}$

b. The total resistance of the circuit is now $R_{total} = V/I$ $= (120 \text{ V})/(0.315 \text{ A}) = 380 \text{ Ω}$. Therefore, $R_{res} = R_{total} - R_{lamp} = 380 \text{ Ω} - 190 \text{ Ω} = 190 \text{ Ω}$.

c. $P = VI = (60 \text{ V})(0.315 \text{ A}) = 19 \text{ W}$

13. a. $I = V/R = (120 \text{ V})(15 \text{ Ω}) = 8.0 \text{ A}$

b. $E = I^2Rt = (8.0 \text{ A})^2(15 \text{ Ω})(30.0 \text{ s}) = 2.9 \times 10^4 \text{ J}$

c. $2.9 \times 10^4 \text{ J}$ since all electrical energy is converted to thermal energy

14. a. $I = V/R = (60 \text{ V})/(30 \text{ Ω}) = 2.0 \text{ A}$

b. $E = I^2Rt = (2.0 \text{ A})^2(30 \text{ Ω})(5 \text{ min})(60 \text{ s/min})$
$= 3.6 \times 10^4 \text{ J}$

15. a. $E = Pt = (0.2)(100 \text{ J/s})(60 \text{ s}) = 1200 \text{ J}$

b. $E = Pt = (0.8)(100 \text{ J/s})(60 \text{ s}) = 4800 \text{ J}$

16. a. $I = V/R = (220 \text{ V})/(11 \text{ Ω}) = 20 \text{ A}$

b. $E = I^2Rt = (20 \text{ A})^2(11 \text{ Ω})(30.0 \text{ s}) = 1.3 \times 10^5 \text{ J}$

c. $Q = mC\Delta T$ with $Q = 0.70 E$
$\Delta T = 0.70 E/mC$
$= (0.70)(1.3 \times 10^5 \text{ J})/(1.20 \text{ kg})(4180 \text{ J/kg} \cdot \text{C}°) = 18°C$

17. a. $P = IV = (15.0 \text{ A})(120 \text{ V}) = 1800 \text{ W} = 1.80 \text{ kW}$

b. $E = Pt = (1.8 \text{ kW})(5 \text{ h/day})(30 \text{ days}) = 270 \text{ kWh}$

c. Cost $= (0.11 \text{ \$/kWh})(270 \text{ kWh}) = \$29.70$

18. a. $I = \dfrac{V}{R} = \dfrac{(115 \text{ V})}{(12\ 000 \text{ Ω})} = 9.6 \times 10^{-3} \text{ A} = 9.6 \text{ mA}$

b. $P = \dfrac{V^2}{R} = \dfrac{(115 \text{ V})^2}{(12\ 000 \text{ Ω})} = 1.1 \text{ W}$

c. Cost $=$
$(1.1 \times 10^{-3} \text{ kW})(\$0.09/\text{kWh})(30 \text{ days})(24 \text{ h/day}) = \$0.07$

Chapter 24

1. **a.** $R = R_1 + R_2 + R_3 = 20\ \Omega + 20\ \Omega + 20\ \Omega = 60\ \Omega$
   b. $I = V/R = (120\ \text{V})/(160\ \Omega) = 2.0\ \text{A}$
2. **a.** $R = 10\ \Omega + 15\ \Omega + 5\ \Omega = 30\ \Omega$
   b. $I = V/R = (90\ \text{V})/(30\ \Omega) = 3.0\ \text{A}$
3. **a.** It will increase.
   b. $I = V/R$, so it will decrease.
   c. No. It does not depend on the resistance.
4. **a.** $R = V/I = (120\ \text{V})/(0.06\ \text{A}) = 2000\ \Omega$
   b. $2000\ \Omega/10 = 200\ \Omega$
5. **a.** $R = 20.0\ \Omega + 30.0\ \Omega = 50.0\ \Omega$
   b. $I = V/R = (120\ \text{V})/(50.0\ \Omega) = 2.40\ \text{A}$
   c. $V = IR$. Across 20.0 Ω-resistor,
   $V = (2.40\ \text{A})(20.0\ \Omega) = 48.0\ \text{V}$. Across 30.0
   Ω-resistor, $V = (2.40\ \text{A})(30.0\ \Omega) = 72.0\ \text{V}$
   d. $V = 48.0\ \text{V} + 72.0\ \text{V} = 120\ \text{V}$
6. **a.** $R = 3.0\ \text{k}\Omega + 5.0\ \text{k}\Omega + 4.0\ \text{k}\Omega = 12.0\ \text{k}\Omega$
   b. $I = V/R = (12\ \text{V})/(12.0\ \text{k}\Omega)$
   $= 1.0\ \text{mA} = 1.0 \times 10^{-3}\ \text{A}$
   c. $V = IR$,
   so $V = 3.0\ \text{V}, 5.0\ \text{V}$, and $4.0\ \text{V}$
   d. $V = 3.0\ \text{V} + 5.0\ \text{V} + 4.0\ \text{V}$
   $= 12.0\ \text{V}$
7. $V_2 = VR_2/(R_1 + R_2) =$
   $(45\ \text{V})(235\ \text{k}\Omega)/(475\ \text{k}\Omega + 235\ \text{k}\Omega) = 15\ \text{V}$
8. **a.** $V_2 = VR_2/(R_1 + R_2) =$
   $(9.0\ \text{V})(475\ \Omega)/(500\ \Omega + 475\ \Omega) = 4.4\ \text{V}$
   b. $V_2 = VR_2/(R_1 + R_2) =$
   $(9.0\ \text{V})(4.0\ \text{k}\Omega)/(0.50\ \text{k}\Omega + 4.0\ \text{k}\Omega) = 8.0\ \text{V}$
   c. $V_2 = VR_2/(R_1 + R_2) =$
   $(9.0\ \text{V})(4.0 \times 10^5\ \Omega)/(0.005 \times 10^5\ \Omega + 4.0 \times 10^5\ \Omega)$
   $= 9.0\ \text{V}$
9. **a.** $1/R = 1/R_1 + 1/R_2 + 1/R_3 = 3/15\ \Omega, R = 5.0\ \Omega$
   b. $I = V/R = (30\ \text{V})/(5.0\ \Omega) = 6.0\ \text{A}$
   c. $I = V/R = (30\ \text{V})/(15.0\ \Omega) = 2.0\ \text{A}$
10. **a.** $1/R = 1/15.0\ \Omega + 1/12.0\ \Omega$, so
    $R = 6.67\ \Omega$
    b. $I = V/R = (15\ \text{V})/(6.67\ \Omega) = 2.25\ \text{A}$
    c. $I = V/R = (15\ \text{V})/(15.0\ \Omega)$
    $= 1.0\ \text{A}, (15\ \text{V})/(12.0\ \Omega)$
    $= 1.25\ \text{A}$
11. **a.** Smaller.
    b. Gets larger.
    c. No. It remains the same. Currents are independent.
12. **a.** $1/R = 1/120.0\ \Omega + 1/60.0\ \Omega + 1/40.0\ \Omega$,
    $R = 20.0\ \Omega$
    b. $I = V/R = (12.0\ \text{V})/(20.0\ \Omega)$
    $= 0.600\ \text{A}$

c. $I = V/R = (12.0\ \text{V})/(120.0\ \Omega)$
$= 0.100\ \text{A}, (12.0\ \text{V})/(60.0\ \Omega)$
$= 0.200\ \text{A}, (12.0\ \text{V})/(40.0\ \Omega)$
$= 0.300\ \text{A}$

13. **a.**

b. $\dfrac{1}{R} = \dfrac{1}{60\ \Omega} + \dfrac{1}{60\ \Omega} = \dfrac{2}{60\ \Omega}$

$R = \dfrac{60\ \Omega}{2} = 30\ \Omega$

c. $R_{eff} = 30\ \Omega + 30\ \Omega = 60\ \Omega$

d. $I = \dfrac{V}{R} = \dfrac{120\ \text{V}}{60\ \Omega} = 2\ \text{A}$

e. $V_3 = IR_3 = (2\ \text{A})(30\ \Omega) = 60\ \text{V}$

f. $V = IR = (2\ \text{A})(30\ \Omega) = 60\ \text{V}$

g. $I = \dfrac{V}{R_1} = \dfrac{V}{R_2} = \dfrac{60\ \text{V}}{60\ \Omega} = 1\ \text{A}$

14. **a.**

b. $\dfrac{1}{R} = \dfrac{1}{15\ \Omega} + \dfrac{1}{15\ \Omega} + \dfrac{1}{15\ \Omega} = \dfrac{3}{15\ \Omega}$

$R = \dfrac{15\ \Omega}{3} = 5.0\ \Omega$

c. $R_{eff} = 5\ \Omega + 10\ \Omega = 15\ \Omega$

d. $P = \dfrac{V}{R_{eff}} = \dfrac{45\ \text{V}}{15\ \Omega} = 3.0\ \text{A}$

e. $V = IR = (3.0\ \text{A})(10\ \Omega) = 30\ \text{V}$

15. Series: $68\ \Omega + 68\ \Omega + 68\ \Omega = 204\ \Omega$,
    Parallel: $68\ \Omega/3 = 23\ \Omega$,
    Series Parallel: $68\ \Omega + 68\ \Omega/2 = 102\ \Omega$

Chapter 25

1. The induced north pole of the filing points in the direction of the field lines.

2. **a.** repulsive **b.** attractive

3. **a.** from south to north **b.** west

4. Since magnetic field strength varies inversely with the distance from the wire, it will be
   a. half as strong.
   b. one-third as strong.

5. It will point toward the top of the page.

6. The pointed end.

7. $F = BIL$,
$$B = \frac{F}{IL} = \frac{0.04 \text{ N}}{(2.0 \text{ A})(0.10 \text{ m})} = 0.2 \text{ T}$$

8. $F = BIL = (0.40 \text{ N/A} \cdot \text{m})(8.0 \text{ A})(0.5 \text{ m}) = 1.6 \text{ N}$

9. $B = \frac{F}{IL} = \frac{0.6 \text{ N}}{(6.0 \text{ A})(0.75 \text{ m})} = 0.13 \text{ T} = 0.1 \text{ T}$

10. $F = BIL$, F = weight of wire.
$$B = \frac{F}{IL} = \frac{0.35 \text{ N}}{(6.0 \text{ A})(0.40 \text{ m})} = 0.15 \text{ T}$$

11. $F = Bqv = (0.50 \text{ T})(1.6 \times 10^{-19} \text{ C})(4.0 \times 10^6 \text{ m/s})$
    $= 3.2 \times 10^{-13} \text{ N}$

12. $F = Bqv =$
    $(9.0 \times 10^{-2} \text{ T})(2)(1.6 \times 10^{-19} \text{ C})(3.0 \times 10^4 \text{ m/s})$
    $= 8.6 \times 10^{-16} \text{ N}$

13. $F = Bqv$
    $= (4.0 \times 10^{-2} \text{ T})(3)(1.6 \times 10^{-19} \text{ C})(9.0 \times 10^6 \text{ m/s})$
    $= 1.7 \times 10^{-13} \text{ N}$

14. $F = Bqv$
    $= (5.0 \times 10^{-2} \text{ T})(2)(1.6 \times 10^{-19} \text{ C})(4.0 \times 10^{-2} \text{ m/s})$
    $= 6.4 \times 10^{-22} \text{ N}$

Chapter 26

1. **a.** $EMF = BLv = (0.4 \text{ N/A} \cdot \text{m})(0.5 \text{ m})(20 \text{ m/s}) = 4\text{V}$
   b. $I = \frac{V}{R} = \frac{4 \text{ V}}{6.0 \text{ }\Omega} = 0.7 \text{ A}$

2. **a.** $EMF = BLv = (5.0 \times 10^{-5} \text{ T})(25 \text{ m})(125 \text{ m/s}) = 0.16 \text{ V}$
   b. $I = V/R = (0.16 \text{ V})/(315 \text{ }\Omega) = 5.0 \times 10^{-4} \text{ A} = 0.50 \text{ mA}$

3. Using the right-hand rule, the north pole is at the bottom.

4. **a.** $EMF = BLv = (1.0 \text{ T})(30.0 \text{ m})(2.0 \text{ m/s})$
    $= 60 \text{ V}$
   b. $I = \frac{V}{R} = \frac{60 \text{ V}}{15.0 \text{ }\Omega} = 4.0 \text{ A}$

5. **a.** $V_{eff} = (0.707) V_{max} = (0.707)(170 \text{ V}) = 120 \text{ V}$
   b. $I_{eff} = (0.707) I_{max} = (0.707)(0.70 \text{ A}) = 0.49 \text{ A}$

6. **a.** $V_{max} = \frac{V_{eff}}{0.707} = \frac{117 \text{ V}}{0.707} = 165 \text{ V}$

   b. $I_{max} = \frac{I_{eff}}{0.707} = \frac{5.5 \text{ A}}{0.707} = 7.8 \text{ A}$

7. **a.** $V_{eff} = (0.707) V_{max} = (0.707)(425 \text{ V}) = 300 \text{ V}$
   b. $I_{eff} = V_{eff}/R = (300 \text{ V})(500 \text{ }\Omega) = 0.60 \text{ A}$

8. Since $P_{eff} = V_{eff}I_{eff} = (0.707 V_{max})(0.707 I_{max}) = \frac{1}{2} P_{max}$,
   $P_{max} = 2 P_{eff} = 2(100 \text{ W})$
   $= 200 \text{ W}$

9. **a.** $\frac{V_S}{V_P} = \frac{N_S}{N_P}$

   $V_S = \frac{V_P N_S}{N_P} = \frac{(7200 \text{ V})(125)}{7500}$
   $= 120 \text{ V}$

   b. $V_P I_P = V_S I_S$

   $I_P = \frac{V_S I_S}{V_P} = \frac{(120 \text{ V})(36 \text{ A})}{7200 \text{ V}}$
   $= 0.60 \text{ A}$

10. **a.** $\frac{V_P}{V_S} = \frac{N_P}{N_S}$

    $V_S = \frac{V_P N_S}{N_P} = \frac{(120 \text{ V})(1500)}{50} = 3600 \text{ V}$

    b. $V_P I_P = V_S I_S$

    $I_P = \frac{V_S I_S}{V_P} = \frac{(3600 \text{ V})(3.0 \text{ A})}{120 \text{ V}} = 9.0 \times 10^1 \text{ A}$

    c. $V_P I_P = (120 \text{ V})(9.0 \times 10^1 \text{ A}) = 1.1 \times 10^4 \text{ W}$
    $V_S I_S = (3600 \text{ V})(3.0 \text{ A}) = 1.1 \times 10^4 \text{ W}$

11. **a.** $V_S = \frac{V_P N_S}{N_P} = \frac{(3600 \text{ V})(50)}{(1500)} = 120 \text{ V}$

    b. $I_S = \frac{V_P I_P}{V_S} = \frac{(3600 \text{ V})(3.0 \text{ A})}{120 \text{ V}} = 90 \text{ A}$

12. **a.** $V_S = \frac{V_P N_S}{N_P}$

    $= \frac{(60.0 \text{ V})(90\ 000)}{300}$
    $= 1.80 \times 10^4 \text{ V}$

    b. $I_P = \frac{V_S I_S}{V_P}$

    $= \frac{(1.80 \times 10^4 \text{ V})(0.50 \text{ A})}{60.0 \text{ V}}$
    $= 1.5 \times 10^2 \text{ A}$

Chapter 27

1. $Bqv = Eq$,

   $v = \frac{E}{B} = \frac{4.5 \times 10^3 \text{ N/C}}{0.6 \text{ T}} = 8 \times 10^3 \text{ m/s}$

2. $Bqv = \dfrac{mv^2}{r}$,

$r = \dfrac{mv}{Bq} = \dfrac{(1.7 \times 10^{-27}\ \text{kg})(7.5 \times 10^3\ \text{m/s})}{(0.6\ \text{T})(1.6 \times 10^{-19}\ \text{C})}$

$= 1 \times 10^{-4}\ \text{m}$

3. $Bqv = Eq$,

$v = \dfrac{E}{B} = \dfrac{3.0 \times 10^3\ \text{N/C}}{6.0 \times 10^{-2}\ \text{T}} = 5.0 \times 10^4\ \text{m/s}$

4. $Bqv = \dfrac{mv^2}{r}$,

$r = \dfrac{mv}{Bq} = \dfrac{(9.11 \times 10^{-31}\ \text{kg})(5.0 \times 10^4\ \text{m/s})}{(6.0 \times 10^{-2}\ \text{T})(1.6 \times 10^{-19}\ \text{C})}$

$= 4.7 \times 10^{-6}\ \text{m}$

5. a. $Bqv = Eq$,

$v = \dfrac{E}{B} = \dfrac{6.0 \times 10^2\ \text{N/C}}{1.5 \times 10^{-3}\ \text{T}} = 4.0 \times 10^5\ \text{m/s}$

b. $Bqv = \dfrac{mv^2}{r}$,

$m = \dfrac{Bqr}{v} = \dfrac{(0.18\,\text{T})(1.6 \times 10^{-19}\ \text{C})(0.165\ \text{m})}{4.0 \times 10^5\ \text{m/s}}$

$= 1.2 \times 10^{-26}\ \text{kg}$

6. $m = \dfrac{B^2 r^2 q}{2V}$

$= \dfrac{(5.0 \times 10^{-2}\ \text{T})^2 (0.106\ \text{m})^2 (2)(1.6 \times 10^{-19}\ \text{C})}{2(66\ \text{V})}$

$= 6.8 \times 10^{-26}\ \text{kg}$

7. $m = B^2 r^2 q / 2V$

$= (7.2 \times 10^{-2}\ \text{T})^2 (0.085\ \text{m})^2 (1.6 \times 10^{-19}\ \text{C})/2(110\ \text{V})$

$= 2.7 \times 10^{-26}\ \text{kg}$

Chapter 28

1. a. $KE = \tfrac{1}{2} mv^2 = (\tfrac{1}{2})(5.0 \times 10^{-3}\ \text{kg})(1.0 \times 10^{-2}\ \text{m/s})^2$
$= 2.5 \times 10^{-7}\ \text{J}$

b. $E = hf = (7 \times 10^{-34}\ \text{J/Hz})(5.0 \times 10^{14}\ \text{Hz})$
$= 4 \times 10^{-19}\ \text{J}$

c. $(2.5 \times 10^{-7}\ \text{J})/(4 \times 10^{-19}\ \text{J/step}) = 6 \times 10^{11}$ steps

2. $KE = qV_0 = (1.6 \times 10^{-19}\ \text{C})(3.2\ \text{J/C}) = 5.1 \times 10^{-19}\ \text{J}$

3. $KE = qV_0 = (1.6 \times 10^{-19}\ \text{C})(5.7\ \text{J/C})/(1.6 \times 10^{-19}\ \text{J/eV})$
$= 5.7\ \text{eV}$

4. a. $c = f_0 \lambda$

$f_0 = \dfrac{c}{\lambda} = \dfrac{3.00 \times 10^8\ \text{m/s}}{310 \times 10^{-9}\ \text{m}} = 9.7 \times 10^{14}\ \text{Hz}$

b. $hf_0 = (6.6 \times 10^{-34}\ \text{J/Hz})(9.7 \times 10^{14}\ \text{Hz})$
$= (6.4 \times 10^{-19}\ \text{J})(1\ \text{eV}/1.6 \times 10^{-19}\ \text{J}) = 4.0\ \text{eV}$

c. $KE_{max} = \dfrac{hc}{\lambda} - hf_0$

$= \dfrac{(6.6 \times 10^{-34}\ \text{J/Hz})(3.00 \times 10^8\ \text{m/s})(1\ \text{eV}/1.6 \times 10^{-19}\ \text{J})}{240 \times 10^{-9}\ \text{m}}$

$- 4.0\ \text{eV} = 5.2\ \text{eV} - 4.0\ \text{eV} = 1.2\ \text{eV}$

5. a. $E = (1240\ \text{eV} \cdot \text{nm})/\lambda$ where λ has units of nm and E has units of eV. $\lambda = (1240\ \text{eV} \cdot \text{nm})/E$
$= (1240\ \text{eV} \cdot \text{nm})/(1.96\ \text{eV}) = 633\ \text{nm}$.

b. $KE_{max} = hf - hf_0 = E_{photon} - hf_0 = (1240\ \text{eV} \cdot \text{nm})/\lambda$
$- hf_0 = (1240\ \text{eV} \cdot \text{nm})/(425\ \text{nm}) - 1.96\ \text{eV}$
$= 2.92\ \text{eV} - 1.96\ \text{eV} = 0.96\ \text{eV}$.

6. a. $\tfrac{1}{2}mv^2 = qV_0$, $v^2 = 2qV_0/m$
$= 2(1.60 \times 10^{-19}\ \text{C})(250\ \text{J/C})/(9.11 \times 10^{-31}\ \text{kg})$
$= 8.78 \times 10^{13}\ \text{m}^2/\text{s}^2$,
$v = 9.4 \times 10^6\ \text{m/s}$

b. $\lambda = h/mv =$
$(6.6 \times 10^{-34}\ \text{J} \cdot \text{s})/(9.11 \times 10^{-31}\ \text{kg})(9.4 \times 10^6\ \text{m/s})$
$= 7.7 \times 10^{-11}\ \text{m}$

7. a. $\lambda = \dfrac{h}{mv}$

$= \dfrac{6.6 \times 10^{-34}\ \text{J} \cdot \text{s}}{(7.0\ \text{kg})(8.5\ \text{m/s})} = 1.1 \times 10^{-35}\ \text{m}$

b. The wavelength is too small to show observable effects.

8. a. $mv = \dfrac{h}{\lambda} = \dfrac{6.6 \times 10^{-34}\ \text{J} \cdot \text{s}}{5.0 \times 10^{-23}\ \text{kg} \cdot \text{m/s}}$

$= 1.32 \times 10^{-22}\ \text{kg} \cdot \text{m/s}$

b. The mass is too small to have observable effects when it collides with particles of ordinary size.

9. a. They have momentum and energy, they can be diffracted and interfere.

b. An electron has mass and charge, a photon does not.

Chapter 29

1. Height is not, number of siblings and mass of gas are. Mass is always an integer times the mass of a gas atom.

2. Only certain energy levels are possible.

3. a. $hf = E_{excited} - E_{ground}$
$= 3.4\ \text{eV} = (3.4\ \text{eV})(1.6 \times 10^{-19}\ \text{J/eV})$
$= 5.4 \times 10^{-19}\ \text{J}$,
$f = (5.4 \times 10^{-19}\ \text{J})/(6.6 \times 10^{-34}\ \text{J/H}_z)$
$= 8.2 \times 10^{14}\ \text{Hz}$

b. $\lambda = \dfrac{c}{f} = \dfrac{3.0 \times 10^8 \text{ m/s}}{8.2 \times 10^{14} \text{ H}_z} = 3.6 \times 10^{-7}$ m

c. ultraviolet

4. Four times as large since orbit radius is proportional to n^2, where n is the integer labeling the level.

5. $r_n = n^2 k$, where $k = 5.3 \times 10^{-11}$ m
$r_2 = (2)^2 (5.3 \times 10^{-11} \text{ m}) = 2.1 \times 10^{-10}$ m
$r_3 = (3)^2 (5.3 \times 10^{-11} \text{ m}) = 4.8 \times 10^{-10}$ m
$r_4 = (4)^2 (5.3 \times 10^{-11} \text{ m}) = 8.5 \times 10^{-10}$ m

6. $E_n = \dfrac{-13.6 \text{ eV}}{n^2}$

$E_2 = \dfrac{-13.6 \text{ eV}}{(2)^2} = -3.4$ eV

$E_3 = \dfrac{-13.6 \text{ eV}}{(3)^2} = -1.5$ eV

$E_4 = \dfrac{-13.6 \text{ eV}}{(4)^2} = -0.85$ eV

7. Using the results of Practice Exercise 6,
$E_3 - E_2 = (-1.5 \text{ eV}) - (-3.4 \text{ eV}) = 1.9$ eV
$E_4 - E_3 = (-0.85 \text{ eV}) - (-1.5 \text{ eV}) = 0.65$ eV

Chapter 30

1. $A - Z = 15 - 8 = 7$ neutrons
2. $A - Z = neutrons$
   $234 - 92 = 142$ neutrons
   $235 - 92 = 143$ neutrons
   $238 - 92 = 146$ neutrons
3. $A - Z = 200 - 80 = 120$ neutrons
4. $^1_1\text{H}, ^2_1\text{H}, ^3_1\text{H}$
5. $^{234}_{92}\text{U} \rightarrow ^{230}_{90}\text{Th} + ^4_2\text{He}$
6. $^{230}_{90}\text{Th} \rightarrow ^{226}_{88}\text{Ra} + ^4_2\text{He}$
7. $^{226}_{88}\text{Ra} \rightarrow ^{222}_{86}\text{Rn} + ^4_2\text{He}$
8. $^{214}_{82}\text{Pb} \rightarrow ^{214}_{83}\text{Bi} + ^0_{-1}\text{e}$
9. 24.6 years $= 2(12.3 \text{ years})$ which is 2 half-lives. Since $^1/_2 \times ^1/_2 = ^1/_4$ there will be $(1.0 \text{ g})(\frac{1}{4}) = 0.25$ g remaining
10. Amount remaining $=$ (original amount)$(^1/_2)^N$ where N is the number of half-lives elapsed. Since $N = 8 \text{ days}/2.0 \text{ days} = 4$, Amount remaining $= (4.0 \text{ g})(^1/_2)^4 = 0.25$ g
11. The half-life of $^{210}_{84}\text{Po}$ is 138 days.

    There are 273 days or about 2 half-lives between September 1 and June 1.
    So the activity is
    $$= \left(2 \times 10^6 \frac{\text{decays}}{\text{s}}\right)\left(\frac{1}{2}\right)\left(\frac{1}{2}\right) = 5 \times 10^5 \frac{\text{decays}}{\text{s}}$$
12. From Table 30–1, 6 years is approximately 0.5 half-life for tritium. Since Figure 30–4 indicates that approxi-

mately $^{11}/_{16}$ of the original nuclei remain after 0.5 half-life, the brightness will be about $^{11}/_{16}$ of the original.

13. **a.** $E = mc^2 = (1.67 \times 10^{-27} \text{ kg})(3.00 \times 10^8 \text{ m/s})^2$
    $= 1.50 \times 10^{-10}$ J

    b. $E = \dfrac{1.50 \times 10^{-10} \text{ J}}{1.60 \times 10^{-19} \text{ J/eV}} = 9.38 \times 10^8 \text{ eV} = 938$ MeV

    c. The pair will be $(2)(938 \text{ MeV}) = 1.88$ GeV

Chapter 31

1. **a.**
6 protons = (6)(1.007825 u) =	6.046950 u
6 neutrons = (6)(1.008665 u) =	6.051990 u
total	12.098940 u
mass of carbon nucleus	−12.000000 u
mass defect	0.098940 u

   b. (0.098940 u)(931 MeV/u) = 92.1 MeV

2. **a.**
1 proton =	1.007825 u
1 neutron =	1.008665 u
	2.016490 u
mass of hydrogen nucleus ÷	2.0140 u
mass defect	0.00249 u

   b. (0.00249 u)(931 MeV/u) = 2.32 MeV

3. **a.**
7 protons = (7)(1.007825 u) =	7.054775 u
8 neutrons = (8)(1.008665 u) =	8.069320 u
total	15.124095 u
mass of nitrogen nucleus	−15.00011 u
mass defect =	0.123985 u
=	0.12399 u

   b. (0.12399 u)(931 MeV/u) = 115 MeV

4. **a.**
8 protons = (8)(1.007825 u) =	8.062600 u
8 neutrons = (8)(1.008665 u) =	8.069320 u
total	16.131920 u
mass of oxygen nucleus	−15.99491 u
mass defect	0.13701 u

   b. (0.13701 u)(931 MeV/u) = 128 MeV

5. **a.** $^{14}_6\text{C} \rightarrow ^{14}_7\text{N} + ^0_{-1}\text{e}$
   b. $^{55}_{24}\text{Cr} \rightarrow ^{55}_{25}\text{Mn} + ^0_{-1}\text{e}$
6. $^{238}_{92}\text{U} \rightarrow ^{234}_{90}\text{Th} + ^4_2\text{He}$
7. $^{214}_{84}\text{Po} \rightarrow ^{210}_{82}\text{Pb} + ^4_2\text{He}$
8. **a.** $^{210}_{82}\text{Pb} \rightarrow ^{210}_{83}\text{Bi} + ^0_{-1}\text{e}$
   b. $^{210}_{83}\text{Bi} \rightarrow ^{210}_{84}\text{Po} + ^0_{-1}\text{e}$
   c. $^{234}_{90}\text{Th} \rightarrow ^{234}_{91}\text{Pa} + ^0_{-1}\text{e}$
   d. $^{239}_{93}\text{Np} \rightarrow ^{239}_{94}\text{Pu} + ^0_{-1}\text{e}$
9. **a.** Input masses 2.014102 u + 3.016049 u
   = 5.030151 u.
   Output masses 4.002603 u + 1.008665 u
   = 5.011268 u.
   Difference is 0.018883 u
   b. (0.018883 u)(931 MeV/u) = 17.6 MeV

Equations

Mechanics

Chapter 1 Physics: A Mathematical Science

$M \times 10^n$

Chapter 2 Mathematical Relationships

$y = mx + b$

$y = kx^2$

$xy = k$

Chapter 3 Motion in a Straight Line

$\bar{v} = d/t$

$a = \dfrac{v_f - v_i}{t}$

$v_f = v_i + at$

$\bar{v} = \dfrac{v_f + v_i}{2}$

$d = v_i t + \frac{1}{2}at^2$

$v_f^2 = v_i^2 + 2ad$

Chapter 5 Forces

$F = ma$

$W = mg$

$F_f = \mu F_N$

$F_{net} = F_{applied} + F_f$

Chapter 6 Vectors

$c^2 = a^2 + b^2$

Chapter 7 Motion in Two Dimensions

$F_c = \dfrac{mv^2}{r}$

$v = \sqrt{gr}$

$T = 1/f$

$T = 2\pi\sqrt{l/g}$

Chapter 8 Universal Gravitation

$F_g = G\dfrac{m_1 m_2}{d^2}$

Chapter 9 Momentum and Its Conservation

$Ft = m\Delta v$

$p = mv$

Chapter 10 Work, Power, and Simple Machines

$W = Fd$

$P = W/t$

$eff = W_o/W_i \times 100\%$

$eff = MA/IMA \times 100\%$

Chapter 11 Energy

$PE = mgh$

$KE = \frac{1}{2}mv^2$

Thermodynamics and States of Matter

Chapter 12 Thermal Energy

$Q = mC\Delta T$

Chapter 13 Gas Laws

$P_1 V_1 = P_2 V_2$

$\dfrac{V_1}{T_1} = k' = \dfrac{V_2}{T_2}$

$\dfrac{P_1 V_1}{T_1} = \dfrac{P_2 V_2}{T_2}$

Chapter 14 States of Matter

$\dfrac{F_1}{A_1} = \dfrac{F_2}{A_2}$

$\dfrac{L - L_o}{L_o} = \dfrac{\Delta L}{L_i} = a\Delta T$

$\lambda = \dfrac{xd}{L} = d\sin\theta$

Wave Theory, Sound, Light, and Optics

Chapter 15 Waves and Energy Transfer

$v = f\lambda$

Chapter 16 Sound

$f' = f(v - v_d)/(v - v_s)$

Chapter 17 Light

$E \propto \dfrac{I}{d^2}$

$c = f\lambda$

Chapter 18 Reflection and Refraction

$n = \dfrac{\sin i}{\sin r}$

$n_1 \sin\theta_1 = n_2 \sin\theta_2$

$n_s = \dfrac{c}{v_s}$

Electricity and Magnetism

Chapter 21 Static Electricity

$F = \dfrac{Kqq'}{d^2}$

Chapter 22 The Electric Field

$E = \dfrac{F_{on\ test\ charge\ q'}}{q'}$

$V_B - V_A = W/q$

$V = Ed$

Chapter 23 Current Electricity

$P = VI$

$I = V/R$

$P = I^2 R$

$Q = I^2 Rt$

Chapter 24 Series and Parallel Circuits

$R = R_1 + R_2 + R_3$

$\dfrac{1}{R} = \dfrac{1}{R_1} + \dfrac{1}{R_2} + \dfrac{1}{R_3}$

Chapter 25 Magnetic Fields

$B = \dfrac{F}{IL}$

Chapter 26 Electromagnetic Induction

$EMF = BLv$

$I_{eff} = \sqrt{\frac{1}{2}(I_{max}^2)} = 0.707\ I_{max}$

$V_{eff} = 0.707\ V_{max}$

$\dfrac{V_s}{V_p} = \dfrac{N_s}{N_p}$

Chapter 27 Electric and Magnetic Fields

$\dfrac{m}{q} = \dfrac{Br}{v}$

Modern Physics

Chapter 28 Quantum Theory

$KE_{max} = q\ V_o$

$KE_{max} = hf - hf_o$

Chapter 29 The Atom

$r = \dfrac{h^2}{4\pi^2 Kmq^2}\ n^2$

$E = \dfrac{-2\pi^2 K^2 mq^4}{h^2} \times \dfrac{1}{n^2}$

TABLE C–1
SI Base Units

Measurement	Unit	Symbol
length	meter	m
mass	kilogram	kg
time	second	s
electric current	ampere	A
temperature	kelvin	K
amount of substance	mole	mol
intensity of light	candela	cd

TABLE C–2
SI Prefixes

Prefix		Multiplication Factor	Prefix		Multiplication Factor
exa	E	$1\ 000\ 000\ 000\ 000\ 000\ 000 = 10^{18}$	deci	d	$0.1 = 10^{-1}$
peta	P	$1\ 000\ 000\ 000\ 000\ 000 = 10^{15}$	centi	c	$0.01 = 10^{-2}$
tera	T	$1\ 000\ 000\ 000\ 000 = 10^{12}$	milli	m	$0.001 = 10^{-3}$
giga	G	$1\ 000\ 000\ 000 = 10^{9}$	micro	μ	$0.000\ 001 = 10^{-6}$
mega	M	$1\ 000\ 000 = 10^{6}$	nano	n	$0.000\ 000\ 001 = 10^{-9}$
kilo	k	$1\ 000 = 10^{3}$	pico	p	$0.000\ 000\ 000\ 001 = 10^{-12}$
hecto	h	$100 = 10^{2}$	femto	f	$0.000\ 000\ 000\ 000\ 001 = 10^{-15}$
deka	da	$10 = 10^{1}$	atto	a	$0.000\ 000\ 000\ 000\ 000\ 001 = 10^{-18}$

TABLE C–3
Units with Special Names Derived from SI Base Units

Measurement	Unit	Symbol	Expressed in Base Units
energy, work	joule	J	$kg \cdot m^2/s^2$
force	newton	N	$kg \cdot m/s^2$
frequency	hertz	Hz	$1/s$
illuminance	lux	lx	$cd \cdot sr/m^2 (lm/m^2)$
luminous flux	lumen	lm	$cd \cdot sr$
potential difference	volt	V	$kg \cdot m^2/A \cdot s^3 (W/A)$
power	watt	W	$kg \cdot m^2/s^3 (J/s)$
pressure	pascal	Pa	$kg/m \cdot s^2 (N/m^2)$
quantity of electric charge	coulomb	C	$A \cdot s$
resistance	ohm	Ω	$m^2 \cdot kg/s^3 \cdot A^2 (V/A)$
magnetic induction	tesla	T	$kg/C \cdot s (1\ N/A \cdot m)$

TABLE C-4
Reference Data: Physical Constants, Conversion Factors, Useful Equations

Physical Constants

Absolute zero temperature: $0 \text{ K} = -273.15°C$

Acceleration due to gravity at sea level (Washington D.C.): 9.801 m/s^2

Avogadro's number: $N_o = 6.022 \times 10^{23}$ particles/mole

Charge of an electron: $e = -1.6021 \times 10^{-19} \text{ C}$

Constant in Coulomb's law: $K = 8.988 \times 10^9 \text{ N} \cdot \text{m/C}^2$

Gravitational constant: $G = 6.670 \times 10^{-11} \text{ N} \cdot \text{m}^2/\text{kg}^2$

Mass of an electron: $m_e = 9.109 \times 10^{-31} \text{ kg}$

Mass of a proton: $m_p = 1.672 \times 10^{-27} \text{ kg}$

Mean wavelength of yellow sodium light: $5.893 \times 10^{-7} \text{ m}$

Planck's constant: $h = 6.626 \times 10^{-34} \text{ J/Hz} = 4.136 \times 10^{-15} \text{ eV} \cdot \text{s}$

Speed of light in a vacuum: $c = 2.99792458 \times 10^8 \text{ m/s}$ (exact)

Conversion Factors

1 atomic mass unit $= 1.661 \times 10^{-27} \text{ kg} = 931.5 \text{ MeV/c}^2$

1 electronvolt $= 1.602 \times 10^{-19} \text{ J}$

1 joule $= 1 \text{ N} \cdot \text{m}$

1 joule $= 1 \text{ V} \cdot \text{C}$

1 coulomb $= 6.242 \times 10^{18}$ elementary charge units

Useful Equations

Quadratic equation: A quadratic equation may be reduced to the form

$$ax^2 + bx + c = 0$$

then

$$x = \frac{-b \pm \sqrt{b^2 - 4ac}}{2a}$$

Remember that the sign immediately preceding the coefficient is carried with the coefficient in solving for the two values of x.

Circumference of a circle: $C = 2\pi r$ or $C = \pi d$

Area of a circle: $A = \pi r^2$

Volume of a cylinder: $V = \pi r^2 h$

Surface area of a sphere: $A = 4\pi r^2$

Volume of a sphere: $V = \dfrac{4\pi r^3}{3}$

TABLE C–5
International Atomic Masses

Element	Symbol	Atomic number	Atomic mass	Element	Symbol	Atomic number	Atomic mass
Actinium	Ac	89	227.02777*	Neodymium	Nd	60	144.24
Aluminum	Al	13	26.98154	Neon	Ne	10	20.179
Americium	Am	95	243.06139*	Neptunium	Np	93	237.04819
Antimony	Sb	51	121.75	Nickel	Ni	28	58.70
Argon	Ar	18	39.948	Niobium	Nb	41	92.9064
Arsenic	As	33	74.9216	Nitrogen	N	7	14.0067
Astatine	At	85	209.98704*	Nobelium	No	102	255.093*
Barium	Ba	56	137.33	Osmium	Os	76	190.2
Berkelium	Bk	97	247.07032*	Oxygen	O	8	15.9994
Beryllium	Be	4	9.01218	Palladium	Pd	46	106.4
Bismuth	Bi	83	208.9804	Phosphorus	P	15	30.97376
Boron	B	5	10.81	Platinum	Pt	78	195.09
Bromine	Br	35	79.904	Plutonium	Pu	94	244.06424*
Cadmium	Cd	48	112.41	Polonium	Po	84	208.98244*
Calcium	Ca	20	40.08	Potassium	K	19	39.0983
Californium	Cf	98	251.07961*	Praseodymium	Pr	59	140.9077
Carbon	C	6	12.011	Promethium	Pm	61	144.91279*
Cerium	Ce	58	140.12	Protactinium	Pa	91	231.03590*
Cesium	Cs	55	132.9054	Radium	Ra	88	226.0254
Chlorine	Cl	17	35.453	Radon	Rn	86	222*
Chromium	Cr	24	51.996	Rhenium	Re	75	186.207
Cobalt	Co	27	58.9332	Rhodium	Rh	45	102.9055
Copper	Cu	29	63.546	Rubidium	Rb	37	85.4678
Curium	Cm	96	247.07038*	Ruthenium	Ru	44	101.07
Dysprosium	Dy	66	162.50	Samarium	Sm	62	150.4
Einsteinium	Es	99	254.08805*	Scandium	Sc	21	44.9559
Erbium	Er	68	167.26	Selenium	Se	34	78.96
Europium	Eu	63	151.96	Silicon	Si	14	28.0855
Fermium	Fm	100	257.09515*	Silver	Ag	47	107.868
Fluorine	F	9	18.998403	Sodium	Na	11	22.98977
Francium	Fr	87	223.01976*	Strontium	Sr	38	87.62
Gadolinium	Gd	64	157.25	Sulfur	S	16	32.06
Gallium	Ga	31	69.72	Tantalum	Ta	73	180.9479
Germanium	Ge	32	72.59	Technetium	Tc	43	96.90639*
Gold	Au	79	196.9665	Tellurium	Te	52	127.60
Hafnium	Hf	72	178.49	Terbium	Tb	65	158.9254
Helium	He	2	4.00260	Thallium	Tl	81	204.37
Holmium	Ho	67	164.9304	Thorium	Th	90	232.0381
Hydrogen	H	1	1.0079	Thulium	Tm	69	168.9342
Indium	In	49	114.82	Tin	Sn	50	118.69
Iodine	I	53	126.9045	Titanium	Ti	22	47.90
Iridium	Ir	77	192.22	Tungsten	W	74	183.85
Iron	Fe	26	55.847	Uranium	U	92	238.029
Krypton	Kr	36	83.80	Vanadium	V	23	50.9414
Lanthanum	La	57	138.9055	Xenon	Xe	54	131.30
Lawrencium	Lr	103	256.099*	Ytterbium	Yb	70	173.04
Lead	Pb	82	207.2	Yttrium	Y	39	88.9059
Lithium	Li	3	6.941	Zinc	Zn	30	65.38
Lutetium	Lu	71	174.97	Zirconium	Zr	40	91.22
Magnesium	Mg	12	24.305	Element 104†		104	257*
Manganese	Mn	25	54.9380	Element 105†		105	260*
Mendelevium	Md	101	258*	Element 106†		106	263*
Mercury	Hg	80	200.59	Element 107†		107	258*
Molybdenum	Mo	42	95.94	Element 108†		108	265*
				Element 109†		109	266*

*The mass of the isotope with the longest known half-life.
†Names for elements 104 and 105 have not yet been approved by the IUPAC. The USSR has proposed Kurchatovium (Ku) for element 104 and Bohrium (Bh) for element 105. The United States has proposed Rutherfordium (Rf) for element 104 and Hahnium (Ha) for element 105.

TABLE C–6 Trigonometric Functions

Angle	sin	cos	tan	Angle	sin	cos	tan
0°	.0000	1.0000	.0000	45°	.7071	.7071	1.0000
1°	.0175	.9998	.0175	46°	.7193	.6947	1.0355
2°	.0349	.9994	.0349	47°	.7314	.6820	1.0724
3°	.0523	.9986	.0524	48°	.7431	.6691	1.1106
4°	.0698	.9976	.0699	49°	.7547	.6561	1.1504
5°	.0872	.9962	.0875	50°	.7660	.6428	1.1918
6°	.1045	.9945	.1051	51°	.7771	.6293	1.2349
7°	.1219	.9925	.1228	52°	.7880	.6157	1.2799
8°	.1392	.9903	.1405	53°	.7986	.6018	1.3270
9°	.1564	.9877	.1584	54°	.8090	.5878	1.3764
10°	.1736	.9848	.1763	55°	.8192	.5736	1.4281
11°	.1908	.9816	.1944	56°	.8290	.5592	1.4826
12°	.2079	.9781	.2126	57°	.8387	.5446	1.5399
13°	.2250	.9744	.2309	58°	.8480	.5299	1.6003
14°	.2419	.9703	.2493	59°	.8572	.5150	1.6643
15°	.2588	.9659	.2679	60°	.8660	.5000	1.7321
16°	.2756	.9613	.2867	61°	.8746	.4848	1.8040
17°	.2924	.9563	.3057	62°	.8829	.4695	1.8807
18°	.3090	.9511	.3249	63°	.8910	.4540	1.9626
19°	.3256	.9455	.3443	64°	.8988	.4384	2.0503
20°	.3420	.9397	.3640	65°	.9063	.4226	2.1445
21°	.3584	.9336	.3839	66°	.9135	.4067	2.2460
22°	.3746	.9272	.4040	67°	.9205	.3907	2.3559
23°	.3907	.9205	.4245	68°	.9272	.3746	2.4751
24°	.4067	.9135	.4452	69°	.9336	.3584	2.6051
25°	.4226	.9063	.4663	70°	.9397	.3420	2.7475
26°	.4384	.8988	.4877	71°	.9455	.3256	2.9042
27°	.4540	.8910	.5095	72°	.9511	.3090	3.0777
28°	.4695	.8829	.5317	73°	.9563	.2924	3.2709
29°	.4848	.8746	.5543	74°	.9613	.2756	3.4874
30°	.5000	.8660	.5774	75°	.9659	.2588	3.7321
31°	.5150	.8572	.6009	76°	.9703	.2419	4.0108
32°	.5299	.8480	.6249	77°	.9744	.2250	4.3315
33°	.5446	.8387	.6494	78°	.9781	.2079	4.7046
34°	.5592	.8290	.6745	79°	.9816	.1908	5.1446
35°	.5736	.8192	.7002	80°	.9848	.1736	5.6713
36°	.5878	.8090	.7265	81°	.9877	.1564	6.3138
37°	.6018	.7986	.7536	82°	.9903	.1392	7.1154
38°	.6157	.7880	.7813	83°	.9925	.1219	8.1443
39°	.6293	.7771	.8098	84°	.9945	.1045	9.5144
40°	.6428	.7660	.8391	85°	.9962	.0872	11.4301
41°	.6561	.7547	.8693	86°	.9976	.0698	14.3007
42°	.6691	.7431	.9004	87°	.9986	.0523	19.0811
43°	.6820	.7314	.9325	88°	.9994	.0349	28.6363
44°	.6947	.7193	.9657	89°	.9998	.0175	57.2900
45°	.7071	.7071	1.0000	90°	1.0000	.0000	∞

APPENDIX D

D:1 Law of Cosines

To use the trigonometry of the right triangle, two of the sides of a triangle must be perpendicular. That is, you must have a right triangle. But sometimes you will need to work with a triangle that is not a right triangle. The law of cosines applies to all triangles. Consider the two triangles shown in Figure D-1. They are not right triangles. When angle C is known, the lengths of the sides obey the following relationship.

$$c^2 = a^2 + b^2 - 2ab \cos C$$

If a, b, and angle C are known, the length of side c is

$$c = \sqrt{a^2 + b^2 - 2ab \cos C}$$

In triangle 1 of Figure D-1, the length of side a is 4.00 cm, side b is 5.00 cm, and angle C is 60.0°. Substituting the values in the equation, side c is obtained. Substituting the appropriate values yields

$$a^2 = (4.0 \text{ cm})^2 = 16.0 \text{ cm}^2$$

$$b^2 = (5.0 \text{ cm})^2 = 25.0 \text{ cm}^2$$

$$2ab \cos \theta = 2(4.00 \text{ cm})(5.00 \text{ cm})(\cos 60.0°)$$
$$= 2(4.00 \text{ cm})(5.00 \text{ cm})(0.500)$$
$$2ab \cos \theta = 20.0 \text{ cm}^2$$

Therefore,

$$c = \sqrt{a^2 + b^2 - 2ab \cos \theta}$$
$$= \sqrt{16.0 \text{ cm}^2 + 25.0 \text{ cm}^2 - 20.0 \text{ cm}^2}$$
$$= \sqrt{21.0 \text{ cm}^2}$$
$$c = 4.58 \text{ cm}$$

If angle C is larger than 90°, its cosine is negative and is numerically equal to the cosine of its supplement. In triangle 2, Figure D-1, angle C is 120.0°. Therefore, its cosine is the negative of the cosine of (180.0° − 120.0°) or 60.0°. The cosine of 60.0° is 0.500. Thus, the cosine of 120.0° is −0.500.

D:2 Law of Sines

Just as the law of cosines applies to all triangles, the law of sines also applies to all triangles. The relationship is

$$\frac{a}{\sin A} = \frac{b}{\sin B} = \frac{c}{\sin C}$$

Using the values for triangle 1 shown in Figure D-1, angle A can be calculated by the law of sines.

$$\frac{a}{\sin A} = \frac{c}{\sin C}$$

$$\sin A = \frac{a}{c} \sin C$$

$$\sin A = \frac{4.00 \text{ cm}}{4.50 \text{ cm}} \sin (60.0°)$$

$$= \frac{(4.00 \text{ cm})(0.867)}{(4.58 \text{ cm})}$$

$$= 0.757$$

$$A = 49.2°$$

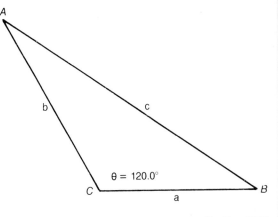

FIGURE D–1.

Physics-Related Careers

Careers in physics-related fields are many and varied. They may require only on-the-job training. Others may consist of seven or eight years of formal college training plus experience through on-the-job programs.

Training and Education Key

Job	= On-the-job training	BS	= Bachelor of Science degree
VoTech	= Vocational or technical school	MS	= Master of Science degree
CC	= Community college (2 yr)	PhD	= Doctor of Philosophy degree (science)

PHYSICIST

Experimental physicists perform research to observe and measure matter and its interactions. Theoretical physicists use mathematics and computers to construct theories to explain the results and predict new ones. Many physicists are also involved in teaching in colleges and universities.

Career	Training	Job Description
Acoustical scientist	BS, MS, PhD	does research in the control of sound; develops acoustical systems
Astrophysicist	BS, MS, PhD	studies the structure and motion of the universe and all its bodies
Biophysicist	BS, MS, PhD	applies physics to biology, medical fields, and related areas
Condensed matter physicist	BS, MS, PhD	studies the behavior of materials and constructs new ones
Elementary-particle physicist	BS, MS, PhD	studies properties of leptons and baryons using high energy accelerators
Geophysicist	BS, MS, PhD	studies the composition and physical features of Earth
Nuclear physicist	BS, MS, PhD	studies the structure of atomic nuclei and their interactions with each other
Optical scientist	BS, MS, PhD	develops optical systems; does laser research
Plasma physicist	BS, MS, PhD	studies matter in the plasma state; does research directed toward the control of fusion
Radiological physicist	BS, MS, PhD	detects radiation and plans health and safety programs at nuclear power plants and in hospital radiation treatment centers
Teacher (High school)	BS, MS	instructs students about general areas of physics
Teacher (College)	BS, MS, PhD	instructs students about general and specific areas of physics and does research

ENGINEER

Generally, engineers design equipment, develop new materials, and find methods for making raw materials and power sources into useful products. Engineers are also frequently involved in management. Others teach in universities.

Career	Training	Job Description
Aerospace engineer	BS, MS, PhD	designs and develops flight systems, aircraft, and spacecraft
Biomedical engineer	BS, MS, PhD	develops instruments and systems to improve medical procedures; studies the engineering aspects of biological systems
Ceramic engineer	BS, MS, PhD	develops methods for processing clay and other nonmetallic minerals into a variety of products, such as glass and heat-resistant materials

Chemical engineer	BS, MS, PhD	plans, designs, and constructs chemical plants; develops processes
Civil engineer	BS, MS, PhD	designs bridges, buildings, dams, and many other types of structures
Computer engineer	BS, MS, PhD	designs new computers and programs
Electrical engineer	BS, MS, PhD	designs electric equipment and systems for the generation and distribution of power, TV, radio, stereo systems
Mechanical engineer	BS, MS, PhD	designs and develops machines that produce power, such as engines and nuclear reactors
Metallurgical engineer	BS, MS, PhD	develops methods to process metals and convert them into useful products

Computer-Related

Careers in the field of computers exist at all levels. People using computers for scientific or engineering applications will need training in the physical sciences as well as computer science.

Career	Training	Job Description
Computer engineer	BS, MS, PhD	designs new computers and programs
Computer programmer	BS	develops the detailed instructions followed by a computer in processing information
Systems analyst	BS, MS	analyzes data flows in an organization and designs more useful and efficient data processing systems
Computer technician	VoTech, CC	operates and services sophisticated computers

TECHNICIAN

Technicians work directly with physicists and engineers. They are trained in specific aspects of science, math, and technology. They help develop and test lab and industrial equipment and processes, and frequently work in sales

Career	Training	Job Description
Aeronautical technician	VoTech, CC	works with engineers and scientists to develop aircraft; works in field service
Chemical technician	CC	helps to develop, sell, distribute chemical products and equipment; conducts routine tests
Civil engineering technician	CC, Job	assists civil engineers in planning, designing and constructing bridges, dams, and other structures
Electronics technician	VoTech, Job	develops, constructs, and services a wide range of electronic equipment
Laser technician	CC, Job	uses and repairs lasers in industry and medicine
Mechanical technician	VoTech, Job	helps to develop and construct automotive tools and machines
Nuclear technician	Job, CC	operates monitoring systems; supports and assists nuclear engineers

Additional Information

Following is a list of addresses for a few sources of additional information. Further information about physics-related careers and a more complete listing of additional sources can be found in the *Occupational Outlook Handbook* and *Keys to Careers in Science and Technology*. Check also with your school guidance counselors for any information they may be able to supply.

American Institute of Physics
335 East 45th Street
New York, NY 10017

Encyclopedia of Careers and Vocational Guidance
Doubleday and Co., Inc.
501 Franklin Avenue
Garden City, NY 11530

Keys to Careers in Science and Technology
National Science Teachers Association
1742 Connecticut Avenue, N.W.
Washington, D.C. 20009

Occupations
Armed Forces Vocational Testing Group
Universal City, TX 78148

Occupational Outlook Handbook
U.S. Department of Labor
Bureau of Labor Statistics
Washington, D.C. 20212

U.S. Civil Service Commission
Washington, D.C. 20415

GLOSSARY

absolute zero: Temperature at which gas would have zero volume.

absorption spectrum: Spectrum of electromagnetic radiation absorbed by the gaseous atoms of an element when white light is passed through the gas.

acceleration: Rate of change of velocity.

accuracy: Closeness of a measurement to the standard value of a quantity.

action-reaction forces: A pair of equal and opposite forces involved in an interaction.

activity: The number of decays per second of a radioactive substance.

adhesion: Attraction between unlike particles.

alpha decay: A process that emits an alpha particle.

alpha particles: Helium nuclei consisting of two protons and two neutrons.

ammeter: Electric device used to measure current.

ampere: Unit for the rate of flow of charged particles. One ampere equals a flow of one coulomb of charge per second.

amplitude: Maximum displacement from zero of any periodic phenomenon.

angle of incidence: Angle between a light ray and a line perpendicular to the surface that the ray is striking.

angle of reflection: Angle between a normal and a reflected ray.

angle of refraction: Angle between a refracted ray and a line perpendicular to the surface that the ray is leaving.

antenna: Device used to receive or transmit electromagnetic waves.

antinode: A point of maximum displacement of two pulses with equal amplitude.

antiparticle: Particle having the same mass and spin as its counterpart but opposite charge and magnetic moment.

Archimedes' principle: An object immersed in a fluid is buoyed up by a force equal to the weight of the fluid displaced by the object.

atomic mass unit: A unit of mass equal to 1/2 of the atomic mass of the carbon-12 atom.

atomic number: Number of protons in the nucleus of an atom.

average acceleration: Ratio of change in velocity to the time interval.

average speed: Ratio of total distance traveled to the total time interval.

back-*EMF*: Potential difference across a coil created by a change in magnetic field.

barometer: Device for measuring the pressure of the atmosphere.

baryon: A subatomic particle that is composed of three quarks; its mass is equal to or greater than that of a proton.

battery: Two dissimilar conductors and an electrolyte that produces a potential difference; converts chemical to electrical energy.

beat: Oscillation in amplitude of complex wave.

Bernoulli's principle: The pressure exerted by a fluid decreases as its velocity increases.

beta particles: High-speed electrons emitted by a radioactive nucleus.

binding energy: Energy equivalent of the mass defect representing the amount of energy required to separate the nucleus into individual nucleons.

boiling point: The temperature at which a substance changes from a liquid to a vapor state.

breeder reactor: A nuclear reactor that converts nonfissionable material to fissionable material with the production of energy.

bubble chamber: An instrument of superheated liquid in which the path of ionizing particles are made visible as trails of tiny bubbles.

candela: Unit of luminous intensity.

capacitor: Device used in electrical circuits to store charge.

capillary action: Rise of a liquid in a narrow tube due to surface tension.

centripetal acceleration: Acceleration always at right angles to the velocity of a particle.

chain reaction: A nuclear reaction producing energy or products that cause further reactions of the same kind.

charging by conduction: Touching a neutral body with a charged body.

chromatic aberration: Failure of a lens to bring all wavelengths of light to focus at the same point.

coefficient of friction: A value describing the nature of surfaces in contact.

coherent light: Light in which all waves are in phase.

cohesive force: Attraction between like particles.

combined gas law: $p_1 V_1 / T_1 = p_2 V_2 / T_2$

complementary colors: Primary and secondary colors that when added produce white light.

components of a vector: Two or more vectors (usually perpendicular) that when added together, produce the original vector.

Compton effect: Interaction of X rays and electrons as the X rays traverse matter resulting in a lengthening of the X-ray wavelength.

concave lens: A diverging lens thinner at the middle than at the edges.

concurrent forces: Forces acting on the same point.

condensation: Change of a gas to a liquid.

conductor: (electrical) Material through which charged particles move readily; (heat) material through which heat flows readily.

consonance: Complex sound wave perceived as pleasant.

constructive interference: The superposition of two equal wave pulses resulting in a combined wave of larger amplitude than its components.

control rods: Devices in a nuclear reactor used to regulate the rate of the nuclear reaction.

conventional current: The direction in which a positive current flows.

converging lens: Lens, thick in the middle and thin at the edge, that causes rays to converge.

converging mirror: Concave mirror capable of causing rays to converge.

convex lens: A converging lens thicker at the center than at the edges.

convex mirror: A spherical mirror that reflects light from its outer surface.

coulomb: Unit of quantity of electric charge equal to the charge found on 6.24×10^{18} electrons.

crest: High point of a wave motion:

critical angle: Minimum angle of incidence that produces total internal reflection.

de Broglie principle: Material particles have wavelike characteristics; wavelength varies inversely with momentum.

dependent variable: The responding variable.

destructive interference: The superposition of two wave pulses with equal but opposite amplitudes.

deuteron: Nucleus of the hydrogen isotope deuterium, consisting of one proton and one neutron.

diffraction: Bending of light waves around an object in their path.

diffraction gratings: Material containing many thousands of parallel lines per centimeter that is used to produce a light spectrum by interference.

diffuse reflection: Reflected light scattered in many directions.

dispersion: Refraction of light into a spectrum of the wavelengths composing the light.

displacement: Vector quantity representing the net change in position of an object.

dissonance: Complex sound wave perceived as unpleasant.

diverging lens: Lens, thin in the middle and thick at the edge, that causes light rays to diverge.

diverging mirror: Convex mirror capable of causing light rays to diverge.

domain: Region of a metal in which magnetic fields in atoms are aligned in a common direction.

Doppler shift: Decrease (or increase) in wavelength as the source and detector of waves move toward (or away from) each other.

dynamics: Study of the motion of particles acted upon by forces.

effective resistance: Resistance of a single resistor that could replace a combination of resistors.

efficiency: Ratio of output work to input work.

effort force: The effort exerted on a machine.

elastic collision: Collision in which the total kinetic energy of two objects is the same after the collision as before.

elasticity: Ability of an object to return to its original form after removal of deforming forces.

electric circuit: Continuous path of conductors that can be followed by charged particles.

electric current: Flow of charged particles.

electric field: The property of space around a charged object that causes forces on other charged objects.

electric field intensity: Ratio of the force exerted by a field on a charged particle to the charge on the particle.

electric field lines: Lines representing the direction of the electric field.

electric generator: Device using mechanical energy to produce electric energy.

electric potential: The ratio of potential energy to the charge.

electromagnet: Device in which a magnetic field is generated by an electric current.

electromagnetic force: One of the fundamental forces. The force that exists between electric charges.

electromagnetic induction: Generation of an electric current by having a wire cut (or cut by) magnetic flux lines.

electromagnetic wave: Wave consisting of electric and magnetic fields that move at the speed of light in space.

electromotive force (EMF): Potential difference generated by electromagnetic induction.

electron: Subatomic particle of small mass and negative charge found in every atom.

electron cloud: Region of high probability of finding an electron about an atom.

elementary charge: The charge of an electron.

emission spectrum: Spectrum produced by the excited atoms of an element.

energy: Capacity to do work or cause heat to flow.

energy levels: The different amounts of energy of an atomic electron.

entropy: Measure of disorder of a system.

equilibrant force: Force equal in magnitude to a resultant, but opposite in direction.

equilibrium: Condition in which the net force on an object is zero.

evaporation: Change from liquid to gas.

excited state: A higher energy level of electrons.

extrapolation: Extending a graph beyond measured points.

first law of thermodynamics: See law of conservation of energy.

first-order line: The first bright band of light on either side of the central band.

fission: Division of nucleus into two or more fragments.

fluid: A material that flows, e.g., liquids and gases.

fluorescence: Phenomenon in which atoms emit light when excited by an outside source. The light emission ceases as soon as the exciting source is removed.

focal length: Distance from the focal point to the vertex of a mirror or center of a lens.

focal point: Point of convergence, real or apparent (virtual), of parallel rays reflected by a mirror or refracted by a lens.

force: Action that results in accelerating or deforming an object.

frame of reference: Coordinate system used to describe motion.

Fraunhofer lines: Absorption lines in the sun's spectrum due to gases in the solar atmosphere.

frequency: Number of occurrences in a unit of time.

friction: Force opposing motion between two objects that are in contact.

fundamental: Lowest frequency sound produced by an instrument.

fuse: A metal safety device in an electric circuit that stops current flow, thus preventing overload.

galvanometer: A device used to measure very small currents.

gamma rays: Electromagnetic waves of extremely high frequency emitted by nuclei.

Geiger-Muller tube: Device used to detect radiation by using the ionizing property of radiation.

gravitational field: Distortion of space due to the presence of a mass.

gravitational force: Attraction between objects due to their masses.

gravitational mass: Mass found by measuring an object on a beam balance.

grounding: Connecting a charged object to Earth to remove the object's charge.

ground state: The lowest energy level of an electron.

half-life: Length of time for half of a sample of a radioactive material to decay.

heat: Quantity of thermal energy transferred from one object to another object because of a difference in temperature.

heat engine: A device that converts thermal energy to mechanical energy.

heat of fusion: Energy required to change 1 kg of a substance from solid to liquid at the melting point.

heat of vaporization: Energy required to change 1 kg of a substance from liquid to vapor (gas) at the boiling point.

Heisenberg uncertainty principle: The more accurately one determines the position of a particle, the less accurately the momentum is known, and vice versa.

hertz: Unit of frequency equal to one event (cycle) per second.

hypotenuse: The side of a right triangle opposite the right angle.

illuminance: Rate at which light energy falls on a surface.

illuminated body: Object on which light is falling.

image: The reproduction of an object formed with lenses or mirrors.

impulse: Product of a force and the time during which it acts.

impulse-momentum theorem: The impulse given to an object is equal to the change in its momentum; $F\Delta t = \Delta p$.

independent variable: The variable that is manipulated or changed by the experimenter.

index of refraction: $n = c/v$ where c is the speed of light in a vacuum and v is its speed in the material.

inductive reactance: Opposition to electric current flow due to self-induction.

inelastic collision: Collision in which some of the kinetic energy of colliding objects is changed to another form of energy.

inertia: Tendency of an object not to change its motion.

inertial mass: The ratio of an unbalanced force exerted on an object to its acceleration.

insulator: Material through which the flow of charged particles or heat is greatly restricted.

interference: Combining of two waves (disturbances) arriving at the same point at the same time.

interference fringes: A pattern of light and dark bands resulting from interference of light waves through slits.

International System of Units (SI): See SI.

isolated system: System not being acted upon by outside forces or into which energy does not enter or leave.

isotopes: Two or more atoms of the same element differing in masses due to different numbers of neutrons.

joule: Unit of energy (or work or heat) equal to a newton-meter.

Kelvin temperature scale: Scale with 0 K = absolute zero and 273.15 K = freezing point of water.

kilogram: The standard unit of mass.

kilowatt hour: Amount of energy equal to 3.6×10^6 J.

kinetic energy: Energy of an object due to its motion.

kinetic theory: Concept that all matter is made of small particles that are in constant motion.

laser: Device for producing coherent light

law of conservation of energy: In a closed, isolated system, the total energy does not change.

law of conservation of mass-energy: The sum of matter and energy in the universe is a constant.

law of conservation of momentum: In a system free of external forces, the total momentum is always the same.

law of reflection: The angle of incidence is equal to the angle of reflection when a light ray strikes a surface.

lens: An optical device with a refractive index larger than that of air.

lens equation: See *mirror equation.*

Lenz's law: The magnetic field generated by an induced current always opposes the field generating the current.

longitudinal wave: Wave in which the direction of the disturbance is the same as the direction of travel of the wave.

loudness: A function of the amplitude of a sound wave; intensity.

lumen: Unit of luminous flux.

luminous body: An object emitting light.

luminous flux: Flow of light from a source.

luminous intensity: Measure of light emitted by a source.

magnetic field: Space around a magnet in which magnetic forces can be detected.

magnetic flux: All the magnetic flux lines associated with a magnet.

magnetic flux density: Number of magnetic flux lines per unit area.

magnetic flux lines: Imaginary lines indicating the magnitude and direction of a magnetic field.

magnetic induction: Strength of a magnetic field.

magnification: The ratio of the size of an image to the size of an object.

mass: Quantity of matter in an object measured by its resistance to a change in its motion (inertia).

mass defect: Difference in mass between the actual atomic nucleus and the sum of the particles from which the nucleus was made.

mass number: Number of protons and neutrons (nucleons) in an atom.

mass spectrograph: Device used to measure the mass of atoms and molecules.

mechanical advantage (MA): Ratio of resistance force to effort force in a machine.

mechanical energy: The sum of potential and kinetic energy.

mechanical resonance: Increase in the amplitude of a vibrating object by applying forces at regular time intervals.

mechanical wave: Disturbance traveling through a material medium.

melting point: The temperature at which a substance changes from a solid to a liquid.

mesons: Medium mass subatomic particles.

meter: The standard SI unit of length.

mirror equation: $1/d_o + 1/d_i = 1/f$

moderator: Material used to decrease speed of fast neutrons in a nuclear reactor.

momentum: Product of an object's mass and velocity.

monochromatic light: Light of a single wavelength.

mutual inductance: The induction of an *EMF* in a secondary coil by varying the magnetic flux in a primary coil.

neutrino: A chargeless, massless particle emitted along with beta particles. A type of lepton.

neutron: Subatomic particle of approximate mass 1 u and no charge.

newton: SI unit of force.

Newton's laws of motion: Laws relating force and motion: first law, see page 74; second law, see page 76; third law, see page 78

node: Point in a medium or field that remains unchanged when acted upon by more than one disturbance simultaneously.

normal force: Force perpendicular to a surface.

nuclear equation: Equation representing a nuclear reaction.

nuclear fission: Splitting a large atomic nucleus into two approximately equal parts.

nuclear fusion: Combining of small nuclei into a larger nucleus.

nuclear moderator: Substance used to slow neutrons in a nuclear reactor.

nuclear (strong) force: Very short range force holding protons and neutrons together in the atomic nucleus.

nuclear reaction: A reaction that occurs whenever the number of protons or neutrons changes.

nucleon: Proton or neutron.

nucleus: Core of an atom containing the protons and neutrons.

nuclide: The nucleus of an isotope.

object: A source of diverging light rays.

octave: The interval between two frequencies with a ratio of 2 to 1.

ohm: Unit of electric resistance.

opaque material: Material that does not transmit light.

optical density: Property determining the speed of light, and thus index of refraction, in a medium.

optical fiber: Light-transmitting glass or plastic fibers that make use of the principle of total internal reflection to transmit light along irregular paths.

overtones: Sound waves of higher frequency than the fundamental.

parallax: Change in relative position of objects with change in viewing angle.

parallel circuit: Circuit in which there are two or more paths for the charged particles to follow as they complete the circuit.

parallel connection: A connection of two or more electrical devices to the same two points of a circuit to provide more than one path for current flow.

pascal: Unit of pressure equal to a newton per square meter.

Pascal's principle: Applied pressure is transmitted undiminished throughout a fluid.

period: Time duration of a periodic phenomenon.

phosphorescence: Emission of light by atoms excited by an outside source. The emission persists for a time after the outside source is removed.

photoelectric effect: Ejection of electrons from the surface of a metal exposed to light.

photon: Quantum of electromagnetic waves.

photovoltaic cell: Device for converting light into electric energy; solar cell.

piezoelectricity: Production of electric current by deforming certain crystals.

pigment: A colored material that absorbs certain colors and reflects others.

pitch: Perceived sound characteristic that is equivalent to frequency.

plane mirror: A flat, smooth surface that reflects light in a regular way.

planetary model: Model of an atom in which the electron(s) orbit(s) the nucleus much as planets orbit the sun.

plasma: High temperature state of matter in which atoms are separated into electrons and positive ions or nuclei.

polarized light: Light in which the electric fields are in the same plane.

position: The separation between an object and a reference point.

positron: Positively-charged antimatter equivalent of electron.

potential difference: Difference in electric potential energy at two points.

potential energy: Energy of an object due to its position or state.

potentiometer: Variable resistor.

power: Rate of doing work.

precision: The degree of exactness in a measurement.

pressure: Force per unit area.

primary coil: A transformer coil that creates a varying magnetic flux when connected to a voltage source.

primary color: Red, green, or blue light.

primary pigment: Yellow, cyan, or magenta pigment.

principal axis: Radius connecting the center of curvature of a spherical mirror with its geometric vertex.

principle of superposition: The displacement of a medium caused by two or more waves is the algebraic sum of the displacements caused by the individual waves.

projectile motion: Motion of objects moving in two dimensions under the influence of gravity.

proton: Subatomic particle of mass approximately 1 u and a positive charge; nucleus of hydrogen atoms.

quantized: Subdivided into small increments.

quantum number: A discrete quantity of energy.

quantum mechanics: Study of matter using a wave-particle model.

quantum model: The present day model of the atom that only predicts the probability of the location of an electron.

quark: Basic building block of protons and neutrons.

radioactive materials: Materials that exhibit the phenomenon of radioactivity.

radioactive decay: Spontaneous decay of unstable nuclei.

ray: Line drawn to represent the path traveled by a wave front.

Rayleigh criterion: If the central bright band of one star falls on the first dark band of the second, the two stars are just resolved.

ray model of light: Model that shows light travels in a straight path.

ray optics: The study of light using ray diagrams.

real image: Image formed by rays that actually recombine.

receiver: Device used to detect electromagnetic waves.

refraction: Change in direction of a wave front as it passes from one medium to another.

regular reflection: Parallel light rays reflected from a smooth surface.

resistance: Opposition to flow of electric current; $R = V/I$.

resistance force: The force exerted by a machine.

resistor: A device with a specific resistance.

resolve: To find the component of a vector in a given direction.

resonance: Large motion of a system due to periodic excitation at its natural oscillation frequency.

resultant: Single force that has the same effect as two or more concurrent vectors.

right-hand rules: Rules to determine the direction of an electric current in a magnetic field: rule 1, see page 429; rule 2, see page 430; rule 3, see page 433.

scalar quantity: Quantity having magnitude (size) only.

schematic diagram: Diagram of an electric circuit using symbols.

scientific notation: Expressing numbers in the form: $M \times 10^n$ where $1 < M > 10$ and n is an integer.

scintillation: Flash of light emitted when a substance is struck by radiation.

second: The standard unit of time.

secondary coil: A transformer coil in which a varying *EMF* is induced.

secondary light color: Yellow, cyan, or magenta light.

secondary pigment: Red, green, or blue pigment.

second law of thermodynamics: Heat flows only from a region of high temperature to a region of lower temperature.

self-inductance: An effect in which the induced *EMF* in a coil creates a magnetic field that opposes the field originally inducing the *EMF.*

semiconductor: Material in which only a few free electrons move.

series circuit: Circuit in which the charged particles must flow through each component of the circuit, one after the other.

series connection: Arrangement of electrical devices in a line so that there is a single path through which the current may pass.

short circuit: an occurrence resulting from a low resistance and a very large current.

SI: An internationally agreed-upon consistent method of using the metric system of measurement.

significant digits: The reliable digits reported in a measurement.

simple harmonic motion: Motion in which a particle repeats the same path periodically due to a linear restoring force.

sliding friction: The force between two surfaces that are already in relative motion.

sound level: A quantity of sound measured in decibels.

spark chamber: A device used to detect the path of charged subatomic particles by the light flashes they emit.

specific heat: Energy required to change the temperature of 1 kg of a substance 1 kelvin.

spectroscope: An instrument used to study the emission spectrum of an atom.

spectrum: Array of the various wavelengths composing electromagnetic radiation.

speed: Ratio of distance traveled to the time interval.

speed of light: 3.00×10^8 m/s (in vacuum).

spherical aberration: Failure of a mirror or lens to bring all rays parallel to the principal axis to focus at the same point.

standard atmospheric pressure: 1.01325×10^5 Pa = 101.325 kPa = 1 atm = 760 mm Hg = 760 Torr.

standing wave: A wave whose nodes are stationary.

state: Physical condition of a material.

static friction: The force that opposes the start of motion between two surfaces that are not already in relative motion.

step-down transformer: A device in which the voltage output is smaller than the voltage input.

step-up transformer: A device in which the secondary voltage is larger than the primary voltage.

stimulated emission: The emission of photons from an excited atom when it has been struck by another photon.

superconductivity: State of some materials at very low temperatures in which the material exhibits zero electric resistance.

surface tension: Strong attraction of surface particles for each other due to unbalanced forces.

surface wave: Surface disturbance with characteristics of both transverse and longitudinal waves.

symmetry: Property that is unchanged by altering operations or reference frames.

synchroton: A particle accelerator that employs a high-frequency electric field and a low-frequency magnetic field.

system: A defined collection of objects.

temperature: Measure of the average kinetic energy of molecules.

terminal velocity: Velocity of a falling object when the force of air resistance is equal to the weight.

thermal (internal) energy: Sum of potential energy and kinetic energy of random motion of particles in an object.

thermonuclear reaction: Nuclear fusion reaction.

timbre: Quality of sound.

time: Interval between two events.

total internal reflection: Refraction of a light ray at such a large angle that the ray remains in the original medium.

trajectory: Path of a projectile.

transformer: Device used to transfer energy from one circuit to another circuit by mutual inductance between two coils.

translucent material: Material transmitting light but distorting it during passage.

transmutation: Nuclear change of one element into another.

transparent material: Material transmitting light undistorted.

transuranium element: Element with an atomic number greater than 92.

transverse wave: Wave in which the disturbance is perpendicular to the direction of travel of the wave.

traveling wave: Traveling disturbance in a field or medium.

trough: The low point of a wave motion.

vaporization: Change of a liquid to a gas.

vector quantity: Quantity having both magnitude (size) and direction.

vector resolution: The process of finding the effective value of a component in a given direction.

velocity: Rate of change of position.

virtual image: Image whose rays appear to emanate from a point without actually doing so.

viscous fluids: Slow-flowing fluids.

volatile fluid: Fluid that is easily evaporated.

volt: Unit of potential difference.

voltage divider: A single resistor or a series of resistors used to provide various potential differences from a single power source.

voltmeter: Electric device used to measure potential difference.

watt: Unit of power equal to 1 J/s.

wavelength: Distance between corresponding points on two successive waves.

wave pulse: A single disturbance traveling through a medium.

weak force: Force involved in the decay of atomic nuclei and nuclear particles. A type of electromagnetic force.

weight: Gravitational attraction of Earth or celestial body for an object.

Wilson cloud chamber: A chamber containing supersaturated water vapor in which charged particles appear as trails of visible droplets.

work: Product of force and displacement.

work-energy theorem: The net work done on an object is equal to its change in kinetic energy.

work function: Energy needed to remove an electron from metal as in the photoelectric effect.

X rays: High frequency electromagnetic waves of very short wavelength.

INDEX

Image, 318, 320; real, 322–325, 331–333; virtual, 318, 323, 326 330, 333–334
Impulse, 148–150
Impulse-momentum theorem, 149
Incandescent body, 480–483
Incidence, angle of, 262, 302
Incident wave, 257–258
Inclined plane, 103–105
Incoherent light, 509
Independent variable, 24
Index of refraction, 306; speed of light and, 308–309; table, 307
Induction: charging by, 357; electromagnetic, 446; magnetic, 433, 435; mutual, 454; self-, 453–454
Inelastic collision, 190
Inertia, 75
Inertial confinement, 548
Inertial mass, 81
Insulator, 354–355
Interference, 260–261, 263–264, 295–296, 340–343, 349
Interference fringes, 342
International System of Units (SI), 7, 10; table, 10
Inverse square law, 134–136
Inverse variation, 27
Ion: negative, 354; positive, 354
Isolated system, 186
Isotope, 520–521, 542–543; half-life of, 524–525; table, half-life, 525

Joliot, Frederic, 526, 542
Joule, James Prescott, 166
Joule (unit), 164, 166, 200, 398

Kamerlingh Onnes, Heike, 5
Kelvin, Lord (William Thomson), 199
Kelvin temperature scale, 198–199
Kepler, Johannes, 130, 133
Kepler's laws of planetary motion, 130–132, 135–136
Kilogram, 7
Kilowatt, 169
Kilowatt hour, 398–399
Kinetic energy, 178, 180–182, 243; of photoelectron, 485–486; table, 182
Kinetic-molecular theory, 194–196, 216, 218

Laser, 509, 513; illus., 511; table, 512
Law: Boyle's, 220–222; Charles', 223–224; combined gas, 225, 227; of conservation of energy, 186–190, 206–208; of conservation of momentum, 153–160, 190; Coulomb's, 358–359, 360–361; gas, 220–229; Hooke's, 120–121; ideal gas, 225–227; inverse square, 134–136; Kepler's, 130–132; Lenz's, 451–453; Newton's first, 74–76, 148; Newton's second, 76–78, 148; Newton's third, 78–79, 151–152; Ohm's, 391–392; of reflection, 262, 302; Snell's, 305–307; of thermodynamics, 200–204; of univer-

sal gravitation, 135–137
Length, 14
Lens, 330; achromatic, 335; concave, 330, 334–335; convex, 330 336; objective, 336; resolving power of, 348
Lenz, H. F. E., 452
Lenz's law, 451–453
Leptons, 529–530; tables, 530, 533
Leyden Jar, 382
Light, 286–299, 302–315, 340–348; absorption of, 292; coherent, 342, 509–513; color and, 292–296; diffraction of, 341–346; dispersion of, 313–315; dual nature of, 491; gravitational effect on, 141–142; incoherent, 509; monochromatic, 342; polarization of, 296–298; quantum theory of, 480–491; reflection of, 302, 309–312; refraction of, 302–309, 312–313; sources of, 290–292; speed of, 14, 288–290, 302, 308–309, 313; total internal reflection of, 309–312; transmission of, 292; white, 343
Light wave, 252, 286, 295, 475; wavelength of, 343–344
Linear accelerator, 526–527
Linear equation, 25–26
Linear motion, 34–52
Liquid, 238–241; viscous, 241; volatile, 241. See also Fluid
Longitudinal wave, 252
Loudness, 272–274
Lumen, 290
Luminous body, 290
Luminous flux, 290–291

Machines, 170–173
Magnet, properties of, 424–426
Magnetic field, 424–440, 464–466; around a coil, 429–430; electric currents and, 432–435; table, 434
Magnetic field lines, 426–427
Magnetic flux, 427
Magnetic force, 432–435
Magnetic induction, 433, 435
Magnetic material, 431–432
Malleability, 242
Marsden, Ernest, 496
Mass, 79–80; of Earth, 8–9; of electron, 9, 462–466; gravitational, 81; inertial, 81; of neon atom, 469; of nucleus, 520
Mass defect, 540–541
Mass number, 518
Mass spectrograph, 467–469
Matter waves, 252, 489–490
Maxwell, James Clerk, 462, 470
Measurement: accuracy and precision of, 14–15; atomic mass, 469; mass of electron, 9; of temperature, 198–199; uncertainty of, 13–14; of wavelength, 343–344
Mechanical advantage, 171–174
Mechanical energy, 187
Mechanical resonance, 122

Mechanical wave, 252–253
Meitner, Lise, 544
Melting point, 209
Mercury barometer, 219
Mersenne, Marin, 268
Mesons, 534
Meter, 7; illus., 10
Metric system, 7, 10–11; table, prefixes, 10
Michelson, Albert A., 289
Micrometer, illus., 15
Microscope, 336
Microwave, 475
Microwave-powered aircraft, 264
Millikan, Robert A., 377–378, 486
Mirage, 312
Mirror: concave, 321–322, 323–327; converging, 321; convex, 329 330; diverging, 329; parabolic, 322; plane, 318, 320
Moderator, 545
Momentum, 146–160; conservation of, 153–160, 190; impulse and, 146–150; Newton's third law and, 151–152; unit for, 148
Monochromatic light, 342
Moog, Robert, 282
Motion: of energy, 178; first law of, 74–76, 148; graphical analysis of, 56–66; linear, 34–52; planetary, 128–132; projectile, 114–116; second law of, 76–78, 148; simple harmonic, 120–123; third law of, 78–79, 151–152; two-dimensional, 110–123; uniform circular, 116–119
Motor, 389; electric, 437–438
Mutual inductance, 454

National Institute of Standards and Technology, 7
Negative acceleration, 43–44
Negative ion, 354
Neutrino, 531
Neutron, 352, 354, 497–498, 540
Newton, Sir Isaac, 72, 76, 133–136, 148, 292
Newton (unit), 76
Newton's laws of motion: first, 74–76, 148; second, 76–78, 148; third, 78–79, 151–152
Nodal line, 264, 343
Node, 261, 276
Noise, 281
Normal, 262
Normal force, 82
Nuclear bombardment, 525–526
Nuclear equation, 522–524
Nuclear fission, 544–545
Nuclear force, 74; strong, 74, 538, 540
Nuclear fusion, 546–548
Nuclear moderator, 545
Nuclear reaction, 522–524
Nuclear reactor, 545–546
Nucleon, 538; quark model of, 532–535; table, 533
Nucleus, 352, 518–520; binding energy

PHOTO CREDITS

3, Freeman and Malin; **4,** Melinda Vasela; **5,** Dan McCoy from Rainbow; **6** bl, George Anderson; br, Tersch; **7,** George Anderson; **8,** I.M. Whillans, Institute of Polar Studies, Ohio States University; **10,** Morgan Photos; **12** Tom Pantages; **14** Allen Zak; **16** l, George Anderson; r, Courtesy of Fisher Scientific; **17,** Ted Rice; **23,** E.C. Boughn/After Image; **24,** Doug Martin; **30,** Historical Pictures Service, Inc.; **35,** Roger K. Burnard; **37** t, Library of Congress; **37** c, Tim Courlas; **37** b, courtesy of Ford Motor Company; **38,** French National Railroad; **42,** Michael Collier; **44,** Luther C. Goldman; **50** t, Edith G. Hawn/Stock, Boston; **50** b, Kodansha; **57,** John Jaszcak; **63,** David Frazier, **65,** Not Approved; **73,** Sports Chrome, Inc.; **74,** Bezzvoli, Experiment on an Inclined Plane, Museo Zoologico de ''La Specolo'' Tribunadi Galileo, Florence. Scala/Art Resources, New York; **75** Ted Rice; **77,** Max Dunham/Photo Researchers Inc.; **81** l, Hickson-Bender; r, George Anderson; **84,** Shostal Associates; **87,** NASA; **93,** Steve Lissau; **98,** Mindy Paderewsky; **100,** Greg Sailor; **111,** Andrew Graham, Department of Physics and Astronomy, Appalachian State University; **112,** PSSC Physics, D.C. Heath & Co., Lexington, 1965; **114,** John Zimmerman © Time, Inc. 1980; **115,** Kodansha; **117,** Shostal Associates; **118,** Hickson-Bender; **120,** George Anderson; **122,** Tom Pantages; **123** t, Greg Sailor; b, Richard Buettner/Bruce Coleman; **129,** NASA; **130,** The Bettmann Archive, Inc.; **131** l, NASA; c, JPI; r, NASA; **134,** Ward's Natural Science Establishment; **135,** NASA; **136,** Reprinted by permission from Nature, Vol 311, No. 5983, Cover Copyright © 1984 Macmillan Journals Limited; **140,** NASA; **142,** Arthur Selby; **147,** courtesy of the National Highway Safety Administration; **148** Doug Martin; **149,** courtesy of General Motors; **151,** Hickson-Bender; **157,** NASA; **160,** PSSC Physics; **165,** Comstock; **166** Young/Hoffhines; **167,** Edwin L. Shay; **169,** Joe Brilla; **172,** Doug Martin; **179,** Photo Researchers; **180** t, Wide World Photos, Inc.; **180** b, Peter Saloutos/After Image; **182,** David M. Dennis; **183,** Doug Martin; **185** l, Frank Cezus; **185** r, Jim Bradshaw; **186** l, Chris Minerva, FPG.; **186** r, Morgan Photos; **187,** Hickson-Bender; **195,** Chris Collins/Stock Market; **198** l, Mary Lou Uttermohlen/Latent Images; **198** r, Pictures Unlimited; **199** tr, Lyn Campbell; **199** trm, Studio Ten; **199** trb, Paul Nesbit; **199** tlb, Doug Martin; **199** tlm, J.L. Adams; **199** tl, file photo; **199** b, Dan McCoy/Rainbow; **203,** Pictures Unlimited; **206,** Hickson-Bender; **208,** courtesy of Texas Gulf Chemicals Company; **209,** Spitzburg/Gamma-Liaison; **217,** Joey Jacques; **218,** Don C. Nieman; **220,** Tim Courlas; **221,** National Center for Atmospheric Research; **223,** Hickson-Bender; **233,** Blair Seitz Inc.; Photo Researchers; **235,** Dennis Holloman/FPG; **236** t, Pictures Unlimited; **236** b, Scripps Institution of Oceanography, University of California, San Diego; **237,** David M. Dennis; **238** t, Ruth Dixon; **238** b, file photo; **239,** Dr. Gary Settles/Photo Researchers; **240** tl, courtesy of Harold E. Edgerton, Massachusetts Institute of Technology; **240** tr, file photo **240** Hickson-Bender; **241,** Pictures Unlimited; **242,** file photo; **243** t, Doug Martin; **243** b, Lawrence Livermore Laboratory; **244,** Doug Martin; **245,** Hickson-Bender/Ohio State University, Marion Campus; **246** t, Tom Myers; **246** b, AP/Wide World Photos; **251,** Pictures Unlimited; **252,** Shostal Associates; **253** t, PSSC Physics, **253** b, Tom Pantages; **255** Doug Martin; **257** George Anderson; **258** t, George Anderson; **258** b, George Anderson; **261,** Kodansha; **262,** courtesy of Education Development Center; **263** t both, courtesy of Education Development Center; b, Steve Allan Bissell; **264** t, courtesy Education Development Center; b, Reprinted from Popular Science with permission © 1988 Time Mirror Magazines, Inc.; **269,** Russ Kinne/Comstock; **270** t, file photo; **272** t, The Ealing Corporation; b, Billy Grimes/Leo de Wys, Inc.; **275,** Tim Courlas; **281,** The Sharper Image, San Francisco; **282,** Doug Martin; **287,** Craig Kramer; **292,** Doug Martin; **293** t, Eastman Kodak Co., 1977; **293** b, Shostal Associates; **294,** Larry Hamill; **295,** Kodansha; **296,** Sinclair Stammers/Science Photo Library; **297,** file photo; **298,** Kodansha; **303,** William D. Popejoy; **302,** E.R. Degginger; **304, 305** t, Kodansha; b, Berenice Abbott/Photo Researchers, Inc.; **306,** George Anderson; **307,** George Anderson; **310,** George Anderson; **311** S.L. Craig, Jr./Bruce Coleman, Inc.; **312,** Eric Lessing/Magnum; **313** t, file photo **313** b, Stewart M. Green/Tom Stack & Assoc; **314,** courtesy of the European Southern Observatory/Karl-Schwarzschel; **319,** Tim Courlas; **320,** Kodansha; **322** l, Alan Benoit; tr, Kodansha; br, Tom Pantages; **328,** Tom Pantages; **330** both, David Parker/Photo Researchers, Inc.; **331,** Craig Kramer; **332,** Philip M. Jordain; **341,** Kjell B. Sandved; **342** t, D.C.H. Plowes; c, CSIRO, Division of Materials Science & Technology; **342** b, **346,** Kodansha; **347,** Hickson-Bender; **348** t, Kodansha; b, file photo; **349,** Dan McCoy/Rainbow; **353,** courtesy of the Ohio Disaster Services Agency; **354,** Ted Rice; **355,** Bob Krist/Leo de Wys, Inc.; **356,** PSSC Physics, D.C. Heath and Co., Lexington, 1965; **360,** Comstock; **362,** Grace Davis/Leo de Wys, Inc.; **362,** courtesy of Xerox Corp.; **363,** file photo; **369,** file photo; **371** courtesy of COSI, Columbus, Ohio; **375,** Education Development Center; **377,** Robert MacNaughton; **381,** Doug Martin; **382,** Tom Pantages; **387,** Rich Brommer; **388** t, Grace Davies/Leo de Wys, Inc.; **386** r, John Yates/Shostal Associates; l, Mark Antman/Stock, Boston; b, Brian Parker/Tom Stack and Assoc.; c, Four by Five Inc.; **395,** Grace Davies/Leo de Wys, Inc.; **396** Tom Pantages; **398,** Frank Cezus/FPG; **399** l, William Maddox; **399** r, Thomas Russell; **405,** Craig Kammer; **409,** Mary Lou Uttermohlen; **413,** George Anderson; **414,** Ted Rice; **417,** Cobalt Productions; **418** tl, Ted Rice; tr, George Anderson; b, courtesy Radio Shack, Inc.; **425,** Gabe Palmer/Stock Market; **426,** Philip M. Jordain; **428,** Paul Chesley; **429,** A.D. Little Co.; **430,** Kodansha; **435,** Tom Pantages; **445,** Craig Kramer; **447,** Tom Pantages; **453,** Craig Kammer; **455** l, George Hunter; r, file photo; **463,** Kay Chernush/Image Bank; **464,** The Science Museum, London; **465,** Brookhaven National Laboratory; **471,** Michael Collier; **476** t, Kodansha; b, file photo; **481,** file photo; **483,** Thomas Russell; **495,** First Image; **498, 499,** Ted Rice/Ohio State University Physics Department; **500** t and c, Kodansha; b, file photo; **501** l, USAEG, San Francisco Operations Office; r, Acton Research Corp.; **504,** Sea Sports/Robert G. Bachand; **511,** Ad Image; **512,** Chuck O'Rear/West Light; **513,** Bill Pierce from Rainbow; **514,** courtesy of IBM; **519,** Patrice Loiez, Cern/Science Photo Library/Photo Researchers, Inc.; **528,** Fermilab; **529,** Cern/Photo Researchers, Inc.; **531,** courtesy Lawrence Berkeley Laboratory; **534,** University of Tokyo © DISCOVER magazine 4/84, Time Inc.; **539,** Craig Kramer; **543** l, Dan McCoy/Rainbow; r, Phototake; **545,** Dave Spier/Tom Stack and Assoc.; **548,** Phototake.